VALUES OF PHYSICAL AND CHEMICAL CONSTAN[TS]

(In SI units and based on the ^{12}C scale)

Speed of light	c	=	2.997[...]
Mass of electron	m	=	9.1095×10^{-31} kg
Electronic charge	e	=	1.6022×10^{-19} C
Planck constant	h	=	6.6262×10^{-34} J s
Boltzmann constant	k	=	1.3807×10^{-23} J K^{-1}
Avogadro constant	$\mathfrak{N}$	=	6.0220×10^{23} mol^{-1}
Gas constant	$R = \mathfrak{N}k$	=	8.3144 J K^{-1} mol^{-1}
		=	0.08206 liters atm K^{-1} mol^{-1}
Faraday constant	$\mathfrak{F} = \mathfrak{N}e$	=	$96{,}485$ C mol^{-1}
Permittivity	$4\pi\epsilon_0$	=	1.11264×10^{-10} C^2 N^{-1} m^{-2}
	$\dfrac{e^2}{4\pi\epsilon_0}$	=	2.3072×10^{-28} J m
Bohr radius	a_0	=	0.5292×10^{-10} m $= 0.5292$ Å
Atomic mass unit	1 amu	=	1.66053×10^{-27} kg
Standard molar gas volume			24.414 liters
kT at 25°C (298.15 K)			4.116×10^{-21} J
RT at 25°C (298.15 K)			2.479 kJ mol^{-1}

ENERGY CONVERSION FACTORS†

		kJ mol^{-1}	kcal mol^{-1}	J molecule^{-1}	e.v.	cm^{-1}
1 kJ mol^{-1}	=	1	0.23901	1.6605×10^{-21}	0.010363	83.591
1 kcal mol^{-1}	=	4.1840	1	6.9478×10^{-21}	0.043360	349.73
1 J molecule^{-1}	=	6.0220×10^{20}	1.4393×10^{20}	1	6.2414×10^{18}	5.034×10^{22}
1 eV	=	96.490	23.062	1.6022×10^{-19}	1	8066
1 cm^{-1}	=	0.011963	2.8594×10^{-3}	1.9865×10^{-23}	1.2397×10^{-4}	1

†Electron volts and wave numbers (cm^{-1}) are defined as amounts of energy per particle.

PHYSICAL CHEMISTRY

PHYSICAL CHEMISTRY

Fourth Edition

Gordon M. Barrow

INTERNATIONAL STUDENT EDITION

McGRAW-HILL INTERNATIONAL BOOK COMPANY

Auckland Bogotá Guatemala Hamburg Johannesburg Lisbon
London Madrid Mexico New Delhi Panama Paris San Juan
São Paulo Singapore Sydney Tokyo

PHYSICAL CHEMISTRY

INTERNATIONAL STUDENT EDITION

Copyright © 1979
Exclusive rights by McGraw-Hill Kogakusha, Ltd. for
manufacture and export. This book cannot be re-exported
from the country to which it is consigned by McGraw-Hill.
6th Printing 1982

This book was set in Times Roman by York Graphic Services, Inc.
The editors were Donald C. Jackson and Stephen Wagley;
the designer was Charles A. Carson;
the production supervisor was John F. Harte.
New drawings were done by J & R Services, Inc.

Library of Congress Cataloging in Publication Data

Barrow, Gordon M
    Physical chemistry.

    Bibliography: p.
    Includes index.
    1. Chemistry, Physical and theoretical. I. Title.
QD453.2.B37 1979   541'.3   78-17080
ISBN 0-07-003825-2

When ordering this title use ISBN 0-07-066170-7

KOSAIDO PRINTING CO., LTD. TOKYO, JAPAN

CONTENTS

*Sections preceded by an asterisk may be omitted without loss of continuity.

PREFACE

Physical chemistry is a unit in the undergraduate chemistry program that introduces, or develops, many distinct topics. Some, such as thermodynamics and kinetics, are long-recognized as major areas of study. Others, such as quantum mechanics, spectroscopy, statistical mechanics, and photochemistry, have come into the physical chemistry course more recently. A single course in which such varied areas are treated is valuable if it provides coherence to the study of these different topics. A textbook for such a course must make it clear that the whole is greater than the sum of the parts. This has been the goal of previous editions, and it remains the goal of this fourth edition.

Each topic is treated in such a way that the knowledge of the entire subject of physical chemistry, as well as that of the particular area, is advanced. But what is the subject of physical chemistry if it is not just a collection of distinct topics? We see it as the quantitative interpretation of the macroscopic world in terms of the atomic-molecular world. To achieve this interpretation, we must organize our observations of macroscopic phenomena, as we do in thermodynamics and in parts of kinetics. We must advance our studies of atoms and molecules, as we do, for example, in quantum mechanics and spectroscopy. Then we must bring these studies together. This coming together is woven into much of the fabric of a modern physical chemistry course.

The principal changes in this fourth edition come from our desire to introduce more serious studies of the atomic-molecular world into the undergraduate physical chemistry course. Thus quantum mechanics is given a fuller introduction and applied in somewhat more detail. Symmetry and group theory are introduced and used. Additional aspects of spectroscopy are presented. A chapter is devoted to photochemistry.

When the first edition of this book was prepared, it was necessary to argue that studies of the atomic-molecular world belonged, along with the traditional topics, in the physical chemistry course. Now it seems necessary to insist that the traditional macroscopic studies be not completely driven out. Physical chemistry should offer much more to the undergraduate student than an introduction to the specialized topics that now constitute the research frontier. The enthusiasm of the specialists for more and more extensions into the new, and often exciting, aspects of these topics has, I hope. been held in check. All additions remain within the framework of physical chemistry. Even so, these additions can be accommodated in a textbook suitable for a year's course only by economies in other areas. Reorganization, rather than deletion, is the route that has been taken. The study of liquids and solids, for example, is now placed along with the thermodynamic, kinetic, and diffraction studies that form the basis for studies of these states. Many such efficiencies of presentation have been realized in this revision.

In the several years since the previous edition, SI units have been very generally accepted in physical chemistry. As in the third edition, SI units are used with only minor exceptions. Pressures are still expressed in the units of atmospheres and molecular dimensions are reported in angstroms.

I would like to express my thanks to Clyde Metz for the great help he has given me in working through both the manuscript and the galleys to ensure a correct, error-free edition.

Gordon M. Barrow
Carmel Valley
California

PROPERTIES OF GASES

The study of the nature of gases provides an ideal introduction to physical chemistry. This study, undertaken in the first two chapters, has three clearly recognizable aspects. One is the organization of the experimental results that are obtained from studies of the world around us, the macroscopic world, into general statements, or *laws*. Second is the development of a molecular model, i.e., a study of the microscopic, or molecular, world. Finally, these two approaches are brought together to give a molecular-level interpretation of the observed macroscopic phenomena.

A considerable appreciation of the world of molecules can be obtained from the second and third steps, and this comes about without recourse to the more elaborate and more powerful theories and experiments that will be discussed later in this text. The deduction of some of the innermost details of the molecular world from the simple experimental results of Chap. 1 and the equally simple theory of Chap. 2 should be appreciated as an elegant accomplishment of science.

Seldom are the experimental and theoretical aspects of a study so neatly separated as they are here. A clear illustration is provided of how these two aspects of scientific study go hand in hand to lead to a more profound interpretation of our physical world. The division of the subject into its empirical and theoretical aspects, it must be admitted, ignores the historical sequence of events. However, most of the results reported in this chapter predate the theoretical deductions of the following chapter. For reference one can recall that the molecular view of matter was born with the nineteenth century and became quite mature and respectable by the end of that century. The earlier dates attached to some of the empirical studies should emphasize the fact that these studies were indeed purely empirical and were not appreciably guided by any existing theory.

1-1 The Dependence of the Volume of a Gas on Pressure: Boyle's Law

As early as 1660 Robert Boyle performed a series of experiments in which he determined the effect of pressure on the volume of a given amount of air with

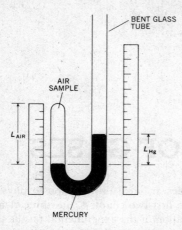

BENT GLASS TUBE

AIR SAMPLE

L_{AIR}

L_{Hg}

MERCURY

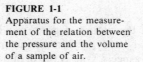

FIGURE 1-1
Apparatus for the measurement of the relation between
the pressure and the volume
of a sample of air.

the apparatus illustrated in Fig. 1-1. A little mercury was added through the open end of the tube to seal off a quantity of air in the closed end. The volume of the enclosed air, for various amounts of mercury added through the open end, could then be measured. Table 1-1 shows some of the results Boyle obtained.

Qualitatively, it is immediately obvious that as the pressure on the air increases, the volume of the air decreases. Such data prompt one to go further and see if there is a simple quantitative relation between the pressure P and the volume V. One tries the relation

$$V \propto \frac{1}{P} \qquad \text{or} \qquad V = \frac{\text{const}}{P} \qquad \text{or} \qquad PV = \text{const} \tag{1-1}$$

The data are easily compared with the final form of this relation. Included in Table 1-1 is the calculated product of the effective length of the column of mercury and the length of the air column. (The units used are not pertinent since it is only the constancy of the result that is of interest.) Within experimental error a constant value is obtained. We now are able to conclude that the volume of air varies inversely as the pressure. Later experiments showed that this relation requires the temperature to be maintained constant and, furthermore, that many gases, as well as air, conform quite closely to this behavior. Boyle's law can now be written as follows: *The volume of a given quantity of a gas varies inversely as the pressure, the temperature remaining constant.*

Processes which are performed at constant temperature are said to be *isothermal*. The pressure-volume data obtained at constant temperature in demonstrating Boyle's law are frequently exhibited on a plot of P versus V. The hyperbolic curve obtained, as in Fig. 1-2, at any given temperature, is an example of an *isotherm*.

According to Boyle's law, the pressure and volume of a given amount of gas at a fixed temperature vary so that the product PV always has the same value. Sometimes one deals with an isothermal process which takes the gas from

TABLE 1-1 Data of Boyle on the Pressure-Volume Relation for Air

The pressure of the atmosphere acting in the open end of the mercury column is equal to $29\frac{1}{8}$ inches of Hg

L_{air}, arbitrary units	L_{Hg}, inches	$L_{Hg} + 29\frac{1}{8}$, inches	$(L_{Hg} + 29\frac{1}{8}) \times L_{air}$
12	0	$29\frac{2}{16}$	349
10	$6\frac{3}{16}$	$35\frac{5}{16}$	353
8	$15\frac{1}{16}$	$44\frac{3}{16}$	353
6	$29\frac{11}{16}$	$58\frac{13}{16}$	353
4	$58\frac{2}{16}$	$87\frac{4}{16}$	349
3	$88\frac{7}{16}$	$117\frac{9}{16}$	353

the initial values P_1 and V_1 to some new values P_2 and V_2. Since the product of P and V is constant, one can write a frequently convenient form of Boyle's law as

$$P_1 V_1 = P_2 V_2 \tag{1-2}$$

Later it will be shown that more accurate or more extensive measurements reveal that gases do not, in fact, behave exactly in accordance with Boyle's law. It is convenient, to begin with, to ignore these additional complications of gas behavior and to restrict our attention to what is known as *ideal behavior*, a term implying a simply described and generally followed behavior.

The simplicity of Boyle's law and its frequent presentation in elementary chemistry courses should not lead to the view that this is the "expected" behavior. For liquids and solids, by contrast, no simple relation exists between

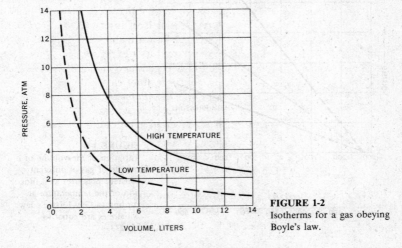

FIGURE 1-2
Isotherms for a gas obeying Boyle's law.

V and P. The fact, for example, that doubling the pressure on any of a wide variety of gases reduces the volume of the gas sample to half its original value is a rather remarkable result that the theory of the next chapter must explain.

1-2 The Volume-Temperature Behavior of Ideal Gases

More than a century elapsed before the counterpart of Boyle's law, a relation between the temperature and gas volume, was discovered. The reason for this long interval stems from the difficulty of the concept of temperature compared with that of pressure. Although qualitative differences between hot and cold can be readily recognized, the means for making quantitative measurements of the "degree of heat" are not so easily devised. Toward the end of the eighteenth century, however, the use of the expansion of a liquid in a glass tube, i.e., a modern thermometer, was generally accepted as a satisfactory method for measuring temperature. On the continent of Europe, furthermore, some agreement had been reached to assign 0 as the scale value for the freezing point of water and 100 as the value for the normal boiling point. The existence of thermometers, with agreed-upon scales, allowed investigations to be made of the variation of the volume of a gas with the temperature.

The early work of the French scientist Jacques Charles in 1787 and then further work by J. L. Gay-Lussac, also French, in 1808 showed that if the pressure is kept constant, the volume of a sample of gas varies linearly with the temperature in a manner indicated by the solid lines of Fig. 1-3.

The extrapolation to low temperatures of curves like those of Fig. 1-3 is revealing. One finds that all the curves extrapolate to $V = 0$ at a temperature of about $-273°C$. In view of this common behavior, it is often convenient to

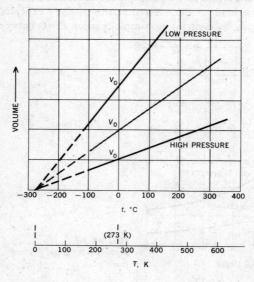

FIGURE 1-3
Variation of the volume of a sample of gas at different constant pressures as a function of the temperature according to Gay-Lussac's law. All slopes are equal to $V_0/273$.

measure temperatures from this point, i.e., from $t = -273\,°C$, rather than from the zero of the Celsius scale. If the size of the degree is kept the same as in the Celsius scale but the zero is shifted, the *absolute Kelvin temperature scale* is obtained. Temperatures T on this scale are related to Celsius scale temperatures t by

$$T = t + 273.15 \tag{1-3}$$

A temperature on this absolute scale is denoted by the symbol K (read "kelvins"), after Lord Kelvin.

With the introduction of this absolute temperature scale, shown below the Celsius scale in Fig. 1-3, a relation paralleling the PV relation of Boyle can be written for V and T. The linear curves of Fig. 1-3, all extrapolating to $V = 0$ at $T = 0$, allow us to write

$$V \propto T \quad \text{or} \quad V = \text{const } T \quad \text{or} \quad \frac{V}{T} = \text{const} \tag{1-4}$$

This result is Gay-Lussac's law, also sometimes referred to as Charles' law: *The volume of a given mass of gas varies directly as the absolute temperature if the pressure remains constant.* Like Boyle's law, this relation is approximately followed by many gases, and obedience of a gas to Gay-Lussac's law constitutes another feature of ideal-gas behavior.

Often we deal with the volume of a gas sample at two different temperatures. Then we can use the general ideal-gas temperature-volume relation in the form

$$\frac{V_1}{T_1} = \frac{V_2}{T_2} \tag{1-5}$$

1-3 The PVT Behavior of Ideal Gases

The gas laws of Boyle and Gay-Lussac separately describe the dependence of the volume of a gas sample on the pressure and temperature. The dependence on both variables can be illustrated by the surface of Fig. 1-4. Any cross section perpendicular to the T axis, i.e., a section for constant temperature, would show a Boyle's-law hyberbolic curve. Any section perpendicular to the P axis, i.e., a section for constant pressure, would show the linear temperature-volume relation of Gay-Lussac's law.

For its mathematical description, the surface of Fig. 1-4 requires an expression of the form

$$V = f(P,T)$$

where $f(P,T)$ implies some function of the variables P and T. The proportion-

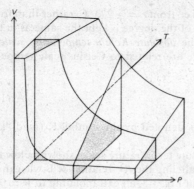

FIGURE 1-4
A section of the surface depicting the dependence of the volume of a gas sample on pressure and temperature.

ality to which this equality corresponds must give, as special cases, the proportionalities of Boyle and Gay-Lussac, and on this basis we can write

$$V \propto \frac{T}{P} \tag{1-6}$$

For a gas sample whose volume is specified at some temperature and pressure, the equality

$$V = \text{const} \frac{T}{P} \tag{1-7}$$

can be written to describe the surface for that sample on a display like Fig. 1-4.

Laboratory studies often lead us to use Eq. (1-7) to calculate the volume of a gas sample at pressures and temperatures other than those existing under the experimental conditions.

To calculate changes in gas volume from Eq. (1-7), or to make estimates from a figure like Fig. 1-4, the gas sample can be specified by a statement of its volume at some indicated temperature and pressure.

Alternatively, the sample can be described by the number of moles of gas it contains. You recall that the mole unit is defined as the amount that contains as many particles of a specified type as there are ^{12}C atoms in an exactly 12-g sample of ^{12}C. When we deal with gases, the particles usually are molecules. A mole of a gas is the amount that contains as many molecules as there are carbon atoms in 12 g of ^{12}C.

The proportionality of Eq. (1-6) can be written to include the volume dependence on the amount of gas, as measured by the number of moles n, as

$$V \propto n \frac{T}{P} \tag{1-8}$$

The convenience of the mole unit in gas-volume calculations can be seen by recalling Avogadro's hypothesis, which states that equal volumes of gases at the same conditions of temperature and pressure contain equal numbers of molecules. It follows that a 1-mol sample of any gas occupies the same volume as a 1-mol sample of any other gas at given conditions of temperature and pressure. With R written for the proportionality constant, the equality that can be written is

$$V = Rn \frac{T}{P}$$

or

$$PV = nRT \tag{1-9}$$

Furthermore, R will have a single value, applicable to all gases that behave ideally.

This result is useful in making gas-volume calculations and is, moreover, a summary of the empirical laws of Boyle and Gay-Lussac and the hypothesis of Avogadro. The theory of the nature of gases, to be developed in the next chapter, will show the molecular basis of this important result.

A numerical value for the gas constant can be obtained from the result that at 0°C and 1 atm, conditions known as standard temperature and pressure (STP), 1 mol of a gas that behaves ideally occupies 22.414 liters. Substitution of these data in the gas-law expression (1-9) gives

$$R = \frac{(1 \text{ atm})(22.414 \text{ liters})}{(1 \text{ mol})(273.15 \text{ K})} = 0.082056 \text{ l atm K}^{-1} \text{ mol}^{-1}$$

If the number of moles of gas in a gas sample is known, this value of R and the relation of Eq. (1-9) allow the volume of the sample to be calculated at any given temperature and pressure. Alternatively, the temperature can be deduced if values of n, V, and P are given, or the pressure can be deduced if values of n, V, and T are given.

The mass of a mole of a gas can be calculated from Eq. (1-9) and a measured value of the density of the sample at some temperature and pressure. The number of moles n can be expressed as m/M, where m is the mass of the sample and M is the molar mass. The density d can be expressed as m/V. Rearrangement of $PV = nRT$ first to $PV = (m/M)RT$, then to $PM = (m/V)RT$, and to $M = (m/V)RT/P$ gives

$$M = d \frac{RT}{P} \tag{1-10}$$

Thus the molar mass of the gas is given in terms of its density at some pressure and temperature.

1-4 The Gas Constant: Energy Units

The gas constant R not only enters into PVT calculations but, as will frequently be seen in succeeding chapters, also plays a very important role in all phenomena involving the energies of molecular systems. This aspect of the gas constant is less surprising when one sees that R includes the dimensions of work, or energy.

If pressure is written as force per unit area and the volume as area times length, one sees that dimensionally

$$\text{Pressure} \times \text{volume} = \frac{\text{force}}{\text{area}} \times \text{area} \times \text{length} = \text{force} \times \text{length}$$

The dimensions of force times length are those of energy, which you recall can be based on the force times the distance through which the force acts. It follows that R has the dimensions of energy per kelvin per mole.

A numerical value for R involving an energy unit will now be obtained. In so doing we shall begin the introduction of the consistent set of units that are referred to as SI (for Système International d'Unités). You will recognize them as mks units, i.e., the meter-kilogram-second system generally used by physicists. Appendix D summarizes some of the basic and derived SI units and their relation to other units with which chemical quantities have been reported.

Chemists have often used the cgs, i.e., centimeter-gram-second, system and moreover have added special units outside this system. Two of these, the pressure unit of the atmosphere and the volume unit of the liter or the related unit of the milliliter (ml), equal to 10^{-3} liter, have already been introduced. These units are so convenient in chemical studies and are in such common use that we shall continue to report pressures and volumes in these nonsystematic units. To work from them to pressures and volumes expressed in SI units use the conversions

$$1 \text{ liter} = 10^{-3} \text{ m}^3 \quad \text{and} \quad 1 \text{ atm} = 101,325 \text{ N m}^{-2}$$

The name pascal (Pa) is given to the pressure unit newtons per square meter.

Now R in the SI energy units of joules (J), *joule* being the special name for the SI unit *newton meter*, can be evaluated as

$$R = 0.082056 \text{ liter atm K}^{-1} \text{ mol}^{-1}$$

$$= 0.082056 \frac{\text{liter atm}}{\text{K mol}} \frac{1 \text{ m}^3}{10^3 \text{ liters}} \frac{101,325 \text{ N m}^{-2}}{1 \text{ atm}}$$

$$= 8.3143 \text{ J K}^{-1} \text{ mol}^{-1} \tag{1-11}$$

In the chemical literature, R has generally been used with the energy units of *calories*. The calorie unit and the joule unit are related by

$$1 \text{ cal} = 4.1840 \text{ J}$$

With this conversion factor we obtain

$$R = (8.3143 \text{ J K}^{-1} \text{ mol}^{-1}) \frac{1 \text{ cal}}{4.1840 \text{ J}} = 1.9872 \text{ cal K}^{-1} \text{ mol}^{-1}$$

1-5 Some Properties of Gas Mixtures

The ideal gas-law expression $PV = nRT$ can be applied to gases that are mixtures of different components or are pure, single-component gases. In the former case it is often necessary to relate the properties of the gas mixture to those of its components.

The pressure exerted by the individual components separately, and together, in a chamber of fixed volume can be determined. If the pressure of the gas mixture P is found to be equal to the sum of the pressures P_1, P_2, etc., exerted by each component by itself, the gas mixture is said to follow *Dalton's law of partial pressures*. More generally we can write this law as

$$P = P_1 + P_2 + P_3 + \cdots = \sum P_i \qquad (1\text{-}12)$$

Dalton's law of partial pressures, like the laws of Boyle and Gay-Lussac, is followed quite closely by mixtures of many gases. Even if the separate components behave like ideal gases, the mixture need not, however, follow Dalton's law. Obvious examples are provided by gas mixtures in which ideal-gas components react chemically with each other.

Dalton's law is obeyed when each component in the gas mixture and the mixture itself follow the ideal-gas laws as expressed by $PV = nRT$. Let n_1, n_2, ... be the number of moles of the various components, and let n be the total number of moles in the gas mixture. Thus

$$n = n_1 + n_2 + n_3 + \cdots \qquad (1\text{-}13)$$

The pressure exerted by the gas mixture and by each of the component gases in a container of volume V can be described by the relations

$$P = \frac{nRT}{V} \qquad P_1 = \frac{n_1 RT}{V} \qquad P_2 = \frac{n_2 RT}{V} \qquad \cdots$$

These relations can be rearranged to

$$n = \frac{PV}{RT} \qquad n_1 = \frac{P_1 V}{RT} \qquad n_2 = \frac{P_2 V}{RT} \qquad \cdots$$

Substitution in Eq. (1-13) then gives

$$\frac{PV}{RT} = \frac{P_1 V}{RT} + \frac{P_2 V}{RT} + \cdots \qquad \text{or} \qquad P = P_1 + P_2 + \cdots$$

The pressure-volume behavior of gas mixtures can also be studied by adding the components separately or together to a chamber of variable volume in which the gas is subjected to some fixed constant pressure. Results could be obtained for the volume of the gas mixture and the volumes of the components put separately in the chamber and subjected to the same pressure as that on the gas mixture. If the result

$$V = V_1 + V_2 + V_3 + \cdots \tag{1-14}$$

is obtained, the gas mixture is said to obey *Amagat's law of partial volumes*. This law can be shown to depend upon ideal behavior of the gas mixture and the components in the gas mixture by the procedure used above for Dalton's law.

In dealing with mixtures we frequently make use of the fractional contribution of each component to some total property of the mixture. Such contributions can be expressed in terms of the *mole fraction* x_i of the ith component, defined as

$$x_i = \frac{n_i}{n} \tag{1-15}$$

By writing

$$n = n_1 + n_2 + n_3 + \cdots$$

and then dividing by n we obtain

$$1 = \frac{n_1}{n} + \frac{n_2}{n} + \frac{n_3}{n} + \cdots$$

or

$$1 = x_1 + x_2 + x_3 + \cdots \tag{1-16}$$

Thus the sum of such fractional quantities over all the components of the mixture is unity.

We can similarly define the *pressure fraction* as P_i/P and the *volume fraction* as V_i/V. When the ideal-mixture laws hold, we can express these as

$$\frac{P_i}{P} = \frac{n_i RT/V}{nRT/V} = \frac{n_i}{n} = x_i \qquad (1\text{-}17)$$

and

$$\frac{V_i}{V} = \frac{n_i RT/P}{nRT/P} = \frac{n_i}{n} = x_i \qquad (1\text{-}18)$$

Thus, both the pressure fraction and the volume fraction are equal to the mole fraction in these ideal-gas mixtures.

The mass of a mole of a gas can be determined, as illustrated in Sec. 1-3, from a measurement of the mass of a gas sample and the volume it occupies at some temperature and pressure. For a gas mixture we write the molar mass as M_{av}, and we can use Eq. (1-10) again to deduce its value.

The mass of 1 mol of a gas mixture is related to the mole fractions of the components and the molar masses of these components by

$$M_{av} = x_i M_1 + x_2 M_2 + x_3 M_3 + \cdots \qquad (1\text{-}19)$$

From this relation a value of M_{av} can be calculated from given values of the x_i's and M_i's. From a measured value of M_{av}, the mole fractions of the components can be deduced, however, only for a two-component mixture. Then there are only two mole-fraction terms, x_1 and x_2 in Eq. (1-19), and they are related by the expression $x_1 + x_2 = 1$. The two equations in the two unknowns x_1 and x_2 can be solved for these quantities.

If one can refrain from anticipating the explanation of gas properties in terms of molecular theory, the properties of gas mixtures embodied in Dalton's and Amagat's laws seem quite remarkable. If gases are thought of as nothing more than homogeneous fluids, it is not at all obvious that they should obey such simple laws. The independent behavior of the components of a gas mixture was, in fact, one of the results that stimulated the concept of the molecular nature of matter.

1-6 The Nonideal Behavior of Gases

The PVT behavior of gases has so far been presumed to follow Boyle's and Gay-Lussac's laws and, with the mole concept, to lead to the result $PV = nRT$. When measurements are extended to higher pressures, or even when very accurate measurements are made at ordinary pressures, it is found that deviations from these laws do exist.

An actual gas exhibits, to some extent, deviations from the ideal-gas law, and when these deviations are recognized, the gas is said to behave as a *real*, *nonideal*, or *imperfect gas*.

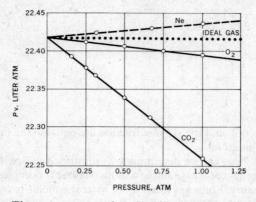

FIGURE 1-5
Accurate data for the product PV for 1 mol of the gas as a function of pressure at 0°C. (*Adapted from L. P. Hammett, "Introduction to the Study of Physical Chemistry," Copyright 1952 by McGraw-Hill, Inc. Used by permission of McGraw-Hill Book Company.*)

The very accurate data for a few gases at relatively low pressures shown in Fig. 1-5 indicate that ideal behavior, which requires the product PV to be independent of P, is not strictly followed. To represent such behavior analytically, the expression $PV = nRT$ must be modified. To do so it is convenient to specify 1 mol of a gas and to indicate this stipulation by writing a special symbol V. Then behavior like that shown in Fig. 1-5 can be described by

$$PV = RT(1 + bP) \qquad (1\text{-}20)$$

where b is characteristic of the gas and moreover is a function of temperature.

This nonideal gas behavior sometimes must be considered when gas densities are used to obtain molecular masses. For ideal behavior, Eq. (1-10), which can be rewritten as

$$\frac{d}{P} = \frac{M}{RT} \qquad (1\text{-}21)$$

applies. For ideal behavior the gas density is proportional to the pressure, and the same value of the ratio d/P will be obtained at any pressure. For real gases, as Fig. 1-6 illustrates, d/P is a function of P. The linearity of the curves of Fig. 1-6 suggests the relation

$$\frac{d}{P} = \frac{M}{RT}(1 + b'P) \qquad (1\text{-}22)$$

where b' is a constant dependent on the nature of the gas and on the temperature. The molecular mass is obtained from the value of d/P in the limit of zero pressure, where the nonideal effects, responsible for the b' term, make no contribution. [The empirical constant b' of Eq. (1-22) can be related to b of Eq. (1-20), as suggested in Prob. 1-24.]

The equations that are written to describe the PVT behavior of gases or other states of matter are known as *equations of state*. The equation $PV = nRT$

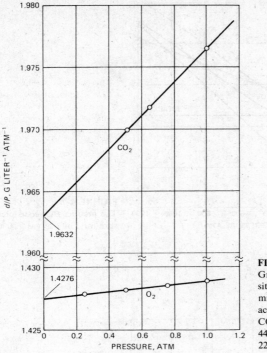

or $PV = RT$ is the equation of state for an ideal gas. Equation (1-20) is the first of several equations of state we shall encounter in our studies of real gases. Various equations are used. This variety results from the highly individualistic behavior of real gases, to the extent that they deviate from ideal behavior, and the need for equations which deal with various pressure and temperature ranges.

Examples of the dependence of PV on pressure at higher pressures are shown in Fig. 1-7. For a given gas, the shapes of the curves displayed for different temperatures are illustrated in Fig. 1-8.

The deviation from ideality is conveniently shown by plotting the ratio PV/RT versus pressure. For ideal behavior this ratio will be unity for all pressures and temperatures. For real gases deviation from unity will occur.

The quantity PV/RT is so convenient in the discussion of the nonideality of gases that it is given the symbol Z, according to

$$Z = \frac{PV}{RT} \tag{1-23}$$

Z is called the *compressibility factor*.

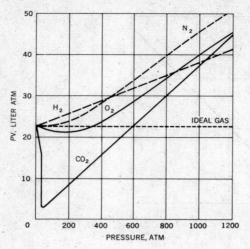

FIGURE 1-7
The product PV versus pressure for 1 mol of gas at 0°C.

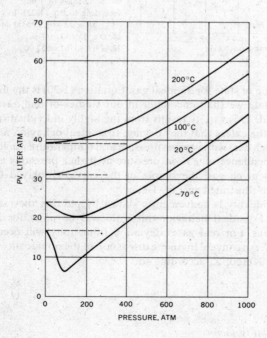

FIGURE 1-8
PV-versus-P curves for methane at four different temperatures. [*From H. M. Kvalnes and V. L. Gaddy, J. Am. Chem. Soc.,* **53**:*394 (1931).*]

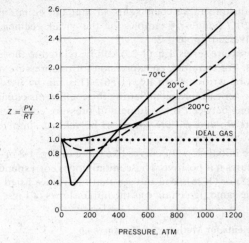

$$Z = \frac{PV}{RT}$$

PRESSURE, ATM

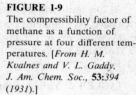

FIGURE 1-9
The compressibility factor of methane as a function of pressure at four different temperatures. [*From H. M. Kvalnes and V. L. Gaddy, J. Am. Chem. Soc.*, **53**:*394* (*1931*).]

Ideal behavior requires Z to have the value unity at all pressures and temperatures. Any gas imperfection is immediately apparent as the difference between the observed value of Z and unity. The compressibility factor for methane at a number of temperatures is shown in Fig. 1-9.

Analytical expressions to represent gas behaviors like those of Fig. 1-9 can be developed by adding additional terms to Eq. (1-16). Thus we could write

$$\frac{PV}{RT} = 1 + B_P(T)P + C_P(T)P^2 + \cdots \tag{1-24}$$

or, for n mol,

$$\frac{PV}{nRT} = 1 + B_P(T)P + C_P(T)P^2 + \cdots \tag{1-25}$$

Such an equation of state is known as a *virial equation.* The coefficients $B_P(T)$ and $C_P(T)$, known as *virial coefficients,* are written with a subscript P to show that they are members of a pressure-term series. The parenthetical T's remind us that the virial coefficients are temperature-dependent.

You will see in Sec. 2-16 that an alternative virial equation involving a series of volume terms has a particular importance. For 1 mol of gas the volume-series equation is

$$\frac{PV}{RT} = 1 + \frac{B_V(T)}{V} + \frac{C_V(T)}{V^2} + \cdots \tag{1-26}$$

The values of $B_V(T)$, $C_V(T)$ and higher coefficients in the volume-series equation can be obtained by adjusting these coefficients so that the equation is consistent with measured PVT values. Examples of the virial coefficients reported for methane are given in Table 1-2.

The coefficients of the pressure series, Eq. (1-25), can be related to those of the volume series, Eq. (1-26). For example, an expression for the pressure as a function of the volume can be written from Eq. (1-26). This can be used in Eq. (1-25) to obtain a volume-series expression. Setting the coefficients equal to B_V, C_V, etc., gives the relations between the volume and pressure coefficients. The *second virial* coefficients B_P and B_V are found to be related simply by $B_P = B_V/RT$.

At low temperatures, the initial slope of curves like those of Fig. 1-8 or 1-9 is negative. At high temperatures it is positive. These initial slopes correspond to the B coefficients of Eq. (1-25) or (1-26). You can see that the values listed for $B(T)$ in Table 1-2 undergo the same sign change as the initial slopes of Figs. 1-8 and 1-9.

TABLE 1-2 Virial Coefficients for Methane for Pressures up to About 400 atm

For $PV/RT = 1 + B_V/V + C_V/V^2 + D_V/V^3$			
t, °C	B_V, liters mol^{-1}	C_V, liters^2 mol^{-2}	D_V, liters^3 mol^{-3}
0	−0.05335	0.002393	26×10^{-5}
25	−0.04282	0.002102	15
50	−0.03423	0.002150	1.3
100	−0.02100	0.001834	2.7
150	−0.01140	0.001640	3.5
200	−0.00416	0.001514	4.3
250	0.00149	0.001420	5.2
300	0.00598	0.001360	5.7
350	0.00966	0.001330	5.9

For $PV/RT = 1 + B_P P + C_P P^2 + D_P P^3$			
t, °C	B_P, atm^{-1}	C_P, atm^{-2}	D_P, atm^{-3}
0	−0.002380	-0.900×10^{-6}	30×10^{-9}
25	−0.001750	$+0.450 \times 10^{-6}$	18
50	−0.001291	1.390	8.2
100	−0.000686	1.486	4.3
150	−0.000328	1.252	2.1
200	−0.000107	0.993	1.03
250	0.000035	0.769	0.58
300	0.000127	0.599	0.32
350	0.000188	0.473	0.17

Source: D. R. Douslin, R. H. Harrison, R. T. Moore, and J. P. McCullough, *J. Chem. Eng. Data,* **9**:358 (1964).

One isotherm, in a plot like that of Fig. 1-9, has an initial slope of zero. For that temperature, in the limit of zero pressure, $d(PV)/dP$ is zero and PV is a constant. The temperature of this isotherm is appropriately called the *Boyle temperature*. Thus at the Boyle temperature the coefficient $B_P(T)$ or $B_V(T)$ is zero.

1-7 Condensation of Gases, the Critical Point, and the Law of Corresponding States

A set of isotherms which extend into the region where condensation occurs is shown for CO_2 in Fig. 1-10. The data for this figure came from the pioneering work of Andrews in 1869 on the behavior of gases. The higher-temperature isotherms show only slight deviations from the hyperbolic curves expected for an ideal gas. Lower-temperature isotherms also conform somewhat, at the low-pressure large-volume end, to ideal behavior. As the pressure is increased at such temperatures, the volume decreases approximately according to Boyle's law, until a point on the dotted line of Fig. 1-10 is reached. At this point the gas begins to condense to a liquid. Now the volume decreases as the gas is continually converted into a liquid, the pressure staying constant at the equilibrium vapor pressure for that temperature. When the left limit marked off by the dotted line is reached, the entire gas has been condensed and further application of pressure results in only a minor decrease in volume, as shown by the steep section at the left end of the isotherm. The region beneath the dotted curve represents situations in which liquid and vapor coexist. Outside that region the system contains a single fluid.

Consider an isotherm that passes through the liquid-vapor region. It can be followed from the low-pressure right-hand side of Fig. 1-10 through the liquid-vapor region that lies below the dotted curve and then up through the

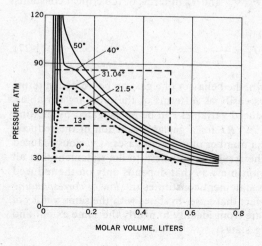

FIGURE 1-10
Isotherms of CO_2 near the critical point. (*From E. D. Eastman and G. K. Rollefson, "Physical Chemistry." Copyright 1947 by McGraw-Hill, Inc. Used by permission of McGraw-Hill Book Company.*)

left-hand region above the dotted curve. Through the liquid-vapor region the proportion of liquid will increase as we move from right to left. All this tempts us to describe the region to the right of the liquid-vapor region as gas and that to the left as liquid.

Now suppose that a sample is moved from one of these regions to the other, as suggested in Fig. 1-10, so that the two-phase region is not traversed. The sample will consist of a single fluid while these pressure and temperature changes are occurring. Thus there will be a gradual change in properties, and at no stage will there be a discontinuity that suggests a conversion from one type of fluid, a gas, into another type, a liquid. Thus states which we call gas and liquid can be reached from each other without a discontinuous change. We thus recognize the *continuity of states*.

The continuity of states suggests that we can treat the parts of the isotherms on both the right and the left sides of the liquid-vapor region just as we do the isotherms that do not pass through this region. Only the two-phase region itself introduces new features not encountered in studies of nonideal "gases."

Of particular interest in the study of the nonideal behavior of gaseous systems is the unique isotherm that touches the top of the dotted curve of Fig. 1-10. This isotherm is called the *critical isotherm*. Its temperature, the *critical temperature*, is seen to be the highest temperature at which the two-phase gas-liquid combination can exist. The point at which this isotherm shows its horizontal point of inflection is called the *critical point*, and the pressure and volume per mole at this point are known as the *critical pressure* and *critical volume*. Some data for the critical points are shown in Table 1-3.

The deviations from ideal behavior shown by real gases appear to depend on the difference between the conditions of the gas and those of the critical point. This suggests that it might be convenient to introduce new variables that relate P, V, and T to the value of these variables at the critical point. To do this, we define the *reduced variables* P_R, V_R, and T_R in terms of the critical constants P_C, V_C, and T_C as

$$P_R = \frac{P}{P_C} \qquad V_R = \frac{V}{V_C} \qquad T_R = \frac{T}{T_C} \qquad (1\text{-}27)$$

If the critical constants are known, the behavior of a gas can be treated in terms of the reduced variables just as easily as in terms of the ordinary variables.

The usefulness of these reduced variables can be investigated by plotting the compressibility factor $Z = PV/RT$ for a gas as a function of the reduced pressure. When this is done for a number of different gases at various reduced temperatures, as in Fig. 1-11, the result is equivalent to the statement that all gases deviate from ideal behavior in a way that depends only on the reduced pressure and temperature. This statement constitutes the *law of corresponding states*. The name expresses the fact that gases in states with the same values of the reduced variables will deviate from ideality to nearly the same extent and are said to be in corresponding states.

TABLE 1-3 Values of P, V, and T at the Critical Point

Gases in order of molecular mass

Gas	P_C, atm	V_C, liters mol^{-1}	T_C, K
H_2	12.8	0.070	33.3
He	2.26	0.062	5.3
CH_4	45.6	0.099	190.2
NH_3	112.2	0.072	405.6
H_2O	217.7	0.056	647.2
CO	35.0	0.090	134.4
Ne	26.9	0.044	44.8
N_2	33.5	0.090	126.0
NO	65	0.058	179
O_2	49.7	0.074	154.4
CH_3OH	78.5	0.118	513.1
HCl	81.6	0.087	324.6
Ar	48.0	0.076	150.7
CO_2	72.8	0.094	304.2
SO_2	77.7	0.123	430.4
$n-C_5H_{12}$	33.0	0.310	470.3
Cl_2	76.1	0.124	417
C_6H_6	47.9	0.256	561.6
Kr	54.3	0.107	209.4
Xe	57.9	0.120	289.8

The law of corresponding states introduces a considerable simplification into the treatment of nonideal gases. The uniform behavior of such gases in terms of the reduced variables should not, however, obscure the fact that critical data, which are characteristic of each gas, are implicit in the reduced variables. No "ideal" generalization such as $PV = nRT$ is possible when the behavior of gases is studied accurately or over a wide range of pressures and temperatures.

1-8 Graham's Law of Effusion

Let us now turn from the PVT behavior of gases to two properties of a different type.

The process by which a gas moves from a higher to a lower pressure through a porous wall or a tube of very small diameter is known as *diffusion*. If the process consists of molecular rather than bulk flow through an orifice, the word *effusion* is used. The rate with which a gas effuses under given conditions is a property characteristic of the gas. Since it is rather difficult, both experimentally and theoretically, to deal with the absolute rates of effusion of gases through an orifice of well-defined dimensions, attention is usually confined to the relative rates of effusion of gases.

Measurements of the effusion ratios of a number of gases were made by Thomas Graham in 1829. He found that at a constant temperature and at a

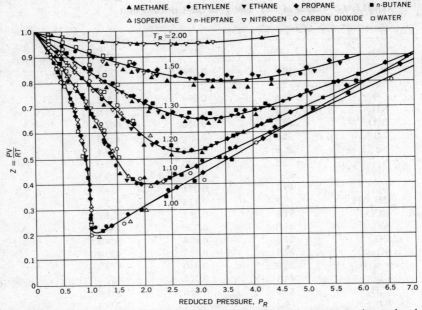

FIGURE 1-11 The compressibility as a function of the reduced pressure at various reduced temperatures. [*From Gouq-Jen Su, Ind. Eng. Chem.,* **38**:*803* (*1946*).]

constant pressure drop the rates of effusion of various gases are inversely proportional to the square roots of the densities of the gases. This relationship resulted when the rates of effusion were measured in terms of the volume of gas at a particular temperature and pressure that effused per unit time. If the effusion rate is denoted by v and the density by d, this result, for gases 1 and 2, is written

$$\frac{v_1}{v_2} = \sqrt{\frac{d_2}{d_1}} \qquad (1\text{-}28)$$

An alternative and frequently convenient form of this law can be obtained by recalling the relation between gas density and molar mass given by Eq. (1-10). The density ratio of two gases at the same pressure and temperature is seen to be equal to the ratio of the molar masses of the two gases. With this result Graham's law becomes

$$\frac{v_1}{v_2} = \sqrt{\frac{M_2}{M_1}} \qquad (1\text{-}29)$$

20 PROPERTIES OF GASES

This effusion law makes itself evident, for example, in the fact that a system which is satisfactorily leakproof to air, molar mass about 29 g mol⁻¹, may fail to hold gases like hydrogen, molar mass 2 g mol⁻¹, or helium, molar mass 4 g mol⁻¹.

Graham's law provides yet another property of gases for which the theory of the nature of gases must account.

1-9 The Viscosity of Gases

When a fluid flows through a pipe, tube, or trough, flow occurs only as a result of the application of a driving force to the fluid. The resistance to flow which this force overcomes depends on the viscosity of the fluid.

A quantitative definition of the viscosity can be made by considering the flow of a fluid near the bottom of a rectangular container as shown in Fig. 1-12. A gas or liquid flowing in a tube or trough forms a very thin stationary layer in contact with the walls of the container. The force required to make the fluid flow results from having to push the fluid relative to this stationary layer. The flow can be understood in terms of a force required to move a layer of fluid relative to another layer. This force is proportional to the areas A of the layers and to the difference in velocity v maintained between the layers and is inversely proportional to the distance l between the layers. The *coefficient of viscosity*, or simply the viscosity, is introduced as a proportionality factor, and the equation

$$\text{Force} = \eta \frac{Av}{l} \tag{1-30}$$

can be written. The viscosity can be thought of as the force required to make a layer of unit area move with a unit velocity greater than that of another layer a unit distance away. Thick liquids, such as molasses, have high viscosities; thin liquids, such as gasoline, have low viscosities. Gases have relatively much lower (but not zero) viscosities.

In practice, one often measures viscosity from the rate of flow through a cylindrical tube. Again, the fluid forms a stationary layer along the wall, and a force is required to make the fluid flow through the tube. By integrating the force required to move the annular layers of the fluid relative to this layer,

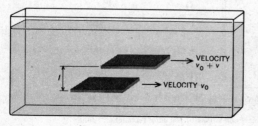

FIGURE 1-12
The relative motion of two layers of a fluid. The viscosity of the fluid requires a force to be applied to the upper layer to keep it moving relative to the lower layer.

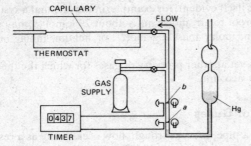

FIGURE 1-13
The components of a gas vis-
cosimeter. The flow of about
5 cm³ of gas, the volume between a and b, through a 0.2-
mm-diameter tube 30 cm long
is timed. [*From J. Olbregts
and J. P. Walgraeve, J. Chem.
Educ.,* 53:602 (1976).]

Eq. (1-30) can be extended to give the rate of flow through a cylindrical tube as a function of the viscosity η, the radius of the tube R, and the pressure difference $P_2 - P_1$ applied over the tube of length l. The result is

$$\text{Rate of flow} = \frac{\pi(P_1 - P_2)R^4}{8l\eta} \qquad (1\text{-}31)$$

Measurement of all the quantities other than η in Eq. (1-31) would allow this quantity to be determined.

In practice an apparatus like that of Fig. 1-13 is used to measure gas viscosity. The time it takes for a given volume of the gas under study to be driven through a capillary is measured. This result is compared with the time it takes for the same volume of a reference gas, such as nitrogen, to be driven through the same capillary. The measured times are inversely proportional to the rates of flow; i.e., a short time corresponds to a large flow rate and vice versa. Since the terms $P_1 - P_2$, R, and l of Eq. (1-31) are the same for the two gases, we can set up the ratio

$$\frac{t}{t_{\text{ref}}} = \frac{\eta}{\eta_{\text{ref}}} \qquad (1\text{-}32)$$

TABLE 1-4 Gas Viscosities at 25°C

Gas	Viscosity, μP†	Gas	Viscosity, μP†
H_2	90	O_2	208
He	197	Ar	227
H_2O	98	CO_2	150
CO	176	HI	172
N_2	178	Hg	250

† The unit of poise is related to SI units by $1\text{ P} = 10^{-1}\text{ kg m}^{-1}\text{ s}^{-1}$ and $1\,\mu\text{P} = 10^{-7}\text{ kg m}^{-1}\text{ s}^{-1}$.
Source: S. Dushman, "Scientific Foundations of Vacuum Techniques," John Wiley & Sons, Inc., New York, 1949.

TABLE 1-5 Viscosity of Propane Gas at Atmospheric Pressure

T, K	μP	T, K	μP
307.6	86.6	488.4	127.0
343.7	93.0	542.9	141.5
386.3	102.5	603.2	155.0
440.7	117.2	652.0	168.0

Source: J. Olbergts and J. P. Walgraeve, *J. Chem. Educ.*, **53**:602 (1976).

Thus, measurement of t and t_{ref} together with a known value of η_{ref} allows a value of η to be deduced. Some results for different gases are shown in Table 1-4, and results for the single gas propane at different temperatures are given in Table 1-5.

When all the quantities in Eq. (1-31) are given in cgs units, the viscosity η is obtained in cgs units, which are given the name *poise* (P). This unit, not in the SI system, is that with which viscosity data have generally been reported. In systematic calculations the conversion $1 \text{ P} = 10^{-1} \text{ kg m}^{-1} \text{ s}^{-1}$ must be used. In the following chapter use will be made of the measured viscosities to obtain information on the size of the molecules and other features of their behavior.

PROBLEMS

1-1. What volume will a gas behaving ideally occupy at a pressure of 0.032 atm if its volume is 3.00 liters at 12.0 atm and the temperature is held constant?

1-2. An ideal gas occupies a volume of 8.93 liters at 100°C. What volume will it occupy at 0°C, the pressure remaining constant?

1-3. Plot P versus V at 0 and 100°C for a sample of gas that obeys Boyle's and Gay-Lussac's laws and has a volume of 1 liter at 0°C and 1 atm. Use any convenient volume and pressure ranges.

1-4. The pressure unit of 1 atm is defined as 760 mmHg (read "millimeters of mercury"), or 760 torr. Show that this definition is consistent with the relation $1 \text{ atm} = 101{,}325 \text{ N m}^{-2}$. The density of mercury is 13.59 g ml^{-1}, and the acceleration due to gravity is 9.81 m s^{-2}.

1-5. (*a*) Sketch a surface showing the pressure, as the variable along the vertical axis, as a function of the volume and the temperature of a sample of a gas that behaves ideally. (*b*) What is the mathematical expression for this surface?

1-6. A gas sample of constant composition has a volume of 1.00 liter at the sea-level conditions of 1 atm and 15°C. What is its volume at 500 km, where the pressure is 1.6×10^{-11} atm and the temperature is 1580 K?

1-7. Calculate the factor by which the volume and the diameter of a balloon would increase as it rose from sea level and 20°C to the stratosphere at 40 km. At that altitude the pressure is 0.0030 atm, and the temperature is about -12°C.

1-8. Calculate the average molecular mass in the earth's atmosphere at 500 km. At that altitude the pressure is 1.6×10^{-11} atm, the temperature is, on the average, 1580 K, and the density is 2.2×10^{-12} g liter^{-1}.

1-9. Assuming ideal-gas behavior, calculate the mass of 1 mol of gas if the gas is found to have a density of 0.9816 g liter^{-1} at $\frac{1}{2}$ atm pressure and 0°C.

1-10. Assuming ideal-gas behavior, what is the density in grams per liter of uranium hexafluoride gas at its normal boiling point, 56°C?

1-11. An evacuated 1-liter bulb weighs 57.4923 g. What will it weigh filled with helium to a pressure of 1 atm if the temperature is 21°C?

1-12. In a laboratory study, a reaction produced a gaseous product which just filled a 200-ml collection chamber when an open-ended mercury leveling device was raised so that the mercury in the open arm was 22.6 mm above the level confining the gas. Atmospheric pressure that day was 752.6 mmHg and room temperature was 22°C. (*a*) What was the STP volume of the gas? (*b*) How many moles of the gas were collected?

1-13. What would be the volume of a helium-filled balloon with a lifting power of 100 lb, or 45 kg? Assume an air temperature of 20°C and 1 atm pressure.

1-14. In 1804, Gay-Lussac ascended to 23,000 ft over Paris in an army (Napoleon's) balloon. He collected air samples by opening previously evacuated glass bulbs. (He found the composition of the air to be unchanged, except for water content, at all altitudes.) If he used $\frac{1}{2}$-liter bulbs, about how many moles and how many grams of oxygen did he have to analyze for in the bulbs opened at sea level and at the highest altitude?

*1-15. The pressure of the earth's atmosphere at any altitude is the result of the weight of the atmosphere above that altitude. (*a*) For a column of the atmosphere of unit cross section express the change in pressure dP for an increment in height dh. Assume ideal-gas behavior and let M be the average mass per mole. (*b*) Assuming constant composition, constant temperature, and a constant gravitational force, integrate the expression of part (*a*) to obtain the barometric equation for the variation of pressure with altitude.

1-16. Experiments by Sir William Ramsey and by Lord Rayleigh around 1894 led to a gas residue remaining when all the then known components of air had been removed. The density of the residue was 1.63 g liter^{-1} at 25°C and 1 atm. What element had they obtained?

1-17. At an altitude of 500 km the earth's atmosphere consists primarily of nitrogen molecules and oxygen atoms. From the results of Prob. 1-8, estimate the proportion of these species.

1-18. The density of acetic acid vapor at its normal boiling point, 118.5°C, is 3.15 g liter^{-1}. If the vapor is assumed to behave ideally, what value does this lead to for the mass of 1 mol of acetic acid? Compare with the value calculated from the formula CH_3COOH.

1-19. The density of the vapor in equilibrium with solid NH_4Cl was found [W. H. Rodebush and J. C. Michalek, *J. Am. Chem. Soc.*, **51**:748(1929)] to be 0.1373 g liter^{-1} at a temperature of 596.9 K and a pressure of 0.253 atm. From these data deduce the nature of the vapor of ammonium chloride under these conditions.

1-20. Extrapolation of density-divided-by-pressure data at the ice point, 0°C, to zero pressure gives the limiting d/P value for CO_2 as 1.96346 g liter^{-1} atm^{-1} and the value for O_2 as 1.42764. Using only these values and the formulas CO_2 and O_2, obtain a value for the atomic mass of oxygen on the $^{12}C = 12.000$ atomic-mass scale. (Note that on this scale the atomic mass of carbon is 12.011 amu.)

1-21. Using the data of the Prob. 1-20, obtain values for the gas constant R.

1-22. The following pressure-density data have been reported for CO_2 at 0°C.

Make a graph of d/P versus P and extrapolate to $P = 0$. (a) If the atomic-mass data in the endpapers are accepted, what value does this result give for the gas constant R? (b) If the value of the gas constant is accepted, what value is obtained for the mass of 1 mol of CO_2?

Pressure, atm	1	$\frac{2}{3}$	$\frac{1}{2}$	$\frac{1}{3}$	$\frac{1}{4}$	$\frac{1}{6}$
Density, g liter^{-1}	1.976757	1.314850	0.985047	0.655957	0.491691	0.327609

*1-23. Using the data of Prob. 1-22, develop virial equations for CO_2 at $0°C$ (a) of the type of Eq. (1-24) and (b) of the type of Eq. (1-26).

1-24. Writing Eq. (1-20) for a sample containing n mol gives $PV = nRT(1 + bP)$. If bP is small compared with unity, the empirical constant b can be related to the corresponding constant b' of Eq. (1-22). Find this relation and use the data for CO_2 in Fig. 1-5 and Prob. 1-22 to test it.

1-25. A gas mixture contains 100 g of hydrogen and 100 g of nitrogen. Assuming ideal behavior of the gas mixture, calculate the volume if the pressure is 1 atm and the temperature is $25°C$. What are the mole fractions, volume fractions, and pressure fractions of each gas?

*1-26. In acetic acid vapor both monomer, CH_3COOH, and dimer, $(CH_3COOH)_2$, molecules are generally present. The volume of 1.00 g of acetic acid vapor at $25°C$ and 0.020 atm was found [F. H. MacDougall, *J. Am. Chem. Soc.*, **58**:2585(1936)] to be 11.04 liters. (a) Obtain a relation between the number of moles n_m of monomer and the number of moles n_D of dimer by describing a 1.00-g mass of acetic acid. (b) Obtain another relation involving n_m and n_D by describing the volume occupied by 1.00 g of acetic acid, assuming that the monomer-dimer mixture behaves as an ideal gas. (c) Calculate values for n_m and n_D and for the partial pressures of monomer and dimer. (d) Calculate the equilibrium constant $P_D/P_m{}^2$ for the 2 monomer $\rightleftharpoons$ dimer reaction at $25°C$.

*1-27. The density of acetic acid vapor at the normal boiling point, $118.5°C$, is given as 3.15 g liter^{-1}. (a) Calculate the fraction of the vapor that is monomer and the fraction that is dimer. (b) What are the partial pressures and the equilibrium constant?

1-28. The density of steam at $100°C$ and 1 atm is 0.5976 g liter^{-1}. (a) What is the compressibility factor? (b) Since water molecules tend to associate with each other, the imperfection of water vapor might be attributed to the formation of dimers or other polymers. With this view the compressibility factor is less than unity because the number of gas molecules is reduced. Calculate the moles of gas molecules in 1 mol of water vapor to account for the compressibility factor. (c) What, according to part (b), is the fraction of dimer water molecules present?

1-29. Using the data of Table 1-2, plot the compressibility factor of methane at 0, 200, and $350°C$ for pressures up to 350 atm.

1-30. From the data of Table 1-2 calculate d/P in grams per liter-atmosphere for CH_4 at $\frac{1}{3}, \frac{1}{2}, \frac{2}{3}$, and 1 atm for a temperature of $0°C$. Treat these values as if they were direct experimental quantities and deduce the mass of 1 mol of CH_4.

*1-31. The following pressure–molar-volume data at $25°C$ have been given for CH_4 by D. R. Donslin, R. H. Harrison, R. T. Moore, and J. P. McCullough, *J. Chem. Eng. Data*, **9**:358(1964). Obtain the virial coefficients B, C, and D for the virial equation (1-26) and compare with the coefficients given for CH_4 at $25°C$ in Table 1-2. (A graphical treatment in which the intercept is B and the slope is C can be set up, or a data-fitting computer program can be used.)

V, liters mol^{-1}	P, atm	V, liters mol^{-1}	P, atm
1	23.4749	$\frac{1}{7}$	140.549
$\frac{1}{2}$	45.2050	$\frac{1}{8}$	159.756
$\frac{1}{3}$	65.5470	$\frac{1}{9}$	180.084
$\frac{1}{4}$	84.8673	$\frac{1}{10}$	202.147
$\frac{1}{5}$	103.539	$\frac{1}{11}$	226.684
$\frac{1}{6}$	121.969	$\frac{1}{12}$	254.577

1-32. (a) Write volume-series and pressure-series virial equations to include only the second, B, and the third, C, coefficient terms. (b) Show that the coefficients are related by $B_P = B_V/RT$ and $C_P = (C_V - B_V^2)/(RT)^2$.

*1-33. The following data for CO_2 at $0°C$ are given by E. B. Millard, "Physical Chemistry for Colleges," 5th ed., McGraw-Hill Book Company, New York, 1941.

P, atm	Density, g liter^{-1}	P, atm	Volume per mole, liters
$\frac{1}{6}$	0.327609	15.07	1.320
$\frac{1}{4}$	0.491691	17.70	1.100
$\frac{1}{3}$	0.655957	21.22	0.880
$\frac{1}{2}$	0.985047	26.67	0.660
$\frac{2}{3}$	1.314850		
1	1.976757		

(a) Obtain values of B and C to fit these data to a $PV = RT(1 + B_P P + C_P P^2)$ equation. (b) What are the corresponding values of B and C for the equation

$$PV = RT\left(1 + \frac{B_V}{V} + \frac{C_V}{V^2}\right)?$$

1-34. The density of CO_2 at $0°C$ and 34 atm is 97 g liter^{-1}. At $0°C$ and 50 atm the density is 925 g liter^{-1}. (a) Use the equation obtained in Prob. 1-33 to prepare a graph of PV versus P and extend the curve past 50 atm. (b) Plot the points obtained from the measured densities at 34 and 50 atm. Explain.

1-35. Use the virial-coefficient data of Table 1-2 and the critical-point data of Table 1-3 to calculate several different points for T_R corresponding to $0°C$ for methane on a Z-versus-P_R graph like that of Fig. 1-11. Compare with the curves of Fig. 1-11.

1-36. Use the data of Fig. 1-11 and Table 1-3 to estimate the value of Z for methane at $-70°C$ and 200 atm. Compare with the value estimated from Fig. 1-9. Repeat for $20°C$ and 200 atm.

1-37. Attempt to sketch the P-versus-V isotherms for 1 mol of water in the temperature range 25 to $400°C$. Use the following data, as guides, and indicate what parts of the sketch are determined by these data. (The range of data is such that linear P and V scales are awkward. You may want to resort to logarithmic scales.)

1. The critical point has $t_C = 374°C$, $P_C = 218$ atm, and the critical density $d_C = 0.4$ g ml^{-1}.
2. The normal boiling point of water is $100°C$.

3. The equilibrium vapor at the normal boiling point behaves nearly ideally.
4. The vapor pressure of water at 25°C is 0.03 atm, and the vapor then behaves ideally.
5. The density of liquid water is 1 g ml^{-1} and is not very sensitive to temperature or pressure.

1-38. The curve for $T_R = 1.00$ of Fig. 1-11 has a vertical section. In view of the horizontal section of the critical curve of Fig. 1-10, explain why this is to be expected.

1-39. A tube with a porous wall allows 0.53 liter of N_2 to escape per minute from a pressure of 1 atm to an evacuated chamber. What amount will escape under the same conditions for (a) He, (b) CCl_4, and (c) UF_6?

1-40. In 1846 Graham reported the following results for the time taken, relative to air, for given volumes of various gases to effuse. How well do these data substantiate Graham's law of effusion?

Gas	Air	O_2	CO	CH_4	CO_2
Time	1.000	1.053	0.987	0.765	1.218

REFERENCES

NEVILLE, R. G.: The Discovery of Boyle's Law, *J. Chem. Educ.*, **39**:356 (1962). The circumstances, apparatus, and results of Boyle's pressure-volume experiments.
ROGERS, E. M.: "Physics for the Enquiring Mind," pp. 416–424, Princeton University Press, Princeton, N.J., 1960. An entertaining but thought-provoking discussion of temperature and temperature-measuring devices.
PARTINGTON, J. S.: "An Advanced Treatise on Physical Chemistry," vol. 1, pp. 551ff, Longmans, Green & Co., Ltd., London, 1949. A very informative and rather complete summary of studies of gases, including information on all aspects of gases dealt with in this text. Many references to original work.
MIDDLETON, W. E. KNOWLES: "A History of the Thermometer," The Johns Hopkins Press, Baltimore, 1966. An attractively illustrated account of the early developments of thermometers and temperature scales.
"International Critical Tables," vol. 3, p. 3, McGraw-Hill Book Company, New York, 1928. A collection of data on the *PVT* behavior of gases.
OTT, J. B., J. R. COATES, and H. T. HALL, JR.: Comparisons of Equations of State in Effectively Describing *PVT* Relations, *J. Chem. Educ.*, **48**:515 (1971).

2 THE KINETIC-MOLECULAR THEORY OF GASES

In the empirical study of the physical behavior of gases in Chap. 1, no answers were given to such natural questions as: Why is it that a gas obeys Boyle's law? Gay-Lussac's law? Why does it show the nonideality it does? In this chapter an attempt will be made to understand gases so that some questions of this type can be answered. The ideas that are developed, however, are not primarily introduced to provide an explanation of the gas laws. It is the quantitative look into the molecular world provided by this theory that is our principal interest.

It is not possible to deduce the molecular nature of gases directly from the measured properties. These data must be used in a roundabout manner. The procedure is to guess at the underlying characteristics of gases and on this basis to deduce their physical properties. A comparison of the deduced properties with those observed allows the usefulness of the guesses to be estimated. A body of assumptions, such as that concerning gases, is called a *model*.

2-1 The Kinetic-Molecular Gas Model

The gas laws and the properties of gases described in Chap. 1 can be understood through a model according to which gases are composed of a large number of small particles, called *molecules,* that move about and collide with each other and with the walls of the container. The complex mass of chemical knowledge that led to thinking in terms of molecules need not be investigated here. It is enough to recognize that the concept of chemical substances as being composed of particles evolved gradually and that during the 1800s the concept of atoms and molecules became generally accepted. This idea was applied primarily to chemical studies and proved valuable in explaining the compositions and transformations of chemical substances, but such applications do not lead to information on the size, shape, or properties of the individual molecules.

This molecular concept of matter, however, provided the basis on which the behavior of gases could be studied. In this application, known as the *kinetic-molecular theory of gases,* much information on the properties of individual molecules appeared. The work of Ludwig Boltzmann, James Clerk Maxwell, and R. J. E. Clausius during the late 1800s was primarily responsible for the development of the theory.

The kinetic-molecular model for a gas is described by the following statements:

1. A gas is made up of a large number of particles, or molecules, that are small in comparison with both the distances between them and the size of the container.

2. The molecules are in continuous, randomly directed motion.

3. Newtonian mechanics, in particular the relation $f = ma$ or $f = md(mu)/dt$, can be used to describe the interaction of the molecules with the walls of the vessel containing the gas.

4. The molecules are independent of each other and interact only during brief collisions. These collisions, on the average, are perfectly elastic; i.e., none of the translational energy is lost by conversion into internal energy of the molecules.

5. The kinetic energy due to the translational motion of a mole of gas molecules is equal to $\frac{3}{2}RT$.

The first step with this model is to show that it does lead to the observed properties of gases.

2-2 The Pressure of a Gas

The force exerted by N molecules, each of mass m, contained in a cubic container of side l can be calculated on the basis of the kinetic-molecular model. The outward-directed force exerted by these molecules is the result of their collisions with the walls of the container. To maintain a fixed volume, an inward-directed pressure must be applied through the agency of the walls of the container.

To begin with, only one of the N molecules will be considered. Let its velocity, i.e., its speed and direction, be **u**. Boldface type is used to indicate a *vector* quantity. The symbol u will indicate the magnitude of the velocity, i.e., the speed. The velocity can be resolved into the components with magnitudes u_x, u_y, and u_z, which are perpendicular to the walls of the container, as drawn in Fig. 2-1.

The force exerted when a molecule collides with the wall of a container can be calculated from Newton's second law of motion. This law states that the rate of change of the momentum of a particle in a given direction is equal to the force acting on the particle in that direction. The momentum with which the molecule approaches wall A of Fig. 2-1 is mu_x. After the collision the molecule moves away from the wall. The u_y and u_z components are unchanged, but the direction along the x axis is reversed, as shown in Fig. 2-2. The momentum of the molecule is now $-mu_x$. Thus at impact the wall exerts a force directed in toward the gas that produces a momentum change of $mu_x - (-mu_x) = 2mu_x$.

The number of such momentum changes per second at wall A is the number of collisions per second which the molecule makes with wall A. Since

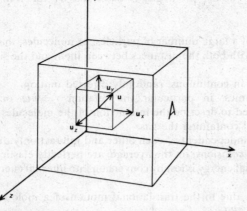

FIGURE 2-1
Coordinate and molecular velocity and velocity components for the derivation of gas pressure.

the molecule travels a distance u_x along the x direction in 1 s, and since the distance traveled between collisions with side A is $2l$, the number of collisions per second with A is $u_x/2l$.

The force exerted by wall A on this one molecule is the rate of change of momentum, i.e., the change of momentum per second, it produces. This force is $(2mu_x)(u_x/2l)$.

Since the pressure is the force per unit area, the pressure exerted by side A is

$$\frac{(2mu_x)(u_x/2l)}{l^2} = \frac{mu_x^2}{l^3} = \frac{mu_x^2}{V}$$

where $V = l^3$ is the volume of the container. Now we can recognize that the pressure is the same for all walls of the container. Thus we can discard the restriction "by side A." We therefore have

$$P = \frac{mu_x^2}{V} \tag{2-1}$$

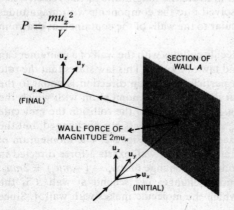

SECTION OF WALL A

(FINAL)

WALL FORCE OF MAGNITUDE $2mu_x$

(INITIAL)

FIGURE 2-2
The reversal of u_x as a result of a collision with wall A.

Now let us consider N molecules, instead of just one, to be in the cubic container. Our model claims that these molecules act independently of each other and that each molecule will make a contribution to the pressure according to a term like that of Eq. (2-1). Summation of the pressure contributions of the N molecules can be indicated as

$$P = \sum_{i}^{N} \frac{(mu_x^2)_i}{V} \tag{2-2}$$

We can consider all molecules to have the same mass, but the model assumes that the molecules move in various directions with various speeds. Thus u_x and u_x^2 will be different for each molecule. If the average value of u_x^2 for the N molecules of the gas is denoted by $\overline{u_x^2}$, Eq. (2-2) can be developed to show the pressure required to confine N molecules to a volume V to be

$$P = \frac{m}{V} \sum_{i} (u_x^2)_i = \frac{m}{V} N \overline{u_x^2} = \frac{Nm\overline{u_x^2}}{V} \tag{2-3}$$

More convenient, however, is a relation between the pressure due to the N molecules and an average of the speeds of the molecules. The relation between the square of the components of the velocities and the square of the magnitude of the velocity itself is, as will be recalled from the more familiar resolution along two perpendicular directions,

$$u^2 = u_x^2 + u_y^2 + u_z^2 \tag{2-4}$$

For a large number of molecules moving in random directions

$$\overline{u_x^2} = \overline{u_y^2} = \overline{u_z^2} \tag{2-5}$$

and therefore

$$\overline{u^2} = 3\overline{u_x^2} \tag{2-6}$$

Substitution of Eq. (2-6) in Eq. (2-3) gives the desired relation between P and $\overline{u^2}$:

$$P = \frac{\frac{1}{3}Nm\overline{u^2}}{V} \quad \text{or} \quad PV = \tfrac{1}{3}Nm\overline{u^2} \tag{2-7}$$

This important equation is as far as one can go in explaining the basis for the pressure of a gas from the first four of the kinetic-molecular postulates of Sec. 2-1. The fifth postulate will be introduced in the following section. A result that can be compared with the empirical gas laws will then be obtained.

2-3 Kinetic Energies and Temperature

Frequently it is convenient to deal with kinetic energies rather than with the molecular speeds. The average kinetic energy of one molecule of a gas is written as $\overline{ke}$. This quantity is related to the average squared molecular speed by

$$\overline{ke} = \tfrac{1}{2}m\overline{u^2} \tag{2-8}$$

Equation (2-7) can thus be developed from $PV = \tfrac{2}{3}N(\tfrac{1}{2}m\overline{u^2})$ to

$$PV = \tfrac{2}{3}N\overline{ke} \tag{2-9}$$

The empirical results of Chap. 1 dealt with molar quantities of gases. The present theoretical results involve the properties of individual molecules, such as $\overline{ke}$. These can be brought together through Avogadro's number $\mathfrak{N}$, which relates the number of molecules N to the number of moles n by the relation

$$N = n\mathfrak{N} \tag{2-10}$$

Equation (2-7) can now be written

$$PV = \tfrac{2}{3}n(\mathfrak{N}\overline{ke}) \tag{2-11}$$

Furthermore, we introduce the term KE to denote the kinetic energy of an Avogadro's number of molecules and rewrite Eq. (2-11) as

$$PV = \tfrac{2}{3}n\,\text{KE} \tag{2-12}$$

Now we can introduce the fifth postulate of Sec. 2-1, that the kinetic energy due to the translational motions of 1 mol of gas molecules is equal to $\tfrac{3}{2}RT$. Introduction of this expression in Eq. (2-12) brings the kinetic-molecular derivation to the result

$$PV = nRT \tag{2-13}$$

Some of the empirical results given in Chap. 1 have now been derived. The expression $PV = \tfrac{2}{3}n\,\text{KE}$, together with the postulate $\text{KE} = \tfrac{3}{2}RT$, in effect reproduces Boyle's and Gay-Lussac's laws. Furthermore, the derived result $PV = nRT$ holds, to the extent that the postulates of the kinetic-molecular theory are followed, for any gas; i.e., it is independent of the molecular mass or any other property characteristic of the molecules of the gas. This expression can hold for two different gases at the same temperature and pressure only if equal volumes of the different gases contain the same number of moles or molecules. Thus Avogadro's hypothesis is derived. Dalton's and Amagat's laws follow directly from the original postulates since, on the assumption that molecules are noninteracting and occupy no appreciable volume, one set of gas molecules will have no effect on another set.

2-4 Numerical Values for Molecular Energies and Molecular Speeds

The intention in this chapter is to reveal some of the properties, in particular energies and speeds, of the molecules of which a gas is composed. It has been shown so far that the qualitative postulates of the kinetic-molecular theory are a sufficiently accurate description of the molecular world to lead to the ideal-gas laws. Quantitative information is obtained from the postulate that the translational kinetic energy of an Avogadro's number of molecules is $\frac{3}{2}RT$.

The value of 8.3143 J K^{-1} mol^{-1} obtained in Sec. 1-4 for R yields for the translational-motion contribution to the energy of 1 mol of any ideal gas at 25°C the result

$$\tfrac{3}{2}RT = \tfrac{3}{2}(8.314 \text{ J K}^{-1} \text{ mol}^{-1})(298 \text{ K}) = 3720 \text{ J mol}^{-1}$$

The average kinetic energy of one molecule of the gas can be expressed as

$$\overline{ke} = \frac{KE}{\mathfrak{N}} = \frac{3}{2} \frac{R}{\mathfrak{N}} T \tag{2-14}$$

Since much of our subsequent work will be concerned with the energies of individual molecules and atoms, it is useful to introduce a new constant k, called *Boltzmann's constant,* as

$$k = \frac{R}{\mathfrak{N}} = 1.3806 \times 10^{-23} \text{ J K}^{-1} \tag{2-15}$$

Boltzmann's constant is therefore the gas constant per molecule, and the average kinetic energy of one molecule is

$$\overline{ke} = \tfrac{3}{2}kT \tag{2-16}$$

The average kinetic energy of a gas molecule at 25°C is

$$\overline{ke} = \tfrac{3}{2}(1.3806 \times 10^{-23} \text{ J K}^{-1})(298 \text{ K}) = 6.17 \times 10^{-21} \text{ J}$$

Although the values of these kinetic energies are very important and will become progressively more meaningful, they are at first difficult to appreciate. It is therefore worthwhile to consider a related and more readily visualized molecular property, the speeds with which molecules travel.

The kinetic energy of an Avogadro's number of molecules can be written

$$\text{KE} = \mathcal{N}(\tfrac{1}{2}m\overline{u^2}) = \tfrac{1}{2}M\overline{u^2} \tag{2-17}$$

where M is the molar mass. A molecular-speed term is obtained by combining this result with the kinetic-molecular-theory postulate $\text{KE} = \tfrac{3}{2}RT$ to get $\overline{u^2} = 3RT/M$, or

$$\sqrt{\overline{u^2}} = \sqrt{\frac{3RT}{M}} \tag{2-18}$$

The cumbersome term $\sqrt{\overline{u^2}}$ is known as the *root-mean-square* (rms) *speed*. This term implies that the magnitude of each of the molecular velocities is squared; then the average value of the squared terms is taken; and finally the square root of this average is determined. The rms speed is different from a simple average speed but only by about 10 percent, as will be seen in Sec. 2-7. For the present, the values of $\sqrt{\overline{u^2}}$ will be taken as indicative of average molecular speeds.

For N_2 at 25°C, for example, M has the SI unit value 0.02802 kg, and we obtain, with the unit relation $1\ \text{J} = 1\ \text{kg m}^2\ \text{s}^{-2}$,

$$\sqrt{\overline{u^2}} = \sqrt{\frac{3(8.3143)(298)}{0.02802}} = 515\ \text{m s}^{-1} = 1150\ \text{mi h}^{-1} \tag{2-19}$$

Table 2-1 shows additional results for a few simple molecules. Notice that since the average kinetic energy at a given temperature is the same for all molecules regardless of their mass, light molecules have greater speeds than heavy molecules.

You should also notice that just as molecular speeds can be interpreted in terms of components in three perpendicular directions by

TABLE 2-1 Average Speeds of Gas Molecules (Equal to 0.921 $\sqrt{\overline{u^2}}$) at 25°C (298 K) and 1000°C (1273 K)

Gas	25°C		1000°C	
	m s^{-1}	mi h^{-1}	m s^{-1}	mi h^{-1}
H_2	1770	3960	3660	8180
He	1260	2820	2600	5830
H_2O	590	1320	1220	2730
N_2	470	1060	970	2190
O_2	440	990	910	2050
CO_2	380	840	780	1740
Cl_2	300	670	620	1380
HI	220	490	450	1010
Hg	180	400	370	830

$$u^2 = u_x{}^2 + u_y{}^2 + u_z{}^2$$

so also can the average kinetic energy. Multiplication by $\frac{1}{2}m$ gives

$$\tfrac{1}{2}m\overline{u^2} = \tfrac{1}{2}m\overline{u_x{}^2} + \tfrac{1}{2}m\overline{u_y{}^2} + \tfrac{1}{2}m\overline{u_z{}^2}$$

or

$$\overline{ke} = (\overline{ke})_x + (\overline{ke})_y + (\overline{ke})_z \tag{2-20}$$

It follows, since the average component energies are equal and $\overline{ke} = \frac{3}{2}kT$, that

$$(\overline{ke})_x = (\overline{ke})_y = (\overline{ke})_z = \tfrac{1}{2}kT \tag{2-21}$$

The three perpendicular directions in which a velocity can be resolved are examples of *degrees of freedom*. We thus can say that *the average translational energy of a molecule per degree of freedom is $\frac{1}{2}kT$*. You will see that this statement is a far-reaching and important guide in the studies of molecular energies.

2-5 Distribution of Molecular Velocities in One Dimension

Having considered and tabulated some average molecular speeds, it is now appropriate to investigate in more detail the molecular speeds that contribute to the average values already worked out.

The basic relation for handling questions regarding the number of molecules that have various speeds, or energies, is *Boltzmann's distribution*. The deduction of this important relationship is best done after the quantum rules that govern molecular behavior are studied. Here the results of the derivation, which will be given in Chap. 4, will be anticipated, and the Boltzmann distribution will be used to obtain the desired information on the distribution of molecular speeds.

According to the model on which the kinetic-molecular theory is based, the molecules of a gas are moving with a variety of speeds and directions, i.e., with various velocities. These velocities can be pictured on a diagram, like that of Fig. 2-3, where each point represents, by its distance from the origin, the magnitude of the velocity, i.e., the speed of a particle, and, by its direction from the origin, the direction in which the particle is moving. It helps to claify the diagram, even if it is really not necessary, to add the vector velocity arrows.

Since gases behave similarly in all directions, i.e., are *isotropic*, a diagram like that of Fig. 2-3 for a large enough number of molecules must be the same in all directions. The nature of the variation in the density of the velocity points as one goes out from the origin is the distribution of molecular speeds, which will be investigated in this and the following sections.

First we investigate the distribution along a particular direction, say the x direction. We must find the fraction dN/N of the velocity points in the interval

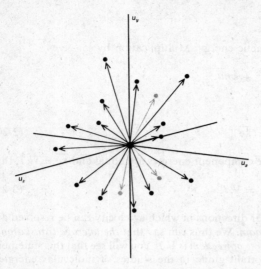

FIGURE 2-3
The velocities of molecules. Each magnitude and direction is represented by the length and direction of the arrow.

u_x to $u_x + du_x$. Molecules moving to the front in Fig. 2-3 have positive u_x values; those to the back have negative u_x values. Thus, for a given absolute value of u_x, corresponding to a given x-component speed, there will be du_x intervals along the positive and negative u_x axes, as shown in Fig. 2-4. The x-component energy of the molecules whose velocity dots lie in these du_x intervals is $\frac{1}{2}mu_x^2$. According to the Boltzmann distribution expression, the fraction of the molecules in such ranges is proportional to an exponential term whose exponent is the ratio of the kinetic energy $\frac{1}{2}mu_x^2$ to kT. Explicitly,

$$\frac{dN}{N} = Ae^{-(1/2)mu_x^2/kT}\,du_x \qquad (2-22)$$

where A is a proportionality constant. This constant can be evaluated by recognizing that integration of the right side of Eq. (2-22) over all possible

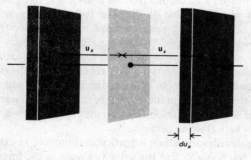

FIGURE 2-4
The two volume elements that together contain all the molecules moving with speeds between u_x and $u_x + du_x$ for u_x positive or negative.

values of u_x, that is, from $u_x = -\infty$ to $u_x = +\infty$, must account for all the velocity points. Thus we can write

$$\int_{-\infty}^{+\infty} Ae^{-(1/2)mu_x^2/kT}\,du_x = 1 \tag{2-23}$$

so that the proportionality constant A is given by

$$A = \frac{1}{\displaystyle\int_{-\infty}^{+\infty} e^{-(1/2)mu_x^2/kt}\,du_x} \tag{2-24}$$

The value of the integral is seen from Appendix A-1 to be $\sqrt{2\pi kT/m}$, and we obtain

$$A = \sqrt{\frac{m}{2\pi kT}} \tag{2-25}$$

Finally, the equation for the distribution over the velocities along the x direction for a sample of N molecules can be written as

$$\frac{dN/N}{du_x} = \sqrt{\frac{m}{2\pi kT}}e^{-(1/2)mu_x^2/kT} \tag{2-26}$$

Graphs of this one-dimensional distribution function are shown for two temperatures for the example of nitrogen in Fig. 2-5.

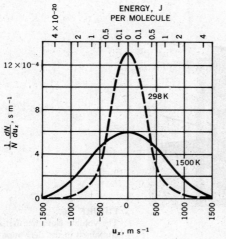

FIGURE 2-5
The distribution of velocities in the x direction for N_2 molecules at 298 and 1500 K.

2-6 Distribution of Molecular Velocities in Three Dimensions

Let us now pass over the distribution of molecular speeds in two dimensions and proceed directly to the more important case of the distribution in three-dimensional space. Again the Boltzmann distribution will provide the basis on which the distribution expression is derived. The original derivation of the result that will be obtained was given by Maxwell, and the result itself is now known as the *Maxwell-Boltzmann distribution* expression.

In the one-dimensional problem that we have solved we dealt with the density of points along any direction, e.g., along the direction of the x axis. These one-dimensional distributions can be combined to give the fraction of the molecules that have velocity components between u_x and $u_x + du_x$, u_y and $u_y + du_y$, and u_z and $u_z + du_z$. This is equal to the fraction of points that occur in the outlined cubic element of volume in Fig. 2-6. It is given analytically as the product of the fractions of the molecules that lie in the appropriate volume elements perpendicular to the axes. Thus we can write

$$\frac{dN}{N} = \left(\sqrt{\frac{m}{2\pi kT}} e^{-(1/2)mu_x^2/kT} \, du_x \right) \left(\sqrt{\frac{m}{2\pi kT}} e^{-(1/2)mu_y^2/kT} \, du_y \right)$$

$$\left(\sqrt{\frac{m}{2\pi kT}} e^{-(1/2)mu_z^2/kT} \, du_z \right)$$

or

$$\frac{dN/N}{du_x du_y du_z} = \left(\frac{m}{2\pi kT} \right)^{3/2} e^{-(1/2)m(u_x^2 + u_y^2 + u_z^2)/kT} \tag{2-27}$$

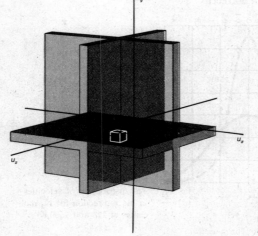

FIGURE 2-6
The volume elements that are combined in the derivation of $dN/N \, du_x \, du_y \, du_z$.

This result gives the distribution of the molecular velocities in that it expresses the density of points in volume elements such as that of Fig. 2-6.

What is wanted, however, is the density of points within a volume element like that of Fig. 2-7, because all points lying in such an element correspond to the same speed u. Since this spherical shell has a volume $4\pi u^2\, du$, the number of points in this element is obtained by multiplying Eq. (2-27) by the ratio of $4\pi u^2\, du$ to $du_x\, du_y\, du_z$. In this way, and with the substitutions $u^2 = u_x^2 + u_y^2 + u_z^2$, one obtains the three-dimensional speed-distribution equation

$$\frac{dN/N}{du} = 4\pi \left(\frac{m}{2\pi kT}\right)^{3/2} u^2 e^{-(1/2)mu^2/kT} \tag{2-28}$$

This Maxwell-Boltzmann distribution expression is plotted for N_2 at two temperatures in Fig. 2-8. Notice that at low temperatures the molecules tend to have speeds bunched in a relatively narrow range. At higher temperatures the distribution is broader, and—what is for some purposes very important—the high-speed end of the curve tends to spread out to much higher speeds.

From Eq. (2-28) the distribution of molecules over the range of kinetic energy, rather than over speeds, can be obtained. The relation $\epsilon = \frac{1}{2}mu^2$ converts Eq. (2-28) into

$$\frac{dN/N}{d\epsilon} = \frac{2}{\sqrt{\pi}(kT)^{3/2}} \sqrt{\epsilon}\ e^{-\epsilon/kT} \tag{2-29}$$

At a given temperature a single curve describes the distribution of molecules of any mass over the possible translational energies.

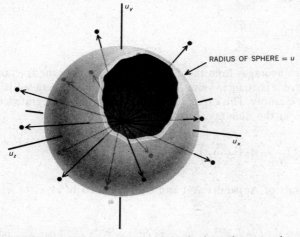

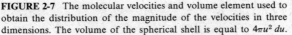

FIGURE 2-7 The molecular velocities and volume element used to obtain the distribution of the magnitude of the velocities in three dimensions. The volume of the spherical shell is equal to $4\pi u^2\, du$.

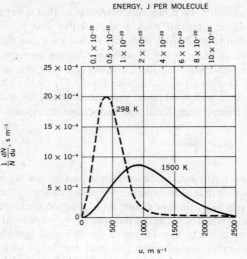

ENERGY, J PER MOLECULE

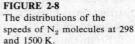

FIGURE 2-8
The distributions of the speeds of N_2 molecules at 298 and 1500 K.

2-7 The Root-Mean-Square, the Average, and the Most Probable Speeds

Knowledge of the distribution curve allows the calculation of any desired kind of average speed. The Maxwell-Boltzmann distribution can, for example, be used to calculate a rms speed which, by other means, has already been shown (Sec. 2-4) to have the value

$$\sqrt{\overline{u^2}} = \sqrt{\frac{3kT}{m}} = \sqrt{\frac{3RT}{M}}$$

To obtain such averages from the distribution expression, the fraction of molecules that have a particular value of the quantity to be averaged is first multiplied by that quantity. This expression is then summed, or integrated, over all possible values of the quantity. Thus $\overline{u^2}$ is given by

$$\overline{u^2} = \int_{u=0}^{u=\infty} u^2 \frac{dN}{N} = 4\pi \left(\frac{m}{2\pi kT}\right)^{3/2} \int_0^\infty u^4 e^{-(1/2)kT} \, du$$

One of the integrals of Appendix A-1 can then be used to give for $\overline{u^2}$ the result

$$\overline{u^2} = 4\pi \left(\frac{m}{2\pi kT}\right)^{3/2} \left(\frac{2kT}{m}\right)^{5/2} \tfrac{3}{8}\sqrt{\pi} = \frac{3kT}{m} \tag{2-30}$$

Finally, $\sqrt{\overline{u^2}} = \sqrt{3kT/m}$, as obtained from the kinetic-molecular treatment of Sec. 2-4.

In a similar way one obtains the average speed from

$$\bar{u} = \int_{u=0}^{u=\infty} u \frac{dN}{N}$$

Substitution of the distribution relation and evaluation of the integral gives

$$\bar{u} = \sqrt{\frac{8kT}{\pi m}} = \sqrt{\frac{8RT}{\pi M}} \qquad (2\text{-}31)$$

Finally, one sometimes deals with the most probable speed, i.e., the speed corresponding to the maxima of the curves like those of Fig. 2-8. To determine this speed it is only necessary to differentiate the distribution expression, set the result equal to zero, and determine the value of u this relation implies. In this way, if α denotes the most probable speed,

$$\alpha = \sqrt{\frac{2kT}{m}} = \sqrt{\frac{2RT}{M}} \qquad (2\text{-}32)$$

These three speeds, the rms, the average, and the most probable, are not very different, being in the ratio

$$\sqrt{\overline{u^2}} : \bar{u} : \alpha = 1.00 : 0.92 : 0.82$$

One or the other of these usually provides sufficient information on the molecular speeds in any given problem. Where a more detailed knowledge of the molecular-speed distribution is required, reference must be made to the distribution expression or to graphs like those of Fig. 2-8.

As a consequence of the Boltzmann distribution, we have learned a great deal more about the speeds with which molecules travel than we did by our earlier comparison of the result $PV = \frac{1}{3}\mathfrak{N}m\overline{u^2}$ and $PV = RT$. While obtaining the detailed distribution of molecular speeds, we were able to verify, by recalculating $\sqrt{\overline{u^2}}$, that the approach of this section is consistent with the simple kinetic-molecular-theory result.

2-8 Effusion and Molecular Beams

Most phenomena that we deal with depend on the average three-dimensional properties of the many molecules of a gas sample. The pressure of a gas is an example. But some phenomena depend in a more detailed way on the collisions of gas molecules with a surface, as in absorption and heterogeneous catalysis;

and some depend on the passage of gas molecules through a pinhole or slit in a container, as in effusion and molecular-beam studies. In such cases, a knowledge of the randomly directed velocities of gas molecules, as developed in Sec. 2-7, is not sufficient. The necessary extensions are now presented.

Molecular beams now provide a valuable technique for studies of the properties and reactions of molecules, and the analysis here can be directed toward an understanding of some of their features. Such beams result when a gas is allowed to pass through a small hole in a sample container into an evacuated region in such a way that molecular collisions are infrequent. Then the molecules travel in straight lines, and a beam of molecules can be selected by appropriate baffles.

Let us first calculate the average speed of the molecules of such a beam, which is taken to be in the positive x direction. The required average of only those molecules having a velocity component in the positive x direction is

$$\bar{u}_{x(+)} = \frac{\int_0^\infty u_x \frac{dN/N}{du_x} du_x}{\int_0^\infty \frac{dN/N}{du_x} du_x}$$

or with Eq. (2-26),

$$\bar{u}_{x(+)} = \frac{\sqrt{\frac{m}{2\pi kT}} \int_0^\infty u_x e^{-(1/2)mu_x^2/kT} du_x}{\sqrt{\frac{m}{2\pi kT}} \int_0^\infty e^{-(1/2)mu_x^2/kT} du_x}$$

The denominator, the fraction of molecules having x-component velocities in the positive x direction, is found, with the integrals of Appendix A-1, to have the expected value of $\frac{1}{2}$. Evaluation of the numerator, again using the integrals of Appendix A-1, then yields

$$\bar{u}_{x(+)} = \sqrt{\frac{2kT}{\pi m}}$$

With $\bar{u} = \sqrt{8kT/\pi m}$ from Sec. 2-7, we can write

$$\bar{u}_{x(+)} = \frac{1}{2}\bar{u} \tag{2-33}$$

Thus the average speed in the x direction of molecules moving in the positive x direction is equal to half the average speed of the molecules of the gas.

Since the speed distributions in the x, y, and z directions are independent of each other, the result $\bar{u}_{x(+)} = \frac{1}{2}\bar{u}$ applies both to molecules moving in random directions in a container and to the directionally selected molecules in a molecular beam.

With this result we can immediately obtain an effusion equation that shows the rate with which molecules will escape from a hole in a container. This equation applies when the gas pressure is low enough and the hole, a "pinhole," is small enough for the molecules to pass through in individual rather than collective flow.

Consider a unit area of a container wall. How many molecules per second will collide with this area or, if the area represents a hole, will pass through it? Let there be N^* molecules per unit volume so that $N^*/2$ are moving in the positive x direction. The number of these reaching the unit surface area per second is equal to the number in the region with unit cross-section area and length $\bar{u}_{x(+)} = \bar{u}/2$. Thus

$$\text{Rate of effusion} = \frac{N^*}{2}\bar{u}_{x(+)} = \tfrac{1}{4}N^*\bar{u}$$

or

$$\text{Rate of effusion} = N^*\sqrt{\frac{kT}{2\pi m}} = N^*\sqrt{\frac{RT}{2\pi M}} \tag{2-34}$$

This is the important effusion equation that gives the rate with which the molecules of a gas escape in an effusion process. The result is in agreement with the empirical Graham's law that sets the number of molecules escaping per unit time inversely proportional to the square root of the molecular mass. Non-ideality of gases enters, as for other ideal-gas expressions, to upset this mass dependence and the predicted temperature dependence. (The equation is often claimed to apply and to be found to be valid when the conditions for molecular effusion are not met. Confusion results from the fact that a diffusion process, which consists of a gas flow involving intermolecular and wall collisions, has the same dependence on variables as the effusion process.)

The effusion process has been used to determine the low vapor pressures exerted by rather nonvolatile solids. In this method, the *Knudsen method*, a sample is enclosed in a heated chamber with a small effusion hole. The pressure within the Knudsen cell is the equilibrium vapor pressure of the solid. The value of this pressure is deduced by measuring the weight loss of the sample that results from the effusion of its vapor out of the effusion hole.

The rate of effusion is expressed by Eq. (2-34) in terms of molecules per unit time per unit effusion hole area. A rate of sample weight loss can be obtained by multiplying the expression of Eq. (2-34) by m, or $M/\mathfrak{N}$, the mass of a molecule. We obtain, still for a unit-area aperture

$$\text{Rate of weight loss} = \frac{MN^*}{\mathfrak{N}}\sqrt{\frac{RT}{2\pi M}}$$

Then, if w represents the change in weight of the sample in unit time, we can write

$$w = \frac{MN^*}{\mathfrak{N}} \sqrt{\frac{RT}{2\pi M}} \tag{2-35}$$

This result can be put in more convenient form by expressing N^* as $n\mathfrak{N}/V$ and inserting the ideal-gas-law relation $V = nRT/P$ for V. The pressure within the Knudsen cell, i.e., the vapor pressure of the sample, can then be written as

$$P = w \left(\frac{2\pi RT}{M}\right)^{1/2} \tag{2-36}$$

where w is the sample weight loss per unit time as a result of effusion through a hole of unit cross-section area. If SI units are used for the quantities on the right of Eq. (2-36), the pressure will be obtained in units of newtons per square meter. Conversion to atmospheres depends on the relation 1 atm = 101,325 N m^{-2}.

2-9 The Mean Free Path, Collision Diameter, and Collision Number

So far we have been able to treat molecules as point particles, i.e., to ignore the size of molecules and the possibility of collisions between molecules. This implies that information about these molecular collisions cannot be obtained from calculations, such as those of Sec. 2-2, of the pressure of a gas.

Section 2-10 will show that, in contrast, the viscosity of a gas is dependent on the collisions of the gas molecules with each other. A kinetic-molecular derivation of the viscosity of a gas will therefore lead to added information about the experiences of the rapidly moving gas molecules. Three questions might come to mind about the collision properties of the molecules of a gas: How far, on the average, does a molecule travel between collisions? How many collisions per second does a molecule experience on the average? And how many collisions per second take place in a given volume of a gas? How little we are at home in the molecular world is impressed on us when we try to guess the answers to these questions.

Before proceeding to the calculation of gas viscosities, we shall show that the answers to all three questions can be related to one molecular property, i.e., the diameter of the molecules of the gas. The use of only one quantity, the diameter, to define the size of the molecules means that the simplifying assumption of spherical molecules is being made and furthermore that the effective size of the molecules is independent of the energy involved in the molecular collision. Molecules are treated as hard spheres with no mutual attractions.

Let us consider a particular molecule A with diameter d in Fig. 2-9, moving in the direction indicated. If the speed of molecule A is $\bar{u}$, it will travel a distance

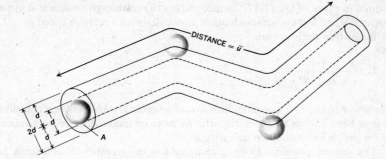

FIGURE 2-9 Path swept out by molecule A in 1 s. Molecules are shown greatly enlarged compared with the distance between them, and under conditions such as STP many more collisions will occur in a 1-s interval.

of $\bar{u}$ m in 1 s. Furthermore, if only A is assumed to move and all the other molecules remain stationary, molecule A will collide in 1 s with all the molecules that have their centers within the cylinder of Fig. 2-9. The volume of the cylinder whose radius is equal to the molecular diameter d is $\pi d^2 \bar{u}$. The number of molecules in the cylinder is $\pi d^2 \bar{u} N^*$, where N^* is the number of molecules per unit volume. The mean free path, i.e., the distance traveled between collisions, is the length of the cylinder $\bar{u}$ divided by the number of collisions occurring as the molecule traverses this length. Thus, if L is introduced to denote the mean-free-path length,

$$L = \frac{\bar{u}}{\pi d^2 \bar{u} N^*} = \frac{1}{\pi d^2 N^*} \tag{2-37}$$

A more detailed calculation shows that this result is not exactly correct. The assumption that only molecule A moves implies a relative speed of the colliding molecules of $\bar{u}$. In fact, as Fig. 2-10 suggests, if the molecules are all moving with speed $\bar{u}$, all types of collisions will occur, ranging from glancing collisions, where the relative speed may be very small, to head-on collisions, where the relative speed is $2\bar{u}$. It turns out that in an average collision the molecules move at right angles to each other and the relative speed is $\sqrt{2}\bar{u}$. A correct result can be

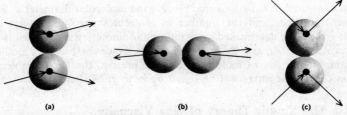

(a)   (b)   (c)

FIGURE 2-10 Types of molecular collisions. The relative velocity in an average collision is $\sqrt{2}\bar{u}$. (a) Relative velocity $= 0$. (b) Relative velocity $= 2\bar{u}$. (c) Relative velocity $= \sqrt{2}\bar{u}$.

obtained in place of Eq. (2-37) by recognizing that although molecule A moves a distance $\bar{u}$ in 1 s, it collides with other molecules with a relative speed of $\sqrt{2}\,\bar{u}$. The mean free path is then

$$L = \frac{1}{\sqrt{2}\pi d^2 N^*} \tag{2-38}$$

The answer to the first question, how far a molecule travels between collisions, has now been shown to depend on the number of molecules per unit volume and on the as yet unknown quantity d.

The second problem to be investigated is the number of collisions per second that a molecule makes. This *collision frequency* is denoted by Z_1. In relation to the other molecules, the molecule A travels with an effective speed equal to $\sqrt{2}\,\bar{u}$. The number of collisions per second of this molecule is therefore equal to the number of molecules in a cylinder of radius d and of length $\sqrt{2}\,\bar{u}$. We thus have

$$Z_1 = (\sqrt{2}\,\bar{u})(\pi d^2)N^* = \sqrt{2}\pi d^2 \bar{u} N^* \tag{2-39}$$

The last of the three problems to be investigated is the number of collisions occurring in a unit volume per unit time. As can be imagined, this quantity is of considerable importance in understanding the rates of chemical reactions. The number of collisions per second per unit volume is called the *collision rate*, denoted by Z_{11}.

The collision rate Z_{11} is closely related to the collision frequency Z_1. Since there are N^* molecules per unit volume and each of these molecules has Z_1 collisions per second, the total number of collisions per second in a unit volume will be $\frac{1}{2}N^*Z_1$. The factor $\frac{1}{2}$ ensures that each collision will not be counted twice. We therefore obtain

$$Z_{11} = \frac{1}{2}\sqrt{2}\pi d^2 \bar{u}(N^*)^2 = \frac{1}{\sqrt{2}}\pi d^2 \bar{u}(N^*)^2 \tag{2-40}$$

The collision frequency, the collision rate, and the mean free path have now been expressed in equations that involve the molecular diameter d. Since the molecular speeds and the number of molecules per cubic meter of a particular gas can be determined, only molecular diameters need be known in order to evaluate L, Z_1, and Z_{11}. Many methods, as we shall see, are available for determining the size of molecules. For the present, the kinetic-molecular derivation of gas viscosities will be relied upon to yield these values.

2-10 The Kinetic Theory of Gas Viscosity

The molecular theory, in accordance with which molecules move freely about, with large spaces between them, might seem at first to imply a complete absence of viscous forces. The source of viscous drag in gases can be understood, however, by focusing attention on two layers of a gas moving parallel to each other but with different flow rates. Over and above their random thermal motion, the molecules in the faster-moving layer will have a greater velocity component in the direction of flow than the molecules in the slower layer. But because of their random movement, some of the molecules of the faster layer will move into the slower layer, imparting to it their additional momentum in the direction of flow and thus tending to speed it up. Likewise, some of the molecules of the slower layer will reach the faster layer and tend to slow it down. The net effect of this exchange of molecules is a tendency toward equalizing the flow rates of the different parts of the gas. The viscous effect is just the difficulty of moving one part of a fluid with respect to another part.

A simplified kinetic-molecular theory of viscosity can be given on this basis. Consider two layers of unit area, separated by a distance equal to the mean free path, of a gas flowing as in Fig. 2-11. The gas flows in the y direction with a velocity v and a velocity gradient dv/dz; that is, the flow rate increases by an amount dv for each increment of distance dz in the z direction. Since the layers under consideration are a mean free path apart, on the average, a molecule leaving one layer will arrive in the other layer, collide, and contribute its greater or lesser momentum in the flow direction to that layer. According to a simple approach which gives almost the correct result, one-third of the molecules have an x component of velocity, one-third a y component, and one-third a z component. Only the third with a z component are effective in the momentum exchange between the gas layers.

The momentum increment with each transferred molecule adds to or

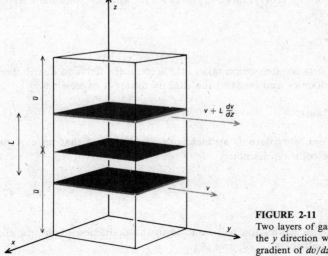

FIGURE 2-11
Two layers of gas moving in the y direction with a velocity gradient of dv/dz.

subtracts from a new layer is $mL\, dv/dz$, that is, m times the difference in flow velocity of the two layers. The force between the two layers can be calculated from the rate of change of momentum. It is now necessary, therefore, to calculate the number of these molecular transfers per second.

The numbers of molecules that move up from the lower layer and down from the upper layer in 1 s are those which are in the lower volume shown and have a z component of velocity upward and those which are in the upper volume shown and have a z component of velocity downward. These two volumes are both drawn with a length $\bar{u}$ m, so that in 1 s all the molecules with the appropriate direction of flight will have passed the shaded cross section. If there are N^* molecules per cubic meter, there will be $\frac{1}{6}N^*\bar{u}$ molecules in the lower volume, all of which will move into the upper volume in 1 s. A similar number will move down into the lower volume in 1 s. The total interchanges per second between layers is therefore $\frac{1}{3}N^*\bar{u}$.

The rate of change of momentum is then $(\frac{1}{3}N^*\bar{u})mL\, dv/dz$, and according to Newton's law this is the force exerted by the layers on each other. Thus

$$f = \tfrac{1}{3}N^*\bar{u}mL\frac{dv}{dz} \tag{2-41}$$

The coefficient of viscosity η has previously been defined by Eq. (1-30). In differential form, and for the unit-layer areas of this derivation, the equation, comparable to Eq. (1-30), is

$$f = \eta\frac{dv}{dz} \tag{2-42}$$

Comparison of Eqs. (2-41) and (2-42) gives for the kinetic-molecular derivation of viscosity

$$\eta = \tfrac{1}{3}N^*\bar{u}mL \tag{2-43}$$

A more detailed derivation takes into account the detailed distribution of molecular velocities and leads to the slightly different expression

$$\eta = \tfrac{1}{2}N^*\bar{u}mL \tag{2-44}$$

It is convenient to replace L by means of Eq. (2-38) so that an expression involving the collision diameter,

$$\eta = \frac{\bar{u}m}{2\sqrt{2\pi}d^2} \tag{2-45}$$

is obtained. This expression will be used in the deduction of the molecular properties d and then L, Z_1, and Z_{11}.

This important result permits the calculation of the collision diameter of a gas molecule from measurements of the viscosity of the gas.

For a given gas, m and d are constants, and $\bar{u}$ varies, according to Eq. (2-31), as the square root of T. The theoretical derivation therefore makes the prediction that the viscosity of a gas should be independent of the pressure and proportional to the square root of the absolute temperature. This rather remarkable result (it seems "reasonable" that the viscosity of a gas should increase as the gas is compressed and becomes more dense) was one of the few theoretical deductions to be made before the experimental measurements had been performed. Maxwell's prediction of this behavior and its subsequent experimental verification provided one of the most dramatic triumphs of the kinetic-molecular theory. (It should be pointed out, however, that at higher pressures the nonideal behavior of gases seriously interferes with these deduced relations.)

2-11 Numerical Values of Collision Properties

As an example, consider the calculation of the collision properties d, L, Z_1, and Z_{11} for N_2 at 1 atm and 25°C. Table 1-4 gives the viscosity as

$$\eta = 178\,\mu P = 1.78 \times 10^{-5}\,kg\,m^{-1}\,s^{-1}$$

The number of molecules in 1 m³ at 25°C and 1 atm is obtained from the number 6.022×10^{23} in 22.4 liters, or 0.0224 m³, at STP, as

$$N^* = \frac{6.022 \times 10^{23}}{0.0224}\frac{273}{298} = 2.46 \times 10^{25}\,m^{-3}$$

The average molecular speed is

$$\bar{u} = \sqrt{\frac{(8)(8.314)(298)}{\pi(0.02802)}} = 0.475 \times 10^3\,m\,s^{-1}$$

and the mass of one molecule is

$$m = \frac{0.02802}{6.022 \times 10^{23}} = 4.65 \times 10^{-26}\,kg$$

With these data the collision diameter of the N_2 molecule can be calculated from a rearrangement of Eq. (2-45) as

$$d = \sqrt{\frac{\bar{u}m}{2\sqrt{2}\pi\eta}} = 3.74 \times 10^{-10}\,m$$

With this value of the molecular diameter, Eqs. (2-38) to (2-40) can be used to obtain the remaining collision properties of N_2 at the specified conditions. Thus

$$L = \frac{1}{\sqrt{2}\pi d^2 N^*} = 6.56 \times 10^{-8} \text{ m}$$

$$Z_1 = \sqrt{2}\pi d^2 \bar{u} N^* = 7.24 \times 10^9 \text{ collisions s}^{-1}$$

$$Z_{11} = \frac{1}{\sqrt{2}}\pi d^2 \bar{u}(N^*)^2 = 8.91 \times 10^{34} \text{ collisions m}^{-3} \text{ s}^{-1}$$

Table 2-2 shows similar results for a few other simple molecules.

The data of Table 2-2 indicate the details which can be obtained about the molecular world from the kinetic-molecular theory. A valuable insight into molecular phenomena is provided by these data, and an effort should be made to become familiar with the order of magnitude of these quantities.

Notice, for example, that molecules are indeed small compared with the size of the region which a gas sample occupies under ordinary conditions. Molecular dimensions, as Table 2-2 shows, are of the order of 10^{-10} m. In spite of the small scale of the molecular world, it is not difficult to become accustomed to thinking in terms of molecular dimensions. One aid is an appropriate unit of length. The *angstrom* (Å) is the unit in which molecular dimensions are almost always expressed. It is defined as $1 \text{ Å} = 10^{-10}$ m. Although the angstrom unit of length is not consistent with the SI system, it has been used so extensively and is so convenient for molecular dimensions that at times we shall report lengths in angstroms.

It is important to realize that the diameters of Table 2-2 reflect the particular method by which the size of the molecules was measured. The determination of a collision diameter requires, to begin with, the assumption of a spherical molecule so that its size can be specified by the single variable, the diameter. This single-parameter assumption, moreover, implies that the molecules are being considered to be hard spheres with no mutual attractive forces. The effect of relaxing this restriction will be developed (Sec. 19-9) in the study of the rates of chemical reactions.

The mean free paths of gases at 1 atm pressure, as the sample calculation for N_2 showed, though hundreds of times larger than the molecular diameter, are short compared with the size of ordinary containers. The molecules of a gas in such a container will therefore collide many times with each other between the collisions they make with the walls of the container. But the mean free path, for a given gas, is inversely proportional to the number of molecules per unit volume, and thus it is inversely proportional to the pressure. At very low pressures, e.g., in the upper atmosphere, mean free paths can become very large.

Finally, the collision numbers Z_1 and Z_{11} should be considered. Under the conditions indicated in Table 2-2, the very many collisions per second, very short distance traveled between collisions, and the very high molecular speeds

TABLE 2-2 Some Kinetic-Molecular-Theory Gas Properties (at 25°C and 1 atm)

	Collision diameter d		Mean free path L, m($\times 10^{-8}$)	Collision frequency Z_1, s^{-1}($\times 10^9$)	Collision rate Z_{11}, m^{-3} s^{-1}($\times 10^{34}$)
	m($\times 10^{-10}$)	Å			
H_2	2.73	2.73	12.4	14.3	17.6
He	2.18	2.18	19.1	6.6	8.1
N_2	3.74	3.74	6.56	7.2	8.9
O_2	3.57	3.57	7.16	6.2	7.6
Ar	3.62	3.62	6.99	5.7	7.0
CO_2	4.56	4.56	4.41	8.6	10.6
HI	5.56	5.56	2.96	7.5	10.6

all indicate the tremendous activity in the molecular world. At low pressures, again, although the molecular speeds are unchanged, the collisions experienced by a molecule in a unit time decrease and the total collisions occurring in a given volume of gas drops off even more rapidly, a consequence of the inverse-square dependence on the particle density.

2-12 Theory of Nonideal Behavior; van der Waals' Equation

The simple model of the kinetic-molecular theory is satisfactory in that it leads to the derivation of the ideal-gas laws. We have seen, however, that real gases show PVT relations that deviate more or less widely from the ideal laws. The question naturally arises whether it is possible to understand these deviations by using a more elaborate model for a gas than that used previously. This can be done, and in our quest for molecular information it is of interest to investigate what refinements of the previous treatment are necessary.

In 1873, the Dutch chemist J. D. van der Waals showed that the addition of two items to the molecular model of Sec. 2-1 could account for much of the deviation of real gases from ideal behavior. He attributed the failure of the derived $PV = nRT$ relation to duplicate the behavior of real gases to the neglect of (1) the volume occupied by the gas molecules and (2) the attractive forces between the molecules. The corrections introduced by the recognition of these two factors will be treated one at a time.

When n mol of a gas is placed in a container of volume V, the volume in which the molecules are free to move is equal to V only if the volume occupied by the molecules themselves is negligible. The presence of molecules of non-vanishing size means that a certain volume, called the *excluded volume*, is not available for the molecules to move in. If the volume excluded by 1 mol of a gas is represented by b, then instead of writing $PV = nRT$, a more appropriate equation would be

$$P(V - nb) = nRT \tag{2-46}$$

The excluded volume b is usually treated as a constant which is characteristic of each gas and must be determined empirically so that a good correction to the simple gas-law expression is obtained.

The relation of b to the size of the molecules can be seen by considering Fig. 2-12. The molecules are again assumed to be spherical and to have a diameter d. The volume in which the centers of two molecules cannot move because of each other's presence is indicated by the lightly shaded circle in Fig. 2-12. The radius of this sphere is equal to the molecular diameter. The volume excluded per pair of molecules is $\frac{4}{3}\pi d^3$. We thus obtain

$$\text{Excluded volume per molecule} = \frac{1}{2}(\frac{4}{3}\pi d^3) = 4\left[\frac{4}{3}\pi\left(\frac{d}{2}\right)^3\right] \tag{2-47}$$

Since the expression in the square brackets is the volume of a molecule with diameter d, the excluded volume is 4 times the actual volume of the molecules. Since b is the excluded volume *per mole*, we have

$$b = 4\mathfrak{N}\left[\frac{4}{3}\pi\left(\frac{d}{2}\right)^3\right] \tag{2-48}$$

where $\mathfrak{N}$ is Avogadro's number. (This result, that the excluded volume is 4 times the volume of all the molecules, applies only if the volume that is excluded results from the coming together of pairs of molecules. At rather high gas pressures more than one molecule might be adjacent to a given molecule, and the excluded volume *per* molecule is then reduced.)

We might be tempted to make use of our previously determined values of d to calculate b. It is more satisfactory, however, to adjust b so that the derived equation corresponds as well as possible to the observed PVT data. This procedure, required principally by the difficulties caused by the second correction term, results in van der Waals' equation being *semiempirical*. The form of the derived equation follows from a theoretical treatment, but the numerical values of the constants appearing in the equation are obtained from the experimental PVT data. Semiempirical equations are not uncommon in chem-

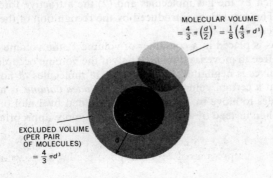

MOLECULAR VOLUME
$$= \frac{4}{3}\pi\left(\frac{d}{2}\right)^3 = \frac{1}{8}\left(\frac{4}{3}\pi d^3\right)$$

EXCLUDED VOLUME
(PER PAIR
OF MOLECULES)
$$= \frac{4}{3}\pi d^3$$

FIGURE 2-12
The excluded volume (light shade) for a pair of molecules according to van der Waals' treatment.

istry and frequently are considerably more satisfactory than completely empirical relations.

The second van der Waals correction term concerns the attractive forces between molecules. That such forces exist is clearly demonstrated by the tendency of all gases to condense at temperatures low enough for these forces to be able to overcome the kinetic energy of the molecules. That these attractions exist is clear; exact knowledge of their source and quantitative values are much harder to come by. The semiempirical approach, however, requires only that a suitable term representing the effect of these attractions be inserted. Its value can be obtained by adjusting it, as is done with b, to give an equation that best fits the PVT data.

The attraction a molecule exerts on its neighbors tends to draw them in toward itself; i.e., the attraction acts with the confining pressure to hold the molecules together. Complete analysis of the consequence of this is difficult, but qualitatively the effect is that of reducing the independence of each molecule. The pressure exerted by the gas is thus reduced just as it would be if the number of independent molecules decreased. The effect of one molecule in helping to hold the gas together through these forces of attraction is proportional to the number of nearby molecules on which it can act. If there is n mol of gas in a volume V, this number is proportional to n/V, the number of moles per unit volume. Since each of the neighboring molecules is likewise attracting its neighbors, the total pulling together of the gas due to these interactions is proportional to $(n/V)^2$. Without this intermolecular-attraction term we would expect the pressure needed to confine the gas to the volume V to be related to n, V, and T by

$$P = \frac{nRT}{V - nb}$$

The attractions between molecules reduce the pressure necessary to confine the gas, and with the proportionality factor a we write

$$P = \frac{nRT}{V - nb} - \frac{an^2}{V^2}$$

or

$$\left(P + \frac{an^2}{V^2}\right)(V - nb) = nRT \tag{2-49}$$

The success of this equation in fitting the PVT behavior of real gases is judged by choosing different values of a and b for each gas and for each temperature to give as good a fit to the observed data as possible. Although perfect agreement of calculated and observed volumes over a wide range of pressure is not obtained, the improvement over the ideal-gas-law expression

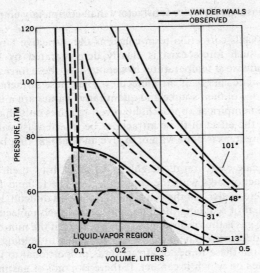

- - - VAN DER WAALS
—— OBSERVED

FIGURE 2-13

Comparison of van der Waals PV curves for CO_2 with the observed behavior near the critical point.

$PV = nRT$ is considerable. Figure 2-13 and Table 2-3 indicate the amount of improvement in regions of very nonideal behavior. The success of van der Waals' equation in representing PVT behavior is very much better than would be expected for any purely empirical expression with only two adjustable constants.

The behavior within the two-phase region, such as shown in Fig. 2-13, however, cannot be followed in detail by van der Waals' equation. The van der Waals curves in this region can be related to the actual straight-line behavior, but the curves themselves do not correspond to real behavior. The continuity of states described in Sec. 1-7, however, suggests that we might hope to describe the isotherms on both sides of this region by a single equation of state. Simple equations of state, such as van der Waals', are only moderately successful in this regard, as seen in Fig. 2-13.

Van der Waals' equation is just one of many equations of state that have

TABLE 2-3 Molar Volumes of CO_2 at 320 K

Comparison of van der Waals' equation and the ideal-gas law near the critical temperature

	V, liters		
P, atm	Observed	van der Waals	Ideal
1	26.2	26.2	26.3
10	2.52	2.53	2.63
40	0.54	0.55	0.66
100	0.098	0.10	0.26

been suggested for real, i.e., nonideal, gases. We dwell on it partly because it is relatively simple but quite successful. Furthermore it includes factors that can be thought about in terms of the repulsions and the attractions between the molecules of the gas. As you will see in Secs. 2-15 and 2-16, it thus anticipates the molecular features that enter when a sound treatment of the effect of molecular interactions on gas behavior is attempted.

2-13 Van der Waals' Equation and the Critical Point

As Fig. 2-13 shows, van der Waals' equation follows the behavior of a gas near the region of liquid-vapor equilibrium reasonably well. Moreover, there will be one temperature for which van der Waals' equation with given values of a and b will show the horizontal point of inflection that is to be identified with the critical isotherm. This identification provides a convenient (but not always the most satisfactory) way of obtaining values for a and b.

Equation (2-49) can be written for 1 mol and rearranged to give

$$P = \frac{RT}{V - b} - \frac{a}{V^2} \tag{2-50}$$

To investigate the horizontal point of inflection on a plot of P versus V we obtain

$$\frac{dP}{dV} = \frac{-RT}{(V - b)^2} + \frac{2a}{V^3} \tag{2-51}$$

and

$$\frac{d^2P}{dV^2} = \frac{2RT}{(V - b)^3} - \frac{6a}{V^4} \tag{2-52}$$

At the critical point the first and second derivatives are zero, and the pressure, volume per mole, and temperature can be written as P_C, V_C, and T_C. At this point, Eqs. (2-50) to (2-52) become, respectively,

$$P_C = \frac{RT_C}{V_C - b} - \frac{a}{V_C^2} \tag{2-53}$$

$$0 = \frac{-RT_C}{(V_C - b)^2} + \frac{2a}{V_C^3} \tag{2-54}$$

and

$$0 = \frac{2RT_C}{(V_C - b)^3} - \frac{6a}{V_C^4} \tag{2-55}$$

These three equations can be solved for a, b, and R in terms of P_C, V_C, and T_C. After some manipulation, the following relations are obtained:

$$b = \tfrac{1}{3}V_C \quad \text{and} \quad a = 3P_CV_C^2 \tag{2-56}$$

and

$$R = \frac{8P_CV_C}{3T_C} \tag{2-57}$$

With these relations, if R is treated as another adjustable parameter, R and the van der Waals constants a and b can be evaluated from the critical-point data of Table 1-3. Usually, however, the gas-constant value of R is maintained, and adjusted values are assigned only to a and b. Furthermore these empirical parameters are generally chosen so that the isotherm with the horizontal point of inflection occurs at the critical temperature and the point of inflection occurs at the critical pressure. The relations used are obtained from Eqs. (2-56) and (2-57) and are

$$a = \frac{27R^2T_C^2}{64P_C} \quad \text{and} \quad b = \frac{RT_C}{8P_C} \tag{2-58}$$

With this procedure, since van der Waals' equation describes the actual behavior only approximately, the value calculated for V at $T = T_C$ and $P = P_C$ will not necessarily be V_C. Values of a and b obtained from Eqs. (2-58) and the data of Table 1-3 are given in Table 2-4.

The values of the empirical constants calculated from critical-point data should result in a good fit of curves, calculated from van der Waals' equation, to the experimental results in the neighborhood of the critical point. If the PVT behavior in some other region is of particular interest, it might be advantageous to adjust the values of a and b to something other than those calculated from Eqs. (2-58).

Also included in Table 2-4 are values of the molecular diameter d based on the interpretation given to b by Eq. (2-48). The molecular diameters calculated from van der Waals' equation are seen to be in rough agreement with those obtained from viscosity measurements, and this encourages confidence in these numbers as giving some measure of the effective diameters of molecules.

Some discussion of the values of the van der Waals constant a is called for, but we postpone this subject of intermolecular forces until Sec. 2-16.

In spite of the success of van der Waals' equation in handling the PVT behavior of real gases, in much of our subsequent work we shall revert to the simple ideal-gas expression $PV = nRT$. At low pressures and not too low temperatures, deviations from this relation are often not significant. Further-

TABLE 2-4 Values of the Constants *a* and *b* of van der Waals' Equation Calculated from the Critical-Point Data of Table 1-3 by Means of Eqs. (2-58)

Gases in order of molecular mass

Gas	a, atm liters^2 mol^{-2}	b, liters mol^{-1}	Molecular diameter d, Å
H_2	0.25	0.027	2.78
He	0.035	0.024	2.67
CH_4	2.25	0.043	3.24
NH_3	4.17	0.037	3.08
H_2O	5.47	0.030	2.88
CO	1.47	0.039	3.14
Ne	0.21	0.017	2.38
N_2	1.35	0.038	3.11
NO	1.40	0.028	2.81
O_2	1.36	0.032	2.94
CH_3OH	9.53	0.067	3.76
HCl	3.67	0.041	3.19
Ar	1.34	0.032	2.94
CO_2	3.61	0.043	3.24
SO_2	6.77	0.057	3.56
$n\text{-}C_5H_{12}$	19.04	0.146	4.88
Cl_2	6.49	0.056	3.54
C_6H_6	18.07	0.120	4.57
Kr	2.29	0.040	3.16
Xe	4.12	0.051	3.43

more, the simplicity of the ideal-gas expression and the fact that it can be used for all gases without adjustment of any constants make its use very advantageous.

2-14 Van der Waals' Equation and the Law of Corresponding States

The empirical data plotted in Fig. 1-11 show that, as the law of corresponding states claims, many gases behave in a similar manner when they are treated in terms of the reduced variables P_R, V_R, and T_R. It is interesting to show that van der Waals' equation is consistent with the law of corresponding states. We must show that when it is written in terms of the reduced variables, no quantities remain to be empirically adjusted for the particular gas to which it is applied.

The constants a, b, and R are related to the critical-point constants by Eqs. (2-56) and (2-57). These relations can be substituted for a, b, and R and used to write van der Waals' equation in a form that shows the critical constants explicitly. Rearrangement of this equation leads to only the terms P/P_C, V/V_C, and T/T_C. Introducing the reduced variables P_R, V_R, and T_R to represent these ratios, we have, for 1 mol of gas,

$$\left(P_R + \frac{3}{V_R^2}\right)(V_R - \tfrac{1}{3}) = \tfrac{8}{3}T_R \tag{2-59}$$

It can now be seen that van der Waals' equation is consistent with the empirical law of corresponding states. This form of van der Waals' equation applies without the evaluation of any additional constants and illustrates the fact that, in terms of the reduced variables, gases behave approximately in a like manner.

2-15 Van der Waals' Equation and the Virial Equation

Van der Waals' equation is based on an imaginative introduction of correction terms into the equation for ideal-gas behavior. By contrast, the virial equation (1-26) has the form expected for an equation based on a methodical, sound treatment of molecular interactions. In particular, as you will see in the following section, the second virial coefficient $B_V(T)$ can be related to the way in which one molecule interacts with another. Now let us see that the virial coefficient $B_V(T)$ can be related to empirical constants of van der Waals' equation.

We begin with van der Waals' equation for 1 mol of gas written in the form of Eq. (2-50). The compressibility factor $Z = PV/RT$ is then given by

$$\frac{PV}{RT} = \frac{V}{V-b} - \frac{a}{RTV} = \frac{1}{1-b/V} - \frac{a}{RTV} \tag{2-60}$$

The binomial expansion

$$(1-x)^{-1} = 1 + x + x^2 + \cdots$$

which is valid for $x < 1$, can now be used on the $(1 - b/V)^{-1}$ term. If we exhibit just the first three terms of the series, we can develop Eq. (2-60) to

$$\frac{PV}{RT} = 1 + \left(b - \frac{a}{RT}\right)\frac{1}{V} + \frac{b^2}{V^2} + \cdots \tag{2-61}$$

Comparison with the virial equation, Eq. (1-26), shows that van der Waals' equation interprets the second virial coefficient in terms of $b - a/RT$.

The $b - a/RT$ term varies with temperature, as do the typical $B_V(T)$ values of Table 1-2. At high temperatures the b term dominates, and $b - a/RT$ approaches a constant value equal to that of b. [Direct deduction of $B_V(T)$ from PVT data, however, typically shown $B_V(T)$ values falling off somewhat at high temperatures.] At lower temperatures the a/RT term becomes important and ultimately dominates the b term. Thus $b - a/RT$ takes on a negative sign for

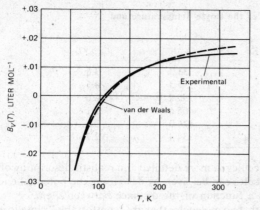

FIGURE 2-14
The second virial coefficient $B_V(T)$ of Eq. (1-26) for neon. The curve labeled "van der Waals" is calculated from $B_V(T) = b - a/RT$ with a and b values of Table 2-4.

small T values. A comparison of $b - a/RT$ and a directly deduced $B_V(T)$ function is shown in Fig. 2-14.

As pointed out in Sec. 1-6, the temperature at which $B_P(T)$, and thus $B_V(T)$, is zero is the Boyle temperature. Now you see that this temperature is related to van der Waals' constants by

$$b = \frac{a}{RT_{\text{Boyle}}}$$

or

$$T_{\text{Boyle}} = \frac{a}{bR} \tag{2-62}$$

If a, b, and R are expressed by means of Eqs. (2-56) and (2-57), the Boyle temperature and the critical temperature are simply related by

$$T_{\text{Boyle}} = \tfrac{27}{8} T_C$$

In fact, this relation is only roughly followed, as can be seen with the Boyle-temperature data of Table 2-5.

2-16 Intermolecular Forces and the Nonideality of Gases

Van der Waals' equation is arrived at by assuming that the molecules of a gas attract each other and that when they come close together, they sharply repel each other. How attractions between molecules leads to the a term of van der Waals' equation was not spelled out in any satisfying detail. In contrast, deduction of the excluded volume term b was carried out with the very specific

TABLE 2-5 Examples of the Boyle Temperature and the Ratio T_{Boyle}/T_C

Gas	T_{Boyle}, K	T_C, K	T_{Boyle}/T_C
H_2	117	33.3	3.5
He	24	5.3	4.5
CH_4	497	190.2	2.6
NH_3	860	405.6	2.1
N_2	332	126.0	2.6
O_2	423	154.4	2.7

hard-sphere model of molecules. A more detailed and realistic description of the interaction between molecules can be given by describing the potential energy of a pair of molecules as a function of the distance between them.

Consider, to begin with, two molecules that are "comfortably" close to each other. To separate them completely from each other work would have to be done to pull them apart. The amount of work that must be done contributes to the potential energy of the molecular pair. Thus the potential energy of this system increases as the molecules are pulled apart from their intermediate positions. At very large separations the interaction between the molecules falls off, and potential energy reaches some limiting value.

If the molecules are brought or pushed very close together, they begin to bump into each other and repel each other. Work must be done on the molecular pair to drive them together. Thus, at separations that are much smaller than the intermediate separation, the potential energy also rises. Moreover it rises steeply and (on the scale with which we deal) without limit.

In general we do not know the mathematical form of the potential-energy curve that describes the interaction of molecules. A much used, satisfactory equation, however, stems from the work of the English chemist J. E. Lennard-Jones, who made use of the expression

$$U(r) = 4\epsilon_{\text{LJ}}\left[\left(\frac{\sigma_{\text{LJ}}}{r}\right)^{12} - \left(\frac{\sigma_{\text{LJ}}}{r}\right)^{6}\right] \tag{2-63}$$

The twelfth-power term rises as the intermolecular distance r decreases. It thus corresponds to the repulsive contribution to the potential energy. The negative of the sixth-power term produces a decrease in the potential energy as r decreases. It corresponds to the attractive contribution.

The form of the potential-energy curve and the attractive and repulsive components are shown in Fig. 2-15. The potential energy is taken as zero for $r = \infty$. The minimum value is $-\epsilon_{\text{LJ}}$. Thus the magnitude of ϵ_{LJ} for a particular molecular type is a measure of the extent of attraction between pairs of molecules. Some values of ϵ_{LJ} are listed in Table 2-6.

As the intermolecular distance is decreased, the potential energy rises from the minimum value of $-\epsilon_{\text{LJ}}$ and reaches a zero value when r is equal to σ_{LJ}.

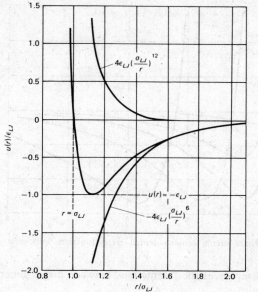

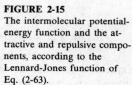

FIGURE 2-15
The intermolecular potential-energy function and the attractive and repulsive components, according to the Lennard-Jones function of Eq. (2-63).

The value of σ_{LJ} corresponds to a molecular separation at which the potential energy is rising rapidly with decreasing molecular separation. Thus σ_{LJ} can be taken as a measure of the size of the molecules. The values of σ_{LJ} included in Table 2-6 are seen to be consistent with this idea.

Examples of the Lennard-Jones, or "6-12," potential curves for several types of molecules are shown in Fig. 2-16.

The Lennard-Jones potential appears to be a satisfactory representation of the interaction between simple molecular species, e.g., the noble-gas atoms, and other small nonpolar molecules, e.g., those of nitrogen. No similar simple

TABLE 2-6 Values of the Parameters ϵ_{LJ} and σ_{LJ} for the Lennard-Jones Intermolecular Potential Function of Eq. (2-63)

Gas	ϵ_{LJ}, J molecule^{-1} ($\times 10^{-21}$)	σ_{LJ}, Å	Gas	ϵ_{LJ}, J molecule^{-1} ($\times 10^{-21}$)	σ_{LJ}, Å
H_2	0.52	2.92	Ar	1.68	3.41
He	0.14	2.56	Kr	2.49	3.60
CH_4	1.96	3.85	CO_2	2.61	4.24
Ne	0.49	2.77	Xe	3.11	4.07
N_2	1.28	3.69	C_2H_4	2.68	5.22
O_2	1.59	3.51	$C(CH_3)_4$	3.22	7.42

Source: Calculated from the results given by J. O. Hirshfelder, C. F. Curtiss, and R. B. Bird, "Molecular Theory of Gases and Liquids", John Wiley & Sons, Inc., New York, 1954.

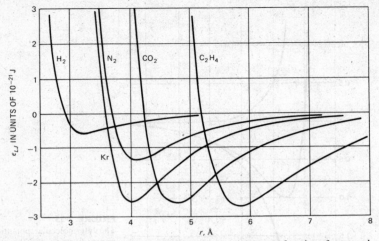

FIGURE 2-16 Lennard-Jones intermolecular potential-energy functions for several gases.

expression is available to represent the interactions between large, generally shaped, and polar molecules.

A long, complex, and still not completely traveled path leads from potential functions for pairs of molecules, like those of Fig. 2-16, to the PVT behavior of gases containing these molecules. Most attempts, however, lead to an equation of state with the form of the virial equation. These theories show that the second virial coefficient $B_V(T)$ is the result of the molecules interacting with each other two at a time. Higher coefficients show the contributions of more complex interactions.

An important result that we can explore but not derive is the relation between $B_V(T)$ and the interaction potential between a pair of molecules. This result is

$$B_V(T) = 2\pi \mathfrak{N} \int_0^\infty (1 - e^{-U(r)/kT}) r^2 \, dr \qquad (2\text{-}64)$$

We can explore this relation by dividing up the potential curve into two parts, that between $r = 0$ and $r = \sigma_{LJ}$, as in Fig. 2-15, and that from $r = \sigma_{LJ}$ to $r = \infty$. The potential in the first region can be approximated by an infinitely high potential-energy region. Such an approximation corresponds to the incompressible-sphere model used in the van der Waals derivation.

The potential function in the region $r = \sigma_{LJ}$ to $r = \infty$ cannot profitably be replaced by any such simple function. Here let us assume only that in this region $U(r) < kT$. (The curves of Fig. 2-16 and the value of 4.12×10^{-21} J for kT at 25°C suggest the validity of this assumption.) With this approximation we can use the series expansion

$$e^{-x} = 1 - x + \frac{x}{2!} - \cdots \qquad \text{for } x < 1$$

to write

$$1 - e^{-U(r)/kT} \approx \frac{U(r)}{kT}$$

With these ideas the form of $B(T)$ given by Eq. (2-64) can be shown as

$$B(T) \approx 2\pi \mathfrak{N} \int_0^{\sigma_{LJ}} r^2 \, dr + \frac{2\pi \mathfrak{N}}{kT} \int_{\sigma_{LJ}}^{\infty} r^2 U(r) \, dr$$

$$= \tfrac{2}{3}\pi \mathfrak{N} \sigma_{LJ}^3 + \frac{2\pi \mathfrak{N} \left[\int_{\sigma_{LJ}}^{\infty} r^2 U(r) \, dr \right]}{kT} \tag{2-65}$$

This incompletely worked out result can be compared with the van der Waals relation $B(T) = b - a/RT$ obtained in Sec. 2-15. Again we recognize that the first term is due to the repulsion between molecules that sets in at small intermolecular distances. The first term in fact is identical to the van der Waals excluded-volume term of Eq. (2-48) if we identify σ_{LJ} with d. The second term has the same inverse-temperature form as that deduced from the relation of van der Waals' equation and the virial equation. The numerator of Eq. (2-65) suggests the type of attractive-interaction term that the van der Waals constant term a is intended to represent.

PROBLEMS

2-1. The smallest gas bubble that can be seen in a microscope has a diameter of about 1 μm. If the pressure is 1 atm and the temperature 25°C, how many molecules, assuming they are air molecules, are present?

2-2. (a) Calculate the pressure exerted by 10^{23} gas particles, each of mass 10^{-25} kg, in a 1-liter container. The rms speed is 100 m s^{-1}. What is (b) the total kinetic energy of these particles and (c) the temperature?

2-3. A 1-liter gas bulb contains 1.03×10^{23} H$_2$ molecules. If the pressure exerted by these molecules is 1 atm, what must (a) the average squared molecular speed and (b) the temperature be?

2-4. Estimate the number of molecules left in a volume the size of a pinhead, about 10^{-9} m^3, when air is pumped out to give a vacuum of 10^{-9} atm at 25°C.

2-5. (a) For a gas sample of N molecules that consists of N_1 molecules of mass m_1 and N_2 molecules of mass m_2, follow through a derivation like that of Secs. 2-2 and 2-3, which led to the result $PV = \frac{1}{3}Nm\overline{u^2}$ and $PV = nRT$. (b) What assumptions are necessary for the derivation to give the empirical result $PV = nRT$ regardless of the masses of the molecules of the sample?

2-6. At an altitude of 300 km the atmosphere consists principally of oxygen atoms and nitrogen molecules in equal numbers. At that altitude the pressure is about 2.5×10^{-10} atm and the temperature is 1400 K. Calculate the number of each of these species per cubic centimeter.

2-7. For 25°C calculate and compare the average gas-phase kinetic energies, speeds, and momenta of the molecules of He and Hg.

2-8. (a) Calculate the molecular rms speeds of He atoms at 10, 100, and 1000 K in units of meters per second and miles per hour. (b) What values would be obtained if the pressure were specified to be 10^{-9} atm?

2-9. The kinetic-molecular theory attributes an average kinetic energy of $\frac{3}{2}kT$ to each particle. Find the speed a mist particle of mass 1×10^{-15} kg would have at room temperature according to the kinetic-molecular theory and compare with the molecular speeds of Table 2-1.

2-10. How much heat must be added to 3.45 g of neon in a 10-liter bulb to raise the temperature from 0 to 100°C? By what ratio is the average squared speed changed by this temperature change?

2-11. How much would the temperature of 1 mol of liquid water be raised by the addition of an amount of energy equal to the translational kinetic energy at 25°C of 1 mol of water vapor? It takes 18 cal K^{-1} mol^{-1}, or 75 J K^{-1} mol^{-1} to raise the temperature of 1 mol of liquid water by 1 K.

2-12. The following values are given for the speed of sound in air.

t (°C)	20	100	500	1000
Speed, m s^{-1}	344	386	553	700

Compare them with the rms speeds of N_2 molecules at these temperatures.

2-13. Obtain Eq. (2-29) from Eq. (2-28).

2-14. Verify that the fraction of molecules in the complete energy range zero to infinity is correctly given as unity by Eq. (2-29). $\left(\text{You can use the integral} \int_0^\infty \sqrt{x}e^{-nx}\,dx = \frac{1}{2n}\sqrt{\frac{\pi}{n}}.\right)$

2-15. Plot the one-dimensional and three-dimensional population-versus-speed curves for H_2 molecules at 0°C.

2-16. Obtain an expression for the distribution of the molecules of a gas throughout x-component translational energies; i.e., obtain an expression for $\frac{1}{N}\frac{dN}{d\epsilon_x}$. $\Big[$Make use of the derivative relation $\frac{dN}{d\epsilon_x} = \frac{dN}{du_x}\frac{du_x}{d\epsilon_x}$. The value of dN/du_x without regard to the sign of du_x, is twice that given by Eq. (2-26).$\Big]$

* 2-17. By graphical means show that the population-energy function of Prob. 2-16 is consistent with an average translational energy of $\frac{1}{2}kT$ per degree of freedom. $\Big[$Plot $\epsilon_x\left(\frac{dN/N}{d\epsilon_x}\right)$ versus ϵ_x.$\Big]$

2-18. From the one-dimensional distribution expression of Prob. 2-16, determine by integration the average kinetic energy for the motion of a molecule in one dimension.

2-19. Repeat the distribution and average-value deductions of Probs. 2-17 and 2-18 but for the total, three-dimensional translational energies of gas-phase molecules. $\Big($Use the integral $\int_0^\infty x^{3/2} e^{-ax}\,dx = \dfrac{3\sqrt{\pi}}{4a^{5/2}}.\Big)$

2-20. (a) Obtain an expression for the ratio of the number of molecules that have a speed of h times the most probable speed to the number that have the most probable speed. (b) Obtain corresponding expressions for h times the average speed and h times the rms speed. (c) What is perhaps surprising about all the relations obtained in parts (a) and (b)? (d) Plot the function obtained in part (a). Notice how the graph shows how the velocities are concentrated about the most probable, or average, velocity, at *any* temperature.

2-21. (a) From Eq. (2-29) obtain an expression for the ratio of the number of molecules that have kinetic energy h times the average energy $\tfrac{3}{2}kT$ to the number that have this average energy. (b) What features of the system remain in the function? (c) Plot the function.

2-22. A Knudsen cell containing a sample of beryllium showed a weight loss of 9.54 mg in 60.1 min at 1457 K. The diameter of the effusion hole was 0.318 cm. What is the vapor pressure of beryllium at this temperature?

2-23. At 25°C, at what pressure is the mean free path of N_2 molecules equal to 1.00 cm?

2-24. Using the value of d from Table 2-2 for argon, calculate (a) the mean free path, (b) the average number of collisions a molecule experiences per second, and (c) the average number of collisions per cubic meter per second for the molecules of argon at 0°C and 1 atm pressure. (d) What values would be obtained at 1000°C and 1 atm? (e) At 0°C and 100 atm?

2-25. (a) Derive an expression for the mean free path for any gas in terms of the collision diameter, the temperature, and the pressure. (b) Prepare a convenient graph showing the variation of the mean free path with pressure for 0°C and the pressure range 10^{-9} to 1 atm if the gas is nitrogen.

2-26. (a) Using Eq. (2-31) for the average speed of a gas, obtain expressions for the Z_1 and Z_{11} as functions of d, M, P, and T. (b) For the pressure range 10^{-9} to 1 atm show graphically the variation of Z_1 and Z_{11} with pressure for N_2 at 0°C.

2-27. What is the mean free path and the average time between collisions of a helium atom in the earth's atmosphere at 700 km (a) during the daytime, when the temperature is 2000 K, and (b) at night, when the temperature is 700 K? The average pressure and density data at 700 km are 2×10^{-12} atm and 2.3×10^{-13} g liter^{-1}.

2-28. (a) The vapor pressure of ice and of liquid water at the triple point, 0.010°C, is 0.0060 atm. How many molecules strike 1 m^2 of the liquid or solid surface each second in an equilibrium ice-liquid-vapor system? (b) From the diameter of water molecules we can estimate that there are about 10^{19} molecules in a surface of 1 m^2. If the rate of departure of surface molecules equals the rate with which molecules strike the surface, what is the average lifetime of a surface molecule?

2-29. (a) What expression for the product PV would you obtain if you calculated it from the product of the average number of collisions per unit surface area, using the effusion equation of Sec. 2-8, and the average momentum change per collision, using the average x velocity component of that section? (b) Explain why this result deviates as it does from the correct result, i.e., is larger or smaller.

2-30. In a study of the effect of a solid catalyst on a gas-phase reaction, a gas mixture at 25°C and at a total pressure of 10^{-8} atm was exposed to the solid catalyst for

15 min. How many molecules and how many moles of the gas mixture came in contact with a surface area of 10^{-4} m^2 of the catalyst during this reaction time? Assume a molecular mass of 30 amu. (Ignore the fact that the same molecules may have been responsible for repeated collisions.)

2-31. How long would it take 1 mol of (a) hydrogen and (b) xenon to escape by effusion into a vacuum through a pinhole of diameter 10^{-6} m if the pressure and temperature of the gases were 10^{-5} atm and 0°C?

*__2-32.__ Calculate the fraction of helium molecules that have upward speeds great enough to escape from the earth for a temperature of 2000 K, as occurs in the daytime in the thermosphere. (The escape speed from the earth is 1.12×10^4 m s^{-1}.)

*__2-33.__ There are about 5 million million (5×10^{12}) cells in a mature human being. Respiration provides on the average, about $\frac{1}{3}$ liter of oxygen, measured at 1 atm pressure, each minute to support the metabolic activity of these cells. (a) Estimate the mass, volume, and (on the basis of a spherical cell) the diameter of each of your cells. (You will need to estimate your body volume.) (b) How many molecules of oxygen are, on the average, supplied to each of your cells per second? (c) How many molecules of oxygen per second would arrive at a cell of the size calculated in part (a) if the cell were completely exposed to fresh air? (d) The respiratory surface of the lungs has an area of about 70 m^2, about 40 times the area of the rest of the human body. What fraction is this of the area of all the cells, taken separately, of the body? (e) How many molecules per second could be provided to each cell of the body if the lung surface area were bathed in fresh air?

2-34. Compare the volume of 20 g of H_2O at 100°C and 0.50 atm pressure given by the ideal-gas law with that given by van der Waals' equation.

2-35. At 200°C a pressure of 41.9 atm is required to reduce the molar volume of NH_3 to 0.851 liter. What pressure would have been calculated on the basis of (a) ideal-gas behavior and (b) van der Waals' equation with the constants of Table 2-4?

2-36. (a) From the molar volumes for CO_2 at any two pressures and temperatures for which data are available in Prob. 1-31, calculate values of van der Waals a and b constants. (b) Then choose two other pressure and temperature conditions and calculate new values of a and b. (c) Compare the two sets of values with each other and with the values in Table 2-4.

2-37. What value of V_C do the van der Waals constants for water, as given in Table 2-4, imply? Compare with the value listed in Table 1-3.

2-38. Use the data for V_C, T_C, and P_C for any gas to obtain values of a, b, and R so that van der Waals' equation correctly describes the critical point. Compare with the a and b values of Table 2-4 and the value 0.08206 liter atm mol^{-1} K^{-1} for R.

2-39. The molar volume of saturated water vapor at 300°C and 84.78 atm is 0.3895 liter. (a) What is the ideal-gas molar volume under these conditions? (b) Use van der Waals' equation with the constants of Table 2-4 to calculate the molar volume under these conditions.

2-40. According to the van der Waals treatment of the nonideality of gases, what is the ratio of the volume of a gas at the critical point to the actual volume of the molecules of the gas?

2-41. (a) According to van der Waals' equation expressed in terms of the reduced variables P_R, T_R, and V_R, plot isotherms for $T_R = 0.8$, 1.0, and 1.2 for V_R up to about 10 and P_R up to about 2. (b) You can identify the point at which condensation occurs for $T_R = 0.8$ by selecting any substance for which the vapor pressure is known at that temperature. Sketch the two-phase liquid-vapor region.

2-42. Show that at fairly low pressures, where $PV = nRT$ can be inserted in the van der Waals correction term, van der Waals' equation for 1 mol can be reduced to

$$PV = RT[1 + B_P(T)] \quad \text{where} \quad B_P(T) = \frac{b}{RT} - \frac{a}{(RT)^2}$$

Use this approximation to calculate virial coefficients at several temperatures from the van der Waals constants for CH_4. Compare with the values given in Table 1-2.

2-43. The ϵ_{LJ} and σ_{LJ} parameters of Eq. (2-63) for N_2 molecules are given in Table 2-6. (a) Plot the Lennard-Jones potential curve using these values. (b) To see that σ_{LJ} is a measure of the size of the molecules, superimpose on the figure of part (a) a curve based on the same value of ϵ_{LJ} but with a value of σ of $2\sigma_{LJ}$. (c) To see that the parameter ϵ_{LJ} measures the attraction between molecules but has little effect on their size, add to the graph containing the curves of parts (a) and (b), one based on σ_{LJ} but with $\epsilon = 2\epsilon_{LJ}$.

2-44. From Fig. 2-16 estimate the value of σ_{LJ} for the molecules shown and compare the values with the van der Waals diameters of Table 2-4.

2-45. The attraction term in the expression for the potential energy between molecules can be compared with the gravitational attraction between particles. For particles of mass m_1 and m_2 separated by a distance r the gravitational force of attraction is given by Gm_1m_2/r^2, where $G = 6.67 \times 10^{-11}$ N m² kg⁻². The corresponding potential-energy term is $-Gm_1m_2/r$. Investigate this term for argon atoms. In what two general ways is the gravitational force between molecules different from the actual force?

2-46. According to Eq. (2-61), the third virial coefficient can be identified with the square of the van der Waals b term. Compare the implied temperature dependence and magnitude of this virial coefficient with the available data for methane.

2-47. What point on the graph of Fig. 2-14 corresponds to the Boyle temperature?

2-48. The van der Waals a term reflects a net force of attraction between molecules and the Lennard-Jones ϵ_{LJ} parameter, an attractive potential-energy term. We might expect some parallel between these terms. Use the data of Tables 2-4 and 2-6 to see whether there is any relation between these quantities.

REFERENCES

TABOR, D.: "Gases, Liquids, and Solids," Penguin Books, Inc., Baltimore, 1969. Further treatment of the kinetic theory of ideal and real gases and related material on solids and liquids.

HILDEBRAND, J. H.: "An Introduction to Kinetic Theory," Reinhold Publishing Corporation, New York, 1963. A brief, readable discussion of the nature of ideal gases, real gases, and the kinetic-molecular theory.

LOEB, L. B.: "Kinetic Theory of Gases," Dover Publications, Inc., New York, 1961. A more complete treatment of the kinetic-molecular theory so presented and at a level that makes it a very suitable extension to the material of this chapter.

JEANS, J. H.: "The Dynamical Theory of Gases," Dover Publications, Inc., New York, 1954. A comprehensive but rather mathematical treatment of the kinetic-molecular theory of gases.

KENNARD, E. H.: "Kinetic Theory of Gases," McGraw-Hill Book Company, New York, 1938. Similar to the treatise by Jeans in scope and approach.

BRUSH, S. G.: "Kinetic Theory," vols. 1 and 2, Pergamon Press, Oxford, 1965 and 1966. Well-chosen selections, with orienting introductory remarks, of the original contributions to the development of kinetic theory. An excellent introduction to the history of the subject.

HIRSHFELDER, J. O., C. F. CURTIS, and R. B. BIRD: "Molecular Theory of Gases and Liquids," John Wiley & Sons, Inc., New York, 1964. An extensive and detailed treatment that can be referred to in many areas of physical chemistry. Chapters 1 to 5 are particularly pertinent.

KAUZMANN, W.: "Thermal Properties of Matter," vol. I, "Kinetic Theory of Gases," W. A. Benjamin, New York, 1966. Chapters 1 and 2.

OLBERGTS, J., and J. P. WALGRAEVE: Determining the Intermolecular Potential in a Gas: A Physical Chemistry Experiment, *J. Chem. Educ.*, **53**:602 (1976). Based on measurement of gas viscosities.

BLINDER, S. M.: "Advanced Physical Chemistry: A Survey of Modern Theoretical Principles," The Macmillan Company, Collier-Macmillan Canada, Ltd., Toronto, 1969. An excellent source of material on gases (chaps. 6 to 8) and kinetic-molecular theory (chaps. 9 to 12).

INTRODUCTION TO QUANTUM MECHANICS

The kinetic-molecular theory of gases provides a great deal of information on the nature and behavior of molecules. This information results, so to speak, from an external view of the molecules. They are treated as structureless spherical particles. Much of the physical chemistry with which we shall deal in later chapters requires a more detailed treatment of the molecules, atoms, or ions of which a system is composed. Any attempt to learn about the internal structure and properties of individual molecules may seem to be a bold undertaking. The small size of molecules is immediately forbidding. More troublesome is the fact, which became evident as the actual investigations were pursued, that molecules and the electrons and atoms of which they are made exhibit behavior that is quite outside our ordinary experience.

3-1 Categories of Thermal Energies of Molecules of Gases

Think of a molecule as a collection of atoms held more or less firmly in a particular spatial arrangement by chemical bonds. The model corresponds to a set of balls joined together by springs. We shall seek to describe the energy of such a system that results from the jostling of any one such molecule by its neighbors, a picture we began to develop in the kinetic-molecular-theory study. (When we consider chemical reactions, in which molecules are torn apart and new ones are assembled, or temperatures so high that additional, excited electronic states are involved, we shall have to consider also the energy associated with the electronic structure of the molecules. Here the energies of molecules not exposed to conditions that disrupt their electronic structure will be dealt with.)

As would be immediately apparent if an actual ball-and-spring model were tossed around, the motions by which the system could have energy would be most conveniently described in terms of three types of motion:

Translation, consisting of motion of the center of gravity of the molecule

Rotation, consisting of a motion in which the molecule turns about axes through the center of gravity of the molecule

Vibration, involving the oscillation of the particles of the system, i.e., the atoms of the molecule, in such a way that there is no net contribution to the motion of the center of gravity or to rotation about this center

The analytical basis for treating these different types of motion separately can be seen by describing the motion of a diatomic molecule. We attempt to express the energy of a freely moving gas-phase diatomic molecule. The only potential-energy contribution, assuming a ball-and-spring type of model for the molecule, arises from variations in the distance between the atoms of the molecule. If this variable distance is r, the potential-energy term can be represented by $U(r)$. The kinetic energy depends on the motion of the two atoms, atom 1 and atom 2, of the molecule. We can introduce the symbols $\dot{x}_1$, $\dot{y}_1$, and $\dot{z}_1$ to represent the velocity components $dx_1/dt, dy_1/dt$, and dz_1/dt. Likewise we use the notation $\dot{x}_2$, $\dot{y}_2$, and $\dot{z}_2$ for the velocity components of atom 2. Now the energy of the molecule can be written as

$$\epsilon = \tfrac{1}{2}m_1(\dot{x}_1{}^2 + \dot{y}_1{}^2 + \dot{z}_1{}^2) + \tfrac{1}{2}m_2(\dot{x}_2{}^2 + \dot{y}_2{}^2 + \dot{z}_2{}^2) + U(r) \tag{3-1}$$

Separate translational, rotational, and vibrational components of this energy can be recognized if a different coordinate system is introduced. Part of this new system consists of the coordinates X, Y, and Z, which locate the center of gravity of the molecule. These, as illustrated for a two-dimensional system in Fig. 3-1, are related to the atomic coordinates by the expressions

$$
\begin{aligned}
(m_1 + m_2)X &= m_1 x_1 + m_2 x_2 \\
(m_1 + m_2)Y &= m_1 y_1 + m_2 y_2 \\
(m_1 + m_2)Z &= m_1 z_1 + m_2 z_2
\end{aligned}
\tag{3-2}
$$

The orientation of the molecule is expressed by the polar angular coordi-

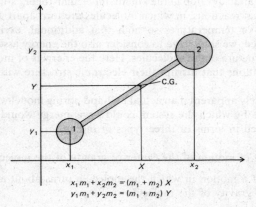

$$x_1 m_1 + x_2 m_2 = (m_1 + m_2)X$$
$$y_1 m_1 + y_2 m_2 = (m_1 + m_2)Y$$

FIGURE 3-1
The location of the center of gravity of a diatomic molecule in terms of the x and y coordinates of its atoms.

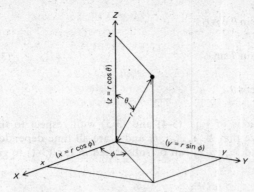

FIGURE 3-2
The relation between polar and cartesian coordinates.

nates θ and ϕ of Fig. 3-2. Figure 3-3 shows how these and the internuclear distance r can be used to develop the relations

$$x_2 - x_1 = r \sin \theta \cos \phi$$
$$y_2 - y_1 = r \sin \theta \sin \phi \qquad (3\text{-}3)$$
$$z_2 - z_1 = r \cos \theta$$

Now either x_1, y_1, z_1 or x_2, y_2, z_2 can be eliminated from Eqs. (3-2) and (3-3), giving

$$x_1 = X - \frac{m_2}{m_1 + m_2} r \sin \theta \cos \phi$$

$$y_1 = Y - \frac{m_2}{m_1 + m_2} r \sin \theta \sin \phi \qquad (3\text{-}4)$$

$$z_1 = Z - \frac{m_2}{m_1 + m_2} r \cos \theta$$

and

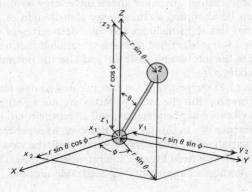

FIGURE 3-3
The cartesian coordinates of the atoms of a diatomic molecule expressed in terms of the interatomic distance r and the angles θ and ϕ.

$$x_2 = X - \frac{m_1}{m_1 + m_2} r \sin \theta \cos \phi$$

$$y_2 = Y - \frac{m_1}{m_1 + m_2} r \sin \theta \sin \phi \qquad (3\text{-}5)$$

$$z_2 = Z - \frac{m_1}{m_1 + m_2} r \cos \theta$$

The derivatives of expressions of Eqs. (3-4) and (3-5) with respect to time can be taken if we recognize that X, Y, Z, r, θ, and ϕ are all time-dependent. The results for $\dot{x}_1$, $\dot{y}_1$, $\dot{z}_1$ and $\dot{x}_2$, $\dot{y}_2$, $\dot{z}_2$ can be substituted in Eq. (3-1) to give, after rearrangement,

$$\epsilon = \tfrac{1}{2}(m_1 + m_2)(\dot{X}^2 + \dot{Y}^2 + \dot{Z}^2) + \tfrac{1}{2}\frac{m_1 m_2}{m_1 + m_2}[\dot{r}^2 + r^2\dot{\theta}^2$$
$$+ r^2 (\sin^2 \theta)\dot{\phi}^2] + U(r) \quad (3\text{-}6)$$

The mass relation $m_1 m_2/(m_1 + m_2)$ often occurs in studies of the dynamics of two-particle systems. We call this mass term the *reduced mass* and denote it by μ. Thus

$$\mu = \frac{m_1 m_2}{m_1 + m_2} \qquad (3\text{-}7)$$

The energy expression can now be sorted out to give three types of terms

$$\epsilon = \tfrac{1}{2}m(\dot{X}^2 + \dot{Y}^2 + \dot{Z}^2) + \tfrac{1}{2}\mu r^2[\dot{\theta}^2 + (\sin^2 \theta)\dot{\phi}^2] + [\tfrac{1}{2}\mu\dot{r}^2 + U(r)] \qquad (3\text{-}8)$$

where $m = m_1 + m_2$ is the mass of the molecule.

The first term of Eq. (3-8) is clearly the energy contribution due to the translational motion of the molecule as a whole. Notice that neither the orientation of the molecule nor the interatomic distance affects this energy term. The second term of Eq. (3-8) can be identified as the energy contribution of the rotational motion. Notice that this term includes the time derivatives of the angles. The third term of Eq. (3-8) is identified with the vibrational motion. It includes the time derivative of the interatomic distance and also the potential-energy variation with this coordinate.

The three terms of Eq. (3-8) suggest that we use the descriptive terms translation, rotation, and vibration. But the last two terms are not rigorously separated. Variations in r, a vibrational phenomenon, will affect the rotational term, as you see from the presence of r in this term. If, however, as is generally the case with molecules, the variation of r due to vibration is small, the value of r in the second term can be taken as a fixed average interatomic distance. Thus we can treat rotation and vibration as approximately separable motions.

From Eq. (3-8) you see that three variables X, Y, and Z are required to describe the motion of the center of gravity of the molecule. Two variables, θ and ϕ, are required to describe the rotational motion and one, r, is required to describe the vibrational motion. We say that this diatomic molecule has three translational *degrees of freedom,* two rotational degrees of freedom, and one vibrational degree of freedom. The total number of degrees of freedom is 6.

The number of degrees of freedom could also have been calculated when we began our studies of the diatomic molecule at the stage of Eq. (3-1). Then we treated its motion in terms of three cartesian coordinates on each atom. The molecule would have been said to have 6 degrees of freedom corresponding to the x-, y-, or z-directed motion of each atom.

The total number of degrees of freedom of a system of particles can always be calculated by thinking of the three cartesian coordinates, or 3 degrees of freedom, of each of the particles. We can choose to describe the degrees of freedom differently, but a system of n particles will retain the $3n$ degrees of freedom that we recognize by associating cartesian coordinates with each particle. Listing the total degrees of freedom and the number of them that can be associated with each type of motion of the system as a whole is often a useful analytical step.

Consider, for example, a linear molecule containing n atoms. It will have a total of $3n$ degrees of freedom, as we calculate from the three cartesian coordinates required to follow the motion of each of the n atoms. We prefer, however, to think of translational, rotational, and vibrational motions of the molecule. In view of our treatment of the diatomic case we see that any linear molecule will have 3 translational degrees of freedom and 2 rotational degrees of freedom. It follows that a linear molecule of n atoms must have $3n - 5$ vibrational degrees of freedom.

Now consider a generally shaped, nonlinear molecule. It also, of course, will have the 3 translational degrees of freedom that correspond to the motion of its center of mass. It will have 3, rather than 2, rotational degrees of freedom. You can think of the third of these as resulting from the twirling of the molecule about an axis, as suggested in Fig. 3-4. (For a linear molecule the corresponding twirling motion is not classed as a molecular rotation. Increasing the twirling about the axis of such a molecule would depend upon an increase in the rotational motion of the electrons of the molecule about the internuclear axis. Such motions can occur, but they are classed as electronic motions which typically do not change except at very high temperatures.) Thus for a generally shaped molecule the translational and rotational motions account for 6 degrees of freedom. If the molecule contains n atoms and thus has a total of $3n$ degrees of freedom, the remaining $3n - 6$ degrees of freedom must be vibrational.

3-2 Quantization of Rotational Motion

Two different types of motion can be recognized from the treatment of molecular motions in the preceding section. One is longitudinal. Translation and

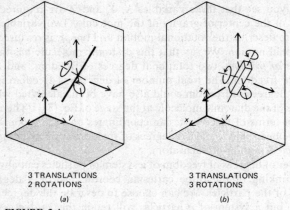

3 TRANSLATIONS
2 ROTATIONS

(a)

3 TRANSLATIONS
3 ROTATIONS

(b)

FIGURE 3-4
The translational and rotational degrees of freedom of a linear molecule and a generally shaped molecule.

vibrational motions are of this type. The other is rotational. Molecular rotations obviously are examples of this type of motion. For both types of motion and for more complex intermediate or mixed motions, the particle or particles carrying out the motion can generally have only certain energies. These, we say, are the *allowed energies*. These energies and the corresponding description of the motion and position of the particle or particles can be deduced by *quantum mechanics*. General techniques applicable to all types of atomic and molecular problems are now available. A subset of these techniques allows the energies and states of rotating systems of particles or of particles each spinning about an axis to be described. Here we shall apply these methods to rotating molecules. In Sec. 3-4 we shall see how the quantum restrictions that apply to longitudinal and more complex motions are treated.

The theory of the hydrogen atom by Niels Bohr in 1913 was the first successful treatment of a quantized rotating system. Bohr's recognition of *quantized angular momentum,* although applied specifically to the hydrogen atom, provided the basis for the deduction of the allowed states and energies of all types of rotating particles and systems of particles in the atomic molecular world. (We shall follow through his deduction of the properties of the hydrogen atom in Sec. 11-2.)

Before seeing the implications of the restrictions that are placed on angular momentum, some of the quantities, such as angular momentum itself, that are used for rotating systems will be introduced. Consider a particle rotating about a fixed point. The speed of rotation can be described in terms of the particle's velocity v or by the number of revolutions per second, i.e., the frequency v. Since the particle travels a distance v each second and the distance for one revolution is $2\pi r$, we have the relation

$$v = \frac{v}{2\pi r} \tag{3-9}$$

The *angular velocity* ω is the number of radians (rad) swept through per second. Since there are 2π rad in a revolution, $\omega = 2\pi v$ and

$$\omega = \frac{v}{r} \tag{3-10}$$

For a rotating many-particle rigid system the angular velocity ω is particularly convenient. Whereas each particle moves with a velocity v that depends on its distance r from the axis of rotation, all particles move around this axis with the same value of ω.

The kinetic energy of a particle, $\frac{1}{2}mv^2$, can be rearranged to a form more convenient for rotary systems. We first rewrite $\frac{1}{2}mv^2$ as

$$\epsilon = \frac{1}{2}mr^2\left(\frac{v}{r}\right)^2 = \frac{1}{2}(mr^2)(\omega^2) \tag{3-11}$$

The term mr^2 is a one-particle example of a frequently occurring collection of terms. It is convenient to introduce I, the *moment of inertia*, for mr^2, where m is the mass of the particle and r is its distance from the axis of rotation. (For many-particle systems the moment of inertia is $I = \Sigma m_i r_i^2$, where the summation is over all the particles and m_i is the mass of the ith particle, which is a distance r_i from the axis of gravity.)

If $I = mr^2$ is substituted in Eq. (3-11), we obtain

$$\epsilon = \frac{1}{2}I\omega^2 \tag{3-12}$$

This expression, developed here for a single rotating particle, is applicable to a system of particles, such as molecule. Notice that in expressions for rotary systems, compared with those for linear systems, I plays the role of m and ω plays the role of v.

Now we can return to the angular momentum. It is defined as $I\omega$ and thus is analogous to linear momentum, defined as mv. One can also see that

$$I\omega = mr^2\frac{v}{r} = mvr \tag{3-13}$$

The rotational energy $\frac{1}{2}I\omega^2$ can be expressed in terms of the angular moment as

$$\epsilon = \frac{1}{2}I\omega^2 = \frac{(I\omega)^2}{2I} \tag{3-14}$$

Expressions which contain I and ω terms can, with suitable interpretation of I, be carried over to any rotating system. Quantum restrictions expressed in terms of these quantities are widely applicable.

In treating the hydrogen-atom problem Bohr postulated that only those orbits were allowed for which the angular momentum $I\omega$ of the electron was some integral multiple of $h/2\pi$. We now know that for rotating particles or rotating systems of particles a somewhat different angular-momentum restriction than that introduced by Bohr is necessary to give results in complete agreement with experiments. The basic quantum restrictions for rotational motion are as follows:

1. The total angular momentum $I\omega$ can have only the values

$$I\omega = \sqrt{l(l+1)}\,\frac{h}{2\pi} \qquad l = 0, 1, 2, \ldots \tag{3-15}$$

It follows that the rotational kinetic energy, according to Eq. (3-14), can have only the values

$$\tfrac{1}{2}I\omega^2 = \frac{(I\omega)^2}{2I} = l(l+1)\,\frac{h^2}{8\pi^2 I} \qquad l = 0, 1, 2, \ldots \tag{3-16}$$

2. If a direction is imposed on the rotating system, e.g., by the presence of a neighboring particle or application of an electric or magnetic field, the angular-momentum component in this direction can have only the values

$$m\,\frac{h}{2\pi} \qquad m = -l, -l+1, \ldots, -1, 0, 1, \ldots, l-1, l \tag{3-17}$$

Each value of m corresponds to a different *rotational state*.

For a given value of l there are $2l + 1$ different possible values of m. (There are l values of m from 1 to l and l more values from -1 to $-l$, plus the zero value.) Thus for each value of l there are $2l + 1$ states. In the presence of a directional field these states can correspond to different energies. In the absence of such a field all $2l + 1$ states corresponding to a given value of l, and thus to a given total angular momentum, will have the same energy. The energy level corresponding to a given value of l contains $2l + 1$ states.

In quantized systems, i.e., those in which only certain energies occur, a number of different states often correspond to a particular allowed energy. The number of states at a given energy is said to be the *degeneracy* of that energy level. A rotational energy level, as dealt with above, with energy $l(l+1)h^2/8\pi^2 I$ is said to have a *degeneracy* equal to $2l + 1$. (The term degeneracy arises by thinking, for example, of a rotating system subjected to a

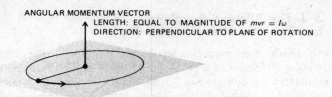

ANGULAR MOMENTUM VECTOR
LENGTH: EQUAL TO MAGNITUDE OF $mvr = I\omega$
DIRECTION: PERPENDICULAR TO PLANE OF ROTATION

FIGURE 3-5 The angular-momentum vector.

directional field. Suppose this field gives different energies to the states with different angular-momentum components in the direction of the field. Each state, even those for a given value of l, will then have a different energy. But as the field is turned down, the energy effects of the field will diminish and the $2l + 1$ energy levels corresponding to a given l value will "degenerate" into a single, field-free energy level that contains all $2l + 1$ states.)

The angular momentum, as is shown in the simple case of a particle rotating about a point in Fig. 3-5, is a vector quantity. The orientation of the rotating system and the magnitude of the angular momentum are depicted, as in Fig. 3-5, by a vector arrow perpendicular to the plane of rotation. Such a vector representation can be carried over to the total allowed angular momentum of Eq. (3-15) and the components of Eq. (3-17). These angular-momentum vectors are related as illustrated in Fig. 3-6. The stipulations of Eqs. (3-15) and (3-17) are such that the total angular-momentum vector never points exactly along any given direction, that of the imposed directional field for example. Our inability to know both the energy of rotation and the plane in which the rotation is occurring exactly is an example of the *uncertainty principle*.

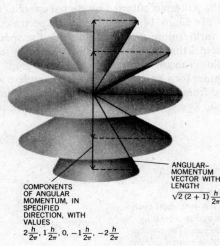

COMPONENTS OF ANGULAR MOMENTUM, IN SPECIFIED DIRECTION, WITH VALUES
$2\frac{h}{2\pi}, 1\frac{h}{2\pi}, 0, -1\frac{h}{2\pi}, -2\frac{h}{2\pi}$

ANGULAR-MOMENTUM VECTOR WITH LENGTH
$\sqrt{2(2+1)}\frac{h}{2\pi}$

FIGURE 3-6
A vector representation of the five states that correspond to an angular-momentum quantum-number value of 2.

3-3 The Allowed Rotational Energies of a Molecule of a Gas

Now the results of the preceding section can be applied to the particular case of the rotating molecules of a gas. The rotational motion of linear molecules is easiest to treat. As shown in Sec. 3-1, such molecules undergo a relatively simple end-over-end rotational motion. The quantum restrictions developed in the preceding section can be applied directly.

The integers, or quantum numbers, that index the allowed total angular momenta of a rotating molecule are usually represented by the symbol J. Thus, according to Eq. (3-15) the allowed angular momenta of the rotating molecule are given by

$$\sqrt{J(J+1)}\,\frac{h}{2\pi} \qquad J = 0, 1, 2, \ldots \tag{3-18}$$

The allowed rotational kinetic energies ϵ_J, according to Eq. (3-16), are given by

$$\epsilon_J = J(J+1)\frac{h^2}{8\pi^2 I} \qquad J = 0, 1, 2, \ldots \tag{3-19}$$

Each rotational energy level, corresponding to a particular value of J, consists of $2J + 1$ states. This is the degeneracy of the rotational energy levels, and with the symbol g_J for this degeneracy we write

$$g_J = 2J + 1 \tag{3-20}$$

A general diagram showing the pattern of allowed rotational energies of a linear molecule is given in Fig. 3-7. In Chap. 14 you will see that spectroscopic studies confirm this pattern and furthermore provide values for the spacing between the energy levels for molecules that have been studied. Generally these spectral studies make use of radiation in the microwave spectral region.

A rotational energy-level diagram for a particular molecule, complete with an energy scale, can be constructed from Eq. (3-19) if a value of the moment of inertia of the molecule is available. Spectral studies (Chap. 14) provide such

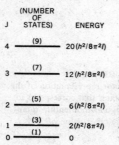

J	(NUMBER OF STATES)	ENERGY
4	(9)	$20\,(h^2/8\pi^2 I)$
3	(7)	$12\,(h^2/8\pi^2 I)$
2	(5)	$6\,(h^2/8\pi^2 I)$
1	(3)	$2(h^2/8\pi^2 I)$
0	(1)	0

FIGURE 3-7
The first few rotational energy levels allowed to a rotating linear molecule. The number of states g_J is related to J by the expression $g_J = 2J + 1$.

data. Also, the diffraction studies of Chap. 15 provide molecular-structure data from which moment-of-inertia values can be calculated. Thus the information needed to calculate the energies which any gas-phase molecule has as a result of its rotational motion is generally available.

Let us take as an example the molecule N_2. The mass of each N atom is $0.0140/(6.02 \times 10^{23})$ kg, and the distance between the atoms of the molecule is 1.100 Å, or 1.100×10^{-10} m. The distance of each atom from the rotational axis is $\frac{1}{2} \times 1.100 \times 10^{-10}$ m. The moment of inertia is therefore

$$I = 2 \times \frac{0.0140}{6.02 \times 10^{23}} [(\tfrac{1}{2})(1.100 \times 10^{-10})]^2 = 14.1 \times 10^{-47} \text{ kg m}^2$$

With this value the rotational-energy spacing factor $h^2/8\pi^2 I$ of Eq. (3-19) can be calculated. We obtain, for this N_2 example,

$$\frac{h^2}{8\pi^2 I} = 0.039 \times 10^{-21}$$

Thus the N_2 molecules of nitrogen gas rotate with one of the energies given by

$$\epsilon_J = J(J + 1)(0.039 \times 10^{-21}) \text{ J} \qquad J = 0, 1, 2, \ldots$$

(The value is written for easy comparison with the room-temperature value of $\frac{1}{2}kT$ of 2×10^{-21} J).

Here, in this introduction to quantum mechanics you should see that the idea of quantized angular momentum has led us to a detailed description of the energies of the states of rotating molecules.

3-4 An Introduction to Wave Mechanics

In 1923 Louis de Broglie suggested that wave properties could be associated with particles. This suggestion pointed the way to the very general wave-mechanics method for handling atomic and molecular systems. The wavelength of the wave which is to be associated with a particle is suggested by combining the electromagnetic wave equation $\Delta\epsilon = h\nu$ and the Einstein relation $\Delta\epsilon = mc^2$. These can be combined to give $h\nu = mc^2$. Introduction of the wavelength according to $\lambda = c/\nu$ and rearrangement then gives

$$\lambda = \frac{h}{mc} \tag{3-21}$$

This expression, as its derivation shows, applies only to electromagnetic radiation. For particles, de Broglie suggested that the wavelength could be deduced from the parallel expression

$$\lambda = \frac{h}{mv} \tag{3-22}$$

where v is the velocity of the particle. Thus a wave, with wavelength $\lambda = h/mv$, could be associated with a stream of particles, each of mass m, moving with velocity v or, more briefly, with momentum mv.

The wave nature of particles and the quantization of angular momentum provide calculation procedures that are intimately connected. Some problems can be treated most conveniently by one approach, other problems by the other approach. The relation between the wave and angular-momentum procedures can be seen by considering a simple system of a particle moving in a circular path, or orbit, about a fixed point. (You can think of this particle as the electron of a hydrogen atom if you like.)

According to de Broglie, the particle will have a wave associated with it. The wavelength of this wave will be related to the mass and velocity of the particle by the relation $\lambda = h/mv$.

For a general orbit and particle velocity, the wave, if drawn around the orbit path, will not fit. Successive cycles of the waves will tend to interfere destructively, as in Fig. 3-8a. For certain orbits constructive interference can occur, as shown in Fig. 3-8b. The relation for constructive interference is

$$2\pi r = n\lambda \tag{3-23}$$

where n is an integer showing the number of waves that fit in the orbit path. Substitution of the de Broglie relation for λ now gives, after rearrangement,

$$mvr = n\frac{h}{2\pi} \qquad n = 1, 2, 3, \ldots \tag{3-24}$$

The collection of terms mvr is, as shown in Sec. 3-3, the angular momentum $I\omega$. Thus, the wave-fitting procedure has led us to the angular-momentum restriction

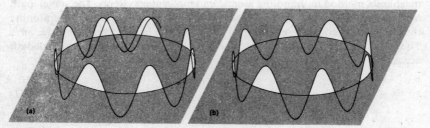

FIGURE 3-8 The de Broglie wave associated with an electron in a Bohr orbit. (a) Destructive interference occurs; (b) constructive interference leads to the formation of a standing wave.

$$I\omega = n\frac{h}{2\pi} \qquad n = 1, 2, 3, \ldots \tag{3-25}$$

The result is similar to the angular-momentum restriction that was the basis of the quantization procedure of Sec. 3-2. The present result is in error in that it assigns integer multiples of $h/2\pi$ instead of the square root of integer products of Eq. (3-15). Early attempts at solving quantized systems, such as Bohr's treatment of the hydrogen atom in 1913, made use of the simple, integral multiple of $h/2\pi$ condition. Later it was recognized that only with the square-root factor could the total angular momentum and the angular-momentum components be related in a way consistent with the uncertainty principle. The de Broglie relation leads to the erroneous result because of the assumption of orbits confined to a particular plane.

The validity of the de Broglie relation was later to be verified directly when experiments were performed in which a beam of electrons, and later of neutrons, behaved in a wavelike manner and showed diffraction, or interference, effects. Some of these effects will be studied in a later chapter. For the present, the suggestion of de Broglie is important in that it introduces the useful concept of the wave nature of particles.

Fitting de Broglie waves into a region in which a particle is free to move can lead to an expression that shows the restrictions placed on the behavior of the particle. For this approach to be used for the wide range of atomic and molecular problems that are of interest to chemists we must have a generally applicable procedure for fitting in the waves. Such an approach is provided by the *wave equation* introduced by Erwin Schrödinger in 1926 and in a different form independently by W. Heisenberg in the same year. Schrödinger's method is based on an equation and a set of rules that allow calculation of the behavior of matter, particularly in systems in which a particle is restricted to regions with the dimensions of atoms and molecules. This method is the counterpart of Newton's laws of motion. Newton's laws, which are always presented without any derivation or proof, let one calculate the mechanical behavior of objects of ordinary and even planetary size. Schrödinger's equation is likewise presented without derivation or proof and is of particular interest in chemistry because it is applicable to the behavior of objects down to molecular and atomic (but probably not subnuclear) dimensions. Just as one uses and trusts $f = ma$, so must one use and, to the extent that seems justifiable, trust the Schrödinger equation.

In a study of molecules or atoms the quantities that might be of prime interest are the energies and the positions of the particles. The Schrödinger method yields the energies directly. It leads, however, to less specific information about the positions of the particles of the system. Only the *probability* that the particle is at a given position is obtained from wave mechanics. The lack of information about the exact position of a particle at some specific time seems to be a characteristic of the problem and not a defect in the Schrödinger method.

Just as one practices applying the ordinary laws of motion to simple problems, such as inclined planes and pulley systems, so also is it helpful to practice using the Schrödinger equation on some simple systems of atomic dimensions. Study of the Schrödinger equation is conveniently begun with problems in which the particle under consideration is required to move along one dimension only. For such a particle, the potential energy will be some function of this one dimension, which can be taken along the x axis and can be represented by $U(x)$. The information which will go into the Schrödinger equation in a particular problem will be the nature of $U(x)$ and the mass m of the particle. The information which we attempt to obtain is the allowed values of the energy of the particle and the relative probabilities of the particle's being at various positions along the x axis. Solution of the Schrödinger equation will yield a function of x. denoted by $\psi(x)$ or simply ψ, which is called the *wave function* for the particle. It is the square of this function which gives the relative probability of the particle's being at various distances along the x axis.

The Schrödinger equation in one dimension is

$$-\frac{h^2}{8\pi^2 m}\frac{d^2\psi}{dx^2} + U(x)\psi = \epsilon\psi \qquad (3\text{-}26)$$

The behavior of a particle is deduced, according to Schrödinger, by finding some function which will solve this differential equation when the appropriate values of $U(x)$ and m have been substituted. Satisfactory solution functions ψ will generally exist only for certain values of ϵ, and these are the allowed energies of the particle. Finally, the probability function ψ^2 is readily obtained from the solution function ψ. (In general, ψ may be either a real or complex function, and to allow for the second possibility, we should write not ψ^2 but $\psi^*\psi$, implying that the probability function is obtained by taking the product of it and its complex conjugate. Here we shall not carry out any calculations with complex wave functions, and we can therefore use the simple squared function symbol ψ^2.)

The example of the following section will illustrate the necessary inputs to the Schrödinger equation, the treatment that must be given to the equation, and the results that this treatment yields.

3-5 An Illustration of the Schrödinger Equation in One Dimension: A Particle in a One-dimensional Square Potential Well

As a sample application of the Schrödinger equation we investigate the energy of a particle constrained to move along a one-dimensional track of fixed length, as in Fig. 3-9. A particle will be so confined if it is subjected to the square-well potential-energy function.

Between $x = 0$ and $x = a$ the potential energy has a constant value, which can be taken as zero. Outside this region, for $x < 0$ and $x > a$, the potential

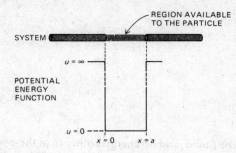

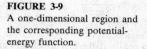

FIGURE 3-9
A one-dimensional region and the corresponding potential-energy function.

energy of the particle would be infinitely high. Let us proceed with this model problem without specifying what the particle is or what imposes the square-well potential-energy function on the particle. In the following sections specific situations will be dealt with.

Outside the region between $x = 0$ and $x = a$ the potential energy is infinitely high, and there will be zero probability of finding the particle in these regions. It follows that since ψ^2 must be zero for $x < 0$ and $x > a$, ψ must be zero in these regions. In the region $0 < x < a$ the potential-energy function is $U(x) = 0$, and the Schrödinger equation in this region is

$$-\frac{h^2}{8\pi^2 m}\frac{d^2\psi}{dx^2} = \epsilon\psi \tag{3-27}$$

It is now necessary to find well-behaved solutions for this equation. To be well behaved and avoid a discontinuity at $x = 0$ and $x = a$, the function ψ must be such that it equals zero at $x = 0$ and $x = a$. Functions which solve the differential equation and also satisfy these boundary conditions can be seen by inspection to be

$$\psi = A \sin\frac{n\pi x}{a} \qquad \text{where } n = 1, 2, 3, \ldots \tag{3-28}$$

and A is some constant factor. The expression $n\pi x/a$ has been arranged, as can be checked, so that the function goes to zero at $x = 0$ and at $x = a$ for any integral value of n. That the function satisfies the Schrödinger equation can be tested by substitution in Eq. (3-27) to give

$$\text{Left side} = -\frac{h^2}{8\pi^2 m}\left(-\frac{n^2\pi^2}{a^2}\right)A \sin\frac{n\pi x}{a} = \frac{n^2 h^2}{8ma^2}\left(A \sin\frac{n\pi x}{a}\right) \tag{3-29}$$

$$\text{Right side} = \epsilon\left(A \sin\frac{n\pi x}{a}\right) \tag{3-30}$$

The left and right sides are equal, and the expression

$$\psi = A \sin \frac{n\pi x}{a}$$

is therefore a solution if

$$\epsilon = \frac{n^2 h^2}{8ma^2} \qquad n = 1, 2, 3, \ldots \tag{3-31}$$

No really different solution can be found, and no energies other than these will result. [The value $n = 0$ in Eq. (3-28) provides a solution to Eq. (3-27) but gives a wave function that is everywhere zero. This leads to a zero probability of a particle's being anywhere in the box and is therefore unacceptable.] The allowed energies ϵ, which are represented in Fig. 3-10, are seen to be quantized as a result of the quite natural introduction of the integers in the solutions of the Schrödinger equation. A ψ function for each value of n is included in Fig. 3-10 alongside the energy to which it corresponds. The requirement that the ψ functions be well behaved limits these functions to ones which "fit," like those of Fig. 3-10, into the region available to the particle. Thus it is the confinement of the particle, or the *boundary conditions,* that leads to the quantization.

The function ψ^2 is also shown in Fig. 3-10 alongside the corresponding energy level for the first few states. The ψ^2 functions show the relative probability of the particle's being at various positions when the quantum number has some particular value. If one assigns a value to A such that the total probability of the particle's being between $x = 0$ and $x = a$ is unity, the wave functions are said to be *normalized.* The ψ^2 curves of Fig. 3-10 represent the probability density at various positions along a one-dimensional track. This can be emphasized by using dot-density diagrams, included in Fig. 3-10. These can properly remind you of the dot-density or electron-cloud diagrams frequently used to describe the electron positions in atoms or molecules.

The probability curves of Fig. 3-10, which are typical of those obtained in other such problems, are by no means understandable in terms of the behavior of ordinary-sized objects. The presence of positions at which the probability of finding the particle is zero is most striking. Furthermore, we learn that a particle in a "box" can have only certain allowed energies and that it is not even permitted to have zero energy. Only the success of the Schrödinger method in treating a number of problems where the solutions can be tested against experiment makes us put up with such strange results.

This particle-in-a-box problem should be appreciated as being typical of those encountered in applying the Schrödinger equation to problems of chemical interest. In general, three dimensions will be involved, and the potential-energy function will be somewhat more complicated. The procedure, however, will consist in writing the Schrödinger equation with the particular potential function and particle mass and then looking for suitable solution functions. This process will generally lead to only certain allowed energies.

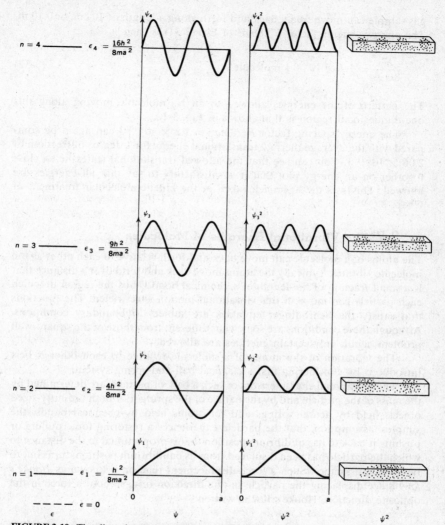

$$n = 4 \underline{} \quad \epsilon_4 = \frac{16h^2}{8ma^2}$$

$$n = 3 \underline{} \quad \epsilon_3 = \frac{9h^2}{8ma^2}$$

$$n = 2 \underline{} \quad \epsilon_2 = \frac{4h^2}{8ma^2}$$

$$n = 1 \underline{} \quad \epsilon_1 = \frac{h^2}{8ma^2}$$

$$----\; \epsilon = 0$$

FIGURE 3-10 The allowed energies ϵ, the wave function ψ, and the probability functions ψ^2 for the first few Schrödinger-equation solutions for the potential of Fig. 3-9.

3-6 Application of the One-dimensional Square-Well Results to the Molecules of a Gas

Now let us consider the translational motion in one dimension of a molecule of an ideal gas. To be specific we deal with an N_2 molecule. An N_2 molecule has a mass of $0.0280/(6.02 \times 10^{23}) = 4.65 \times 10^{-26}$ kg. Suppose the molecules of a gas sample can move freely back and forth along a length of 10 cm, or 0.10 m. The energy spacing factor $h^2/8ma^2$ of Eq. (3-31) is then

$$\frac{h^2}{8ma^2} = 1.2 \times 10^{-40} \text{ J molecule}^{-1} \tag{3-32}$$

The pattern of the energies allowed to an N_2 molecule moving along this one-dimensional region is that shown in Fig. 3-10.

The energy spacing factor $h^2/8ma^2 = 1.2 \times 10^{-40}$ J can again be compared with the average thermal translational energy for 1 degree of freedom of 2.06×10^{-21} J. You can see that the allowed translational states lie so close together on an energy plot that it is satisfactory to say that all energies are allowed. This was the approach taken in the kinetic-molecular treatment of Chap. 2.

3-7 The Vibrational Energies of Molecules

The atoms of a molecule can move back and forth relative to each other as the molecule vibrates. Typically the atoms move back and forth over a distance that is a small fraction of the length of a chemical bond. Thus the region in which each particle can move in this vibrational motion is restricted. The functions that satisfy the Schrödinger equation are subject to boundary conditions. Although these conditions are somewhat different from those of the square-well problem, again only certain energies are allowed.

The vibration of the atoms of a molecule relative to each other is best introduced by considering first a classical ball-and-spring system.

The vibrational characteristics of such a ball, or particle, are determined by the mass of the particle and by the nature of the spring. For both ordinary-sized objects held by actual springs and for atoms held by chemical bonds, the simplest assumption, that the particle experiences a restoring force pulling or pushing it back to its equilibrium position that is proportional to the distance to which the particle has been displaced from its equilibrium position, turns out to be quite satisfactory. Such a force-displacement relation is known as *Hooke's law*. Since displacing the particle in one direction brings about a force in the opposite direction, Hooke's law is written

$$f = -kx \tag{3-33}$$

where f is the restoring force and x is the displacement from the equilibrium position. The proportionality constant k is known as the *force constant* and is a measure of the stiffness of the spring. The force constant is equal to the restoring force operating for a unit displacement from the equilibrium position.

The classical motion of a particle, such as that of Fig. 3-11, can be deduced from Newton's law $f = ma$. If $f = -kx$ and $a = d^2x/dt^2$ are substituted, one obtains

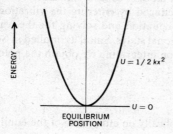

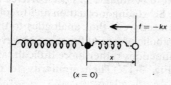

FIGURE 3-11
Hooke's law of force for a single particle.

$$m\frac{d^2x}{dt^2} = -kx \quad \text{or} \quad \frac{m}{k}\frac{d^2x}{dt^2} = -x \tag{3-34}$$

A solution to this equation can be seen by inspection and verified by substitution to be

$$x = A \sin\sqrt{\frac{k}{m}}\,t \tag{3-35}$$

A is a constant that is equal to the maximum value of x; that is, it is the vibrational amplitude. The position of the particle therefore varies sinusoidally with time, since every time t increases by $2\pi\sqrt{m/k}$, the quantity $\sqrt{k/m}\,t$ increases by 2π and the particle traces out one complete cycle. The time corresponding to one oscillation, or vibration, is therefore $2\pi\sqrt{m/k}$. More directly useful is the reciprocal of this quantity, which is the frequency of vibration, i.e., the number of cycles performed per second. If this quantity is denoted by ν_{vib}, we have

$$\nu_{\text{vib}} = \frac{1}{2\pi}\sqrt{\frac{k}{m}} \tag{3-36}$$

For a system of ordinary dimension there is therefore a natural frequency of oscillation that depends on the values of k and m. Any amount of energy can be imparted to the vibrating system, and this energy changes only the amplitude of the vibration.

The quantum-mechanical solution to this problem provided by the

Schrödinger equation differs, of course, in that only certain amounts of vibrational energy are allowed. These can be deduced by entering the vibrational potential function U into the Schrödinger equation and solving for the wave functions and energies of the allowed vibrational states. Since, as implied in Sec. 2-16, $f = -dU/dx$ and, here, $f = -kx$, upon integrating we obtain the potential function as

$$U = \tfrac{1}{2}kx^2 \tag{3-37}$$

The potential energy therefore rises parabolically on either side of the equilibrium position, as illustrated in Fig. 3-11.

Once a potential function for the motion to be studied has been arrived at, it is possible to substitute this function in the Schrödinger equation and to solve for the allowed energy-level pattern. The procedure is thus analogous to that used for the square well in Sec. 3-5. The parabolic potential function, however, makes determination of the solution wave functions rather more difficult, and these are shown, without derivation, in Fig. 3-12. Their similarity to the square-well functions is readily apparent.

The energies of the allowed vibrational states would also be given by solution of the Schrödinger equation. Again, only the result is given, and with the symbol v to represent the integers that enter, the energies of the allowed states are

$$\epsilon_{\text{vib}} = (v + \tfrac{1}{2})\frac{h}{2\pi}\sqrt{\frac{k}{m}} \qquad v = 0, 1, 2, \ldots \tag{3-38}$$

This quantum-mechanical result therefore indicates a pattern of energy levels with a constant spacing $(h/2\pi)\sqrt{k/m}$, shown in Fig. 3-12.

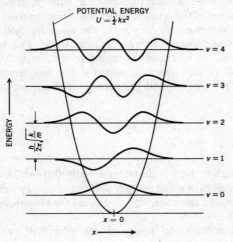

FIGURE 3-12
The allowed energies and the wave functions for the first few states of a particle subjected to a Hooke's-law potential.

It is interesting that the quantum-mechanical solution introduces the collection of terms $(1/2\pi)\sqrt{k/m}$ that correspond to the natural vibrational frequency of a classical oscillator. Equation (3-38) can therefore be written

$$\epsilon_{vib} = (v + \tfrac{1}{2})h\nu_{vib} \tag{3-39}$$

where the term ν_{vib} is interpreted according to Eq. (3-36).

The values of the vibrational-energy spacing factor $h\nu_{vib}$ or $(h/2\pi)\sqrt{k/m}$ can be deduced from spectroscopic studies, as will be shown in Sec. 14-3. Here we need only see the importance of the quantum restrictions on the energy.

The vibrational-energy spacing factors, which depend on the stiffness of the chemical bonds and on the masses of the vibrating atoms, are again characteristic of each molecule. A typical energy value, however, is 20×10^{-21} J. Here then, the quantum restrictions are very significant, and we must think of most molecules as having the least possible vibrational energy, or the next higher, and so forth. We cannot use the classical view that any vibrational energy is allowed.

Thus, although the quantum restrictions on translational motion can be ignored in considerations of the energy of a collection of molecules (as they can for the rotational motion of most molecules), those on vibrational energies cannot.

The energy gap between allowed vibrational energies is much greater than that between allowed rotational energies, and this gap in turn is much greater than that between allowed translational energies. This ordering can be attributed to the different sized regions in which the particles can move in the various types of motion. In vibrational motion the atoms move back and forth in a region whose length is only a fraction of a chemical-bond length. In rotational motion the atoms can be thought of as moving along a circular path around the axis about which the molecule is rotating. This path will have a length equal to that of several chemical bonds. Finally, in translational motion, the region available is that of the container, which is assumed to be very much larger than the molecular dimensions.

3-8 A Three-dimensional Illustration of the Schrödinger Equation: A Particle in a Cubic Potential Well

So far only one-dimensional problems have been solved by application of the Schrödinger equation. Now the allowed energies and the probability functions for a particle that is free to move in three dimensions will be deduced. A molecule of a gas enclosed in a cubic container provides a specific example that will be dealt with later in the section after the general procedure has been developed.

For any three-dimensional problem the potential energy will in general be a function of three coordinates. For a cubic potential box the cartesian coordi-

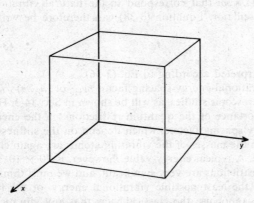

FIGURE 3-13
The three-dimensional square-well potential-energy function. The potential U is infinitely high except within the box, where it can be assigned the value zero.

nates of Fig. 3-13 are convenient. Again, the potential energy can be taken as zero everywhere inside the box, but it becomes infinite at the walls. The differential equation that must be solved is now the Schrödinger equation in three dimensions

$$-\frac{h^2}{8\pi^2 m}\left(\frac{\partial^2\psi}{\partial x^2} + \frac{\partial^2\psi}{\partial y^2} + \frac{\partial^2\psi}{\partial z^2}\right) + U(x,y,z)\psi = \epsilon\psi \qquad (3\text{-}40)$$

The solution function ψ will depend on the three coordinates x, y, and z.

For such differential equations it is often profitable to see whether they can be separated into parts, as was done for a diatomic molecule of a gas in Sec. 3-1. For the cubic container of Fig. 3-13 the potential energy can be written $U(x) + U(y) + U(z)$, where each function is like the one-dimensional potential-energy well of Fig. 3-9. Now one can try the substitution

$$\psi(x,y,z) = \phi(x)\phi(y)\phi(z) \qquad (3\text{-}41)$$

to see whether such a separated function simplifies Eq. (3-40). Substitution of Eq. (3-41) into Eq. (3-40) gives

$$-\frac{h^2}{8\pi^2 m}\left[\phi(y)\phi(z)\frac{d^2\phi(x)}{dx^2} + \phi(x)\phi(z)\frac{d^2\phi(y)}{dy^2} + \phi(x)\phi(y)\frac{d^2\phi(z)}{dz^2}\right]$$
$$+ [U(x) + U(y) + U(z)]\phi(x)\phi(y)\phi(z) = \epsilon[\phi(x)\phi(y)\phi(z)] \quad (3\text{-}42)$$

Division by $\phi(x)\phi(y)\phi(z)$ gives

$$-\frac{h^2}{8\pi^2 m}\left[\frac{1}{\phi(x)}\frac{d^2\phi(x)}{dx^2} + \frac{1}{\phi(y)}\frac{d^2\phi(y)}{dy^2} + \frac{1}{\phi(z)}\frac{d^2\phi(z)}{dz^2}\right]$$
$$+ [U(x) + U(y) + U(z)] = \epsilon \quad (3\text{-}43)$$

For the equation to be satisfied for all values of x, y, and z, each term on the left must equal a component of ϵ, and we can write

$$\epsilon = \epsilon_x + \epsilon_y + \epsilon_z \tag{3-44}$$

The Schrödinger equation (3-44) can then be broken down into three identical equations of the type

$$-\frac{h^2}{8\pi^2 m} \frac{1}{\phi(x)} \frac{d^2\phi(x)}{dx^2} + U(x) = \epsilon_x$$

or

$$-\frac{h^2}{8\pi^2 m} \frac{d^2\phi(x)}{dx^2} + U(x)\phi(x) = \epsilon_x \phi(x) \tag{3-45}$$

These equations are identical with that written for the one-dimensional problem. The solution to the three-dimensional square-box problem is therefore

$$\psi = \phi(x)\phi(y)\phi(z)$$

with

$$\phi(x) = A \sin \frac{n_x \pi x}{a} \qquad \epsilon_x = \frac{n_x^2 h^2}{8ma^2} \qquad n_x = 1, 2, 3, \ldots$$

$$\phi(y) = A \sin \frac{n_y \pi y}{a} \qquad \epsilon_y = \frac{n_y^2 h^2}{8ma^2} \qquad n_y = 1, 2, 3, \ldots \tag{3-46}$$

$$\phi(z) = A \sin \frac{n_z \pi z}{a} \qquad \epsilon_z = \frac{n_z^2 h^2}{8ma^2} \qquad n_z = 1, 2, 3, \ldots$$

One might try to visualize the probability distribution ψ^2 which is obtained from this wave function, but a graphical representation will be seen to be rather difficult. One can proceed by repeating the curves of Fig. 3-10 to show the separate factors of the wave-function components $\phi(x)$, $\phi(y)$, and $\phi(z)$ and their squares and leaving it to the viewer to imagine a three-dimensional graphical display of the product.

To depict the combined result, one must show the values of ψ or of ψ^2 throughout the region of the cubic box, and this, at best, leads to qualitative displays like that of Fig. 3-14.

The allowed energy levels for a particle in this three-dimensional cubic potential-energy box are

$$\epsilon = \epsilon_x + \epsilon_y + \epsilon_z = (n_x^2 + n_y^2 + n_z^2) \frac{h^2}{8ma^2} \tag{3-47}$$

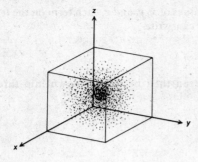

FIGURE 3-14
The function ψ^2 for the lowest energy state, $n_x = n_y = n_z = 1$, for a particle in a cubic box. The density of the dots is intended to be proportional to the value of the ψ^2 function.

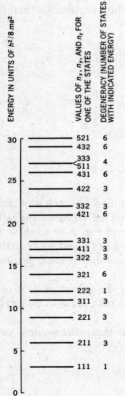

ENERGY IN UNITS OF $h^2/8\,ma^2$	VALUES OF n_x, n_y, AND n_z FOR ONE OF THE STATES	DEGENERACY (NUMBER OF STATES WITH INDICATED ENERGY)
30	521	6
	432	6
	333	4
	511	
	431	6
25		
	422	3
	332	3
	421	6
20		
	331	3
	411	3
	322	3
15	321	6
	222	1
	311	3
10	221	3
5	211	3
	111	1
0		

FIGURE 3-15
The energy-level pattern formed by the lower energy states of a particle in a cubic box, according to Eq. (3-46).

The pattern of energies of the allowed states differs from that for the one-dimensional case (Fig. 3-10) in two ways: (1) As Fig. 3-15 shows, the pattern is much less regular. This follows from the reduced regularity of the sum of the squares of the three integers compared with the squares of integers themselves. (2) Some of the energies are degenerate. Thus, although the energy $3(h^2/8ma^2)$ corresponds to only the state specified by $n_x = 1, n_y = 1, n_z = 1$, the energy $6(h^2/8ma^2)$ corresponds to the three states $n_x = 2, n_y = 1, n_z = 1$; $n_x = 1, n_y = 2, n_z = 1$; and $n_x = 1, n_y = 1, n_z = 2$.

The model of an ideal gas used in Chap. 2 pictures the molecules as moving freely within the confines of the impenetrable walls of the container. The corresponding quantum-mechanical problem treats a particle subject to a three-dimensional square-well potential with dimensions equal to that of the gas container.

Consider again the specific example of a gas containing N_2 molecules in a 1-liter container that we take to be cubic with dimensions of 0.10 m. The energy spacing factor $h^2/8ma^2$ was calculated in Sec. 3-6 to be

$$\frac{h^2}{8ma^2} = 1.2 \times 10^{-40} \text{ J}$$

and thus the energies of the allowed states are

$$\epsilon = (n_x{}^2 + n_y{}^2 + n_z{}^2)(1.2 \times 10^{-40}) \qquad \text{J molecule}^{-1} \tag{3-48}$$

Again we can conclude that the energy spacing for three-dimensional molecular translation is very much smaller than the room-temperature value of kT.

PROBLEMS

3-1. How many translational, rotational, and vibrational degrees of freedom are there for the molecules Ne, H_2, O_2, N_2O (linear), CO_2 (linear), H_2O (bent), NH_3 (pyramidal), CH_4 (tetrahedral), and benzene C_6H_6 (planar hexagonal)?

3-2. Twirling one end of an ethane molecule relative to the other end is described as an *internal rotation*. It accounts for one of the degrees of freedom of the molecule. How many translational, rotational, and vibrational degrees of freedom does an ethane molecule have in addition to this internal rotation?

3-3. Obtain Eqs. (3-4) and (3-5) from Eqs. (3-2) and (3-3).

3-4. Obtain Eq. (3-8) from Eqs. (3-1), (3-4), (3-5), and (3-7).

3-5. Express the reduced mass μ in terms of the atomic mass m of the atoms of a homonuclear diatomic molecule.

3-6. (*a*) What is the reduced mass of a diatomic molecule containing a light atom of mass m_l and a heavy atom of mass m_h in the limit as m_h/m_l approaches infinity? (*b*) Calculate the reduced mass of the HCl molecule and compare with the mass of the H atom and the Cl atom. (*c*) Calculate the reduced mass of the hydrogen atom, consisting of a proton and electron.

3-7. A ball of mass 100 g on the end of a 1-m string twirls around making one revolution each second. Find the angular momentum and the rotational energy using (a) the mass, the velocity, and the radius and (b) the angular velocity ω and the moment of inertia I.

3-8. The moment of inertia of the CO_2 molecule is 71.7×10^{-47} kg m^2. If it rotates about an axis so that its rotational energy is equal to $\frac{1}{2}kT$ at 25°C, that is, 2.06×10^{-21} J, what is (a) its angular momentum and (b) its angular velocity? (c) How many revolutions does it make per second? (d) The distance from the center of gravity, at the carbon atom, to an oxygen atom is 1.16 Å. What is the velocity of the oxygen atoms? Compare with translational velocities obtained in Chap. 2.

3-9. If a molecule has a rotational energy of 2.06×10^{-21} J and a moment of inertia of 2×10^{-47} kg m^2, what is the approximate value of its rotational quantum number?

3-10. If the rotational quantum number of a molecule with a moment of inertia of 2×10^{-47} kg m^2, as in Prob. 3-9, is known to be 100, what are (a) the angular momentum and (b) the rotational energy of the molecule?

3-11. Calculate the moment of inertia of (a) a hydrogen molecule, for which the internuclear distance is 0.74 Å, and (b) a chlorine molecule, for which the internuclear distance is 1.99 Å. (c) If a hydrogen molecule and a chlorine molecule have rotational states with the same value of the rotational quantum number, what is the ratio of their rotational energies?

3-12. (a) What is the magnitude of the angular momentum of a rotating system in a state for which the rotational quantum number is 5? (b) What are the possible magnitudes of the component of this angular momentum along any imposed direction? (c) What is the degeneracy of the rotational state in the absence of an imposed direction?

3-13. Draw a vector diagram to illustrate the relation between the total and the component angular momenta in Prob. 3-12.

3-14. A representative small-molecule moment of inertia is 1×10^{-45} kg m^2. How many rotational energy levels are there between the lowest-energy, $J = 0$, state and the state with an energy equal to $\frac{1}{2}kT$ at 25°C?

3-15. The energy pattern of the rotational states of a molecule spreads out so that for very large values of J or very large rotational energies the energy spacing between adjacent levels becomes large. (a) For a molecule with $I = 1 \times 10^{-45}$ kg m^2, for what value of J is the energy between the J state and the $J + 1$ state equal to $\frac{1}{2}kT$ at 25°C? (b) What is the energy of this state?

3-16. A representative small-molecule moment of inertia is 1×10^{-45} kg m^2. What is the energy separation between adjacent rotational states at a rotational energy equal to the 25°C value of $\frac{1}{2}kT$?

3-17. The π electrons of the benzene molecule can be treated as being free to travel around a circular track of radius 1.40 Å. (a) On the basis of this model obtain an expression for the allowed energies of the π electrons. (b) If two electrons can be assigned to each state, what energy would be required to raise one of the uppermost electrons to the next available energy level? (c) What wavelength of radiation would have quanta of the necessary energy? (d) In fact benzene absorbs radiation in the near-ultraviolet region at about 3000 Å. To what extent is the simple model of freely rotating delocalized π electrons satisfactory?

3-18. Calculate the wavelength of the de Broglie waves associated with (a) an electron accelerated by a voltage of 50 kV, as it is in an electron microscope. If we ignore relativistic effects which begin to become important, the velocity acquired by the electron is then about 1.5×10^8 m s^{-1}. (b) A molecule of nitrogen with a translational energy of $\frac{3}{2}kT$ at 25°C. (c) A beam of thermal neutrons, whose average energy is $\frac{1}{2}kT$ at 25°C. (d) A golf ball, of mass 46 g, traveling at 100 mi h^{-1}.

3-19. The absorption of a quantum of infrared radiation by a molecule is said, in most cases, to raise the molecule from the lowest energy vibrational state to the next higher energy state. Is this expectation consistent with the typical vibrational-energy spacing of 2×10^{-20} J mentioned in Sec. 3-7?

3-20. The probability density for a particle at a given position is given by ψ^2. If the wave function for a particle in a square well is $\psi = A \sin(n\pi x/a)$, by a suitable integration find the total probability that the particle will be found between $x = 0$ and $x = a$. Replace A by a suitable term so that $\int_0^a \psi^2 \, dx$ is always unity, i.e., so that one particle will be found somewhere in the well.

3-21. (a) Attempt to represent graphically and qualitatively the probability density for a particle at various positions in a cubic potential box for the quantum states $n_x = n_y = n_z = 1$ and $n_x = 2, n_y = n_z = 1$. (b) What are the energies of these states if the box is cubic with dimension 5 Å and the particle is an electron?

3-22. (a) Deduce an expression for the energies of the translational states of a molecule in a rectangular box with sides of length a, a, and b. (b) Draw energy-level diagrams at the left and at the right sides of a page to show the first dozen or so energy levels for a cubic box of dimension a and a rectangular box with dimension a, a, and $b = 2a$. (c) Add to the diagram *correlation lines* showing the qualitative way in which the energies of the states of a particle in a cubic box would change if some of the degeneracy were removed by elongating the box.

3-23. Calculate the energy spacing factor $h^2/8ma^2$ and the translational-energy spacing at a translational energy of $\frac{3}{2}kT$ for a hydrogen molecule in a cubic 0.10-m box at 25°C.

3-24. A general guide is that quantum restrictions become important when particles are confined to regions in space that are of the order of angstroms. Calculate the energy spacing factors for an electron, a hydrogen molecule, and a nitrogen molecule confined to a 10-Å cubic box.

3-25. If radiation were absorbed or emitted by molecules when they changed from a state with one translational energy to a state with the next higher or next lower translational energy, what region of the electromagnetic spectrum would be involved? (In fact, translational energies are not directly affected by radiation.)

3-26. (a) Calculate the energy that would be required to confine an electron to a region the size of a nucleus. A representative small-atom nucleus has a diameter of 10^{-15} m. Recognize that this is a very large energy by calculating the mass equivalent to this energy. You now see that although electrons, or β particles, are produced in nuclear reactions, they are not thought of as being present in nuclei. (b) Repeat the calculations for a neutron or a proton.

3-27. Repeat the benzene π-electron energy calculation in Prob. 3-17 by fitting de Broglie waves into the circular ring.

REFERENCES

HOFFMANN, B.: "The Strange Story of the Quantum," 2d ed., Dover Publications, Inc., New York, 1959. One of the best—accurate and amusing—of the popular stories of the development of quantum-mechanical concepts.

SHERWIN, C. W.: "Basic Concepts of Physics," Holt, Rinehart and Winston, Inc., New York, 1961. Chapter 6 deals with some of the key experiments and ideas in the development of quantum mechanics.

ATKINS, P. W., J. S. E. HOLKER, and A. K. HOLLIDAY (eds.): "Quanta: A Handbook of Concepts," Oxford University Press, Oxford, 1974. An unusual but excellent collection of treatments of both simple and complex topics related to quanta and quantum mechanics.

HUND, F.: "The History of Quantum Theory," trans. G. Reece, Barnes and Noble Books (Harper & Row), New York, 1974. A "review," some of which will be fully appreciated only as you proceed further with your studies of quantum mechanics.

HERZBERG, G.: "Atomic Spectra and Atomic Structure," Dover Publications, Inc., New York, 1944. A classic introduction to atomic spectra that provides the background in quantum mechanics necessary for an understanding of the principal features of atomic-spectral analysis.

SEMAT, H.: "Introduction to Atomic and Nuclear Physics," 4th ed., Chapman & Hall, Ltd., London. Includes a detailed treatment of the pre-Schrödinger equation material that is touched on in this chapter.

HEITLER, W.: "Elementary Wave Mechanics," Oxford University Press, New York, 1945. A short, quite readable presentation that deals with some of the material of this chapter as well as that of Chap. 10.

SLATER, J. C.: "Quantum Theory of Atomic Structure," chaps. 1 and 2, McGraw-Hill Book Company, New York, 1960, and L. PAULING and E. B. WILSON, JR.: "Introduction to Quantum Mechanics," McGraw-Hill Book Company, New York, 1935. Introductory material in these two books deals with some of the topics of this chapter as a preliminary to further work on quantum mechanics.

THE ENERGIES OF COLLECTIONS OF MOLECULES: THE MOLECULAR APPROACH

The introductory material of the preceding chapter has shown that molecules exist in a world of quantum restrictions. This implies that a molecule or an atom or an electron must exist in one of the allowed states and must have the energy corresponding to that state. Collections of large numbers of molecules, like those one deals with in ordinary-sized, or *macroscopic,* systems, must therefore consist of these molecules distributed throughout the allowed states. Many of the properties of chemical materials can be deduced if the energies of the quantum states and the distribution throughout these states are known. In practice the deduction of properties of macroscopic samples from such detailed calculations is often impossibly difficult. Nevertheless, the way this is done for such samples as ideal gases allows us to understand the molecular basis of many properties. Here, therefore, we shall investigate how some properties related to the energy of a gas sample are deduced.

4-1 The Boltzmann Distribution for Quantized Energies

The distribution expression that will be used to deduce the relative population of the energies available to the molecules of a gas has already been introduced in the study (Sec. 2-5) of the distribution of speeds and translational energies of gas molecules. Then energies were treated classically. The distribution expression for translational motion in one dimension was introduced as

$$\frac{dN}{N} = Ae^{-(1/2)mu_x^2/kT} du_x$$

The corresponding expression for quantized energies is

$$\frac{N_i}{N} = Ae^{-(\epsilon_i - \epsilon_0)/kT}g_i$$

The number of molecules N_i with energy ϵ_i is the counterpart of dN. The term $\epsilon_i - \epsilon_0$, the difference between the energy ϵ_i and the lowest allowed energy ϵ_0, is the counterpart of the kinetic-energy term $\frac{1}{2}mu_x^2$. Finally, g_i, the degeneracy or number of states with energy ϵ_i, is the counterpart of du_x, the interval of u_x. The Boltzmann distribution expression for quantized energies is usually written in the order

$$\frac{N_i}{N} = Ag_i e^{-(\epsilon_i - \epsilon_0)/kT} \tag{4-1}$$

It is often convenient to deal with the ratio of the populations of states at different energies, for this avoids the constant term of Eq. (4-1). First recognize that if N_i is the number of molecules with energy ϵ_i and g_i is the number of states at this energy, then N_i/g_i is the number of molecules *per state* at this energy. Then the ratio of the number of molecules per state at energy ϵ_i to the number per state at some other energy ϵ_j can be written from Eq. (4-1) as

$$\frac{N_i/g_i}{N_j/g_j} = e^{-(\epsilon_i - \epsilon_j)/kT} \tag{4-2}$$

It is often convenient to refer the populations of states to that of the lowest energy state. If this state is denoted by $j = 0$, we can write

$$\frac{N_i/g_i}{N_0/g_0} = e^{-(\epsilon_i - \epsilon_0)/kT} = e^{-(\Delta\epsilon_i)/kT} \tag{4-3}$$

where $\Delta\epsilon_i = \epsilon_i - \epsilon_0$. The terms in Eq. (4-3) are illustrated in Fig. 4-1.

Now you can see that if $\Delta\epsilon_i$ is large compared with kT, the ratio $(N_i/g_i)/(N_0/g_0)$ will be very small. Such is the case, generally, for all electronically excited states. Thus the energies of the molecules of a gas can often be

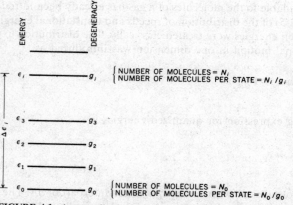

FIGURE 4-1 A generalized set of energies available to the molecules of a sample as a result of a particular type of motion.

adequately dealt with in terms of the translational, rotational, and vibrational energies of the ground electronic state.

The constant term A of Eq. (4-1) can be expressed by setting the summation of N_i over all states equal to the total number of molecules N. We write

$$N = \Sigma N_i = A\Sigma g_i e^{-(\epsilon_i - \epsilon_0)/kT}$$

or

$$A = \frac{N}{\Sigma g_i e^{-(\epsilon_i - \epsilon_0)/kT}}$$

The Boltzmann distribution can then be written as

$$N_i = \frac{N}{\Sigma g_i e^{-(\epsilon_i - \epsilon_0)/kT}} g_i e^{-(\epsilon_i - \epsilon_0)/kT} \qquad (4\text{-}4)$$

In the following two sections the origin of the Boltzmann distribution expression will be investigated. Then the expression will be applied to the various molecular motions of gas-phase molecules. You can proceed to those applications without working through Secs. 4-2 and 4-3 if you accept Eqs. (4-1) and (4-4).

4-2 Derivation of the Boltzmann Distribution Expression

A *distribution* is a statement of the number of molecules that occupy each of the energy levels that the quantum restrictions allow.

Consider the general energy-level pattern, including multiplicities, shown in Fig. 4-1. We must now see whether we can deduce (without depending on the Boltzmann distribution expression that was revealed in advance in the preceding section or even on the hint given there that the temperature is involved) how molecules distribute themselves throughout this pattern of energy levels. We proceed by looking for the most probable distribution, and we begin by seeing how the probability of a distribution is expressed.

A problem which in this regard is identical with that of the distribution of molecules throughout the pattern of Fig. 4-1 is that in which one asks about the probabilities of various distributions of marbles thrown randomly into a box with various-sized compartments. Figure 4-2 suggests a specific marble-compartment analog to the molecule energy-level problem. If one could construct such a compartmentalized box and have a suitably random throwing device, one could verify that the expression for the probabilities of the different arrangements (which is worked out in introductory chapters of texts dealing with probability) contains two factors.

The first factor involves the relative sizes of the compartments. The probability of each marble's landing in a given compartment is proportional to the size of the

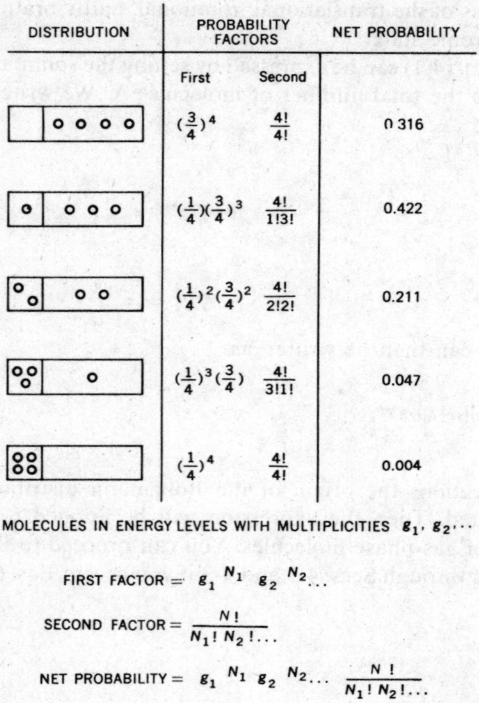

DISTRIBUTION	PROBABILITY FACTORS		NET PROBABILITY
	First	Second	
o o o o	$(\frac{3}{4})^4$	$\frac{4!}{4!}$	0.316
o o o o	$(\frac{1}{4})(\frac{3}{4})^3$	$\frac{4!}{1!3!}$	0.422
o o o o	$(\frac{1}{4})^2(\frac{3}{4})^2$	$\frac{4!}{2!2!}$	0.211
o o o o	$(\frac{1}{4})^3(\frac{3}{4})$	$\frac{4!}{3!1!}$	0.047
o o o o	$(\frac{1}{4})^4$	$\frac{4!}{4!}$	0.004

MOLECULES IN ENERGY LEVELS WITH MULTIPLICITIES $g_1, g_2 \cdots$

$$\text{FIRST FACTOR} = g_1{}^{N_1} g_2{}^{N_2} \ldots$$

$$\text{SECOND FACTOR} = \frac{N!}{N_1! N_2! \ldots}$$

$$\text{NET PROBABILITY} = g_1{}^{N_1} g_2{}^{N_2} \ldots \frac{N!}{N_1! N_2! \ldots}$$

FIGURE 4-2
A marble-and-compartment illustration of the probability factors that enter into the expression for the probability of a distribution of molecules throughout an energy-level pattern.

compartment. This consideration implies that in the expression for the probability of a particular distribution of the four marbles of Fig. 4-2, there is a term that is the product of the sizes of the compartments occupied by each marble or, more conveniently, the product of the sizes of the compartments each raised to the power corresponding to the number of marbles occupying that compartment in that particular distribution. (The corresponding factor for the molecules distributed throughout energy levels will be written $g_1{}^{N_1}, g_2{}^{N_2}, g_3{}^{N_3}, \ldots$.) This first factor implies that the most probable distribution will be the one in which all the marbles are in the largest compartment. This is clearly not the case.

The second factor expresses the tendency of the marbles to distribute themselves. It can be formed by seeing for each distribution the number of ways the individual marbles can be rearranged without altering the total number of marbles in each compartment. The ways in which four numbers or numbered marbles can be arranged in two boxes to give each of the possible distributions are illustrated in Fig. 4-3. There is a total of 4! ways of arranging four numbers. Of these 4! ways, some consist of rearrangements within a compartment. The net significant arrangements, as illustrated in Fig. 4-3, are obtained by dividing 4! by the insignificant interchanges: 4! in the first distribution, 3! in the second, and so forth. (For molecules in energy levels this factor has the form $N!/N_1!N_2!N_3! \cdots$.)

The total probabilities for the marble distributions are shown in Fig. 4-2. (If you

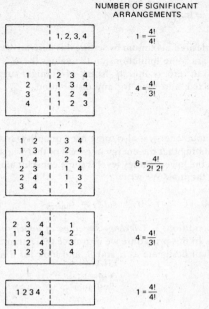

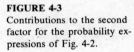

FIGURE 4-3
Contributions to the second
factor for the probability expressions of Fig. 4-2.

are not familiar with such probability expressions, you should investigate further examples to convince yourself that the combination of the two factors dealt with here leads to probabilities for various distributions that seem reasonable.)

In a similar way, we should express the probability W of a given distribution of a total of N molecules throughout energy levels as

$$W = (g_1{}^{N_1}g_2{}^{N_2}g_3{}^{N_3}\cdots)\frac{N!}{N_1!N_2!N_3!\cdots} \tag{4-5}$$

The goal, it will be recalled, was to find the values of $N_1, N_2, N_3, \ldots$ that maximize W. It is mathematically more convenient to look for a maximum in $\ln W$, which occurs also when W is a maximum. (The logarithmic expression allows Stirling's approximation $\ln x! = x \ln x - x$ for large numbers, which is derived in Appendix A-2, to be applied.) When Stirling's approximation is used for the N_i terms, we obtain

$$\ln W = N_1 \ln g_1 + N_2 \ln g_2 + \cdots + \ln N!$$
$$- N_1 \ln N_1 - N_2 \ln N_2 - \cdots + N_1 + N_2 + \cdots$$
$$= N_1 \left(1 + \ln \frac{g_1}{N_1}\right) + N_2 \left(1 + \ln \frac{g_2}{N_2}\right) + \cdots + \ln N! \tag{4-6}$$

To find the maximum in $\ln W$, we first take the derivative, and recognizing that $N!$ is a constant, we obtain for any N_i

$$\frac{\partial \ln W}{\partial N_i} = \frac{\partial}{\partial N_i}\left[N_i\left(1 + \ln\frac{g_i}{N_i}\right)\right] = \ln\frac{g_i}{N_i} \tag{4-7}$$

We cannot now proceed directly to the desired maximum by setting this derivative equal to zero. We must recognize that there are some limitations on the values the N_i's may take. [They cannot, for example, all go to zero, or infinity, as Eq. (4-7) might suggest.] The total number of molecules N is fixed, and thus, for any distribution,

$$N_1 + N_2 + N_3 + \cdots = \Sigma N_i = N \tag{4-8}$$

At a given temperature, moreover, the total energy is also some fixed quantity, and this requirement can be expressed by stipulating that the energy in excess of that which the system would have for all molecules in the lowest energy level is some constant amount E_{therm} where the subscript stands for thermal. We write

$$N_0(0) + N_1(\epsilon_1 - \epsilon_0) + N_2(\epsilon_2 - \epsilon_0) + \cdots = \Sigma(\epsilon_i - \epsilon_0)N_i = E_{\text{therm}} \tag{4-9}$$

The method for imposing such conditions is *Lagrange's method of undetermined multipliers,* discussed in Appendix A-3. In this procedure we introduce two parameters, the Lagrange multipliers, which we shall designate as α and β, and look for a maximum in

$$\ln W - \alpha\Sigma N_i - \beta\Sigma(\epsilon_i - \epsilon_0)N_i \tag{4-10}$$

We find the maximum, with respect to each N_i, by forming

$$\frac{\partial}{\partial N_i}[\ln W - \alpha\Sigma N_i - \beta\Sigma(\epsilon_i - \epsilon_0)N_i] = 0$$

or

$$\frac{\partial \ln W}{\partial N_i} - \alpha - \beta(\epsilon_i - \epsilon_0) = 0 \tag{4-11}$$

for each energy level i.

Now the values of N_i that produce the desired maximum in $\ln W$ can be obtained by substituting Eq. (4-7) in Eq. (4-11) to yield

$$\ln\frac{g_i}{N_i} - \alpha - \beta(\epsilon_i - \epsilon_0) = 0$$

or

$$N_i = g_i e^{-\alpha}e^{-\beta(\epsilon_i - \epsilon_0)} \tag{4-12}$$

This result for the population of the states in the most probable distribution remains mysterious until we eliminate or investigate the parameters α and β.

The term involving α can be eliminated by considering a sample of given size. One containing an Avogadro's number $\mathfrak{N}$ of molecules is convenient. For the summation of all N_i to give $\mathfrak{N}$,

$$\mathfrak{N} = \sum_i N_i = e^{-\alpha} \sum_i g_i e^{-\beta(\epsilon_i - \epsilon_0)}$$

Rearrangement gives

$$e^{-\alpha} = \frac{\mathfrak{N}}{\sum g_i e^{-\beta(\epsilon_i - \epsilon_0)}} \tag{4-13}$$

With this expression, the $e^{-\alpha}$ term can be eliminated from our expression Eq. (4-12) for the population of the states in a sample containing a total of $\mathfrak{N}$ molecules to give

$$N_i = \frac{\mathfrak{N}}{\sum_i g_i e^{-\beta(\epsilon_i - \epsilon_0)}} g_i e^{-\beta(\epsilon_i - \epsilon_0)} \tag{4-14}$$

You should notice that the summation term is characteristic of the system and is not identified with any one of the states. As a result, we can form the ratio of the populations of two states, which is easier to interpret, and for this quantity our derivation gives us

$$\frac{N_i}{N_j} = \frac{g_i e^{-\beta(\epsilon_i - \epsilon_0)}}{g_j e^{-\beta(\epsilon_j - \epsilon_0)}} = \frac{g_i}{g_j} e^{-\beta(\epsilon_i - \epsilon_j)}$$

or

$$\frac{N_i/g_i}{N_j/g_j} = e^{-\beta(\epsilon_i - \epsilon_j)} \tag{4-15}$$

The result clearly parallels the Boltzmann distribution expression of Eq. (4-2), but to complete the derivation of the Boltzmann expression we must proceed, as in the following section, to show that β can be identified with $1/kT$.

4-3 The Thermal Energy Due to the Translational Motion of the Molecules of a Gas and the Deduction that $\beta = 1/kT$

Let us now apply Eq. (4-14), the expression for the population of each state when molecules are distributed throughout available states, to the molecules of a one-dimensional gas to deduce the translational energy of an Avogadro's number of gas molecules. The answer will be in terms of the remaining unknown parameter β. We shall evaluate this parameter by using the fact that this energy must be equal to $\frac{1}{2}RT$, the translational energy of a mole of gas molecules due to their motion in one dimension. (In later sections we follow a similar procedure for rotational and vibrational energies, but then, having already interpreted β, we shall be able to deduce the thermal energies for these motions.)

The energy we calculate is E_{therm}, the energy of the system in excess of that which it would have if all molecules of a mole were at the lowest energy. E_{therm} can also be denoted by introducing E for the total energy of the system and E_0 for the energy of the system with all molecules in the lowest energy level. Then we can write

$$E_{therm} = E - E_0$$

The kinetic energy of translation of $\frac{1}{2}RT$, for example, is such a thermal energy term because it is the average energy over and above that which the molecules would have in the lowest translational energy level.

The thermal energy resulting from the distribution of molecules throughout the available energies can be written

$$E - E_0 = N_0(0) + N_1(\epsilon_1 - \epsilon_0) + N_2(\epsilon_2 - \epsilon_0) + \cdots = \sum_i N_i(\epsilon_i - \epsilon_0) \qquad (4\text{-}16)$$

To carry out the calculation we must use the information that Eq. (4-14) gives for the N_i's. Substitution of Eq. (4-14) into Eq. (4-16) yields, with Avogadro's number $\mathfrak{N}$ as the total number of molecules,

$$E - E_0 = \frac{\mathfrak{N}}{\sum_i g_i e^{-\beta(\epsilon_i - \epsilon_0)}} \sum_i g_i(\epsilon_i - \epsilon_0)e^{-\beta(\epsilon_i - \epsilon_0)} \qquad (4\text{-}17)$$

This general expression can be applied to the one-dimensional translational motion. The energy levels for this motion, as you saw in Sec. 3-6, are all single; that is, $g_i = 1$ for all i. The allowed energies form a pattern according to the equation

$$\epsilon_i = \frac{i^2 h^2}{8ma^2} \qquad i = 1, 2, 3, \ldots$$

Such large values of i will occur for most of the states that contribute to the summations of Eq. (4-17) that we can replace the lowest energy, $1h^2/8ma^2$, by zero, and thus obtain

$$E - E_0 = \frac{\mathfrak{N} \sum (i^2 h^2/8ma^2)e^{-\beta i^2 h^2/8ma^2}}{\sum e^{-\beta i^2 h^2/8ma^2}} \qquad (4\text{-}18)$$

The steps corresponding to successive i values are small compared with the range over which the summation extends, and so the summations can be replaced by integrations, giving

$$E - E_0 = \frac{\mathfrak{N} \int_0^\infty (i^2 h^2/8ma^2)e^{-\beta i^2 h^2/8ma^2}\, di}{\int_0^\infty e^{-\beta i^2 h^2/8ma^2}\, di} \qquad (4\text{-}19)$$

Both integrals are listed in Appendix A-1, and these lead us to the result

$$E - E_0 = \tfrac{1}{2}\mathfrak{N}\,\frac{1}{\beta} \tag{4-20}$$

Thus $1/\beta$ must be interpreted as a quantity which is proportional to the thermal energy. One can proceed from this result in a number of ways. One way is to realize that $1/\beta$ could be used in all the roles that we attribute to temperature and could thus be the basis for the establishment of a temperature function. More straightforward is the recognition that the temperature scale we have been using is such that the one-dimensional translational energy of a mole of gas is

$$E - E_0 = \tfrac{1}{2}RT = \tfrac{1}{2}\mathfrak{N}(kT) \tag{4-21}$$

For the Boltzmann distribution result obtained in Eq. (4-20) to be consistent with this value, we must make the identification

$$\beta = \frac{1}{kT} \tag{4-22}$$

Then, returning to Eq. (4-14), we see that we now have produced the result

$$N_i = \frac{\mathfrak{N}}{\Sigma g_i e^{-(\epsilon_i - \epsilon_0)/kT}}\, g_i\, e^{-(\epsilon_i - \epsilon_0)/kT} \tag{4-23}$$

or from Eq. (4-15),

$$\frac{N_i/g_i}{N_j/g_j} = e^{-(\epsilon_i - \epsilon_j)/kT} \tag{4-24}$$

Thus we have deduced that the most probable distribution is that given by the expressions, such as Eqs. (4-23) and (4-24), that constitute Boltzmann distribution expressions. Molecules generally distribute themselves throughout the allowed energy levels according to this most probable Boltzmann distribution. In some cases additional restrictions enter to cause deviations from the Boltzmann distribution when the available states are highly occupied. The most probable Boltzmann distribution is that reached when the molecules have had sufficient time to adjust to the conditions. It is the equilibrium distribution. If a system is suddenly formed or changed, a nonequilibrium distribution is momentarily created. Such a distribution, as you will see in Sec. 20-7, is the basis of laser action. In most chemical systems, however, the most probable equilibrium Boltzmann distribution can be assumed to have been reached.

4-4 The Partition Function

The distribution expression (4-4) for a collection of particles is rather clumsy. In overcoming this fault, we are led to the introduction of a quantity with widespread significance. The summation that appears in the denominator of

Eq. (4-4) turns out to be important enough to warrant a symbol, q, and a name, the *partition function*. Thus we define q by

$$q = \sum_i g_i e^{-(\epsilon_i - \epsilon_0)/kT} \qquad (4\text{-}25)$$

The calculation of a value or an expression for q for a particular type of motion requires information only about the pattern of allowed energies and the degeneracies of these levels.

Some of the implications of the name partition function can be seen by returning to Eq. (4-4) and writing it as

$$N_i = \frac{\mathfrak{N}}{q} g_i e^{-(\epsilon_i - \epsilon_0)/kT} \qquad (4\text{-}26)$$

For the ground state, $i = 0$, this becomes

$$\frac{N_0}{g_0} = \frac{\mathfrak{N}}{q} \qquad (4\text{-}27)$$

The N_0 particles could be said to be distributed or partitioned throughout the g_0 states that are available to them at energy ϵ_0. Likewise, the total number of particles $\mathfrak{N}$ can be said, as a result of the Boltzmann distribution, to be distributed, or partitioned, throughout q states. Thus q is a measure of the *availability of states*, a sort of net degeneracy, that results from the energy pattern throughout which the molecules are distributed and from the temperature which controls the distribution.

The convenience, even elegance, that enters when q is used to denote the summation of Eq. (4-25) can be seen by developing the general expression for the thermal energy.

The thermal energy $E - E_0$, the energy in excess of that which the system would have if all molecules were in their lowest energy states, is obtained, as in Eq. (4-16), as

$$E - E_0 = N_0(0) + N_1(\epsilon_1 - \epsilon_0) + N_2(\epsilon_2 - \epsilon_0) + \cdots = \sum_i N_i(\epsilon_i - \epsilon_0)$$

Now, with Eq. (4-26) this can be developed as

$$E - E_0 = \sum_i \frac{\mathfrak{N}}{q} g_i(\epsilon_i - \epsilon_0) e^{-(\epsilon_i - \epsilon_0)/kT}$$

$$= \frac{\mathfrak{N}}{q} \sum_i g_i(\epsilon_i - \epsilon_0) e^{-(\epsilon_i - \epsilon_0)/kT} \qquad (4\text{-}28)$$

The first derivative of q, as well as q itself, turns out to be involved. The derivative is

$$\frac{dq}{dT} = \sum_i g_i e^{-(\epsilon_i - \epsilon_0)/kT} \frac{\epsilon_i - \epsilon_0}{kT^2}$$

and multiplication by kT^2 leads to the useful relation

$$kT^2 \frac{dq}{dT} = \sum_i g_i (\epsilon_i - \epsilon_0) e^{-(\epsilon_i - \epsilon_0)/kT} \tag{4-29}$$

Comparison with Eq. (4-28) shows that the thermal energy can be expressed by

$$\mathsf{E} - \mathsf{E}_0 = \frac{\mathfrak{N}}{q} kT^2 \frac{dq}{dT} = \frac{RT^2}{q} \frac{dq}{dT} \tag{4-30}$$

Thus, for *any type of motion,* the thermal energy can be calculated if an expression which can be differentiated with respect to temperature is obtained for $q = \Sigma g_i e^{-(\epsilon_i - \epsilon_0)/kT}$.

In a similar way it will be found that other energy-related properties that result from the distribution of molecules throughout an energy pattern can be expressed in terms of the partition function.

In most of the molecular problems that we deal with, the state of a molecule can conveniently be described as the result of the translational, the rotational, the vibrational, and the electronic states, which make up the overall state. It is important to see that this separation of energies at the molecular level leads with Eq. (4-30) to a corresponding separation of the energy terms for the system of $\mathfrak{N}$ molecules.

Consider molecules whose energy is described in terms of the two types of motion, say a and b, they can undergo. Then if these motions can be treated separately, we can write for some allowed energy, compared with the lowest energy,

$$\epsilon_i = \epsilon_j{}^a + \epsilon_k{}^b \tag{4-31}$$

Furthermore, if the degeneracy of energy level $\epsilon_j{}^a$ is $g_j{}^a$ and that of level $\epsilon_k{}^b$ is $g_k{}^b$, the number of states with energy $\epsilon_j{}^a + \epsilon_k{}^b$ will be

$$g_i = g_j{}^a g_k{}^b \tag{4-32}$$

The partition function q for the system can be interpreted in terms of the separate motions. We show this by writing

$$q = \sum_i g_i e^{-\epsilon_i/kT} = \sum_{j,k} g_j{}^a g_k{}^b e^{-(\epsilon_j{}^a + \epsilon_k{}^b)/kT}$$

$$= \sum_j g_j{}^a e^{-\epsilon_j{}^a/kT} \sum_k g_k{}^b e^{-\epsilon_k{}^b/kT} = q_a q_b \qquad (4\text{-}33)$$

The energy consequences for a collection of particles are seen by rewriting Eq. (4-30) as

$$\mathrm{E} - \mathrm{E}_0 = RT^2 \frac{d \ln q}{dT}$$

which, with $\ln q = \ln q_a a_b = \ln q_a + \ln q_b$, becomes

$$\mathrm{E} - \mathrm{E}_0 = RT^2 \frac{d \ln q_a}{dT} + RT^2 \frac{d \ln q_b}{dT} = (\mathrm{E} - \mathrm{E}_0)_a + (\mathrm{E} - \mathrm{E}_0)_b \qquad (4\text{-}34)$$

Thus, when separate energy patterns for molecular motions are recognized, the total partition function is the product of the partition functions for the separate motions and the total energy of the system is calculated as the sum of energy contributions from the separate motions. The translational, rotational, and vibrational motions of gas-phase molecules, as illustrated in Sec. 3-1, are (at least approximately) separable. Thus we can write the partition function for the molecule as

$$q = q_{\text{trans}} q_{\text{rot}} q_{\text{vib}} \qquad (4\text{-}35)$$

and the thermal energy as

$$\mathrm{E} - \mathrm{E}_0 = (\mathrm{E} - \mathrm{E}_0)_{\text{trans}} + (\mathrm{E} - \mathrm{E}_0)_{\text{rot}} + (\mathrm{E} - \mathrm{E}_0)_{\text{vib}} \qquad (4\text{-}36)$$

4-5 The Three-dimensional Translational Energy of a Mole of Gas

That the translational energy of an Avogadro's number of gas molecules is $\frac{3}{2}RT$ will come as no surprise, but calculation of this result will illustrate the procedure that is based on partition-function expressions.

The translational states have energies that are expressed by

$$\epsilon = \epsilon_x + \epsilon_y + \epsilon_z = (n_x{}^2 + n_y{}^2 + n_z{}^2) \frac{h^2}{8ma^2} \qquad \begin{matrix} n_x = 1, 2, 3, \ldots \\ n_y = 1, 2, 3, \ldots \\ n_z = 1, 2, 3, \ldots \end{matrix} \qquad (4\text{-}37)$$

The partition function, again with the assumption that the ground state has an energy so close to zero that a zero value can be assigned to it, is

$$q_{\text{trans}} = \sum_{i,j,k} e^{-(n_x^2 + n_y^2 + n_z^2)h^2/8ma^2kT}$$

$$= \sum_i e^{-n_x^2 h^2/8ma^2kT} \sum_j e^{-n_y^2 h^2/8ma^2kT} \sum_k e^{-n_z^2 h^2/8ma^2kT}$$

$$= q_x q_y q_z \tag{4-38}$$

(Notice that the summation is over all states, not over all energy levels. Thus the degeneracy that would enter for an energy-level summation does not appear.)

Replacing the summations by integrations, and using an integral of Appendix A-1, gives

$$q_x = q_y = q_z = \int_0^\infty e^{-n_x^2 h^2/8ma^2kT} \, dn_x = \frac{\sqrt{2\pi ma^2 kT}}{h}$$

Thus

$$q_{\text{trans}} = \left(\frac{2\pi ma^2 kT}{h^2} \right)^{3/2}$$

It is convenient also to replace a by $V^{1/3}$ to avoid the requirement of a cubic container, and this replacement gives

$$q_{\text{trans}} = \left(\frac{2\pi mkT}{h^2} \right)^{3/2} V \tag{4-39}$$

A typical value of q_{trans} can be obtained by considering an N_2 molecule of a mole of N_2 gas at 25 °C and 1 atm pressure. The value of m is 4.65×10^{-26} kg, and the volume V in which the molecules are contained is $V = 24.5$ liters $= 0.0245$ m^3. Equation (4-39) gives

$$q_{\text{trans}} = 0.350 \times 10^{30} \tag{4-40}$$

If the three-dimensional motion is interpreted in terms of three one-dimensional components, the contribution to q_{trans} for each of the translational degrees of freedom can be calculated. We obtain, in view of Eq. (4-38),

$$q_x = q_y = q_z = 0.705 \times 10^{10} \tag{4-41}$$

These q values can be interpreted as measures of the number of states available to the particles of the gas.

Notice that the value of q_{trans} (or of q_x, q_y, or q_z) increases with increasing particle mass, container volume, or temperature. The dependence on mass and container volume stems from the way these terms affect the energy-level spacing. The temperature dependence stems from the availability of states, as expressed by the Boltzmann distribution.

The average translational energy can be calculated from the expression for q_{trans} and its derivative.

$$\frac{dq_{trans}}{dT} = \frac{(2\pi mk)^{3/2}}{h^3} V \left(\tfrac{3}{2}T^{1/2}\right)$$

We immediately obtain

$$(E - E_0)_{trans} = \frac{RT^2}{q} \frac{dq}{dT}$$

$$= \frac{RT^2}{(2\pi mkT)^{3/2}V/h^3} \frac{(2\pi mk)^{3/2}V}{h^3} \left(\tfrac{3}{2}T^{1/2}\right) = \tfrac{3}{2}RT \qquad (4\text{-}42)$$

Although q_{trans} depends on the mass of the particles and the volume of the container, the thermal energy $(E - E_0)_{trans}$ always has the value $\tfrac{3}{2}RT$.

For other molecular motions the result is not so well known.

4-6 The Thermal Energy Due to the Rotational Motion of the Molecules of a Gas

Now, let us calculate the rotational energy of an Avogadro's number of molecules which, like the molecules of a gas at not too high a pressure, are freely rotating. The allowed energies for a rotating linear molecule with 2 rotational degrees of freedom were shown in Sec. 3-3 to be given by

$$\epsilon_{rot} = J(J + 1) \frac{h^2}{8\pi^2 I}$$

and the degeneracies by

$$g_J = 2J + 1 \qquad J = 0, 1, 2, \ldots$$

Now we must develop

$$q_{rot} = \sum_{J=0}^{\infty} (2J + 1)e^{-J(J+1)h^2/8\pi^2 IkT} \qquad (4\text{-}43)$$

For most molecules at not too low a temperature the values of J that will lead to most of the contributing terms in this summation are very large compared with unity. We can write

$$q_{rot} \approx \sum_{J=0}^{\infty} 2J e^{-J^2 h^2/8\pi^2 IkT} \qquad (4\text{-}44)$$

Furthermore, the large number of summation terms that contribute allow us to treat J as a continuous variable so that the summation can be replaced by an integral. Thus we have

$$q_{rot} \approx 2 \int_0^\infty J e^{-J^2(h^2/8\pi^2 IkT)} \, dJ \tag{4-45}$$

Use of the appropriate integral from Appendix A-1 allows this to be evaluated to give

$$q_{rot} = \frac{8\pi^2 IkT}{h^2} \tag{4-46}$$

One additional feature needs to be recognized to make this partition function applicable to diatomic molecules containing identical atoms or to symmetric linear molecules. When a molecule, diatomic or linear, has like atoms, e.g., homonuclear diatomic molecules and linear molecules like acetylene, H—C≡C—H, a further restriction (not mentioned in Sec. 3-3) on the allowed rotational states enters. The wave function for an allowed state of a many-particle atom or molecule must have a particular symmetry; it must change sign or not change sign, depending on the nature of the identical particles, when the roles of equivalent particles are interchanged. This restriction, in a way we cannot deal with here, enters to eliminate half the rotational states when, as for homonuclear diatomic molecules N_2, O_2, H_2, etc., and linear molecules like H—C≡C—H, a rotation can turn the molecule so that it appears unchanged. (The restriction, in fact, enters only when the like nuclei are truly identical, i.e., are isotopically the same.) For such molecules the overall availability of rotational states is reduced to half what it otherwise would be.

This reduction in rotational states is often shown by introducing the *symmetry number* σ for the molecule and including this in the denominator of the previously obtained rotational-partition-function expression. Thus, for diatomic and linear molecules, we write

$$q_{rot} = \frac{8\pi^2 IkT}{\sigma h^2} \tag{4-47}$$

The symmetry number represents the number of ways the molecule can be rotated to give back the original molecule, identical except for labels attached to indistinguishable nuclei. Thus, for molecules such as HCl and HCN, σ is unity, but for N_2, CO_2, and H—C≡C—H, σ is 2.

As an example of the value of q_{rot} we can calculate that for N_2 at 25°C. The moment of inertia was calculated in Sec. 3-4 to be 14.1×10^{-47} kg m². The value for q_{rot} for N_2 molecules at 25°C is, according to Eq. (4-47),

$$q_{rot} \, (N_2 \text{ at } 25°C) = 52.2$$

The rotational partition function per degree of freedom for this example is

$$q_{rot} \text{ (per degree of freedom)} = \sqrt{52.2} = 7.2$$

This value can be contrasted with the q_{trans} value of the preceding section.

The rotational energy of a mole of gas-phase linear molecules can be calculated from the expression for q_{rot} and its derivative

$$\frac{dq_{rot}}{dT} = \frac{8\pi^2 Ik}{\sigma h^2} \tag{4-48}$$

With Eqs. (4-47) and (4-48) the thermal-energy contribution is obtained from Eq. (4-30) as

$$(E - E_0)_{rot} = \frac{RT^2(8\pi^2 Ik/\sigma h^2)}{8\pi^2 IkT/\sigma h^2} = RT \tag{4-49}$$

Thus for the linear molecule considered here, with 2 rotational degrees of freedom we achieve the value expected on a classical basis of $\frac{1}{2}RT$ thermal energy per degree of freedom. Again the value of q, here q_{rot}, depends on the factors that affect the allowed energy pattern, but as long as the spacings between the allowed energies are not too great, the thermal energy is simply $\frac{1}{2}RT$ per degree of freedom.

For a generally shaped molecule, rotation can be described in terms of component rotations about three perpendicular axes. The moments of inertia about these axes are known as the *principal moments of inertia* and are represented by I_A, I_B, and I_C. Since now the pattern of allowed energies is not so easily expressed, the partition function will be cited without derivation.

For a generally shaped molecule with identical atoms that can be interchanged by a rotation of the molecule a symmetry number appears in the denominator as it did in Eq. (4-47). The symmetry number is again the number of different ways the molecule can be turned to give back an original position. The symmetry number of H_2O is 2, of NH_3 is 3, and of CH_4 is 12.

The rotational partition function for a generally shaped molecule is

$$q_{rot} = \left(\frac{8\pi^2 kT}{h^2}\right)^{3/2} \frac{(\pi I_A I_B I_C)^{1/2}}{\sigma} \tag{4-50}$$

The general relation to the 2-degrees-of-freedom equation, Eq. (4-47), is straightforward.

For molecules with very low moments of inertia, H_2 being the most conspicuous example, or for all molecules at rather low temperatures, the assumptions $J \gg 1$ for most of the terms in the summation and the replacement of the summation by an integration are not justified. In such a case, other approaches to the evaluation of the partition-function sum must be taken. A similar problem which forces us to a term-by-term summation occurs when the net vibrational energy of a collection of molecules is considered.

4-7 The Thermal Energy Due to the Vibrational Motion of Molecules

The one vibrational mode of a diatomic molecule and the $3n - 6$ or $3n - 5$ modes of a polyatomic molecule each have associated with them a set of vibrational states with energies, as shown in Sec. 3-7, given by

$$\epsilon_{\text{vib mode}} = (v + \tfrac{1}{2}) \frac{h}{2\pi} \sqrt{\frac{k}{m}} = (v + \tfrac{1}{2}) h\nu_{\text{vib}} \qquad v = 0, 1, 2, \ldots \tag{4-51}$$

For each vibrational mode we can thus write

$$q_{\text{vib mode}} = \sum_{v=0}^{\infty} e^{-[(v+1/2)h\nu_{\text{vib}} - (1/2)h\nu_{\text{vib}}]/kT} = \sum_{v=0}^{\infty} e^{-vh\nu_{\text{vib}}/kT} \tag{4-52}$$

Now, in contrast to the situation in the two preceding sections, the vibrational spacings are appreciable compared with kT, and therefore only a few of the terms in the series contribute. The sum cannot be replaced by an integral, but we can obtain an expression by developing the summation

$$q_{\text{vib}} = 1 + e^{-h\nu_{\text{vib}}/kT} + e^{-2h\nu_{\text{vib}}/kT} + \cdots \tag{4-53}$$

With the introduction of the convenient symbol

$$x = \frac{h\nu_{\text{vib}}}{kT}$$

this becomes

$$q_{\text{vib mode}} = 1 + e^{-x} + e^{-2x} + \cdots = 1 + (e^{-x})^1 + (e^{-x})^2 + \cdots \tag{4-54}$$

This series can be recognized as the binomial expansion of $(1 - e^{-x})^{-1}$, and thus we have

$$q_{\text{vib mode}} = \frac{1}{1 - e^{-x}} = \frac{1}{1 - e^{-h\nu_{\text{vib}}/kT}} \tag{4-55}$$

A typical energy spacing $h\nu_{\text{vib}}$ between vibrational states is 2×10^{-20} J per molecule. At 25°C

$$x = \frac{h\nu_{\text{vib}}}{kT} = \frac{2 \times 10^{-20}}{(1.38 \times 10^{-23})(298)} = 5$$

The representative value of q that we calculate is

$$q_{\text{vib mode}} = \frac{1}{1 - e^{-5}} = 1.007$$

The vibrational energy levels are so widely spaced that little more than a single vibrational state is available, in this representative example, in each vibrational degree of freedom.

The derivative of $q_{\text{vib mode}}$ with respect to T is

$$\frac{dq_{\text{vib mode}}}{dT} = \frac{(h\nu_{\text{vib}}/kT^2)e^{-h\nu_{\text{vib}}/kT}}{(1 - e^{-h\nu_{\text{vib}}/kT})^2} = \frac{(x/T)e^{-x}}{(1 - e^{-x})^2} \tag{4-56}$$

The thermal energy contributed by a vibrational mode is then obtained from Eq. (4-30) as

$$(E - E_0)_{\text{vib mode}} = \frac{RT^2(x/T)e^{-x}}{1 - e^{-x}} = RT\frac{x}{e^x - 1} \tag{4-57}$$

Alternatively, with x replaced by $h\nu_{\text{vib}}/kT$ and R by $\mathfrak{N}k$, this can be written

$$(E - E_0)_{\text{vib mode}} = \frac{\mathfrak{N}(h\nu_{\text{vib}})}{e^{h\nu_{\text{vib}}/kT} - 1} \tag{4-58}$$

Plots of $(E - E_0)_{\text{vib mode}}$, for various values of T as a function of the vibrational-energy-level spacing, are shown in Fig. 4-4.

We can note immediately that only as $x \to 0$, that is, as $h\nu_{\text{vib}}$ becomes very much less than kT, does this expression reduce to our classical expectations. For then we can write

$$e^x \approx 1 + x$$

and

$$RT\frac{x}{e^x - 1} \approx RT\frac{x}{1 + x - 1} \approx RT$$

In this limit, the average kinetic energy is $\frac{1}{2}RT$, and this, together with the equal potential energy that characterizes a harmonic oscillator, gives the deduced result RT.

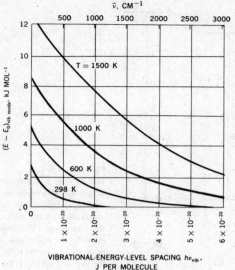

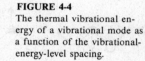

VIBRATIONAL-ENERGY-LEVEL SPACING $h\nu_{vib}$,
J PER MOLECULE

FIGURE 4-4
The thermal vibrational energy of a vibrational mode as a function of the vibrational-energy-level spacing.

The thermal energy for oscillators with the representative energy spacing of 2×10^{-20} J distributed according to Boltzmann's distribution is, by Eq. (4-57),

$$(E - E_0)_{vib} = RT\frac{x}{e^x - 1} = (8.314)(298)\frac{5}{e^5 - 1} = 84 \text{ J mol}^{-1}$$

Classically, where no quantum restrictions apply, an average potential and kinetic energy of RT, or about 2500 J mol^{-1}, would be expected at 25°C. The difference between 2500 and the calculated value of 84 is attributable to the effect of the rather widely spaced vibrational quantum levels.

Each of the vibrational degrees of freedom of a polyatomic molecule has a pattern of vibrational energies associated with it. The total vibrational energy of a polyatomic molecule is obtained by adding together the thermal energy contributed by each of these degrees of freedom, using Eq. (4-57) or (4-58) or Fig. 4-4 to calculate these contributions.

The thermal vibrational energy of a mole of SO_2 can be calculated as an illustration. Spectroscopic studies, which will be discussed in Sec. 14-3, show that the 3 vibrational degrees of freedom $(3n - 6 = 3)$ have the spacings indicated in Fig. 4-5. (The ways in which the atoms move in the three vibrations are not important here, but are included in Fig. 4-5.) The thermal vibrational energy can now be calculated from Eq. (4-57) or (4-58) or, for certain temperatures, read, approximately, off Fig. 4-4. At room temperature, for example, the 3 vibrational degrees of freedom contribute $550 + 51 + 22 = 623$ J mol^{-1}. At 1000 K, where more molecules are spread throughout higher energy levels, the total thermal vibrational energy is $5580 + 3220 + 2670 = 11,470$ J mol^{-1}.

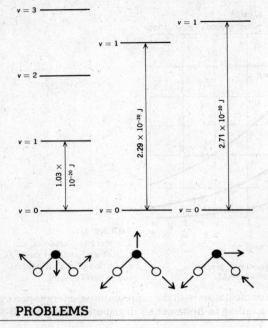

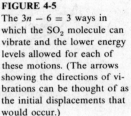

FIGURE 4-5
The $3n - 6 = 3$ ways in which the SO_2 molecule can vibrate and the lower energy levels allowed for each of these motions. (The arrows showing the directions of vibrations can be thought of as the initial displacements that would occur.)

PROBLEMS

4-1. Calculate the ratio of the number of molecules per state for two states separated by an energy equal to the value of kT at $T = 298$ K for (a) $T = 0$ K, (b) $T = 298$ K, (c) $T = 1000$ K.

4-2. At what temperature would the population of the states at a higher energy be one-tenth that of the states at a lower energy if the difference in energy is 1 kJ mol^{-1}?

4-3. In how small a one-dimensional box must an N_2 molecule be confined for the population of the $n = 2$ state to be appreciably less, say less by 1 percent, than the population of the $n = 1$ state if the temperature is 25°C?

4-4. A large number of particles are confined to a cubic container for which the size of the container, the mass of the particles, and the temperature are such that $h^2/8ma^2 = 0.1kT$. Calculate the ratio of the number of particles (a) in a state with $n_x = 1$, $n_y = 2$, $n_z = 3$ compared with the number in a state with $n_x = n_y = n_z = 1$; (b) at the energy $(1^2 + 2^2 + 3^2)h^2/8ma^2$ compared with the number at an energy $(1^2 + 1^2 + 1^2)h^2/8ma^2$.

4-5. For N_2 molecules in a 1-liter cubic container at 25°C $h^2/8ma^2kT$ is 2.87×10^{-20}. What is the value of n for the most probable speed, where, as in Sec. 4-5, $n^2 = n_x^2 + n_y^2 + n_z^2$.

4-6. Assume an imaginary gas whose molecules have none of the ordinary types of energies. Instead the only available energies are the singly degenerate ground state and one other energy level, of degeneracy g, at an energy equal to kT at $T = 100$ K above the ground state. (a) Calculate the partition function at several temperatures up to 1000 K and plot q versus T for g equal to 1, 3, and 10. (b) What is the infinite temperature limit in each case?

4-7. Using the imagined energy-level patterns of the preceding problem, calculate and plot the energy as a result of distribution of the molecules throughout the two-energy-level pattern for the cases of the upper-level degeneracy of (a) 1, (b) 3, and (c) 10. (d) What are the high-temperature limits in each case?

4-8. Gaseous iodine atoms have an electronic ground state that is fourfold-degenerate and a higher energy electronic state, with twofold degeneracy, 15.11×10^{-20} J above the ground state. (Additional electronic states are of very much higher energy.) What is the electronic partition function for $I(g)$ at (a) 298 K, (b) 1000 K, (c) 2000 K, (d) in the limit at $T = 0$, (e) if no other electronic states are taken into account in the limit at $T \to \infty$?

4-9. Calculate q_{trans} for (a) He molecules and (b) Xe molecules at 1 atm pressure and 25°C. (c) What is the average translational energy in each case?

4-10. To a very rough approximation an electron of an atom can be treated as an electron confined to a region of uniform potential which can be taken as cubic with dimensions 10^{-10} m. (a) According to this model, what is the partition function, which now could be called q_{elec}, for the electrons of such a system of atoms at 25°C? (b) In view of the definition of q, what is the smallest value, for any type of system, that q can have?

4-11. (a) What is the value of q_{trans} for nitrogen gas molecules in a 1-liter container at 25°C? (b) What would the value be if the pressure in the container were stipulated as 100 atm, the temperature still being 25°C and the volume still 1 liter?

4-12. Calculate the value of q_{trans} for one mole of water vapor at the standard state of an ideal gas, 1 atm, at (a) 25°C and (b) 100°C.

4-13. Without any information other than the fact that CO_2 is a linear molecule and SO_2 is bent, which do you think will have the larger partition-function product $q_{rot}q_{vib}$?

4-14. Why is it that the volume occupied by a gas or the pressure of a given amoung of gas must be specified for the calculation of q_{trans} but not for the calculation of q_{rot} or q_{vib}?

*4-15. Compare the values of q_{rot} at 25°C for CH_4, which has a relatively small moment of inertia, and SF_6, which has a relatively large moment of inertia. Both are *spherical top* molecules with $I_A = I_B = I_C$. The moment of inertia of the CH_4 molecule can be calculated from its tetrahedral shape and the C—H bond length of 1.094 Å. The moment of inertia of SF_6 is calculated from its octahedral shape and the S—F bond length of 1.48 Å. (The symmetry number of CH_4 is 12; that of SF_6 is 24.)

*4-16. For molecules with small moments of inertia and therefore widely spaced rotational energies, the replacement of a summation by an integration in the derivation of Eq. (4-46) or (4-47) is not entirely justified. Calculate q_{rot} at 25°C for HCl, moment of inertia 2.7×10^{-47} kg m², using (a) a term-by-term summation based on Eq. (4-43) (a computer program is a convenience) and (b) Eq. (4-46). (c) What error, if any, is introduced by using Eq. (4-46)?

4-17. What is the thermal energy of an Avogadro's number of rigid, i.e., non-vibrating, diatomic molecules (a) at 298 K and (b) at 1000 K?

4-18. Consider a reaction in which two monatomic molecules combine to give a rigid, i.e., nonvibrating, diatomic molecule. (a) Express the energy content of each species in terms of the zero-state energy and the translational- and rotational-energy contribution. (b) Write an expression for the difference in energy between the product and the sum of the reactants. (c) Will more or less energy be given out by the reaction as the temperature is raised?

*4-19. (a) If you have access to a computer and a suitable program, calculate q_{rot} for a diatomic molecule by a term-by-term summation of Eq. (4-43). (Choose a particular molecule, or take a representative moment of inertia in the range 10^{-46} to 10^{-45} kg m².) Include a symmetry number if necessary. (b) Plot the results versus T and add to the graph the curve based on the classical result of Eq. (4-46) or (4-47).

*4-20. The energy stored in any energy pattern is given in terms of q and the energy pattern by Eq. (4-28). (a) Recast this general expression to apply to a rotational energy pattern for which $g_J = 2J + 1$ and $\epsilon = J(J + 1)h^2/8\pi^2 I$. (b) Using the partition-function results from Prob. 4-19 and a suitable modification of the program used there, calculate $(E - E_0)_{rot}$ for the diatomic molecule. Plot the results versus temperature. (c) Add to the graph the classical limit for $E - E_0$ of a rotating diatomic molecule.

4-21. Calculate the vibrational partition function at 25°C for HCl molecules, which have the fairly high vibrational-energy spacing of 2885 cm⁻¹ or 5.73×10^{-20} J, and for Br_2 molecules, which have the very low vibrational spacing of 322 cm⁻¹, or 0.64×10^{-20} J.

4-22. Calculate q_{vib} at 25°C for HCl and Br_2 by the term-by-term summation of Eq. (4-54).

4-23. The three sets of vibrational levels of the SO_2 molecule have spacings 1.03×10^{-20}, 2.29×10^{-20}, and 2.71×10^{-20} J. What is the vibrational partition function for SO_2 at 25°C?

4-24. The vibrational energy levels of HCl consist of an evenly spaced set with a separation of 5.94×10^{-20} J. Calculate the ratio of the number of molecules in one energy level to the number of molecules in the next lower level at 25°C. Do the same for I_2, for which the vibrational energies are spaced by 0.42×10^{-20} J.

4-25. Compare the limits, the $h\nu_{vib}$ equal to zero or $T = \infty$, of the energy curves of Fig. 4-4 with the values that would be expected if a vibrational mode behaved classically.

4-26. Calculate the total thermal energy of 1 mol of gaseous SO_2 at 1500 K.

REFERENCES

These references include material that is related to the topics treated in the following three chapters. Some of the references at the end of Chap. 5 can be used in connection with this chapter.

GUGGENHEIM, E. A.: "Boltzmann's Distribution Law," Interscience Publishers, Inc., New York, 1955. A short readable treatment of the Boltzmann distribution and of some developments of thermodynamic functions.

SHERWIN, C. W.: "Basic Concepts of Physics," Holt, Rinehart and Winston, Inc., New York, 1961. Chapter 7 offers a very clear presentation of some of the basic features of statistical mechanics. No mathematical complexities obscure the treatment, and many simple systems are used to illustrate the concepts.

ANDREWS, F. C.: "Equilibrium Statistical Mechanics," John Wiley & Sons, Inc., New York, 1963. Treatment of probability and distributions followed by applications, thermodynamic functions, and ideal and real gases.

KITTEL, C.: "Elementary Statistical Physics," John Wiley & Sons, Inc., New York, 1958. Treatment of many topics of this chapter dealt with in a particularly straightforward manner.

DAVIDSON, N.: "Statistical Mechanics," McGraw-Hill Book Company, New York, 1962. A detailed and mathematical development of mathematical procedures in chap. 5, distributions in chaps. 6 and 7, and application to the thermodynamic properties of diatomic molecules in chap. 8 and of polyatomic molecules in chap. 11.

GURNEY, R. W.: "Introduction to Statistical Mechanics," chap. 1, Probability in Molecular Systems, and chap. 2, The Method of Undetermined Multipliers and the Boltzmann Distribution Expression, McGraw-Hill Book Company, New York, 1949.

BLINDER, S. M.: "Advanced Physical Chemistry: A Survey of Modern Theoretical Principles," The Macmillan Company, Collier-Macmillan Canada, Ltd., Toronto, 1969. An excellent reference. Some of the material on statistical mechanics (chaps. 17 to 23) can be studied before thermodynamics is dealt with.

5 THE FIRST LAW OF THERMODYNAMICS

A powerful method for studying chemical phenomena, which can be developed quite independently of the atomic and molecular theory of the preceding chapters and can be applied to systems of any complexity, is that of *thermodynamics*. The name implies a study of the flow of heat, but it will be seen that the subject treats the more general quantity energy. The energy changes associated with chemical reactions are themselves of considerable importance and will be dealt with in this and the following chapter. Even greater chemical interest, however, stems from the fact that the equilibrium position of a reacting system can be related to these energy changes. Much of the succeeding thermodynamic development will be directed toward associating thermal properties with the equilibrium state of a chemical system.

Thermodynamics is a logical subject of great elegance. Three concise statements, the three laws of thermodynamics, are made that sum up our experiences with energy and natural processes. From these statements logical deductions are then drawn that bear on almost every aspect of chemistry.

One should note that the great contribution of thermodynamics is that it *systematizes* the information we obtain from various experiments or measurements and allows us to draw conclusions about other aspects of the behavior of the system than that measured. The initial statements, for example, of the first law of thermodynamics may seem now to be so obvious as to be unnecessary and not very useful. As one proceeds through this and the following chapter, however, it will be noticed that the logical developments that follow from this first law allow important quantitative conclusions to be drawn that do not follow immediately or obviously from the statement of the first law.

The validity of thermodynamics depends only on the three generalizations and on the logic of the succeeding deductions. Thus since thermodynamics is independent of any model or theory, such as the molecular theory, for the nature of matter, any alteration in our present ideas and theories about the nature of molecules would in no way affect the validity of any thermodynamic result. Thermodynamics has a permanence which might, for example, be compared with that of Euclid's geometric theorems in plane geometry, but which is not shared by our ever-changing views on the nature of atoms and molecules.

Modern physical chemistry, however, attempts to understand the nature of the chemical world and does so primarily in terms of the atomic and molecular theory. Although thermodynamics can be kept aloof from these molecular ideas, it need not be. In practice, one deals with thermodynamics most frequently when detailed molecular ideas are used to try to explain or calculate some thermodynamic result. It will be found that the ability to understand thermodynamic quantities on a molecular basis, although not at all necessary for the study of thermodynamics, is a very valuable aid to the study of chemistry and the molecular world.

The introduction from time to time of molecular explanations will provide a concrete model as a basis on which thermodynamic quantities can be understood. Most students find this quite helpful. It cannot be emphasized too strongly, however, that the molecular model need not be introduced in our study of thermodynamics.

5-1 Thermal and Mechanical Energy: The Mechanical Equivalent of Heat

The forms of energy that are most easily and directly dealt with are thermal energy and mechanical energy. Thermal energy, or heat, is usually thought of as being measured by the change in temperature it produces in a given amount of material. Thus, the most familiar unit in which heat is measured is the *calorie,* defined originally as the amount of heat required to raise the temperature of one gram of water by one degree celsius. Mechanical energy can be thought of in terms of the potential energy that is stored when work is used to raise a weight against the force of gravity. Such a system can also deliver mechanical energy if a downward movement of the weight is suitably harnessed. Then the decrease in potential energy appears as work. Joules, the energy units of the SI system, are the traditional units in which mechanical energy is measured. (The related smaller unit, the erg, equal to 10^{-7} J, is used in most older chemical studies.) The joule is defined in terms of a force, one newton, acting through a distance, one meter. Furthermore, since a newton is defined through $f = ma$ as 1 kg (m s^{-2}), a joule has the units of kg m^2 s^{-2}. This definition reveals the mechanical basis of the unit.

Now we use the single unit, the joule, to measure both thermal energy, or heat, and mechanical energy, or work. That we can do so stems from early studies, most notably those of James Joule in 1849, on the mechanical equivalent of heat. Joule's apparatus consisted of a falling weight connected to a system of paddles which turned in an insulated container filled with water. Various weights falling various distances were used, and for each experiment the temperature rise of the water was recorded. Joule's experiments showed a proportionality between the work done, or loss of mechanical energy by the falling weight, and the heat gained, or increase in thermal energy of the water. The amount of mechanical energy that was lost could be made equal to the

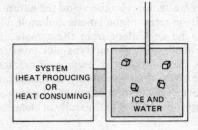

FIGURE 5-1
A thermal reservoir, and ice calorimeter, that can be used to measure the thermal energy gained or lost by the system.

SYSTEM (HEAT PRODUCING OR HEAT CONSUMING)

ICE AND WATER

amount of thermal energy that was gained if the units used for these two forms of energy were given the relation, using the modern factor,

$$1 \text{ cal} = 4.184 \text{ J}$$

Once this step is taken, the two-unit system with one unit for heat and a different unit for work can be dispensed with.†

Recognition that there is a mechanical equivalent of heat has much greater consequences than a simplification of units. It leads us to think of heat and work as different forms of energy. It establishes, for these two energy forms, the principle that energy is conserved, i.e., energy can change its form from work to heat or vice versa, but the amount of energy remains constant. This principle is now extended beyond energies that can be described as thermal or mechanical. Then it is known as the *conservation-of-energy principle*. In the following section you will see that this idea, when put into a more readily applicable form, constitutes the first law of thermodynamics.

In thermodynamics we study a *system*, a collection of materials that undergo some physical, chemical, or biological change. Deductions about the system are based on measurements of the heat that flows into or out of the system and of the work that the system does or has done on it.

The amount of heat transferred to (or from) any simple or complex system can be supplied by (or received by) a *thermal reservoir*. A simple thermal reservoir that avoids any need for a temperature-scale definition is an ice calorimeter, shown schematically in Fig. 5-1. If heat flows into the calorimeter from some outside source, some of the ice will melt, the total ice-water volume will decrease, and the indicator level will fall. We can use the change in the height of the indicator level as a measure of the thermal energy the calorimeter has gained. Such a device, which could be imagined to be made with other materials or operated at other pressures, provides a means of measuring thermal energies. The type of calorimeter used in practice is the counterpart of the ice calorimeter; when heat flows into it or out of it from a process under study, an

---

†Only recently have chemists actually done so. Until the recent adoption of SI units thermal quantities such as heat of combustion, heat of vaporization, heat capacity, and so forth were expressed in calories. Mechanical quantities, e.g., those occurring in studies of the mechanics or dynamics of molecules, were expressed in a variety of units such as ergs, joules, and electronvolts.

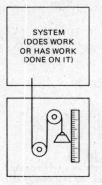

FIGURE 5-2
A schematic mechanical reservoir that would show the mechanical energy gained or lost by the system.

amount of thermal energy is added to, or taken from, the calorimeter to maintain constant temperature. Then this energy is determined from the electrical devices used for the addition or removal of energy. We shall frequently use schematic representations of thermal reservoirs that can exchange heat with some system in which we are interested. You can picture these as one or a series of *isothermal* calorimeters like the ice calorimeter that can be set at any desired temperature.

A mechanical-energy reservoir is best pictured as a weight-and-pulley system, like that in the Joule experiment. If, for simplicity, we accept the constant gravitational pull at some point on the earth's surface, the storage of mechanical energy in a system like that of Fig. 5-2 is measured by the height to which a given mass is raised. This schematic device will be used to measure, or represent, the gain or loss of mechanical energy that results when a system of interest does work or requires work to be done on it. The symbols $\Delta E_{\text{ther res}}$ and $\Delta E_{\text{mech res}}$ will be used to denote increases in the energies of the thermal and mechanical reservoirs.

5-2 The First Law of Thermodynamics

In practice it is not the energy changes that occur in the thermal and mechanical reservoirs that are of interest but what these energy changes can tell us about what is happening in a *system*, the collection of materials undergoing the physical, chemical, or biological change. The first law of thermodynamics helps us to deduce the energy changes in the system from the measurable energy changes in the reservoirs. (When you reach the second law, you will see the merits of keeping separate track of the thermal and mechanical energies.)

The system and the thermal-energy reservoir and the mechanical-energy reservoir that can be related to it are shown in the block diagram of Fig. 5-3. The three blocks provide the *universe* for the system and any process occurring in the system. Nothing else is affected by happenings in the system, and it is in this sense that the word universe is used.

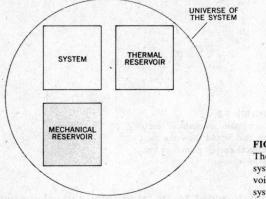

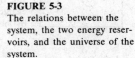

FIGURE 5-3
The relations between the system, the two energy reservoirs, and the universe of the system.

Consider some change, e.g., a chemical reaction, that occurs in the system and changes it from some state a, which implies certain chemical constituents at some pressure or temperature, to some other state b, implying different chemical constituents or pressure or temperature. Without any detailed information on the process that is occurring in the system, we can measure $\Delta E_{\text{therm res}}$ and $\Delta E_{\text{mech res}}$. We can use the conservation-of-energy principle to deduce the energy change $\Delta E_{a \to b}$ that has occurred in the system. The conservation principle applied to the universe of the process is expressed by

$$\Delta E_{\text{univ}} = 0 \quad \text{or} \quad \Delta E_{\text{therm res}} + \Delta E_{\text{mech res}} + \Delta E_{a \to b} = 0$$

The desired information about the system is then given by

$$\Delta E_{a \to b} = -\Delta E_{\text{therm res}} - \Delta E_{\text{mech res}} \tag{5-1}$$

For any change in the system, the energy change that must be attributed to the system to maintain the conservation-of-energy principle can be deduced from Eq. (5-1). In general, however, there are many ways of carrying a system from one state a to another state b. At this stage, different values might be expected to be obtained for $\Delta E_{a \to b}$ for each of these different processes.

To be specific, imagine that in going from state a to state b by path 1 of Fig. 5-4 the system gains energy from the reservoirs. Now suppose that when the system is restored to state a by path 2 of Fig. 5-4 the system pays back less energy to the reservoirs than it gained in the a-to-b process. We now could imagine this cyclic process of a to b by path 1 and then back by the alternate route, path 2. During each cycle, the reservoirs gain a certain amount of energy and the system is returned to the initial state a as a result of each cycle. Thus we have a perpetual motion machine, one that is described as a perpetual motion machine of the first kind. Our experience is that such machines, which in a

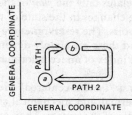

FIGURE 5-4
Alternate routes between
states a and b that together
constitute a cyclic process.

cyclic process produce an increase in energy, are impossible. This recognition implies that if the system gains an amount of energy from the reservoirs in going from state a to state b, it must contribute an equal amount to the reservoirs in returning from state b to a, even if the return route is different from the forward route. It follows that there is some energy difference between states a and b that depends only on these states and not on the way in which the system is changed from one state to the other. We thus are entitled to interpret $\Delta E_{a \to b}$ according to

$$\Delta E_{a \to b} = E_b - E_a \tag{5-2}$$

We now can state the conservation-of-energy principle in the useful form that constitutes the *first law of thermodynamics*.

The energy change of a system for any process that takes the system from state a to state b can be deduced from

$$\Delta E = -\Delta E_{\text{therm res}} - \Delta E_{\text{mech res}} \tag{5-3}$$

and ΔE is dependent only on the states a and b and can be treated in terms of the state function E according to

$$\Delta E = E_b - E_a \tag{5-4}$$

The first-law expressions (5-3) and (5-4) put the idea that the energy of the universe of a system is constant into a usable form. The quantity E, which you now see implies a property of the system, just like the volume V, is known as the *internal energy*.

In writing and using the first-law expression

$$\Delta E = -\Delta E_{\text{therm res}} - \Delta E_{\text{mech res}}$$

or for infinitesimal changes $dE = -dE_{\text{therm res}} - dE_{\text{mech res}}$ you must recognize that E is a function of the state of the system and that $E_{\text{therm res}}$ and $E_{\text{mech res}}$ are functions of the states of the thermal and mechanical reservoirs.

Processes that carry a system from state a to state b can have various values for $\Delta E_{\text{therm res}}$ and $\Delta E_{\text{mech res}}$. The first law relates only the *sum* of these quantities to ΔE. Thus the variables that determine changes in the state of the system cannot be used to treat changes in the reservoirs. The reservoir energies are determined by the "states" of the reservoirs, and these are simply dependent, in one case, on an indicator such as the volume index of an ice calorimeter and, in the other case, on the height of a weight.

Often, in thermodynamic treatments, we take a "system-centered" view, rather than one that treats the system and the thermal and mechanical surroundings on an equal basis. We specify only the state of the system. Then only the system has state functions. With this point of view and the new variables

q = heat gained by system
w = work gained by or done on system

we can write

$$\Delta E = q + w \qquad (5\text{-}5)$$

The new terms q and w are written with lowercase letters to indicate that they are not functions of the state of the system. In a similar way, if an infinitesimal change in the state of the system is considered, we write

$$dE = \delta q + \delta w \qquad (5\text{-}6)$$

where the symbols remind us that δq and δw are not derivatives of system state functions.

As we proceed we shall sometimes use the relation

$$\Delta E = -\Delta E_{\text{therm res}} - \Delta E_{\text{mech res}}$$

and have in mind the components of the universe of the system as shown in Fig. 5-3. At other times the system-centered viewpoint and the more convenient words heat and work and symbols q and w will be adequate.

5-3 Determination of ΔE:
Reversible and Irreversible Processes

The value of ΔE, the energy change of the system, can be deduced from measurements on the thermal and mechanical reservoirs. The fact that it is only the total of the changes in these energy reservoirs that is fixed for a given change in the system will now be illustrated. Of the infinite variety of processes imaginable that can change a system from one state to another, two extreme cases described as *irreversible* and *reversible* will be shown. The first term is applied to any process that occurs at other than a state of balance; the second is applied to a process in which the driving forces making the reaction proceed are offset only infinitesimally from a state of balance. The term reversible for this latter case is used because an infinitesimal change from the state of balance could reverse the process. The importance of the reversible and irreversible classifications of processes will be apparent in second-law studies. Here they serve to categorize the many different ways in which processes can occur.

In the first example (Fig. 5-5a) state a consists of a weight attached to a "ceiling," and state b consists of the weight on the "floor." If the string holding the weight in state a is cut, state b is reached by the unbalanced or irreversible process of free fall. The potential energy lost by the system would appear as thermal energy that would be collected from the floor and the weight by the thermal reservoir. No mechanical work would be done. The energy transfers between the system and the thermal and mechanical reservoirs are shown in Fig. 5-5b. Alternatively, state b can be reached from state a by a balanced, reversible process, as illustrated in Fig. 5-5c. Now, with the supposition of frictionless pulleys, no energy is transferred to the thermal reservoir. The potential energy lost by the system is collected by the mechanical reservoir.

As a second example of the energy transfers in different processes, consider the expansion of a gas. States a and b are shown in Fig. 5-6a. Free expansion, as in Fig. 5-6b, will produce no changes in the mechanical reservoir. In general, as you will see in Sec. 8-11, there will be some cooling or heating of the gas as it expands. The thermal reservoir will thus be called upon to supply or remove this relatively small amount of heat to return the gas to its initial temperature. In the reversible process of Fig. 5-6c the expansion is balanced by the weight and pulley system of the mechanical reservoir. Mechanical energy is stored in this system, and one would find that a corresponding amount of heat is transferred from the thermal reservoir to the system. For ideal gases, as you will see in Sec. 5-7, these two amounts of energy will be equal.

Finally consider the more chemical example of Fig. 5-7. In the irreversible process, H_2 and Cl_2 are allowed to react in the gas phase to produce HCl gas, which is then added to the water. A considerable amount of heat must be transferred to the thermal reservoir to maintain the system at its initial temper-

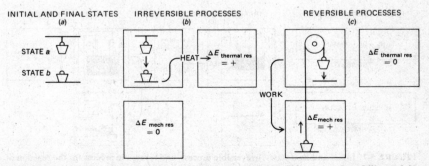
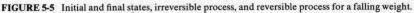

FIGURE 5-5 Initial and final states, irreversible process, and reversible process for a falling weight.

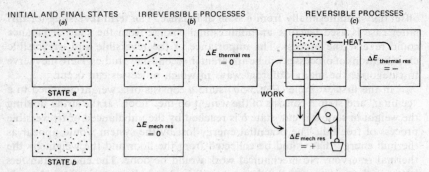

FIGURE 5-6 Initial and final states, irreversible process, and reversible process for the expansion of a gas.

ature. A relatively small amount of work, corresponding to the change in volume of the system, will be done by the mechanical reservoir. A reversible process involving the electrochemical cell of Fig. 5-7c can carry the system from the same initial to the same final state. Now a large amount of work is transferred from the system to the mechanical surroundings. A relatively small amount of heat will be transferred between the system and the thermal reservoir.

In the three examples of Figs. 5-5 to 5-7, the energy change ΔE of the system can be deduced from changes in the thermal and mechanical reservoirs. For different paths the energy changes in these reservoirs can be quite different. Thus we write $\Delta E = q + w$ to show that ΔE can be interpreted as $E_b - E_a$ but that various values of q and of w can be involved in these a-to-b processes.

5-4 The Work of Expansions and Contractions

In almost all the chemical examples to be considered in the first half of this book, the mechanical surroundings will gain or lose energy only as a result of the work done as the system expands or contracts against the confining pressure.

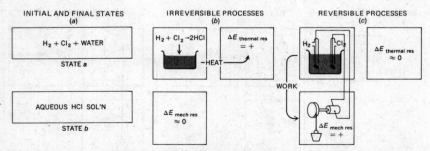

FIGURE 5-7 Initial and final states, irreversible process, and reversible process for the reaction of H_2, Cl_2, and water.

(In later chapters electrochemical cells will be treated, and then the electrical output provides an additional route for the transfer of energy to the mechanical reservoir.) Here we develop an expression for the energy changes corresponding to expansions and contractions.

Consider the system to occupy the cylinder of a piston arrangement, as in Fig. 5-8. The energy that can be transferred to the mechanical reservoir depends on the force that the connection to this reservoir exerts and the distance through which this force acts. Let f_{ext} be the force exerted by the piston shaft on the piston. Work is done by the mechanical reservoir if this force drives the piston down and compresses the system. Work is done by the system and stored in the mechanical reservoir if the piston shaft exerts a force that overbalances f_{ext} and drives it up. Thus we can write

$$w = -\int_{l_1}^{l_2} f_{ext}\, dl$$

Insertion of the piston cross-section area A into the denominator and numerator converts this into

$$w = -\int_{l_1}^{l_2} \frac{f_{ext}}{A} A\, dl$$

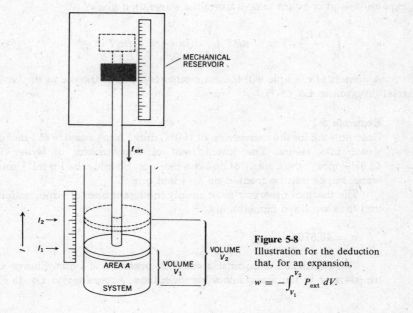

MECHANICAL RESERVOIR

f_{ext}

$l_2 \rightarrow$

$l_1 \rightarrow$

AREA A

SYSTEM

VOLUME V_1

VOLUME V_2

Figure 5-8
Illustration for the deduction that, for an expansion,

$$w = -\int_{V_1}^{V_2} P_{ext}\, dV.$$

Since pressure is force per unit area, the quantity f_{ext}/A can be written P_{ext}, the pressure that drives the piston. Furthermore, $A\,dl$ can be recognized as the change in volume of the system and can be replaced by the symbol dV. Thus we can write

$$w = -\int_{V_1}^{V_2} P_{ext}\,dV \qquad (5\text{-}7)$$

If the gas expands, dV is positive and w is negative: work is done by the gas. If the gas is compressed, dV is negative and w is positive: work is done on the gas. Calculations with Eq. (5-7) can be made only if the nature of the expansion or compression, i.e., the relation between P_{ext} and V, is specified.

For example, expansion against a constant external pressure, as in systems which are open to the atmosphere, leads to

$$w = -P_{ext}\int_{V_1}^{V_2} dV = -P_{ext}(V_2 - V_1) = -P_{ext}\Delta V \qquad (5\text{-}8)$$

Other special and important expansions are ones in which the expansion is balanced, or reversible, implying that the external pressure is only infinitesimally less than the internal pressure throughout the expansion. The piston pressure P_{ext} can be equated to the gas pressure P. The integration of Eq. (5-7) then requires a relation between P_{ext} or P and the volume. If, for example, the system consists of n mol of an ideal gas, this relation is $PV = nRT$, and if the expansion is at constant temperature, the integration gives

$$w = -\int_{V_1}^{V_2} \frac{nRT}{V}\,dV = -nRT\int_{V_1}^{V_2} d(\ln V) = -nRT\ln\frac{V_2}{V_1} \qquad (5\text{-}9)$$

A numerical example will illustrate other features of the use of the basic relation given in Eq. (5-7).

Example 5-1
Calculate ΔE for the conversion at 100°C and 1 atm pressure of 1 mol of water into steam. The latent heat of vaporization of water is 40,670 J mol^{-1}, the density of liquid water can be taken as 1 g ml^{-1}, and water vapor can be treated as an ideal gas.

The thermal reservoir must supply the latent heat of vaporization, and thus we have immediately

$$q = 40{,}670 \text{ J}$$

The expansion is against a constant pressure of 1 atm. Energy is transferred to the mechanical surroundings. According to Eq. (5-8),

$$w = -P_{ext}(V_2 - V_1)$$

The required quantities are

$P_{ext} = 1 \text{ atm} = 101,325 \text{ N m}^{-2}$
$V_1 = \text{volume of 1 mol of liquid water} = 18 \text{ ml} = 18 \times 10^{-6} \text{ m}^3$
$V_2 = \text{volume of 1 mol of water vapor}$
$\quad = 0.0224 \times \frac{373}{273} = 0.0306 \text{ m}^3$

Thus

$$w = -101,325(0.0306) - 18 \times 10^{-6}) = -101,325(0.0306) = -3100 \text{ J}$$

Finally,

$$\Delta E = q + w = 40,670 - 3100 = +37,570 \text{ J}$$

Most of the energy received by the water from the thermal reservoir goes into raising the internal energy of the water as it goes from liquid to vapor. A small amount, shown by the increase in energy of the mechanical surroundings, is used in pushing back the atmosphere.

5-5 The Enthalpy Function

In studies of the energy changes associated with reactions of chemical interest, a great variety of chemical materials and transformations will be dealt with. The transformations will be carried out in many ways, but it is convenient to consider two conditions that are special and occur frequently: (1) the *volume* of the system is kept constant and (2) the *pressure* on the system is held constant. The latter situation, for example, is that existing for reactions or other processes carried out in containers open to the atmosphere.

For a constant-volume process the schematic thermal and mechanical surroundings, as in Fig. 5-3, can be used without any complication. We write

$$\Delta E = q + w \tag{5-10}$$

For a constant-volume process, no PV work of the type treated in Sec. 5-4 is done, and therefore only some other form of work, e.g., that resulting from an electrical output, could lead to a work term. If, as is often the case, no such work is done,

$$w = 0 \tag{5-11}$$

and for such constant-volume processes we have the result, which is specially convenient for calorimetric studies,

$$\Delta E = q \qquad \text{[const volume, only } PV \text{ work]†} \qquad (5\text{-}12)$$

where q is the heat absorbed by the system.

Constant-pressure processes are different in that generally the volume of the system changes and work is done on or by the surroundings. In particular, if the system expands by an amount ΔV against a constant external pressure P an amount of energy $P \Delta V$ is gained by the mechanical reservoir and lost by the system. Again, in many processes carried out at constant pressure, no mechanical work, other than through expansion, is done. For such constant-pressure processes, we have

$$\Delta E = q - P \Delta V \qquad (5\text{-}13)$$

We could proceed using Eq. (5-13), but it is, in fact, a nuisance for all reactions carried out open to the atmosphere to have to include this $P \Delta V$ term along with the calorimeter term q. It is more convenient to recognize that both ΔE and ΔV are changes in the system and to rearrange Eq. (5-13) to read

$$\Delta E + P \Delta V = q \qquad (5\text{-}14)$$

This lumping together of ΔE and $P \Delta V$ can be made part of our thermodynamic treatment by introducing a new energy term H, called the *enthalpy* or *heat content,* defined by

$$H = E + PV \qquad (5\text{-}15)$$

For any process the change in H will then be

$$\Delta H = \Delta E + \Delta(PV) \qquad (5\text{-}16)$$

For any *constant-pressure* process,

$$\Delta H = \Delta E + P \Delta V \qquad (5\text{-}17)$$

and, with Eq. (5-14),

$$\Delta H = q \qquad \text{[const press., only } PV \text{ work]} \qquad (5\text{-}18)$$

Thus, for constant-pressure processes, calorimetric measurements which meas-

---

†To emphasize the special conditions under which equations apply, reminders like this will be added to the equations where these restrictions are easily overlooked.

ure the energy change of the thermal reservoir lead directly to ΔH, that is, to a value of the change in $H = E + PV$ of the system.

Very generally, it is convenient to deal with E in connection with constant-volume processes and with $H = E + PV$ in connection with constant-pressure processes. Of course, for either type of process, one can calculate and deal with either or both the quantities ΔE and ΔH.

The enthalpy, like the energy, is a state function; i.e., for a particular state of a system, the enthalpy has some particular value. This follows directly from the definition of H as the sum of two other state functions E and PV.

5-6 Some Properties of State Functions

To describe the properties of chemical substances and of the reactions they undergo, we shall need to know how some of these properties are related to each other and how they are related to other variables. Some quite general mathematical relations are helpful.

We shall restrict our attention to properties that can be expressed in terms of two variables. If we select a sample of given size, 1 mol of a substance for example, properties such as the volume, the internal energy, and the enthalpy are such functions. It is frequently convenient to think of the temperature and the pressure as the variables on which these properties depend. Then we can express the functional dependence by relations such as

$$E = f(T,P) \tag{5-19}$$

Let us now see what follows from the fact that for a variety of properties of the system we can write relations like Eq. (5-19) for the internal energy. This analytical expression could, alternatively, be shown graphically, as is suggested in Fig. 5-9. From either the analytical or graphical approach, if the actual dependence were known, one could determine the separate dependence of E on P and T. In this way one would obtain the partial derivatives

$$\left(\frac{\partial E}{\partial T}\right)_P \quad \text{and} \quad \left(\frac{\partial E}{\partial P}\right)_T$$

where, it will be recalled, the subscript signifies the variable that is held constant. A general infinitesimal change in E can be written in terms of these slopes, or rates of change, and of the changes dT and dP that are involved in the general process. This leads to the *total differential*

$$dE = \left(\frac{\partial E}{\partial T}\right)_P dT + \left(\frac{\partial E}{\partial P}\right)_T dP \tag{5-20}$$

The internal energy E is, in fact, usually more conveniently dealt with as a

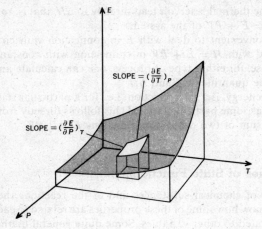

SLOPE $= \left(\frac{\partial E}{\partial T}\right)_P$

SLOPE $= \left(\frac{\partial E}{\partial P}\right)_T$

FIGURE 5-9
Two partial derivatives of the state function E.

function of T and V. The enthalpy H more often is treated as a function of T and P. The most useful starting points for the development of many relationships are therefore

$$dE = \left(\frac{\partial E}{\partial V}\right)_T dV + \left(\frac{\partial E}{\partial T}\right)_V dT \qquad (5\text{-}21)$$

and

$$dH = \left(\frac{\partial H}{\partial P}\right)_T dP + \left(\frac{\partial H}{\partial T}\right)_P dT \qquad (5\text{-}22)$$

Four generally useful relationships involving partial derivatives can now be pointed out.

1. The partial derivatives $(\partial E/\partial V)_T$ and $(\partial E/\partial T)_V$ of Eq. (5-21), for example, are themselves functions of V and T. Thus partial derivatives, such as $\left[\frac{\partial}{\partial V}\left(\frac{\partial E}{\partial T}\right)_V\right]_T$, which implies the derivative of $(\partial E/\partial T)_V$ with respect to volume at constant temperature, can be formed. Since the order in which derivatives are taken is of no consequence,

$$\left[\frac{\partial}{\partial V}\left(\frac{\partial E}{\partial T}\right)_V\right]_T = \frac{\partial^2 E}{\partial V \partial T} = \frac{\partial^2 E}{\partial T \partial V} = \left[\frac{\partial E}{\partial T}\left(\frac{\partial E}{\partial V}\right)_T\right]_V \qquad (5\text{-}23)$$

2. For processes in which the function for which the total derivative is written remains constant we can write, again using Eq. (5-21) as an example, $dE = 0$. Thus, specifying that E remains constant, we have

$$\left(\frac{\partial E}{\partial V}\right)_T dV + \left(\frac{\partial E}{\partial T}\right)_V dT = 0 \tag{5-24}$$

Rearrangement of this expression with introduction of the partial derivative notation gives

$$\left(\frac{\partial V}{\partial T}\right)_E = -\frac{(\partial E/\partial T)_V}{(\partial E/\partial V)_T} \quad \text{or} \quad \left(\frac{\partial T}{\partial V}\right)_E = -\frac{(\partial E/\partial V)_T}{(E/\partial T)_V} \tag{5-25}$$

3. A derivative can be formed from the total differential. Thus, again using Eq. (5-21) as an example, we can divide by dT or by dV to obtain

$$\frac{dE}{dT} = \left(\frac{\partial E}{\partial V}\right)_T \frac{dV}{dT} + \left(\frac{\partial E}{\partial T}\right)_V \quad \text{or} \quad \frac{dE}{dV} = \left(\frac{\partial E}{\partial V}\right)_T + \left(\frac{\partial E}{\partial T}\right)_V \frac{dT}{dV} \tag{5-26}$$

4. Derivatives and partial derivatives with the same variables held constant can be manipulated like fractions. For example, dV/dP can be written as

$$\frac{dV}{dP} = \frac{dV}{dE}\frac{dE}{dP} \tag{5-27}$$

A similar partial derivative relation can be written if the constancy of a single variable is applied to each term. If, for example, the above relation is applied while T is held constant, we write

$$\left(\frac{\partial V}{\partial P}\right)_T = \left(\frac{\partial V}{\partial E}\right)_T \left(\frac{\partial E}{\partial P}\right)_T \tag{5-28}$$

Expressions like these will be used in the next section, in which ideal-gas behavior is explored.

5-7 The Expansion of an Ideal Gas: The Dependence of H and E of an Ideal Gas on Pressure and Volume

An important experiment by Joule in 1843 was directed at the study of the internal energy of a gas. These early, insensitive experiments led to a conclusion that we now recognize as characterizing ideal-gas behavior. The experiment performed in an apparatus like that depicted in Fig. 5-10 consisted in filling one of the two bulbs with air at a pressure of about 20 atm, the other bulb being evacuated. The gas-bulb assembly was then immersed in a water bath which was insulated from the surroundings.

The experimental arrangement ensures that no work will be done on or by, and no heat will be gained or lost by, the gas-bulb assembly and the water in

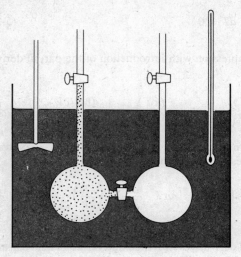

FIGURE 5-10
Apparatus for the Joule experiment on the heat effect of the expansion of a gas.

which it is immersed. Thus, for these gas and water components of the system we can write

$$E_{gas} + E_{water} = \text{const} \quad \text{or} \quad dE_{gas} + dE_{water} = 0 \qquad (5\text{-}29)$$

The gas and water-bath contributions can be described by total differentials in the form

$$dE = \left(\frac{\partial E}{\partial V}\right)_T dV + \left(\frac{\partial E}{\partial T}\right)_V dT$$

The experimental arrangement provides for a change in the volume term only for the gas. Thus, Eq. (5-29) can be expressed as

$$\left[\left(\frac{\partial E}{\partial V}\right)_T dV\right]_{gas} + \left[\left(\frac{\partial E}{\partial T}\right)_V dT\right]_{gas} + \left[\left(\frac{\partial E}{\partial T}\right)_V dT\right]_{water} = 0 \qquad (5\text{-}30)$$

When the experiment was carried out by opening the stopcock of Fig. 5-10, the result was no detectable temperature change. Thus $dT = 0$ can be inserted into the description of the process as given by Eq. (5-30). Only the first term of Eq. (5-30) remains, and since dV of the gas is not zero, it follows that

$$\left(\frac{\partial E}{\partial V}\right)_T = 0 \qquad (5\text{-}31)$$

This deduced result, that at a fixed temperature the internal energy of a gas is independent of its volume, is now taken as an additional characteristic of ideal behavior. The mathematical formulation of the consequences is seen by returning to the total differential for E, shown in Eq. (5-21), and inserting this ideal-gas characteristic $(\partial E/\partial V)_T = 0$. Then one has

$$dE = \left(\frac{\partial E}{\partial T}\right)_V dT \quad \text{or} \quad \frac{dE}{dT} = \left(\frac{\partial E}{\partial T}\right)_V \qquad \text{[ideal gas]} \qquad (5\text{-}32)$$

Thus, for an ideal gas, E changes with T for *any* process in the same way that it does for the volume or the pressure held constant. [Here the expression $(\partial E/\partial V)_T = 0$ has been added to the PVT relation $PV = nRT$ to characterize ideal-gas behavior. In fact, as will be seen in Sec. 8-11 after the second law of thermodynamics has been introduced, $(\partial E/\partial V)_T = 0$ is a *consequence* that can be deduced from PVT behavior following the ideal-gas law $PV = nRT$.]

The result expressed by Eq. (5-31) or (5-32) is immediately understandable on the basis of our kinetic-molecular model and the discussion of thermal energy in the preceding chapter. The absence of attractions and repulsions between the molecules of a gas was seen to be the basis for obedience to the $PV = nRT$ law. Furthermore, the absence of such interactions means that the energy of the gas will be unaffected by the average distance between molecules and will depend only on their distribution throughout their allowed energy levels. For nonideal gases and for liquids and solids, on the other hand, these interactions do occur, and the molecules have a different average potential energy when the average intermolecular distance is changed. In general, therefore, E does depend on P or V as well as on T.

For an ideal gas H as well as E is a function only of the temperature. From the defining equation $H = E + PV$, the derivative of H with respect to pressure at constant temperature can be formed as

$$\left(\frac{\partial H}{\partial P}\right)_T = \left(\frac{\partial E}{\partial P}\right)_T + \left[\frac{\partial(PV)}{\partial P}\right]_T \qquad (5\text{-}33)$$

Recognition that for an ideal gas $(\partial E/\partial P)_T = 0$ and, from $PV = nRT$, that $[\partial(PV)/\partial P]_T = 0$ leads us to

$$\left(\frac{\partial H}{\partial P}\right)_T = 0 \qquad \text{[ideal gas]} \qquad (5\text{-}34)$$

A similar result would be found for $(\partial H/\partial V)_T$. Thus we can write, for the enthalpy of an ideal gas,

$$\left(\frac{\partial H}{\partial T}\right)_P = \left(\frac{\partial H}{\partial T}\right)_V = \frac{dH}{dT} \qquad \text{[ideal gas]} \qquad (5\text{-}35)$$

Again, ideal-gas behavior has converted the specific temperature dependence of H to the simple result of Eq. (5-35), which shows that H as well as E varies with temperature in a way that is independent of any restriction or lack of restriction on the pressure and volume.

5-8 The Dependence of H and E on Temperature: The Heat Capacities C_P and C_V of Ideal Gases

The energies of chemical systems are influenced mostly by chemical reactions and by temperature changes. Reactions will be dealt with in the following chapter. Temperature effects can be treated here, and are done so in terms of the *heat capacities*.

As for the energy content, it is convenient to deal separately with heat capacities measured at constant volume, indicated by C_V, and those measured at constant pressure, C_P. The definitions of these heat capacities, which can be appreciated by imagining the type of experiment that provides heat-capacity data, are

$$C_V = \lim_{\Delta T \to 0} \left(\frac{q}{\Delta T} \right)_{V \text{ of syst const}} \tag{5-36}$$

$$C_P = \lim_{\Delta T \to 0} \left(\frac{q}{\Delta T} \right)_{P \text{ of syst const}} \tag{5-37}$$

That is, the heat capacities are the thermal energy that must be added to the system per unit temperature rise under the specified conditions.

Furthermore, for all constant-volume processes for which only PV work is involved we can write $q = \Delta E$, and for all constant-pressure processes for which only PV work is involved we can write $q = \Delta H$. These relations allow the definitions of C_V and C_P to be converted into

$$C_V = \left(\frac{\partial E}{\partial T} \right)_V \tag{5-38}$$

$$C_P = \left(\frac{\partial H}{\partial T} \right)_P \tag{5-39}$$

Notice that these are quite generally applicable, no assumption of ideal-gas behavior having been made.

Now let us see how C_V and C_P are related. Let us form the difference and then reduce the result to one involving only E, instead of E and H, by using $H = E + PV$. We have

$$C_P - C_V = \left(\frac{\partial H}{\partial T} \right)_P - \left(\frac{\partial E}{\partial T} \right)_V = \left(\frac{\partial E}{\partial T} \right)_P + P \left(\frac{\partial V}{\partial T} \right)_P - \left(\frac{\partial E}{\partial T} \right)_V \tag{5-40}$$

At this stage you might see the simplification that results from the assumption of ideal-gas behavior, but let us proceed to a more generally useful equation before this is done. The first term of Eq. (5-40) can be converted into an equation involving a $(\partial E/\partial T)_V$ term by using the total differential result of (5-26), namely,

$$\frac{dE}{dT} = \left(\frac{\partial E}{\partial V}\right)_T \frac{dV}{dT} + \left(\frac{\partial E}{\partial T}\right)_V \tag{5-41}$$

and, stipulating constant pressure,

$$\left(\frac{\partial E}{\partial T}\right)_P = \left(\frac{\partial E}{\partial V}\right)_T \left(\frac{\partial V}{\partial T}\right)_P + \left(\frac{\partial E}{\partial T}\right)_V \tag{5-42}$$

Substitution of this result for the first term of Eq. (5-40) and rearranging gives

$$C_P - C_V = \left[P + \left(\frac{\partial E}{\partial V}\right)_T\right]\left(\frac{\partial V}{\partial T}\right)_P \tag{5-43}$$

This general relation can be used now to investigate ideal-gas behavior. The term $(\partial E/\partial V)_T$ is then zero, and the remaining term $P(\partial V/\partial T)_P$ is found, with the relation $PV = RT$ for 1 mol of an ideal gas, to have the value R. Thus

$$C_P - C_V = R \qquad \text{[1 mol of an ideal gas]} \tag{5-44}$$

For real gases, as well as liquids and solids, the internal energy does depend on the volume, and thus $(\partial E/\partial V)_T$ cannot be set equal to zero. Furthermore, $(\partial V/\partial T)_P$ has a value that depends on the characteristics of the particular material. In Sec. 5-12 you will see how the difference in heat capacities is related to measurable properties of materials.

5-9 Adiabatic Expansions of Ideal Gases

A process that occurs in an insulated or isolated system so that no heat is gained or lost is *adiabatic*. Adiabatic processes are important in the development of many thermodynamic concepts. It is worthwhile here investigating, for the simple case of an ideal gas, the PVT behavior of a gas expanding adiabatically and reversibly. These results will be most immediately appreciated by comparing them with the PVT behavior for an isothermal expansion, for which T (and therefore PV) is constant.

For n mol of an ideal gas, we can write, according to Sec. 5-8,

$$\frac{dE}{dT} = n C_V \qquad \text{or} \qquad dE = n C_V \, dT \tag{5-45}$$

For a reversible expansion process work w done on the gas is

$$w = -P \, dV = -\frac{nRT}{V} \, dV \tag{5-46}$$

For an adiabatic process $q = 0$, and the first law required $dE = w$, or

$$nC_V \, dT = -nRT \frac{dV}{V} \qquad \text{or} \qquad \frac{C_V}{R} \frac{dT}{T} = -\frac{dV}{V} \tag{5-47}$$

For a process that takes the gas from a volume V_1 at a temperature T_1 to a new volume V_2 at a temperature T_2, if C_V is taken to be constant, one has

$$\frac{C_V}{R} \int_{T_1}^{T_2} \frac{dT}{T} = -\int_{V_1}^{V_2} \frac{dV}{V} \qquad \text{or} \qquad \frac{C_V}{R} \ln \frac{T_2}{T_1} = -\ln \frac{V_2}{V_1} \tag{5-48}$$

On rearrangement, and after antilogarithms have been taken, this result can be written

$$V_1 T_1^{C_V/R} = V_2 T_2^{C_V/R} \tag{5-49}$$

An arrangement that is frequently more useful is obtained by substituting for T_1 and T_2 the ideal-gas-law expression $T = PV/nR$ and $C_P = C_V + R$ to get

$$P_1 V_1^{C_P/C_V} = P_2 V_2^{C_P/C_V} \tag{5-50}$$

The ratio of the two heat capacities frequently occurs, and is given the designation

$$\gamma = \frac{C_P}{C_V} \tag{5-51}$$

With this notation the variation of pressure and volume of a reversible adiabatic process involving an ideal gas is given by

$$P_1 V_1^{\gamma} = P_2 V_2^{\gamma} \tag{5-52}$$

or

$$PV^{\gamma} = \text{const} \tag{5-53}$$

On plots of P versus V, curves for reversible adiabatic processes are steeper than are those for isothermal processes, as is indicated in Fig. 5-11. When a gas expands isothermally, heat is absorbed to make up for the work done by the gas.

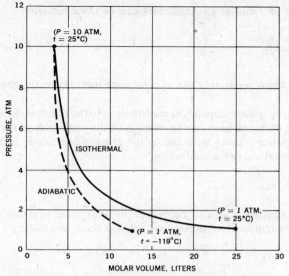

FIGURE 5-11 Reversible isothermal and adiabatic expansions of 1 mol of N_2 from 10 atm and 25°C to 1 atm. (For N_2 at 25°C, $\gamma = 1.40$.)

For reversible adiabatic expansion the work of expansion uses up the thermal energy of the gas. As a result the temperature falls, and the pressure change, for a given expansion, is greater than in the corresponding isothermal expansion.

Adiabatic expansions using a flow system and a pressure-reducing *throttling valve* are used industrially to produce the low temperatures needed to form liquid air and the liquid forms of other "permanent" gases. Such expansions can be shown to occur at constant enthalpy. The temperature coefficient $(\partial T/\partial P)_H$, known as the *Joule-Thomson coefficient,* is itself dependent on the temperature. At room temperature this coefficient is positive for most gases. Cooling occurs when the pressure is reduced. For hydrogen and helium the room-temperature values of the coefficient are negative. Only below the *inversion temperature,* 193 K for H_2 and 36 K for He, do cooling and subsequent liquefaction occur.

5-10 The Molecular Interpretation of E and H of Ideal Gases

The descriptions of the energies of molecules of Chap. 4 can now be brought together with the thermodynamic internal-energy and enthalpy functions. If an expression for the partition function for the molecules of an ideal gas can be developed from

$$q = q_{\text{trans}}q_{\text{rot}}q_{\text{vib}}q_{\text{elec}} \tag{5-54}$$

the thermal energy of 1 mol of gas molecules can be obtained from

$$E - E_0 = \frac{RT^2}{q}\frac{dq}{dT}$$ (5-55)

In practice we calculate separately the various contributions to the thermal energy $E - E_0$.

The thermal temperature-dependent contribution to the internal energy of an ideal gas can be deduced from our knowledge of the molecules of the gas. This thermal component, along with the temperature-independent E_0 term, constitutes the internal energy according to

$$E = E_0 + (E - E_0)$$ (5-56)

The enthalpy function can also be broken up into a temperature-independent term and a temperature-dependent thermal term. We write

$$H = H_0 + (H - H_0)$$ (5-57)

The terms E_0 and H_0 are the energy and the enthalpy that a mole of substance would have if all the molecules were in their lowest allowed energy states. This is the distribution that would result if the temperature were reduced to zero while the pattern of allowed energies remained unchanged. Both E_0 and H_0 are temperature-independent quantities.

The relation between E_0 and H_0 can be seen by substituting Eqs. (5-56) and (5-57) in $H = E + PV$. We obtain

$$H_0 + (H - H_0) = E_0 + (E - E_0) + PV$$ (5-58)

For an ideal gas, the PV term is given by RT. Since the temperature-independent and temperature-dependent terms must separately satisfy the equality, it follows that

$$H - H_0 = (E - E_0) + RT \quad \text{and} \quad H_0 = E_0 \quad \text{[ideal gas]}$$ (5-59)

A calculation of the thermal-energy functions $E - E_0$ and $H - E_0$ for SO_2 will illustrate the molecular approach to thermodynamic quantities. This molecule, which will later be shown to be nonlinear, has 3 translational degrees of freedom, 3 rotational degrees, and $3n - 6 = 3$ vibrational degrees. A spectroscopic study shows that the three vibrational modes have energy-level schemes with spacings of 518, 1151, and 1362 cm^{-1}.

With these data we can calculate the energy that 1 mol of SO_2 gas has as a result of the molecules occupying energy levels other than the lowest available ones. The calculation is summarized in Table 5-1. As will be recalled from

TABLE 5-1 Calculation of the Thermal Energy
$E - E_0$ of $SO_2(g)$ at 25°C

Contributing term		Energy, J mol^{-1}	
Translation	$\frac{3}{2}RT =$	3718	
Rotation	$\frac{3}{2}RT =$	3718	
Vibration:			
$\bar{\nu} = 518 \text{ cm}^{-1}$ $x = 2.50$	$\dfrac{RTx}{e^x - 1} = 554$		
$\bar{\nu} = 1151 \text{ cm}^{-1}$ $x = 5.56$	$= 53$		
$\bar{\nu} = 1362 \text{ cm}^{-1}$ $x = 6.58$	$= 23$	630	
		8066	

Chap. 4, only the vibrational contribution requires a detailed calculation. The thermal-enthalpy function $H - E_0$ is obtained by reference to Table 5-1 as

$$(H - E_0) = (E - E_0) + RT = 8066 + 2479 = 10{,}545 \text{ J}$$

At first it is perhaps more informative to write

$$E = E_0 + 8066 \text{ J} \qquad H = E_0 + 10{,}545 \text{ J} \tag{5-60}$$

In this form the breakdown of the enthalpy into a lowest-level energy and a thermal-energy component is more apparent.

The calculation of such quantities should further emphasize that although in thermodynamic calculations changes in E and H are often calculated from measured changes in the thermal and mechanical reservoirs, the functions E and H are state functions and can be calculated for particular conditions without regard to changes or paths. The calculations leading to Eqs. (5-60), furthermore, again show that *for ideal gases* E and H are functions only of the temperature. The thermal contributions to E and H for an ideal gas can be calculated if (in addition to the properties of the molecules of the gas) only the value of the temperature is given.

Although the lowest-level energy term E_0 has yet to be dealt with, one should see that the molecular approach to thermodynamic properties provides an additional valuable way in which to look at and understand the internal energy and the enthalpy. It is also true that such calculations provide very useful information on thermodynamic properties that are difficult to obtain by the classical thermodynamic methods. The thermal-enthalpy terms of Table 5-2, for example, are taken from an extensive tabulation that has been prepared for practical use from calculations like that illustrated above. After following through the calculation for SO_2, one should notice that the calculations of such functions can be done at any temperature, such as 1000 and 1500 K, and that in this way thermodynamic data for relatively inaccessible conditions can easily be obtained.

TABLE 5-2 The Enthalpy Function $H - E_0 = E - E_0 + RT$, in J mol^{-1}, at Various Temperatures

	298.15 K	600 K	1000 K	1500 K
H_2	8,467	17,274	29,145	44,744
O_2	8,660	17,904	31,367	49,272
CO	8,672	17,612	30,361	47,525
CO_2	9,364	22,269	42,769	71,145
H_2O	9,906	20,427	36,016	57,540
CH_4	10,029	23,217	48,367	88,408
Ethane	11,950	33,539	76,484	144,348
Ethylene	10,565	28,167	61,756	113,386
Acetylene	10,008	25,635	50,585	85,969
Benzene	14,230	51,400	126,202	239,952

Source: F. A. Rossini et al. (eds.), Tables of Selected Values of Chemical Thermodynamic Properties, *Natl. Bur. Stand. (U.S.) Circ.* 500, 1952.

Use of these functions for problems of chemical interest will be postponed until the following chapter. There the procedures for dealing with the E_0 term, which our molecular approach has introduced but failed to treat, will be developed.

5-11 The Molecular Interpretation of C_V and C_P of Ideal Gases

The heat capacity C_V is given by the derivative with respect to temperature of E. The explicit expressions for the thermal, temperature-dependent contributions to the internal energy, obtained in Chap. 4, can be used to obtain the corresponding contributions to C_V. The necessary derivatives are shown in Table 5-3. With these expressions and information on the linear or nonlinear

TABLE 5-3 Factors Entering the Calculation of C_V for 1 mol of an Ideal Gas

Translation
$$\frac{d}{dT}\left(\tfrac{3}{2}RT\right) = \tfrac{3}{2}R$$

Rotation:

Linear molecule
$$\frac{d}{dT}\left(\tfrac{3}{2}RT\right) = \tfrac{3}{2}R$$

Nonlinear molecule
$$\frac{d}{dT}\left(\tfrac{3}{2}RT\right) = R$$

Vibration (per degree of freedom)
$$\frac{d}{dT}\left(\frac{\mathfrak{N}h\nu_{\text{vib}}}{e^{h\nu_{\text{vib}}/kT} - 1}\right) = \frac{Rx^2e^x}{(e^x - 1)^2}$$

Electronic
$$\frac{d}{dT}(E - E_0)_{\text{elec}} = R\frac{d}{dT}\left(\frac{T^2}{q_{\text{elec}}}\frac{dq_{\text{elec}}}{dT}\right)$$

structure of the molecule and on the energy spacings in the vibrational modes, the heat capacities can be calculated according to

$$C_V = C_{\text{trans}} + C_{\text{rot}} + C_{\text{vib}} + C_{\text{elec}} \qquad (5\text{-}61)$$

and

$$C_P = C_V + R \qquad (5\text{-}62)$$

Usually only the C_{vib} term requires appreciable calculations to be made. For many purposes the graphical treatment of the C_{vib} function, as in Fig. 5-12, provides adequate values. The heat-capacity contribution of a vibrational mode as a function of temperature for various vibrational-energy spacings is shown in Fig. 5-13. Notice that for any spacing the heat-capacity contribution approaches the classical value of R at high temperatures but that this limit is reached more easily by the vibrational modes with small steps between the allowed energies. Notice also that at low temperatures the heat-capacity contributions approach zero, a result that is understood by the inability of the molecules at these temperatures to acquire enough energy to move to any level higher than that of the lowest $v = 0$ state.

For most molecules only the ground electronic state is appreciably populated until quite high temperatures are reached. If, however, low-lying electronic states occur, or if high-temperature heat capacities are to be calculated, there will be an electronic contribution to the heat capacity. This contribution is obtained by taking the derivative with respect to temperature of the expression

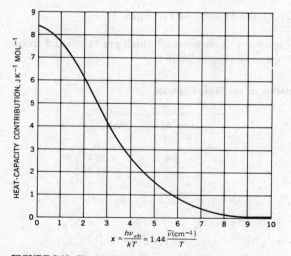

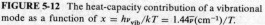

FIGURE 5-12 The heat-capacity contribution of a vibrational mode as a function of $x = h\nu_{\text{vib}}/kT = 1.44\bar{\nu}(\text{cm}^{-1})/T$.

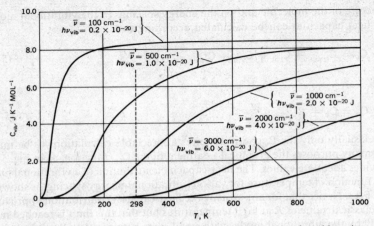

FIGURE 5-13 The heat-capacity contributions of vibrational modes with various energy spacings as a function of temperature.

for the thermal energy, which can be obtained from $E - E_0 = (RT^2/q) \, dq/dT$. The electronic partition function must be calculated from a term-by-term summation.

Again, SO_2 vapor can be used as an example to illustrate the calculation of thermodynamic properties from molecular data. The contributions to C_V are evaluated in Table 5-4 and give the result $C_V = 31.50$ J K^{-1} mol^{-1}. With this result, furthermore,

$$C_P = C_V + R = 31.50 + 8.31 = 39.81 \text{ J K}^{-1} \text{ mol}^{-1}$$

Additional heat-capacity values, some of which are calculated from molecular properties, are given in Appendix B-1.

TABLE 5-4 Calculation of the Heat Capacity C_V of SO_2 at 25°C

Contributing term		Heat-capacity contribution, J K^{-1} mol^{-1}	
Translation		$\frac{3}{2}R =$	12.47
Rotation		$\frac{3}{2}R =$	12.47
Vibration:			
$\bar{\nu} = 518$ cm^{-1}	$x = 2.50$	$\dfrac{Rx^2 e^x}{(e^x - 1)^2} = 5.06$	
$\bar{\nu} = 1151$ cm^{-1}	$x = 5.56$	1.00	
$\bar{\nu} = 1362$ cm^{-1}	$x = 6.58$	0.50	6.56
Electronic			0
			31.50

These heat-capacity calculations are the first of a number of valuable thermodynamic results that can be completely deduced by a molecular approach. The calculation of a property, such as the heat capacity, from the properties of the molecules which make up the gas is a considerable feat. Such calculations, furthermore, are of very great practical value. Heat capacities at high temperatures, for example, are frequently needed and are not easily measured. The molecular calculation, however, often provides a fairly easy way of obtaining otherwise inaccessible values of C_V and C_P.

In some cases, on the other hand, it is easier to make direct thermal measurements of C_P for gases than it is to do the calculation like that illustrated for SO_2. For example, spectroscopic data might not be available to show the energy-level spacing in one of the vibrational degrees of freedom. Such is the case for the "torsional" motion in ethane, in which one CH_3 group executes a hindered rotation relative to the other CH_3 group. In such cases, measured values for the thermodynamic quantity C_P can be used to deduce something about the molecular motion.

Finally, you should notice that the heat capacity is completely determined by the distribution of the molecules of a sample throughout the available energy levels. This contrasts with the internal-energy and enthalpy properties. Their thermal, temperature-dependent parts, which depend on the distribution of the molecules throughout the allowed energy levels, are often only minor components of E and H. Yet to be introduced is another thermodynamic property, entropy, which stands with internal energy and enthalpy in importance but, like the heat capacity, is completely determined by the distribution of the molecules throughout the available states.

5-12 The Difference $C_P - C_V$ for Real Gases, Liquids, and Solids

Heat capacity provides an excellent meeting ground on which the results from calorimetric or thermodynamic studies can be compared with those based on the details of the molecules of the system. In the preceding section you saw that the measured heat capacities of ideal gases could be completely understood in terms of various molecular contributions. Similar but not quite so successful attempts can be made to interpret heat-capacity data for real, nonideal gases and for liquids and solids. These attempts will be begun here and completed in the following section.

Measurements of the heat capacities of liquids and solids are often performed in a constant-pressure apparatus and therefore give values of C_P directly. Unfortunately, these constant-pressure results are not easily approached from a molecular viewpoint. Constant-pressure heat capacities contain appreciable contributions from the energy absorbed in overcoming the intermolecular attractive forces as expansion with increasing temperature occurs. We now must see how a value for C_V can be obtained from a measured value for C_P.

You might expect that measurements of C_V or of the difference $C_P - C_V$ will have to be made. Interrelations, which are the heart of thermodynamics, allow values of $C_P - C_V$ to be deduced from quantities that at first seem to be quite unrelated to heat capacities. A beginning was made in Sec. 5-8, where we obtained the relation

$$C_P - C_V = \left[P + \left(\frac{\partial E}{\partial V} \right)_T \right] \left(\frac{\partial V}{\partial T} \right)_P$$

This difference $C_P - C_V$ can be related to PVT behavior if we borrow an expression based on the second law of thermodynamics. In Sec. 8-11 it will be shown that

$$\left(\frac{\partial E}{\partial V} \right)_T = T \left(\frac{\partial P}{\partial T} \right)_V - P \tag{5-63}$$

With this expression the equation for $C_P - C_V$ becomes

$$C_P - C_V = T \left(\frac{\partial P}{\partial T} \right)_V \left(\frac{\partial V}{\partial T} \right)_P \tag{5-64}$$

The ideal-gas equation of state $PV = RT$ again leads to the result

$$C_P - C_V = R$$

The pressure-temperature coefficient $(\partial P/\partial T)_V$, as appears in Eq. (5-64), is conveniently replaced by volume-pressure and volume-temperature coefficients. A relation of the type illustrated in Eq. (5-25) lets us write

$$\left(\frac{\partial P}{\partial T} \right)_V = - \frac{(\partial V/\partial T)_P}{(\partial V/\partial P)_T} \tag{5-65}$$

Then Eq. (5-64) can be recast as

$$C_P - C_V = - \frac{T(\partial V/\partial T)_P^2}{(\partial V/\partial P)_T} \tag{5-66}$$

If an equation of state for a gas is available, the partial derivatives of Eq. (5-66) can be obtained. For example, van der Waals' equation (Sec. 2-15) can be expanded to

$$\frac{PV}{RT} = 1 + \left(b - \frac{a}{RT} \right) \frac{1}{V} + \frac{b^2}{V^2} + \cdots \tag{5-67}$$

If only the first of the variable terms on the right is retained and V is replaced by RT/P in this term, we get

$$V = \frac{RT}{P} + b - \frac{a}{RT} \tag{5-68}$$

The derivatives of Eq. (5-66) can be worked out, and again if only the linear term in P is retained, we arrive at

$$C_P - C_V = R\left(1 + \frac{2a}{R^2 T^2} P\right) \tag{5-69}$$

Experimental results over much wider ranges of temperature and pressure than those for which this equation is applicable are illustrated for nitrogen in Fig. 5-14.

For liquids and solids, the description of PVT behavior, needed in Eq. (5-66), is usually reported in terms of the *thermal expansivity* α, defined by

$$\alpha = \frac{1}{V}\left(\frac{\partial V}{\partial T}\right)_P \tag{5-70}$$

and the *isothermal compressibility* β, defined by

$$\beta = -\frac{1}{V}\left(\frac{\partial V}{\partial P}\right)_T \tag{5-71}$$

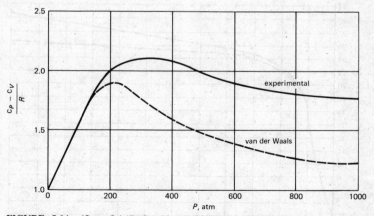

FIGURE 5-14 $(C_P - C_V)/R$ for N_2 at 0°C as a function of pressure. (*From S. M. Blinder, Advanced Physical Chemistry: A Survey of Modern Theoretical Principles, The Macmillan Company, New York, 1969.*)

With these expressions Eq. (5-66) can be written in terms of α and β as

$$C_P - C_V = \frac{\alpha^2 VT}{\beta}$$

or for molar quantities

$$\mathsf{C}_P - \mathsf{C}_V = \frac{\alpha^2 \mathsf{V} T}{\beta} \tag{5-72}$$

Data for the various quantities in this expression are given for several liquids and solids in Table 5-5. For many liquids the difference $\mathsf{C}_P - \mathsf{C}_V$ is appreciable compared with the heat capacities themselves. For solids the difference is generally much less.

For both solids and liquids both α and β, as well as V, increase with temperature. The temperature term T in Eq. (5-72), however, dominates the temperature dependence, and $\mathsf{C}_P - \mathsf{C}_V$ generally increases as the temperature increases. [The opposite occurs in real gases according to Eq. (5-69).] An illustration of the divergence of C_P and C_V for a solid with increasing temperature is shown in Fig. 5-15.

5-13 The Heat Capacity of Crystals and Liquids

A very early generalization of the heat capacity of crystals was made by Pierre Dulong and Alexis Petit in 1819. The data available at that time consisted of

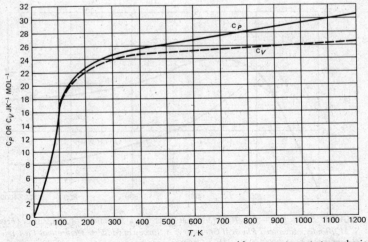

FIGURE 5-15 The variation of C_P and C_V of copper with temperature at atmospheric pressure.

TABLE 5-5 Values of C_P and the Quantities Needed to Obtain C_V by Means of Eq. (5-72) at 25°C and 1 atm

	C_P, J K⁻¹ mol⁻¹	$\alpha = \dfrac{1}{V}\left(\dfrac{\partial V}{\partial T}\right)_P$, K⁻¹	$\beta = -\dfrac{1}{V}\left(\dfrac{\partial V}{\partial P}\right)_T$, m² N⁻¹	V, m³	$C_P - C_V$, J K⁻¹ mol⁻¹	C_V, J K⁻¹ mol⁻¹
Ideal gas	—	$\dfrac{1}{T} = 33.5 \times 10^{-4}$	$\dfrac{1}{P^2} = 9.74 \times 10^{-11}$	$24{,}500 \times 10^{-6}$	$R = 8.314$	—
Liquids:						
Hg	27.8	1.81×10^{-4}	3.4×10^{-11}	14.8×10^{-6}	4.25	23.6
CS₂	75.7	12.4	96	60	28.6	47.1
CCl₄	131.7	12.5	107	97	42.2	89.5
C₆H₆	134.3	12.5	97	89	42.7	91.6
CHCl₃	116.3	13.3	97	80	43.5	72.8
H₂O	75.5	2.35	46	18	0.63	74.9
Solids:						
C (diamond)	6.07	0.035×10^{-4}	0.68×10^{-11}	3.4×10^{-6}	0.0018	6.07
SiO₂ (quartz)	44.5	0.35	2.65	22.6	0.31	44.2
NaCl	49.7	1.21	4.2	27.0	2.8	46.9
H₂O (ice, 0°C)	36.6	2.55	12	19.6	3.2	33.4
Fe	25.0	0.35	0.59	7.1	0.44	24.6
Cu	24.5	0.48	0.72	7.1	0.68	23.8
Ag	25.5	0.57	0.99	10.2	1.00	24.5
Zn	24.6	0.89	1.69	9.2	1.28	23.3
Pb	26.8	0.86	2.37	18.7	1.74	25.1

heat capacities measured at atmospheric pressure and room temperature. Dulong and Petit recognized that these data indicated that the heat capacity C_P of solid elements, mostly metals, at room temperature all had values of about 26 J K^{-1} mol^{-1}. This generalization holds fairly well also for C_V's, as the data of Table 5-5 suggest.

The kinetic theory of gases provides a background that leads to a ready explanation of the *law of Dulong and Petit*. Each vibrational degree of freedom would be expected, on the classical, i.e., non-quantum-mechanical, approach to have an average kinetic energy of $\frac{1}{2}RT$ for an Avogadro's number of particles. The average kinetic energy for the three perpendicular vibration modes of the particles in a crystal lattice would then be $\frac{3}{2}RT$. On the average, also, for a vibrational motion, there is an equal amount of potential energy. We therefore expect

$$E_{vib} \text{ (classical)} = E_{kin} + E_{pot} = \tfrac{3}{2}RT + \tfrac{3}{2}RT = 3RT \tag{5-73}$$

The heat capacity is readily calculated by differentiating this result with respect to temperature. Thus one deduces

$$C_V = \left(\frac{\partial E}{\partial T}\right)_V = 3R \tag{5-74}$$

This calculation indicates that a heat capacity of about 25 J K^{-1} mol^{-1} should be expected and that this value should apply to all crystals made up of a lattice of single particles. The indication of the calculation, furthermore, is that the heat capacity should be independent of temperature. The nice, if approximate, success of this derivation was soon disrupted by additional experimental results.

Figure 5-16 shows more extensive C_P data for crystals of elements to which the Dulong and Petit rule presumably applies. One sees that the rule is more or less valid at room temperature if only the heavy metals are considered but that at lower temperatures the heat capacities show no correlation with this rule. The classical derivation and its prediction of a heat capacity independent of temperature are completely disproved. In the days of classical treatments, before 1900, these results presented a very perplexing problem. There seemed no way to avoid the erroneous deductions of the theory.

With the development of the quantum theory, it was soon recognized that the classical treatment of the vibrations, i.e., with any vibrational energy allowed, was faulty. In 1907 Einstein showed that when a vibrational frequency is assigned to the vibrations of the crystal particles and the motion is treated quantum-mechanically, curves of the general shape of Fig. 5-16 can be obtained if it is assumed that some energy separation $h\nu$ can be assigned to the energy of the vibration modes of the particles of the crystal.

The calculation of the heat capacity resulting from vibrational modes has already been treated in Sec. 5-11. It is only necessary to note that for a gram

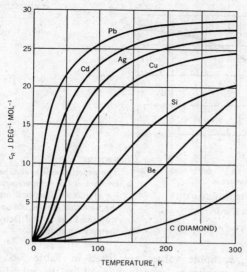

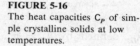

FIGURE 5-16
The heat capacities C_P of simple crystalline solids at low temperatures.

atom there are $\mathfrak{N}$ particles, each with 3 vibrational degrees of freedom. The previous formula given in Table 5-3 for molecular vibrations is completely applicable and leads to the heat-capacity prediction for a crystalline solid containing an Avogadro's number of single particles of

$$C_V = 3R \left(\frac{h\nu}{kT} \right)^2 \frac{e^{h\nu/kT}}{(e^{h\nu/kT} - 1)^2} \tag{5-75}$$

By choosing a value of the vibrational-energy-level spacing $h\nu$ for each crystal, Einstein was able to obtain approximate agreement with each of the curves of Fig. 5-16, as illustrated by the data for aluminum in Fig. 5-17.

An improvement on Einstein's theory which gives results in even better agreement with the experimental data was soon forthcoming. It was recognized by Debye that the assumption that all the particles of a crystal vibrate with the same frequency was not entirely valid. Although all the particles may be bound by similar forces, the motions of the particles will couple so that vibrations of a wide range of frequencies will result. On the assumption of a range of vibrational frequencies, Debye derived a heat-capacity equation in a manner similar to that used by Einstein. Debye's expression relates the heat capacity to the term $h\nu_{max}/kT$, where ν_{max} is the maximum of a whole range of frequencies. Like the single frequency of the Einstein theory, the value of ν_{max} must be deduced empirically for each crystal. Figure 5-17 shows how well this theory fits the data of aluminum, and particularly how the fit at temperatures approaching absolute zero is greatly improved.

It has become customary to introduce the *Debye characteristic temperature*

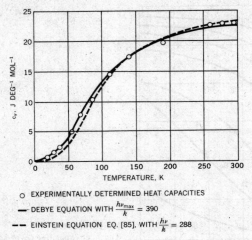

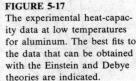

FIGURE 5-17
The experimental heat-capacity data at low temperatures for aluminum. The best fits to the data that can be obtained with the Einstein and Debye theories are indicated.

O EXPERIMENTALLY DETERMINED HEAT CAPACITIES

— DEBYE EQUATION WITH $\frac{h\nu_{max}}{k} = 390$

‑ ‑ EINSTEIN EQUATION EQ. [85], WITH $\frac{h\nu}{k} = 288$

θ_D, defined by $\theta_D = h\nu_{max}/k$. Some values are listed in Table 5-6. The values of $h\nu_{max}$ indicate the maximum energy spacing for the vibrational energies of the crystal particles.

The vibrational frequencies of free molecules were shown (Sec. 3-7) to indicate the force constants of the bonds between the atoms of the molecule. The Debye or Einstein frequencies indicate the rigidity with which the atoms or

TABLE 5-6 The Debye Characteristic Temperatures, the Debye Frequencies, and the Force-Constant Factors for Some Monatomic Crystalline Materials

Crystal	$\theta_D = \dfrac{h\nu_{max}}{k}$, K	$\bar{\nu}_{max}$, cm^{-1}	Force-constant factor $M\bar{\nu}^2_{max} \times 10^{-5}$
Ne	63	44	0.4
K	100	70	1.5
Xe	55	38	1.9
Na	150	104	2.5
Li	385	270	5.0
Pb	88	61	7.7
Hg	96	67	9.0
KCl	227	157	9.2
Ca	230	160	10
Al	390	271	20
Au	170	118	27
Cu	315	218	30
Be	1000	695	43
Fe	420	292	48
W	310	214	84
C (diamond)	1840	1280	197

ions are held at their crystal-lattice sites. The frequencies depend, however, on both the force constants and the particle masses through a relation of the type $\nu = (1/2\pi)\sqrt{k/m}$, where m is the mass of the vibrating particle. For force-constant comparisons it is sufficient to calculate $M\bar{\nu}_{max}^2$, where M is the atomic mass in amu. This quantity, exhibited in Table 5-6, is a measure of the stiffness of the crystal bonds uncomplicated by the effect of the mass of the crystal particles. The gradation from soft, weakly bonded crystals to hard, strongly bonded materials is evident and is given in a quantitative way by the data of Table 5-6.

The vibrational spacings themselves, ν or ν_{max}, determine the heat-capacity behavior. Crystals with closely spaced levels, as a result of weak bonds or heavy atoms, as in lead, reach the classical heat-capacity value at relatively low temperatures. On the other hand, crystals with large vibrational spacings, as a result of high force constants or light atoms, reach this limit of $3R$ for C_V only at relatively high temperatures. This latter type, as Fig. 5-16 shows, is illustrated more emphatically by the example of diamond.

It is a matter of considerable practical importance to be able to predict how the heat capacity of a crystalline solid will behave as the absolute temperature approaches zero. The success of the Debye theory in correlating the measurable heat capacities has led to reliance on its predictions of how C_V approaches zero. Since the details of the Debye theory have not been given, it is necessary to state simply that the low-temperature limit predicts the behavior

$$C_V = \alpha T^3 \tag{5-76}$$

where α is a constant characteristic of each material. With this low-temperature limiting expression it is possible to extrapolate heat-capacity data to absolute zero. The Debye curve for aluminum in Fig. 5-17 shows the form of this predicted behavior. Entropy values deduced on the basis of the third law of thermodynamics (Sec. 7-7) depend on this extrapolation of measured heat capacities to absolute zero.

Now the C_V data of liquids can be considered. Most informative, initially, is the value, shown in Table 5-5, of just about $3R$ for mercury. The simplest explanation of this result comes from considering that the mercury atoms of the liquid have, not 3 translational degrees of freedom, which would lead to a heat capacity of only $\frac{3}{2}R$, but 3 vibrational degrees of freedom. If the atoms are only loosely bound and the vibrational frequencies are low, each vibrational contribution will be equal to R and the total contribution will be $3R$.

With the assumption of a contribution of $3R$ from the liquid-state counterpart of translational motion, we can proceed to polyatomic molecules. The new feature that enters is the counterpart of the molecular rotation. The contribution from the rotational-type motion however, is not easily handled. If the motion were entirely free, there would be contributions of $\frac{1}{2}R$ per degree of freedom. If, however, the interference of neighboring molecules is such that this motion is more like a low-frequency vibrational motion, the contribution could

TABLE 5-7 Calculations of the Heat Capacity C_V of Some Liquids at 25°C, J K^{-1} mol^{-1}

Calculations for free rotation and for a restricted rotation or libration

	Hg		CS$_2$		CCl$_4$	
Motion of center of mass	$3R = 24.9$		$3R = 24.9$		$3R = 24.9$	
Intramolecular vibrational motion (see Sec. 5-11)	0		10.3		45.1	
	Free rotation	Libration	Free rotation	Libration	Free rotation	Libration
Rotationlike motion	0	0	$R = 8.3$	$2R = 16.6$	$\frac{3}{2}R = 12.5$	$3R = 24.9$
C_V, calculated	24.9	24.9	43.5	51.8	82.5	94.9
Observed		23.6		47.1		89.5

rise to values equal to about R per degree of freedom. The way to proceed is not yet clear, but the examples of Table 5-7 indicate that the principal contributions to the heat capacity at constant volume of simple liquids have been recognized.

5-14 The Heat-Capacity Contribution of the Electrons of Metallic Crystals

Metals are distinguished by their luster and their electrical conductivity. These characteristics lead directly to the idea of relatively free electrons moving throughout the crystal lattice. The study of metallic crystals becomes primarily the study of how these electrons can be described and how their behavior can be investigated.

The results presented in Figs. 5-16 and 5-17 show that the heat capacities of metallic crystals are of a magnitude and have a temperature dependence similar to that of simple ionic or covalent crystals. At first, this result should be surprising. The relatively free electrons of a metal might be expected to lead to an additional heat-capacity contribution of about $3(\frac{1}{2}R)$ if each atom of the metal contributes one electron that is not tightly bound to the atom. A closer look at the heat-capacity data for metals is therefore called for.

Data for the heat capacity of silver down to low temperatures are given in Table 5-8. Close inspection of these data shows that although at the higher temperatures they are in line with the Debye theory and to a lesser extent with the Einstein theory, they are not consistent with these theories at the lower temperatures. In fact, at temperatures low enough for the Debye law to reduce to the T^3 relation, the data can be fitted by an empirical equation of the form

$$C_V = \alpha T^3 + \gamma T \tag{5-77}$$

The first term can be looked on as arising from the lattice vibrations, in the

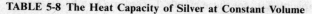

TABLE 5-8 The Heat Capacity of Silver at Constant Volume

T, K	C_V obs, J K^{-1} mol^{-1}	T, K	C_V obs, J K^{-1} mol^{-1}	T, K	C_V obs, J K^{-1} mol^{-1}
1.35	0.00106	12	0.347	74.56	16.90
2	0.00262	14	0.559	83.91	18.10
3	0.00657	16	0.845	103.14	20.07
4	0.0127	20	1.671	124.20	21.27
5	0.0213	28.56	4.297	144.38	22.48
6	0.0373	36.16	7.088	166.78	22.86
7	0.0632	47.09	10.80	190.17	23.34
10	0.199	65.19	15.37		

Source: C. Kittel, "Introduction to Solid State Physics," John Wiley & Sons, Inc. New York, 1953.

manner shown by Debye and dealt with in the preceding section. The linear-temperature term can be attributed to the electronic contribution of the metallic crystal. Heat-capacity data can be compared with Eq. (5-77) if it is first rearranged to

$$\frac{C_V}{T} = \alpha T^2 + \gamma \qquad (5\text{-}78)$$

Then, if a plot of C_V/T versus T^2 yields a straight line, the slope gives the value of α and the intercept is the value of γ. Such plots are shown in Fig. 5-18. It is

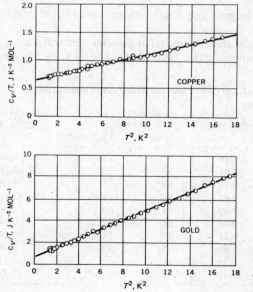

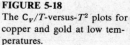

FIGURE 5-18
The C_V/T-versus-T^2 plots for copper and gold at low temperatures.

5-14 THE HEAT CAPACITY DUE TO THE ELECTRONS OF METALLIC CRYSTALS **157** clear that the heat-capacity data for these metals do conform to a heat-capacity equation of the form of Eq. (5-77) or (5-78).

Similar behavior is found for other metals, and data in Table 5-9 show the values of γ that are found. The contributions γT of this electronic term at room temperature are also included. There is an electronic heat-capacity term for metals, but it is exceedingly small compared with R or $3R$ at ordinary temperatures.

We now must consider the behavior of the electrons of a metal to see whether their small heat-capacity contribution can be understood. The simplest model for this purpose, which also has the advantage of leading into more detailed theoretical treatments, is the *free-electron model*. Electrons, perhaps one from each atom, are considered to be free to move throughout a region of uniform potential provided by the metal crystal. These electrons are treated like particles-in-a-box. This treatment yields allowed energy levels according to the formula

$$\epsilon = (n_x^2 + n_y^2 + n_z^2)\frac{h^2}{8ma^2} \qquad \text{where } \begin{matrix} n_x = 1, 2, 3, \dots \\ n_y = 1, 2, 3, \dots \\ n_z = 1, 2, 3, \dots \end{matrix} \qquad (5\text{-}79)$$

or

$$\epsilon = n^2\frac{h^2}{8ma^2} \qquad \text{where } n^2 = n_x^2 + n_y^2 + n_z^2$$

Now m is the mass of the electron, and a is the dimension of the crystal, here assumed to be a cube.

The N electrons of a gram atom of a metal at absolute zero will occupy the lowest-energy-available quantum states. Two electrons with spins oppositely

TABLE 5-9 The Values of γ of Eq. (5-77) and the Electronic Contribution γT to C_V at Room Temperature

Metal	γ, J K^{-2} mol^{-1}	γT at 25°C, J K^{-1} mol^{-1}	Metal	γ, J K^{-2} mol^{-1}	γT at 25°C, J K^{-1} mol^{-1}
Ag	0.62×10^{-3}	0.18	Na	1.8×10^{-3}	0.54
Al	1.38	0.41	Ni	7.3	2.18
Au	0.71	0.21	Pb	3.3	0.98
Bi	0.04	0.01	Pd	(11)	(3.3)
Co	5.0	1.49	Pt	6.8	2.02
Cr	1.5	0.45	Sn	1.8	0.54
Cu	0.7	0.21	Th	5.0	1.49
Fe	5.0	1.49	Ti	3.3	0.98
Mg	1.3	0.39	U	10.8	3.21
Mn	(16)	(4.8)	W	(1.3)	(0.4)

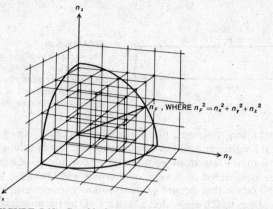

n_F, WHERE $n_F{}^2 = n_x{}^2 + n_y{}^2 + n_z{}^2$

FIGURE 5-19 Graphical representation of the values of the quantum numbers n_x, n_y, and n_z for a particle in a three-dimensional box. All the points lying within the spherical segment with radius n_F correspond to energies less than the energy corresponding to n_F.

directed can occupy each state. It follows, as can be seen by considering the states displayed by points as in Fig. 5-19, that to accommodate all N electrons in the lowest available states, all states will be occupied up to those with $n = n_F$, where n_F is given by

$$2 \times \tfrac{1}{8}(\tfrac{4}{3}\pi n_F{}^3) = N \tag{5-80}$$

The subscript on n designates that this value of n corresponds to what is known as the *Fermi level*. The energy corresponding to this level, below which at absolute zero all states are occupied and above which all states are empty, is designated by ϵ_F and is given by

$$\epsilon_F = \frac{n_F{}^2 h^2}{8ma^2} = \frac{h^2}{8m}\left(\frac{3N}{\pi a^3}\right)^{2/3} \tag{5-81}$$

The ratio N/a^3 can be recognized as the electron density, which, if one free electron is provided by each atom, is the number of atoms per unit volume.

How the available states are occupied can be shown by a diagram like that of Fig. 5-20. The solid line shows that at absolute zero all states are occupied up to the Fermi energy. For a typical metal, as insertion of numerical values in Eq. (5-81) will show, the Fermi energy is about 160×10^{-21} J per electron, and this value allows the comparison with the room-temperature value of kT of about 4.1×10^{-21} J to be made in Fig. 5-20.

To proceed to a treatment of the occupation of the available states and the total energy of the system at temperatures other than absolute zero, we would

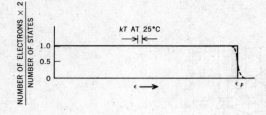

FIGURE 5-20
The occupation of the available states by the free electrons of a metal at absolute zero (solid line) and at room temperature (broken line).

have to develop distribution functions, like those obtained in Chap. 4. This derivation is somewhat lengthy and will not be carried out. Instead the energy and the heat capacity of the electrons of a metal, according to the model assumed here, will be considered in a very qualitative way. Because of the exponential $e^{-\text{energy}/kT}$ factor that occurs in distribution expressions, we can expect that only those states which are within about kT of the Fermi energy will become populated when the temperature is raised from 0 K to T. The dashed curve of Fig. 5-20 suggests the curve for the population of the states at room temperature.

Furthermore, we can reach the known linear heat-capacity term of Eq. (5-77) by arguing that only a fraction kT/ϵ_F of the electrons, indicated by the shaded area of Fig. 5-20, gain energy in the temperature interval 0 to T and that on the average they each acquire an energy equal to kT. It follows that the thermal electronic energy would be

$$\mathsf{E}_{\text{therm elec}} = \frac{NkT}{\epsilon_F}(kT) = \frac{Nk^2}{\epsilon_F}T^2 \tag{5-82}$$

The electronic contribution to the heat capacity would be

$$\mathsf{C}_{V,\text{ elec}} = 2\frac{Nk^2}{\epsilon_F}T = \frac{2Rk}{\epsilon_F}T \tag{5-83}$$

Equation (5-83) shows the electronic heat-capacity term as linearly dependent on the temperature, in agreement with the form shown in Eq. (5-77). We can now identify the quantity $2Rk/\epsilon_F$ of Eq. (5-83) with γ, values of which are presented in Table 5-9. Substitution of numerical values for R and k and the representative value of 160×10^{-21} J per electron for ϵ_F leads to a value of 10^{-3} J K^{-2} for $2Rk/\epsilon_F$. This result is in general agreement with the experimentally determined values of γ shown in Table 5-9.

By means of a very simple model, we thus have come to an understanding of the contribution of the electrons of metals to their heat capacities. The distribution of electrons throughout the available energy levels, suggested in Fig. 5-20, consists of a crowding into the states of lower energy. A result is the very small ability of the system to acquire energy as the temperature is raised. This situation is to be contrasted with uncrowded systems, where the Boltzmann distribution applies and relatively large amounts of energy are acquired as the temperature is raised.

PROBLEMS

5-1. The acceleration due to gravity on the earth's surface is about 9.8 m s^{-2}. (a) What is the force of gravity on a 1-kg mass? (b) How much work could be done by fully harnessing the downward movement of a 1-kg mass through a distance of 58 m, the height of Niagara Falls? (c) How much heat would be produced if the mass were allowed to fall freely through this distance? (d) If the mass consisted of water and all the heat were absorbed by the water, how much would the temperature of the water rise?

5-2. What is the heat of vaporization of benzene if 1.34 A of current passing through an electric heater of 50-Ω resistance for 5.62 min vaporizes 78.1 g of benzene? (Electrical heat is calculated from I^2R, where I is the current and R the resistance.)

5-3. One mole of an ideal gas is allowed to expand against a piston that supports 0.4 atm pressure. The initial pressure is 10 atm and the final pressure is 0.4 atm. The temperature is kept constant at 0°C. (a) How much energy is transferred to the mechanical surroundings from the gas during the expansion? (b) What is the change in internal energy and in the enthalpy of the gas? (c) How much heat is absorbed from the thermal surroundings?

5-4. One mole of an ideal gas is allowed to expand reversibly, i.e., against a confining pressure that is at all times infinitesimally less than the gas pressure, from an initial pressure of 10 atm to a final pressure of 0.4 atm, the temperature being kept constant at 0°C. (a) How much work is done by the gas? (b) What is the change in E and in H? (c) How much heat is absorbed by the gas?

5-5. A chemical reaction in a gas mixture at 500°C decreases the number of moles of gas, which can be assumed to behave ideally, by 0.347. If the internal-energy change is -23.8 kJ, what is the enthalpy change?

5-6. The densities of ice and water at 0°C are 0.9168 and 0.9998 g ml^{-1}, respectively. (a) Calculate the difference between ΔH and ΔE of fusion for 1 mol under atmospheric pressure. The density of liquid water at 100°C is 0.9584 and of water vapor at 100°C and 1 atm is 0.000596 g ml^{-1}. (b) Calculate the difference between ΔH and ΔE for the vaporization of water at atmospheric pressure.

5-7. A cylinder containing 1 mol of liquid water at 100°C is heated until the liquid is converted into vapor. The cylinder is fitted with a piston which just resists a pressure of 1 atm. (a) How much work is done by the expanding gas? (b) If the heat of vaporization of water is 40,670 J, what is the change in internal energy?

5-8. A system consists of an open beaker of water at its normal boiling point. The thermal reservoir consists of an electrical hot plate rated at 500 W. (a) If the hot plate is turned on for 10 min and all the heat it produces goes into the water system, what is the value of $\Delta E_{\text{therm res}}$? The heat required to convert liquid water into water vapor at its normal boiling point is 40,670 J mol^{-1}. (b) How many moles of water are evaporated in the 10-min heating period? (c) If water vapor behaves ideally, how much work is done by the system on the mechanical surroundings, which here is the atmosphere? (d) What is the value of $\Delta E_{\text{mech res}}$? (e) What is the value of ΔE of the system?

5-9. In Prob. 5-8 what are the values of q and w?

5-10. (a) If 1 mol of liquid water in an open beaker at 100°C and 1 atm is converted into vapor, also at 100°C and 1 atm, how much work of expansion is done against the atmosphere? (b) What is the change in internal energy of the water? The heat of vaporization of water at its normal boiling point is 40,670 J mol⁻¹.

5-11. After 1 g of metallic zinc is added to a beaker containing dilute hydrochloric acid, returning the solution to its original temperature would require the removal of 2330 J of heat. What are the values of q, w, and ΔE for the zinc–hydrochloric acid system.

5-12. Helium is released from a large cylinder, in which the helium pressure is 6000 lb in⁻² gauge, 409 atm, into a stratospheric balloon. The volume of the partially inflated balloon at sea level, where the temperature is 20°C and the pressure approximately 1 atm, is 500 m³. Treat the helium that is released into the balloon as the system. Describe the thermal and mechanical reservoirs and calculate q, w, and ΔE.

*5-13. One mole of an ideal gas is enclosed in a cylinder fitted with a piston. The piston is not friction-free, and it resists movement by a force which when divided by the piston area corresponds to a pressure on the piston of 0.1 atm. (a) If the gas, initially at 10 atm, is allowed to expand while the temperature is maintained at 25°C to 1 atm, producing as much work as possible, how much energy can be stored in the mechanical surroundings? The gas is then compressed to its original volume now using as little work as possible and again with the temperature maintained at 25°C. (b) How much mechanical energy is required for this compression? (c) What is the value of w for the combined expansion and compression? (d) What is the value of ΔE_{system}? (e) What is the value of q?

5-14. What would be the values of w, ΔE, and q for the combined expansion and compression in Prob. 5-13 if the piston had been frictionless?

5-15. What is the change in E and H suffered by 10 mol of CO_2 if the temperature is raised from 100 to 500°C, the pressure remaining constant at 0.1 atm? The heat capacity of CO_2 is given by $C_P = 44.2 + 8.79 \times 10^{-3}T - 8.62 \times 10^5T^{-2}$ J mol⁻¹ K⁻¹.

5-16. Nitrogen gas is expanded reversibly and adiabatically from a volume of 1 liter at 0°C and 1 atm until the volume is 2 liters. The heat capacities C_V and C_P can be taken to be constant at the values 20.8 and 29.1 J mol⁻¹ K⁻¹ respectively. (a) Assuming ideal-gas behavior, calculate the final temperature and pressure. (b) Calculate q, w, ΔE, and ΔH.

5-17. One liter of air, with molecular mass 28.2 and $C_V = \frac{5}{2}R$ and $C_P = \frac{7}{2}R$, is heated by the addition of 40 J of heat. (a) What is the final volume if the pressure remains at 1 atm? (b) What is the final pressure if the volume remains at 1 liter?

5-18. A space capsule develops a leak, and suddenly the air pressure drops from 1 to $\frac{1}{2}$ atm. (a) Is this a reversible expansion process? (b) What temperature change would be noticed in the cabin?

5-19. On the same graph plot the pressure-volume changes when 1 mol of a gas is expanded from 1 atm and 400 K to 0.1 atm by (a) an isothermal expansion of any ideal gas, (b) a reversible adiabatic expansion of benzene vapor (for benzene $C_V = 73.36$ and $C_P = 81.67$ J mol⁻¹ K⁻¹), and (c) a reversible adiabatic expansion of argon, for which $C_V = 12.48$ and $C_P = 20.79$ J mol⁻¹ K⁻¹.

5-20. What is the change in enthalpy when 1 mol of gas in a 1-liter container is heated from −20 to +20°C if (a) the gas is N_2, for which C_P can be taken as 29.12 J mol⁻¹ K⁻¹, and (b) the gas is He, for which C_P is 20.79 J mol⁻¹ K⁻¹?

5-21. Hydrogen gas is expanded reversibly and adiabatically from a volume of 1.43 liters, at a pressure of 3 atm and temperature of 25°C, until the volume is 2.86 liters. The heat capacity C_P of hydrogen can be taken to be 28.8 J K⁻¹ mol⁻¹. (a) Calculate the pressure and temperature of the gas, assumed to be ideal, after the expansion. (b) Calculate $\Delta E_{therm\,res}$, $\Delta E_{mech\,res}$, ΔE, and ΔH for the gas.

5-22. The value of γ for CH_4 is 1.31, and near room temperature and at pressures less than about 1 atm the gas behaves ideally. An adiabatic and reversible expansion is performed which reduces the pressure of a CH_4 sample, initially at 100°C and with volume 3 liters, from 1 to 0.1 atm. (a) What are the final temperature and volume of the gas? (b) How much work is done by the gas? (c) What is the difference between ΔH and ΔE for the process?

5-23. Assume, as in Prob. 4-6, an imaginary gas whose molecules do not have the normal translational, rotational, and vibrational energies. Instead they have only a singly degenerate ground state and one upper energy level, at an energy equal to kT at $T = 100$ K, with degeneracy of (a) 1, (b) 3, and (c) 10. Calculate the heat-capacity contribution from these energy patterns and plot this heat capacity versus temperature. A temperature range of 0 to 100 K is convenient in this case.

5-24. Calculate (a) the thermal contribution $E - E_0$ to the internal energy and (b) $H - E_0$ to the enthalpy of Cl_2 at 25 and at 1000°C. Assume ideal-gas behavior, and use the vibrational-energy-level spacing of 1.10×10^{-20} J per molecule.

5-25. Obtain an expression for the thermal energy $E - E_0$ contributed by the electronic states of gaseous iodine atoms. Data on the degeneracy and the energy spacing are given in Prob. 4-8. Calculate the value of $(E - E_0)_{elec}$ at (a) 298 K, (b) 1000 K, (c) 2000 K, (d) in the limit as $T \to 0$, (e) if no other electronic states are taken into account, in the limit as $T \to \infty$.

5-26. Using the results of Prob. 5-25, obtain expressions for the internal energy and for the enthalpy of 1 mol of $I(g)$ at 298 and 1000 K.

5-27. Using the expression for the electronic thermal energy for gaseous iodine atoms obtained in Prob. 5-25, develop an expression for the electronic contribution to the heat capacity of $I(g)$. What is the electronic contribution to the heat capacity of 1 mol of $I(g)$ at (a) 298 K, (b) 1000 K, (c) 2000 K, (d) in the limit as $T \to 0$, (e) if no other electronic states are taken into account, in the limit as $T \to \infty$.

5-28. Using the results of Prob. 5-27, calculate the heat capacity C_P of 1 mol of gaseous iodine atoms at 298 and at 1000 K.

5-29. Calculate the molar heat capacity of Cl_2 at (a) 25 and at (b) 1000°C using the data of Prob. 5-24, and compare with the values obtained from the empirical equation $C_P = 37.0 + 0.67 \times 10^{-3}T - 2.84 \times 10^5 T^{-2}$ J mol^{-1} K^{-1}.

5-30. (a) Using the thermal-energy data of Prob. 5-24 and assuming ideal-gas behavior, calculate ΔE, ΔH, q, and w when 1 mol of Cl_2 is heated at a constant pressure of 1 atm from 25 to 1000°C. (b) Repeat the calculation using the empirical heat-capacity expression of Prob. 5-29.

5-31. Using the data of Table 5-2, determine the *difference in* ΔH of the reaction at 1500 and at 298 K, that is, $\Delta H_{1500} - \Delta H_{298}$, for the reactions (a) $2CO + O_2 \to 2CO_2$ and (b) $2H_2 + O_2 \to 2H_2O$.

*5-32. The slope of the curve obtained in Prob. 4-20 gives the heat-capacity contribution from the rotational motion of the diatomic molecule. Use the results from that problem to prepare a graph of C_{rot} versus T. Add the line for the classical value for C_{rot}.

5-33. The vibrational-energy spacing of N_2 is 2330 cm^{-1}. Calculate C_P at (a) 300, (b) 500, and (c) 1000 K.

5-34. The vibrational spacings of gaseous F_2, Cl_2, Br_2, and I_2 are 894, 554, 322, and

213 cm^{-1}. Use Fig. 5-12 and estimate values of C_p at 298 K. Compare with the values given in Appendix B-1.

5-35. What vibrational spacing, in (a) joules and (b) in wave-number units of cm^{-1}, gives a vibrational heat-capacity contribution of $\frac{1}{2}R$ at 25°C?

5-36. (a) Calculate the number of Br_2 molecules that are in the $v = 0$, $v = 1$, $v = 2$, and $v = 3$ energy levels when 1 mol of Br_2 is held at 100°C. The vibrational-energy-level spacing is 0.64×10^{-20} J. (b) Calculate at this temperature the vibrational contribution to $E - E_0$ of the molecules in the $v = 1$, and the $v = 2$, and in the $v = 3$ levels. Compare the sum of these contributions with the total thermal vibrational energy obtained using Eq. (4-57).

5-37. The heat capacity C_p at 298 K of methane gas is 35.71 J mol^{-1} K^{-1}, and that calculated for carbon tetrachloride vapor is 83.51 J mol^{-1} K^{-1}. (a) What contributions do the vibrations of CH_4 and of CCl_4 make to the heat capacities of these substances? (b) Use Fig. 5-12 to estimate an average vibrational-energy spacing for the vibrations of CH_4 and for those of CCl_4. (c) On what basis are these values related in a way that is expected?

5-38. (a) Under what conditions is the rejection of the final term of Eq. (5-67) to obtain Eq. (5-68) justified? (b) For nitrogen at 0°C up to about what pressure is this justified?

5-39. From the results for $(C_p - C_V)/R$ shown for N_2 in Fig. 5-16, estimate the van der Waals constant a and compare with the value given in Table 2-4.

5-40. At 20°C liquid ethanol has a thermal expansivity α of 1.12×10^{-3} K^{-1}, an isothermal compressibility β of 1.10×10^{-9} m^2 N^{-1}, and a density of 0.789 g ml^{-1}. What is the difference between C_p and C_V?

5-41. Explain why KCl can be included in Table 5-6, which otherwise contains calculated values of the force-constant factor only for monatomic substances.

5-42. (a) Calculate the force-constant factors, as defined in Table 5-6, for CH_4 and H_2O, which have Debye temperatures of 78 and 192 K, respectively. Assume that the molecule as a whole vibrates in the lattice vibrations, i.e., that the mass in the force-constant-factor calculation can be taken as that of the whole molecule. (b) Are the values obtained for CH_4 and H_2O in line with what would be expected in view of the data of Table 5-6?

* 5-43. (a) Determine a value of the lattice frequency for KCl so that the Einstein heat-capacity relation fits as well as possible the experimental values for C_V. (b) Compare this value with the value of ν_{max} required by the Debye theory and shown in Table 5-6. (c) Show graphically the fit obtained to the experimental data by the Einstein relation. Heat-capacity measurements by W. T. Berg and J. A. Morrison, *Proc. R. Soc. Lond.*, **A242**:467 (1957), for KCl give the values tabulated. (Use the conversion factor 1 cal = 4.184 J.)

T, K	10	20	30	40	60	80	100	140	180	220	260
C_V, cal K^{-1} mol^{-1}	0.008	0.71	1.99	3.56	6.31	8.16	9.31	10.52	11.09	11.39	11.56

* 5-44. Fit the data of Table 5-8 to the Einstein and the Debye T^3 functions, and verify that although the fit can be made satisfactory at most temperatures, large discrepancies occur with the very low temperature data.

5-45. Deduce from the data of Table 5-8 the value of γ for the electronic-heat-capacity term for silver.

5-46. Assuming each atom contributes one free electron, obtain the necessary density data for several metals and calculate values of the Fermi energy ϵ_F.

REFERENCES

TRIPP, T. B.: The Definition of Heat, *J. Chem. Educ.,* **53:**782 (1976).

Treatments of classical thermodynamics:

NASH, L. K.: "Elements of Chemical Thermodynamics," Addison-Wesley Publishing Company, Inc., Reading, Mass., 1962.
MAHAN, B. H.: "Elementary Chemical Thermodynamics," W. A. Benjamin, Inc., New York, 1963.
KLOTZ, I., and R. M. ROSENBERG: "Chemical Thermodynamics," W. A. Benjamin, Inc., New York, 1972.
PITZER, K. S., and L. BREWER: "Thermodynamics," McGraw-Hill Book Company, New York, 1961. Brings up to date the classic treatment of thermodynamics by G. N. Lewis and M. Randall. Includes very valuable summaries of available data, references to original literature, and examples of the application of thermodynamics to chemical problems.
DENBIGH, K.: "The Principles of Chemical Equilibrium," Cambridge University Press, New York, 1961. A very clear and careful development, with emphasis, as the title indicates, on equilibria in chemical systems. The last third of the book deals with the calculation of thermodynamic properties from molecular properties.
ZEMANSKY, M. W.: "Heat and Thermodynamics," 4th ed., McGraw-Hill Book Company, New York, 1957. A treatment with more emphasis on systems of interest in physics and engineering than chemistry, but the presentation enables the reader to follow this extension readily.

Two books that emphasize biochemical systems:

KLOTZ, I.: "Energy Changes in Biochemical Reactions," Academic Press, Inc., New York, 1967.
LEHNINGER, A. L.: "Bioenergetics," W. A. Benjamin, Inc., New York, 1965.

A number of books that weave together, in various ways, classical thermodynamics and the molecular interpretation of thermodynamic properties:

DICKERSON, R. E.: "Molecular Thermodynamics," W. A. Benjamin, Inc., New York, 1969.
NASH, L. K.: "Chemthermo: A Statistical Approach to Chemical Thermodynamics," Addison-Wesley Publishing Company, Inc., Reading, Mass., 1971.
NASH, L. K.: "Review of Elements of Statistical Thermodynamics," Addison-Wesley Publishing Company, Inc., Reading, Mass., 1974.
KAUZMANN, W.: "Thermal Properties of Matter," vol. II, "Thermodynamics and Statistics: With Applications to Gases." W. A. Benjamin, Inc., New York, 1967.
RAPP, D.: "Statistical Mechanics," Holt, Rinehart and Winston, Inc., New York, 1972.
ANDREWS, F. C.: "Equilibrium Statistical Mechanics," John Wiley & Sons, Inc., New York, 1963.
MOELWYN-HUGHES, E. A.: "Physical Chemistry," chaps. 7–9, Cambridge University Press, New York, 1951.
MAYER, J. E., and M. G. MAYER: 'Statistical Mechanics," 2d ed., chaps. 5–9, John Wiley & Sons, Inc., New York, 1977. A more detailed development of the relation between thermodynamic functions and molecular properties.

6 THERMOCHEMISTRY

The specific application of the first law of thermodynamics to the study of chemical reactions is referred to as *thermochemistry*. Thermochemistry deals with the measurement or calculation of the heat absorbed or given out in chemical reactions. The subject has therefore great immediate practical importance. Thermochemistry also provides the data from which the relative energy or enthalpy contents of chemical compounds can be deduced. This aspect implies that thermochemistry is basic to the study of chemical bonding. As you will see, thermochemistry also provides data necessary for the thermodynamic study of chemical equilibria.

6-1 Measurements of Heats of Reaction

The approaches used in thermochemistry will be more understandable if some of the methods and the scope of the more common experimental techniques are mentioned first.

Only a very few of the many possible chemical reactions are such that their heats of reaction can be accurately determined directly. To be suitable for a precise calorimetric study, a reaction must be fast, complete, and clean. A fast reaction is required so that the heat of the reaction will be given out or absorbed in a short time. It is then easier to prevent heat from flowing away from the reaction system or into it from the surroundings while the measurement of the temperature change of the system is being made. The completeness of the reaction is required so that difficult corrections for unreacted material need not be made. Finally, a clean reaction implies one that goes completely to a given set of products with no complicating side reactions. These stipulations are rather severe and rule out all but a few types of reactions.

In the field of organic chemistry the combustion reactions are of great utility. In the presence of excess oxygen, burning a compound containing only carbon, hydrogen, and oxygen usually leads to the formation of the sole products CO_2 and H_2O. For organic compounds containing other elements, the products are not always so well defined, but combustion reactions are frequently practical.

The heat of combustion is usually determined in a *bomb calorimeter*.

166

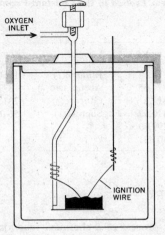

OXYGEN
INLET

IGNITION
WIRE

FIGURE 6-1
A combustion bomb.

Figure 6-1 shows some of the features of the bomb in which the combustion occurs. A weighed sample is placed in the cup inside the reaction chamber, or bomb, and the bomb is then filled with oxygen under a pressure of about 30 atm. A fine wire dipping into the sample is heated by an electric current to start the reaction. Once started, the reaction proceeds rapidly with the evolution of a large amount of heat. This heat is determined by the temperature rise of the water around the calorimeter. It is customary to calibrate the apparatus by the measurement of the temperature rise resulting from the combustion of a sample with a known heat of combustion. The bomb and water chamber are carefully insulated from the surroundings so that no heat can flow into or out of it. Such an arrangement is called an *adiabatic calorimeter.*

Heats of combustion are usually very large, of the order of hundreds or thousands of kilojoules per mole, and with careful work these can be measured with an accuracy of better than 0.01 percent. This accuracy is necessary because it often is the difference in energy contents of two compounds that is of interest. This is often a small difference between two large numbers.

Table 6-1 shows some heats of combustion of a number of organic compounds.

A second important type of reaction that is occasionally suitable for organic compounds is hydrogenation. Unsaturated materials can sometimes be made to add hydrogen in a reaction that is suitable for calorimetric study. Such reactions give out less heat than oxidation reactions and are therefore more useful in giving information on small energy differences between compounds.

The heats of inorganic reactions, e.g., those occurring in aqueous solution, can be measured in a calorimeter that is essentially an insulated container open to the atmosphere. Heats of neutralization, solution, and complex formation can be so studied. The same stringent requirements as previously mentioned still apply, of course, if accurate results are to be obtained.

TABLE 6-1 Enthalpies of Combustion, i.e., Heat *Evolved* in the Constant-Pressure Combustion Reaction, at 25°C

Products are $CO_2(g)$ and $H_2O(l)$

	kJ mol^{-1}		kJ mol^{-1}		kJ mol^{-1}
H_2	285.84	n-Butane(g)	2878.51	Ethanol(l)	1366.95
C(graphite)	393.51	Isobutane(g)	2871.65	Acetic acid(l)	872.4
CO(g)	282.99	n-Heptane(g)	4811.2	Glucose(s)	2815.8
$CH_4(g)$	890.35	Ethylene(g)	1410.97	Sucrose(s)	5646.7
$C_2H_6(g)$	1559.88	Acetylene(g)	1299.63		
$C_3H_8(g)$	2220.07	Benzene(g)	3301.51		

6-2 Internal-Energy and Enthalpy Changes in Chemical Reactions

Thermochemistry deals with the particular process of a chemical reaction. If such reactions are represented as

$$\text{Reactants} \rightarrow \text{products} \tag{6-1}$$

the internal-energy and enthalpy changes for the process are related to the energy and enthalpy contents of the reactants and products by

$$\Delta E = E_{prod} - E_{react} \tag{6-2}$$

and

$$\Delta H = H_{prod} - H_{react} \tag{6-3}$$

For example, the enthalpy change ΔH for the reaction

$$C + \tfrac{1}{2}O_2 \rightarrow CO \tag{6-4}$$

gives the enthalpy of 1 mol of carbon monoxide compared with the enthalpy of 1 mol of carbon plus one-half the enthalpy of 1 mol of oxygen; i.e.,

$$\Delta H = H_{CO} - H_C - \tfrac{1}{2}H_{O_2} \tag{6-5}$$

When chemical reactions are dealt with, the Δ notation, which previously signified any change, means the difference of some property for the products and the reactants in amounts corresponding to the written chemical equation.

If heat is absorbed in the reaction and the products contain more energy than the reactants, then ΔE (if the process is at constant volume) and ΔH (if the process is at constant pressure) are positive; that is, H and E increase as a result of the reaction. Such reactions are called *endothermic*. Reactions for which ΔE and ΔH are negative proceed with a decrease in E and H. Heat is therefore given out, and the reaction is said to be *exothermic*. To summarize:

ΔH or ΔE	positive	heat absorbed	endothermic
ΔH or ΔE	negative	heat given out	exothermic

The combustion experiments previously mentioned are all exothermic, and therefore for these reactions ΔH and ΔE are negative.

6-3 Relation between ΔE and ΔH

A measurement of a heat of reaction usually gives directly either the internal-energy change or the enthalpy change, but either datum can be used to calculate the other. If the reaction is performed in a constant-volume apparatus, such as the bomb calorimeter, no work of expansion is performed and the heat of the reaction is equal to the internal-energy change. If a constant-pressure system is used, the heat of the reaction, as pointed out in Sec. 5-5, is equal to the enthalpy change.

The difference between ΔH and ΔE for a reaction can be deduced by applying the defining equation for H to the reactants and products, as they occur in the equation for the reaction. Collection of the various types of terms gives

$$\Delta H = \Delta E + \Delta(PV) \tag{6-6}$$

For reactions that involve only solid or liquid reactants and products, the $\Delta(PV)$ term (or for constant pressures a $P\,\Delta V$ term) is small and often negligible.

If gases are involved in the reaction, an appreciable value of $\Delta(PV)$ can occur and ΔH and ΔE will be significantly different. Suppose that the reaction produces a net change Δn_g in the number of moles of gas. To the accuracy of the ideal-gas laws and neglecting the volumes of liquids and solids, the PV term will be greater for the products than for the reactants by an amount

$$\Delta(PV) = \Delta(n_g RT) = RT\,\Delta n_g \tag{6-7}$$

The enthalpy change for the reaction will differ from the internal-energy change by $RT\,\Delta n_g$. Thus

$$\Delta H = \Delta E + RT\,\Delta n_g \tag{6-8}$$

Consider, as an example, the reaction

$$2CO(g) + O_2(g) \rightarrow 2CO_2(g)$$

where g stands for gas. A bomb-calorimetric study would give the heat of this reaction, i.e., the combustion of 2 mol of carbon monoxide, as 563,500 J given out. Since this is a constant-volume experiment, we have immediately

$$\Delta E = -563,500 \text{ J} \qquad (6\text{-}9)$$

The product contains 2 mol of gas, and the reactants contain 3 mol. The value of Δn_g is -1, and at 25°C the enthalpy change is calculated as

$$\Delta H = \Delta E + RT \Delta n_g = -563,500 + (8.3143)(298.15)(-1)$$
$$= -563,500 - 2480 = -565,980 \text{ J} = -565.98 \text{ kJ} \qquad (6\text{-}10)$$

It has now been pointed out that the heats of some reactions can be measured and that ΔE and ΔH for these reactions can be calculated.

6-4 Thermochemical Equations

An elaboration of the form in which chemical-reaction equations are usually written is sometimes advisable in thermochemical work.

Since the heat of a reaction depends on whether a reagent is solid, liquid, or gas, it is necessary to specify the state of the reagents. This is usually done by adding s, l, or g after the compound. Occasionally a more careful description is necessary. When carbon is involved in a reaction, for instance, it is necessary to state whether it is graphite or diamond. One must be especially careful with water, which can quite reasonably be involved as a gas or a liquid.

Another characteristic of thermochemical equations is the appearance of fractional numbers of moles of some of the reactants or products. If one were interested in the heat of a reaction which produces 1 mol of water, for instance, one would write the reaction and the enthalpy change as

$$H_2(g) + \tfrac{1}{2}O_2(g) \rightarrow H_2O(l) \qquad \Delta H = -285.84 \text{ kJ} \qquad (6\text{-}11)$$

The reaction written with integers corresponds to the formation of 2 mol of water, and twice as much heat is evolved. Such a reaction would be written

$$2H_2(g) + O_2(g) \rightarrow 2H_2O(l) \qquad \Delta H = -571.68 \text{ kJ} \qquad (6\text{-}12)$$

Combustion reactions are usually written for the combustion of 1 mol of material. For benzene, for example, one would usually write

$$C_6H_6(g) + \tfrac{15}{2}O_2(g) \rightarrow 6CO_2(g) + 3H_2O(l) \quad \Delta H = -3301.51 \text{ kJ} \quad (6\text{-}13)$$

One additional comment is necessary. Unless the information is otherwise given, it is convenient to attach the temperature and pressure at which the reported enthalpy applies. A superscript degree sign indicates that the pressure is 1 atm, a usual reference, or standard, state. (This superscript, meaning standard state, must be distinguished from the previously used subscript zero, meaning the lowest energy-level quantity.) The temperature is indicated by a subscript giving the absolute temperature. An equation for the formation of water at 25°C and 1 atm would then be

$$H_2(g) + \tfrac{1}{2}O_2(g) \rightarrow H_2O(l) \qquad \Delta H^\circ_{298} = -285.84 \text{ kJ} \qquad (6\text{-}14)$$

6-5 Indirect Determination of Heats of Reaction

For reactions which are not suitable for direct calorimetric study, the internal-energy or enthalpy changes can often be obtained by an indirect method. This was originally suggested by Hess in 1840, and is often known as *Hess's law of heat summation*. We now recognize that it is merely an application of the first law of thermodynamics.

The indirect determination of the enthalpy change can be illustrated with the reaction in which carbon is converted from graphite into diamond, i.e.,

$$C(\text{graphite}) \rightarrow C(\text{diamond}) \qquad \Delta H = ? \qquad (6\text{-}15)$$

Although this reaction can be made to occur, it is certainly very unsuitable for any direct calorimetric study.

The combustion of both graphite and diamond can be conveniently studied, and these reactions and the heats of combustion are

$$C(\text{graphite}) + O_2(g) \rightarrow CO_2(g) \qquad \Delta H^\circ_{298} = -393.51 \text{ kJ} \qquad (6\text{-}16)$$

$$C(\text{diamond}) + O_2(g) \rightarrow CO_2(g) \qquad \Delta H^\circ_{298} = -395.40 \text{ kJ} \qquad (6\text{-}17)$$

The enthalpy changes of these reactions clearly differ as a result of the different enthalpies of graphite and diamond, as shown by writing

$$-393.51 \text{ kJ} = H_{CO_2} - H_{C(\text{graphite})} - H_{O_2} \qquad (6\text{-}18)$$

$$-395.40 \text{ kJ} = H_{CO_2} - H_{C(\text{diamond})} - H_{O_2} \qquad (6\text{-}19)$$

Subtraction of these algebraic equations with cancellation of the enthalpies of CO_2 and O_2 gives, on rearrangement,

$$H_{C(\text{diamond})} - H_{C(\text{graphite})} = -393.51 + 395.40 = +1.89 \text{ kJ} \qquad (6\text{-}20)$$

The result of 1890 J is the enthalpy change for the original graphite-to-diamond reaction.

The same result could have been obtained by subtracting the two combustion-reaction equations (6-16) and (6-17) as though they were algebraic equations. Canceling the O_2 and CO_2 terms and moving the C(diamond) term to the right side with a change of sign gives

$$C(\text{graphite}) \rightarrow C(\text{diamond}) \qquad \Delta H_{298} = -393.51 - (-395.40)$$
$$= +1.89 \text{ kJ} \qquad (6\text{-}21)$$

This treatment of the reaction equation is always possible and saves writing out the heat contents of each of the species before the subtraction is made.

Combining reactions by either of these methods is equivalent to calculating ΔH for the desired reaction by an indirect but experimentally more feasible path. The preceding example can be illustrated as

$$\Delta H = -393.51 \text{ kJ} \nearrow \overset{CO_2}{\searrow} \Delta H = +395.40 \text{ kJ}$$
$$C(\text{graphite}) + O_2 \rightarrow C(\text{diamond}) + O_2$$

The fact that the enthalpy is a state function requires ΔH to be the same by the indirect path, that is, $-393.51 + 395.40 = +1.89$ kJ, as by the direct path. It is this fact which allows the previous reaction subtractions to be performed.

One additional example can be given. The heat of the reaction by which a compound is formed from its elements is, as we shall see, of special interest. In few cases can such reactions be studied directly. Consider, for example, the formation of methane according to the equation

$$C(\text{graphite}) + 2H_2(g) \rightarrow CH_4(g) \qquad (6\text{-}22)$$

Again combustion reactions can be used and give

(a) $\qquad CH_4(g) + 2O_2(g) \rightarrow CO_2(g) + 2H_2O(l) \quad \Delta H^{\circ}_{298} = -890.35 \text{ kJ}$
(b) $\qquad H_2(g) + \tfrac{1}{2}O_2(g) \rightarrow H_2O(l) \qquad\qquad \Delta H^{\circ}_{298} = -285.84 \text{ kJ}$
(c) $\qquad C(\text{graphite}) + O_2(g) \rightarrow CO_2(g) \qquad\quad \Delta H^{\circ}_{298} = -393.51 \text{ kJ}$

$-(a) + 2(b) + (c)$:
$$C(\text{graphite}) + 2H_2(g) \rightarrow CH_4(g) \qquad\qquad \Delta H^{\circ}_{298} = -74.84 \text{ kJ}$$

6-6 Standard Heats of Formation

Methods for obtaining the enthalpies of many reactions either directly or indirectly have been given. Although it is not at all practical to compile a table of all the reactions for which such data are available, it would be feasible to tabulate information for each of the compounds for which thermal data have been obtained. The *standard heats of formation* provide a means of making such a table. Furthermore, from these data it is possible to work out the heats of any reactions involving the listed compounds.

If, for the moment, we consider only the elements, we are at liberty to choose some *standard* state for each element and to specify enthalpies in other states relative to that state. It is customary to take this *standard state as that of 1 atm pressure with the element in the physical state and stable form under these conditions*. The enthalpy of the elements in the standard state is arbitrarily given the value zero. Enthalpies based on this standard state are called *standard enthalpies*. The assignment of the arbitrary value of zero for the standard enthalpy to all elements is allowed because no chemical reaction converts one element into another.

Once standard enthalpies are assigned to the elements, it is possible to determine standard enthalpies for compounds. These enthalpies are usually called *standard heats of formation*. Consider, for example, the reaction

$$C(\text{graphite}) + O_2(g) \rightarrow CO_2(g) \tag{6-23}$$

The enthalpy change for the reaction at 25°C is −393.51 kJ. This value is equal to the standard enthalpy of CO_2 less the standard enthalpies of C and O_2. Since the latter are elements in their standard state, their standard enthalpies are zero. The standard enthalpy, or standard heat of formation, of CO_2 at 25°C must therefore be −393.51 kJ. The enthalpy of the reaction by which the compound is formed from its elements, all in their standard states, is seen to be equal to the standard heat of formation of the compound. As a result of this, one uses the symbol ΔH_f° for this standard heat of formation.

By combining reactions one can frequently deduce the enthalpy of formation of a compound from its elements, as illustrated for CH_4 in Sec. 6-5. Furthermore, when the standard enthalpies of some compounds have been determined, they can be used in working out the standard enthalpies of other compounds.

Appendix B-1 includes standard enthalpies at 25°C of some common compounds. Such a table of enthalpies can be used to determine the enthalpy for any reaction at 1 atm and 25°C involving the elements and any of the compounds appearing in the table.

The heat of hydrogenation of ethylene can be calculated as an illustration. One writes

$$CH_2CH_2(g) \quad + \quad H_2(g) \rightarrow \quad CH_3CH_3(g) \tag{6-24}$$
$$\text{At } 25°C: \Delta H_f^\circ = +52.30 \text{ kJ} \quad \Delta H_f^\circ = 0 \quad \Delta H_f^\circ = -84.68 \text{ kJ}$$

The enthalpy of the reaction is the difference in enthalpy of the products and the reactants. Thus

$$\Delta H_{298}^\circ = \Delta H_f^\circ(CH_3CH_3) - \Delta H_f^\circ(H_2) - \Delta H_f^\circ(CH_2CH_2)$$
$$= -84.68 - 0 - 52.30 = -136.98 \text{ kJ} \tag{6-25}$$

The calculated enthalpy for the reaction has, of course, no necessary connection with the arbitrary assignment of zero enthalpy to the elements in their standard states. The value displayed in Eq. (6-25) is the enthalpy change occurring when 1 mol of ethylene is hydrogenated.

6-7 Standard Heats of Formation of Ions in Aqueous Solutions

So far we have presumed that the reagents of each reaction are in the form of pure solids, liquids, or gases or that if a solution was involved, the solution process involved a negligible heat effect. Many reactions of chemical interest do not fall in this category, and the reactions involving ions in aqueous solution constitute the most important type of reactions not so far dealt with. Here it will be shown that as long as we deal with very dilute solutions (or to be strictly correct, infinitely dilute solutions), a procedure similar to that developed in Sec. 6-6 can be used to provide a table of standard heats of formation of ions. These standard heats can then be used to calculate the heats of reactions involving ions in dilute aqueous solutions.

The direct approach to the heat of formation of ions would be that of considering reactions in which such ions are formed. For example, we might consider the solution of 1 mol of HCl gas in a large amount of water. In solution the dissociation is complete and hydrated H^+ (or if you like, H_3O^+) and Cl^- ions are formed. The reaction can be represented as

$$HCl(g) \xrightarrow{\text{H}_2\text{O}} H^+(aq) + Cl^-(aq) \tag{6-26}$$

where the symbol (aq) implies that the ion is present in a large amount of water. The heat evolved in the reaction, at $25°C$, is 75.14 kJ, and thus for the reaction one writes

$$\Delta H_{298}^\circ = -75.14 = \Delta H_f^\circ[H^+(aq) + Cl^-(aq)] - \Delta H_f^\circ[HCl(g)]$$

With the value of ΔH_f° for $HCl(g)$ given in Appendix B-1, this can be arranged to

$$\Delta H_f^\circ[H^+(aq) + Cl^-(aq)] = -75.14 + (-92.30) = -167.44 \text{ kJ} \tag{6-27}$$

In this way we have obtained the standard heat of formation of the *pair* of ions H^+ and Cl^- in aqueous solution, and furthermore, we see a method for obtaining the standard heats of formation of the groups of ions that result from the solution of any acid, base, or salt.

The fact that all reactions of this sort lead to an electrically neutral solution means that no procedure involving ordinary chemical reactions will give only a single type of ion as a product. Therefore only the heats of formation of collections of ions can be measured.

We wish, of course, to be able to tabulate ΔH_f° values for individual ions. First, we must be sure that the enthalpy of a dilute solution can in fact be treated in terms of contributions attributed to the separate types of ions in the solution. Experiments in which dilute solutions of nonreacting electrolytes are mixed, e.g., mixing dilute solutions of HCl and KBr, show no heats of reaction. It follows that the heat of a sufficiently dilute solution can be attributed to separate contributions from the ions that are present, and each contribution is independent of the other ions that are present.

The absence of reactions involving only a single type of ion does not frustrate our attempt to tabulate the standard heats of formation of ions. Instead it permits the assignment of an arbitrary value to the standard heat of formation of any one ion. Values for the heats of formation of all other ions will then follow.

It is generally agreed to assign the value of zero to the heat of formation of H^+ ions in dilute aqueous solution; that is,

$$\Delta H_f^\circ[H^+(aq)] = 0$$

Once this step has been taken, one can use, for example, Eq. (6-27) to obtain the heat of formation of the chloride ion at 25°C as

$$\Delta H_f^\circ[Cl^-(aq)] = -167.44 - 0 = -167.44 \text{ kJ} \tag{6-28}$$

Likewise, the heat of solution of potassium chloride at infinite dilution is 17.18 kJ at 25°C, and the standard heat of formation of $KCl(s)$ is -435.87 kJ at this temperature. From these data, one obtains, for 25°C,

$$\Delta H_f^\circ[K^+(aq)] + \Delta H_f^\circ[Cl^-(aq)] = 17.18 - 435.87 = -418.69 \text{ kJ}$$

The value for the chloride ion can now be used to obtain, again for 25°C,

$$\Delta H_f^\circ[K^+(aq)] = -418.69 - (-167.44) = -251.25 \text{ kJ}$$

This procedure, which depends on the arbitrary assignment of zero for the value of ΔH_f° for the H^+ ion, provides data like that of Appendix B-2. With such data the heats of reactions at 25°C of any reaction involving dilute solutions of these ions can be calculated.

As an example of the use of standard enthalpy data we can calculate the heat of reaction in which calcium carbonate precipitates from a solution as a result of the addition of CO_2 to an aqueous solution containing Ca^{2+} ions in low concentration. The reaction can be written

$$Ca^{2+}(aq) + CO_2(g) + H_2O(l) \rightarrow CaCO_3(s) + 2H^+(aq) \tag{6-29}$$

We first write

$$\Delta H = 2\Delta H_f^\circ[H^+(aq)] + \Delta H_f^\circ[CaCO_3(s)] - \Delta H_f^\circ[Ca^{2+}(aq)]$$
$$- \Delta H_f^\circ[CO_2(g)] - \Delta H_f^\circ[H_2O(l)]$$

and then use the data of Appendix B to obtain

$$\Delta H = 2(0) + (-1206.87) - (-542.96) - (-393.51) - (-285.84)$$
$$= +15.44 \text{ kJ}$$

Only one water is shown explicitly in the equation. No doubt each Ca^{2+} and each H^+ ion is strongly hydrated, and such hydrations involve an appreciable heat effect. All this, however, is taken into account by the procedure used to set up the standard heats of formation of the ions. These heats include the contribution of the ion and all the water molecules involved in the hydration of the ion.

6-8 Temperature Dependence of Heats of Reaction

The enthalpies of reactions calculated from a table of standard heats of formation usually apply to a temperature of 25°C, the temperature most often used for tabulations of thermodynamic data. For these data to be of wider value, a means for determining the heats of reactions at other temperatures must be available. This can be done by writing the enthalpy of the reaction as

$$\Delta H = H_{prod} - H_{react} \tag{6-30}$$

and differentiating with respect to temperature to get

$$\left[\frac{\partial(\Delta H)}{\partial T} \right]_P = \left(\frac{\partial H_{prod}}{\partial T} \right)_P - \left(\frac{\partial H_{react}}{\partial T} \right)_P \tag{6-31}$$

The change in enthalpy with respect to temperature at constant pressure was shown in Sec. 5.8 to be the heat capacity at constant pressure, so that we can write

$$\left[\frac{\partial(\Delta H)}{\partial T} \right]_P = (C_P)_{prod} - (C_P)_{react} = \Delta C_P \tag{6-32}$$

and in a similar manner,

$$\left[\frac{\partial(\Delta E)}{\partial T} \right]_V = \Delta C_V \tag{6-33}$$

It is therefore necessary to know only the difference in the heat capacities of the products and the reactants in order to determine how the enthalpy of a reaction changes with temperature for temperature ranges that do not encompass any phase changes. Experimental heat capacities are sometimes expressed by an empirical relation such as

$$C_P = a' + b'T + c'T^2 + \cdots \tag{6-34}$$

In practice, however, it is somewhat more satisfactory to use an equation of the form

$$C_P = a + bT + cT^{-2} \tag{6-35}$$

Representative values of the coefficients are given in Table 6-2.

If each of the C_P's of the products and the reactants is so written, one can see that ΔC_P will have the same form as that shown for C_P. The previous differential equation (6-32), which corresponds to the integral form

$$\Delta H_{T_2} - \Delta H_{T_1} = \int_{T_1}^{T_2} \Delta C_P \, dT \tag{6-36}$$

can then be integrated. One obtains a relation of the form

$$\Delta H_{T_2} - \Delta H_{T_1} = \Delta a \, (T_2 - T_1) + \tfrac{1}{2}\Delta b \, (T_2{}^2 - T_1{}^2) - \Delta c \left(\frac{1}{T_2} - \frac{1}{T_1} \right) \tag{6-37}$$

Thus, from equations based on experimental data for the heat capacities of all the reagents involved in the reaction, the difference in heats of a reaction at two different temperatures can be calculated from the appropriate integrated form of Eq. (6-36).

Likewise, an expression for the general dependence of the heat of reaction on the temperature can be obtained from the indefinite integral corresponding to Eq. (6-36). One then has

$$\Delta H_T = \int \Delta C_P \, dT + \text{const} \tag{6-38}$$

and if an empirical equation of the form of Eq. (6-35) is used,

$$\Delta H_T = \Delta a T + \tfrac{1}{2}\Delta b \, T^2 - \Delta c \frac{1}{T} + \text{const} \tag{6-39}$$

It is then most convenient to refer to 25 °C, so that the standard enthalpies can be used to determine the integration constant.

6-9 Temperature Dependence of Heat of Vaporization

A special case of the variation of ΔH with temperature arises when the reaction consists of the conversion of a liquid or a solid to its equilibrium vapor. Then

TABLE 6-2 Heat Capacities in J K^{-1} mol^{-1} at Constant Pressure

Parameters for the equation $C_P^\circ = a + bT + cT^{-2}$

	a	b	c
Gases (in temperature range 298 K to 2000 K)			
He, Ne, Ar, Kr, Xe	20.79	0	0
S	22.01	-0.42×10^{-3}	1.51×10^5
H_2	27.28	3.26	0.50
O_2	29.96	4.18	-1.67
N_2	28.58	3.76	-0.50
S_2	36.48	0.67	-3.76
CO	28.41	4.10	-0.46
F_2	34.56	2.51	-3.51
Cl_2	37.03	0.67	-2.84
Br_2	37.32	0.50	-1.25
I_2	37.40	0.59	-0.71
CO_2	44.22	8.79	-8.62
H_2O	30.54	10.29	0
H_2S	32.68	12.38	-1.92
NH_3	29.75	25.10	-1.55
CH_4	23.64	47.86	-1.92
TeF_6	148.66	6.78	-29.29
Liquids (from melting point to boiling point)			
I_2	80.33	0	0
H_2O	75.48	0	0
NaCl	66.9	0	0
$C_{10}H_8$	79.5	407.5×10^{-3}	0
Solids (from 298 K to melting point, or 2000 K)			
C(graphite)	16.86	4.77×10^{-3}	-8.54×10^5
Al	20.67	12.38	0
Cu	22.63	6.28	0
Pb	22.13	11.72	0.96
I_2	40.12	49.79	0
NaCl	45.94	16.32	0
$C_{10}H_8$	-115.9	937	0

Source: Calculated from data of G. N. Lewis and M. Randall, "Thermodynamics," 2d ed. (rev. by K. S. Pitzer and L. Brewer), McGraw-Hill Book Company, New York, 1961.

ΔH is the *heat of vaporization*. The variation of the heat of vaporization with temperature for a few liquids is shown in Table 6-3. Heats of vaporization decrease with increasing temperature. A zero value is reached at the critical temperature, at which temperature the liquid and the equilibrium vapor become identical.

TABLE 6-3 The Heats of Vaporization in kJ mol⁻¹ of Liquids to Their Equilibrium Vapor at Various Temperatures

t, °C	H_2O	C_2H_5OH	$(C_2H_5)_2O$	CCl_4
0	44.8	42.4	28.8	33.5
25	44.01			
40	43.2	41.5	25.7	
80	41.6	39.2	22.3	29.8
100	40.67			
120	39.7	35.1	18.9	27.2
160	37.4	30.0	13.6	24.6
200	34.8	22.1		21.1
240		7.4		16.5
250	30.7			
280				6.7
300	24.9			
350	15.7			

Source: "International Critical Tables," vol. 5, p. 138, McGraw-Hill Book Company, New York, 1975.

The heat of vaporization can be treated in terms of the enthalpy of the "product" of the reaction, the equilibrium vapor, and the reactant, the liquid, by

$$\Delta H_{vap} = H_v - H_l \tag{6-40}$$

The variation of H_v and H_l can be displayed as in the water example of Fig. 6-2. There the enthalpies are given in terms of the standard heat of formation of $H_2O(g)$ at 25°C.

The situation described by Fig. 6-2 is distinctive in that the enthalpy of the vapor *decreases* with increasing temperature as the critical temperature is approached. In this region the vapor acts as a nonideal gas, subject to both the increasing temperature and the increasing pressure, the equilibrium vapor pressure.

6-10 Heats of Reaction from Tabulated Enthalpy Functions

The reference energy H_0°, or E_0° as appears in Table 5-2, is natural and convenient for the calculation of the enthalpies of substances. When the enthalpy changes for chemical reactions are treated, it is more convenient to have tables of $H^\circ - H_{298}^\circ$. Then standard enthalpy-of-formation data, which are listed at 25°C, can be used to obtain the ΔH_{298}° values that go along with these functions.

Some tabulations of thermodynamic functions, such as that of Table 5-2, provide $H^\circ - H_0^\circ$ values. Other tabulations give $H^\circ - H_{298}^\circ$ values. The latter, which use H_{298}° as a reference value, are smaller than the former, which use H_0

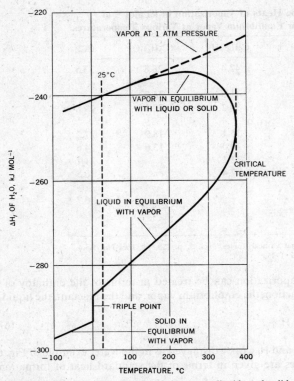

FIGURE 6-2 The heat content of the vapor, liquid, and solid phases of water as a function of temperature.

as a reference, by an amount $H_{298}^{\circ} - H_0^{\circ}$. Thus, for any substance, the different tabulations are shifted by this constant amount. Some values of $H^{\circ} - H_{298}^{\circ}$ for simple atomic and molecular species are given in Appendix B-3. Included in the table are values of $H_{298}^{\circ} - H_0^{\circ}$.

Either calorimetric data, consisting of heat-capacity and heat-of-transition data, or calculations from molecular properties provide $H^{\circ} - H_{298}^{\circ}$ or $H^{\circ} - H_0^{\circ}$ values. The latter route, however, is the only one available for high temperatures, where calorimetric results can not be obtained.

The use of tabulations like Table 5-2 can be illustrated by calculating the heat of the *shift-conversion* reaction

$$CO(g) + H_2O(g) \rightarrow CO_2(g) + H_2(g)$$

at 1000 and 1500 K.

First, the heat of the reaction at 298 K is obtained from the $\Delta H_f^{\circ}(298)$ values of Appendix B-1.

$$\Delta H^\circ_{298} = (-393.51 + 0) - (-110.52 - 241.83) = -41.16\,kJ$$

A value of ΔH°_0 can then be calculated from the data of the first column of Table 5-2 as

$$\Delta H^\circ_0 = \Delta H^\circ_{298} - \Delta(H^\circ_{298} - H^\circ_0)$$
$$= -41.16 - (9.364 + 8.467 - 8.672 - 9.906) = -40.41\,kJ$$

Now we can use

$$\Delta H^\circ_T = \Delta(H^\circ - H^\circ_0)_T + \Delta H^\circ_0$$

At 1000 K the result is

$$\Delta H^\circ_{1000} = (42.768 + 29.145 - 30.361 - 36.016) - 40.41 = -34.87$$

and at 1500 K

$$\Delta H^\circ_{1500} = (71.145 + 44.744 - 47.525 - 57.940) - 40.41 = -29.99\,kJ$$

Calculations like these can give the heats of reactions at any temperature if a single heat of reaction is known. Great use of this approach has been made, particularly in the field of hydrocarbon reactions. Predictions of the heats of rearrangements, of combustion, and so forth, of petroleum-fraction molecules can be made at temperatures at which actual measurements would be very difficult.

6-11 Bond Enthalpies and Bond Energies

A type of reaction that provides insight into the molecular basis of the energetics of chemical reactions is that in which molecules are completely disrupted to give free atoms. The enthalpies of such reactions lead to *bond enthalpies;* these quantities interpret the enthalpy of the molecule in terms of the enthalpies of the chemical bonds drawn to represent the bonding. This molecular-enthalpy component has until now been left as a part of E_0 and ΔE_0, and only the enthalpy due to the motions of the intact molecule has been treated.

The enthalpy of atomization of a molecule can be calculated from the values of ΔH°_f for the parent molecule and the free gaseous atoms, as given in Appendix B-1.

The data for the atomic species of elements whose standard state consists of gaseous diatomic molecules come from spectroscopic studies of the dissociation of the parent diatomic molecule. The value of ΔH°_f for the atomic gaseous state for elements whose standard state is not that of gaseous diatomic molecules must be obtained by other means. Most important is the element carbon, with graphite as its standard state. Measurements of the heat of sublimation of carbon, and analysis of the equilibrium gas-phase species, which include molecules like C_2 as well as atomic carbon, lead to the value 718.38 kJ mol^{-1} for ΔH_f° for free carbon atoms.

For diatomic species, the bond enthalpy is calculated directly from the listed enthalpies for the atomic species, the diatomic species being the standard-state species. Thus, for O_2,

$$O_2(g) \rightarrow 2O(g) \qquad \Delta H^\circ = 2(247.52) - 0 = 495.04 \text{ kJ} \qquad (6\text{-}41)$$

The energy of the reaction is the bond enthalpy for the O_2 molecule.

In a similar way the bond enthalpies of polyatomic molecules containing a single type of chemical bond can be calculated. For CH_4, for example, we can write, with all data applying to 25°C,

$$CH_4(g) \rightarrow C(g) + 4H(g)$$
$$\Delta H^\circ, \text{kJ mol}^{-1}: \quad -74.85 \qquad 718.38 \quad 4(217.94)$$

$$\Delta H^\circ = +1590.14 - (-74.85) = +1664.99 \text{ kJ} \qquad (6\text{-}42)$$

With the molecular view of CH_4 that we usually adopt, this is the enthalpy required to break the four C—H bonds. The C—H bond enthalpy in methane is thus obtained as

$$\frac{1664.99}{4} = 416.25 \text{ kJ}$$

In a similar way the bond enthalpy for other bonds can be obtained by considering molecules with a single type of bond.

Difficulties arise, however, when we attempt to determine bond enthalpies for bonds that occur in molecules that also have other bond types. For example, consider the C—O bond of methanol, CH_3OH. We have, using the data of Appendix B-1,

$$CH_3OH(g) \rightarrow C(g) + 4H(g) + O(g)$$

$$\Delta H^\circ = 1837.66 - (-201.25) = +2038.91 \text{ kJ} \qquad (6\text{-}43)$$

This result, the enthalpy required to overcome the bonding in CH_3OH, must now be interpreted as the enthalpy required to break three C—H, one C—O, and one O—H bonds. One way of assigning the total to the different bond types is to assume that the C—H and O—H bonds have the same bond enthalpies as in the CH_4 and H_2O molecules. On this basis, and with the value 463 kJ for the O—H bond enthalpy, the C—O bond enthalpy in CH_3OH is

$$2039 - 3(416) - 463 = 328 \text{ kJ} \qquad (6\text{-}44)$$

TABLE 6-4 Bond Enthalpies for Chemical Bonds in kJ mol⁻¹

Single bonds						Multiple bonds	
H—H	436	N—H	391	F—F	158	C=C	615
H—F	563	N—N	159	Cl—Cl	243	C≡C	812
H—Cl	432	N—O	175	Br—Br	193	C=O	724
H—Br	366	N—F	270	I—I	151		
H—I	299	N—Cl	200			N=N	418
				Cl—F	251	N≡N	946
C—H	415	O—H	463	Br—Cl	218		
C—C	344	O—O	143	I—Cl	210		
C—Cl	328	O—F	212	I—Br	178		
C—Br	276						
C—O	350	S—H	368				
C—N	292	S—S	266				

Source: From a more extensive table by L. Pauling, "General Chemistry," W. H. Freeman and Company, San Francisco, 1970.

Carryover of values, such as the C—O bond energy deduced here, to other molecules, CH_3—O—CH_3 for example, depends on the useful but inexact assumption that a particular bond has an energy that is independent of its molecular environment. The difficulties introduced often lead to discrepancies of several kilojoules per bond between the actual enthalpy of atomization of a molecule and that calculated from bond energies. As a result, bond enthalpies that are tabulated are often "best" values that apply reasonably well to a variety of molecular types. Examples are given in Table 6-4.

6-12 Thermochemical Determination of the Lattice Energies of Ionic Crystals

In the preceding section thermodynamic data were used to deduce bond energies, which in turn were used to interpret the energy changes occurring when chemical, or covalent, bonds are broken or formed. An analogous treatment can be given for simple ionic solids. Thermodynamic data are first used to obtain a quantity that is suitable for a molecular-level interpretation. Then an ionic model is developed and shown to be, at least approximately, consistent with the experimental results. Here thermochemical data will be used to obtain the *lattice energy* of simple ionic crystals. In the following section the molecular-level basis of these energies will be explored.

The *lattice energy,* which we shall find to be that directly approached by theoretical considerations of crystal energies, is the energy absorbed in processes such as

$$NaCl(c) \rightarrow Na^+(g) + Cl^-(g) \tag{6-45}$$

Since the energy of such processes cannot be obtained by a direct experimental method, we must resort, as we did in Sec. 6-5, to indirect methods. A procedure based on the *Born-Haber cycle* accomplishes this for simple ionic crystals.

The process of Eq. (6-45) can be performed in the example of NaCl by the indirect route, indicated by solid arrows in Fig. 6-3. The enthalpy and energy terms involved in the indirect route of the cycle are

$$\Delta H_f^\circ = \text{standard heat of formation of NaCl}$$
$$\Delta H_{sub} = \text{heat of sublimation of Na}$$
$$D_0 = \text{dissociation energy of } Cl_2$$
$$I = \text{ionization potential of Na}$$
$$A = \text{electron affinity of Cl}$$

A is usually given as a positive number, but since energy is given out in the process $Cl + e^- \rightarrow Cl^-$, the energy change for the reaction is negative, i.e., is $-A$.

The dissociation energy, the ionization energy, and the electron affinity are deduced from spectral or mass-spectroscopic studies rather than from calorimetric measurements. They usually are presented as energies rather than enthalpies. A correction to enthalpies by the addition of RT is necessary only for the dissociation energy.

For salts containing the bromide or the iodide ions, the heat-of-formation term ΔH_f° is that for the formation of the salt from the element as a liquid for bromine and as a solid for iodine. These heats of formation can be corrected to show formation from the gaseous elements by subtracting from ΔH_f° half the heat of vaporization, 32 kJ/mol, for bromine and half the heat of sublimation, 62 kJ/mol, for iodine.

Born-Haber cycle calculations can now be carried out with the data accumulated in Table 6-5. The enthalpy change for the formation of gaseous ions from a crystal is given by

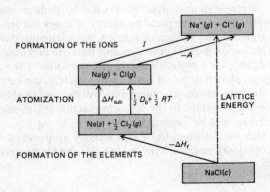

FORMATION OF THE IONS $\quad I$

$Na^+ (g) + Cl^- (g)$

$-A$

$Na(g) + Cl(g)$

ATOMIZATION $\quad \Delta H_{sub} \quad \frac{1}{2} D_0 + \frac{1}{2} RT$

LATTICE ENERGY

$Na(s) + \frac{1}{2} Cl_2 (g)$

$-\Delta H_f$

FORMATION OF THE ELEMENTS

$NaCl(c)$

FIGURE 6-3
An illustration of the Born-Haber cycle.

TABLE 6-5 Crystal Enthalpies from Born-Haber-Cycle Calculations [Eq. (6-46)]

All energies in kJ mol^{-1}

Crystal	ΔH_f°	ΔH_{sub} (metal)	I (metal)	$\frac{1}{2}(D_0 + RT)$ (halide)	A† (halide)	ΔH (Born-Haber) Eq. (6-46)
LiF	−612	161	520	80	322	1051
NaF	−569	108	496	80	322	931
KF	−563	89	419	80	322	829
LiCl	−409	161	520	122	349	863
NaCl	−411	108	496	122	349	788
KCl	−436	89	419	122	349	717
NaBr	−376§	108	496	97	325	752
KBr	−408§	89	419	97	325	688
NaI	−319§	108	496	77	295	705
KI	−359§	89	419	77	295	649

† From E. C. Chen and W. E. Wentworth, *J. Chem. Educ.*, **52**:486 (1975).
§ Calculated for formation from gas-phase Br_2 and I_2.

$$\Delta H = -\Delta H_f^\circ + \Delta H_{sub} + (\tfrac{1}{2}D_0 + \tfrac{1}{2}RT) + I - A \qquad (6\text{-}46)$$

The results are listed in the last column of Table 6-5.

6-13 Calculation of the Lattice Energies of Ionic Crystals

Crystals of simple salts consist of ordered structures of anions and cations. Each ion can be taken to be spherical. The attractions between ions are predominantly due to coulombic electrostatic forces.

The relative ease with which binding energies of ionic crystals can be calculated stems from our ability to express (to a good approximation) the potential-energy term due to the coulombic interactions. For a pair of ions the potential energy is given by

$$U = \frac{(Z_i e)(Z_j e)}{4\pi\epsilon_0 r_{ij}} \qquad (6\text{-}47)$$

where i and j identify the ions, which have charges Z_i and Z_j times the electronic charge e and are separated by a distance r_{ij}. The factor $4\pi\epsilon_0$, with the value 1.113×10^{-10} C^2 m^{-1}J^{-1}, allows the charges to be expressed in coulombs and yields energy values in joules.

Now we must express the net electrostatic interactions between the many ions of a crystal. The potential-energy term for one ion, e.g., a cation, interacting with all the other ions of the crystal can be written in view of Eq. (6-47) as

$$U_+ = \frac{Z_+e}{4\pi\epsilon_0} \sum_i \frac{Z_ie}{r_i^+} \tag{6-48}$$

It is convenient to express r_i^+, the distance from the reference positive ion to the ith ion, by the dimensionless ratio r_i^+/r, where r is the shortest cation-anion distance in the crystal. Let $R_i^+ = r_i^+/r$. The value of R_i^+ for any particular ith ion will be the same for any crystal with a given structural arrangement. In terms of R_i^+, Eq. (6-48) can be written

$$U_+ = \frac{Z_+e}{4\pi\epsilon_0 r} \sum_i \frac{Z_ie}{r_i^+/r} = \frac{Z_+e^2}{4\pi\epsilon_0 r} \sum_i \frac{Z_i}{R_i^+} \tag{6-49}$$

One additional manipulation converts Eq. (6-49) into a form that serves later purposes. Multiplying and dividing by Z_-, the charge of the anion, gives

$$U_+ = \frac{Z_+Z_-e^2}{4\pi\epsilon_0 r} \sum_i \frac{Z_i/Z_-}{R_i^+} \tag{6-50}$$

In a similar way the potential energy of an anion that results from its coulombic interaction with other anions and with the cations of the crystal is given by

$$U_- = \frac{Z_+Z_-e^2}{4\pi\epsilon_0 r} \sum_i \frac{Z_i/Z_+}{R_i^-} \tag{6-51}$$

In general, the environment of the cations and anions of a crystal will not be identical, and the summation of Eq. (6-51) will not be the same for a given crystal type as that of Eq. (6-50).

The coulombic energy of a crystal, with this model of simple coulombic-ion interactions, with $\mathfrak{N}$ cations and $\mathfrak{N}$ anions, is

$$U_{coul} = \tfrac{1}{2}\mathfrak{N}(U_+ + U_-) \tag{6-52}$$

where the factor of $\tfrac{1}{2}$ prevents each ion-ion interaction from being counted twice. Then

$$U_{coul} = \mathfrak{N} \frac{Z_+Z_-e^2}{4\pi\epsilon_0 r} \left[\frac{1}{2} \left(\sum_i \frac{Z_i/Z_-}{R_i^+} + \sum_i \frac{Z_i/Z_+}{R_i^-} \right) \right] \tag{6-53}$$

The term in parentheses depends only on the geometric arrangement of the ions in the crystal and the charges of these ions. This term, known as the *Madelung constant*, has been calculated and tabulated for many crystal types. If

TABLE 6-6 Madelung Constants Defined by Eqs. (6-53) and (6-54) for Some Crystal Types

Structure	Stoichiometry	Madelung constant $\mathfrak{M}$
Rock salt	AB	1.7476
Cesium chloride	AB	1.7627
Zinc blende	AB	1.6380
Wurtzite	AB	1.6413
Fluorite	AB_2	2.5194
Rutile	AB_2	2.3850

$\mathfrak{M}$ is introduced to represent the Madelung constant, values of which are given in Table 6-6, Eq. (6-53) can be written as

$$U_{\text{coul}} = \frac{\mathfrak{N} Z_+ Z_- e^2}{4\pi\epsilon_0 r} \mathfrak{M} \tag{6-54}$$

The short-range repulsion between ions is less easily treated. Expressions like those mentioned in Sec. 2-16 to represent the repulsion between molecules appear to be suitable. An inverse power dependence r^{-n} with n in the range 6 to 12 is sometimes used to represent the repulsion potential-energy term. Here we shall use an alternative exponential expression

$$U_{\text{rep}} = b e^{-r/\rho} \tag{6-55}$$

where again, r is the distance between nearest-neighbor ions. The constant ρ, which is a measure of the "firmness" of the ions, can be deduced from data on crystal compressibilities. A value of 0.3×10^{-10} m for ρ seems to be satisfactory for all the simple ions with which we shall be dealing.

The total repulsive potential-energy term is the sum of the terms for all nearest neighbors. We can write simply

$$U_{\text{rep}} = B e^{-r/\rho} \tag{6-56}$$

where B is an empirical constant.

The potential energy of a simple A^+B^- ionic crystal has now been expressed as

$$U_{\text{tot}} = -\frac{\mathfrak{N} e^2}{4\pi\epsilon_0 r} \mathfrak{M} + B e^{-r/\rho} \tag{6-57}$$

To proceed to the goal of calculating this crystal energy we must now make use of some experimental data in order to evaluate the remaining unknown, B. (We take the other empirical constant, ρ, to have the value 0.3×10^{-10} m.)

The empirical factor B can be eliminated by requiring dU/dr to be zero at the equilibrium interionic spacing. From Eq. (6-57) we obtain

$$\frac{dU}{dr} = \frac{\mathfrak{N}e^2\mathfrak{M}}{4\pi\epsilon_0 r^2} - \frac{B}{\rho}e^{-r/\rho} \tag{6-58}$$

Setting $dU/dr = 0$ for r equal to the equilibrium distance r_0 gives

$$B = \frac{\mathfrak{N}\mathfrak{M}e^2\rho e^{r_0/\rho}}{4\pi\epsilon_0 r_0^2} \tag{6-59}$$

This result allows Eq. (6-57) to be written as

$$U_{\text{tot}} = -\frac{\mathfrak{N}\mathfrak{M}e^2}{4\pi\epsilon_0 r_0}\left(\frac{r_0}{r} - \frac{\rho}{r_0}e^{(r_0-r)/\rho}\right) \tag{6-60}$$

The potential energy of the crystal in its equilibrium structure, i.e., when $r = r_0$, except for small thermal vibrational-energy terms, is the negative of the lattice energy $\Delta E(\text{lattice})$, which measures the energy required to form free ions from 1 mol of the crystal. We thus calculate

$$\Delta E(\text{lattice}) = \frac{\mathfrak{N}\mathfrak{M}e^2}{4\pi\epsilon_0 r_0}\left(1 - \frac{\rho}{r_0}\right)$$

and

$$\Delta H(\text{lattice}) = \frac{\mathfrak{N}\mathfrak{M}e^2}{4\pi\epsilon_0 r_0}\left(1 - \frac{\rho}{r_0}\right) + 2RT \tag{6-61}$$

Results for crystal enthalpies calculated from Eq. (6-61) with $\rho = 0.3 \times 10^{-10}$ m are shown in Table 6-7 along with the values of ΔH from the Born-Haber cycle.

The success with which the theoretical values of ΔH follow the experimental values is seen to be quite good and confirms the assumption that the attractive and repulsive terms used in the theory are indeed those of principal importance. [Additional, attractions of the van der Waals type between the ions would add to the values calculated from Eq. (6-61) and would improve the agreement with the Born-Haber values.]

Such calculations, it must be admitted, cannot be carried out with similar success for ionic crystals involving polyatomic ions or for crystals of polyatomic molecules. Then neither the attractive nor repulsive forces are as simply expressed, and in general more empirical constants would enter into these expressions than could be evaluated.

TABLE 6-7 Comparison of the Crystal Enthalpies Calculated from Eq. (6-61) with $\rho = 0.3 \times 10^{-10}$ m and the Thermodynamic Born-Haber-Cycle Results from Table 6-4

Crystal	$r_0,$ 10^{-10} m	Eq. (6-61)	Born-Haber
		ΔH, kJ mol^{-1}	
LiF	2.01	1033	1051
NaF	2.31	919	931
KF	2.67	812	829
LiCl	2.57	839	863
NaCl	2.81	776	788
KCl	3.14	704	717
NaBr	2.97	739	752
KBr	3.29	675	688
NaI	3.23	686	705
KI	3.53	633	649

6-14 Solvation Energies of Ions

In the preceding section we saw that the energy change accompanying the formation of an ionic crystal from free gaseous ions can be determined. Here we shall obtain values for the heat of formation of an aqueous solution from the addition of the free gaseous ions to water. The unique role of water as a solvent is suggested by the fact that these heats of solution, or *solvation energies,* are comparable to the crystal energies deduced in the preceding section.

Results for the heat of solution of electrolytes, which can be obtained calorimetrically, can be listed, and some values are given in Table 6-8. These data are the enthalpies of the solutions *compared with* those of the solid salts.

TABLE 6-8 Values of ΔH in kJ mol^{-1} for the Solution of Crystalline Metal Halides and Gaseous Hydrogen Halides in Water at 25°C

	F$^-$	Cl$^-$	Br$^-$	I$^-$
H$^+$	−48.5	−72.8	−83.5	−80.4
Li$^+$	+4.2	−35.1	−47.1	−61.7
Na$^+$	+2.5	+4.3	+0.4	−5.2
K$^+$	−15.1	+17.2	+19.8	+21.8
Rb$^+$	−24.3	+18.4	+24.9	+27.2
Cs$^+$	−36.0	+20.0	+28.2	+34.5
Ag$^+$	−14.2	+66.1	+84.0	+111.8
Tl$^+$		+42.3	+54.4	+73.3
Mg^{2+}	−11.6	−150.3	−181.2	−208.4
Zn^{2+}		−65.4	−62.8	−47.3

The enthalpy effects of the solution process are exhibited if enthalpies for reactions of the type

$$\text{Na}^+(g) + \text{Cl}^-(g) \xrightarrow{\text{H}_2\text{O}} \text{Na}^+(aq) + \text{Cl}^-(aq)$$

are deduced. To obtain such data it is only necessary to have, in addition to the data of Table 6-8 for the ionic crystals, the enthalpies of processes such as

$$\text{NaCl}(s) \rightarrow \text{Na}^+(g) + \text{Cl}^-(g)$$

Results for such processes were obtained from the Born-Haber cycle. With such results, the equations for the NaCl example are

$$\text{NaCl}(s) \xrightarrow{\text{H}_2\text{O}} \text{Na}^+(aq) + \text{Cl}^-(aq) \qquad \Delta H = 4.3 \text{ kJ}$$

and, from Table 6-7,

$$\text{NaCl}(s) \rightarrow \text{Na}^+(g) + \text{Cl}^-(g) \qquad \Delta H = 788 \text{ kJ}$$

These give, on subtraction, the desired reaction and enthalpy value

$$\text{Na}^+(g) + \text{Cl}^-(g) \xrightarrow{\text{H}_2\text{O}} \text{Na}^+(aq) + \text{Cl}^-(aq) \qquad \Delta H = -784 \text{ kJ}$$

The corresponding calculation for the hydrogen halides requires, instead of the lattice energy, the enthalpy of the reaction

$$\text{HX}(g) \rightarrow \text{H}^+(g) + \text{X}^-(g) \qquad \text{(6-62)}$$

This can be obtained from available data on dissociation energies, ionization potentials, and electron affinities, as illustrated for HCl.

$$
\begin{array}{ll}
\text{HCl}(g) \rightarrow \text{H}(g) + \text{Cl}(g) & \Delta H = +\ 432 \text{ kJ} \\
\text{H}(g) \rightarrow \text{H}^+(g) + e^- & \Delta H = +1310 \\
\underline{\text{Cl}(g) + e^- \rightarrow \text{Cl}^-(g)} & \underline{\Delta H = -\ 349} \\
\text{HCl}(g) \rightarrow \text{H}^+(g) + \text{Cl}^-(g) & \Delta H = +1393 \text{ kJ}
\end{array}
$$

Combination of this result with the value of $-72.8 \text{ kJ mol}^{-1}$ for ΔH for the solution of $\text{HCl}(g)$ gives, finally,

$$\text{H}^+(g) + \text{Cl}^-(g) \xrightarrow{\text{H}_2\text{O}} \text{H}^+(aq) + \text{Cl}^-(aq) \qquad \Delta H = -1466 \text{ kJ}$$

In such ways the data presented for the solution of a variety of gaseous ions of electrolytes in Table 6-9 can be obtained.

TABLE 6-9 Values of ΔH in kJ mol^{-1} for the Solution of Gaseous Ions of Metal Halides and Hydrogen Halides in Water at 25°C

The data are for processes of the type

$$M^+(g) + X^-(g) \xrightarrow{H_2O} M^+(aq) + X^-(aq)$$

	F$^-$	Cl$^-$	Br$^-$	I$^-$
H$^+$	−1599	−1466	−1435	−1384
Li$^+$	−1047	−897		
Na$^+$	−929	−784	−752	−710
K$^+$	−844	−700	−668	−627

This is as far as we can go with a thermodynamic treatment. The fact, however, that the difference between successive values in adjacent columns or rows of Table 6-9 are approximately constant leads us to recognize that the heat of solution of the ions of an electrolyte, at infinite dilution, can be interpreted in terms of separate contributions made by the ions of the electrolyte. It remains now to see how the values of Table 6-9 can be divided up so that contributions from the separate ions can be obtained.

A variety of evidence suggests that the ions present in an aqueous solution have associated with them water molecules that are said to *solvate* or *hydrate* the ion. The associations involve various numbers of water molecules and occur with varying energies, and the complexes of ion-plus-water molecules persist for varying lengths of time.

Attempts to separate the heat of hydration of the ions of an electrolyte into ionic components have been made. Most of these start with the calculation of the relative work required to charge a sphere, which represents the ion, in the gas phase compared with the work required in a dielectric medium.

A result of such a derivation suggests that the hydration energy should be proportional to the square of the charge and inversely proportional to its effective radius in aqueous solution. With such a guide, results like those of Table 6-9 can be divided into contributions from each of the ions of the electrolyte. One set of values, which can be looked on as based on the assumption of −1090 kJ mol^{-1} for the H$^+$ ion, is given in Table 6-10.

Some of the trends of the data of Table 6-10 are those expected from the sizes and charges of the ions. (For more extensive data a closer look into the arrangement of the outer electrons of the ion and the way these electrons interact with the adjacent water molecules must be taken.) Of special note, however, is the very large value for the proton. Some understanding of this value is provided by an estimate that the heat of the reaction

$$H^+(g) + H_2O(g) \rightarrow H_3O^+(g)$$

is −760 kJ mol^{-1}. If this reaction is considered to be a step in the solution of a

TABLE 6-10 Some Values of ΔH in kJ mol^{-1} for the Hydration of Gas-Phase Ions Based on the Value of 1090 kJ mol^{-1} for

$$H^+(g) \xrightarrow{H_2O} H^+(aq)$$

H$^+$	(−1090)	Ca^{2+}	−1580	F$^-$	−510
Li$^+$	−530	Zn^{2+}	−2040	Cl$^-$	−380
Na$^+$	−410	Al^{3+}	−4680	Br$^-$	−350
K$^+$	−330	La^{3+}	−3300	I$^-$	−300

proton, and if we recall that the heat of vaporization of water is about 40 kJ, the entire heat of solution is accounted for by ascribing 370 kJ mol^{-1} to the heat of solution of the H_3O^+ ion. This value is in line with the values given in Table 6-10 for other singly charged cations.

Noteworthy also are the very large values that are commonly to be found for the highly charged ions such as Al^{3+}. If these values are divided by 6, a reasonable value for the number of water molecules that can come in direct contact with the ion, may lead to hydration energies for each nearest-neighbor water molecule. Thus, for these ions the hydration process must be regarded as involving the formation of bonds with strengths comparable to those of covalent bonds (Table 6-4). For the singly charged ions, on the other hand, the energy per nearest-neighbor water molecule is considerably less, and a very strong hydrogen bond or ion-dipole association is indicated. Thus, although the ion hydration energies cannot be easily understood at this stage in a quantitative way, they are clearly significant data in the analysis of the nature of ions in aqueous solution.

PROBLEMS

6-1. A sample of ethanol weighing 0.7663 g is burned in a bomb calorimeter for which the heat capacity, including the sample, is 5643 J K^{-1}. A temperature rise from 20.62 to 24.64°C is observed. (*a*) How much heat is given out per gram of ethanol? (*b*) What are the values of $\Delta E_{\text{therm res}}$, $\Delta E_{\text{mech res}}$, and ΔE, all per mole of ethanol? (*c*) What is the change in the number of moles of gaseous reagents per mole of ethanol? (*d*) What is the value of ΔH for the reaction?

6-2. What temperature rise is expected if 0.2347 g of glucose, $C_6H_{12}O_6$, is burned in a bomb calorimeter? The heat capacity of the calorimeter is such that an electrical heating in which 2512 J is added produces a temperature rise of 0.512°C. The heat of combustion of glucose is listed in Table 6-1.

6-3. The compounds for which the heats of combustion are given in Table 6-1 all have formulas of the type CH_mO_n. Set up a general expression for the difference between ΔE and ΔH for the combustion reactions.

6-4. One milliliter of liquid 100% H_2SO_4 is added to water to produce 100 ml of dilute H_2SO_4 solution. The heat-of-formation values of liquid H_2SO_4 and dilute solution H_2SO_4 are -811.3 and -907.5 kJ mol^{-1}. If the heat capacity of the solution is taken as equal to that of water and the initial temperature is 25°C, what is the approximate final temperature? [The density of $H_2SO_4(l)$ is given as 1.834 g ml^{-1}.]

6-5. The heats evolved when 1 mol of carbon, C, sulfur, S, and liquid carbon disulfide, CS_2 at 25°C are burned to the products $CO_2(g)$ and $SO_2(g)$ are 393.5, 296.1, and 1073.5 kJ mol^{-1}, respectively. Calculate the standard heat of formation of $CS_2(l)$ at 25°C and compare with the value of Appendix B-1.

6-6. The heat of combustion, i.e., the heat liberated per mole at 25°C of liquid ethanol, C_2H_5OH, hydrogen gas, and graphite, all to form $CO_2(g)$ and $H_2O(l)$, are 1366.9, 285.8, and 393.5 kJ mol^{-1}, respectively. Calculate the heat of formation, ΔH_f° for liquid ethanol at 298 K.

6-7. (a) Which would release the greater amount of heat, oxidation of 1 mol of carbon to give $CO_2(g)$ or the oxidation of 1 mol of silicon to give $SiO_2(c)$? (b) Will the answer be different if the comparison is made on a mass rather than mole basis? Use the heat-of-formation data of Appendix B-1.

6-8. Which releases the more energy, the combustion of the hydrocarbon n-heptane or the carbohydrate glucose if (a) the comparison is based on a unit mass of the fuels n-heptane and glucose; (b) the comparison is based on a unit mass of oxygen that is required for the combustion process?

6-9. According to the data of Prob. 2-33, how much oxygen, measured as a number of moles, is utilized by an average adult each 24 h? (a) Use results like those of Prob. 6-8 to estimate how much heat is released by the use of this much oxygen in the combustion of foodstuffs per day. (b) Does this value coincide with what you know on other grounds?

6-10. It is estimated that a man expends about 2 kJ of energy per pound of body weight in walking a mile. Which has the better performance rating based on pound-miles per unit mass of fuel, a man using glucose as a fuel or a car using gasoline as a fuel? (Assume any particular car you like, or take a representative value of a 1-ton car and a 15-miles-per-gallon fuel consumption; 1 U.S. gal = 3.785 liters, and the density of gasoline is about 0.68 g ml^{-1}.)

6-11. G. B. Kistiakowsky, J. R. Ruhoff, H. A. Smith, and W. E. Vaughan [*J. Am. Chem. Soc.,* **57**:65 (1935)] reported the value of -32.82 kcal, or -137.32 kJ, for the heat of hydrogenation of ethylene at 355 K. (a) Compare this result with the value at 25°C that is calculated from the data of Appendix B-1. (b) To what can the difference in these values be attributed?

6-12. G. B. Kistiakowsky, J. R. Ruhoff, H. A. Smith, and W. E. Vaughan [*J. Am. Chem. Soc.,* **57**:876 (1935)] reported the value of -49.80 kcal, or -208.36 kJ, as the heat of the reaction in which 3 mol of hydrogen gas is added to 1 mol of benzene gas at 355 K. (a) Compare this value with that calculated for 25°C (298 K) from the ΔH_f° value of -156.2 kJ for C_6H_{12}. (b) Is the difference in the direction what you would expect? (c) What is the basis for your expectation?

6-13. Once the heat of formation of $HCl(g)$ is known, the heat of formation of $HBr(g)$ can be obtained from convenient reactions in which aqueous solutions are mixed or gases are dissolved in aqueous solutions. Very early thermochemical data obtained by J. J. Thomson, which have been converted to joules but otherwise unchanged, are tabulated as follows:

	ΔH(kJ)
$\frac{1}{2}H_2(g) + \frac{1}{2}Cl_2(g) \longrightarrow HCl(g)$	-92.0
$HCl(g) \xrightarrow{H_2O} HCl(aq)$	-72.4
$KBr(aq) + \frac{1}{2}Cl_2(g) \longrightarrow KCl(aq) + \frac{1}{2}Br_2(aq)$	-48.1
$KOH(aq) + HCl(aq) \longrightarrow KCl(aq)$	-57.3
$KOH(aq) + HBr(aq) \longrightarrow KBr(aq)$	-57.3
$\frac{1}{2}Br_2(g) \xrightarrow{H_2O} \frac{1}{2}Br_2(aq)$	-2.1
$HBr(g) \xrightarrow{H_2O} HBr(aq)$	-83.3

Calculate a value for the standard heat of formation of HBr(g) and compare with the $\Delta H_f^\circ(298)$ value of Appendix B-1.

6-14. A flow process converts 0.5 mol of acetylene per minute into benzene by passing acetylene gas over a catalyst bed. At what rate must heat be added or removed in order to keep the catalyst bed and the product benzene vapor at the same temperature, 25°C, as the incoming acetylene?

6-15. Combustion of diborane, B_2H_6, at a constant pressure proceeds according to the equation

$$B_2H_6(g) + 3O_2(g) \rightarrow B_2O_3(s) + 3H_2O(g)$$

For each mole of diborane consumed 2020 kJ of heat is liberated. Combustion of elemental boron also proceeds to the product B_2O_3 and gives out 1264 kJ per mole of B_2O_3. What is the standard heat of formation of diborane at 25°C?

6-16. Compare the heat of solution of equal weights of anhydrous sodium sulfate and the decahydrate, known as *Glauber's salt*.

6-17. A dilute aqueous ammonia solution is added to a dilute solution of copper sulfate. Will the temperature rise or fall because of the reaction in which the complex $Cu(NH_3)_4^{2+}$ ion is formed?

6-18. (a) Calculate $H_{298}^\circ - H_0^\circ$ for CO_2 given that the vibrational spacings are 667, 667, 1343, and 2349 cm^{-1} and the moment of inertia is 71.7×10^{-47} kg m^2. The molecule is linear. (b) Compare with the values for this quantity that can be found in Table 5-2 and in Appendix B-4. (c) Calculate $H^\circ - H_0^\circ$ and $H^\circ - H_{298}^\circ$ at 1000 K and compare with the values of Table 5-2 and Appendix B-4.

*6-19. Carbon monoxide can be formed from CO_2 or from O_2 by the action of hot carbon according to the equations

$$CO_2(g) + C(s) \rightarrow 2CO(g) \quad \text{and} \quad O_2(g) + 2C(s) \rightarrow 2CO(g)$$

(a) Calculate the heat of each reaction at a reasonable operating temperature of 1200 K. The reactions of part (a) can be carried out together by passing a mixture of carbon dioxide and oxygen over a bed of hot charcoal. (b) What would be the mole ratio of CO_2 to O_2 in a gas stream preheated to 1200 K to give a net reaction such that no heating or cooling of the reaction zone was required? (c) What would be the mole ratio if the gas stream were not preheated and entered the reaction chamber at 25°C?

6-20. Using the heat-capacity data of Table 6-2, calculate $H^\circ - H_{298}^\circ$ at 1000 K for any gas for which data are also given in Appendix B-4. Compare the value you obtain with that given in Appendix B-4.

6-21. Calculate the thermal contribution $E° - E_0°$ to the internal energy and $H° - E_0°$ to the enthalpy of Cl_2 at 298 and at 1000 K. Assume ideal-gas behavior, and use the vibrational-energy-level spacing of 1.10×10^{-20} J per molecule.

6-22. Calculate the molar heat capacity of Cl_2 at 298 and at 1000 K using the data of Prob. 6-21 and compare with the values obtained from the empirical equation $C_P° = 37.03 + 0.67 \times 10^{-3}T - 2.84 \times 10^5 T^{-2}$ J K^{-1}.

6-23. (a) Using the thermal-energy data of Prob. 6-21 and assuming ideal-gas behavior, calculate ΔE, ΔH, $\Delta E_{\text{therm res}}$, and $\Delta E_{\text{mech res}}$ when 1 mol of Cl_2 is heated at a constant pressure of 1 atm from 298 to 1000 K. (b) Repeat the calculation using the empirical heat-capacity expression of Prob. 6-22.

6-24. Draw to scale a diagram for the reaction $CO(g) + \frac{1}{2}O_2(g) \rightarrow CO_2(g)$, showing the enthalpies of reactants and products from 298 to 1000 K. Make use of the data of Appendix B-4 and Table 6-2.

6-25. The dissociation energy of $I_2(g)$ as determined by spectroscopic studies is 1.5417 eV, or 148.76 kJ mol^{-1}. The enthalpy of sublimation of iodine at 25°C is 65.52 kJ mol^{-1}. What is the standard free energy of formation of $I(g)$ at 25°C?

6-26. The heat of combustion of cyclopropane has been reported as 2091.2 kJ mol^{-1}. Use this value to obtain an estimate of the C—C bond enthalpy in cyclopropane and compare with the value given in Table 6-4.

6-27. From data found elsewhere in the text verify the N—H bond enthalpy value given in Table 6-4.

6-28. If the C—H bonds of n-butane and i-isobutane are assumed to have the same bond enthalpies, what values for the C—C bond energies in these two butanes would be obtained? Use the data of Table 6-1.

6-29. Explain why the C—C bond enthalpy can be estimated to be half the heat of sublimation of diamond.

*6-30. (a) Use an inverse power of r for the repulsion term to obtain an expression for the lattice energy ΔE. (b) What value of n must be used to have the same repulsion-term effect as a ρ value of 0.3×10^{-10} m?

*6-31. By what percentage will a calculated value of ΔE change, according to the expression developed in Prob. 6-30, if the value of n is changed from 9 to 6?

6-32. (a) Crystalline MgO, periclase, adopts the NaCl structure. Use a Born-Haber cycle and a lattice-energy calculation to estimate the affinity of oxygen atoms for two electrons. The following data, all in kilojoules per mole, can be used. The standard heat of formation of $MgO(c)$ is -601.2, the heat of sublimation of Mg is 147.6, the dissociation energy of O_2 is 498.4, and the sum of the first two ionization potentials of Mg atoms is 2178. The unit cell dimension of the MgO crystal is 4.213 Å. (b) The electron affinity of oxygen atoms for one electron is reported as 1.465 eV, or 141.4 kJ. What is the electron affinity of $O^-(g)$?

6-33. The *heat of solution*, i.e., the heat given off when a substance is dissolved, is listed for 18°C, as $+15.89$ kcal mol^{-1} for anhydrous $CuSO_4$ and -2.796 kcal mol^{-1} for the pentahydrate. Are these data consistent with the heat-of-formation data of Appendix B? (The difference between 25°C and 18°C will introduce only a minor discrepancy.)

6-34. Use the data of Tables 6-8 and 6-9 to recover a value for ΔH for the reaction $Na^+(g) + Cl^-(g) \rightarrow NaCl(c)$.

REFERENCES

The general treatments of chemical thermodynamics listed at the end of Chap. 5 contain material on thermochemistry. References to compilations of thermochemical data can be found particularly in the book by Pitzer and Brewer. The following books and articles are also pertinent to the subject of thermochemistry.

COTTRELL, T. L.: "The Strengths of Chemical Bonds," Butterworth & Co. (Publishers), Ltd., London, 1958. Presents the experimental methods for obtaining bond-dissociation energies in diatomic and polyatomic molecules and summarizes the available data.

JANAF Thermochemical Tables, 2d ed., Natl. Stand. Ref. Data Ser., *Natl. Bur. Stand.* (*U.S.*), no. 37, 1971. Thermodynamic data for many inorganic compounds.

ROSSINI, F. W., et al. (eds.): Tables of Selected Values of Chemical Thermodynamic Properties, *Natl. Bur. Stand.* (*U.S.*) *Circ.* 500, 1952. An excellent collection of thermodynamic properties of chemical substances, with references to original sources.

SMITH, D. W.: Ionic Hydration Enthalpies, *J. Chem. Educ.*, **54**:540 (1977).

HOLM, J. L.: Enthalpy Cycles in Inorganic Chemistry, *J. Chem. Educ.*, **51**:460 (1974).

ENTROPY AND THE SECOND AND THIRD LAWS OF THERMODYNAMICS

A very large part of chemistry is concerned, in one way or another, with the state of equilibrium and the tendency of systems to move in the direction of the equilibrium state. Thermodynamics is the basic approach to the study of equilibria. Enthalpy and internal-energy changes themselves are not reliable indications of the tendency of a reaction to proceed; i.e., they do not indicate where the equilibrium lies. The thermodynamic and molecular treatments that we now take up are concerned with the following questions: (1) Can the equilibrium state of a chemical system be determined by the use of some additional thermodynamic function? (2) If so, can this function, and therefore the equilibrium state, be understood in terms of the properties of the molecules involved?

After a preliminary discussion of the general statements of the second law of thermodynamics, a new thermodynamic function will, rather arbitrarily, be introduced. This function will allow the second law of thermodynamics to be applied to chemical systems. It will be seen that the second law and the new function are concerned with the equilibrium state and the tendency of processes, or reactions, to occur spontaneously. A molecular interpretation of the new thermodynamic function will then be suggested.

Not until the following chapter will the thermodynamic study of equilibria be completed by the introduction of another, more convenient function.

7-1 General Statements of the Second Law of Thermodynamics

Although the second law can be stated in a number of ways, all statements can be shown to generalize our knowledge that natural processes tend to go to a state of equilibrium. The second law sums up our experiences with equilibria, just as the first law summed up our experience with energy. The general statements of the second law, like the conservation-of-energy statement of the first law, are not immediately applicable to chemical problems. After general statements of the law are presented, it will be shown that the law can be expressed in a chemically useful form.

Two important statements of the second law have been given. One, due to

Lord Kelvin, is that *it is impossible by a cyclic process to take heat from a reservoir and convert it into work without at the same time transferring heat from a hot to a cold reservoir.*

This statement can be illustrated by the fact that a ship cannot derive work from the energy in the sea on which it moves. A moment's thought about all types of engines will show that there is always both a hot source and a cold sink. A steam engine, for example, could not be made to produce work if it were not for the high pressure and high temperature of the steam *compared* with the surroundings.

This statement of the second law is related to equilibria when it is realized that work can be obtained from a system only when the system is not already at equilibrium. If a system is at equilibrium, no process tends to occur spontaneously and there is nothing to harness to produce work. A nonchemical example is the production of hydroelectric power. Here work is obtained when the spontaneous tendency of water to flow from a high to a low level is used. Lord Kelvin's statement recognizes that the spontaneous process is the flow of heat from a higher to a lower temperature and that only from such a spontaneous process can work be obtained.

The second classic statement, given by Clausius, is that *it is impossible to transfer heat from a cold to a hot reservoir without at the same time converting a certain amount of work into heat.*

This statement is readily illustrated by the operation of a refrigerator. Again we recognize that the spontaneous flow of heat is from a high to a low temperature and that the reverse is possible only when work is expended.

Neither the Kelvin nor the Clausius statement follows from the first law. No conflict with the first law would be encountered if heat were completely converted into work or if heat were to simply flow from a lower to a higher temperature. The second law is a different generalization about heat and work from that provided by the first law.

A rather more sophisticated approach than will be used here concerns itself with how the high and low temperatures referred to in these statements are defined. The statements of Kelvin and Clausius, in fact, provide fundamental definitions for temperature. Temperature so defined, however, can be shown to be identical with the temperature scale that makes the relation $PV = nRT$ hold for ideal gases.

The chemist's interest in the second law of thermodynamics is aroused by the possibility of this law's saying something about the position of equilibrium in a chemical process.

7-2 Entropy and Another Statement of the Second Law of Thermodynamics

In considering the thermodynamics of changes, chemical or otherwise, we must focus on the initial and the final states that are connected by a real or imagined process. We would like to know whether there is a property (and if there is, how it can be evaluated) that lets us deduce whether a natural, spontaneous process might change the system from the one state to the other.

Chemical terminology would have it that spontaneous processes are those in which a *driving force* tends to make the reaction or process occur. The study of any property that might be associated with the tendency of processes or chemical reactions to proceed, and thus might give a measure to the driving force of chemical reactions, is of obvious chemical interest. (A process or reaction for which there is no tendency to proceed in either direction has been described as balanced, or *reversible*. By contrast, a spontaneous process is unbalanced, or *irreversible*: no small change in the conditions could overcome the natural driving force.) In the search for such a property it turns out to be profitable to deal with $\Delta E_{\text{therm res}}/T$ rather than with q or $\Delta E_{\text{therm res}}$ itself. Such a quantity is sufficiently important to merit a symbol $\Delta S_{\text{therm res}}$ and a name, the change in *entropy* of the thermal reservoir. More generally, there will be thermal reservoirs at a number of different temperatures, or the reservoir might operate over a range of temperatures. In the latter case the entropy change of the thermal reservoir would be calculated by a suitable integration of

$$dS_{\text{therm res}} = \frac{dE_{\text{therm res}}}{T} \qquad (7\text{-}1)$$

We are at liberty to ascribe any features to this new entropy function that we like, the requirement being that we construct a function that is self-consistent and allows us to form a useful expression for the second law. In this vein we further specify that, for all processes,

$$dS_{\text{mech res}} = 0 \qquad (7\text{-}2)$$

Now we are at a stage comparable with that in the development of the first law where we knew how to determine the energy changes in the thermal and mechanical surroundings. The next step is to use this information to learn about the change in the property, now the entropy, of the *system* and to see how it can be used.

We proceed by making two statements that together express a law of nature, which we call the second law of thermodynamics. (A law of nature is, you recall, a generalization, and you accept it if you find that it agrees with observations.)

The two following statements constitute the second law:

1. *When a process is carried out reversibly, the entropy change in the universe of the process is zero.* (Notice that since we know how to calculate $\Delta S_{\text{therm res}}$ and we have required $\Delta S_{\text{mech res}}$ to be zero, this statement provides a means for deducing the entropy change ΔS of the system.)
2. *For processes that proceed irreversibly, i.e., out of balance and therefore spontaneously, the entropy of the universe of the process increases.* (Thus, if

by some means the entropy change of the system ΔS and $\Delta S_{\text{therm res}}$ are known, the possibility of this process occurring spontaneously can be deduced by inspecting the sign of $\Delta S + \Delta S_{\text{therm res}}$.)

That the first statement can lead to a value for the entropy change of the system can first be illustrated.

Example 7-1:

By how much does the entropy of 1 mol of liquid water at 1 atm and 100°C change when the water is converted into vapor at the same temperature and pressure?

Solution:

The system and the surroundings are illustrated in Fig. 7-1. The numerical entries result from the use of the heat of vaporization, 40,670 J, to obtain, first,

$$\Delta S_{\text{therm res}} = \frac{-40,670}{373} = -109 \text{ J K}^{-1} \tag{7-3}$$

The value of $\Delta S_{\text{mech res}}$ is zero according to our description of entropy. Since the vaporization can be imagined to occur reversibly with only an infinitesimal temperature difference between the reservoir and the system, the first of the two second-law statements requires $\Delta S_{\text{univ}} = 0$. With ΔS implying the entropy change in the system, we can write

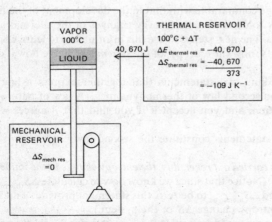

FIGURE 7-1 The formation of 1 mol of steam from 1 mol of liquid water at 1 atm and 100°C.

$$\Delta S_{\text{therm res}} + \Delta S = 0$$

or

$$\Delta S = -\Delta S_{\text{therm res}} = +109 \text{ J K}^{-1} \qquad (7\text{-}4)$$

The entropy of 1 mol of steam is 109 J K^{-1} greater than that of liquid water both at 100°C and 1 atm.

Now let us turn to a process which we know to be spontaneous and see whether, as the second statement claims, the entropy of all concerned increases.

Example 7-2:

Consider a vessel containing liquid water and steam at 1 atm and therefore at 100°C to be brought in contact with a vessel containing liquid water and ice at 1 atm and therefore at 0°C. What is the entropy change for the flow of some amount of heat Q from the hot to the cold vessel? (The water-and-steam and water-and-ice containers are used so that their temperatures will remain constant even though heat, if not too much, is transferred. If temperatures were allowed to change, the calculations would be similar in principle but a little more involved.)

Solution:

First a reversible way of performing this energy transfer must be devised so that the constancy of the entropy of all concerned in a reversible process can be used to calculate the entropy change of the system, which consists of the two containers. (Heat flowing directly from a high to a low temperature corresponds to an irreversible process, and for such processes we have no direct way of calculating this entropy change.) A reversible process results if we connect each of the two parts of the system to separate heat reservoirs, as shown in Fig. 7-2b, one at a temperature infinitesimally lower than 100°C, the other infinitesimally higher than 0°C. The heat flows indicated in the figure give the net result, as far as the system is concerned, of transferring energy from the hot to the cold body. The addition of the thermal reservoirs, however, makes the process reversible.

The entropy change suffered by the thermal reservoirs is now calculated as

$$\Delta S_{\text{therm res}} = \Delta S_{\text{hot res}} + \Delta S_{\text{cold res}} = \frac{Q}{373} + \frac{-Q}{273}$$

$$= -0.00098Q \quad (7\text{-}5)$$

Since the process of Fig. 7-2b is reversible, $\Delta S_{\text{univ}} = 0$ and thus

$$\Delta S = -\Delta S_{\text{therm res}} = +0.00098Q \qquad (7\text{-}6)$$

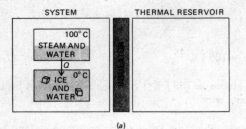

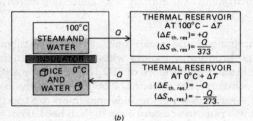

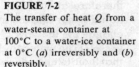

FIGURE 7-2
The transfer of heat Q from a water-steam container at 100°C to a water-ice container at 0°C (a) irreversibly and (b) reversibly.

The entropy change of the system has been calculated by means of the arrangement of Fig. 7-2b, but, as will be shown, the entropy change of the *system* is independent of how the process is performed and depends only on the initial and final states. The result therefore gives the entropy change ΔS of the system when heat Q is transferred from water-steam to water-ice by *any* process, including that of Fig. 7-2a.

Now we can consider the entropy change of the universe for the direct heat transfer, as in the arrangement of Fig. 7-2a. No heat reservoirs are involved, and an entropy change results, therefore, only from that which occurs in the system. This we have deduced to be the positive quantity $+0.00098Q$. Thus, for the direct heat transfer,

$$\Delta S_{\text{univ}} = \Delta S = +0.00098Q = \text{a positive quantity} \qquad (7\text{-}7)$$

If we did not know that heat would flow spontaneously from hot to cold, this result, and the statements of the second law, would tell us that this would happen!

Let us consider one final example.

Example 7-3:
Determine the entropy change for the isothermal expansion of n mol of an ideal gas at temperature T from a volume V_1 to a volume V_2.

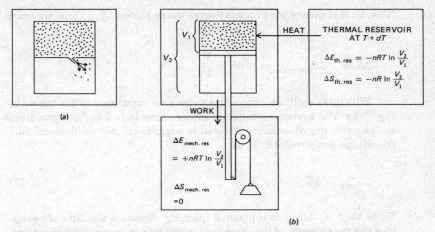

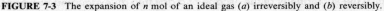

FIGURE 7-3 The expansion of n mol of an ideal gas (a) irreversibly and (b) reversibly.

Solution:

The expansion can be performed irreversibly by simply opening a stopcock and allowing the gas to rush into the previously evacuated compartment, as represented by Fig. 7-3a. We have no method for analyzing this process directly to find the entropy difference between the expanded gas and the initial gas. It is necessary to devise an alternative process that can be carried out reversibly and that takes the system from the same initial to the same final state. Figure 7-3b shows one possibility.

For this isothermal ideal-gas expansion, the internal energy does not change and the thermal surroundings give up an amount of energy equal to that gained by the mechanical surroundings. Since for the reversible expansion $P_{ext} = P$, we calculate

$$\Delta E_{mech\,res} = \int P_{ext}\, dV = \int P\, dV = \int_{V_1}^{V_2} \frac{nRT}{V}\, dV = nRT \ln \frac{V_2}{V_1} \quad (7\text{-}8)$$

and

$$\Delta E_{therm\,res} = -nRT \ln \frac{V_2}{V_1} \quad (7\text{-}9)$$

This allows us to obtain

$$\Delta S_{therm\,res} = \frac{\Delta E_{therm\,res}}{T} = -nR \ln \frac{V_2}{V_1} \quad (7\text{-}10)$$

Now, for this reversible process to give the required $\Delta S_{univ} = 0$, we must have

$$\Delta S = -\Delta S_{therm\,res} = +nR \ln \frac{V_2}{V_1}$$

With this result, we can return to the free expansion of the gas as in Fig. 7-3a. The system changes from the same initial to the same final states as in the alternative reversible expansion, but no thermal surroundings are involved. Thus

$$\Delta S_{univ} = \Delta S = +nR \ln \frac{V_2}{V_1} \qquad (7\text{-}11)$$

Since $V_2 > V_1$, ΔS_{univ} is a positive quantity. Again, if we did not recognize the spontaneity of the escape of a gas into an evacuated chamber, this result, an increase in the entropy of all that is affected by the process, would lead us to this expectation.

Some of the importance attached to entropy, as a result of such deductions, can be seen by its position alongside energy in the famous maxim of Clausius: *The energy of the universe is constant; the entropy of the universe always tends toward a maximum.* Since all natural processes are spontaneous, they must occur with an increase of entropy, and therefore the sum total of the entropy in the universe is continually increasing. Recognition of this trend leads to some interesting philosophical discussion, e.g., Sir Arthur Eddington's idea that "entropy is time's arrow."

We are now in a position to summarize the results of this and the preceding section and thereby to indicate the use that can be made of the function called entropy. Suppose one wishes to investigate the possibility of a reaction, either chemical or physical, proceeding from one state a to another state b. If the entropy difference ΔS_{univ} for the process can be calculated, use can be made of the following statements:

If ΔS_{univ} is positive, the reaction will tend to proceed spontaneously from state a to state b.

If ΔS_{univ} is zero, the system is at equilibrium and no spontaneous process will occur.

If ΔS_{univ} is negative, the reaction will tend to go spontaneously in the reverse direction, i.e., from b to a.

That these properties of entropy sum up our experience with naturally occurring phenomena has been illustrated by the simple examples given above.

For the type of process used in these examples, it is certainly cumbersome and unnecessary to introduce the entropy function. On the other hand, when dealing with a chemical reaction

Reactants → products

one would be greatly aided by a thermodynamic property which could be determined for the reactants and the products and any surroundings involved and which would tell whether or not the reaction would tend to proceed spontaneously.

The above considerations all depend on the use of results obtained from measurements on the thermal surroundings to deduce, for a reversible process, the entropy change that is occurring in the system. (The procedure is parallel to that used in applications of the first law, where measurements on the energy changes in the thermal and mechanical surroundings allowed the change in energy in the system to be deduced.) But again, there generally are a number of reversible ways of going from some initial state of the system to some final state. Have we any assurance that the values calculated for ΔS for all these will be the same; i.e., are we entitled to interpret a value for ΔS deduced for some process that takes the system from state a to state b as $S_b - S_a$? (There is, you should note, some good reason to be uncertain of the answer. In our first-law deduction that E was a state function, we used the fact that the sum of $\Delta E_{\text{therm res}}$ and $\Delta E_{\text{mech res}}$ is independent of path, even though the separate terms are quite path-dependent.)

That entropy is a state function can be deduced by considering a specific cyclic process from which the results can be extended to a large class of processes.

7-3 The Carnot Cycle

Although chemists are not necessarily interested in the conversion of heat into work, consideration of a particularly simple engine for doing this leads us to the recognition that a system in a given state has a certain amount of entropy; i.e., entropy, like internal energy or enthalpy, is a state function.

The engine we consider was analyzed originally by the French engineer Sadi Carnot in 1824. This engine is very convenient for analysis, but although the pattern of operation is not entirely different from that of a steam or internal-combustion engine, it is not a practical device. One cycle of this engine has the net effect of using heat from a hot thermal reservoir, producing some mechanical energy, and giving some heat to a cold thermal reservoir. The engine would operate by continually repeating this cycle.

A diagram of a Carnot-engine system and the thermal and mechanical reservoir is shown in Fig. 7-4. Any material could be assumed to be present in the cylinder, but the analysis is greatly simplified if the working material in the cylinder is an ideal gas. We shall assume further that there is 1 mol of this gas.

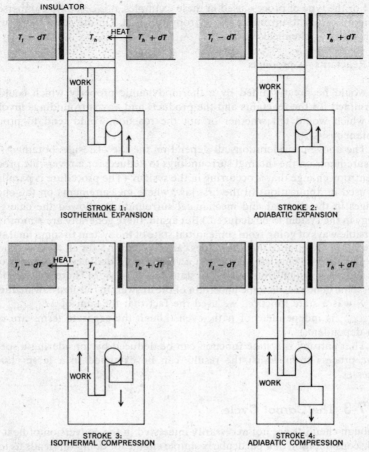

FIGURE 7-4 The four strokes of the Carnot cycle.

The Carnot cycle consists of four steps, shown in Fig. 7-5. Each step is performed reversibly; i.e., the pressure of the gas is only infinitesimally different from that of the piston, and the heat flows across an infinitesimal temperature gradient. First the energy exchanged between the system and the thermal and mechanical reservoirs will be deduced for each step.

Step 1 The gas is expanded isothermally at a high temperature T_h from an initial volume V_1 to a volume V_2. Work is done by the gas, and heat flows from the hot reservoir to the gas.

The work w done on the gas is

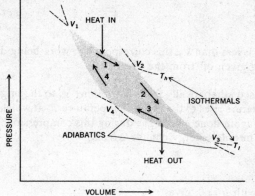

FIGURE 7-5
The Carnot cycle on a PV diagram. (The four strokes are numbered as in Fig. 7.4.)

$$w = -\int P\, dV = -RT_h \int_{V_1}^{V_2} \frac{dV}{V} = -RT_h \ln \frac{V_2}{V_1} \tag{7-12}$$

Since the gas is ideal and the temperature is constant, $\Delta E = 0$. It follows, from $\Delta E = q + w$, that

$$q = -w = RT_h \ln \frac{V_2}{V_1} \tag{7-13}$$

Step 2 The gas is expanded adiabatically from a volume V_2 to a volume V_3, and the temperature drops to a low temperature T_l. Work is done by the gas, and since the insulators are in place for this adiabatic step, no heat is transferred.

The fact that the working substance is an ideal gas lets us write

$$\Delta E_2 = C_V(T_l - T_h)$$

and the first law then gives

$$w = C_V(T_l - T_n) \tag{7-14}$$

Step 3 The gas is compressed isothermally at the lower temperature T_l from the volume V_3 to a volume V_4. Work is now done *on* the gas by the piston, and heat flows from the gas to the cold reservoir.

$$w = -\int P\, dV = -RT_l \int_{V_3}^{V_4} \frac{dV}{V} = -RT_l \ln \frac{V_4}{V_3} \tag{7-15}$$

Again, as in step 1, the temperature is constant and $\Delta E = 0$. Thus

$$q = -w = +RT_l \ln \frac{V_4}{V_3} \qquad (7\text{-}16)$$

We note that since V_4 is less than V_3, this corresponds to work being done on the gas and heat being given off from the gas.

Step 4 The gas is compressed adiabatically from the volume V_4 to the original volume V_1, and the temperature rises to the higher temperature T_h at which the cycle was started. Work is again done *on* the gas during this compression, and no heat is absorbed. The internal-energy change ΔE_4 is

$$\Delta E_4 = C_V(T_h - T_l)$$

The first-law expression, with $q = 0$, gives

$$w = C_V(T_h - T_l) \qquad (7\text{-}17)$$

In this step work is done on the gas and w is a positive quantity.

That the entire cycle obeys the first law of thermodynamics can now be checked. Since the effects in steps 2 and 4 nullify each other, the net work done on the gas is

$$w = w_1 + w_3$$

or

$$w = -RT_h \ln \frac{V_2}{V_1} - RT_l \ln \frac{V_4}{V_3} \qquad (7\text{-}18)$$

This expression can be simplified by the recognition that the adiabatics of steps 2 and 4 relate the four volumes according to the equations

$$T_h{}^{C_V/R} V_2 = T_l{}^{C_V/R} V_3 \qquad \text{and} \qquad T_h{}^{C_V/R} V_1 = T_l{}^{C_V/R} V_4$$

Division of the first of these by the second gives

$$\frac{V_2}{V_1} = \frac{V_3}{V_4}$$

Thus Eq. (7-18) reduces to

$$w = -R(T_h - T_l) \ln \frac{V_2}{V_1} \qquad (7\text{-}19)$$

or

Work done by gas $= R(T_h - T_l) \ln \dfrac{V_2}{V_1}$ (7-20)

The net heat absorbed by the gas is

$$q = q_1 + q_2 = RT_h \ln \frac{V_2}{V_1} + RT_l \ln \frac{V_4}{V_3}$$

or, with the relation $V_2/V_1 = V_3/V_4$,

$$q = R(T_h - T_l) \ln \frac{V_2}{V_1}$$ (7-21)

For the cycle, in which the working substance is returned to its initial state, the net work done by the working substance is equal to the net heat absorbed. The first law is obeyed.

7-4 The Efficiency of the Transformation of Heat into Work

The performance of an engine is usually computed on the basis of the net work done for a given consumption of thermal energy from the hot reservoir. In an internal-combustion engine, for example, one measures the mechanical energy produced from a given amount of fuel, which is the counterpart of heat from the hot reservoir. The efficiency of the Carnot engine is therefore defined as

$$\text{eff} = \frac{-w}{q_h}$$ (7-22)

Use of Eqs. (7-19) and (7-13) allows this efficiency to be shown as

$$\text{eff} = \frac{R(T_h - T_l) \ln (V_2/V_1)}{RT_h \ln (V_2/V_1)} = \frac{T_h - T_l}{T_h}$$ (7-23)

This formula represents the results of the analysis of the operation of the Carnot engine. The relation of this particular result to the previously given general statements of the second law can now be investigated.

Kelvin's statement that thermal energy cannot be completely converted into mechanical energy leads us to investigate the possibility of an engine with 100 percent thermodynamic efficiency. According to Eq. (7-23), this can happen only if T_h is infinite or T_l is zero. The first is obviously an impracticality, although engines are run at as high a temperature as possible to increase their efficiencies. The second, as we shall see when the third law of thermodynamics is dealt with, is another impossibility.

The Clausius statement requires us to think of a Carnot cycle that is run in the direction opposite that of the preceding derivation. Since all the steps in the cycle are reversible, this could occur if the temperatures of the heat reservoirs were changed by infinitesimal amounts. We now have a refrigerator in which an amount of mechanical energy is expended, some thermal energy is taken from the cold reservoir, and energy equal to the sum of these is delivered to the hot reservoir. Then both the numerator and denominator in Eq. (7-22) have signs opposite from that for operation as an engine. The efficiency is therefore still given by Eq. (7-23). Now it is interpreted as the ratio of the mechanical energy spent to the thermal energy delivered to the hot reservoir. This can only be zero, implying unassisted flow of heat from the cold to the hot reservoir for $T_h = T_l$, a result that is in accordance with the Clausius statement of the second law.

It can be shown that no other engine working between the same two temperatures can convert thermal to mechanical energy with a greater efficiency than the Carnot engine. Other reversible engines, in fact, will have the same efficiency as the Carnot engine; the Carnot assumption of 1 mol of an ideal gas as a working fluid merely allows us to use available expressions for the expansions and compressions in each of the engine's strokes. The Carnot-cycle efficiency can therefore be used to make an estimate of the maximum conversion of heat into work that can be expected for a real engine.

A steam engine, for instance, can be taken as operating between some high temperature around 120°C and a condenser temperature of about 20°C. For such an engine the efficiency can be estimated as

$$\text{eff} = \frac{393 - 293}{393}(100) = 25\% \tag{7-24}$$

Thus, for every four units of heat supplied in the steam, the equivalent of one unit of work can be obtained, and three units of heat is given off at the low temperature. This efficiency is the maximum that could be expected if there were no other inefficiencies in the operation. In addition, of course, there is a mechanical efficiency that limits the available work to some fraction of this theoretically possible amount.

Such a calculation indicates the desirability of operating an engine with as high a value of T_h and as low a value of T_l as possible.

7-5 Entropy Is a State Function

Now the results of the Carnot-cycle derivation can be used to prove the previous assumption that the entropy of the system is a function of the state of the system, so that the entropy difference between two states of a system is the same for *any* process connecting these two states.

Two different reversible paths 1 and 2 that connect states *a* and *b* are shown in Fig. 7-6. Let the entropy change of the system that results from going from *a* to *b* by path 1 be $\Delta S_{a \to b}^{(1)}$, and let the entropy change for path 2 be $\Delta S_{a \to b}^{(2)}$. The

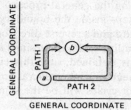

FIGURE 7-6
Two different reversible ways
in which state b can be
reached from state a.

entropy change when the system is carried from b to a is then $-\Delta S^{(1)}_{a\to b}$ if path 1 is retraced or $-\Delta S^{(2)}_{a\to b}$ if path 2 is retraced.

The two different paths between a and b can be thought of as constituting a cyclic process. Consider a cyclic process that starts at state a, goes to state b by path 1, and returns to state a by path 2. The entropy change of the system as a result of this cyclic process is

$$\Delta S_{\text{cycle}} = \Delta S^{(1)}_{a\to b} - \Delta S^{(2)}_{a\to b}$$

or

$$\Delta S^{(1)}_{a\to b} = \Delta S^{(2)}_{a\to b} + \Delta S_{\text{cycle}} \tag{7-25}$$

We can learn about the difference between the entropy changes when different reversible paths are taken by deducing a value for ΔS_{cycle}.

Any reversible cycle involving an ideal gas can be thought of as being made up of a large number of Carnot cycles, as illustrated by Fig. 7-7. A grid of isotherms and adiabatics is drawn through the heavy curve, which represents any reversible cyclic process. The grid can be used to construct a set of Carnot cycles so that the outer parts of the set trace out a curve that approximates that of the general process. If one were to perform all the Carnot cycles in the set, the

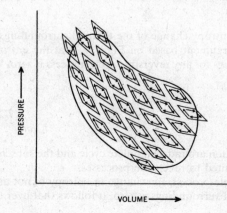

FIGURE 7-7
A cyclic process approximated by a set of schematic Carnot cycles.

net result would be almost the same as performing the general process. This follows from the fact that all the Carnot-cycle steps inside the boundary are canceled out because each is traced in both a forward and a reverse direction. In the limit of an infinitely closely spaced grid, an outline with infinitesimal steps that corresponds to the general cyclic process is obtained, and this curve, furthermore, encloses the same area on the PV diagram as the general process does. The net effect of performing all the Carnot cycles will be the same as performing the general process.

Now let us analyze the entropy changes that occur in the thermal surroundings as a result of each cycle of the Carnot engine. Equating Eqs. (7-22) and (7-23) gives

$$\frac{-w}{q} = \frac{T_h - T_l}{T_h} \tag{7-26}$$

The first-law result for the cycle, $-w = q_h + q_l$, can be used in Eq. (7-26) to obtain

$$\frac{q_h + q_l}{q_h} = \frac{T_h - T_l}{T_h}$$

or, on rearrangement,

$$\frac{q_h}{T_h} + \frac{q_l}{T_l} = 0 \tag{7-27}$$

Now recall that $q_h = -(\Delta E_{\text{therm res}})_h$ and $q_l = -(\Delta E_{\text{therm res}})_l$. We have deduced that

$$\frac{(\Delta E_{\text{therm res}})_h}{T_h} + \frac{(\Delta E_{\text{therm res}})_l}{T_l} = 0 \tag{7-28}$$

Thus for each Carnot cycle the entropy change of the thermal surroundings is zero. It follows also, from the argument based on Fig. 7-7, that the entropy change in the thermal surroundings for any reversible cyclic process is zero. We can express this by writing

$$\oint_{\text{rev}} \frac{dq}{T} = 0 \tag{7-29}$$

where the $\oint$ sign signifies integration around a complete cycle and the subscript reminds us that the result is limited to reversible processes.

Thus, for any cyclic reversible process, the change in entropy of not only the universe but also the thermal surroundings is zero. It follows that over the cycle the entropy change of the *system* must also be zero. Substitution of this result in Eq. (7-25) gives

$$\Delta S_{a \to b}^{(1)} = \Delta S_{a \to b}^{(2)}$$

Thus all paths from a to b must produce the same entropy change. Thus proof of the zero value for the cyclic integral is equivalent to proof that the entropy difference between two states is a function only of those states and is not dependent on the path used to go from one to the other.

Thus the entropy change of a system can be calculated for any reversible process. The result is a valid measure of the difference in the entropy of the system in the initial and final states. This difference is independent of how the process is carried out—even of whether the process is reversible or irreversible. The entropy, like the internal energy, enthalpy, volume, and so forth, is a property of the system, a state function.

7-6 The Unattainability of Absolute Zero

The third and final of the great summations of our experiences with nature on which all the deductions of thermodynamics are based can now be introduced. Full use of thermodynamics can then be made in our subsequent studies of chemical systems.

The second law of thermodynamics has introduced entropy, and this function has been shown to be important when the directions of spontaneous changes are investigated. The second law, moreover, shows how differences in entropy of two states of a system can be determined. The third law gives a method for assigning a value to the entropy of a system. Like the first two laws, the third is an expression of our experiences with nature. The basic experiences for this law come about from attempts to achieve very low temperatures. Such activity is not as readily undertaken as the experiments that form the basis of the first and second laws, and for this reason the third law will appear to be a less general principle. All attempts that have been made to obtain lower and lower temperatures, however, lead to the general statement that *the absolute zero of temperature is unattainable.* This statement can be used as a basis for the expression in the next section for the third law of thermodynamics. First, however, it may be of interest to mention briefly some of the steps that have been taken in the direction toward absolute zero.

It is not the mere attainment of low temperatures that stimulates attempts to achieve them. It will be shown that the measurement of absolute values for entropies requires measurements at temperatures approaching absolute zero. Furthermore, as absolute zero is approached, the reduction of thermal energy leads to the appearance of a number of very interesting phenomena that are obscured or nonexistent at higher temperatures. Interest in such effects has led to the production of lower and lower temperatures.

Liquid nitrogen can now be readily obtained commercially, and the attainment of a temperature of about 77 K presents no problem to the research worker.

Still lower temperatures are obtained by performing a Joule-Thomson expansion on hydrogen, but this gas must first be cooled below its inversion temperature of 193 K, e.g., by means of a liquid nitrogen. Expansion then allows liquid hydrogen, boiling point 22 K, to be formed. Finally, liquid hydrogen can be used to cool helium below its inversion temperature, and subsequent expansion produces liquid helium, which boils at 4 K. Temperatures of somewhat less than 1 K can be produced by reducing the pressure over the helium, but this technique is limited by the large amounts of vapor that must be pumped off. For many low-temperature research problems the temperatures reached by liquid hydrogen or helium are satisfactory and can be reached with commercially available liquid helium or a helium liquefier.

There are now several techniques for reaching temperatures below the 1 K obtainable with liquid helium. Some depend on the special properties of the helium isotopes ^{3}He and ^{4}He, and others make use of the magnetic properties of materials that result from atomic magnetic moments, due to unpaired electrons, or from nuclear magnetic moments. The use of low-temperature magnetization can serve to illustrate the techniques and their limitations.

The temperature-entropy curves for *paramagnetic* salts, like gadolinium sulfate octahydrate, which contain unpaired electrons, and materials like copper, whose nuclei have a magnetic moment, are illustrated in Fig. 7-8. Over

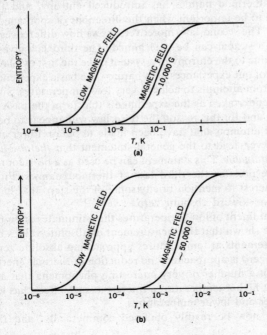

FIGURE 7-8
Representative ST diagrams for a material that (a) is paramagnetic because of unpaired electrons and (b) whose magnetism depends on the magnetic effects of the nuclei.

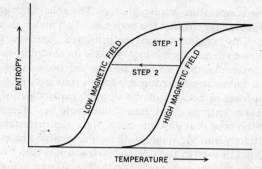

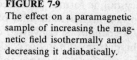

FIGURE 7-9
The effect on a paramagnetic sample of increasing the magnetic field isothermally and decreasing it adiabatically.

a certain temperature range, the entropy of these substances in a low magnetic field is greater than it is in a high magnetic field. (In Sec. 7-8 you will see the basis on which the lower entropy for the magnetized, and thus more ordered, forms is to be expected.)

The adiabatic-demagnetization procedure for producing low temperatures can now be seen by considering a two-step process. In the first step, the magnetic field is gradually increased. The sample tends to heat up, but a temperature rise is prevented by the flow of heat into a thermostating bath, e.g., of liquid helium. This reversible removal of heat produces an increase in the entropy of the bath and a corresponding decrease in the entropy of the sample. In preparation for the second step, the sample is isolated from this bath and any other heat-conducting components. The magnetic field is slowly reduced. The magnetization of the sample is nearly in balance with the magnetic field during this demagnetization process. Thus the process is a nearly reversible one, and the entropy change for the universe of the sample is zero. Since the thermal surroundings are unaffected, in this second step the entropy of the sample remains constant. Thus this step returns the sample to its low magnetization state without an increase in temperature. The two-step temperature-reducing process is illustrated in Fig. 7-9.

Low-temperature, or *cryogenic,* work shows that temperatures very near absolute zero can be obtained, but the entropy difference between any pair of states that can be connected by reversible processes, as in step 1 of Fig. 7-9, appears to approach zero as the absolute zero of temperature is approached. It follows that the temperature reduction that is possible approaches zero as the zero temperature is approached. Absolute zero is thus unattainable.

The chemist's interest in the unattainability of absolute zero stems primarily from the implication of this generalization on the entropy of crystals as the temperature approaches absolute zero.

7-7 Entropy and the Third Law of Thermodynamics

If any entropy differences existed down to absolute zero and a reversible process existed that could connect them, one might expect to be able to use these

entropy changes to reduce the temperature to absolute zero. The generalization that absolute zero is unattainable suggests that the entropies of all materials at absolute zero are the same. This conclusion must be restricted, however, to materials that are in the thermodynamically most stable state for this temperature range. (One finds, for example, that many materials are frozen into a metastable glassy state as the temperature is reduced, and this state may persist even as absolute zero is approached because of the slowness with which the crystalline form is produced. The entropy of the glassy state could be different, in fact higher, than that of the crystal at absolute zero. Since the metastable state cannot be converted directly into the stable state by a reversible process, this entropy difference could not be used in attempts to reach absolute zero.) We can conclude, therefore, that *the entropy of all perfect crystalline substances must be the same at absolute zero.* Furthermore, to be consistent with the molecular interpretation of entropy, we take the entropy at absolute zero to be zero. In this way we come to the chemically useful statement of the third law of thermodynamics, quoted from the classic thermodynamics text by Lewis and Randall:†
"If the entropy of each element in some crystalline state be taken as zero at the absolute zero of temperature, every substance has a finite positive entropy; but at the absolute zero of temperature the entropy may become zero, and does so become in the case of perfect crystalline substances."

The third law makes it possible to assign entropy values, described as *absolute entropies,* to chemical compounds. The difference in entropy between 0 K and a temperature T can be deduced from the defining equation for entropy by considering nearly reversible additions of heat from a variable-temperature heat reservoir. Then for the sample under study we have

$$S_T - S_0 = - \int_0^T \frac{dE_{\text{therm res}}}{T} = \int_0^T \frac{\delta q_{\text{rev}}}{T} \tag{7-30}$$

The third law allows S_0 to be assigned the value of zero for materials that form perfect crystals. Then Eq. (7-30) becomes

$$S_T = \int_0^T \frac{\delta q_{\text{rev}}}{T} \tag{7-31}$$

Recall that an integration of δq itself would give results that depend upon the particular way of carrying out the temperature increase. The integration of $\delta q/T$, however, gives the same result for all reversible paths. Thus S_T can be evaluated by any reversible procedure that provides the necessary calorimetric data.

The integral of Eq. (7-31) can be evaluated from measured heat capacities and heats of transition. If 1 mol of a substance in a given phase is heated from T_1 to T_2 at constant pressure, it gains entropy according to the expression

† G. N. Lewis and M. Randall, "Thermodynamics," McGraw-Hill Book Company, Inc., New York, 1923.

$$S_{T_2} - S_{T_1} = \int_{T_1}^{T_2} \frac{dH}{T} = \int_{T_1}^{T_2} \frac{C_P \, dT}{T} = \int_{T_1}^{T_2} C_P \, d(\ln T) \qquad (7\text{-}32)$$

The integration can be carried out if the necessary values for C_P are measured. The integration is usually performed graphically from a plot of either C_P/T versus T or C_P versus $\ln T$. In either treatment the area under the curve between two temperatures gives, according to Eq. (7-32), the entropy increment for that temperature range. The method is illustrated in Fig. 7-10. Since heat-capacity measurements are usually not taken down below about 15 K,

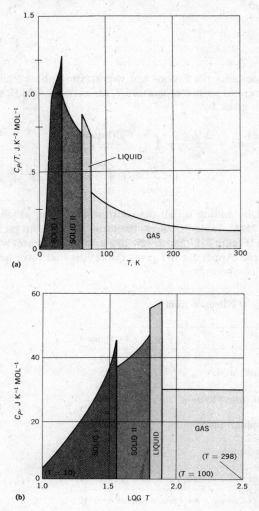

(a)

(b)

FIGURE 7-10
Graphs of C_P/T versus T and C_P versus $\ln T$ for N_2. [*Data of W. F. Giauque and J. O. Clayton, J. Am. Chem. Soc.,* **55:** *4875 (1933).*]

attainable with liquid hydrogen, an extrapolation to absolute zero is necessary. The extrapolation, which introduces a comparatively small term in the total entropy, is based on the T^3 dependence of the heat capacity as given by Eq. (5-76).

In taking a compound from near absolute zero to some temperature such as 25°C a number of phase transitions are generally encountered. At each of these transitions the heat capacity will, generally, change abruptly, and heat will be absorbed. The entropy change corresponding to such transitions can be calculated, as illustrated in Example 7-1, from the measured enthalpy change for the transition by the expression

$$\Delta S_{\text{trans}} = \frac{\Delta H_{\text{trans}}}{T_{\text{trans}}} \tag{7-33}$$

If a substance undergoes only the fusion- and vaporization-phase transitions as it is brought from zero to some temperature T, for example, 298 K, the entropy of the substance is given by

$$S(T) = \int_0^{T_{\text{fus}}} \frac{C_P \text{ (solid)}}{T} dT + \frac{\Delta H_{\text{fus}}}{T_{\text{fus}}} + \int_{T_{\text{fus}}}^{T_{\text{vap}}} \frac{C_P \text{ (liquid)}}{T} dT$$
$$+ \frac{\Delta H_{\text{vap}}}{T_{\text{vap}}} + \int_{T_{\text{vap}}}^{T} \frac{C_P \text{ (gas)}}{T} dT \tag{7-34}$$

The entropy obtained by adding up all the contributions from absolute zero is usually reported at 25°C. Table 7-1 shows the terms that go into such a determination for nitrogen. Figure 7-11 shows how the entropy increases with temperature for this example. Appendix B-1 gives the results that have been obtained for a number of compounds.

TABLE 7-1 The Entropy of Nitrogen from Heat-Capacity Data

	J K^{-1} mol^{-1}
0–10 K extrapolation	1.92
10–35.61 K (graphical integration)	25.25
Transition 228.9/35.61	6.43
35.61–63.14 K (graphical integration)	23.38
Fusion 720.9/63.14	11.42
63.14–boiling point (graphical integration)	11.41
Vaporization 5535.0/77.32	72.13
Correction for gas imperfection	0.92
Ideal gas 77.32–298.2 K	39.20
Entropy of ideal gas at 298.2 K and 1 atm	192.06

Source: W. F. Giauque and J. O. Clayton, *J. Am. Chem. Soc.,* **55:**4875 (1933).

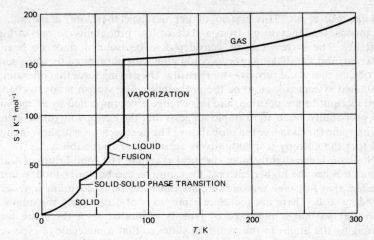

FIGURE 7-11 Graphical display of the third-law entropy components for N_2, as given in Table 7-1.

Such third-law entropy values are of interest to the chemist in two important areas: (1) they provide the data with which molecular calculations of entropy can be compared, and (2) along with values for the enthalpies of reactions, they constitute the thermodynamic basis for treating chemical equilibria.

7-8 The Molecular Basis of Entropy

In the preceding developments it was quite unnecessary to attempt to reach any "explanation" of entropy. The definition of entropy shows how changes in this function can be calculated, and the discussion of the previous sections have shown how entropy changes are related to the spontaneity of reactions. With this information one understands entropy as well, for instance, as one understands a familiar quantity like work. One might notice that one's appreciation of work is pretty well limited to its definition as force times distance and to a familiarity with some of its qualitative features. Entropy differs only in that it is a less familiar function.

It is not immediately obvious what molecular phenomenon is responsible for the entropy of a system. Some idea of what it is that should be calculated can be obtained by trying to discover a quantity that might tend to increase when an isolated system moves spontaneously toward the equilibrium position. A very nonchemical example will reveal such a quantity.

Consider a box containing a large number of pennies. Suppose, furthermore, that the pennies are initially arranged so that they all have heads showing. If the box is now shaken, the chances are very good that some arrangement of higher probability, with a more nearly equal number of heads and tails, will result. This system of pennies has, therefore, a natural, or spontaneous, tendency to go from a state of low probability to one of high probability. The system can be considered to be isolated since no heat is transferred, and the shaking process could almost be eliminated by using some other objects that could turn over more easily. The driving force that operates in this isolated system is seen to be the probability. The system tends to change toward its equilibrium position, and this change is accompanied by an increase in the probability. Such an example suggests that the entropy might be identified with some function like the probability. The next sections will show in more detail that the entropy is quantitatively related to the probability.

Now consider a slightly more chemical example. The equilibrium of A and B in which B has the higher entropy, for example, can be understood in terms of the fact that for some reason there are more available quantum states corresponding to B. There are therefore more ways of distributing the atoms in these states so that a molecule of type B is formed than there are ways of arranging the atoms in the quantum states so that a molecule of type A is formed. The tendency for A to change over to B, even if no energy driving force exists, is therefore understood to be due to the driving force that takes the system from a state of lower probability, i.e., of few quantum states and few possible arrangements, to one of higher probability, i.e., one of many available quantum states and more possible arrangements. The qualitative result from this discussion is: *A substance for which the molecules have more available quantum states has the higher probability and therefore the higher entropy.*

The molecular explanation of the entropy change in a process is basically quite simple. In practice, of course, it is not always easy to see whether a process, or reaction, produces a system with more, or less, available quantum states or energy levels. Thus, for the liquid-to-vapor transition a large entropy increase occurs. The difficulties encountered in a molecular understanding of the liquid state make it very difficult to evaluate this entropy increase from the molecular model.

In the remaining sections of this chapter you will see that these difficulties can be overcome, at least for ideal gases. Then the entropy can be calculated from the properties of the molecules of the gas.

7-9 Entropy and the Probability of a System of Molecules

Let us begin with a postulate that relates probability to entropy. Then, once it is shown what is meant by probability as applied to a system of molecules, the entropy of systems of molecules will be calculated. Agreement between the entropies so calculated and the entropy values obtained from third-law measurements will support the original probability-entropy postulate.

According to the approach of Boltzmann, the entropy of a system is given by the elegantly simple expression

$$S = k \ln W \qquad (7\text{-}35)$$

where k is Boltzmann's constant, with value 1.3806×10^{-23} J K^{-1}, and W is the number of quantum states available to the particles of the system. We can think of W as being a measure of the number of different molecular-level arrangements that the particles of the system can adopt for the specified macroscopic state of the system. W can also be interpreted as the ratio of the probability of the system, with its very many possible different arrangements, to the probability it would have if the system consisted of a single arrangement. Thus we shall talk of W as a probability. Now let us investigate W so that we obtain an equation that allows the calculation of S for some actual system.

The number of arrangements that constitute a particular distribution, or the probability of that distribution, was investigated in Sec. 4-2. There the expression of Eq. (4-5) for the probability of a distribution of an Avogadro's number of particles throughout a set of allowed energies was developed. Equation (4-5) was obtained, as is obvious from Fig. 4-3, when we label the marbles or particles that we distribute throughout the boxes or quantum states. We assumed that the marbles or molecules were distinguishable and thus could be kept track of. If they were not distinguishable, the number of arrangements, or probability, that would be associated with each distribution would be greatly reduced.

The number of different arrangements of the integers $1, 2, 3, \ldots, N$ is $N!$. There is only one arrangement of N identical numbers, e.g., a set of N 1's or 2's. The probability deduced for N items must be reduced by a factor of $N!$ if these items are indistinguishable instead of distinguishable. (Since all distributions are equally affected by this recognition of indistinguishability, this reduction was of no consequence in Sec. 4-2, where we sought the most probable distribution.) To calculate a value for $\ln W$ that will apply to the distribution of gas molecules over the allowed energy levels we must recognize that the molecules cannot be labeled and therefore that the previous value of W must be divided by $N!$ Equation (4-5) becomes

$$W = (g_1{}^{N_1} g_2{}^{N_2} g_3{}^{N_3} \cdots) \frac{1}{N_1! N_2! N_3! \cdots} \qquad (7\text{-}36)$$

Use of Stirling's approximation, $\ln x! = x \ln x - x$ for large numbers, as in Sec. 4-2, gives

$$\ln W = \sum N_i \left(1 + \ln \frac{g_i}{N_i} \right) \qquad (7\text{-}37)$$

A simple illustration of the results obtained by applying these expressions is given in Fig. 7-12. The logarithm of the probability for several different distributions of five particles in the set of six boxes, each of different size, is

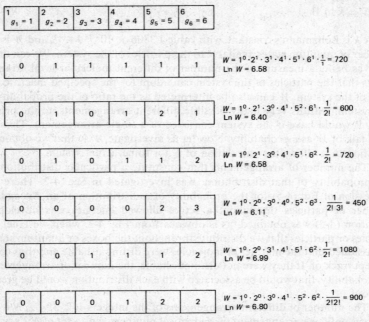

$W = 1^0 \cdot 2^1 \cdot 3^1 \cdot 4^1 \cdot 5^1 \cdot 6^1 \cdot \frac{1}{1} = 720$
Ln $W = 6.58$

$W = 1^0 \cdot 2^1 \cdot 3^0 \cdot 4^1 \cdot 5^2 \cdot 6^1 \cdot \frac{1}{2!} = 600$
Ln $W = 6.40$

$W = 1^0 \cdot 2^1 \cdot 3^0 \cdot 4^1 \cdot 5^1 \cdot 6^2 \cdot \frac{1}{2!} = 720$
Ln $W = 6.58$

$W = 1^0 \cdot 2^0 \cdot 3^0 \cdot 4^0 \cdot 5^2 \cdot 6^3 \cdot \frac{1}{2!\,3!} = 450$
Ln $W = 6.11$

$W = 1^0 \cdot 2^0 \cdot 3^1 \cdot 4^1 \cdot 5^1 \cdot 6^2 \cdot \frac{1}{2!} = 1080$
Ln $W = 6.99$

$W = 1^0 \cdot 2^0 \cdot 3^0 \cdot 4^1 \cdot 5^2 \cdot 6^2 \cdot \frac{1}{2!2!} = 900$
Ln $W = 6.80$

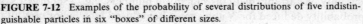

FIGURE 7-12 Examples of the probability of several distributions of five indistinguishable particles in six "boxes" of different sizes.

shown. (The calculations are carried out more easily if W is calculated first, as suggested in Fig. 7-12.) Each box is the counterpart of an allowed energy level, and the size of the box is to be thought of as being proportional to the number of states at that energy.

Now let us return to Eq. (7-37) and deduce the value of ln W not for an arbitrary distribution but for the most probable arrangement of molecules throughout the energy-level pattern. This distribution is given by the Boltzmann equation. From Eq. (4-26) for example, we have

$$\frac{N_i}{g_i} = \frac{\mathfrak{N}}{q} e^{-\Delta\epsilon_i/kT} \tag{7-38}$$

where q is the partition summation $\sum g_i e^{-\Delta\epsilon_i/kT}$ and $\Delta\epsilon_i$ is the difference in energy between the ith energy level and the lowest energy level. The logarithmic form of the reciprocal of Eq. (7-38), which is needed for Eq. (7-37), is

$$\ln\frac{g_i}{N_i} = \frac{\Delta\epsilon_i}{kT} + \ln\frac{q}{\mathfrak{N}} \tag{7-39}$$

Substitution in Eq. (7-37) leads then to the molar entropy

$$S = k \ln W = k \left[\sum_i N_i \left(1 + \frac{\Delta \epsilon_i}{kT} + \ln \frac{q}{\mathfrak{N}} \right) \right]$$

$$= \frac{1}{T} \sum_i (N_i \, \Delta \epsilon_i) + k\mathfrak{N} \left(1 + \ln \frac{q}{\mathfrak{N}} \right) \qquad (7\text{-}40)$$

The summation that remains in Eq. (7-40) is recognized as giving the thermal energy, which we have been representing by $E - E_0$. With R written for $k\mathfrak{N}$ Eq. (7-40) can be rearranged so that we reach the desired result

$$S = \frac{E - E_0}{T} + R \ln \frac{q}{\mathfrak{N}} + R \qquad (7\text{-}41)$$

This expression will be used in the following sections to calculate the entropies of several gases. Comparison of the results with the third-law entropy values of these compounds confirm the basic equation $S = k \ln W$ used in the molecular calculations.

Although for ideal gases the thermal-energy term $E - E_0$ is not dependent on the pressure, we shall see that q and S are pressure-dependent. When the standard state of 1 atm is specified, Eq. (7-41) will be written

$$S^\circ = \frac{E^\circ - E_0^\circ}{T} + R \ln \frac{q^\circ}{\mathfrak{N}} + R \qquad (7\text{-}42)$$

All the terms in Eq. (7-41) or (7-42) are calculable if the energy pattern of the allowed states is known. The entropy is entirely dependent on the distribution of the molecules of the sample throughout these states.

The applicability of Eq. (7-42), it should be pointed out, is limited, and these limitations stem from two sources.

First, we have again the question of distinguishability of the particles. The displayed result, Eq. (7-42), is applicable to gases for which the molecules can in no way be distinguished from each other. Perfect crystalline materials, on the other hand, are different in that the order and rigidity of the crystal lattice allow the atoms or molecules to be labeled, at least in principle, e.g., by their position relative to a point in the crystal. Liquids present some intermediate cases that are difficult to analyze. In the applications to follow, only gases will be dealt with. The qualitative conclusions regarding the factors that influence the entropy, however, can be carried over to liquids and solids even if quantitative results will not be obtained.

The second limitation sets in when the particles are crowded into the states of the lower energy levels. Then the distribution does not conform to the

Boltzmann distribution. The distribution that results depends on the fundamental nature of the particles of the system. Electrons and other particles which, like electrons, have half-integral spin quantum numbers appear to be limited to two particles per quantum state. (This restriction is, in fact, familiar in the context of the electron configurations of atoms.) Particles that behave in this way are said to obey *Fermi-Dirac statistics,* and the importance of this behavior in the treatment of the free electrons in metals was seen in Sec. 5-14. Other fundamental particles, those with integral spin quantum numbers, have no such restriction on the number per state and are said to obey *Bose-Einstein statistics.* Even these, when crowded into available states, do not conform to the Boltzmann distribution. The systems we deal with in the calculation of thermodynamic properties here, however, will have very many more available quantum states than particles. In such situations most of the states will be unoccupied; the special features of *fermions* or *bosons* will be of no consequence. The Boltzmann distribution will then be effectively followed, and when the probability expression is corrected for indistinguishable particles, the resulting $k \ln W$ and entropy result [Eq. (7-42)] are, as you will see, valid.

7-10 The Contributions to the Entropy of an Ideal Gas

For many gases, at temperatures that are not too high, the molecular motions or degrees of freedom that must be recognized for thermodynamic calculations are those of translation, rotation, and vibration. For some molecules at lower temperatures and for all molecules at elevated temperatures electronic states other than the single ground state must be considered.

The energy of the molecules of a gas can be treated, at least approximately, as separable, and we can write

$$E - E_0 = (E - E_0)_{trans} + (E - E_0)_{rot}$$
$$+ (E - E_0)_{vib} + (E - E_0)_{elec} \tag{7-43}$$

The total partition functions, as shown in Sec. 4-4, has the form

$$q = q_{trans} q_{rot} q_{vib} q_{elec} \tag{7-44}$$

These general descriptions of the thermal-energy and partition functions for the molecules of an ideal gas can be inserted into Eq. (7-42). The many terms can then be collected to give

$$S° = \frac{(E - E_0)_{trans}}{T} + R \ln \frac{q_{trans}}{\mathfrak{N}} + R$$
$$+ \frac{(E - E_0)_{rot}}{T} + R \ln q_{rot}$$

$$+ \frac{(E - E_0)_{vib}}{T} + R \ln q_{vib}$$

$$+ \frac{(E - E_0)_{elec}}{T} + R \ln q_{elec} \qquad (7\text{-}45)$$

The assignment of the $\mathfrak{N}$ term and the additional R term to the translational component produces a translational entropy component with the form of the expression for the entropy obtained in the preceding section.

Now we can proceed to the calculation of the entropies of ideal gases.

7-11 The Translational Entropy of an Ideal Gas

It is important to obtain a qualitative understanding of the molecular basis for entropy and energy. It is satisfying also to see that the molecular expressions obtained here in a rather simple manner do lead to quantitative values for thermodynamic functions. In particular, it can be shown that a value can be calculated for the entropy of an ideal gas and that such calculated values agree with the thermodynamic third-law values.

The translational energy of an Avogadro's number of molecules has been shown on both classical and quantum-mechanical grounds to be $\frac{3}{2}RT$. This value can be substituted for $(E - E_0)_{trans}$ of Eq. (7-42) or the first component of Eq. (7-45) to give

$$S_{trans} = \frac{\frac{3}{2}RT}{T} + R \ln \frac{q_{trans}}{\mathfrak{N}} + R = \tfrac{5}{2}R + R \ln \frac{q_{trans}}{\mathfrak{N}} \qquad (7\text{-}46)$$

The translational partition function has been obtained (Sec. 4-5) as

$$q_{trans} = \left(\frac{2\pi mkT}{h^2} \right)^{3/2} \mathsf{V} \qquad (7\text{-}47)$$

Now this expression for the translational partition function can be inserted into Eq. (7-46) to give

$$S_{trans} = R \left[\frac{5}{2} + \ln \left\{ \left(\frac{2\pi mkT}{h^2} \right)^{3/2} \frac{\mathsf{V}}{\mathfrak{N}} \right\} \right] \qquad (7\text{-}48)$$

This equation was obtained by O. Sackur and H. Tetrode in 1912 by a rather unsatisfactory derivation. It has now been frequently checked against third-law entropies and can be relied on to give the translational contribution to the entropy of an ideal gas.

The experimental third-law entropy of argon gas at 1 atm pressure and 87.3 K, its normal boiling point, has been reported as 129.1 J K^{-1} mol^{-1}. The values, in SI units, necessary for the calculation of S_{trans} from Eq. (7-48) are

$$m = 6.63 \times 10^{-26} \text{ kg} \qquad h = 6.62 \times 10^{-34} \text{ J s}$$

$$k = 1.38 \times 10^{-23} \text{ J K}^{-1} \qquad V = \frac{87.3}{273}(0.0224) = 0.00716 \text{ m}^3$$

$$T = 87.3 \text{ K}$$

The entropy S_{trans}, which for the monatomic gas argon is equal to the molar entropy S is calculated for these conditions as

$$S = R[\tfrac{5}{2} + 2.303 \log (4.61 \times 10^5)] = 8.315(2.500 + 13.04)$$
$$= 129.2 \text{ J K}^{-1} \text{ mol}^{-1}$$

The calculated value agrees nicely, therefore, with that of 129.1 based on the third-law calorimetric method.

Such agreement of calculated and third-law entropies can be taken as support either for the molecular postulates of Schrödinger and Boltzmann or for the thermodynamic choice of a zero entropy at absolute zero.

The general expression of Eq. (7-48) can be put in a form more convenient for many numerical calculations by stipulating standard conditions of 1 atm pressure. Then, when numerical values are inserted, we obtain the standard molar entropy as

$$S^\circ \text{ (J K}^{-1}\text{ mol}^{-1}) = 28.72 \log M + 47.86 \log T - 9.79 \qquad \text{[1 atm]} \quad (7\text{-}49)$$

where M is the mass of a molecule in atomic mass units.

At 25°C this expression becomes

$$S^\circ \text{ (J K}^{-1}\text{ mol}^{-1}) = 28.72 \log M + 108.74 \qquad \text{[1 atm, 25°C]} \qquad (7\text{-}50)$$

7-12 The Rotational Entropy of the Molecules of an Ideal Gas

As was pointed out in Sec. 3-3, a rotating molecule has a set of allowed rotational energy levels. For a diatomic, or any linear, molecule the allowed rotational energies of a molecule of moment of inertia I are given approximately by

$$\epsilon_{rot} = \frac{J(J+1)h^2}{8\pi^2 I} \qquad J = 0, 1, 2, \ldots \tag{7-51}$$

Furthermore, the rotational energy corresponding to a given value of J has a degeneracy of $2J + 1$. These features of the rotational-energy patterns allow the rotational partition function to be deduced, as in Sec. 4-6. This result can now be used to obtain the rotational entropy contribution. This rotational contribution to the entropy, which must be added to the translational contribution calculated in Sec. 7-10, is given by

$$S_{\text{rot}} = \frac{(E - E_0)_{\text{rot}}}{T} + R \ln q_{\text{rot}} \tag{7-52}$$

The partition function for rotation of a linear molecule obtained in Sec. 4-6 is

$$q_{\text{rot}} = \frac{8\pi^2 IkT}{\sigma h^2} \tag{7-53}$$

For a linear molecule, which has just 2 rotational degrees of freedom, the value of $E - E_0$ for rotation was found, with this expression, to be RT. The rotational entropy of a diatomic or a linear polyatomic molecule can thus be written

$$S_{\text{rot}} = \left(1 + \ln \frac{8\pi^2 IkT}{\sigma h^2}\right) \qquad \text{[linear molecules]} \tag{7-54}$$

For CO, as determined by the method to be treated in Sec. 14-1, the moment of inertia is 14.5×10^{-47} kg m^2. The rotational entropy contribution at 25°C can therefore be calculated as

$$\begin{aligned} S_{\text{rot}} &= R(1 + 2.303 \log 107.2) = R(1 + 4.676) \\ &= 47.2 \text{ J K}^{-1} \text{ mol}^{-1} \end{aligned} \tag{7-55}$$

For comparison, the translational entropy of CO at 1 atm and 298 K can be calculated from Eq. (7-49) or (7-50) as

$$S^{\circ}_{\text{trans}} = 149.6 \text{ J K}^{-1} \text{ mol}^{-1} \tag{7-56}$$

The much greater translational entropy contribution (compared with the rotational entropy contribution) can be understood in terms of the much closer spacing of the translational energy levels and therefore the much larger number of translational states throughout which the molecules are distributed.

Equation (7-54) is applicable to all diatomic molecules and all linear molecules. Generally shaped molecules, with 3 rather than 2 rotational degrees of freedom, require the use of $\frac{3}{2}RT$ for the rotational energy and the rotational partition function, given in Sec. 4-6. For gases composed of such molecules

$$S_{\text{rot}} = \left[\frac{3}{2} + \ln\left(\frac{8\pi^2 kT}{h^2}\right)^{3/2} \frac{(\pi I_A I_B I_C)^{1/2}}{\sigma}\right] \qquad \text{[nonlinear molecules]} \tag{7-57}$$

When numerical values are inserted for the constants, the rotational contributions to ideal gases are given by the following expressions:
Linear molecules:

$$S_{rot}^{\circ} \, (\text{J K}^{-1} \text{ mol}^{-1}) = 877.37 + 19.14 \, (\log I + \log T - \log \sigma) \qquad (7\text{-}58)$$

Nonlinear molecules:

$$S_{rot}^{\circ} \, (\text{J K}^{-1} \text{ mol}^{-1})$$
$$= 1320.79 + 9.57 \log I_A I_B I_C + 28.72 \log T - 19.14 \log \sigma \quad (7\text{-}59)$$

where each moment of inertia is to be expressed in SI units of kilogram meter squared.

These equations cannot be applied to molecules with very low moments of inertia or at very low temperatures. In both cases the spacing of the energy levels becomes appreciable compared with the thermal energy, and the integration that produced Eq. (7-53), for example, is not valid.

7-13 The Vibrational Entropy of the Molecules of an Ideal Gas

The vibrational contribution to the entropy separates from the translational and rotational contributions as shown in Sec. 7-11. Thus, for each vibrational mode one adds to the translational and rotational contributions the term

$$S_{vib} = \frac{(E - E_0)_{vib}}{T} + R \ln q_{vib} \qquad (7\text{-}60)$$

The first term, the vibrational thermal energy, has been shown in Eq. (4-57) to be given by

$$E - E_0 = RT \frac{x}{e^x - 1} \qquad \text{where} \qquad x = \frac{h\nu_{vib}}{kT}$$

The vibrational partition function for each vibrational degree of freedom was given by Eq. (4-55) as

$$q_{vib} = \frac{1}{1 - e^{-x}}$$

Thus, for each vibrational degree of freedom of the molecules of 1 mol of gas, the entropy contribution is

$$S_{vib} = R \frac{x}{e^x - 1} + R \ln \frac{1}{1 - e^{-x}} \qquad (7\text{-}61)$$

or with numerical values,

$$S_{vib} \, (J \, K^{-1} \, mol^{-1}) = 8.3143 \left[\frac{x}{e^x - 1} - 2.303 \log (1 - e^{-x}) \right] \qquad (7\text{-}62)$$

Application of Eq. (7-62) to the CO example with the vibrational-energy-spacing value of 4.26×10^{-21} J leads to an entropy contribution, 0.003 J mol^{-1} K, that is negligible compared with the translational and rotational contributions.

Qualitatively, it can be recognized that such a small fraction of the molecules are in vibrational states other than the lowest available vibrational level that the entropy contribution from the vibrational states is, in this example, effectively zero. In general, the vibrational entropy contribution is small but, except for wide vibrational spacings as in CO, not negligible.

It follows, therefore, that the total entropy of CO at 1 atm and 298 K is calculated, according to the expressions given here, as

$$S^\circ = S^\circ_{trans} + S^\circ_{rot} + S^\circ_{vib} + S^\circ_{elec} = 150.3 + 47.2 + 0.00 + 0.00$$
$$= 197.5 \, J \, K^{-1} \, mol^{-1} \qquad (7\text{-}63)$$

Calculations that allow for the fact that the rotational-energy term $E - E_0$ is not exactly the classical value give the calculated result 197.9 J K^{-1} mol^{-1}.

The calculation of the entropy of CO is an example of the results that can be deduced for thermodynamic functions from a knowledge of molecular properties. For larger gas-phase molecules, the procedure is usually limited by the difficulty in deducing the energy-level spacings for the $3n - 6$ vibrational modes. For liquids and solids, so little is known about the allowed energy-level patterns that it is not generally possible to perform the summations over energy levels and obtain values for thermodynamic properties.

7-14 Molecular Interpretation of the Third Law

The molecular deductions of the preceding sections have led to the same conclusion as that stated in the third law of thermodynamics, namely, that an absolute value can be assigned to the entropy of a chemical compound. When the entropy values calculated from the details of the molecular energies are compared with those obtained from calorimetric third-law measurements, agreement within experimental error is usually found, but there are some exceptions.

The third-law value obtained for the entropy of CO at 1 atm and 298.15 K is 193.3 J K^{-1} mol^{-1}. This value is significantly lower than the statistical result of 197.9 J K^{-1} mol^{-1} reported in the preceding section. Similar discrepancies, i.e., third-law values too low by about 4.6 J K^{-1} mol^{-1}, are found for NO and N$_2$O. The third-law result for H$_2$O vapor is lower than the statistically calculated value by 3.3 J K^{-1} mol^{-1}. These discrepancies can now be attributed to the failure of these materials to form the perfect crystalline state required at absolute zero for the third law to be applied. It is the perfectly ordered state of the crystal, with all the molecules in the same lowest energy level, that is the molecular basis for the third-law result that the entropy is zero at absolute zero. (The positive values for the entropies of all compounds at temperatures above absolute zero result from the fact that as the temperature is raised, more and more energy levels become accessible to the molecules. The entropies at such temperatures are, of course, very characteristic of the individual molecule, since each molecule has its own particular energy-level pattern.)

The discrepancies between calculated and third-law entropies can now be attributed to a nonzero value of the entropy as absolute zero is approached. Thus we must explain an absolute-zero entropy of, for example, about 4.6 J K^{-1} mol^{-1} for CO.

A disorder to be expected for such a material is that in which the molecular alignment in the crystal is not (CO   CO   CO   CO $\cdots$) but rather a disordered pattern like (CO   CO   OC   CO $\cdots$). A crystal formed initially in this way could have the disorder "frozen" in as the temperature is lowered, there being too little thermal energy for the molecules to rearrange to the ordered structure. Thus, instead of each molecule's having a single state to occupy, the randomness makes two states available to each molecule. The entropy of such a crystal can then be expected to be greater by $k \ln 2^{\mathfrak{N}} = R \ln 2 = 5.8$ J K^{-1} mol^{-1} than it would be for a perfect crystal. This is, in fact, the approximate discrepancy found for CO.

Other types of disorder can now be expected to persist at absolute zero and to lead to apparent discrepancies in the third law. For example, a glassy material at absolute zero will not have the necessary molecular order to guarantee an entropy of zero at absolute zero. In view of such difficulties, the third-law statement must include the restriction that only perfectly ordered crystalline materials have zero entropy at absolute zero.

7-15 The Entropy of Vaporization

So far our attention has been focused primarily on gases but with some consideration for randomness in solids. We are led to some understanding of the entropy of liquid substances by considering an interesting empirical generalization made by F. Trouton in 1884. This generalization, now known as *Trouton's rule,* states that the heat of vaporization divided by the normal boiling point on the absolute temperature scale is approximately the same for all liquids. Now we recognize that

$$\frac{\Delta H_{vap}}{T} = \Delta S_{vap} \qquad (7\text{-}64)$$

and Trouton's rule says that the entropy increases by the same amount when 1 mol of any substance is changed from liquid into vapor at its normal boiling point.

The scope of this rule is remarkable, as the examples of Table 7-2 show. Included in the list are simple and complex inorganic compounds, organic compounds, an ionic substance, and several metals. With only a few exceptions, the entropies of vaporization lie around the value 88 J K^{-1} mol^{-1}.

Two classes of substances that have entropies of vaporization rather far from the average value can be recognized. Those with low normal boiling points, in particular helium and hydrogen, tend to have ΔS_{vap} values much

TABLE 7-2 Heats and Entropies of Vaporization of Liquids at their Normal Boiling Points

Liquid	Formula	Normal bp, K	ΔH_{vap}, kJ mol^{-1}	$\Delta S_{vap} = \dfrac{\Delta H_{vap}}{T}$, J K^{-1} mol^{-1}
Helium	He	4.21	0.84	20
Hydrogen	H_2	20.4	0.904	44
Nitrogen	N_2	77.3	5.56	72
Argon	Ar	87.2	6.52	75
Methane	CH_4	111.7	9.27	83
Xenon	Xe	165.1	12.64	77
Ethane	C_2H_6	184.5	14.71	80
Hydrogen chloride	HCl	188.1	16.15	86
Hydrogen sulfide	H_2S	213.5	18.80	88
Chlorine	Cl_2	239.1	20.41	85
Ammonia	NH_3	239.7	23.26	97†
Sulfur dioxide	SO_2	263.1	24.92	95
Ethyl ether	$(C_2H_5)_2O$	307.7	25.98	84
Methanol	CH_3OH	337.8	35.27	104†
Carbon tetrachloride	CCl_4	349.8	30.00	86
Ethanol	C_2H_5OH	351.6	38.57	110†
Benzene	C_6H_6	353.2	30.76	87
Water	H_2O	373.2	40.67	109†
Formic acid	HCOOH	374.0	24.10	64†
Stannic chloride	$SnCl_4$	385	33.05	86
Acetic acid	CH_3COOH	391.4	24.39	62†
Naphthalene	$C_{10}H_8$	491	40.46	82
Mercury	Hg	629.7	59.27	94
Sodium chloride	NaCl	1738	170.7	98
Lead	Pb	2023	180	89

† Substances for which hydrogen-bonding effects are expected.

lower than the average value. Such substances are brought more into line by a modification of Trouton's rule made by J. Hildebrand. He suggested comparing the entropy of vaporization to vapors with a fixed concentration, such as 1 mol in 22.4 liters, rather than to the equilibrium vapor.

The second class of nonconforming substances are those which are associated in the liquid or the vapor. Acetic acid, for example, forms an equilibrium vapor which is made up largely of dimers. Had these been treated as the molecular form of acetic acid, the ΔS_{vap} value would have been twice that listed, more in line with the average value of ΔS_{vap}. Association through hydrogen bonding in water and the alcohols also occurs in the liquid and to a smaller extent in the equilibrium vapor.

Now let us turn to the majority of compounds that conform to Trouton's rule and show entropies of vaporization near the value 88 J K^{-1} mol^{-1}. We must compare the entropy of 1 mol of molecules in the equilibrium vapor with the entropy of 1 mol of molecules in the liquid. We can attempt to describe these entropies in terms of translational, rotational, and vibrational contributions. The problem is immediately simplified by recognizing that for most molecules the vibrational and rotational contributions, if they exist, are nearly the same for liquid-phase and gas-phase molecules.

Some gas-phase molecules, like CH_4, have, for example, a negligible entropy due to rotation and vibration. Others, like CCl_4, have a large contribution from these motions; about half the entropy of gaseous CCl_4 is due to rotational and vibrational contributions. But molecules like CH_4 and CCl_4 seem to obey Trouton's rule equally well. Thus, it seems that no major changes in the rotational and vibrational entropies are occurring. It is therefore necessary to look to changes in the translational entropy to account for the principal part of the Trouton-rule entropy value.

The translational entropy of vapor molecules is well understood and has been treated in Sec. 7-10. A set of closely spaced translational energy levels exists, and the spacing of these levels can be calculated by treating each gas molecule as a particle-in-a-box. The energy-level spacing decreases with increasing size of the container. The translational entropy includes the term $R \ln V$.

If the volume in which the liquid molecules are free to move, called the *free volume*, is denoted by V_f, the entropy for transformation to the vapor state is given by

$$\Delta S_{vap} = S_v - S_l = R \ln \frac{V_v}{V_f} \tag{7-65}$$

The entropy of vaporization is very insensitive to the value of V_v/V_f. If this ratio is within a factor of about 2 of the value of 40,000, an entropy of vaporization of about 88 J mol^{-1} K^{-1} will be obtained.

The volume of 1 mol of vapor V_v depends on the normal boiling point. For liquids boiling somewhat above room temperature a representative value of V_v

is 30,000 ml. A typical molar volume of liquids that boil just above room temperature is 100 ml, and thus a free volume of about 1 percent of the liquid volume would account for the entropy of vaporization. This value seems not unreasonable.

PROBLEMS

7-1. (a) The heat of fusion of hydrogen at its normal melting point of 14 K is 120 J mol^{-1}. What is its entropy of fusion? (b) Its heat of vaporization at its normal boiling point of 20.4 K is 840 J mol^{-1}. What is its entropy of vaporization?

7-2. Estimate, from the data of Fig. 6-2, the entropy of vaporization of water at 0, 100, 200, 300°C and at the critical temperature, 374°C.

7-3. On a diagram that shows the system and the thermal and mechanical reservoirs show the energy and entropy changes that accompany the conversion of 1 mol of liquid water to ice at 0°C. The thermal reservoir is at a temperature infinitesimally lower than 0°C. The enthalpy of fusion of water is 5.98 kJ mol^{-1}. The density of water and ice at 0°C and 1 atm are 1000 and 0.917 g ml^{-1}, respectively.

7-4. Repeat the calculation and display of Prob. 7-3 for the reversible conversion of steam into liquid water at 100°C and 1 atm. The enthalpy of vaporization is 40.67 kJ mol^{-1}, and the vapor can be assumed to behave as an ideal gas.

7-5. (a) Which is greater, the entropy change when an ideal gas is heated over a certain temperature interval at constant pressure or over the same interval at constant volume? (b) Which has the greater entropy, an ideal gas at high pressure or low pressure?

***7-6.** An expression for the dependence of entropy on pressure will be derived in Chap. 8. An example of the general relation can be obtained by the following three-step calculation for the entropy change of 1 mol of an ideal gas initially at a pressure P_1 and temperature T_1. (a) Obtain an expression for the entropy changes of the gas as its temperature is raised at constant pressure to a new temperature T_2. (b) Repeat part (a) for a temperature change to T_2 at constant volume, the pressure becoming P_2. (c) From the results of parts (a) and (b) obtain the entropy change that must accompany the expansion of the gas at temperature T_2 from pressure P_2 to pressure P_1. Your result should not involve T_1.

7-7. One mole of gas is expanded from an initial pressure of 100 atm to a final pressure of 1 atm, the temperature being maintained at 25°C. (a) Sketch an arrangement for the system and the thermal and mechanical reservoirs that allows the expansion to be carried out reversibly. Enter values for the energy and entropy changes in each of these three components of the universe of the system. (b) Show the changes in energy and entropy of the three components if the expansion occurs against a piston that maintains a force equal to a pressure of 1 atm throughout the expansion. (c) Sketch an arrangement, and show the energy and entropy changes for a free expansion against a piston exerting no restraining force. (d) From these three cases make a statement about the entropy change in the universe of the process and the degree of irreversibility of the process.

7-8. What is the total entropy change of everything involved in the process when 1 kJ of heat flows from an object at 100°C to one at 0°C, both objects being so large that their temperatures do not change appreciably?

7-9. A heat reservoir is at a temperature ΔT above that of a system to which it is delivering thermal energy. The extent to which this heat flow is an irreversible process can be judged by the entropy change for the transmittal of, say, 1 kJ of heat. (a) What is this entropy change if ΔT is 1°C and the system is at 25°C? (b) What is the entropy change if ΔT is 0.01°C and the system is still at 25°C?

7-10. A 10-g piece of ice at 0°C is added to 20 g of water at 100°C in a Dewar flask. The heat of fusion of water is 5980 J mol^{-1}; the specific heat of water can be taken as independent of temperature; and the heat capacity of the Dewar can be ignored. (a) What is the final temperature of the water? (b) How could the process be performed reversibly, and what would the entropy changes of the surroundings and of the system then be? (c) What is the entropy change of the system for the direct addition? (d) What is the entropy change of the surroundings for the direct addition?

*7-11. Refer to the non-friction-free piston and the two-step process of Prob. 5-13. Calculate the entropy changes for the system and the thermal surroundings for each step and also for the entire process.

7-12. Compare the theoretical efficiency of a steam engine operating at 5 atm pressure, at which pressure water boils at 152°C, with one operating at 100 atm, at which pressure water boils at 312°C. The condenser in each case is at 30°C.

*7-13. A Carnot cycle uses 1 mol of an ideal gas, for which $C_V = 25$ J K^{-1} mol^{-1}, as the working substance and operates from a most compressed state of 10 atm pressure and 600 K. It expands isothermally to a pressure of 1 atm and then adiabatically reaches a most expanded state at a temperature of 300 K. (a) Obtain numerical values for $\Delta E_{\text{therm res}}$ and $\Delta E_{\text{mech res}}$ for each stroke. (b) From the results of part (a) calculate the efficiency with which the heat from the high-temperature reservoir is converted into work. (c) Repeat the calculation of part (a) for a maximum compression of 100 atm at 600 K and an expansion to 1 atm and then to 300 K. (d) From the results of part (c) calculate the efficiency of the engine. (e) What expression does the comparison of the results of parts (b) and (d) illustrate?

*7-14. Plot the two Carnot cycles of Prob. 7-13 on a graph of P versus V. The net work delivered to the mechanical surroundings is the summation of $P\,dV$ for all strokes. (a) To what area does this net work correspond? (b) Estimate graphically the net work produced by each cycle and compare with the results of Prob. 7-13.

7-15. Assume that an engine of a type different from the Carnot engine exists which can operate between heat reservoirs at temperatures T_h and T_i with greater efficiency than that calculated for the Carnot engine. Imagine this more efficient engine to be coupled to the Carnot engine so that one engine drives the other to make the second engine operate as a refrigerator. Show that the supposition of an engine with an efficiency greater than that calculated for a reversible engine operating between the temperatures T_h and T_i leads to a violation of the initial statements of the second law of thermodynamics.

*7-16. (a) On a graph of T versus S sketch each of the Carnot cycles of Prob. 7-13. What is the significance of (b) the area under the line for the first step, the isothermal expansion; (c) the area under the line for the third step, the isothermal compression; and (d) the enclosed area? (e) Check the conclusion by comparing the area with values obtained in Prob. 7-13.

7-17. By a suitable graphical or computer integration determine the entropy of metallic silver at 25°C from the data tabulated for the heat capacity per mole which are calculated from these reported by P. F. Meads, W. K. Forsythe, and W. F. Giauque,

J. Am. Chem. Soc., **63**:1902 (1941). Assume that the heat capacity approaches absolute zero according to a T^3 relation; that is, $C_p = \text{const } T^3$, and $C_p = 0$ at $T = 0$.

T, K	C_p, J K^{-1}	T, K	C_p, J K^{-1}	T, K	C_p, J K^{-1}	T, K	C_p, J K^{-1}
15	0.67	90	19.13	170	23.61	250	25.03
30	4.77	110	20.96	190	24.09	270	25.31
50	11.65	130	22.13	210	24.42	290	25.44
70	16.33	150	22.97	230	24.73	300	25.50

7-18. By how much does the entropy of 1 mol of NaCl increase as it is heated from 25°C to its melting point 801°C at constant pressure? Use the heat-capacity equation of Table 6-2.

7-19. Calculate the increase in the entropy of 1 mol of methane when the temperature is raised from 300 to 1000 K at constant pressure. Use the heat-capacity data of Table 6-2.

7-20. Explore distributions besides those shown in Fig. 7-12 to find the one with the highest probability.

***7-21.** At constant volume $dS = (C_V \, dT)/T$ or $(\partial S/\partial T)_V = C_V/T$. Does the statistically based expression for entropy given by Eq. (7-45) conform to this relation?

7-22. It is said that "hard substances have low entropies." Cite examples that substantiate this statement.

7-23. (a) Which of the substances listed in Appendix B-1 has the least entropy per mole? (b) What is the molecular explanation for this?

7-24. (a) Plot the translational entropy of an ideal gas at 298 K and in its standard state as a function of the mass of 1 mol for masses up to 2000 g mol^{-1}. (b) Add a curve for a temperature of 1000 K. (c) On a molecular basis, why does the translational entropy have this mass and temperature dependence?

7-25. (a) By how much does the translational entropy of 1 mol of an ideal gas change if the pressure is doubled? (b) Qualitatively what is the molecular explanation for this change?

7-26. Calculate the entropy of 1 mol of argon in its standard state at 25°C and compare with the value listed in Appendix B-1.

7-27. Discuss why the translational and rotational thermal energies of ideal gases are the same for all gases at a given temperature but the translational and rotational entropy contributions depend on properties of the molecules of the gas.

7-28. (a) Calculate the translational entropy of 1 mol of H_2 in its standard state at 25°C. (b) What fraction of the total entropy of H_2 is due to its translational motion?

7-29. (a) Plot the entropy due to the rotational motion of a heteronuclear diatomic molecule as a function of moment of inertia at 298 and 1000 K. Use a moment-of-inertia range of 10^{-46} to 10^{-44} kg m^2. (b) Add curves for homonuclear molecules.

7-30. (a) What value does Eq. (7-54) or (7-58) give as the moment of inertia I approaches zero? (b) What value should it give? (c) According to Eq. (7-53), what value does q_{rot} have in the limit of $I = 0$? (d) What value should it have? (e) What is the source of these discrepancies?

7-31. (a) Plot the entropy contribution from a vibrational degree of freedom as a function of the vibrational-level spacing, expressed in wave-number units ($x = h\nu_{vib}/kT = hc\bar{\nu}/kT$). Prepare plots for 298 and 1000 K. (Vibrational levels are found spectroscopically to be spaced by values of up to about 4000 cm^{-1}.) (b) Compare these curves with the qualitative statement that the entropy increases as the number of available states increases.

7-32. Calculate the entropy of 1 mol of chlorine at the standard conditions of 1 atm pressure and 25°C. The moment of inertia of the Cl_2 molecule is 1.15×10^{-45} kg m^2, and the vibrational-energy-level spacing is 1.10×10^{-20} J. Compare the answer with the value listed in Appendix B-1.

*7-33. Use graphs prepared in previous problems in this chapter to make a table of the translational, rotational, and vibrational contributions to the entropy of F_2, Cl_2, Br_2, and I_2 gases in their standard states at 25°C. The respective moments of inertia are 31.7, 115.0, 346, and 750 all times 10^{-47} kg m^2, and the respective vibrational spacings are 894, 554, 322, and 213 cm^{-1}.

7-34. Calculate the entropy of 1 mol of carbon disulfide as a gas in its standard state at a temperature of 25°C. The molecule is linear and has a moment of inertia of 2.56×10^{-45} kg m^2. The vibrational spacings are 397, 397, 656, and 1523 cm^{-1}. Compare with the value listed in Appendix B-1.

7-35. Calculate the entropy of $CCl_4(g)$ in its standard state at 25°C. The CCl_4 molecule is tetrahedral, and the C—Cl bond length is 1.76 Å. (The molecule is a spherical top with $I_A = I_B = I_C$.) The vibrational spacings are 218(2), 314(3), 458(1), and 776(3) cm^{-1}, where numbers in parentheses indicate degeneracies.

7-36. Hildebrand's extension of Trouton's rule suggests that the entropy of vaporization be compared for vaporizations from the liquid to a given fixed vapor volume. If a vapor volume of 22.4 liters is selected, the vapors in equilibrium with liquids that boil below 0°C will have to be expanded and those which boil above 0°C will have to be compressed to reach this volume. (a) Calculate the corrections to be applied, on this basis, to the entropy of vaporization values of Table 7-2 for H_2, N_2, CCl_4, and Hg. (b) What are the values of the entropy of vaporization based on Hildebrand's extension? (c) Does this approach improve the consistency of entropy-of-vaporization values?

REFERENCES

BENT, H. A.: "The Second Law: An Introduction to Classical and Statistical Thermodynamics," Oxford University Press, New York, 1965. A very stimulating treatment of the formulation and application of the second law, with many quotations from, and references to, original work.

FAST, J. D.: "Entropy," McGraw-Hill Book Company, New York, 1963. A treatment of thermodynamics from the viewpoint that entropy is an important property and should not be considered to play a role secondary to energy.

WILKE, J.: "The Third Law of Thermodynamics," Oxford University Press, New York, 1961. A monograph dealing entirely with the third law.

HOARE, F. E., L. C. JACKSON, and N. KURTI (eds.): "Experimental Cryophysics," Butterworth & Co. (Publishers), Ltd., London, 1961. A collection of review articles on the methods of attaining and measuring very low temperatures.

MENDELSSOHN, K.: "The Quest for Absolute Zero," McGraw-Hill Book Company, New York, 1966. A nonmathematical account of both the early and the more recent aspects of science that relate to the achievement of low temperatures.

LOUNASMAA, O. V.: New Methods for Approaching Absolute Zero, *Sci. Am.*, **221**(6):26–35 (1969).

NASH, L. K.: Applicability of the Equation $dE = T\,dS - P\,dV$, *J. Chem. Educ.*, **54**:409 (1977).

FREE ENERGY AND CHEMICAL EQUILIBRIA

In Chap. 7 it was shown that for any process, the entropy change in a system plus the entropy change in the thermal surroundings tells us whether that process can proceed spontaneously. Now we introduce a function of the system that by itself indicates the spontaneous direction of a reaction. This function, the *free energy,* lends itself to the treatment of the equilibrium state toward which the process moves. The interrelation of thermodynamic properties and the equilibrium states of chemical reactions is, for chemistry, the most important accomplishment of thermodynamics.

8-1 A Convenient Measure of the Driving Force of a Reaction: The Free Energy

The entropy change that must be considered if the direction of chemical reaction is to be deduced is that of the universe of the reaction. This entropy change is the sum of that occurring in the system and that occurring in the thermal surroundings.

Consider a chemical reaction system in which the reaction occurs at constant temperature and constant pressure and does no work other than that of expansion. Then, according to Eq. (5-18), q, the heat the system gains from the thermal reservoir, is equal to ΔH, the enthalpy change of the system. The entropy change in the thermal reservoir is $-q/T$ or $-\Delta H/T$. Both this thermal-energy-reservoir term $-\Delta H/T$ and ΔS, the entropy change in the system as a result of the reaction, can be deduced from data for the reactants and products. Thus from properties of the system we can evaluate ΔS_{univ}.

With the absence of a subscript implying a function of the system we write

$$\Delta S_{univ} = \Delta S + \Delta S_{therm\,res} = \Delta S - \frac{\Delta H}{T} \qquad (8\text{-}1)$$

It is customary to express this quantity in a somewhat different way. First, to convert the expression to one with the more familiar units of energy, we multiply it by T, the constant temperature of the reaction, to give

$$T \Delta S - \Delta H$$

Then we introduce a symbol and a name for this collection of terms by writing

$$-\Delta G = T \Delta S - \Delta H \quad \text{or} \quad \Delta G = \Delta H - T \Delta S \quad (T \text{ const}) \qquad (8\text{-}2)$$

By considering a particular type of reaction, i.e., one at constant T and P and with no work other than that of expansion, we have come to a very generally useful function. This function, G, whose change is ΔG in the above example, is called the *free energy* or, more completely, the *Gibbs free energy*.

By comparing Eqs. (8-1) and (8-2) we see that for the type of process considered $T \Delta S_{\text{univ}} = -\Delta G$. Now you see the implications

$$\Delta G = \begin{cases} - & \text{reaction can proceed as written} \\ + & \text{reverse reaction can proceed} \end{cases} \qquad (8\text{-}3)$$

For a balanced reversible process the total entropy change ΔS_{univ} is zero. Thus, since $\Delta G = -T \Delta S_{\text{univ}}$, ΔG is also equal to zero for such a process.

The free-energy function, from which the relation of Eq. (8-2) stems, is defined by

$$G = H - TS \qquad (8\text{-}4)$$

Since H and TS are properties of the system, so too is G.

Now let us see the significance of ΔG for balanced processes in which the system might do work over and above that of expansion against its confining pressure. The defining equation, $H = E + PV$, is substituted in Eq. (8-4) to give

$$G = E + PV - TS \qquad (8\text{-}5)$$

For an infinitesimal change in G one now has

$$dG = dE + P\, dV + V\, dP - T\, dS - S\, dT \qquad (8\text{-}6)$$

For constant-temperature constant-pressure processes, Eq. (8-6) reduces to

$$dG = dE + P\, dV - T\, dS \qquad (8\text{-}7)$$

The first-law expression $dE = \delta q + \delta w$ can now be inserted to give

$$dG = \delta q + \delta w + P\, dV - T\, dS \qquad (8\text{-}8)$$

Here let us think of $-\delta w$, the work done *by* the system. Some of this work is work of expansion, and this contribution is $P\, dV$. The remaining component, which we assume can be harnessed to do useful work, is $-\delta w'$. Thus the total work that can be done by the system can be described by

$$-\delta w = P\,dV - \delta w'$$

or

$$\delta w = -P\,dV + \delta w' \tag{8-9}$$

Insertion of Eq. (8-9) in (8-8) gives

$$dG = \delta q - T\,dS + \delta w'$$

or

$$-dG = -\delta q + T\,dS - \delta w'$$

For a balanced, reversible process

$$\frac{\delta q}{T} = dS$$

and

$$-dG = -\delta w' \qquad [T,\ P \text{ const; reversible}] \tag{8-10}$$

The decrease in free energy for a process occurring in a balanced, reversible way is equal to the work (over and above any $P\,dV$ work) that can be obtained. Furthermore, in a reversible process, there is no wasted drive, and the work obtained is the maximum work. The decrease in free energy for a reaction is the maximum work that could be obtained if the reaction were carried out at constant temperature and pressure.

This implication is consistent with the earlier conclusion that a reaction for which ΔG is negative can proceed spontaneously. Reactions for which ΔG is negative, we now see, are ones that can be harnessed to do work. Such reactions must have a driving force, or a spontaneous tendency to occur.

Now let us examine the type of chemical reaction that is used to produce work. An example is provided by an electrochemical cell in which hydrogen is used at one electrode and oxygen at the other. The product is water. The electric current produced by the cell can be used to do work. The reaction is

$$H_2(g) + \tfrac{1}{2}O_2(g) \rightarrow H_2O(l) \tag{8-11}$$

At 25°C and with the gases at 1 atm pressure, the values for the reaction that are obtained from the data of Appendix B-1 are

$$\Delta H = -285.84 \text{ kJ}$$

$$\Delta S = -163.16 \text{ J K}^{-1} = -0.16316 \text{ kJ K}^{-1} \quad \text{and} \quad T\Delta S = -48.65 \text{ kJ}$$

$$\Delta G = \Delta H - T\Delta S = -237.19 \text{ kJ} \tag{8-12}$$

The energy changes in the system and surroundings are shown in Fig. 8-1. According to the first law, the decrease in enthalpy of the system equals the total of the heat given to the thermal reservoir and the work given to the mechanical reservoir. Heat in the amount shown *must* be passed to the thermal reservoir to balance the decrease in entropy of the system itself and thus to allow the system to proceed in a state of balance. Only the remaining energy can be delivered to the mechanical reservoir as work. When we use a system to obtain work, we must first "pay off" any entropy "debt" the system has incurred. Only the fraction of ΔH that remains is *free* to be converted into work. This fraction is $-\Delta G$, and you see the significance of the "free" in free energy.

In the above example, our focus was on obtaining work from a system. In such cases it is convenient to rewrite the constant-temperature expression $\Delta G = \Delta H - T\Delta S$ as

$$-\Delta H = -\Delta G - T\Delta S \tag{8-13}$$

where $-\Delta H$ = energy released by system
$-\Delta G$ = maximum work delivered to mechanical surroundings
$-T\Delta S$ = heat that must be delivered to thermal surroundings

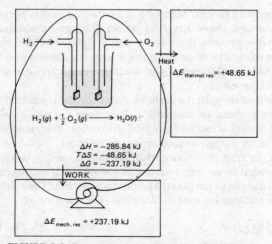

FIGURE 8-1 Energy changes in the system, the thermal reservoir, and the mechanical reservoir for the reversible reaction $H_2 + \frac{1}{2}O_2 \rightarrow H_2O(l)$.

In some reactions the entropy of the system increases as the reaction proceeds. Then no entropy debt is incurred. Now the process proceeds at a state of balance when heat is drawn into the system from the thermal reservoir. The result is that the maximum work $-\Delta G$ that can be obtained is greater than the enthalpy decrease $-\Delta H$.

For the chemist the free energy† is the most important of the thermodynamic functions. This statement assumes that chemical reactions, rather than chemicals themselves, constitute the heart of chemistry. Free energy is the function constructed to indicate directly the spontaneous direction of a chemical reaction and, as will be seen in Sec. 8-4, the position of chemical equilibria.

8-2 Standard Free Energies of Formation

The difference in the free energies of the reactants and the products of a chemical reaction indicates the direction in which the reaction can proceed. It is therefore helpful to have a tabulation of the free energies of chemical compounds. Then the free-energy change of any reaction we want to consider can easily be calculated.

Standard free energies can be determined from free-energy changes of reactions in exactly the same way that standard heats of formation were determined from heats of reaction. The *standard free energy of formation* of a substance is the free-energy change for the reaction by which the substance is formed from its elements when the substance and the elements are in their standard states. The notation ΔG_f° will be used to indicate a standard free energy of formation. It follows from this definition that the standard free energies of the elements in their standard states are zero.

The calculation of standard free energies for compounds can be illustrated by deducing ΔG_f° for ammonia at 25°C. The equation for the formation from the elements can be written as

$$\tfrac{1}{2}N_2(g) + \tfrac{3}{2}H_2(g) \rightarrow NH_3(g)$$

The value of ΔH for the reaction is obtained from the ΔH_f° data of Appendix B-1. The entropy change is similarly calculated from the entropy value of Appendix B-1. Substitution of these results in the expression $\Delta G = \Delta H - T\Delta S$ for the constant temperature of 25°C gives

$$\Delta G = -46.19 - 298.15(-0.09912) = -16.64 \text{ kJ}$$

† The free-energy function G, the Gibbs free energy, is suitable for direct application to constant-pressure processes; another free-energy function is more convenient for constant-volume processes. This function, known as the *Helmholtz free energy A*, is defined as $A = E - TS$. A development like that performed on G in this section would show that in a constant-volume process the decrease in A corresponds to the driving force of the reaction. Thus H and G are functions that are convenient for constant-pressure processes, whereas E and A are more convenient for constant-volume processes. In the introduction to thermodynamics that is presented here, it will be sufficient to develop the applications of H and G.

Finally, since the reaction was written for the formation of 1 mol of $NH_3(g)$ from its elements, this ΔG value is ΔG_f° for ammonia. Thus

$$\Delta G_f^\circ(NH_3) = -16.64 \text{ kJ}$$

The standard free energies of a number of other substances are shown in Appendix B-1.

8-3 The Dependence of Free Energy on Pressure

The standard free energies, like those in Appendix B, allow predictions to be made of the possibility of a reaction at 25°C for each reagent at 1 atm pressure. For these free-energy data to be of real use, a means must be available for calculating free energies at other pressures and temperatures.

Since G is a state function, we can show how it varies with P and T by writing the total differential

$$dG = \left(\frac{\partial G}{\partial P}\right)_T dP + \left(\frac{\partial G}{\partial T}\right)_P dT \tag{8-14}$$

In Eq. (8-6), however, we already have found that

$$dG = dE + P\,dV + V\,dP - T\,dS - S\,dT \tag{8-15}$$

Again, as in Sec. 8-1, let us suppose that we are dealing with states of the systems that can be connected by a reversible process so that we can write $T\,dS = \delta q$. Now, however, T and P will not be held constant, and the only remaining restriction will be to reversible processes in which the only work is PV work, i.e., $P\,dV = -\delta w$. Under these circumstances the first law $dE = \delta q + \delta w$ is $dE = T\,dS - P\,dV$ or $dE - T\,dS + P\,dV = 0$. Three terms of Eq. (8-15) thus cancel, leaving

$$dG = V\,dP - S\,dT \tag{8-16}$$

Comparison with Eq. (8-14) now gives the desired relations involving the coefficients as

$$\left(\frac{\partial G}{\partial T}\right)_P = -S \tag{8-17}$$

[Reversible process, only PV work]

$$\left(\frac{\partial G}{\partial P}\right)_T = V \tag{8-18}$$

These two results show how the free energy of a chemical compound depends on the pressure and the temperature. For the present, only the pressure dependence is considered.

Liquids and solids have small molar volumes compared with gases. For many purposes the pressure dependence of the free energy of liquids and solids can be neglected.

For gases the dependence of free energy on pressure is appreciable and important. For an ideal gas, P and V are related by the ideal-gas law, and the integration of Eq. (8-18) can be performed to give the free-energy change when the pressure is changed from P_1 to P_2 at constant temperature. Thus

$$G_2 - G_1 = \int V\,dP = nRT \int_{P_2}^{P_2} \frac{dP}{P} = nRT \ln \frac{P_2}{P_1} \tag{8-19}$$

Of particular interest is the extent to which the free energy changes from its standard-state value when the pressure changes from 1 atm. If state 1 is the standard state, then

$$P_1 = 1\ \text{atm} \qquad \text{and} \qquad G_1 = G°$$
$$P_2 = P \qquad \text{and} \qquad G_2 = G$$

With this notation for states 1 and 2, Eq. (8-19) can be rewritten for 1 mol as

$$G - G° = RT \ln \frac{P}{1}$$

or

$$G = G° + RT \ln P_{\text{atm}} \qquad [T\ \text{const},\ P\ \text{in atm, ideal gas}] \tag{8-20}$$

Note that here pressures are conveniently expressed in atmospheres, rather than in the SI units of newtons per square meter, because the standard state has been specified to be that with 1 atm pressure. The unit-identifying subscript will be used, where necessary, to indicate this deviation from SI units.

The free energy of a gas at pressure P is, according to Eq. (8-20), made up of the free energy that it has at 1 atm plus an additional term that is positive for P larger than 1 atm and negative for P less than 1 atm.

Equation (8-20) is strictly applicable to ideal gases, since $PV = nRT$ was assumed for the P-versus-V relation in the integration of Eq. (8-19); however, this equation can be assumed to apply approximately for all gases.

8-4 Quantitative Relation of $\Delta G°$ and the Equilibrium Constant

Qualitative arguments have been given in Sec. 8-1 for deciding on the basis of the free-energy change whether a reaction will proceed in one direction or the other. Chemical experience tells us, however, that a reaction will proceed in a given direction only until the system reaches a state of equilibrium. It will now be seen that free energies can be used to show not only the direction in which a reaction tends to proceed but also the equilibrium state to which this reaction carries the system.

Consider a reaction involving four gases A, B, C, and D, all at temperature T, which now will be assumed to behave ideally. Assume that these gases can enter into a reaction that is described by the equation

$$aA + bB \rightarrow cC + dD \qquad (8\text{-}21)$$

Since during the course of the reaction the number of moles of the various reagents in the reaction system will vary, so will the total free energy of the system.

Let us investigate the free energy of the reaction system as the reaction changes the system from that consisting of a mol of A and b mol of B to one consisting of c mol of C and d mol of D. As is customary, let ξ represent the *degree of advancement* of the reaction. This index has the value zero for the initial conditions, in which the number of moles $n_A = a$ and the number of moles $n_B = b$. As the reaction advances, ξ increases to 1, the value it has when $n_A = 0$, $n_B = 0$ and $n_C = c$ and $n_D = d$. The moles of the reagents present at any stage in the reaction are related to the degree of advancement by the relations

No. of moles of A $= n_A = a(1 - \xi)$
No. of moles of B $= n_B = b(1 - \xi)$
No. of moles of C $= n_C = c\xi$ $\qquad (8\text{-}22)$
No. of moles of D $= n_D = d\xi$

At any degree of advancement the partial pressures of the reagents A, B, C, and D will be P_A, P_B, P_C, and P_D. If the individual gases and the reaction system at any degree of advancement behave ideally, the molar free energies of the reagents will be given by expressions of the form

$$G_A = G_A^\circ + RT \ln P_A \qquad (8\text{-}23)$$

Now let us assume that the reaction proceeds, at a constant temperature, by an amount that produces a change in the degree of advancement from ξ to $\xi + d\xi$. The free energy of the reaction system changes at the degree of advancement ξ because of changes in the number of moles of the reagents. The rate of change of G with ξ at any value ξ is thus given by

$$\frac{dG}{d\xi} = G_A \frac{dn_A}{d\xi} + G_B \frac{dn_B}{d\xi} + G_C \frac{dn_C}{d\xi} + G_D \frac{dn_D}{d\xi} \qquad (8\text{-}24)$$

The derivative terms are obtained from Eqs. (8-22) as

$$\frac{dn_A}{d\xi} = -a \qquad \frac{dn_B}{d\xi} = -b \qquad \frac{dn_C}{d\xi} = c \qquad \frac{dn_D}{d\xi} = d$$

The molar free energies of the reagents are given by equations like (8-23). Equation (8-24) can thus be developed to read

$$\frac{dG}{d\xi} = -a(G_A^\circ + RT\ln P_A) - b(G_B^\circ + RT\ln P_B)$$
$$+ c(G_C^\circ + RT\ln P_C) + d(G_D^\circ + RT\ln P_D)$$
$$= cG_C^\circ + dG_D^\circ - aG_A^\circ - bG_B^\circ + RT\ln\frac{P_C{}^c P_D{}^d}{P_A{}^a P_B{}^b} \qquad (8\text{-}25)$$

The reaction will proceed spontaneously, according to the arguments of Sec. 8-1, as long as the advancement lowers the free energy. The equilibrium state is that at which a minimum in a G-versus-ξ curve is reached. At that point, advancement is accompanied by no change in free energy. Thus at the state of equilibrium $dG/d\xi = 0$ and the pressures of the gases are those at the equilibrium state. For this state Eq. (8-25) becomes

$$cG_C^\circ + dG_D^\circ - aG_A^\circ - bG_B^\circ = -RT\ln\left(\frac{P_C{}^c P_D{}^d}{P_A{}^a P_B{}^b}\right)_{\text{equil}} \qquad (8\text{-}26)$$

The expression on the left is the free-energy change that would accompany the transformation indicated by the equation for the reaction, Eq. (8-21), if the reactants, each in its standard state, were transformed into the products, each in its standard state. Thus we can introduce the symbol ΔG° as

$$\Delta G^\circ = cG_C^\circ + dG_D^\circ - aG_A^\circ - bG_B^\circ$$

Then Eq. (8-26) is

$$\Delta G^\circ = -RT\ln\left(\frac{P_C{}^c P_D{}^d}{P_A{}^a P_B{}^b}\right)_{\text{equil}} \qquad (8\text{-}27)$$

The pressure term in parentheses in Eq. (8-27) implies a dimensionless quantity, as it must if its logarithm is to be taken. "Ghost," $P = 1$ atm, terms are implied in each of the four pressure terms, as can be recalled by returning to Eq. (8-20).

Equation (8-27) constitutes a thermodynamic derivation of the familiar equilibrium-constant expression. Since ΔG° for a particular reaction at a given temperature is a fixed quantity, the argument of the logarithmic factor must have some constant value that is independent of the individual pressures. It is customary to call this constant the *equilibrium constant* and to denote it by the symbol K or, since pressures are involved, by K_P. Thus

$$K_P = \left[\frac{(P_C)^c(P_D)^d}{(P_A)^a(P_B)^b}\right]_{\text{equil}} \tag{8-28}$$

and with this notation Eq. (8-27) becomes

$$\Delta G^\circ = -RT \ln K_P \tag{8-29}$$

This equation represents one of the most important results of thermodynamics. By it, the equilibrium constant of a reaction is related to a thermochemical property.

This quantitative relationship can readily be seen to be consistent with the previous qualitative statements about the significance of the free-energy change. For instance, if ΔG° is very negative, the argument of Sec. 8-1 leads to the expectation of a spontaneous reaction. Equation (8-29) confirms this by showing that the equilibrium constant would be a large positive quantity. The reaction therefore would proceed until a large partial pressure of products relative to reactants was built up.

The above derivation applies strictly only to ideal gases. For nonideal gases the free energy does not differ from its standard value exactly according to the equation $G = G^\circ + RT \ln P$. In Secs. 8-8 to 8-10 the effect of nonideal behavior on the equilibrium relationship will be dealt with. Here no great error will be introduced by applying the present equations to most gaseous reagents at relatively low pressures.

Since many equilibria are studied in solution, it is very desirable to have a result that can be applied to the concentration of reagents in addition to one that treats gaseous reagents. Only a minor extension of the present treatment is needed to obtain the corresponding equation with the equilibrium constant expressed in terms of concentrations. This, however, will be postponed to a later chapter.

As an example of the use of the free-energy–equilibrium relation, the industrially important process of the formation of ammonia from its elements can be considered. The reaction is

$$N_2(g) + 3H_2(g) \rightleftharpoons 2NH_3(g)$$

and, from the standard free-energy values of Appendix B-1, we calculate $\Delta G^\circ_{298} = -33,270$ J. Now Eq. (8-29) gives, for pressures in atmospheres

$$K_P = \frac{(P_{NH_3})^2}{(P_{N_2})(P_{H_2})^3} = 6.8 \times 10^5 \qquad \text{at } 25^\circ C$$

It should be pointed out that if the reaction had been written

$$\tfrac{1}{2}N_2(g) + \tfrac{3}{2}H_2(g) \rightleftharpoons NH_3(g)$$

the value of ΔG°_{298} would have been $-16,635\,J$ and the equilibrium constant would have been

$$K_P = \frac{P_{NH_3}}{(P_{N_2})^{1/2}(P_{H_2})^{3/2}} = 8.2 \times 10^2$$

This result is the square root of the result $K_P = 6.8 \times 10^5$.

The synthesis of ammonia would seem to be indicated as certainly feasible by the calculation. It turns out, however, that it is very difficult to get the reagents to react fast enough, i.e., to come to the calculated equilibrium position fast enough, to make the process feasible. To increase the speed of the reaction, it is usually run at higher temperatures, and we must therefore be able to calculate the equilibrium constant at temperatures other than 25°C.

Such an interest in reactions at various temperatures is quite general. Methods for finding the temperature dependence of the equilibrium constant will be developed in Sec. 8-7.

8-5 The Molecular Interpretation of Chemical Equilibria

Consider the simplest gas-phase reaction, one in which molecules of A are converted into molecules of B. The reaction, described by the equation

$$A \rightleftharpoons B$$

will proceed until a state of equilibrium is reached. Then, at a given temperature, there will be some ratio of the number of B molecules to the number of A molecules. Now we investigate what it is about the A molecules and the B molecules that determines the ratio of the numbers of them present in equilibrium. This simple, artificial example will show what molecular-level factors operate to determine the position of a chemical equilibrium.

Consider the generalized patterns of energies of the states of the chemical species A and B in their standard states to be those shown in Fig. 8-2. The difference in the energies of the A and B states of lowest energy is $\Delta \epsilon_0^{\circ}$. This quantity is familiar as the molar quantity ΔE_0°, the difference in energy between a mole of A and a mole of B if all the molecules of both species are in their lowest possible energy states.

On a molecular basis the question of the position of the equilibrium between A and B is phrased in this way. If a large number of molecules are allowed to equilibrate and distribute themselves throughout the energy-level

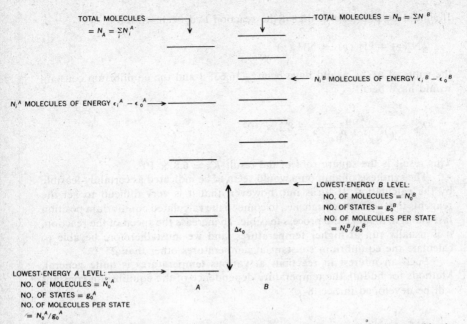

FIGURE 8-2 Schematic energy diagrams for the molecules of reagents A and B connected by the equilibrium A $\rightleftharpoons$ B.

pattern of Fig. 8-2, how many will end up as A molecules, i.e., occupy the A levels, and how many as B molecules, i.e., occupy the B levels? The question is answered by application of the Boltzmann distribution expression.

Let N_0^A be the number of molecules which, at equilibrium, occupy the lowest energy level. This happens, in the example of Fig. 8-2, to be an A level. The number of molecules of A at an energy ϵ_i^A is, with Eq. (4-3),

$$N_i^A = g_i^A \frac{N_0^A}{g_0^A} e^{-\Delta\epsilon_i^A/kT}$$

The total number of molecules N_A is then

$$N_A = \sum_i N_i^A = \sum_i g_i^A \frac{N_0^A}{g_0^A} e^{-\Delta\epsilon_i^A/kT}$$

$$= \frac{N_0^A}{g_0^A} \sum_i g_i^A e^{-\Delta\epsilon_i^A/kT} = \frac{N_0^A}{g_0^A} q_A \tag{8-30}$$

In a similar way the number of molecules N_B distributed throughout the B levels is related to the number in the lowest-energy B states by

$$N_B = \frac{N_0{}^B}{g_0{}^B} q_B \tag{8-31}$$

Since equilibrium is established between the distribution throughout the A and the B states, the population of the lowest B state is related to the population of the lowest A state by the Boltzmann expression

$$\frac{N_0{}^B/g_0{}^B}{N_0{}^A/g_0{}^A} = e^{-\Delta\epsilon_0/kT}$$

or

$$\frac{N_0{}^B}{g_0{}^B} = \frac{N_0{}^A}{g_0{}^A} e^{-\Delta\epsilon_0/kT} \tag{8-32}$$

The population of the B levels, as given by Eq. (8-31), can now be rewritten

$$N_B = \frac{N_0{}^A}{g_0{}^A} e^{-\Delta\epsilon_0/kT} q_B \tag{8-33}$$

The equilibrium constant for the reaction of A to B might be expressed as the ratio of the pressure or the concentration of B to A. Both these terms will be dependent on, and proportional to, the number of moles or molecules of the two reagents. We can therefore write

$$K = \frac{N_B}{N_A} \tag{8-34}$$

The expressions for N_B of Eq. (8-33) and N_A of Eq. (8-30) can now be substituted to give

$$K = e^{-\Delta\epsilon_0/kT} \frac{q_B}{q_A} = e^{-\Delta E_0/RT} \frac{q_B}{q_A} \tag{8-35}$$

This result can be applied to any molecular transformation of the type $A \rightleftarrows B$ (Fig. 8-3). Notice that the formation of B is favored by ΔE_0 values that are small or negative. This term is temperature-independent (although it does enter the temperature-dependent term $e^{-\Delta E_0/RT}$) and is not determined by the pattern of energy levels. The formation of B is also favored by a large value of q_B relative to that of q_A. Large partition-function values result, according to the discussion of Sec. 4-4, when many states are available to the molecules. Thus,

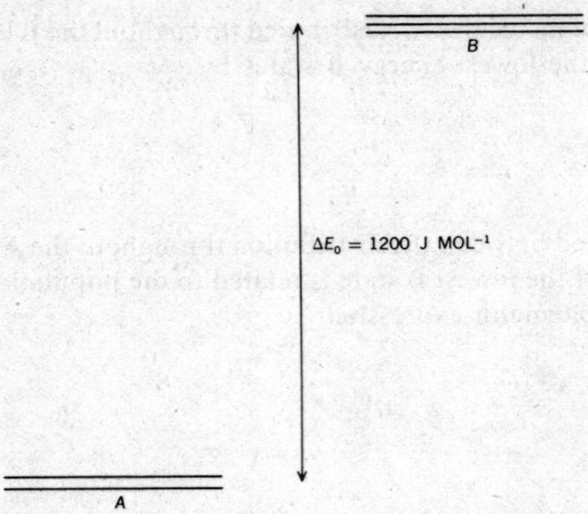

$\Delta E_0 = 1200 \text{ J MOL}^{-1}$

FIGURE 8-3
A simple energy pattern for the molecules A and B to illustrate the effects of q_B/q_A and ΔE_0 on the equilibrium position for the reaction $A \rightleftarrows B$.

the formation of B will be favored if the energies of the states of B are closely spaced and the number of states corresponding to these allowed energies is high.

The very simple example of Fig. 8-3 can be used to illustrate these general conclusions. The partition functions are very simply calculated as

$$q_A = \sum_i (g_i e^{-\Delta \epsilon_i/kT})_A = g_0{}^A e^{-0/kT} = (2)(1) = 2 \tag{8-36}$$

$$q_B = \sum_i (g_i e^{-\Delta \epsilon_i/kT})_B = g_0{}^B e^{-0/kT} = (3)(1) = 3 \tag{8-37}$$

The equilibrium constant for the system can be calculated at the two temperatures of, say, 25 and 1000°C. Equations (8-36) and (8-37) can be used to give

$$K_{298} = e^{-1200/(8.314)(298)}(\tfrac{3}{2}) = 0.92$$
$$K_{1273} = e^{-1200/(8.314)(1273)}(\tfrac{3}{2}) = 1.34 \tag{8-38}$$

It is well worthwhile, even for this artificial example, to notice how the energy term ΔE_0° and the partition-function term combine to determine the equilibrium constant. At the lower temperature, the energy term ΔE_0° dominates and leads to the favoring of A over B. At higher temperatures, this factor becomes less important, and the larger number of states that constitute B swings the equilibrium over to the side of B.

A molecular interpretation of more complex equilibria is best carried out by returning to the free-energy function. The free energy per mole of any reactant or product is defined by the equation

$$G = H - TS \tag{8-39}$$

A molecular-level interpretation of free energy can be given by writing the ideal-gas relations

$$H = E + RT \quad \text{and} \quad S = \frac{E - E_0}{T} + R \ln \frac{q}{\mathfrak{N}} + R$$

Substitution of these expressions in Eq. (8-39) leads to

$$G = E_0 + RT \ln \frac{q}{\mathfrak{N}} \qquad (8\text{-}40)$$

For the standard state (1 atm pressure) we write

$$G^\circ = E_0^\circ + RT \ln \frac{q^\circ}{\mathfrak{N}} \qquad (8\text{-}41)$$

This result, and the thermodynamic relation $\Delta G^\circ = -RT \ln K$, can be used to obtain the expression for the molecular interpretation of the equilibrium constant.

For an $A \rightleftharpoons B$ type reaction we write

$$\Delta G^\circ = \Delta E_0^\circ + RT \ln \frac{q_B^\circ / \mathfrak{N}}{q_A^\circ / \mathfrak{N}}$$

or, with $\Delta G^\circ = -RT \ln K$,

$$K = \frac{q_B^\circ}{q_A^\circ} e^{-\Delta E_0^\circ / RT}$$

Any standard-state stipulation on the reagents A and B would cancel out in the partition-function ratio, and we would arrive again at Eq. (8-35).

Consider now, the more general situation as illustrated by reactions of the type

$$A + B \rightleftharpoons AB$$

Application of Eq. (8-41) to each of the reagents gives

$$\Delta G^\circ = \Delta E_0^\circ - RT \ln \frac{q_{AB}^\circ / \mathfrak{N}}{(q_A^\circ / \mathfrak{N})(q_B^\circ / \mathfrak{N})} \qquad (8\text{-}42)$$

The calculated free-energy change ΔG° applies to the standard state. If this ΔG° is used in the relation $\Delta G^\circ = -RT \ln K$, the equilibrium constant will be based on the standard state used for the partition-function calculations. Usually, for gases, this state is that for 1 atm pressure, as in Eq. (8-20).

Each partition function, for gases, contains a q_{trans} factor of the form

$$q_{trans} = \left(\frac{2\pi mkT}{h^2}\right)^{3/2} V$$

It is the molar volume component of these terms that is affected by the standard-state selection. If this state is that of 1 atm pressure, $V = RT/P = RT/(1 \text{ atm})$. The value of R that must be used is that which gives V the SI units of cubic meters. This R value is $0.08206 \times 10^{-3} \text{ m}^3 \text{ atm}$

8-6 Tabulated Free-Energy Functions

Many calculations of equilibrium constants are based on free-energy functions.

From Eq. (8-41) we can form $G° - E_0°$ or equivalently, for an ideal gas, $G° - H_0°$. Since these quantities are always negative, and become more negative with increasing temperature, it is convenient to deal with the so-called free-energy function, $-(G° - H_0°)/T$. For an ideal gas this function is simply

$$-\frac{G° - H_0°}{T} = R \ln\left(\frac{q°}{\mathfrak{N}}\right) \tag{8-43}$$

Examples of this free-energy function for some inorganic and organic gaseous substances are given in Appendix B-4.

For solids and liquids, calorimetric results must be used to deduce free-energy functions. It is then often more convenient to refer free energies to the properties of the substance at 298 K rather than 0 K. Thus, tabulations, as in Appendix B-3, often show the free-energy function $-(G° - H_{298}°)/T$ for solids and liquids. The $-(G° - H_0°)/T$ values given for gases can be converted to this 298 K function through the calculation

$$\frac{G° - H_{298}°}{T} = \frac{G° - H_0°}{T} - \frac{H_{298}° - H_0°}{T} \tag{8-44}$$

The enthalpy increment $H_{298}° - H_0°$ is included in the tabulations given for gaseous substances in Appendix B-3.

This free-energy function completes the list of thermodynamic functions that we shall calculate for samples of ideal gases. Each function, as shown in Table 8-1, can be calculated from an expression for the partition function. The contributing terms to the partition functions and the thermodynamic functions are included in Table 8-1.

A use of the data of Appendix B-3 can be illustrated by calculating the equilibrium constant for the ammonia synthesis reaction

$$\tfrac{1}{2}N_2(g) + \tfrac{3}{2}H_2(g) \rightleftharpoons NH_3(g) \tag{8-45}$$

TABLE 8-1 Summary of the Expressions Used for the Calculation of Thermodynamic Functions from the Properties of the Molecules of an Ideal Gas

	Translation	Rotation		Vibration†
		Linear	Nonlinear	
$q = q_t q_r q_v$	$q_t = \left(\dfrac{2\pi mkT}{h^2}\right)^{3/2} V$	$q_r = \dfrac{8\pi^2 IkT}{\sigma h^2}$	$q_r = \left(\dfrac{8\pi^2 kT}{h^2}\right)^{3/2}\dfrac{(\pi I_A I_B I_C)^{1/2}}{\sigma}$	$q_v = \dfrac{1}{1-e^{-x}}$
$E - E_0 = \dfrac{RT^2}{q}\dfrac{dq}{dT}$	$\tfrac{3}{2}RT$	RT	$\tfrac{3}{2}RT$	$RT\dfrac{x}{e^x-1}$
$H - E_0 = E - E_0 + RT$	$\tfrac{5}{2}RT$	RT	$\tfrac{3}{2}RT$	$RT\dfrac{x}{e^x-1}$
$C_v = \dfrac{d}{dT}(E - E_0)$	$\tfrac{3}{2}R$	R	$\tfrac{3}{2}R$	$\dfrac{Rx^2 e^x}{(e^x-1)^2}$
$C_P = C_V + R$	$\tfrac{5}{2}R$	R	$\tfrac{3}{2}R$	$\dfrac{Rx^2 e^x}{(e^x-1)^2}$
$S = \dfrac{E-E_0}{T} + R\ln\dfrac{q}{\mathfrak{N}} + R$	$\tfrac{5}{2}R + R\ln\dfrac{q_t}{\mathfrak{N}} + R$	$R + R\ln q_r$	$\tfrac{3}{2}R + R\ln q_r$	$\dfrac{Rx}{e^x-1} + R\ln q_v$
$G - E_0 = RT\ln\dfrac{q}{\mathfrak{N}}$	$RT\ln\dfrac{q_t}{\mathfrak{N}}$	$RT\ln q_r$	$RT\ln q_r$	$RT\ln q_v$

† Per vibrational degree of freedom.

TABLE 8-2 Calculation of the Equilibrium Constant for the Ammonia Synthesis Reaction

$$\tfrac{1}{2}N_2(g) + \tfrac{3}{2}H_2(g) \rightleftharpoons NH_3(g)$$

The value of ΔH_0° is -39.07 kJ

T, K	$\dfrac{\Delta(G^\circ - H_0^\circ)}{T}$ $J\,K^{-1}$	$\Delta(G^\circ - H_0^\circ)$ kJ	$\Delta G^\circ = \Delta(G^\circ - H_0^\circ)$ $+ \Delta H_0^\circ$, kJ	$\log K_P = \dfrac{-\Delta G^\circ}{2.303RT}$	K_P
298	+75.51	+22.51	−16.56	+2.90	7.9×10^2
500	+87.25	+43.63	+4.55	−0.48	3.3×10^{-1}
1000	+100.98	+100.98	+61.91	−3.23	5.9×10^{-4}

Let us calculate the equilibrium constants at the three temperatures 298, 500, and 1000 K.

We first obtain the temperature-independent term ΔH_0°. For the ammonia synthesis reaction of Eq. (8-45), we obtain directly from Appendix B-3 $\Delta H_0^\circ = -39.07$ kJ. Now, for each temperature the steps of the successive columns of Table 8-2 lead to the desired values of the equilibrium constants.

8-7 The Temperature Dependence of the Free Energy and the Equilibrium Constant of a Reaction

Tabulated values of the free-energy function allow the free-energy change and the equilibrium constant to be evaluated at any temperature for which data are given. Now an expression will be developed for the temperature dependence of the equilibrium constant. This expression provides an alternate way of deducing equilibrium constants at various temperatures. It also reveals the factor on which the temperature dependence of an equilibrium constant depends.

The free energy of each compound involved in a reaction depends on the temperature, according to Eq. (8-17) by the relation

$$\left(\frac{\partial G}{\partial T}\right)_P = -S \tag{8-46}$$

For a chemical reaction it is the free energy of the products less that of the reactants which is of interest. Application of Eq. (8-46) to each reagent allows the expression

$$\left[\frac{\partial(\Delta G)}{\partial T}\right]_P = -\Delta S \tag{8-47}$$

to be written, where $\Delta G = G_{\text{prod}} - G_{\text{react}}$ and $\Delta S = S_{\text{prod}} - S_{\text{react}}$. A convenient expression for the temperature dependence of ΔG results if ΔS is eliminated from Eq. (8-47).

At any constant temperature the changes of free energy, enthalpy, and entropy for any reaction are related by

$$\Delta G = \Delta H - T\,\Delta S \quad \text{or} \quad \Delta S = \frac{\Delta H - \Delta G}{T} \quad [T \text{ const}] \quad (8\text{-}48)$$

The second expression can be used to eliminate ΔS from Eq. (8-47) to give

$$\left[\frac{\partial(\Delta G)}{\partial T}\right]_P = \frac{-\Delta H + \Delta G}{T} = -\frac{\Delta H}{T} + \frac{\Delta G}{T}$$

or

$$\left[\frac{\partial(\Delta G)}{\partial T}\right]_P - \frac{\Delta G}{T} = -\frac{\Delta H}{T} \quad (8\text{-}49)$$

The two terms on the left side of Eq. (8-49) can be shown to be equivalent to

$$T\left[\frac{\partial(\Delta G/T)}{\partial T}\right]_P = T\frac{T[\partial(\Delta G/\partial T)]_P - \Delta G}{T^2} = \left[\frac{\partial(\Delta G)}{\partial T}\right] - \frac{\Delta G}{T} \quad (8\text{-}50)$$

Now the left side of Eq. (8-50) can be inserted in place of the left side of Eq. (8-49) to give

$$T\left[\frac{\partial(\Delta G/T)}{\partial T}\right]_P = -\frac{\Delta H}{T} \quad (8\text{-}51)$$

When this relation is applied to the reagents of a reaction, each at the constant pressure corresponding to the standard states, it becomes

$$T\frac{d(\Delta G^\circ/T)}{dT} = -\frac{\Delta H^\circ}{T} \quad [\text{standard-state pressure}, T \text{ const}] \quad (8\text{-}52)$$

Finally, the relation between ΔG° and the equilibrium constant, Eq. (8-29), can be inserted to give, on rearrangement,

$$\frac{d(\ln K)}{dT} = \frac{\Delta H^\circ}{RT^2} \quad (8\text{-}53)$$

This important formula is the goal of the derivation. The rate of change of the equilibrium constant with temperature is seen to depend on the standard heat of the reaction.

The change of $\ln K$ or K can be obtained by an integration of this expression either with the assumption of a constant value of $\Delta H°$ or with the temperature dependence of this quantity expressed by the empirical expressions developed in Sec. 6-8. Integrations can be carried out by first rearranging Eq. (8-53) to

$$\frac{d(\ln K)}{d(1/T)} = -\frac{\Delta H°}{R} \quad \text{or} \quad \frac{d(\log K)}{d(1/T)} = -\frac{\Delta H°}{2.303R} \tag{8-54}$$

The integrated form of these equations, on the assumption that $\Delta H°$ is temperature-independent, is

$$\log K = -\frac{\Delta H°}{2.303R}\frac{1}{T} + \text{const} \tag{8-55}$$

Both the integrated and differential forms show that a plot of $\log K$ versus $1/T$ should give a straight line with a slope equal to $-\Delta H°/2.303R$. The linearity shown by good measurements can be judged by the example of Fig. 8-4. The straight line, furthermore, has been drawn with the slope $\Delta H°/R$, with a value of $\Delta H°$ from the data of Appendix B-1.

Thus a measured value of $\Delta H°$ can be used to calculate the equilibrium constant at temperatures other than that for which it is given. Conversely, it is possible to use measurements of the equilibrium constant at a number of temperatures to evaluate the standard enthalpy change for the reaction.

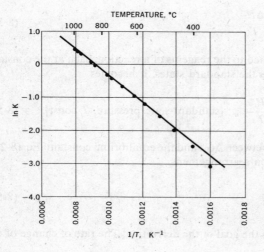

FIGURE 8-4
The temperature dependence of the equilibrium constant for the reaction
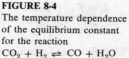
$CO_2 + H_2 \rightleftarrows CO + H_2O$

When much larger temperature ranges are considered, the basis of the dependence of the equilibrium constant on temperature can more clearly be seen by returning to the expressions

$$\Delta G° = \Delta H° - T\Delta S° \quad \text{and} \quad \Delta G° = -RT\ln K$$

or

$$RT\ln K = -\Delta H° + T\Delta S° \tag{8-56}$$

This equation is valid at any temperature when values of $\Delta H°$ and $T\Delta S°$ appropriate to that temperature are used. Generally, the $T\Delta S°$ term, as might be expected from the presence of the explicit T factor, is the more temperature-dependent. At high temperatures this term dominates the $\Delta H°$ term to give an $RT\ln K$ value that is increasingly positive or negative, depending on whether $\Delta S°$ for the reaction is positive or negative. Thus at high temperatures the equilibrium constant generally becomes increasingly greater if $\Delta S°$ is positive or smaller if $\Delta S°$ is negative. Examples of these behaviors are shown by the reactions used as illustrations in Fig. 8-5.

In general, the more gas-phase molecular or atomic particles there are, the higher the entropy. This fact and the overwhelming importance of the entropy of the system at high temperatures lead to the general breakup or dissociation of species at these temperatures. One can generalize that at high temperatures the side of the equation with more gas-phase species will be dominant, a generalization that is not valid unless the $T\Delta S°$ term dominates the $\Delta H°$ term in contributing to $\Delta G°$.

8-8 The Pressure Dependence of the Free Energy of Nonideal Gases: The Fugacity

Now let us begin the steps that allow us to remove the restriction to systems of ideal gases. (The extension to other real systems of interest, reactions in solutions, will be postponed until Chap. 9.) The first step lets us describe the dependence of the free energy of a nonideal gas on pressure. We must begin again with Eq. (8-18)

$$\left(\frac{\partial G}{\partial P}\right)_T = V$$

and develop a counterpart of the ideal-gas expression, Eq. (8-20),

$$G = G° + RT\ln P$$

A straightforward treatment of nonideal gases would use a suitable equation of state, such as van der Waals' equation, to allow the integration of Eq. (8-18) to

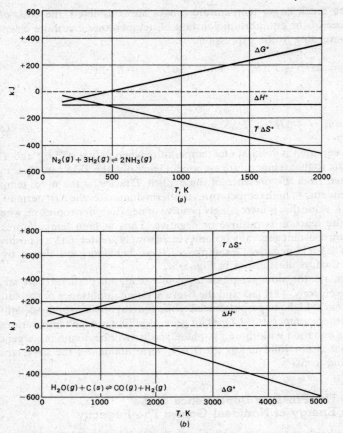

FIGURE 8-5 The temperature dependence of $\triangle G°$, $\triangle H°$, and $T \triangle S°$ over large temperature ranges; the behavior for (*a*) negative $\triangle S°$ and (*b*) positive $\triangle S°$.

be performed. Such a procedure, however, results in an expression for ΔG that is a complicated and unwieldy function of P. The simplicity of the ideal-gas results, Eqs. (8-19) and (8-20), will be found to lead to other important equations with a similar simple form. We can obtain such an expression, even for nonideal gases, by what at first will seem a rather devious approach.

A satisfactory procedure is the introduction of a new function called the *fugacity f*. If G_1 and G_2 are the molar free energies of a gas at two pressures P_1 and P_2, the fugacities f_1 and f_2 of the gas at these pressures are *defined* so that

$$G_2 - G_1 = RT \ln \frac{f_2}{f_1} \tag{8-57}$$

This procedure insists on the free-energy equation having the convenient form of Eq. (8-57). The nonideal complications are hidden in the fugacity terms.

Comparison of this defining equation for fugacity with the ideal-gas equation (8-19) shows that for ideal behavior the fugacity is proportional to the pressure and can be set equal to it. For nonideal behavior we must expect the fugacity of a gas to deviate from its pressure. It is now necessary to show how the fugacity of a gas at a particular pressure and temperature can be deduced.

A number of manipulations are necessary. We begin with the thermodynamic equation for 1 mol of gas at constant temperature,

$$G_2 - G_1 = \int_{P_1}^{P_2} V \, dP \tag{8-58}$$

The quantity RT/P can be added to and subtracted from the integrand to give

$$\begin{aligned} G_2 - G_1 &= \int_{P_1}^{P_2} \left[\frac{RT}{P} + \left(V - \frac{RT}{P} \right) \right] dP \\ &= \int_{P_1}^{P_2} \frac{RT}{P} \, dP + \int_{P_1}^{P_2} \left(V - \frac{RT}{P} \right) dP \\ &= RT \ln \frac{P_2}{P_1} + \int_{P_1}^{P_2} \left(V - \frac{RT}{P} \right) dP \end{aligned} \tag{8-59}$$

Comparison of this expression with Eq. (8-57) gives

$$RT \ln \frac{f_2}{f_1} = RT \ln \frac{P_2}{P_1} + \int_{P_1}^{P_2} \left(V - \frac{RT}{P} \right) dP$$

or

$$RT \ln \frac{f_2/P_2}{f_1/P_1} = \int_{P_1}^{P_2} \left(V - \frac{RT}{P} \right) dP \tag{8-60}$$

Since all gases tend to become ideal as the pressure approaches zero, i.e.,

$$\frac{f}{P} \to 1 \quad \text{as} \quad P \to 0$$

the ratio f_1/P_1 becomes unity when P_1 approaches zero. Furthermore, if P and f are written instead of P_2 and f_2 for the arbitrary pressure and fugacity in Eq. (8-60), we have

$$RT \ln \frac{f}{P} = \int_{P=0}^{P=P} \left(V - \frac{RT}{P} \right) dP \tag{8-61}$$

If information on the dependence of the molar volume V on pressure is available, the integration can be carried out and the ratio f/P at any pressure P can be calculated. The virial-coefficient expression (1-24) for the pressure series is particularly convenient. With this expression for V, integration of Eq. (8-61) leads to

$$\ln \frac{f}{P} = B_P P + \tfrac{1}{2} C_P P^2 + \tfrac{1}{3} D_P P^3 + \cdots \tag{8-62}$$

Thus, the ratio f/P can be calculated at any temperature for which virial-coefficient data are available and for any pressure in the range in which these data are applicable. If the real-gas behavior is expressed by any other equation of state, the integration of Eq. (8-61) can be carried out graphically or with the help of a computer.

For gases for which molar-volume measurements have not been made and an equation of state is not available, the law of corresponding states can be used to estimate the fugacities at various temperatures and pressures. It will be recalled that this law states that in terms of the reduced variables P_R, V_R, and T_R all gases follow the same equation of state. This means that at the same value of P_R and T_R all gases have the same imperfection and therefore the same nonideality. Furthermore, the variation of the compressibility factor Z with the reduced pressure has been represented for various values of T_R in Fig. 1-11. These data are all that are necessary for the integration of Eq. (8-61). Figure 1-11 gives values of

$$Z = \frac{PV}{RT}$$

from which one obtains

$$V = \frac{RT}{P} Z \tag{8-63}$$

With this relation Eq. (8-61) can be written as

$$RT \ln \frac{f}{P} = \int_0^P \left(\frac{RT}{P} Z - \frac{RT}{P} \right) dP = RT \int_0^P (Z - 1) \frac{dP}{P}$$

or

$$\ln \frac{f}{P} = \int_0^P (Z - 1) \frac{dP}{P} = \int_0^P (Z - 1) \frac{dP_R}{P_R} \tag{8-64}$$

The data of Z as a function of P_R for a given value of T_R then allow graphical integrations to be performed to give curves like those of Fig. 8-6.

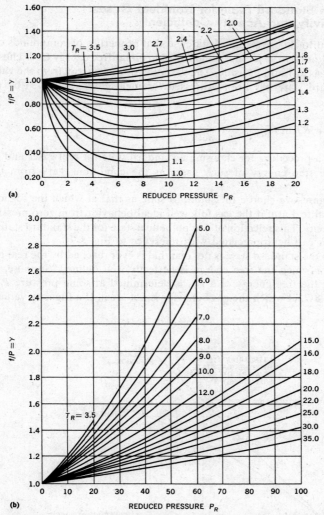

(a)

(b)

FIGURE 8-6 The ratio f/P for gases as a function of the reduced pressure $P_R = P/P_C$ and the reduced temperature $T_R = T/T_C$ (a) at pressures and temperatures near the critical point and (b) at higher pressures and temperatures. [*From R. H. Newton, Ind. Eng. Chem.,* **27**: *302 (1935).*]

8-9 The Standard State for Nonideal Gases: The Activity and Activity Coefficient

It is convenient to choose standard states so that properties of compounds can be tabulated. For ideal gases, the standard-state molar free energy $G°$ is chosen as that of the gas at 1 atm pressure. The variation of free energy from the value for the standard state has been expressed for ideal gases (Sec. 8-3) by the formula

$$G = G° + RT \ln P_{atm}$$

We now need a procedure for choosing a standard state for real gases and for expressing the free energy of such gases as the conditions vary from this standard state.

For real gases we choose the standard state as that at which the fugacity would be equal to 1 atm if the gas followed ideal behavior from zero pressure up to this fugacity. This selection of a hypothetical state for the standard state of nonideal gases can be appreciated with reference to Fig. 8-7.

Although the standard state is not one that is ever reached by the real gas, it is a state for which the free energy is perfectly well defined. Suppose, for example, that the free energy of a gas is determined at some pressure P, as shown in Fig. 8-7, at which the gas behavior is not ideal. If a fugacity value at

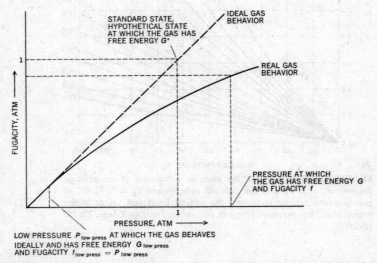

FIGURE 8-7 A schematic representation of the fugacity-pressure relation for a real gas and the relation that would exist if the gas behaved ideally up to a pressure of 1 atm.

pressure P is available, the free energy G at this pressure can be related to the free energy $G_{low\ press}$ at some low pressure $P_{low\ press}$ by

$$G - G_{low\ press} = RT\ln\frac{f}{f_{low\ press}} = RT\ln\frac{f}{P_{low\ press}} \qquad (8\text{-}65)$$

The relation between the free energy $G_{low\ press}$ and the standard-state free energy follows from ideal behavior and is

$$G° - G_{low\ press} = RT\ln\frac{1\ atm}{P_{low\ press}} \qquad (8\text{-}66)$$

Subtraction of Eqs. (8-65) and (8-66) eliminates the common low-pressure terms and gives

$$G - G° = RT\ln\frac{f_P}{1\ atm} \qquad (8\text{-}67)$$

or with the assumption that the fugacity is expressed in atmospheres,

$$G - G° = RT\ln f \qquad (8\text{-}68)$$

Thus, although $G°$ is based on a hypothetical state, free energies of the gas at any pressure can be related to this standard free energy if the fugacity of the gas at that pressure is known.

Comparison of Eq. (8-68) with the ideal-gas relation

$$G - G° = RT\ln P$$

suggests that introduction of a term to exhibit the nonideality of a gas by comparing f with P. The *activity coefficient* γ, defined as

$$\gamma = \frac{f}{P} \qquad (8\text{-}69)$$

is introduced. With this factor the free-energy expression for real gases can be written

$$G - G° = RT\ln\gamma P \qquad (8\text{-}70)$$

The special convenience of γ is that it shows explicitly the importance of nonideality.

The activity coefficients for gases are given graphically on the basis of the law of corresponding states in Fig. 8-6.

8-10 Equilibrium Constants for Systems of Real Gases

The development of expressions comparable with those of Eqs. (8-28) and (8-29) in a way that allows for nonideal-gas behavior of each gas of the reaction mixture begins with relations of the type

$$G - G° = nRT \ln f$$

for each reagent. By a treatment like that followed through for ideal gases in Sec. 8-4 one then obtains the result

$$\Delta G° = -RT \ln \left[\frac{(f_C)^c (f_D)^d}{(f_A)^a (f_B)^b} \right]_{equil} \tag{8-71}$$

Now the factor that must remain constant involves fugacities rather than pressures. Since the treatment here is thermodynamically exact (it will be recalled that f is defined so that $G - G° = RT \ln f$), the constant term will now be labeled K_{th}; that is,

$$K_{th} = \left[\frac{(f_C)^c (f_D)^d}{(f_A)^a (f_B)^b} \right]_{equil} \tag{8-72}$$

This thermodynamically exact expression is more frequently used with the substitution of the relation $f = \gamma P$ for each of the components, which gives

$$K_{th} = \frac{(\gamma_C P_C)^c (\gamma_D P_D)^d}{(\gamma_A P_A)^a (\gamma_B P_B)^b} = \frac{(\gamma_C)^c (\gamma_D)^d}{(\gamma_A)^a (\gamma_B)^b} K_P \tag{8-73}$$

If K_γ is introduced for the activity-coefficient term, Eq. (8-73) can be written

$$K_{th} = K_\gamma K_P \tag{8-74}$$

Only for ideal gases will all the activity coefficients be unity, and only then will $K_{th} = K_P$. Furthermore, the activity-coefficient term may well change as the pressure of the system or as the individual pressures change. Then only K_{th} can be expected to be a constant for any arrangement of pressures, and the pressure term K_P will be a nonconstant "equilibrium constant."

An illustration of the effects of nonideality on the equilibrium constant is provided again by the reaction

$$\tfrac{1}{2}N_2 + \tfrac{3}{2}H_2 \rightleftharpoons NH_3$$

The reaction is generally carried out at high pressures and at a temperature of about 450°C. Analysis of the equilibrium gas mixture provides values for the mole fractions of ammonia, nitrogen, and hydrogen present at equilibrium. Data from the classic studies of Larson for a temperature of 450°C and various pressures are given in Table 8-3.

If ideal behavior is assumed, the mole fractions of each of the components can be used to calculate the partial pressure of that component from $P_i = x_i P_{tot}$. These data at each pressure can be inserted into the equilibrium-constant expression written in terms of pressures. The results of these calculations are given in the K_P column of Table 8-3. The equilibrium "constant" K_P is not constant over this range of pressures.

The activity-coefficient data needed for K_γ of Eq. (8-74) can be deduced for each component. The data of Table 8-4 illustrate the calculation at 1000 atm and 450°C. Such results provide the data of the K_γ column of Table 8-3.

The product of K_P and K_γ is, according to Eq. (8-74), the thermodynamic equilibrium constant K_{th}. The K_γ term is intended to be such that K_{th} is strictly constant. The data of the K_{th} column of Table 8-3 show that the activity-coefficient term has been suitably evaluated up to a total pressure of about 600 atm.

The result at the highest pressure indicates that our treatment, as entered in Table 8-3, is still somewhat approximate. This does not imply any approximation in the formation of K_{th} but stems from the evaluation of the activity coefficients for the individual gases as if they were pure gases at the total pressure of the reaction system. A correct treatment would make use of PVT data on nonreacting gas mixtures so that the activity coefficients of the components in the mixture could be evaluated. The treatment illustrated in Table 8-3 is satisfactory, however, at all but very high pressures.

8-11 The Dependence of Entropy and Internal Energy on Pressure or Volume

The dependence of free energy on pressure, given by Eq. (8-18)

$$\left(\frac{\partial G}{\partial P}\right)_T = V$$

has been explored for ideal and real gases. Derived relations, such as $G = G° + RT \ln P$ and $G = G + RT \ln f$, have led us to the important free-energy–equilibrium-constant expression of Eq. (8-29). Although the pressure dependence of other thermodynamic quantities does not lead to as chemically significant results as Eq. (8-29), these quantities do provide additional insights into the properties of substances.

The pressure dependence of S The dependence of free energy on pressure and the dependence on temperature, as given in Eqs. (8-17) and (8-18), can be related to each other. Since, as shown in Sec. 5-6, the order of differentiation is immaterial, we can write

TABLE 8-3 Equilibrium Constants for the Reaction

$$\tfrac{1}{2}N_2(g) + \tfrac{3}{2}H_2(g) \rightleftharpoons NH_3(g)$$

at 450°C

P, atm	Equilibrium mole fraction[†]			Equilibrium partial pressure, atm			K_P	K_γ	$K_{th} = K_P K_\gamma$
	NH_3	N_2	H_2	NH_3	N_2	H_2			
10	0.0204	0.2296	0.7469	0.204	2.296	7.469	0.00659	0.994	0.0066
30	0.0580	0.2196	0.7192	1.740	6.588	21.58	0.00676	0.975	0.0066
50	0.0917	0.2107	0.6943	4.585	10.54	34.72	0.00690	0.95	0.0066
100	0.1635	0.1917	0.6413	16.35	19.17	64.13	0.00727	0.89	0.0065
300	0.3550	0.1407	0.5000	106.5	42.21	150.0	0.00892	0.70	0.0062
600	0.5360	0.0929	0.3664	321.6	55.74	219.8	0.01322	0.50	0.0066
1000	0.6940	0.0511	0.2498	694.0	51.10	249.8	0.02459	0.37	0.0091

[†] Small amounts of argon are also present in each of the reaction mixtures.

Source: Data from A. J. Larson, *J. Am. Chem. Soc.*, **46**:367 (1924).

TABLE 8-4 Calculation of K_γ for a Reaction Mixture of NH_3, N_2, and H_2 at a Total Pressure of 1000 atm and a Temperature of 450°C (723 K)

	P_C, atm	T_C, K	P_R	T_R	γ (from Fig. 8-6)
NH_3	111.5	405.6	8.97	1.78	0.85
N_2	33.5	126.1	29.8	5.73	1.62
H_2	12.8	33.3	78.1	21.7	1.47

$$K_\gamma = \frac{\gamma_{NH_3}}{\gamma_{N_2}^{1/2}\gamma_{H_2}^{3/2}} = 0.37$$

$$\left(\frac{\partial}{\partial P}\left(\frac{\partial G}{\partial T}\right)_P\right)_T = \left(\frac{\partial}{\partial T}\left(\frac{\partial G}{\partial P}\right)_T\right)_P$$

With Eqs. (8-17) and (8-18) this leads directly to the first of our desired relations

$$\left(\frac{\partial S}{\partial P}\right)_T = -\left(\frac{\partial V}{\partial T}\right)_P \tag{8-75}$$

This is one of the frequently useful relations known as *Maxwell equations*.

Pressure and volume dependence of E The first law, applied to a reversible process in which the only work is that of expansion, gives

$$dE = \delta q + \delta w = T\,dS - P\,dV$$

Division by dP followed by specification of constant temperature gives

$$\left(\frac{\partial E}{\partial P}\right)_T = T\left(\frac{\partial S}{\partial P}\right)_T - P\left(\frac{\partial V}{\partial P}\right)_T \tag{8-76}$$

The pressure dependence of entropy, Eq. (8-75), can be inserted to give

$$\left(\frac{\partial E}{\partial P}\right)_T = -T\left(\frac{\partial V}{\partial T}\right)_P - P\left(\frac{\partial V}{\partial P}\right)_T \tag{8-77}$$

Alternatively, the dependence of internal energy on volume can be obtained. In view of the relations of Sec. 5-6 we can write $(\partial E/\partial P)_T = (\partial E/\partial V)_T(\partial V/\partial P)_T$ and $(\partial V/\partial T)_P/(\partial V/\partial P)_T = (\partial P/\partial T)_V$. These allow Eq. (8-77) to be developed to

$$\left(\frac{\partial E}{\partial V}\right)_T = T\left(\frac{\partial P}{\partial T}\right)_V - P \tag{8-78}$$

Equations (8-77) and (8-78) show that $(\partial E/\partial P)_T$ and $(\partial E/\partial V)_T$, like $(\partial S/\partial P)_T$, are related to the PVT behavior of the system; i.e., the PVT behavior of the system is expressed in terms of a thermodynamic quantity. Such relations are said to be *thermodynamic equations of state*.

Now recall that $PV = nRT$ sums up the PVT behavior of an ideal gas. From $PV = nRT$ we obtain $(\partial P/\partial T)_V = nR/V = P/T$. Thus, according to Eq. (8-78), if $PV = nRT$,

$$\left(\frac{\partial E}{\partial V}\right)_T = 0 \qquad \text{[ideal gas]} \tag{8-79}$$

As mentioned in Sec. 5-7, this ideal-gas characteristic need not be presented as a separate postulate. It can now be seen to be a consequence of the PVT behavior summed up in $PV = nRT$.

PROBLEMS

8-1. A reversible electrochemical cell is used to carry out the formation of 1 mol of aqueous HCl according to the reaction

$$\tfrac{1}{2}H_2(g) + \tfrac{1}{2}Cl_2(g) \xrightarrow{\;H_2O\;} HCl(aq)$$

On a diagram for the system and the thermal and mechanical reservoirs (*a*) show the enthalpy and entropy changes in these three components. (Use the enthalpy and entropy data of Appendix B.) What is the free-energy change of the system? (*b*) Show the enthalpy and entropy changes if the process is carried out irreversibly so that no work is collected.

8-2. Using the data of Appendix B-1, for the combustion of 1 mol of ethane to give $CO_2(g)$ and $H_2O(l)$ at a constant pressure and temperature of 1 atm and 25°C, calculate the heat that would be given out in a free, unharnessed combustion and the maximum work that could in principle be obtained from a reversible reaction. What happens to the energy difference between the two values when the reaction is made to occur reversibly?

8-3. Use the data of Appendix B-1 to compare the values of ΔH and ΔG for the conversion of 1 mol of ozone to $1\tfrac{1}{2}$ mol of oxygen at 1 atm pressure and 25°C.

8-4. Using the data of Appendix B-1, for the conversion of 1 mol of ozone, O_3, to $1\tfrac{1}{2}$ mol of oxygen, O_2, at a constant pressure and temperature of 1 atm and 25°C calculate (*a*) the heat that would be given out by the reaction if no work other than that of expansion was drawn from the reaction and (*b*) the maximum work that could be obtained from the reaction. (*c*) Where does the energy come from that allows the answer to part (*b*) to be greater than that of part (*a*)? (*d*) Is the entropy change of the reaction consistent with your explanation?

8-5. Calculate ΔH, ΔS, and ΔG when 1 mol of water is converted from liquid at 100°C and 1 atm into vapor at the same temperature and pressure. Discuss the influence of the entropy and energy factors on the spontaneity of the reaction.

8-6. Calculate ΔH, ΔS, and ΔG for the conversion of liquid water at 25°C, subjected to its equilibrium vapor pressure of 0.0313 atm, to steam at 100°C and 1 atm. The heat of vaporization of water at its normal boiling point is 40.67 kJ mol^{-1}. You can take the heat capacity of liquid water to be constant at 75.4 J mol^{-1} K^{-1}.

8-7. Given that the heat of vaporization of water at 25°C is 44.01 kJ mol^{-1} and that the heat capacity of water vapor is given by the expression of Table 6-2, obtain values for ΔH, ΔS, and ΔG for the process of Prob. 8-6 by calculation over an alternate route.

8-8. Calculate the free energies at 25°C, based on the standard free energies of Appendix B-1, of (a) 1 mol of $H_2(g)$ at a pressure of 10^{-5} atm and (b) 1 mol of $O_2(g)$ at a pressure of 10^{-5} atm. (c) Calculate the free energy of formation of liquid water from hydrogen and oxygen each at a pressure of 10^{-5} atm and compare with the standard heat of formation of liquid water.

8-9. Use the data of Appendix B-1 to calculate the equilibrium constant at 25°C for the reaction of $Cl_2(g)$ with $CH_4(g)$ to give $CH_3Cl(g)$ and $H_2(g)$.

8-10. Use the data of Appendix B-1 to calculate the equilibrium pressure of oxygen over (a) Ag_2O and (b) Al_2O_3.

8-11. Use the data of Appendix B-1 to calculate the equilibrium water vapor pressure of $CuSO_4 \cdot 5H_2O$ at 25°C.

***8-12.** The following values have been reported for the equilibrium constant for the reaction $Br_2(g) \rightleftharpoons 2Br(g)$. The moment of inertia of Br_2 is 3.46×10^{-45} kg m^2, the vibrational spacing is 322 cm^{-1}, and the symmetry number is 2. The ground electronic state of $Br(g)$ has a multiplicity of 4, and there is a doubly degenerate state at an energy of 3685 cm^{-1}, or 7.325×10^{-20} J. (a) By the method of Sec. 8-5 calculate the equilibrium constants in the temperature range of the experimental results and compare with these results. (b) Use the free-energy data of Appendix B-4 to calculate equilibrium constants and compare these values with the experimental results.

T, K	1123	1173	1223	1273
K_P	0.000403	0.00140	0.00328	0.0071

8-13. For the reaction

$$CO_2(g) + H_2(g) \rightarrow CO(g) + H_2O(g)$$

(a) calculate the equilibrium constant at 25°C. (b) Obtain an expression for the enthalpy of the reaction as a function of temperature. What is a representative value of ΔH for the temperature range 300 to 1400 K? (c) Assuming a constant value of ΔH, calculate $\log K$ for several temperatures and prepare a plot of $\log K$ versus $1/T$. Compare with Fig. 8-4. (d) With the equation for ΔH from part (b) obtain an expression for $\log K$ as a function of temperature and calculate $\log K$ at the values of T chosen in part (c).

8-14. Use the free-energy-function data of Appendix B-4 to obtain equilibrium constants for the reaction of Prob. 8-13 at the selected temperatures. Compare with the results of parts (c) and (d).

8-15. The following data have been reported for the dissociation of silver oxide according to the reaction

$$Ag_2O(s) \rightarrow 2Ag(s) + \tfrac{1}{2}O_2(g)$$

$t\,°C$	150	173	183.1	188.2	191.2	200
P_{O_2} mm Hg	182	422	605	717	790	1050

Estimate from these data the standard heat of formation and the standard free energy of formation of $Ag_2O(s)$ and compare with the 25°C values of Appendix B-1.

8-16. The following data have been given for the dissociation of water vapor according to the reaction $H_2O(g) \rightleftharpoons \frac{1}{2}O_2(g) + H_2(g)$. Calculate equilibrium constants and percent dissociations in this temperature range from the data of Appendix B-4. Compare with the experimental values. A graphical display is convenient.

T, K	1300	1500	1705	2155	2257	2300
Dissociation, %	0.0027	0.02	0.102	1.18	1.77	2.60

8-17. The breakup of NO_2 according to the reaction

$$NO_2(g) \rightleftharpoons NO(g) + \frac{1}{2}O_2(g)$$

has been found to proceed at a total pressure of 1 atm, so that the percentage of NO_2 that is decomposed is

T, K	457	552	767	903
NO_2 decomposed, %	5.0	13.0	56.5	99.0

(a) What value do these data suggest for the heat of the reaction? (b) Compare with the heat of reaction deduced from Appendix B-1 for 298 K.

8-18. (a) At what temperature does O_2 break up so that there are equal numbers of O_2 molecules and O atoms if the total pressure is 1 atm? (b) What temperature is required to dissociate N_2 molecules to the same extent?

8-19. In the thermosphere from about 300 to 500 km oxygen is the principal atmospheric component. Calculate the ratio of O_2 molecules to O atoms in this region at 400 km where the pressure is 5×10^{-11} atm and the temperature is 2000 K.

8-20. The formation of nitric oxide, NO, at the high temperatures of internal-combustion engines is an initial step in smog formation. Calculate the equilibrium partial pressure of NO present in a 4:1 nitrogen-to-oxygen system at 1 atm pressure at (a) 298 K (b) 1000 K, (c) 2000 K, and (d) 3000 K. (In practice it is necessary to consider the rate at which the equilibrium is reached as well as the composition at equilibrium.)

8-21. One process for the industrial formation of acetylene consists of the partial oxidation of methane. The reaction is carried out in a methane-oxygen flame at a temperature of about 1800 K. The reaction can be described by the equation

$$5CH_4 + 3O_2 \rightarrow C_2H_2 + 3CO + 6H_2 + H_2O$$

(a) Use the data of Appendix B-4 to obtain the equilibrium constant at several temperatures and extrapolate to obtain an approximate value at 1800 K. (b) What fraction of the methane is converted into acetylene if the total pressure is 1 atm and the ratio of methane to oxygen is 5:3?

8-22. Hydrogen cyanide is prepared industrially in the United States by the reaction

$$CH_4 + NH_3 + \frac{3}{2}O_2 \rightarrow HCN + 3H_2O$$

The reaction is carried out in the presence of a catalyst at 2000°F, or about 1100°C. Yields of about 20 percent based on methane are reported. The high temperatures are troublesome because other reactions set in. Do you think the high temperature is necessary to speed up the reaction, as in the ammonia synthesis reaction, or to attain a satisfactory equilibrium relation?

8-23. An alternative industrial route to hydrogen cyanide makes use of the reaction

$$CH_4(g) + NH_3(g) \rightarrow HCN(g) + 3H_2(g)$$

Compare the equilibrium constant of this reaction and that of Prob. 8-22 at 25°C.

8-24. In terms of the sources of nonideal behavior recognized by van der Waals, explain what might cause an activity coefficient of a nonideal gas to be greater than unity and what might cause it to be less than unity.

*8-25. "Methanol is produced by the exothermic reaction between hydrogen and carbon monoxide or carbon dioxide over a copper or Cr–Zn catalyst at pressures between 4000 and 6500 psig, and temperatures in the 750°F range" (Albert V. G. Hahn, "The Petrochemical Industry," McGraw-Hill Book Company, New York, 1970). For the reaction

$$2H_2(g) + CO(g) \rightarrow CH_3OH(g)$$

(a) calculate the equilibrium constant at or near the conditions suggested. First assume ideal-gas behavior and then correct for nonideality. (b) If the feed is not preheated, how much heat per mole of H_2 supplied would have to be added or removed to maintain a constant temperature in the reactor? (c) Repeat the calculations for the reaction

$$3H_2(g) + CO_2(g) \rightarrow CH_3OH(g) + H_2O(g)$$

8-26. For pressures up to about 50 atm, the equation of state $PV = RT - 0.072P$ with P in atmospheres and V in liters for CO_2 at 100°C is adequate. Calculate the fugacity and the activity coefficient of CO_2 at 100°C and (a) 1 atm, (b) 50 atm.

8-27. The pressure-volume data for CH_4, on which the virial coefficients at 25°C of Table 1-2 are based, were given in Prob. 1-31. (a) Use these data to obtain the activity coefficient of methane at 25°C and at various pressures. (b) On the same graph plot curves for $\gamma = f/P$ for methane at 0 and at 25°C. (The value of $V - RT/P$ can be obtained from the virial-coefficient data of Table 1-2.)

8-28. At 800 K the values tabulated are reported for the density of steam [Tables of Thermal Properties of Gases, *Natl. Bur. Stand.* (*U.S.*) *Circ.* 564, (rev. 1960)]. What are the fugacity and the activity coefficient of steam at 800 K and 300 atm? Compare these values with those obtained from the critical data and Fig. 8-6.

P, atm	Density g ml^{-1}	P, atm	Density g ml^{-1}	P, atm	Density g ml^{-1}
1	0.00027464	80	0.023344	240	0.08070
10	0.0027648	120	0.036184	280	0.09803
20	0.0055709	160	0.049937	300	0.1073
40	0.011312	200	0.064724		

8-29. The equilibrium constant for the reaction $H_2 + CO_2 \rightleftharpoons H_2O + CO$ at 986°C is 1.60 at rather low pressures, where all the gases behave essentially ideally. Estimate the value that the expression for K_P would have at a total gas pressure of 500 atm and the same temperature.

8-30. For most systems of gases, liquids, or solids, the volume increases with temperature. (*a*) What qualitative feature does this imply for the pressure dependence of the entropy? (*b*) What familiar system behaves contrary to this generalization?

***8-31.** The difference in entropy of a real gas at some pressure P and the entropy the gas would have at 1 atm pressure if it behaved ideally up to this pressure can be obtained by integrating Eq. (8-75) for the real gas from zero pressure to pressure P and subtracting the integral for ideal-gas behavior from zero to 1 atm pressure. In this way, set up a general expression for the entropy of a real gas compared with that of the ideal gas at 1 atm based on the Berthelot equation of state

$$PV = RT + \frac{9RPT_C}{128P_C}\left(1 - 6\frac{T_C^2}{T^2}\right)$$

***8-32.** Use the equation obtained in Prob. 8-31 to verify the gas-imperfection correction applied to nitrogen at its normal boiling point in the third-law entropy deduction of Table 7-1.

***8-33.** Because of hydrogen bonding, the vapor of alcohols shows considerable nonideal behavior. The PVT data for methanol can be represented by a virial-type equation $V = RT/P + B + DP^2$, with $B = -0.100 - 0.002148e^{1986/T}$ liter and $D = -0.835 \times 10^{-14}e^{10,750/T}$ liter atm^{-2}. Perform an analytical integration of Eq. (8-61) to obtain the activity coefficient for the vapor up to 1 atm pressure at a temperature of 64.6°C.

***8-34.** (*a*) Calculate and plot the dependence of the molar enthalpy of the methanol vapor on pressure at the normal boiling point, 64.6°C, from zero pressure up to the vapor pressure of 1 atm. (*b*) Add the curve for ideal behavior. Use the PVT expression of Prob. 8-33 and represent the enthalpy at $P = 0$ by $H_{P=0}$.

***8-35.** Using the data of Prob. 8-34, deduce the heat capacity of methanol in the ideal-gas state at 341 K from the experimental result that at this temperature and at 0.987 atm the heat capacity is 113.0 J K^{-1} mol^{-1}. (Calculations using molecular data suggest a value for C_P° at this temperature of 61.5 K^{-1} mol^{-1}.)

***8-36.** Although Berthelot's equation, given in Prob. 8-31, does not conform very closely to the actual PVT relations of real gases, it is convenient for the estimation of the pressure dependence of thermodynamic quantities. (*a*) Obtain from this equation of state an expression for the value of the inversion temperature. (*b*) What values are calculated for helium and for hydrogen? Compare with the observed values.

REFERENCES

Many of the references listed in the three preceding chapters can be used to supplement this chapter. In addition, the following articles relevant:

GIBBARD, H. F., and M. R. EMPTAGE: Gas Phase Chemical Equilibria, *J. Chem. Educ.*, **53**:218 (1976). Studies of the ammonia synthesis reaction.

HUYBRECHTS, G., and G. PETRE: Determining the K_p for the Ammonia Synthesis as a Function of Temperature, *J. Chem. Educ.*, **53**:443 (1976). A suggested physical chemistry experiment.

SPENCER, J. N.: ΔG and $\partial G/\partial \xi$, *J. Chem. Educ.*, **51**:577 (1974).

THE THERMODYNAMIC TREATMENT OF MULTI-COMPONENT SYSTEMS

In almost all the preceding applications of thermodynamics to chemical systems, only systems of one chemical component have been treated. (An exception was the development in Sec. 8-4 of an expression for the equilibrium constant in a system involving various reagents. In that case the simple and unexplored assumption was made that the thermodynamic properties of the system could be interpreted in terms of the contributions of each component.) Now we must develop the thermodynamic apparatus necessary for a sound treatment of multicomponent systems. We shall then be able to apply the powerful methods of thermodynamics to the many interesting and important solution systems.

First ideal solutions are treated. The results obtained in these easily visualized cases will provide convenient reference results when the more mathematically based relationships needed for real systems are encountered.

9-1 The Ideal Solution

Consider the formation of a mixture of gases, i.e., a gaseous solution from two pure gases. The results that will be obtained for the free-energy change accompanying this process will be generalized to any ideal solution, whether gas, liquid, or solid. If the gases are completely indifferent to each other, the mixing process will be equivalent to the expansion of each gas from its separate compartment of Fig. 9-1 to the entire chamber.

Suppose there are n_A mol of A and n_B mol of B each at the same pressure P and temperature T. The entire volume is V, and, in view of the proportionality between volume and number of moles, as expressed in $V = n(RT/P)$, the volume occupied by A is $[n_A/(n_A + n_B)]V$ and that occupied by B is $[n_B/(n_A + n_B)]V$. When mixing occurs, each gas will expand to fill the entire container. As the volume available to A increases from $[n_A/(n_A + n_B)]V$ to V, the pressure of A will decrease from P to $[n_A/(n_A + n_B)]P$. Now let us write this final pressure of A as $x_A P$, where x_A is the mole fraction of A. Likewise the pressure of B will decrease from P to $x_B P$. The total pressure of the gas remains at P.

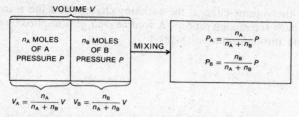

FIGURE 9-1 The mixing of two ideal gases to form an ideal-gas mixture at constant pressure.

The dependence of the free energy of an ideal gas developed in Sec. 8-3 now lets us write

$$G_A \text{ (in mixture)} - G_A \text{ (pure)} = n_A RT \ln \frac{x_A P}{P} = n_A RT \ln x_A \qquad (9\text{-}1)$$

and

$$G_B \text{ (in mixture)} - G_B \text{ (pure)} = n_B RT \ln x_B \qquad (9\text{-}2)$$

The free energy of a mole of a component, A for example, in the mixture is

$$G_A \text{ (in mixture)} = G_A \text{ (pure)} + RT \ln x_A \qquad (9\text{-}3)$$

Remember that G_A (pure) is the free energy of A at the pressure P of the gas mixture.

The free-energy change for the mixing process itself is obtained by adding the free-energy changes of Eqs. (9-1) and (9-2). Thus

$$\Delta G_{mix} = n_A RT \ln x_A + n_B RT \ln x_B \qquad (9\text{-}4)$$

Division of Eq. (9-4) by $n_A + n_B$ gives the free-energy change for the formation of 1 mol of solution as

$$\Delta G_{mix} = x_A RT \ln x_A + x_B RT \ln x_B \qquad (9\text{-}5)$$

Equation (9-5) has been derived for the special, easily treated case of an ideal mixture of ideal gases. Now we shall use it to define an ideal solution. Consider the formation of a mole of solution from the separate components, each in the same physical state and at the same pressure and temperature as the solution that forms. The solution will be said to be ideal if the free energy of mixing as a function of T, P, x_A, and x_B is given by Eq. (9-5).

This definition of an ideal solution by means of Eq. (9-5) carries with it implications about the volume change, the enthalpy change, and the entropy change that accompany the mixing process. A volume change is implied by this free-energy function through relation (8-18)

$$\left(\frac{\partial G}{\partial P}\right)_T = V$$

Here we write

$$\left[\frac{\partial(\Delta G_{mix})}{\partial P}\right]_{T,x} = \Delta V_{mix}$$

Clearly ΔG_{mix} as given by Eq. (9-5) is independent of pressure and therefore

$$\Delta V_{mix} = 0 \tag{9-6}$$

An enthalpy change is implied by Eq. (9-5) through relation (8-51)

$$\left[\frac{\partial(\Delta G/T)}{\partial T}\right]_P = -\frac{\Delta H}{T^2}$$

According to Eq. (9-5), $\Delta G_{mix}/T$ is independent of T and thus

$$\Delta H_{mix} = 0 \tag{9-7}$$

The entropy of mixing in the formation of an ideal solution is obtained

TABLE 9-1 The Entropy and Free-Energy Change at 25°C for the Formation of 1 mol of an Ideal Binary Solution

Mole fraction		$x_A R \ln x_A$, J K^{-1} mol^{-1}	$x_B R \ln x_B$, J K^{-1} mol^{-1}	ΔS_{mix}, J K^{-1} mol^{-1}	$T \Delta S_{mix}$, J mol^{-1}	ΔG_{mix}, J mol^{-1}
x_A	x_B					
1	0	0	0	0	0	0
0.9	0.1	−0.79	−1.91	2.70	805	−805
0.8	0.2	−1.48	−2.68	4.16	1240	−1240
0.7	0.3	−2.08	−3.00	5.08	1510	−1510
0.6	0.4	−2.55	−3.05	5.60	1670	−1670
0.5	0.5	−2.88	−2.88	5.76	1720	−1720
0.4	0.6	−3.05	−2.55	5.60	1670	−1670
0.3	0.7	−3.00	−2.08	5.08	1510	−1510
0.2	0.8	−2.68	−1.48	4.16	1240	−1240
0.1	0.9	−1.91	−0.79	2.70	805	−805
0	1	0	0	0	0	0

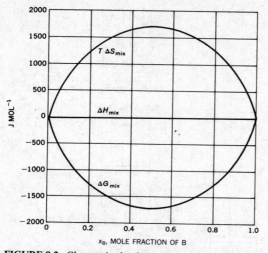

FIGURE 9-2 Changes in the thermodynamic functions for the formation of 1 mol of an ideal solution at 25°C.

either from $\partial(\Delta G_{mix})/\partial T = -\Delta S_{mix}$ or, with $\Delta H_{mix} = 0$, from $\Delta G_{mix} = \Delta H_{mix} - T\Delta S_{mix}$. The result is

$$\Delta S_{mix} = -x_A R \ln x_A - x_B R \ln x_B \tag{9-8}$$

The mixing process in which an ideal solution is formed is thus completely determined by Eq. (9-5). The consequences are $\Delta H_{mix} = 0$, $\Delta V_{mix} = 0$, and ΔS_{mix} according to Eq. (9-8). The free-energy and entropy quantities are shown in Table 9-1 and graphically, along with ΔH_{mix}, in Fig. 9-2. Notice that mixing is accompanied by a decrease in free energy and an increase in entropy, as we expect from the spontaneous nature of the mixing process.

9-2 Thermodynamic Properties of Liquid Solutions

Now let us investigate the changes in the thermodynamic quantities that occur when two liquids are mixed. If an ideal solution is formed, the free-energy change will be given by Eq. (9-5). We must see how the free-energy change that ocurs when two liquids are mixed can be determined so that we can compare observed behavior with ideal behavior.

A way of accomplishing the mixing of two liquids that allows the free energy of the process to be deduced is shown in Fig. 9-3. The vapor pressures of the pure liquids are P_A° and P_B°. The partial pressures of the components above the mixture, which has mole fractions x_A and x_B, are P_A and P_B. We assume that the vapors can be treated as ideal gases.

Now we can calculate the free-energy changes that occur when x_A mol of A

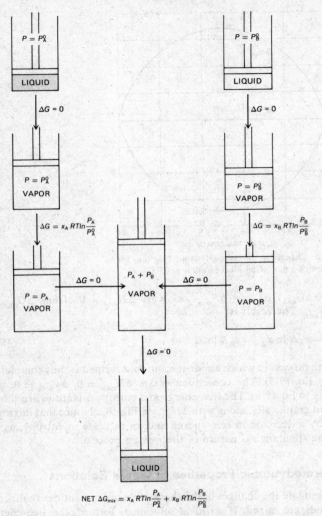

FIGURE 9-3 The free-energy change for the formation of 1 mol of a liquid mixture from x_A mol of A and x_B mol of B. The vapor pressures of pure A and B are P_A^0 and P_B^0. Their vapor pressures in the liquid mixture are P_A and P_B.

and x_B mol of B are taken from the pure liquids and added to the solution to form an additional mole of solution. The steps and the corresponding ΔG values are shown in Fig. 9-3. The net result is

$$\Delta G_{mix} = x_A RT \ln \frac{P_A}{P_A^\circ} + x_B RT \ln \frac{P_B}{P_B^\circ} \tag{9-9}$$

Through this equation measurements of the vapor pressures of the pure liquids P_A° and P_B° and of the partial pressures of the components above a solution give the free-energy change for the formation of 1 mol of solution of mole fractions x_A and x_B.

The free energy of mixing is equal to that of Eq. (9-5) and the solution is ideal only if

$$\frac{P_A}{P_A^\circ} = x_A \qquad \text{and} \qquad \frac{P_B}{P_B^\circ} = x_B$$

or

$$P_A = x_A P_A^\circ \qquad \text{and} \qquad P_B = x_B P_B^\circ \tag{9-10}$$

Obedience to these relations constitutes conformity to *Raoult's law*, which states that *the vapor pressure of a component of a solution is proportional to the mole fraction of the component.*

The vapor pressures of benzene and toluene over benzene-toluene solutions conform to Raoult's law, as shown in Fig. 9-4. In addition the volume change and the enthalpy change accompanying the formation of a benzene-toluene solution would be found to be quite small. (Or, equivalently, it would be found that Raoult's law is obeyed over a range of temperatures and total

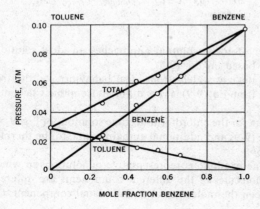

FIGURE 9-4
The vapor pressures of the components and the total vapor pressures for the nearly ideal solution benzene-toluene at 20°C. [*Data from R. Bell and T. Wright, J. Phys. Chem.,* **31:** *1884 (1927).*]

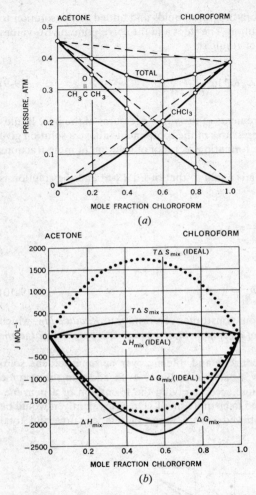

FIGURE 9-5
(a) Vapor-pressure diagram for the system chloroform-acetone at 35°C. [*From data of J. Von. Zawidzki, Z. Phys. Chem.*, **35:** *129* (*1900*).] (b) Changes in the thermodynamic functions for the formation of 1 mol of a chloroform-acetone solution at 25°C. The dotted lines show ideal behavior. (*Based on the data of I. Prigogine and R. Defay, "Thermodynamique chimique," Desoer, Liège, 1950.*)

pressures.) Thus the benzene-toluene solution approaches an ideal solution, according to the definition based on Eq. (9-5).

Other liquid solutions deviate widely from ideal behavior; i.e., the free energy of mixing calculated from Eq. (9-9) is very different from that calculated from Eq. (9-5).

The vapor-pressure data for the chloroform-acetone solutions of Fig. 9-5a, for example, lead, with Eq. (9-9) and additional enthalpy data, to the thermodynamic results of Fig. 9-5b.

This chloroform-acetone example is representative of solutions in which interactions between the molecules of the different components are different from the interactions between the molecules of an individual component. On mixing, these will interact with each other, and in the chloroform-acetone example, this interaction takes the form of hydrogen bonding; i.e.,

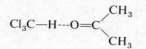

Heat will be evolved when the solution is formed, as can easily be noticed if the two components are mixed in a test tube. The nonideal behavior can be accounted for in part by a negative enthalpy of mixing in contrast to the zero enthalpy of mixing of an ideal solution.

The association of the components on mixing will also change the entropy from that calculated for an ideal solution. Very qualitatively, one might expect that the association in the solution would tend to restrict the motion of the molecules, and in view of the general discussion of entropy and freedom in Chap. 7, this would be expected to give the system less entropy than in the ideal case.

Thus our expectations are consistent with the observation that for a system like chloroform-acetone the enthalpy of mixing should be negative and that the entropy of mixing might be less positive than for an ideal solution.

Deviations from ideal behavior in the opposite direction occur and are illustrated by carbon tetrachloride–methanol solutions in Fig. 9-6a and b. Systems that show this behavior are frequently those made up of a component that is itself associated, as are water and alcohols, and a more or less inert component. Mixing tends to break up some of the association, and a positive enthalpy term can be expected because of the heat required to break up the associated component. The data for the carbon tetrachloride–methanol system (Fig. 9-6b) indicate that it is primarily this enthalpy effect which produces the free-energy effect. The region of negative heat of mixing and the appreciable entropy term, however, should caution against the use of qualitative arguments like those used here when other than very large effects are being considered.

9-3 Properties of the Components of Real Solutions: Partial Molal Quantities

In addition to treating the total thermodynamic changes that occur when a solution is formed, we find it helpful also to be able to distribute the properties of a solution among the components of which it is composed. (This is particularly clear when one component, present in minor amounts, is called the solute and is primarily responsible for the properties or reaction that is being considered.) Now we must see how we can go from measurable properties of the solution to quantities attributable to the components. This was done for ideal solutions in Sec. 9-1. Considerably more development is necessary for real solutions.

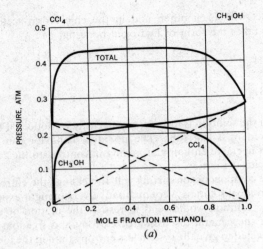

(a)

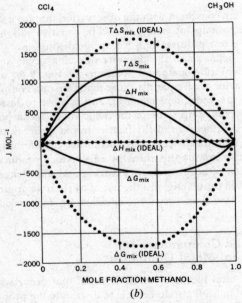

FIGURE 9-6
(a) Vapor-pressure diagram for the system carbon tetrachloride–methanol at 35°C. (*From J. Timmermans, "Physicochemical Constants of Binary Systems," vol. 2, Interscience Publishers, Inc., New York, 1959.*) (b) Thermodynamic changes for the formation of 1 mol of a carbon tetrachloride–methanol solution at 25°C. (*Based on the data of I. Prigogine and R. Defay, "Thermodynamique chimique," Desoer, Liège, 1950.*)

(b)

In the systems that have been investigated thus far in our studies of thermodynamics, the total amount of reagent in the system being considered has been fixed. Such systems are said to be *closed systems,* and the procedures that have been developed are suitable for finding changes that occur when there is some reaction in such systems or when the temperature or pressure changes and affects such systems.

When one treats the components of solutions, it is more convenient to be able to regard a certain amount of the solution as the system and then to investigate what happens when amounts of any of the components are added to the system. Such systems are said to be *open systems,* and we shall see in this and the following sections how we can apply thermodynamic methods to them. To begin with, we shall assume that the pressure and temperature are fixed and that only the amounts of the components of the solution are variable.

The volume of a solution is perhaps the easiest of its properties to visualize. Let us therefore first consider how one might treat the volume of a solution and its dependence on the number of moles of the components present. Experiments that would provide the answers might begin with some amount of one component, e.g., that designated the *solvent,* and then measurements would be made of the total volume of the system as the other component was added.

A curve showing the results that would be obtained from such measurements for rather dilute solutions of magnesium sulfate in water is shown in Fig. 9-7. The total volumes that can be read off such curves depend, of course, on the amounts of solute and solvent present and are therefore not of general use. The slope of the curves, however, gives the rate of change of volume at various points along the abscissa, i.e., at various relative amounts of solute and solvent. If n_A designates the number of moles of solvent and n_B the moles of solute, in calculus notation these slopes are

$$\left(\frac{\partial V}{\partial n_A}\right)_{n_B} \qquad \text{or} \qquad \left(\frac{\partial V}{\partial n_B}\right)_{n_A}$$

It is the value of the second of these partial derivatives that can be obtained from a curve like that of Fig. 9-7. To be more specific, we should write these partial derivatives as

$$\left(\frac{\partial V}{\partial n_A}\right)_{n_B, T, P} \qquad \text{and} \qquad \left(\frac{\partial V}{\partial n_B}\right)_{n_A, T, P}$$

to show that they imply the rate of change of volume with respect to the number of moles of one reagent when both the amount of the other reagent and the temperature and pressure are held constant.

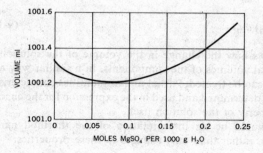

FIGURE 9-7
The volume of solutions containing 1000 g of water and various amounts of $MgSO_4$. (*From G. N. Lewis and M. Randall, "Thermodynamics," 2d ed., revised by K. S. Pitzer and L. Brewer. Copyright McGraw-Hill, Inc., 1961. Used by permission of McGraw-Hill Book Company.*)

Such derivatives, with T,P, and the amounts of the other reagents held constant, are examples of what are called *partial molal quantities*. They play a very important role in the thermodynamic treatment of solutions. Although their derivative nature may make their character and role somewhat obscure at first, one can come to recognize that they do give the contribution of a mole of the material in the solution specified to the property being considered. For example, $(\partial V/\partial n_B)_{n_A}$ for a solution containing 0.1 mol of $MgSO_4$ per 1000 g of water is, according to Fig. 9-7, 0.83 ml mol^{-1}. This means that for a system containing 0.1 mol of $MgSO_4$ and 1000 g of water, the rate of change of volume with the number of moles of $MgSO_4$ is 0.83 ml mol^{-1}. More easily pictured is the situation in which one has a very large amount of this solution, so that 1 mol of solute could be added without significantly changing the concentration. Then the change in volume that results from the addition of the 1 mol would itself be $(\partial V/\partial n_B)_{n_A}$, and we see that this partial molal volume is in fact the volume contributed by 1 mol of $MgSO_4$ in a solution of this composition. Thus in the solution of the specified composition a partial molal quantity is the contribution of a mole of the reagent to the property being dealt with.

Such derivatives also appear if we recognize that, if T and P are considered fixed, a quantity such as the volume of a two-component system is a function of n_A and n_B and therefore that the total differential

$$dV = \left(\frac{\partial V}{\partial n_A}\right)_{n_B} dn_A + \left(\frac{\partial V}{\partial n_B}\right)_{n_A} dn_B \tag{9-11}$$

can be written. The partial derivative coefficients are seen to be the partial molal volumes, which of course are dependent on the composition of the solution. One can in fact carry over the notation procedure of special (sans-serif) letters for molar quantities and add a bar over the symbol to designate a partial molal quantity. In this way the nature of the partial molal derivatives can be emphasized. With

$$\left(\frac{\partial V}{\partial n_A}\right)_{n_B} = (\bar{V}_A) \quad \text{and} \quad \left(\frac{\partial V}{\partial n_B}\right)_{n_A} = (\bar{V}_B)$$

one can rewrite Eq. (9-11) as

$$dV = (\bar{V}_A)\, dn_A + (\bar{V}_B)\, dn_B \tag{9-12}$$

Equation (9-12) shows how the change in the volume of the solution is related to the partial molal volumes of the components. In a similar way any thermodynamic property can be treated. Partial molar quantities characteristic of each component can be determined and used in the expression for the change in a thermodynamic property of the solution itself.

Even more useful would be an interpretation of the thermodynamic properties of the solution, rather than only *changes* in these properties.

First a general mathematical expression, an example of Euler's theorem, must be deduced. This will be done in terms of one representative thermodynamic property, the volume V of the system. Let us investigate the dependence of the volume of a system, any system, on the number of moles $n_A, n_B, \ldots$ of the components present at some fixed temperature and pressure. From experimental results we know that if we were to increase the amounts of all the components by some factor a, the volume would increase by this factor. Thus, if the new amounts of the components $n'_A, n'_B, n'_C, \ldots$ are related to the old amounts n_A, n_B, n_C by

$$n'_A = an_A \qquad n'_B = an_B \qquad \cdots \tag{9-13}$$

the new volume $V(n'_A, n'_B, \ldots)$ is related to the old volume $V(n_A, n_B, \ldots)$ by

$$V(n'_A, n'_B, \ldots) = aV(n_A, n_B, \ldots) \tag{9-14}$$

Now let us differentiate this equation with respect to a. The derivative of $V(n'_A, n'_B, \ldots)$, the left side of Eq. (9-14), with respect to a, can be obtained by writing the total differential and then dividing by da to obtain

$$\frac{dV(n'_A, n'_B, \ldots)}{da} = \frac{\partial V(n'_A, n'_B, \ldots)}{\partial n'_A} \frac{dn'_A}{da} + \frac{\partial V(n'_A, n'_B, \ldots)}{\partial n'_B} \frac{dn'_B}{da} + \cdots$$

$$= \frac{\partial V(n'_A, n'_B, \ldots)}{\partial n'_A} n_A + \frac{\partial V(n'_A, n'_B, \ldots)}{\partial n'_B} n_B + \cdots \tag{9-15}$$

Since $V(n_A, n_B, \ldots)$ is independent of a, the derivative of the right side of Eq. (9-14) with respect to a is simply

$$\frac{d}{da}[aV(n_A, n_B, \ldots)] = V(n_A, n_B, \ldots) \tag{9-16}$$

Equating the results of Eqs. (9-15) and (9-16) gives

$$\frac{\partial V(n'_A, n'_B, \ldots)}{\partial n'_A} n_A + \frac{\partial V(n'_A, n'_B, \ldots)}{\partial n'_B} n_B + \cdots = V(n_A, n_B, \ldots) \tag{9-17}$$

This result is valid for all values of a, and we find that a useful relation is obtained by setting $a = 1$. Then $n_A = n'_A$, $n_B = n'_B$, etc., and we have

$$n_A \frac{\partial V(n_A, n_B, \ldots)}{\partial n_A} + n_B \frac{\partial V(n_A, n_B, \ldots)}{\partial n_B} + \cdots = V(n_A, n_B, \ldots)$$

or more simply

$$n_A \frac{\partial V}{\partial n_A} + n_B \frac{\partial V}{\partial n_B} + \cdots = V \qquad (9\text{-}18)$$

The partial derivatives are the partial molar quantities. With the notation of the bar on the special symbols we have obtained

$$V = n_A \bar{V}_A + n_B \bar{V}_B + \cdots \qquad (9\text{-}19)$$

Similar expressions would be obtained for the other thermodynamic properties H, S, and G on which our attention might be focused.

We thus see that the experimentally accessible partial molar quantities again can be looked on as the molar value for the component in the solution and that the properties of a solution, as well as changes in these properties, can be deduced from the number of moles of the components and the partial molar quantities of each component by means of relations like

$$dV = \bar{V}_A \, dn_A + \bar{V}_B \, dn_B \quad \text{and} \quad V = n_A \bar{V}_A + n_B \bar{V}_B$$

9-4 The Free Energies of the Components of a Solution: Solvents

In view of the development of the preceding section, the free energy of a two-component solution at a given temperature and pressure can be formally described by

$$G = n_A \bar{G}_A + n_B \bar{G}_B \qquad (9\text{-}20)$$

This expression can be applied to any solution, real and nonideal or ideal.

We can also obtain an expression for this solution free energy by considering the formation of any real solution by the process of Fig. 9-3. The free energy of n_A moles of liquid A in its standard state is $n_A \, G_A^\circ$. The free energy of n_B mol of liquid B in its standard state is $n_B G_B^\circ$. The free-energy change accompanying the addition of each mol of A to an amount of solution large enough to ensure that its composition is not changed is, as described in Fig. 9-3, $RT \ln (P_A/P_A^\circ)$. Likewise that for addition of each mole of B is $RT \ln (P_B/P_B^\circ)$. The free energy of the solution is described in terms of that of the pure components and the changes that occur during mixing by

$$G = n_A G_A^\circ + n_B G_B^\circ + n_A RT \ln \frac{P_A}{P_A^\circ} + n_B RT \ln \frac{P_B}{P_B^\circ}$$

$$= n_A \left(G_A^\circ + RT \ln \frac{P_A}{P_A^\circ} \right) + n_B \left(G_B^\circ + RT \ln \frac{P_B}{P_B^\circ} \right) \qquad (9\text{-}21)$$

Comparison of Eq. (9-20) with Eq. (9-21) gives, for example,

$$\overline{G}_A = G_A^\circ + RT \ln \frac{P_A}{P_A^\circ} \tag{9-22}$$

Thus we can deduce the partial molar free energies of the components in any real solution from vapor-pressure data. [The terms like $\overline{G}_A$, here referred to as a partial molar free energy, are often called *chemical potentials* and are given the symbol μ. Then, in addition, the standard-state free energies are designated as a chemical potential. With this terminology, Eq. (9-22) becomes

$$\mu_A = \mu_A^\circ + RT \ln \frac{P_A}{P_A^\circ} \tag{9-23}$$

Here we shall continue to write symbols like G_A° and $\overline{G}_A$ and refer to them as free energies per mole.]

If a solution is ideal, Raoult's law applies and Eq. (9-21) has the form

$$G = n_A G_A^\circ + n_B G_B^\circ + n_A RT \ln x_A + n_B RT \ln x_B$$

$$= n_A G_A^\circ + n_B G_B^\circ + n_A RT \ln \frac{n_A}{n_A + n_B} + n_B RT \ln \frac{n_B}{n_A + n_B} \tag{9-24}$$

The partial molar free energies can now be recognized by forming, $(\partial G/\partial n_A)_{T,n_B}$ and $(\partial G/\partial n_B)_{T,n_A}$. Recalling that $d \ln u = (1/u)\,du$, we obtain

$$\overline{G}_A = \left(\frac{\partial G}{\partial n_A}\right)_{T,n_B} = G_A^\circ + RT \ln x_A \qquad \text{[ideal]} \tag{9-25}$$

with a similar expression for component B.

We now have Eq. (9-25), which shows the free energy contributed by the components of an ideal solution, and Eq. (9-22), which shows the free energy contributed by the components of a liquid solution with partial pressures P_A and P_B when the mole fractions of the components are x_A and x_B.

The solvents of all real solutions approach obedience to Raoult's law in the dilute-solution limit, as can be seen in the examples of Figs. 9-5a and 9-6a. You now see that the characterization of the ideal-solution component behavior given by Eq. (9-25) applies to the *solvent* of all real solutions in the dilute-solution limit. Thus the component contributions to the free energy given by Eq. (9-25) represent the approximate behavior of a few real solutions over the entire concentration range and the behavior in the dilute-solution limit of the solvents of *all* solutions.

It is convenient to have an expression of the form of Eq. (9-25) even when the component of interest is not conforming to ideal behavior. This can be done by introducing the activity a, defined as $a_A = P_A/P_A^\circ$, so that the partial molar free energy is given, even for nonideal solutions, by

$$\overline{G}_A = G_A^\circ + RT \ln a_A \tag{9-26}$$

Since we expect a_A to approach x_A for the solvent of a dilute solution, it is convenient to introduce the *activity coefficient* γ as

$$\gamma = \frac{a_A}{x_A} \quad \text{or} \quad a_A = \gamma x_A \tag{9-27}$$

By its variation from unity the activity coefficient shows the nonideality of the solution. Since the solvents of all solutions that are sufficiently dilute obey Raoult's law, the value of γ approaches unity for the solvent of any solution as the solute concentration approaches zero.

The vapor-pressure data of Figs. 9-5a and 9-6a provide the necessary data for the calculation of activity and activity coefficients according to $a_A = P_A/P_A^\circ$ and $\gamma_A = a_A/x_A = (P_A/P_A^\circ)/x_A$. The activities and activity coefficients for acetone-chloroform solutions are shown in Fig. 9-8. The factors that operate to make the activity coefficients less than unity are of course the same as those mentioned in Sec. 9-2 in connection with the free energy of mixing in the formation of solutions.

It should be noted that the partial molar free energy of a solvent is referred to that of the pure liquid solvent at the temperature and pressure of the solution. This standard state is reached when the value of P_A/P_A° or of a_A approaches unity. A rather different standard state is convenient when solutes are treated.

9-5 The Free Energies of the Components of a Solution: Solutes

For some solutions, particularly those made up from liquid components and those with a wide range of the relative amounts of the components, it is not desirable to designate components as solute and solvent. Then both the components can be treated in the manner indicated in Sec. 9-4, where the pure component was taken as the standard state. For other solutions, particularly when a component is a solid or a gas and is present in relatively small amounts, it is convenient to designate this component as a solute and to refer its thermodynamic properties to a different standard state.

Let us first notice a general result, illustrated by vapor-pressure curves like those of Figs. 9-5a and 9-6a, that the vapor pressure of a *solute* of a dilute solution is proportional to the mole fraction of the solute. Furthermore, the mole fraction and the molal concentration become proportional to each other as the solution becomes more dilute. Thus for these dilute solutions we can write

$$P_B = kx_B \quad \text{or} \quad P_B = k'm \tag{9-28}$$

where x_B and m are the mole fraction and the molal concentration of the solute, component B, of the solution and k and k' are constants. Solutes that obey Eq. (9-28) are said to conform to *Henry's law*.

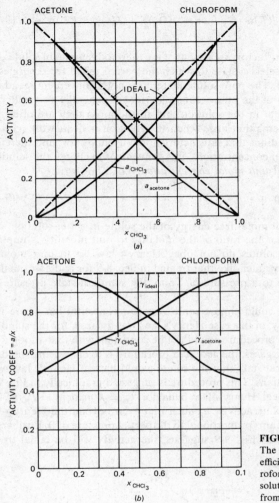

FIGURE 9-8

The activities and activity coefficients of acetone and chloroform in acetone-chloroform solutions at 25°C. Calculated from the data of Fig. 9-5(a).

The difference in partial molal free energies of a solute at two concentrations can be written in terms of the vapor pressures of the solute over the two solutions as

$$(\bar{G}_B)_2 - (\bar{G}_B)_1 = RT \ln \frac{P_2}{P_1} \tag{9-29}$$

Furthermore, if the two solutions are dilute enough to conform to Henry's law, by insertion of Eq. (9-28) one obtains

$$(\bar{G}_B)_2 - (\bar{G}_B)_1 = RT \ln \frac{x_2}{x_1} \quad \text{or} \quad (\bar{G}_B)_2 - (\bar{G}_B)_1 = RT \ln \frac{m_2}{m_1} \quad \text{(9-30)}$$

To proceed to a satisfactory treatment of the thermodynamics of solutes, we must now see how to select a state to which the partial molal free energies of solutes can be referred. The pure solute material is not a convenient standard, because the properties of the pure solute material are generally very different from those of the solute in the solution and furthermore they are often not pertinent to the problems that arise when the solution is dealt with.

For solutes of solutions that satisfactorily obey Henry's law, and therefore Eqs. (9-30), up to molal concentrations, it is convenient to choose the standard state as the solution at *unit molal concentration*. Then one writes

$$\bar{G}_B = \bar{G}_B^\circ + RT \ln m \qquad \qquad \text{(9-31)}$$

where $\bar{G}_B^\circ$ is the partial molal free energy of the solute in a $1\,m$ solution, and where the fact that m is the ratio of the molality to unit molality is implied.

Solutions whose solutes do not obey Henry's law up to unit molality present a situation very much like that treated in Sec. 8-9 for real gases that do not behave ideally up to a pressure of 1 atm, the standard-state pressure for ideal gases.

As for gases, one could choose some very low concentration where uniformity to the ideal law, in this case Henry's law, was assured, for the standard state. However, such a procedure would not be consistent with that adopted for "ideal" systems. As for gases, the accepted procedure is to choose the standard state as the hypothetical state that the solute would have if Henry's law were obeyed up to $1\,m$ solutions. This procedure is suggested graphically in Fig. 9-9.

In the region of ideal, Henry's-law, behavior, $P_B = k'm$, or $m = P_B/k'$. Let us now introduce a solute activity a_B such that even beyond the Henry's-law region this activity remains proportional to the partial pressure of B. Further, let $a_B = P_B/k$, and then, as Fig. 9-9 suggests, the activity will be equal to the

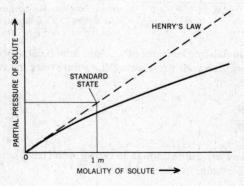

FIGURE 9-9
The standard state of a solute in a solution in which Henry's law is not obeyed up to a concentration of $1\,m$. (The vapor of the solute is assumed to behave ideally, so that its vapor pressure and fugacity can be equated.)

molarity in the limit of low molality but at higher molalities will correspond to a hypothetical solution that still maintains conformity with Henry's law.

Now the standard state for the solute can be defined as that which has unit activity, and we can write

$$\bar{G}_B = \bar{G}_B^\circ + RT \ln a_B \qquad (9\text{-}32)$$

where $\bar{G}_B^\circ$ is the partial molal free energy of the standard state, i.e., the value of G_B when $a_B = 1$.

Comparison of Eq. (9-32) with Eq. (9-31) suggests, again, the introduction of an activity coefficient, usually defined now as

$$\gamma = \frac{a_B}{m} \qquad (9\text{-}33)$$

[Since both a_B in Eq. (9-32) and m in Eq. (9-31) imply the ratio of these quantities to their unit values, they imply dimensionless quantities. Thus γ is likewise dimensionless.]

With the introduction of the activity coefficient, the molal free energy of the solute of a solution can be written

$$\bar{G}_B = \bar{G}_B^\circ + RT \ln \gamma m \qquad (9\text{-}34)$$

It is, of course, also possible to compare the activity of the solute with the mole fraction rather than the molality of the solute. This procedure is more consistent with that used for solvents, but it is not generally used because of the chemist's tendency to deal with solute concentrations in terms of molality.

To illustrate the use of relations like Eqs. (9-32) and (9-34), let us now consider one way of determining the activities and activity coefficients of nonelectrolyte solutes.

9-6 Solute Activities from Solvent Properties: An Application of the Gibbs-Duhem Equation

It is often not feasible to determine the partial molar free energies and the activities of solutes from measurements of the vapor pressure of the solute. For nonvolatile solutes, for example, it is clearly necessary to have an alternative procedure, and here one that depends on the relation between solute and solvent properties as given by the *Gibbs-Duhem equation* will be developed. Specifically, we shall develop the relation between the free energies of a single solute and the solvent of a solution.

One of the relations developed in Sec. 9-3 for partial molal quantities was

$$dG = \bar{G}_A \, dn_A + \bar{G}_B \, dn_B$$

The rate of change of solution free energy with additions of solvent component A is then given by

$$\frac{dG}{dn_A} = \bar{G}_A + \bar{G}_B \frac{dn_B}{dn_A} \qquad (9\text{-}35)$$

Alternatively, dG/dn_A can be obtained by differentiating the expression $G = n_A \bar{G}_A + n_B \bar{G}_B$, also obtained in Sec. 9-3, with respect to n_A, and this gives

$$\frac{dG}{dn_A} = n_A \frac{d\bar{G}_A}{dn_A} + \bar{G}_A + n_B \frac{d\bar{G}_B}{dn_A} + \bar{G}_B \frac{dn_B}{dn_A} \qquad (9\text{-}36)$$

Equating these two expressions for dG/dn_A leads to the desired Gibbs-Duhem equation

$$n_A \frac{d\bar{G}_A}{dn_A} = -n_B \frac{d\bar{G}_B}{dn_A} \qquad (9\text{-}37)$$

An alternative form is obtained by dividing numerators and denominators of both sides by $n_A + n_B$ to obtain mole-fraction terms and the result

$$x_A \frac{d\bar{G}_A}{dx_A} = -x_B \frac{d\bar{G}_B}{dx_A} \qquad (9\text{-}38)$$

Now information on the variation of solvent free energy can be used to deduce the variation of solute free energy.

Expressions for either solvent or solute partial molar free energy have the form

$$\bar{G} = \bar{G}^\circ + RT \ln a$$

Thus

$$\frac{d\bar{G}_A}{dx_A} = RT \frac{d(\ln a_A)}{dx_A} \quad \text{and} \quad \frac{d\bar{G}_B}{dx_A} = RT \frac{d(\ln a_B)}{dx_A} \qquad (9\text{-}39)$$

With these expressions, Eq. (9-38) becomes

$$x_A \frac{d(\ln a_A)}{dx_A} = -x_B \frac{d(\ln a_B)}{dx_A}$$

or

$$d(\ln a_B) = -\frac{x_A}{x_B} d(\ln a_A) \qquad (9\text{-}40)$$

TABLE 9-2 The Activities of Water and Sucrose in Water-Sucrose Solutions at 0°C Obtained from the Vapor Pressure of Water and the Gibbs-Duhem Relation

Molality of sucrose	Mole fractions		Vapor pressure of water, mmHg	a_{water}	$a_{sucrose}$
	Sucrose	Water			
0	0	1.000	4.579	1.000	0
0.2	0.0036	0.996	4.562	0.996	0.0036
0.5	0.0089	0.991	4.536	0.990	0.0089
1.0	0.0177	0.982	4.489	0.980	0.019
3.5	0.059	0.941	4.195	0.916	0.146
4.5	0.075	0.925	4.064	0.888	0.238
5.0	0.082	0.918	3.994	0.872	0.292
6.0	0.098	0.902	3.867	0.845	0.403

Source: Data from "International Critical Tables," vol. 3, p. 293, McGraw-Hill Book Company, New York, 1923.

With this relation and data for the activity for one component of the solution over a range of mole-fraction values a suitable integration procedure provides information on the changes in the activity of the other component. Some results for the activity of sucrose in water deduced from measurements of the water vapor pressure are given in Table 9-2.

9-7 Colligative Properties: The Vapor-Pressure Lowering

The variables that affect the solutions we have been dealing with are pressure, temperature, and composition. The complexities of real solutions are such that in all the developments so far, the pressure and temperature have been presumed to be fixed, so that we could concentrate on the remaining variable, the composition. There are, however, several important properties of dilute solutions that require attention to be paid to all three variables.

Now let us deal with four properties of dilute solutions for which the temperature or the pressure, as well as the concentration of the solute, vary. These four properties are the decrease in vapor pressure of the solvent, the lowering of the freezing point and the raising of the boiling point of the solution, and the development of an osmotic pressure. These properties are known as *colligative properties*. They are "tied together" (Latin *colligatus,* for tied or bound together, as in the other familiar chemical term ligand) by their common dependence on the number of solute particles in a given amount of solvent.

The first of the colligative properties, the lowering of the vapor pressure of the solvent as a result of the addition of a nonvolatile solute, is directly implied by Raoult's law.

Raoult's law is usually expressed in terms of the solvent mole fraction. Then it is written as

$$P_A = x_A P_A^\circ \tag{9-41}$$

If $x_A = 1 - x_B$ is inserted in place of x_A, the dependence of the solvent vapor pressure on the mole fraction of solute can be written as

$$P_A = (1 - x_B)P_A^\circ \quad \text{or} \quad P_A^\circ - P_A = x_B P_A^\circ \tag{9-42}$$

According to this result, the vapor-pressure lowering $P_A^\circ - P_A$ for a given solvent depends only on the mole fraction x_B of the solute.

Raoult's law, as we saw in Sec. 9-4, is followed by the solvent in the dilute-solution limit even if the solvent behavior is nonideal in more concentrated solutions. Thus Eq. (9-42) applies to all solutions in the dilute-solution limit. Thus the lowering of the vapor pressure of a solvent as a result of the presence of a nonvolatile solute depends, at least in the dilute-solution limit, only on the mole fraction of the solute. None of the properties of the solute are involved; it may be ionic or molecular, and the molecules may be small or large. Thus, the lowering of the vapor pressure is one of the colligative properties.

9-8 The Boiling-Point Elevation

Now consider the change in the boiling point that results from the addition of a small quantity of a nonvolatile solute to a solvent. The liquid-vapor equilibrium that exists allows us to write

$$(G_A)_v = \bar{G}_A \tag{9-43}$$

where $(G_A)_v$ is the molar free energy of A in the vapor and $\bar{G}_A$ is the partial molar free energy of A in the solution, both under the same conditions of temperature and pressure.

The molar free energy of the vapor, which is assumed to consist only of the solvent, component A, is a function of T and P. The molar free energy of A in the solution, i.e., its partial molar free energy or chemical potential, is a function of T, P, and the composition. If ideal behavior is assumed, the composition dependence is given by the $RT \ln x$ term and we can write

$$G_A = (G_A^\circ)_l + RT \ln x_A \tag{9-44}$$

where $(G_A^\circ)_l$ is the molar free energy of pure liquid A.

Equations (9-43) and (9-44) can be rearranged to read

$$\frac{(G_A)_v - (G_A^\circ)_l}{T} = \frac{\Delta G_{vap}}{T} = R \ln x_A \tag{9-45}$$

where the free energy of vaporization, ΔG_{vap} has been introduced.

Equation (9-45) relates the mole fraction of A in a boiling solution with a nonvolatile solute to the free energy of vaporization of A. We are interested in the temperature dependence of this relation. To begin with we write

$$\frac{d}{dT}\left(\frac{\Delta G_{vap}}{T}\right) = R \frac{d \ln x_A}{dT} \tag{9-46}$$

The left side can be simplified by using Eq. (8-51):

$$\frac{d(\Delta G/T)}{dT} = -\frac{\Delta H}{T^2}$$

to obtain the result

$$-\frac{\Delta H_{vap}}{RT^2} = \frac{d \ln x_A}{dT} \tag{9-47}$$

The temperature change required to maintain equilibrium when a nonvolatile solute is added to the pure solvent and the solvent mole fraction changes from 1 to x_A can now be determined. The temperature will change from T_{bp}, the boiling point of the pure solvent, to a temperature T. If ΔH_{vap} is assumed to remain constant, the integral is

$$-\frac{\Delta H_{vap}}{R} \int_{T_{bp}}^{T} \frac{1}{T^2} dT = \int_{x_A=1}^{x_A} d \ln x_A$$

and integration yields

$$\frac{\Delta H_{vap}}{R}\left(\frac{1}{T} - \frac{1}{T_{bp}}\right) = \ln x_A \tag{9-48}$$

Now let us rearrange this result so that it expresses the temperature change in terms of the mole fraction of solute x_B and does so for values of $x_B \ll 1$. With the series expansion

$$\ln(1 + y) = y + \frac{y^2}{2} + \frac{y^3}{3} + \cdots$$

we have

$$\ln x_A = \ln(1 - x_B) \approx -x_B$$

Furthermore

$$\frac{1}{T} - \frac{1}{T_{bp}} = \frac{T_{bp} - T}{TT_{bp}} \approx -\frac{\Delta T}{T_{bp}^2}$$

where ΔT is the change $T - T_{bp}$ in the boiling point and it is assumed that ΔT

is small enough for TT_{bp} to equal $T_{bp}{}^2$. These rearrangements and approximations allow Eq. (9-48) to be written as

$$\Delta T_{bp} = \frac{RT_{bp}{}^2}{\Delta H_{vap}} x_B \tag{9-49}$$

It is customary in colligative-property work to use molality rather than mole fraction of the solute. Molality, represented by m, is defined as the moles of solute per 1000 g of solvent, and if n_A is the number of moles of solvent in 1000 g of solvent,

$$x_B = \frac{m}{n_A + m} \approx \frac{m}{n_A} \tag{9-50}$$

The final simplification results because for dilute solutions, m is much less than n_A. For any solvent A the quantity n_A is readily calculated as 1000 divided by the molar mass of A.

In terms of molality, the boiling-point elevation is written

$$\Delta T_{bp} = \frac{RT_{bp}{}^2}{n_A \Delta H_{vap}} m \tag{9-51}$$

The fractional expression is called the *boiling-point elevation constant* or the *ebullioscopic constant* and is frequently represented by K_{bp}. With this notation we have

$$\Delta T_{bp} = K_{bp} m \tag{9-52}$$

where

$$K_{bp} = \frac{RT_{bp}{}^2}{n_A \Delta H_{vap}} \tag{9-53}$$

and $n_A = 1000/M_A$ where M_A is the molar mass of the solvent, A, in grams.

Some results comparing the values of K_{bp} from Eq. (9-52) and measurements of the boiling-point elevation with the values obtained from Eq. (9-53) are shown in Table 9-3. This agreement can be expected to be good, however, only for solutes that are neither associated nor dissociated in solution. If either of these processes occurs, the number of solute particles per 1000 g of solvent is not simply Avogadro's number times the molality.

9-9 The Freezing-Point Depression

Now let us consider the equilibrium between a component in a solution and that component as a solid in equilibrium with the solution. Here we shall think of the

TABLE 9-3 Molal Boiling-Point-Elevation Constants at 1 atm Pressure

Solvent	bp,°C	K_{bp} Observed = $\dfrac{\Delta T_{bp}}{m}$	K_{bp} Calculated [Eq. (9-53)]
Water	100.0	0.51	0.51
Ethanol	78.4	1.22	1.20
Benzene	80.1	2.53	2.63
Ethyl ether	34.6	2.02	2.11
Chloroform	61.3	3.63	3.77

solvent of a solution and the freezing process which leads to the separation of pure solid solvent. As will be shown, the effect of solute in the solution is the depression of the freezing point of the solvent.

In deriving an expression for the lowering of the freezing point we shall obtain, along the way, a relation for the solubility of a solid in an ideal solution. We pass over this expression here and leave it to be dealt with in Sec. 10-10.

The equilibrium maintained at the freezing point between component A in the solution and solid A allows us to write

$$(G_A)_s = \bar{G}_A \tag{9-54}$$

where the subscript s stands for solid. If A in the solution behaves ideally, we can write

$$G_A = (G_A^\circ)_l + RT \ln x_A \tag{9-55}$$

Now we can proceed, as in Sec. 9-8, to a rearrangement and an integration showing the change in freezing point from T_{fp} to T as the mole fraction of A is reduced from 1 to x_A. If $\Delta H_{fus} = H_l^\circ - H_s^\circ$ is assumed to remain constant over this temperature range, we obtain, as in Sec. 9-8,

$$\frac{\Delta H_{fus}}{R}\left(\frac{1}{T_{fp}} - \frac{1}{T}\right) = \ln x_A \tag{9-56}$$

It is this expression that will be used in Sec. 10-10 to treat solubilities.

Assumption of a small change ΔT_{fp} in the freezing point for a small addition x_B of solute (again as in Sec. 9-8) allows this result to be transformed into

$$\Delta T_{fp} = -\frac{RT_{fp}^2}{\Delta H_{fus}} x_B \tag{9-57}$$

TABLE 9-4 Freezing-Point Depressions for Solutions of Mannitol in Water

Molality	fp,°C	$-\dfrac{\Delta T_{fp}}{m}$
0.00402	−0.0075	1.86
0.00842	−0.0157	1.86
0.01404	−0.0260	1.852
0.02829	−0.0525	1.856
0.06259	−0.1162	1.857

Source: From data of L. H. Adams, *J. Am. Chem. Soc.*, **37**:481 (1915).

This result can also be written in terms of molality, and it then becomes

$$\Delta T_{fp} = -K_{fp}m \tag{9-58}$$

where

$$K_{fp} = \frac{R T_{fp}^{2}}{n_A \, \Delta H_{fus}} \tag{9-59}$$

and $n_A = 1000/M_A$ where M_A is the molar mass of the solvent, A, in grams. The constant K_{fp} is known as the *freezing-point-depression constant* and is clearly a function only of the solvent. The freezing-point depression of dilute solutions is therefore a function of the properties of the solvent and is independent of any feature of the solute except its concentration in the solution. The depression of the freezing point is therefore another colligative property.

Table 9-4 shows the accuracy with which freezing-point depressions can be measured and indicates the degree to which the dilute-solution freezing-point-depression equation is obeyed. The heat of fusion of water at 0°C is 6008 J mol^{-1} and the calculated value of K_{fp} is 1.860.

Freezing-point-depression measurements find frequent use in molecular-mass determinations. In the field of organic chemistry it is often very helpful to have a value for the molecular mass of a newly synthesized or isolated material whose structure is being determined.

9-10 Osmotic Pressure

Osmotic pressure needs, perhaps, more of an introduction than the properties of the preceding sections. The phenomenon of osmosis depends on the existence of *semipermeable membranes*. Such membranes are of a great variety, but they are all characterized by the fact that they allow one component of a solution to pass through and prevent the passage of another component. Cellophane and a number of plant or animal membranes, for example, are permeable to water but not to higher-molecular-mass compounds. Mention can also be made of the semipermeability of a palladium foil, which is permeable to hydrogen gas but not to nitrogen and other gases. With such a membrane, osmosis can be studied in the vapor phase.

Any osmosis apparatus depends on the separation of a solution from its pure solvent by means of a membrane, permeable to the solvent but impermeable to the solute. The essential features of the system are shown schematically in Fig. 9-10. When such an arrangement is made, it is found that there is a natural tendency for the solvent to flow from the pure-solvent chamber through the membrane into the solution chamber. This tendency can be opposed by applying pressure to the solution chamber. The excess pressure that must be applied to the solution to produce equilibrium is known as the *osmotic pressure* Π. It is through this quantity that the quantitative aspects of osmosis are studied.

The osmotic pressure developed between any dilute solution and its solvent will be shown to be a colligative property. It is therefore dependent only on the concentration of the solution and on the properties of the solvent. It is important to recognize that the nature of the semipermeable membrane and the mechanism by which it allows solvent to pass through it but prevents the passage of solute is of no importance for the study of osmotic pressure as a colligative property.

The thermodynamic basis of the osmotic pressure can now be shown. Consider the schematic arrangement of Fig. 9-10. The solvent in the pure-solvent compartment will be subject to no pressure or temperature change or solute addition. Thus

$$d(G_A)_{\text{pure solv}} = 0 \tag{9-60}$$

The solvent in the solution compartment, on the other hand, is subject to a pressure change and the addition of solute. The free energy changes as a result of the change in x_A, assuming ideal behavior, according to an $RT \, d(\ln x_A)$ term. The free-energy change due to a pressure change dP is $\bar{V}_A \, dP$, where $\bar{V}_A$ is the partial molar volume of A. Thus, for the solvent in the solution compartment

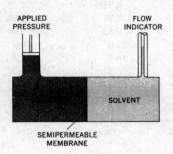

APPLIED PRESSURE

FLOW INDICATOR

SOLVENT

SEMIPERMEABLE MEMBRANE

FIGURE 9-10
Schematic representation of an osmotic-pressure apparatus.

$$d\bar{G}_A = \bar{V}_A \, dP + RT \, d \ln x_A \tag{9-61}$$

For equilibrium to be maintained with the unaffected pure solvent of the solvent compartment, the net change in $\bar{G}_A$ must be zero. Thus

$$\bar{V}_A \, dP = -RT \, d \ln x_A \tag{9-62}$$

Integration from $x_A = 1$, for which the pressure is P_{init} to x_A, for which the pressure is P_{final}, can be carried out if it is assumed that $\bar{V}_A$ is a constant equal to the molar volume V_A of the pure solvent. Then

$$V_A(P_{final} - P_{init}) = -RT \ln x_A \tag{9-63}$$

The excess pressure is the osmotic pressure Π and thus, for $x_A = 1 - x_B$, $x_B \ll 1$, and $\ln x_A \approx -x_B$, Eq. (9-63) gives the desired colligative property relation

$$V_A\Pi = RTx_B \tag{9-64}$$

An interesting variation of this result is obtained by multiplying by n_A, the number of moles of A, which is approximately equal to $n_A + n_B$. This gives

$$n_A V_A \Pi = RTn_A x_B \approx n_B RT \tag{9-65}$$

If $\mathbf{V}$ is introduced to represent $n_A V_A$, which is, approximately, the volume of solution containing n_B mol of solute, we can write

TABLE 9-5 The Osmotic Pressure of Aqueous Solutions of Sucrose at 20°C

Concentration		Observed osmotic pressure, atm	Calculated osmotic pressure	
m (molality)	M (molarity)		From Eq. (9-64)	From Eq. (9-66)
0.1	0.098	2.59	2.40	2.36
0.2	0.192	5.06	4.81	4.63
0.3	0.282	7.61	7.21	6.80
0.4	0.370	10.14	9.62	8.90
0.5	0.453	12.75	12.0	10.9
0.6	0.533	15.39	14.4	12.8
0.7	0.610	18.13	16.8	14.7
0.8	0.685	20.91	19.2	16.5
0.9	0.757	23.72	21.6	18.2
1.0	0.825	26.64	24.0	19.8

Source: Osmotic-pressure data of Morse, reported by A. Findlay, "Osmotic Pressure," Longmans, Green & Co., Inc., New York, 1919.

$$\Pi V \doteq n_B RT \quad \text{or} \quad \Pi = MRT \tag{9-66}$$

where M is the molarity of the solution. The similarity of this expression to the ideal-gas law led van't Hoff and others to some not very fruitful ideas that view the osmotic pressure as arising from a molecular-bombardment process. It is recognized here that Eq. (9-66) is merely an approximate form obtained from the thermodynamic dilute-solution expression (9-64).

A comparison of the observed osmotic pressure as a function of concentration with the behavior expected on the basis of the derived expressions is shown in Table 9-5.

PROBLEMS — You're RIGHT! A Bloody Big one!

9-1. The following vapor-pressure data for solutions of silicon tetrachloride and carbon tetrachloride at 25°C have been reported by S. E. Wood, *J. Am. Chem. Soc.*, **59**:1510 (1937).

Mole fraction SiCl$_4$ in liquid	0	0.266	0.472	0.632	1.00
Mole fraction SiCl$_4$ in vapor	0	0.436	0.648	0.773	1.00
Total vapor pressure, mmHg	114.9	153.0	179.1	198.5	238.3

Prepare a graph of vapor pressures of the components and the total vapor pressure versus mole fraction of SiCl$_4$ in the liquid. Add ideal-solution lines for comparison.

9-2. The system carbon tetrachloride–acetonitrite has been studied by L. Brown and F. F. Smith, *Aust. J. Chem.*, **7**:269 (1954) and L. Brown and W. Foch, *Aust. J. Chem.*, **9**:180 (1956). The following results were reported for a temperature of 45°C:

x_{CCl_4} in liquid	0.0347	0.1914	0.3752	0.4790	0.6049	0.8069	0.9609
x_{CCl_4} in vapor	0.1801	0.4603	0.5429	0.5684	0.5936	0.6470	0.8001
Total vapor pressure, atm	0.3263	0.4421	0.4797	0.4863	0.4882	0.4773	0.4136

and

x_{CCl_4} in liquid	0.128	0.317	0.407	0.419	0.631	0.821
ΔH_{mix}, J mol^{-1}	414	745	862	858	930	736

From these data prepare a figure showing ΔH_{mix}, ΔG_{mix}, and $T \Delta S_{mix}$, for the system CCl$_4$–CH$_3$CN at 45°C. The vapor pressures of pure CCl$_4$ and CH$_3$CN are 0.3405 and 0.2742 atm.

9-3. Draw straight lines representing the solute obedience to Henry's law on copies of Figs. 9-5a and 9-6a.

9-4. Studies of the liquid-vapor equilibrium of ethanol-chloroform solutions at 45°C by G. Scatchard and C. L. Raymond, *J. Am. Chem. Soc.*, **60**:1278 (1938), yield the following data:

$x_{C_2H_5OH}$ in liquid	1.00	0.990	0.980	0.950	0.900	0.800
$x_{C_2H_5OH}$ in vapor	1.00	0.961	0.924	0.820	0.669	0.464
Total vap. press., mmHg	172.76	177.95	183.38	200.81	232.58	298.18

Prepare a graph that shows the extent to which Raoult's law is obeyed by the solvent, ethanol, and Henry's law by the solute, chloroform.

9-5. In studies of the chloroform-rich solutions of the system of Prob. 9-4 the following data, also at 45°C were reported;

x_{CHCl_3} in liquid	1.00	0.990	0.980	0.950	0.900	0.800
x_{CHCl_3} in vapor	1.00	0.979	0.963	0.925	0.887	0.845
Total vapor pressure, mm	433.54	438.59	442.16	449.38	445.16	454.53

Make a graph that allows conformity to Raoult's law and Henry's law to be seen in these chloroform-rich solutions.

9-6. From the data of Probs. 9-4 and 9-5 plot the free energy of mixing of chloroform and ethanol at 45°C.

9-7. (a) Use the tabulated data for sulfuric acid–water solutions at 20°C to show by a graphical display the extent to which these data conform to Raoult's law. (b) What is the activity and, taking pure water as the standard state, the activity coefficient of water in a solution containing 3 mol of sulfuric acid in 1000 g of solution?

Density of solution, g cm^{-3}	1.00	1.05	1.10	1.15	1.20	1.25
H_2SO_4, wt %	0	7.36	14.33	20.97	27.34	33.33
Vapor pressure of H_2O, mmHg	17.4	17.0	16.3	15.4	14.0	12.2

9-8. The following data for glycerol-water solutions at 20°C are given by the "Handbook of Chemistry and Physics," Chemical Rubber Publishing Co., Cleveland, Ohio:

$C_3H_8O_3$, wt %	0	20	40	60	80	100
Sp. gr.	0.9982	1.0470	1.0995	1.1506	1.2079	1.2609

Calculate (a) the volume per 100 g of solution (approximately 100/sp.gr.) for each solution; (b) the volume per 100 g of water for each solution; (c) the moles of glycerol per 100 g of water for each solution. (d) Make a graph like that of Fig. 9-7 showing the volume of solutions containing 100 g of water versus the number of moles of glycerol in the solution. (e) What is the partial molal volume of glycerol in water (1) in an infinitely dilute solution and (2) in a solution containing 4 mol of glycerol per 100 g of water? (f) What is the volume of 1 mol of pure liquid glycerol at 20°C?

9-9. Using the results of Prob. 9-8 and the relation $V = n_1\bar{V}_1 \times n_2\bar{V}_2$ determine the partial molal volume of water in one of the glycerol-water solutions.

9-10. The density at 30°C of solutions of carbon tetrachloride and cyclohexane have been measured by S. E. Wood and J. A. Gray, *J. Am. Chem. Soc.,* **74**:3729 (1952). Some of the values they report for the density for various mole fractions of carbon tetrachloride are

x_{CCl_4}, mole fraction	Density g cm^{-3}	x_{CCl}, mole fraction	Density g cm^{-3}
1.0000	1.57478	0.3751	1.04872
0.8725	1.46041	0.2520	0.95430
0.7485	1.35278	0.1303	0.86364
0.6511	1.27068	0	0.76918
0.4978	1.14561		

From these data deduce the partial molal volumes of carbon tetrachloride and of cyclohexane for solutions ranging from pure tetrachloride to pure cyclohexane.

9-11. Use Fig. 9-5 to estimate the molar free energy of chloroform in an equimolar liquid mixture with acetone at 35°C.

9-12. According to the data of Fig. 9-5, plot the molar free energy of chloroform in a chloroform-acetone solution relative to the free energy of pure liquid chloroform at 35°C.

9-13. The tabulated data for the vapor pressure of the carbon tetrachloride–methanol system at 20°C are from J. Timmermans, "Physicochemical Constants of Binary Systems in Concentrated Solutions," vol. 2, Interscience Publishers, Inc., New York, 1959. (*a*) Use these data to prepare a graph of the activity of each component as a function of the solution composition. Compare with ideal behavior. (*b*) Prepare a figure showing the activity coefficients of the carbon tetrachloride–methanol system using the pure liquids as standard states and compare with ideal behavior.

x_{CH_3OH} Liquid	x_{CH_3OH} Vapor	Total vapor pressure, atm	x_{CH_3OH} Liquid	x_{CH_3OH} Vapor	Total vapor pressure, atm
1.00	1.00	0.126	0.40	0.47	0.211
0.90	0.65	0.178	0.30	0.46	0.210
0.80	0.55	0.200	0.20	0.45	0.209
0.70	0.51	0.207	0.10	0.43	0.204
0.60	0.49	0.210	0.00	0.00	0.119
0.50	0.48	0.211			

9-14. Use the data of Prob. 9-13 or the figure obtained in answer to that problem to show graphically the free energy of methanol relative to pure liquid methanol in liquid solutions with carbon tetrachloride.

9-15. From the data of Prob. 9-2 prepare a figure showing the activities of each component as a function of solution composition. Add lines to show what the variation of activity with composition would be if the solution behaved ideally.

9-16. Using the results of Prob. 9-15, prepare a figure showing the activity coefficients of each component as a function of solution composition. Add ideal-solution behavior lines.

*9-17. Measurements of the solubility of CO_2 in water at 50 and 100°C by R. Weibe and V. L. Gaddy, *J. Am. Chem. Soc.*, **61**:315 (1939) provide the basis for the following data:

P_{CO_2}, atm	25	50	75	100
Molality of CO_2 in solution, 50°C	0.44	0.77	1.00	1.15
Molality of CO_2 in solution, 100°C	0.24	0.45	0.64	0.79

(a) Is Henry's law obeyed? (b) At these high pressures, carbon dioxide gas does not behave ideally. Does correction for nonideality of the gas improve the conformity to Henry's law?

9-18. Illustrate Eq. (9-40) at any molality using the data for the water-sucrose system given in Table 9-2.

9-19. The following data are given for aqueous calcium chloride solutions at 20°C:

Percent $CaCl_2$ by weight	Specific gravity	Percent $CaCl_2$ by weight	Specific gravity
0	0.9982	20	1.1775
4	1.0316	25	1.2284
8	1.0659	30	1.2816
12	1.1015	35	1.3373
16	1.1386	40	1.3957

Determine the partial molal volume of $CaCl_2$ and of water over the range covered by these data.

9-20. Use the data of Prob. 9-7 to find the activity of sulfuric acid in aqueous solutions. Assume the activity of H_2SO_4 can be taken to be equal to the mole fraction of H_2SO_4 at $[H_2SO_4] = 0.014$.

9-21. The following data show the freezing point of solutions of urea in water. (a) Using the freezing-point-depression constant of 1.86 for water, calculate the mass of 1 mol of urea. (b) If the value of the mass of 1 mol based on atomic mass data is accepted, what value do these data give for the freezing-point-depression constant?

Molality	0.3241	0.646	1.521	3.360
$-\Delta T_{fp}$, °C	0.5953	1.170	2.673	5.490

9-22. A solution of 9.0 g of naphthalene, $C_{10}H_8$, in 1000 g of benzene freezes at 5.07°C. The normal boiling and freezing points of benzene are 80.0 and 5.42°C, and the heat of vaporization is 30.76 kJ mol^{-1}. Using these data calculate (a) the vapor pressure of the solution at 80.0°C, (b) the boiling point of the solution, and (c) the heat of fusion of benzene.

9-23. The boiling point of benzene is raised from its normal value of 80.1 to 82.4°C by the addition of 13.76 g of biphenyl, $C_6H_5C_6H_5$, to 100 g of benzene. What are (a) the boiling-point-elevation constant and (b) the heat of vaporization of benzene according to these data?

9-24. Equation (9-51) involves the quantity n_A, the moles of solvent in 1000 g of solvent. Explain why, even if the heat to vaporize a given amount of solvent is measured, Eq. (9-51) cannot be used to obtain the molar mass of the solvent if a measurement of ΔT_{bp} is made with a solute of known molar mass.

9-25. A newly synthesized organic compound is analyzed for carbon and hydrogen and found to contain by weight 63.2 percent carbon, 8.8 percent hydrogen, and the remainder oxygen. A solution of 0.0702 g of the compound in 0.804 g of camphor is found to freeze 15.3 °C lower than the freezing point of the pure camphor. What are the molecular mass and the formula of the new compound? The freezing-point constant for camphor is 40.

9-26. Henry's-law constants k_M^{-1} of the relation $M = k_M^{-1}P$ for nitrogen and oxygen in water at 0 °C are 0.00103 and 0.0022 mol liter^{-1} atm^{-1}, respectively. What will be the difference in freezing point between pure water and water in equilibrium, i.e., saturated, with air?

9-27. The osmotic pressure is measured between water and a solution containing 1 g of glucose, $C_6H_{12}O_6$, and 1 g of sucrose, $C_{12}H_{22}O_{11}$ in 1000 g of water. The temperature is maintained at 25 °C. (*a*) What osmotic pressure would be expected? (*b*) If this pressure is measured without knowing that the solute is a mixture, what molar mass will be calculated? (*c*) The measurement of the osmotic pressure gives an average molar mass of the solute. What kind of average, i.e., number or mass, is this?

9-28. The osmotic pressure of human blood is reported, on the average, to be 7.7 atm at body temperature. (It varies from a low of about 7.2, which usually occurs in the morning, to a high of about 8.0.) What is the freezing and boiling point of blood plasma, i.e., whole blood with the cellular particles removed?

9-29. In view of the data of Prob. 9-28, calculate the concentration of NaCl that could be used as a blood substitute or extender.

9-30. It is reasonable to expect that a number of water molecules, say 5, are bound quite strongly to a sucrose molecule by hydrogen bonding. This would have the effect of decreasing the number of solvent particles relative to the number of solute particles. Calculate what value of the osmotic pressure of the 1 *m* sucrose solution would be expected with this hydration assumption and Eq. (9-64) and compare with the observed value of Table 9-5.

9-31. A solution of 2.58 g phenol in 100 g bromoform freezes at a temperature 2.374 °C lower than pure bromoform. (*a*) What is the apparent molar mass of phenol at this concentration and temperature in bromoform? (*b*) Give a qualitative explanation for this molar mass. For bromoform, $K_{fp} = 14.4$ K m^{-1}.

9-32. The osmotic pressure of a dilute solution of KNO_3 in water is 0.470 atm when measured against water at 25 °C. Find (*a*) the vapor pressure at 25 °C (the vapor pressure of pure water is 0.03126 atm at this temperature), (*b*) the freezing point, and (*c*) the boiling point of the solution.

***9-33.** Obtain an expression for the freezing point as a function of pressure and apply this expression to find the difference in the freezing point of ice at 1 atm pressure and that of ice under its own vapor pressure. The vapor pressure of ice at 0 °C is 6.025×10^{-3} atm. The densities of water and ice at 0 °C are 1.000 and 0.9168 g ml^{-1}, respectively, and the heat of fusion of ice is 6.01 kJ mol^{-1}.

***9-34.** Combine the results of Probs. 9-26 and 9-33 to obtain the difference between the freezing point of water saturated with air at 1 atm and that of pure water under its own vapor pressure.

REFERENCES

In addition to the following references, most of the thermodynamics texts referred to in previous chapters include discussions of the treatment of solutions.

HILDEBRAND, J. H., and **D. L. SCOTT:** "Regular Solutions," Prentice-Hall, Inc., Englewood Cliffs, N.J., 1962. A monograph summarizing Hildebrand's ideas on "regular solutions" that makes use of thermodynamic approaches, and ideas on intermolecular forces and on the liquid state. Excellent material, showing a use and purpose for much of the material that has been presented in this text.

PRIGOGINE, I.: "The Molecular Theory of Solutions," Interscience Publishers, Inc., New York, 1957. The development of a theory of the nature of solutions that builds on the thermodynamic properties of ideal and nonideal systems.

RAWLINSON, J. S.: "Liquids and Liquid Mixtures," Butterworth Scientific Publications, London, 1959. A treatment of many aspects of liquids that brings together the properties and approaches to pure liquids and to liquid solutions. Chapters 4 and 5 contain material on mixtures of simple and complex liquids that supplements the thermodynamic introduction to such systems given in this text.

COVINGTON, A. K., and **P. JONES (eds.):** "Hydrogen-bonded Solvent Systems," Tylor and Francis, 1968. A collection of symposium articles that show the variety of subjects that can be studied in connection with solute-solvent interactions and reactions.

CHAO, K. C., and **R. A. GREENKORN:** "Thermodynamics of Fluids: An Introduction to Equilibrium Theory," vol. 4 of "Chemical Processing and Engineering," Marcel Dekker Inc., New York, 1975. Good treatments of nonideal gases, mixtures, and liquids.

PHASE EQUILIBRIA

PHASE EQUILIBRIA IN
ONE-COMPONENT SYSTEMS

A phase is defined as that part of a system which is chemically and physically uniform throughout. We have, in fact, been studying the characteristics and the molecular makeup of gas, liquid, and solid phases and (in Chap. 9) equilibria involving gas-liquid and solid-liquid systems. An organized study of systems in which two or more phases are present together in equilibrium with each other will now be undertaken.

Phase-equilibria studies will be introduced with the chemically simplest systems, those consisting of a single chemical material, or component. By this it is meant that the composition of each and every phase is completely determined by the specification of a single chemical material for the system. Later, when many-component systems are studied, the implications of the word component used in this technical sense will be explored further.

10-1 Pressure-Temperature Diagrams for One-Component Systems

The phases present in a one-component system at various pressures and temperatures can conveniently be presented on a P-versus-T plot. An example is provided by the diagram for water for moderate pressures and temperatures in Fig. 10-1. The line labeled TC shows the pressures and temperatures at which liquid and vapor exist in equilibrium. It is a vapor-pressure curve. At temperatures higher than that of point C, the critical-point, liquid-vapor equilibria do not occur. Thus this liquid-vapor equilibrium line terminates at C.

Consider the changes that occur as a pressure or temperature change results in the system moving across the line TC. From point 1, for example, the temperature can be lowered to get to point 2 or the pressure can be raised to get to point 3. In either process one crosses the liquid-vapor equilibrium line in the direction of condensation from vapor to liquid. Thus the line TC has "sides" to it that can be labeled as "vapor" or "liquid." Notice, however, that if a sample is

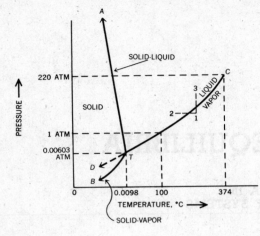

FIGURE 10-1
Phase diagram for water at moderate pressures (not drawn to scale).

carried from point 1 to point 2 or point 3 by a path that goes around C, no phase change will occur.

The line TB of Fig. 10-1 gives the temperatures and pressures at which solid and vapor are in equilibrium; i.e., it is the curve for the vapor pressure of the solid. The line TA gives the temperatures and pressures at which ice and liquid are in equilibrium; i.e., it shows the melting point of ice as a function of pressure. Liquid water can be cooled below its freezing point to give, as indicated by the dashed line TD, *supercooled* water. Supercooled water represents a metastable system because it owes its existence to the fact that the rate of formation of ice has been interfered with by the use of a very clean sample of water and a smooth container.

Figure 10-1 is a convenient representation of all the available information about the phases of water that occur at moderate pressures and temperatures. It is interesting also to consider Fig. 10-2, which shows the phase behavior of water at very high pressures. Many new solid phases, corresponding to ice with different crystal structures, are encountered. The occurrence of different crystalline forms of a given compound is fairly common and is known as *polymorphism*. It is particularly remarkable that the melting point of ice VII, which exists above about 20,000 atm pressure, is over 100°C.

In Figs. 10-1 and 10-2 the occurrence of a single phase corresponds to an area on a PT diagram; i.e., both these variables can be arbitrarily assigned, within limits, without the appearance of a second phase. When two phases are in equilibrium, the diagram shows a line indicating that either P or T may be fixed but that when one is fixed, the other must be such that the system is somewhere on the phase-equilibrium line. Finally, as both Figs. 10-1 and 10-2 show, three phases can exist together, and this occurs at a point on the diagram. Nowhere on the diagram do four phases coexist.

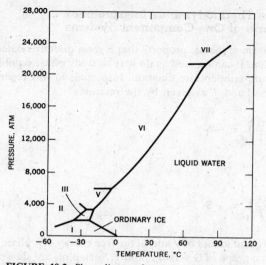

FIGURE 10-2 Phase diagram for water at high pressures.

The most important three-phase equilibrium point, called the *triple point,* is that shown by ordinary ice, liquid, and vapor. The temperature and pressure at the triple point are completely determined by the system itself. (As a result, the triple point is a convenient condition on which to base a temperature scale. It is assigned the value 273.16000 K. The ice point is 0.0098 K lower and thus has the value 273.15 K.)

The most familiar material, water, that we have used as an illustration of *PT* phase diagrams is, in some ways, not at all representative. More suitable, in this regard, is one in which the solid-liquid equilibrium line, *TA* of Fig. 10-1, has a positive slope, as is the case in Fig. 10-3.

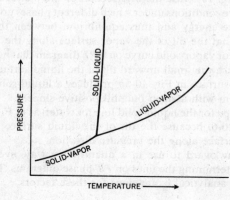

FIGURE 10-3
A representative one-component solid-liquid-vapor phase diagram.

10-2 Qualitative Thermodynamic Interpretation of Phase Equilibria of One-Component Systems

The free energy is the thermodynamic property that is most directly related to the position of equilibrium. It can be used again here to study phase equilibria as portrayed on a pressure-temperature diagram. Important in this regard is the dependence of G on P and T as given by the relations

$$\left(\frac{\partial G}{\partial P}\right)_T = V \qquad \left(\frac{\partial G}{\partial T}\right)_P = -S$$

or for 1 mol,

$$\left(\frac{\partial \mathsf{G}}{\partial P}\right)_T = \mathsf{V} \qquad \left(\frac{\partial \mathsf{G}}{\partial T}\right)_P = -\mathsf{S} \qquad (10\text{-}1)$$

From these relations, and values of V and S, the free energy of a phase can be shown as a surface on a graph of G versus P and T. Such plots are shown for the solid, liquid, and vapor forms in Fig. 10-4. The principal features of such diagrams stem from the relations, applicable to most materials.

S for gas $> \mathsf{S}$ for liquid $> \mathsf{S}$ for solid
V for gas $\gg \mathsf{V}$ for liquid $> \mathsf{V}$ for solid

As a result, the free-energy surface for the vapor slopes steeply up along the direction of increasing pressure and steeply down along the direction of increasing temperature. The free-energy surface for a liquid has similarly directed but smaller slopes. For most substances the surface for a solid has even smaller slopes in both directions.

Composite diagrams, like Fig. 10-5, use the intersection of the planes to show the pressure and temperature conditions under which different phases give the material the same molar free energy and thus equilibrium between the phases. Notice from Fig. 10-5a that the tilt of the vapor surface along the P direction results in a vapor-liquid or vapor-solid curve on a PT diagram that has a relatively small slope. In contrast, the small upward tilt of the liquid surface compared with that of the solid surface in Fig. 10-5b produces a liquid-solid equilibrium line on a PT diagram with a steep but still positive slope.

The exceptional negative slope for the liquid-solid line for water, as in Fig. 10-1, results, as shown in Fig. 10-6, because the tilt of the liquid surface is smaller than that of the solid surface along the pressure direction.

These representations are awkward to use in a quantitative way, even though they reveal the factors determining the lines on PT phase diagrams. To proceed quantitatively, we need analytical expressions for these factors.

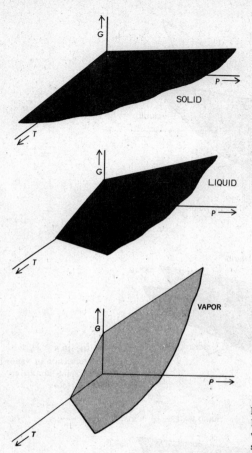

FIGURE 10-4
Representative free-energy
versus T and P surfaces for
solids, liquids, and gases.

10-3 Quantitative Treatment of Phase Equilibria in One-Component Systems: The Clausius-Clapeyron Equation

Let us now obtain an expression for the pressure-temperature dependence of the state of equilibrium between two phases. To be specific, we deal with the liquid-vapor equilibrium.

The free energy of 1 mol of liquid is equal to the free energy of 1 mol of the vapor that is in equilibrium with the liquid. We can therefore write, with subscript l denoting liquid and v denoting vapor,

$$G_l = G_v \tag{10-2}$$

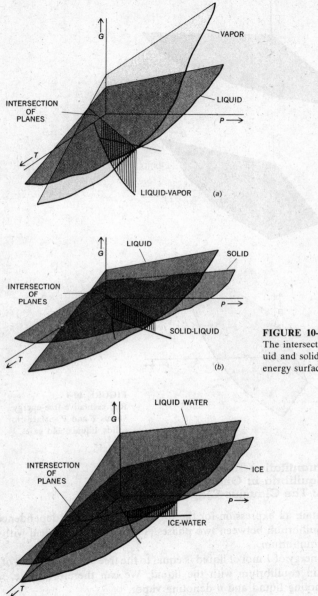

FIGURE 10-5
The intersection of vapor-liquid and solid-liquid free-energy surfaces.

FIGURE 10-6 The intersection of the free-energy surfaces for liquid water and ice and the resulting temperature-pressure plot for equilibrium between these phases.

and for an infinitesimal change in the system for which equilibrium is maintained, the differential equation

$$dG_l = dG_v \tag{10-3}$$

can be written.

Since only one component is present and the composition is not variable, such free-energy changes can be expressed by the total differential

$$dG = \left(\frac{\partial G}{\partial P}\right)_T dP + \left(\frac{\partial G}{\partial T}\right)_P dT \tag{10-4}$$

The partial derivatives are related, as in Sec. 10-2, to the molar volume and entropy, and thus we can write for a molar amount in each phase

$$dG = V\, dP - S\, dT \tag{10-5}$$

Recognizing that although various temperatures and pressures can be considered, both phases are at the same temperature and pressure, we can apply this equation to the liquid and to the equilibrium vapor to give

$$V_l\, dP - S_l\, dT = V_v\, dP - S_v\, dT$$

or

$$\frac{dP}{dT} = \frac{S_v - S_l}{V_v - V_l} = \frac{\Delta S_{vap}}{\Delta V_{vap}} \tag{10-6}$$

More generally, we can write

$$\frac{dP}{dT} = \frac{\Delta S}{\Delta V} \tag{10-7}$$

where ΔS and ΔV signify changes for the two phases being considered.

We thus have an expression for the slope of the phase-equilibrium lines on PT diagrams like those of Figs. 10-1 to 10-3.

The large value of ΔV for solid-vapor or liquid-vapor phases, for example, is related to small values of dP/dT and thus flatter curves than for solid-liquid phases. Also, curves tend to have positive slopes because the molar entropies and volumes both follow the same order, vapor greater than liquid and liquid greater than solid. The most notable exception is that for ice–liquid water, where ΔS and ΔV have opposite signs. This happens also in other cases, as shown by the high-pressure-region diagram for water in Fig. 10-2.

Substitution of

$$S_v - S_l = \frac{\Delta H_{vap}}{T} \qquad (10\text{-}8)$$

in Eq. (10-6) gives

$$\frac{dP}{dT} = \frac{\Delta H_{vap}}{T \Delta V_{vap}} \qquad (10\text{-}9)$$

For liquid-vapor equilibria at temperatures well below the critical temperature, often the condition of interest, the liquid volume V_l can be neglected compared with the vapor volume V_v. With this approximation we can write

$$\frac{dP}{dT} = \frac{\Delta H_{vap}}{V_v T} \qquad (10\text{-}10)$$

This equation is one form of the expression for the temperature–vapor-pressure relation known as the *Clapeyron equation*. It can be modified to apply to other phase equilibria besides the liquid-vapor one dealt with here.

If the equilibrium vapor is treated as an ideal gas, the molar vapor volume can be expressed as RT/P, and substitution of this approximation in Eq. (10-10) gives

$$\frac{dP}{dT} = \frac{\Delta H_{vap} P}{RT^2} \qquad (10\text{-}11)$$

This result rearranges to the most generally used derivative forms of the *Clausius-Clapeyron* equation,

$$\frac{d(\ln P)}{dT} = \frac{\Delta H_{vap}}{RT^2} \qquad (10\text{-}12)$$

and

$$\frac{d(\ln P)}{d(1/T)} = -\frac{\Delta H_{vap}}{R} \qquad (10\text{-}13)$$

The integrated form, with the assumption of a constant value of ΔH_{vap} over the temperature range considered, is written in terms of logarithms to the base 10 as

$$\log P = -\frac{\Delta H_{vap}}{2.303 R} \frac{1}{T} + \text{const} \qquad (10\text{-}14)$$

TABLE 10-1 Vapor Pressures in Atmospheres of Liquids as a Function of Temperature

$t, °C$	H_2O	CCl_4	Acetone	Ethyl ether	Ethanol	n-Octane
0	0.00603	0.043		0.243	0.016	0.004
10	0.01212	0.074	0.153	0.384	0.032	0.008
20	0.02308	0.120	0.243	0.581	0.058	0.013
30	0.04186	0.188	0.372	0.851	0.104	0.024
40	0.07278	0.284	0.554	1.212	0.178	0.041
50	0.1217	0.417	0.806	1.680	0.292	0.064
60	0.1965	0.593	1.140		0.464	0.103
70	0.3075	0.818	1.579		0.713	0.155
80	0.4672	1.109			1.070	0.230
90	0.6918	1.476			1.562	0.333
100	1.0000	1.925				0.466

The preceding derivation indicates that a plot of log P versus $1/T$ should give a straight line and that the slope of such a line is to be identified with $-(\Delta H_{vap}/2.303R)$. When the vapor-pressure data of Table 10-1 and Fig. 10-7a are treated in this way, the essentially linear plots of Fig. 10-7b are obtained. A more careful look at such results, however, reveals deviations from linearity, and these deviations can be attributed to the approximations that have been introduced in obtaining Eqs. (10-10), (10-11), and (10-14).

THE PHASE RULE

Before proceeding to the phase equilibria shown by multicomponent systems, a helpful generalization known as the *phase rule* can be introduced, and it can be illustrated with examples from the one-component systems just studied. First some terms used in the statement of the phase rule must be more carefully defined.

10-4 The Number of Phases

The statement of the thermodynamic rule regarding the phase equilibria that occur in any system requires the precise definition of three quantities. The first of these terms is phase. A *phase* is defined as that part of a system which is chemically and physically uniform throughout. The definition is little different from our ordinary use of the word, and only a few points need be made.

A phase may consist of any amount, large or small, of material and may be in one unit or subdivided into a number of smaller units. Thus ice represents a phase whether it is in a single block or subdivided into fine chips, but this subdivision must not be carried to molecular dimensions. A solution in which

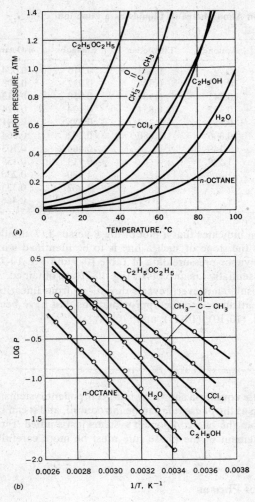

FIGURE 10-7
(a) The dependence of the vapor pressure of some liquids on temperature; (b) log P versus $1/T$ for the vapor pressures of the liquids of part (a).

there are two chemical species, for example, is to be considered as one phase, even though subdivision to a molecular scale would reveal that it was not "uniform throughout."

Of particular importance is the *number of phases P* present in a system. Because of the complete mutual solubility of gases, only one gaseous phase can exist in any system. Some liquids are insoluble in each other, and a number of different liquid phases may therefore exist in a system at equilibrium. Different solids, whether they have different chemical composition or the same chemical composition but different crystal structure, constitute different phases.

10-5 The Number of Components

It is necessary now to consider what information must be given to specify the chemical composition of a system. In this connection, the familiar word components is used, but a strict definition is attached to it. The *number of components C* is defined as the least number of independently variable chemical species necessary to describe the composition of each and every phase of the system.

The composition of a solution of sugar in water, for example, is described by specifying that sugar and water are present. There are two components. If such a solution is cooled, a pure solid sugar phase may begin to separate out. According to the definition, the *system* still has two components even if the solid phase contains only one chemical species.

Some special care is required when the system involves species which are in chemical equilibrium with each other. The number of species that can be arbitrarily varied in a solution of acetic acid in water is 2. A number of equilibria are set up in such a system; in particular,

$$CH_3COOH + H_2O \rightleftharpoons CH_3COO^- + H_3O^+$$

Thus there are many chemical species. It should be clear, however, that if the presence of two species is specified, the presence of the other species is determined by the equilibrium relations that exist. The example should point out that there is no unique set of components among the species in a system. It is only the *number of components* that is unique.

An overstrict attention to the possible equilibria among the species of a system should be avoided. Consider, for example, the gaseous system of water vapor, hydrogen, and oxygen. In the presence of an electric arc or suitable catalyst, the equilibrium

$$2H_2O \rightleftharpoons 2H_2 + O_2$$

is readily established. Under such conditions the system has two components since specification of any two species implies that at equilibrium the third will be present. Alternatively, one can say that the concentration of any two species could be arbitrarily set but that the concentration of the third would then be fixed and could in fact be calculated from the equilibrium constant of the reaction. At room temperature and in the absence of a catalyst, however, this equilibrium is established so slowly that for all practical purposes the reaction connecting the three species can be ignored. Under such conditions the concentrations of all three species can be varied arbitrarily, and the system has three components. A system like this, which appears stable but is not at the thermodynamic equilibrium position with respect to the reaction, is said to be in *metastable equilibrium*. Many systems have thermodynamically feasible reactions, both chemical and physical, which can properly be ignored under certain conditions.

In a similar way the number of components one assigns to a system may depend on the conditions encountered. For example, under most circumstances the solid-vapor equilibrium system set up by NH_4Cl could be said to be a one-component system. The fact that the vapor consists of an equimolar mixture of NH_3 and HCl rather than NH_4Cl molecules would not affect any of the deductions made regarding the behavior of the system. However, if conditions of temperature and pressure could be found so that either the ammonia or the hydrogen chloride separated out from the gas phase, under these conditions the system would have to be defined as one of two components, just as it would be said to be a two-component system if one could add NH_3 or HCl to the NH_4Cl system.

10-6 The Number of Degrees of Freedom

Some properties of each phase of a system are independent of the amount of the phase present. Thus the temperature, pressure, density, molar heat capacity, and refractive index, for example, of a gas are independent of the amount of gas one is dealing with. Properties like these, which are characteristic of the individual phases of the system and are independent of the amounts of the phases, are known as *intensive properties*. Properties like the weight and volume of a phase, which depend on the amount of the phase, are known as *extensive properties*. The latter type of property will not concern us in our study of phase equilibria.

A one-phase system of one component, for example, has a large number of intensive properties. To describe the state of such a simple system, one might measure and report values for many such properties; i.e., one might report the pressure, the temperature, the density, the refractive index, the molar heat capacity, and so forth. We know *from experience,* however, that it is not necessary to specify all these properties to characterize the system completely. All the intensive properties of a sample of pure liquid water, for example, are fixed if the temperature and pressure of the sample are stated. Any two intensive properties instead of temperature and pressure might have been fixed, and one would again have found that the sample was completely characterized. Our experience tells us that only a few of the many intensive properties of a sample can be arbitrarily fixed, i.e., need be specified to define the sample.

The number of *degrees of freedom* of a system is defined as *the least number of intensive variables that must be specified to fix the values of all the remaining intensive variables*. The number of degrees of freedom is denoted by Φ. In the previous example of a one-phase system of one component there are 2 degrees of freedom; that is, $\Phi = 2$.

A rearrangement of the statement of the definition which is sometimes easier to apply is that the number of degrees of freedom is the number of intensive variables that can be independently varied without changing the number of phases of the system. Examples will bring out the significance of this number and of its definition.

10-7 The Phase Rule for One-Component Systems

The identification of an area on a PT diagram with one phase of a one-component system illustrates the two degrees of freedom that exist, these usually being specified as pressure and temperature.

For a two-phase system, the requirement of an equality in the molar free energies of the two phases imposes a relation, such as $dP/dT = \Delta S/\Delta V$, and thus the pressure and temperature cannot both be arbitrarily varied. A two-phase, one-component system thus has a single degree of freedom, as shown by the identification of a line on a PT diagram with two phases in equilibrium.

Finally, for three phases to coexist, the molar free energy of the first pair would have to be equal to that of the additional phase. One more restrictive equation then exists, and thus the last degree of freedom is removed. No arbitrary assignment of variables can be made; the system is entirely self-determined. The one-component PT-diagram feature for three phases is a point.

All this can be summarized by the equation

$$\Phi = 3 - P \qquad \text{[one component]} \tag{10-15}$$

10-8 The Phase Rule

Rules similar to that of Eq. (10-15) can be deduced for systems of more than one component. It is possible, however, to proceed more generally and to obtain the *phase rule,* which gives the number of degrees of freedom of a system with C components and P phases. This rule was first obtained by J. Willard Gibbs in 1878, but it was published in the rather obscure *Transactions of the Connecticut Academy* and overlooked for 20 years.

Consider the C components to be distributed throughout each of the P phases of a system, as schematically indicated in Fig. 10-8. The degrees of freedom of the system can be calculated by first adding up the total number of

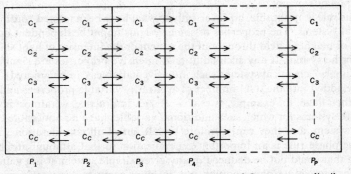

FIGURE 10-8 Schematic representation of a system of C components distributed throughout P phases.

intensive variables required to describe separately each phase and then subtracting the number of these variables, whose values are fixed by free-energy equilibrium relations between the different phases. To begin with, each component is assumed to be present in every phase.

In each phase there are $C - 1$ concentration terms that will be required to define the composition of the phase quantitatively. Thus, if mole fractions are used to measure the concentrations, one needs to specify the mole fraction of all but one of the components, the remaining one being determined because the sum of the mole fractions must be unity. Since there are P phases, there will be a total of $P(C - 1)$ such composition variables. In addition, the pressure and the temperature must be specified, giving a total of $P(C - 1) + 2$ intensive variables if the system is considered phase by phase.

The number of these variables, which is fixed by the equilibrium conditions of the system, must now be determined. Component 1, for example, is distributed between phases P_1 and P_2. When equilibrium is established for any one component distributed between any two phases, a distribution relation can be written. Thus, if the concentration of a component in phase P_1 is specified, its concentration in phase P_2 is automatically fixed. Similar equilibria will be set up for each component between the various pairs of phases. For each component there will be $P - 1$ such relations. Thus, for C components a total of $C(P - 1)$ intensive variables will be fixed by the equilibrium conditions.

The number of degrees of freedom, i.e., the net arbitrarily adjustable intensive variables, is therefore

$$\Phi = P(C - 1) + 2 - C(P - 1) = C - P + 2 \tag{10-16}$$

If a component is not present or is present to a negligible extent in one of the phases of the system, there will be one fewer intensive variable for that phase since the negligible concentration of the one species is of no interest. There will also be one fewer equilibrium relation. The phase rule applies, therefore, to all systems regardless of whether all phases have the same number of components or not.

This rule is applicable, however, only to what have been termed "ordinary" chemical systems. The properties of some systems might be dependent on the electric or magnetic field throughout the system or the intensity of light shining through the system. If any such additional intensive properties are significant (in "ordinary" chemical systems such intensive variables can be ignored), they must be added into the total number of arbitrarily variable properties and one would then have, for example, $\Phi = C - P + 3$. In practice, we almost always deal with systems for which such additional variables have no noticeable effect on the system, and they can therefore be left out of all consideration.

The phase rule is an important generalization in that although it tells us nothing that could not be deduced in any given simple system, it is a valuable guide for unraveling phase equilibrium in more complex systems.

PHASE DIAGRAMS FOR MULTICOMPONENT SYSTEMS: CONDENSED PHASES ONLY

A few representative phase diagrams for two- and three-component systems for which the pressure is high enough for only the condensed solid and liquid phases to occur will now be discussed. Systems including the vapor phase will be treated separately in the final sections of the chapter.

10-9 Two-Component Liquid Systems

The simplest of the two-component phase diagrams are those for liquid systems which can break up into two liquid phases. Such systems are usually treated at some constant pressure, usually atmospheric, high enough to ensure that no vapor can occur in equilibrium with the liquid phases and over a range of temperatures high enough to ensure that no solid phases appear. If the pressure is fixed, the remaining significant variables are the temperature and composition. Diagrams are therefore made showing the phase behavior in terms of these variables. The composition is usually expressed as weight percent of one component or as weight fraction.

Three different types of behavior are recognized. Representatives are shown in Fig. 10-9a to c. The heavy line on each of these diagrams bounds the region in which two liquid phases appear. That the line also gives the composition of the liquid layers can be seen by following, in Fig. 10-9a, the addition of the second component, isobutanol, to an initial quantity of pure water at 60°C. The first additions of butanol dissolve in the water to form a single phase, and this solubility persists until the total composition of the system corresponds to

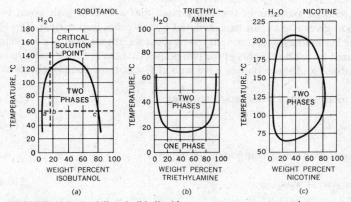

FIGURE 10-9 Partially miscible liquid two-component systems at 1 atm pressure. Measurements were made in a sealed tube in which the pressure was equal to the vapor pressure of the system.

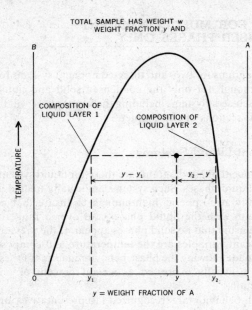

COMPOSITION OF
LIQUID LAYER 1

COMPOSITION OF
LIQUID LAYER 2

$y - y_1$

$y_2 - y$

TEMPERATURE →

0 y_1 y y_2 1

y = WEIGHT FRACTION OF A

FIGURE 10-10
The relative amounts of the
two liquid layers are given in
terms of the liquid-layer compositions and the total-system
composition by $w_1/w_2 =$
$(y_2 - y)/(y - y_1)$.

point a. At this point the solubility of butanol in water is reached, and further addition produces a second layer of composition c. Thus a total composition of b, at 60°C, results in a two-phase system, the phases having compositions a and c. As the amount of the second component increases, the total composition approaches c, at which point all the water-rich layer has finally dissolved in the butanol-rich layer to give a one-phase system again.

The relative amounts of the two phases that a system with given total composition gives rise to can be calculated by the procedure indicated in Fig. 10-10. The system has a total weight w and gross weight fraction of component A designated by y. The weights of the two phases that the system breaks up into are w_1 and w_2, and these phases have weight fractions of component A of y_1 and y_2.

The total weight conservation requires

$$w = w_1 + w_2 \tag{10-17}$$

and the conservation of component A requires

$$yw = y_1 w_1 + y_2 w_2 \tag{10-18}$$

Substitution of the expression for w from Eq. (10-17) in Eq. (10-18) gives

$$y(w_1 + w_2) = y_1 w_1 + y_2 w_2$$

which rearranges to

$$\frac{w_1}{w_2} = \frac{y_2 - y}{y - y_1} \tag{10-19}$$

Thus the weights of the two phases are in the proportion of the two line lengths of the dashed line in Fig. 10-10. This line, which "ties" together the solutions that are in equilibrium, is an example of a *tie line*.

Application of the phase rule to regions of two liquid phases gives

$$\Phi = C - P + 2 = 2 - 2 + 2 = 2 \tag{10-20}$$

If these 2 degrees of freedom are exercised by specifying T and P, then in the process in which the *total* composition of the system is changed there can be no phase-composition degrees of freedom. The compositions of each of the two phases, which is what the phase rule is concerned with, are fixed, and only the relative amounts of the two phases are varied by changes in the total composition.

It is also of interest to investigate the changes that occur when the temperature of a two-phase system, like that of Fig. 10-9a, is raised. If the temperature is increased for the system of total composition of b, the system moves up along the dashed line. The fraction of the system composed of the water-rich layer gradually increases until when the two-phase boundary curve is reached, the last of the butanol-rich layer appears to dissolve in the water-rich layer. By contrast, if a composition equal to that of the curve maximum is picked, the two layers remain in about equal amounts until at the two-phase boundary their composition becomes identical and they form a one-phase system.

The maximum of the curve of Fig. 10-9a is known as the *critical solution temperature* or the *upper consolute temperature*.

The remaining two diagrams of Fig. 10-9 show that liquid systems can also exhibit a *lower consolute temperature* or, in a few cases, both upper and lower consolute temperatures. This behavior of increased mutual solubility at lower temperatures is certainly not that which is normally expected and must be attributed, very qualitatively, to some interaction between the components that can be effective only at lower temperatures.

10-10 Two-Component Solid-Liquid Systems: Formation of a Eutectic Mixture

Consider now a two-component system at some fixed pressure, where the temperature range treated is such as to include formation of one or more solid phases. A simple behavior is shown by systems for which the liquids are completely soluble in each other and in which the only solid phases that occur are the pure crystalline forms of the two components. Such phase behavior is shown in Fig. 10-11 for the system benzene-naphthalene. The curved lines AE

and BE show the temperatures at which solutions of various compositions are in equilibrium with pure solid benzene and pure solid naphthalene, respectively. The horizontal straight line is the temperature below which no liquid phase exists.

It is instructive to consider what happens when solutions of various concentrations are cooled. The data that are obtained give the temperature of the systems as a function of time. These data are plotted as *cooling curves,* some of which, for concentrations indicated in Fig. 10-11, are shown in Fig. 10-12. It is such cooling curves, in fact, that are used to obtain the data shown in the phase diagram.

The relation between the cooling curves and the information on the phase diagram can be illustrated with one of the cooling curves, b, for example. The liquid system cools until the curve BE is reached, at which point solid naphthalene is in equilibrium with the solution and starts to freeze out. As cooling continues, more naphthalene freezes out, the solution becomes richer in benzene, and its composition and temperature move down along the line BE. This stage is represented on the cooling curve by the slowly falling portion, corresponding to the freezing points of solutions of varying composition. It should be noted that although the temperature and overall composition place the system in the area below BE, no phase of such composition exists. Only the two phases, one to the right and the other to the left of the gross-composition point, occur. It is informative, as indicated in Fig. 10-11, to draw a tie line through the gross composition, at c for example, to connect or tie together the two phases that are present and are in equilibrium with each other; however, such lines can be understood and need not be drawn.

Cooling and freezing out of naphthalene proceeds until point E is reached by the liquid phase, at which stage the solution becomes in equilibrium with

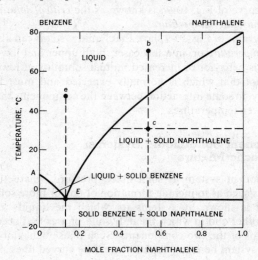

FIGURE 10-11
Freezing-point diagram for the binary system benzene-naphthalene at 1 atm pressure. (*From L. P. Hammett, "Introduction to the Study of Physical Chemistry," McGraw-Hill, Inc. Copyright 1952. Used by permission of McGraw-Hill Book Company.*)

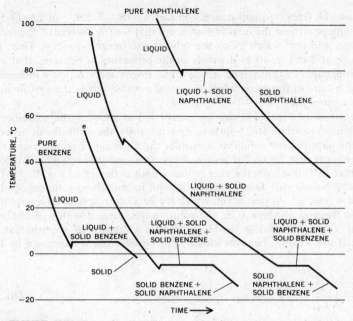

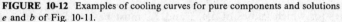

FIGURE 10-12 Examples of cooling curves for pure components and solutions *e* and *b* of Fig. 10-11.

pure solid benzene as well as with pure solid naphthalene. The solution composition and temperature remain constant until the system is entirely converted into the two solids. The point E is called the *eutectic,* from the Greek word meaning "easily melted," and the mixture of solids that separates out is called the *eutectic mixture.*

Application of the phase rule to the system at its eutectic point where there are two solid phases and one liquid phase in equilibrium gives

$$\Phi = C - P + 2 = 2 - 3 + 2 = 1 \tag{10-21}$$

Since this 1 degree of freedom is used by the arbitrarily chosen pressure, we learn that at a given pressure the intensive properties of the system at the eutectic point are entirely fixed. That the constant freezing point of a eutectic system does not imply the freezing out of a compound is experimentally verified by the fact that the eutectic mixture has a different composition at different pressures and that microphotographs show the solid to be a mixture of two crystalline forms.

Two aspects of solid-liquid equilibrium diagrams, like that of Fig. 10-11, can be treated in terms of the relations developed in Sec. 9-9 on freezing-point depression. First, we recognize that the initial slopes at A and B in Fig.

10-11 show the freezing-point-depression factor $-RT_{fp}^2/\Delta H_{fus}$ of Eq. (9-57). The freezing point and the heat of fusion are that for the "solvent," the major component, and that which yields the solid in the freezing process. Thus, the initial slope at A in Fig. 10-11 depends on the properties of benzene; that at B on the properties of naphthalene. These initial slopes, moreover, are independent of the nature of the second component, as pointed out in the treatment of colligative properties.

The curves of Fig. 10-11 can be interpreted as showing the solubility of naphthalene in benzene and, a little more awkwardly, the solubility of benzene in benzene-naphthalene solutions. Consider the addition of naphthalene to a sample of benzene at 20°C. The process will correspond to the movement along a horizontal 20°C line from the pure benzene limit at the left of Fig. 10-11. The added naphthalene will dissolve until the solid naphthalene–solution equilibrium line is reached. At that point, which for 20°C corresponds to a naphthalene mole fraction of about 0.26, the solution is saturated with naphthalene. Thus, the curve EB of Fig. 10-11 shows the solubility of naphthalene in benzene. If the solution behaves ideally, this equilibrium is expressed by Eq. (9-56)

$$\frac{\Delta H_{fus}}{R}\left(\frac{1}{T_{fp}} - \frac{1}{T}\right) = \ln x_A \tag{10-22}$$

The species for which values of ΔH_{fus} and T_{fp} must be used is A, that which forms the solid. In the above discussion that species is naphthalene. Insertion of 80°C (353 K) for the freezing point of naphthalene and 19.29 kJ mol^{-1} for its heat of fusion in Eq. (10-22) gives

$$\log x_{naph} = 2.854 - \frac{1007}{T} \tag{10-23}$$

At 20°C, for example, $\log x_{naph} = -0.58$ and $x_{naph} = 0.264$. This value corresponds to that which would be read from Fig. 10-11.

Notice that the solubility of naphthalene in *any* solvent that follows ideal behavior is given by Eq. (10-23). The curve from B toward E will follow the same path in all such solutions.

A variation on the formation of a simple eutectic occurs when the solids that separate out can accommodate some of the second component. The system silver-copper is illustrated in Fig. 10-13. The areas at the extreme right and left along the abscissa scale show regions in which there is a solid solution of silver in copper and copper in silver, respectively. Each region is bordered by a line showing the maximum solubility of the second component in the solid of the first component. Any solution that is cooled will give rise to these solid solutions. The eutectic mixture will of course also be a mixture of saturated solid solutions.

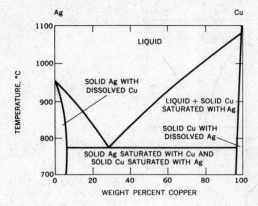

FIGURE 10-13
Freezing-point diagram for
the system formic acid–form-
1 atm pressure.

10-11 Two-Component Solid-Liquid Systems: Compound Formation

Systems in which the components show some attraction for each other some-times show the formation of a solid-state compound consisting of a simple mole ratio of the two components. Such a system is that of formic acid and formam-ide, as shown in Fig. 10-14. Diagrams like this are readily understandable on the basis of the discussion of Sec. 10-10 since each half of Fig. 10-14 corresponds to the simple eutectic diagrams treated there.

Solutions which on cooling reach line *NM* or *RQ* of Fig. 10-14 give rise to solid formic acid or formamide, respectively. Solutions which on cooling reach line *PN* or *PQ* give rise to a solid which is a compound containing equimolar amounts of formic acid and formamide. At point *N* the solution is in equilib-rium with this new compound and with formic acid, and at point *Q* the solution

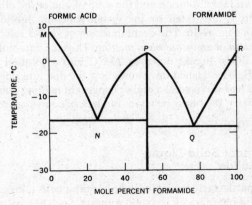

FIGURE 10-14
Freezing-point diagram for
the system formic acid–formamide at 1 atm pressure showing the formation of a one-
to-one compound in the solid
state. (*From L. P. Hammett,
"Introduction to the Study of
Physical Chemistry."* Copyright 1952 McGraw-Hill Inc.
*Used by permission of
McGraw-Hill Book Company.*)

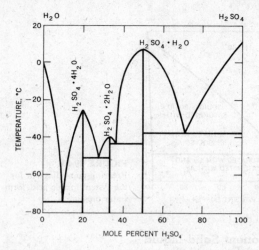

FIGURE 10-15
Freezing-point diagram for
$H_2O \cdot H_2SO_4$ showing multiple
compound formation in the
solid state.

is in equilibrium with the new compound and formamide. Points N and Q represent two eutectics that generally will have different temperatures.

Again, as in the preceding section, the initial slopes of the lines at M, P, and R can be interpreted in terms of the heat of fusion and the freezing point of the substance that separates out as a solid near these points. Likewise, the curves can be interpreted in terms of the solubility of these components and can be compared with the ideal-solution expectations given by Eq. (10-22).

Compound formation in the solid state is frequently encountered with *hydrates*. Figure 10-15 shows the formation of hydrated compounds of sulfuric acid in the solid state. Again, such diagrams are easily understood as a series of simple eutectic diagrams side by side.

A complication does occur when a solid compound does not have sufficient stability to persist up to the temperature at which it would melt. In such cases the unstable solid breaks down into a solution and the solid of one or the other of the two components. This is illustrated by the system calcium fluoride–calcium chloride, as shown in Fig. 10-16. The decomposition of such a solid is referred to as a *peritectic reaction* or an *incongruent melting*. Thus the equimolar crystal $CaF_2 \cdot CaCl_2$ of Fig. 10-16 breaks down as 737°C into a solution of composition B and solid CaF_2. The dashed line shows how the diagram might have looked if the compound had survived to a real or congruent melting point. This line is helpful for visualizing the phase behavior but has, of course, no real significance.

10-12 Two-Component Solid-Liquid Systems: Miscible Solids

Brief mention can be made, particularly in view of their importance as alloys, of systems forming only one solid phase which is a solid solution. Such behavior is

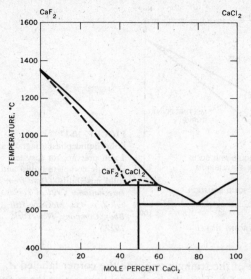

FIGURE 10-16
Freezing-point diagram for the system $CaF_2 \cdot CaCl_2$ showing the incongruent melting of the solid compound CaF_2CaCl_2 at 737°C. (*Data from "International Critical Tables, vol. 4, p. 63, McGraw-Hill Book Company, New York, 1927.*)

a result of complete mutual solubility of the two solid components. In Sec. 10-10 it was pointed out how partial solubility of the solid phases in each other affects the phase diagram of a system showing a simple eutectic. Such partial solubility frequently occurs when the atoms of one component are small and can fit into the interstices of the lattice of the major component. In this way an *interstitial* alloy is formed. The carbon atoms in a carbon-containing alloy are usually so accommodated.

Complete solubility of two solid phases usually results when the atoms of the two components are about the same size and can substitute for each other in the lattice to form a substitutional alloy. The system of copper and nickel (Fig. 10-17) shows this behavior. The upper of the two curves shows the temperature at which solutions of various compositions start to freeze. The lower curve gives the composition of the solid which separates out at that freezing point. In this system the solid is always richer in the higher-melting component than the solution from which it separates. The alloy consisting of 60 percent copper and 40 percent nickel is known as *constantan*.

10-13 Three-Component Systems

To depict the phase behavior of three-component systems on a two-dimensional diagram it is necessary to consider both the pressure and the temperature as fixed. The phases of the system as a function of the composition can then be shown. The relative amounts of the three components, usually presented as percent by weight, can be shown on a triangular plot, as indicated in Fig. 10-18. The corners of the triangle labeled *A*, *B*, and *C* correspond to the pure compo-

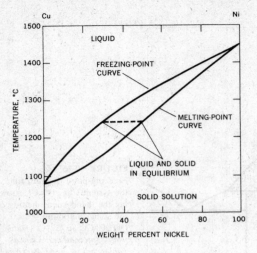

FIGURE 10-17
Solid-liquid phase diagram at
1 atm pressure for a system
showing complete liquid and
solid miscibility. (*Data from
International Critical Tables,
vol. 2, p. 433, McGraw-Hill
Book Company, New York,
1927.*)

nents A, B, and C. The side of the triangle opposite the corner labeled *A*, for
example, implies the absence of A. Thus the horizontal lines across the triangle
show increasing percentages of A from zero at the base to 100 percent at the
apex. In a similar way the percentages of B and C are given by the distances
from the other two sides to the remaining two apices. From the three composition scales of the diagram the composition corresponding to any point can be
read off. This procedure for handling the composition of three-component
systems is possible, and the total composition is always 100 percent, because of
the geometric result that the sum of the three perpendicular distances from any
point to the three sides of the triangle is equal to the height of the triangle.

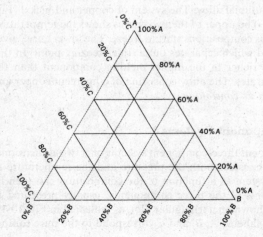

FIGURE 10-18
Diagram for plotting the composition of a three-component
system.

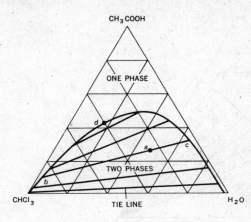

FIGURE 10-19
The liquid system acetic
acid–chloroform–water at
1 atm pressure and 18°C.
[*From R. H. Perry, C. H.
Chilton, and S. D. Kirkpatrick
(eds.), "Chemical Engineers'
Handbook," 2d ed. Copyright
1941 McGraw-Hill, Inc. Used
by permission of McGraw-Hill
Book Company.*]

As with two-component systems, the simplest three-component systems are those in which a liquid system breaks down into two phases. Over a certain range of temperature the system acetic acid–chloroform–water is such a system. A two-phase region occurs in systems with relatively low amounts of acetic acid. A quantitative display of the system at 18°C is given in Fig. 10-19. A necessary part of this diagram are the tie lines through the two-phase region joining the compositions of the two phases that are in equilibrium. (In all previous two-component phase diagrams such lines could have been drawn, but since they would have been horizontal constant-temperature lines, it was unnecessary to exhibit them.) Thus a total composition corresponding to point a in the two-phase region gives two phases, one of composition b and the other of composition c. A unique point on the two-phase boundary is that indicated by d. This point, called the *isothermal critical point* or the *plait point,* is similar to the previously encountered critical-solution temperatures, or consolute points, in that the compositions of the two phases in equilibrium become equal at this point.

Application of the phase rule to a system corresponding to a point in the two-phase region gives

$$\Phi = C - P + 2 = 3 - 2 + 2 = 3 \qquad (10\text{-}24)$$

The 3 degrees of freedom can be accounted for by the pressure, the temperature, and one composition variable. Thus the composition of both phases cannot be arbitrarily fixed. If one is fixed, the tie line from that composition fixes the composition of the second phase.

Three-component systems involving solids and liquids can be introduced by considering systems of two salts and water. The simplest behavior is that shown in Fig. 10-20, where the two salts are somewhat soluble and the diagram gives the curves for the saturated-solution compositions. Such diagrams are perhaps more easily understood if tie lines are also drawn to show that the

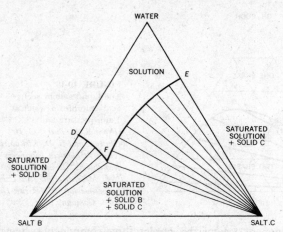

FIGURE 10-20 Phase diagram (schematic) for two salts and water at a fixed temperature and pressure.

saturated solutions along *DF* and *EF* are in equilibrium with the solid salts B and C, respectively. Point *F* corresponds to a system in which the solution is in equilibrium with both salts. Removal of water from point *F* moves the total composition toward the base of the triangle. The effect of this is to form more solid salts, which remain in equilibrium with the decreasing amount but constant concentration of staurated solution.

Finally, three-component systems in which the three components taken in pairs form simple eutectics can be illustrated by the system bismuth-tin-lead. A three-dimensional representation (Fig. 10-21) shows descriptively the phase behavior as a function of composition and temperature at the fixed pressure of 1 atm. For quantitative work it is more suitable to express the data at various constant temperatures on triangular plots. Such diagrams for a few temperatures are therefore included. Tie lines are shown to indicate more clearly the solution compositions that are in equilibrium with the solid components.

If a solution containing 32 percent lead, 15 percent tin, and 53 percent bismuth is cooled, it is found that it remains liquid until, at 96°C, all three solid components start separating out. The phase rule indicates that at such a point, called a *ternary eutectic,* there is

$$C - P + 2 = 3 - 4 + 2 = 1 \text{ degree of freedom} \qquad (10\text{-}25)$$

Since this degree has been used up by the fixed pressure, the system has no remaining variables. It is characteristic of such ternary eutectics that the eutectic point is at a low temperature compared with the melting points of the pure components; e.g., the ternary eutectic of the metal system of the present example will melt in boiling water.

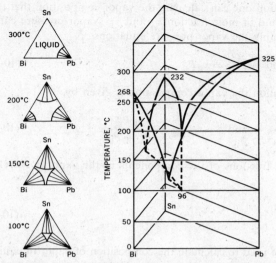

FIGURE 10-21 The three-component system bismuth-tin-lead.

PHASE DIAGRAMS: LIQUID-VAPOR SYSTEMS

Liquid-vapor systems have already been described in our studies of solutions in Chap. 9. Now we can recognize that diagrams like Figs. 9-5a and 9-6a describe, in part, liquid-vapor phase equilibria. We begin our studies by extending these diagrams which show the phase behavior at a fixed temperature. Then diagrams comparable to those presented in condensed-phase studies, which show the phase behavior at a fixed pressure, will be developed.

10-14 Vapor-Pressure Diagrams
Showing Liquid and Vapor Compositions

Vapor equilibrium data are useful in the study of distillations. It is of value to have diagrams showing not only the vapor pressure of a solution of given composition but also the composition of the vapor that is in equilibrium with the liquid. This additional information can be put on the vapor-pressure–composition diagrams.

Since the partial pressure of a gas is proportional to the number of moles of the gas per unit volume, the mole fractions of the vapor can be written

$$x_{A, \text{vap}} = \frac{P_A}{P_A + P_B} \quad \text{and} \quad x_{B, \text{vap}} = \frac{P_B}{P_A + P_B} \tag{10-26}$$

For an ideal solution one can calculate the vapor composition that is in equilibrium with a liquid of mole fraction x_A and x_B. Vapor-pressure curves like that of Fig. 9-4 imply the vapor-pressure equations

$$P_A = x_A P_A^\circ \quad \text{and} \quad P_B = x_B P_B^\circ \tag{10-27}$$

Thus for an ideal solution the vapor composition is given by

$$x_{A,\,vap} = \frac{x_A P_A^\circ}{P_A + P_B} \quad \text{and} \quad x_{B,\,vap} = \frac{x_B P_B^\circ}{P_A + P_B} \tag{10-28}$$

The ratio of the mole fractions of the components in the vapor is therefore given as

$$\frac{x_{A,\,vap}}{x_{B,\,vap}} = \frac{x_A}{x_B} \frac{P_A^\circ}{P_B^\circ} \tag{10-29}$$

This expression can be used to calculate the composition of vapor in equilibrium with an ideal solution of any composition. The qualitative result which should be noticed is that the vapor will be relatively richer in A if P_A° is greater than P_B°, that is, if A is the more volatile component.

The vapor-composition information is added to the vapor-pressure–composition diagram by allowing the abscissa to be used for both liquid and vapor compositions, as illustrated for an ideal solution in Fig. 10-22. At a particular vapor pressure one can read, along the horizontal dashed line, for example, the composition of the liquid that gives rise to this vapor pressure and also the composition of the vapor that exists in equilibrium with this liquid. More often one uses the diagram by starting with a given liquid composition, a of Fig.

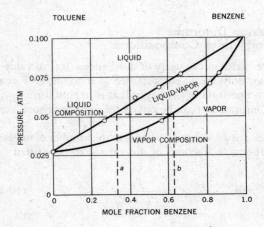

FIGURE 10-22
Vapor-pressure diagram showing liquid and vapor compositions for the nearly ideal system benzene-toluene at 20°C. (Data from Fig. 9-4; curves drawn for ideal behavior.)

10-22, reading off the vapor pressure of this solution and also obtaining the composition b of the vapor in equilibrium with the solution.

For nonideal solutions the composition of the vapor in equilibrium with a given solution must be calculated from Eq. (10-26) and the experimentally determined vapor pressures of the two components. The vapor pressures of the two components of representative nonideal solutions were shown in Figs. 9-5 and 9-6. The vapor composition over an acetone-chloroform solution containing a chloroform mole fraction of 0.2 can be calculated as an example. At this concentration, the vapor pressure of chloroform is, from Fig. 9-5a, 0.045 atm, and that of acetone is 0.350 atm. The total vapor pressure is 0.395 atm. The mole fraction of chloroform in the vapor is $0.045/0.395 = 0.11$; that of acetone is 0.89. Such data can be used to add the vapor-composition curves, as in Figs. 10-23 and 10-24.

It is helpful to notice and remember that on vapor-pressure–composition diagrams (both for ideal and any type of nonideal system) the liquid-composition curve always lies above the vapor-composition curve. Where the curve for the vapor pressure of the liquid shows a maximum or minimum, however, the equilibrium vapor has the same composition as the liquid. Such points will be important when a separation process is considered.

The diagrams of Figs. 10-22 to 10-24 are phase diagrams; i.e., they show the phase or phases present at any pressure at the specified temperature. Consider, for example, a point in the lower region of any of these figures. The pressure is lower than the vapor-pressure curves, and the system exists as a vapor. As the pressure is increased, the point describing the system moves up until it reaches the vapor-composition line. The vapor is then in equilibrium with liquid of the composition given by the liquid-composition curve at that pressure. Attempts to increase the pressure will produce more liquid. In general the liquid composition will be different from that of the vapor. When this process is complete, the system is represented by a point on the upper liquid-composition curve. Further pressure increases merely increase the pressure on

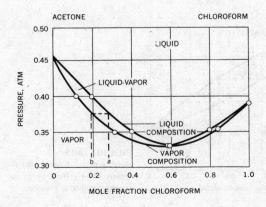

FIGURE 10-23
Vapor-pressure diagram for the system chloroform-acetone at 35°C, showing liquid- and vapor-composition curves.

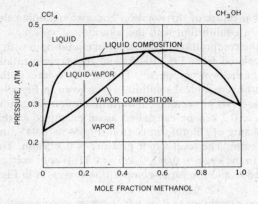

FIGURE 10-24
Vapor-pressure diagram for the system carbon tetrachloride–methanol at 35°C, showing liquid- and vapor-composition curves.

the liquid. It follows from this discussion that the three regions of Figs. 10-22 to 10-24 can be labeled "vapor," "vapor and liquid," and "liquid."

10-15 Boiling-Point–Composition Diagrams

The discussion of liquid-vapor equilibrium has so far concerned itself with the experimental results obtained when the vapor in equilibrium with solutions at some fixed temperature, often 25°C, is studied. Such vapor-pressure data are suited to the theoretical questions that have been discussed, but they are not the results that are of primary importance in studies of the more practical aspects of liquid-vapor equilibria. In practice, it is more common to fix the pressure at some constant value, often, but not always, at 1 atm, and to determine the temperature at which liquid and vapor are in equilibrium. In this way, data are

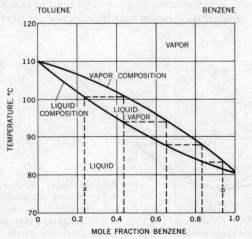

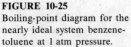

FIGURE 10-25
Boiling-point diagram for the nearly ideal system benzene-toluene at 1 atm pressure.

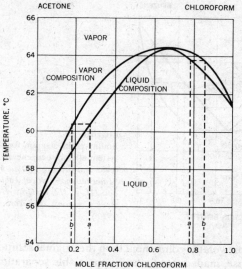

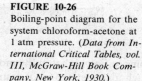

FIGURE 10-26
Boiling-point diagram for the system chloroform-acetone at 1 atm pressure. (*Data from International Critical Tables, vol. III, McGraw-Hill Book Company, New York, 1930.*)

obtained from which a *boiling-point–composition diagram* can be constructed. It is again customary to show the composition of the vapor that is in equilibrium with the liquid on the same diagram. Figure 10-25 shows these curves for the ideal system benzene-toluene. Now one notices that for the vapor to be relatively richer in the more volatile, i.e., *lower*-boiling, component, the liquid-composition curve lies below the vapor-composition curve. The exact shapes of the two curves on the boiling-point diagram, even for an ideal solution, are not deduced as easily as the curves on the vapor-pressure diagram. The curves depend on the behavior of the system as a function of temperature, and this is less easy to generalize than the constant-temperature behavior of the vapor-pressure diagrams.

The boiling-point curves for the two types of nonideal systems are shown in Figs. 10-26 and 10-27. A minimum in the vapor-pressure–composition curve results in a maximum in the boiling-point–composition curve, and vice versa. Also, as for the ideal solutions, the liquid-composition curve lies lower than the vapor-composition curve on a boiling-point diagram. The significance of these diagrams for any separation process can again be appreciated by following paths, like those shown dashed, for the conversion of some of a liquid sample of composition *a* to its equilibrium vapor of composition *b*.

10-16 Distillation

The important process of distillation can now be investigated. From the boiling-point diagram of Fig. 10-25 one can see that if a small amount of vapor were removed from a solution of composition *a*, the vapor would have a

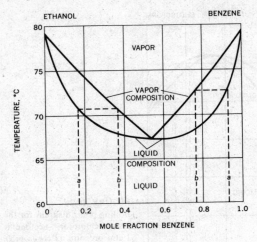

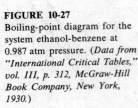

FIGURE 10-27
Boiling-point diagram for the
system ethanol-benzene at
0.987 atm pressure. (*Data from
"International Critical Tables,"
vol. III, p. 312, McGraw-Hill
Book Company, New York,
1930.*)

composition higher in the more volatile component than the original solution *a*.
Such a single step is, of course, inadequate for any appreciable separation of
two components unless they have extremely different boiling points. In practice,
a process of *fractional distillation* is used, in which the separation step just
described is, in effect, repeated by condensing some of the vapor, boiling off
some vapor from this new solution, collecting and revaporizing this product,
and so forth. This procedure has the effect of stepping across the boiling-point
diagram, as indicated by the dashed lines of Fig. 10-25. A distillation *column*
carries out this stepwise process automatically.

The efficiency of a distillation column is determined by the number of
theoretical plates that the separation it performs corresponds to. For example, a
column supplied with a charge of composition *a* in Fig. 10-26 is operated at
total reflux until equilibrium is established. A small sample of distillate is then
drawn off and analyzed and has, say, composition *b*. The separation that has
resulted corresponds to four ideal evaporations and condensations, and the
column is said to have four theoretical plates.

For a solution showing a maximum vapor pressure and a minimum boiling
point, the distillation process is indicated by the dashed lines of Fig. 10-27.
Regardless of the initial solution distillation in a fractional-distillation unit is
seen to result ultimately in a distillate of the composition of the minimum-
boiling-point mixture. One or the other of the pure components could be
prepared only by working with the residue. The most important commercial
solution that shows this behavior is the water-ethanol system. Fermentation
processes result in an ethanol concentration of about 10 percent. The object of
distillation is to increase this concentration and possibly to yield pure ethanol.
The boiling-point diagram of Fig. 10-28 shows that distillation at atmospheric
pressure can yield, at best, a distillate of 95 percent ethanol. It is for this reason
that 95 percent ethanol is a fairly common chemical material. Absolute alcohol

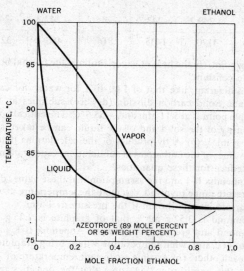

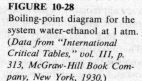

FIGURE 10-28
Boiling-point diagram for the system water-ethanol at 1 atm. (*Data from "International Critical Tables," vol. III, p. 313, McGraw-Hill Book Company, New York, 1930.*)

can be obtained by a distillation procedure using a three-component system, usually alcohol, water, and benzene.

A different situation arises with solutions that show a maximum in their boiling-point curves, like the system of Fig. 10-26. If such a solution is merely boiled away, the residue will approach the composition corresponding to the maximum of the boiling-point curve and the boiling point will also approach that corresponding to this maximum. Once this solution and boiling point have been reached, the remaining solution will boil at this temperature and will not change its composition. Such a solution is known as a *constant-boiling mixture* or *azeotrope*. This same term is applied to a solution having the composition of the minimum of a boiling-point curve.

It is necessary to stress that although in the case of an azeotrope we are dealing with a constant-temperature constant-composition boiling mixture, this mixture is not to be regarded as a compound formed between the two components. A change in the total pressure is usually sufficient to show that the azeotropic composition can be changed.

PROBLEMS

10-1. The normal boiling point of benzene is 80.1°C, and it obeys Trouton's rule quite well. Estimate the vapor pressure of benzene at 25°C.

10-2. The vapor pressure of neon is reported in the "International Critical Tables," vol. III, p. 203, McGraw-Hill Book Company, New York, 1930, as a function of temperature as follows:

$t, °C$	-228.7	-233.6	-240.2	-243.7	-245.7	-247.3	-248.5
p, mmHg	19,800	10,040	3170	1435	816	486	325

What are (a) the normal boiling point, (b) the heat of vaporization at the normal boiling point, and (c) the Trouton-rule constant?

10-3. (a) Prepare a phase diagram, like that of Fig. 10-1 for water, for carbon dioxide. Use the following data. Solid carbon dioxide (dry ice) sublimes at 1 atm pressure and $-78.2°C$. The triple point is at 5.11 atm and $-56.6°C$. The critical point is at 73 atm and 31.1°C. The density of the solid and of the liquid can be taken as the constant values 1.56 and 1.11 g ml^{-1}. (b) A by-product of the calculations that you should have made are average values of the enthalpies of sublimation, vaporization, and fusion. What values do you deduce for these quantities?

10-4. From the data of Appendix B-1 and the assumption that these values do not vary appreciably in the temperature range involved, calculate the temperature at which rhombic and monoclinic sulfur are in equilibrium if the pressure is 1 atm.

10-5. The density of diamond is 3.52 g ml^{-1}; that of graphite is 2.25 g ml^{-1}. Thermodynamic data for diamond and graphite are given in Appendix B-1. (a) Assuming the pressure is 1 atm, what temperature would bring graphite and diamond in equilibrium with each other? (b) Assume a constant temperature of 25°C; what pressure would produce this equilibrium? (Assume that the densities remain constant over this pressure range.)

10-6. At what temperature does water boil at an elevation at which the barometric pressure is 0.66 atm?

10-7. Obtain an approximate expression for the slope of the liquid-vapor equilibrium curve on a P-versus-T graph for any liquid at its normal boiling point.

10-8. (a) Find the slope of the liquid-solid curve for water using the heat of fusion of 6.01 kJ mol^{-1} and the density of ice of 0.92 g ml^{-1}, neither being very sensitive to temperature or pressure. The normal freezing point of water is 0°C. (b) What temperature do you calculate for the triple point if you know it occurs at a pressure of 0.006 atm?

10-9. The integrated form of the Clausius-Clapeyron equation is approximate in part because it treats ΔH_{vap} as a constant. The approximation is most unsatisfactory when large ranges of pressure and temperature are considered. (a) Set up a Clausius-Clapeyron equation for water on the basis of the critical point and the triple point. (b) What does this equation give for ΔH_{vap} and for the normal boiling point?

10-10. Plot the number of degrees of freedom for the silver-copper system of Fig. 10-13 (a) as a function of the percent of copper at 800°C and (b) as a function of temperature at 50 percent copper.

10-11. A remarkable imaginary catalyst quickly converts any hydrocarbon and carbon and hydrogen to the equilibrium carbon-hydrogen products. How many components and how many degrees of freedom are there in a catalyzed system that (a) is made up by charging the system with carbon, hydrogen, and heptane and consists only of a liquid phase; (b) is made up by charging the system with hydrogen and heptane and has gas, liquid, and one solid phase?

10-12. The scientist who discovered the catalyst described in Prob. 10-11 reported that in a particular study with this catalyst three different crystalline hydrocarbon products formed within the mother liquor. No vapor phase was present. What do you think of his claim?

10-13. Ammonium carbamate, $NH_4CO_2NH_2$, is a solid which gives rise to a vapor consisting of CO_2 and NH_3. Ammonium chloride similarly gives rise to a vapor consisting of HCl and NH_3. (*a*) What is the number of components in a reaction system which contains both solid $NH_4CO_2NH_2$ and NH_4Cl and a vapor phase containing HCl, CO_2, and NH_3? (*b*) How many phases are present? (*c*) What is the number of degrees of freedom?

10-14. The equilibria between the phases of a single-component metallic system are affected by the applied magnetic field, in addition to the temperature and pressure. What is the maximum number of phases that can coexist?

10-15. At temperatures approaching 1000°C equilibrium is established in the two reduction reactions

$$FeO(s) + H_2(g) \rightleftharpoons Fe(s) + H_2O(g)$$

and

$$FeO(s) + CO(g) \rightleftharpoons Fe(s) + CO_2(g)$$

(*a*) If a reaction chamber is charged with $FeO(s)$ and $H_2(g)$, how many components, phases, and degrees of freedom does the system have? (*b*) If the reaction chamber is charged with $FeO(s)$, $H_2(g)$, and $CO(g)$, how many components, phases, and degrees of freedom does the system have?

10-16. How many components are there in the systems composed of (*a*) $N_2(g)$ plus $O_2(g)$, (*b*) the system of part (*a*) if a catalyst is present that promotes the formation of the many possible oxides of nitrogen, (*c*) $NaCl(s)$ and an aqueous solution saturated with NaCl and containing some HCl, (*d*) any salt plus water, (*e*) the system of part (*d*) at a high enough temperature for it to consist only of dry solid salt and water vapor, (*f*) the system of part (*d*) cooled until a solid appears that turns out to be the hydroxide of the metal?

10-17. How many remaining degrees of freedom are there in each of the following systems? Suggest variables that could correspond to these degrees of freedom. (*a*) Liquid water and water vapor in equilibrium at a pressure of 1 atm; (*b*) liquid water and water vapor in equilibrium; (*c*) I_2 dispersed between liquid water and liquid CCl_4 at 1 atm pressure with no solid I_2 present; (*d*) the vapor equilibrium system of NH_3, N_2, and H_2; (*e*) an aqueous solution of H_3PO_4 and NaOH at 1 atm pressure; (*f*) a solution of H_2SO_4 in water in equilibrium with the solid hydrate $H_2SO_4 \cdot 2H_2O$ at 1 atm pressure.

10-18. In view of Fig. 10-9*c*, describe the phase situations that arise when nicotine is gradually added to a small quantity of water at 100°C until the system is transformed to nearly 100 percent nicotine.

10-19. In view of Fig. 10-9*c*, describe the phase situations that arise when an aqueous solution that is 60 percent by weight nicotine is heated from 50 to 250°C.

10-20. Estimate from Fig. 10-11 the weight of solution and of solid that will be present when 100 g of solution of composition *b* is cooled to point *c*.

10-21. Calculate the solubility of naphthalene in benzene at 25°C and compare with the observed value of 69 g of naphthalene per 100 g of benzene.

10-22. With the help of Fig. 10-13 describe the phases that form and the temperatures at which phase changes occur when a 20 percent copper-in-silver melt at 1000°C is cooled to 700°C.

10-23. With the help of Fig. 10-13 describe the phase changes when solid silver at 900°C is added to a silver-copper melt containing 40 percent copper at 900°C.

10-24. At about 60 percent by weight, $CaCl_2$ in the system $CaCl_2 \cdot CaF_2$, shown in Fig. 10-16, a peritectic point occurs at 737°C. If the pressure is assumed fixed at 1 atm, apply the phase rule to deduce the number of degrees of freedom at this point.

10-25. Describe the phases that appear and the temperature of their appearance when the solid compound $CaF_2 \cdot CaCl_2$ is heated from 400 to 1400°C at 1 atm pressure.

10-26. Verify that the sum of the three perpendicular distances from any point inside an equilateral triangle to the sides of the triangle is equal to the height of the triangle.

10-27. (a) Estimate from Fig. 10-19 the weights of the three components present in 100 g of the one-phase system at point d. (b) Estimate the compositions and the weights of the two phases that occur for 100 g of the system having the total composition of point a of Fig. 10-19.

10-28. Describe the phases that occur as water is added to an initially anhydrous mixture of 5 percent of the salt B and 95 percent of the salt C in Fig. 10-20.

10-29. Assuming ideal-solution behavior, calculate the equilibrium vapor pressure and the mole-fraction composition of the vapor in equilibrium at 40°C with a solution of carbon tetrachloride–cyclohexane that has 0.4753 mole fraction CCl_4. The vapor pressures at 40°C of pure CCl_4 and cyclohexane are 0.2807 and 0.2429 atm, respectively. Compare with the measured values reported by G. Scatchard, S. E. Wood, and J. M. Mochel [*J. Am. Chem. Soc.*, **61**:3206 (1939)] of 0.2677 for the vapor pressure and 0.5116 for the mole fraction of CCl_4 in the vapor.

10-30. It is found that the boiling point at 1 atm pressure of a solution of 0.6589 mole fraction benzene and 0.3411 mole fraction toluene is 88.0°C. At this temperature the vapor pressures of pure benzene and toluene are 1.259 and 0.4993 atm, respectively. What is the vapor composition that boils off this liquid?

10-31. At 55° a solution of mole fraction 0.2205 ethanol and 0.7795 cyclohexane has a vapor pressure of 0.4842 atm and a vapor composition of 0.5646 mole fraction ethanol and 0.4355 cyclohexane. The vapor pressures of pure ethanol and cyclohexane at 55°C are 0.3683 and 0.2212 atm, respectively. Plot a possible vapor-pressure diagram having liquid and vapor compositions that are compatible with these data.

10-32. (a) Prepare a vapor-pressure–composition diagram showing the vapor composition as well as the vapor pressure in terms of the liquid composition for the system carbon tetrachloride–acetonitrile at 45°C. Data are given in Prob. 9-2. (b) Discuss the consequences of distilling solutions that are originally rich in CCl_4 or in CH_3CN.

10-33. At total reflux, samples from the pot and the still head are withdrawn from an experiment in which ethanol and benzene are refluxing in a packed distillation column operating at 0.987 atm pressure. The pot sample has 0.05 mole fraction benzene, and the still head a composition of about 0.5 mole fraction benzene. According to Fig. 10-27, what would the temperatures in the pot and head be and how many theoretical plates does the column have?

REFERENCES

RICCI, J. E.: "The Phase Rule and Heterogeneous Equilibrium," D. Van Nostrand Company, Inc., Princeton, N.J., 1951.

DENBIGH, K.: "The Principles of Chemical Equilibrium," chaps. 5–8, Cambridge University Press, New York, 1955.

ALPER, A. M. (ed.): "Phase Diagrams," vols. 1–3, "Materials Science and Technology," Academic Press, Inc., New York, 1970.

REISMAN, A.: "Phase Equilibria," Academic Press, Inc., New York, 1970.

PARKER, R. C., and D. S. KRISTOL: Freezing Points, Triple Points, and Phase Equilibria, *J. Chem. Educ.*, **51**:658 (1974).

QUANTUM MECHANICS AND ATOMIC STRUCTURE

Atomic and molecular structure was treated in Chap. 3 only in sufficient detail to allow a molecular interpretation to be given to the thermodynamic functions. A more organized and penetrating direct look into the molecular world will now be taken.

One of the most exciting endeavors in our investigation of the world in which we live has been our attempt to understand the basic units of matter that make up the material world. For the chemist the basic units are the molecules and the atoms of which they are composed. Some of the long sought for answers to the questions of why and how atoms are held together into molecules can now be given. The description of the nature of chemical bonding that is achieved represents the culmination of one aspect of our efforts to unravel the secrets of matter.

In this chapter the methods of quantum mechanics will be developed and the nature and structure of atoms will be explored. The methods of quantum mechanics and this background information on atoms will be brought together again in Chap. 13, when molecules and chemical bonding are studied. (The intervening chapter will show how the properties of symmetric systems, such as atoms and many molecules, are governed by the symmetry of the system. Recognition of these symmetry features often greatly simplifies the application of the methods of quantum mechanics.)

11-1 Atomic Spectra

Even before the detailed nature of atoms was known, it was recognized that the radiation emitted by a hot, or excited, atom presents a body of valuable data on the internal nature of the atom. The actual spectra were of little use, however, until some pattern or relation could be found for the frequencies of the emitted radiation. The initial step in bringing these data to bear on the problem of atomic structure was the completely empirical one of discovering some basic design in the frequencies of the emitted radiation.

Many unsuccessful attempts were made to explain the observed spectral lines of the hydrogen atom, shown in Fig. 11-1, as harmonics or overtones of some set of fundamental frequencies. Gradually, however, a completely em-

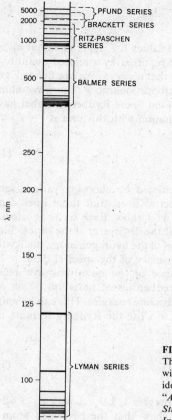

5000 —
2000 —

1000 —

500 —

250 —

200 —

λ, nm

150 —

125 —

100 —

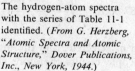

]} PFUND SERIES
]} BRACKETT SERIES
]} RITZ-PASCHEN SERIES
}BALMER SERIES
}LYMAN SERIES

FIGURE 11-1
The hydrogen-atom spectra with the series of Table 11-1 identified. (*From G. Herzberg, "Atomic Spectra and Atomic Structure," Dover Publications, Inc., New York, 1944.*)

pirical approach yielded some understanding of the spectra of the simpler atoms. In 1885, J. J. Balmer showed that the frequencies of some of the observed spectral lines of the hydrogen atom, now known as the *Balmer series,* can be expressed by an empirical equation which we write as

$$\nu \text{ (Hz)} = 3.2880 \times 10^{15} \left(\frac{1}{2^2} - \frac{1}{n_1{}^2} \right) \qquad n_1 = 3, 4, 5, \ldots \qquad (11\text{-}1)$$

This entirely empirical correlation proved a valuable clue, and very shortly it was shown by J. R. Rydberg that a more general expression of this type could be written to correlate the frequencies of all the observed spectral lines of the hydrogen atom. The expression, known as a *Rydberg formula,* is

$$\nu \text{ (Hz)} = 3.2880 \times 10^{15} \left(\frac{1}{n_2{}^2} - \frac{1}{n_1{}^2} \right) \tag{11-2}$$

where n_1 and n_2 are to be assigned integral values 1, 2, 3, ... such that $n_1 > n_2$.

The frequency of a spectral line can be reported by a related quantity, the *wave number*, usually denoted by $\bar{\nu}$. Recall that $\nu = c/\lambda$. We can define $\bar{\nu}$ as ν/c or $1/\lambda$ and thus have a measure that is proportional to ν. The wave-number quantity $\bar{\nu}$ will be seen with the cgs unit of cm^{-1}, the Rydberg number having the value 109,677 cm^{-1}. The Rydberg equation with this unit is

$$\bar{\nu} \text{ (cm}^{-1}) = 109{,}677 \left(\frac{1}{n_2{}^2} - \frac{1}{n_1{}^2} \right) \tag{11-3}$$

Frequencies, or wave numbers, calculated by choosing various sets of integers correspond to the observed spectral lines, and these lines can be grouped in series, as Table 11-1 and Fig. 11-1 show. Each series is calculated from a given value of n_2 and is named after the discoverer of the series. Since it can be used to generate all the spectral lines of the hydrogen atom, the Rydberg formula provides a concise analytical summary of the spectral data.

As was apparent after the acceptance of the quantum-wave relation $\Delta\epsilon = h\nu$, the emission of only specific frequencies of radiation by an atom corresponds to the emission of quanta of discrete energies. This can be emphasized by making use of Planck's relation to write the Rydberg formula more explicitly in terms of energy. The result is

$$\Delta\epsilon \text{ (J)} = 2.1787 \times 10^{-18} \left(\frac{1}{n_2{}^2} - \frac{1}{n_1{}^2} \right) \tag{11-4}$$

again with n_1 and n_2 selected from the integers 1, 2, 3, ... with $n_1 > n_2$.

The spectroscopic results therefore show that the hydrogen atom can change its energy only by the definite amounts calculated from the Rydberg formula. These amounts can be obtained from the spectrum of hydrogen atoms or calculated from the Rydberg expression, which of course is based on the spectral results.

From the energy changes that are determined spectrally, an energy dia-

TABLE 11-1 Hydrogen-Atom Spectral Series and Rydberg Integers for Eq. (11-2) or (11-3)

Series	n_2	n_1	Spectral region
Lyman	1	2, 3, 4, ...	Ultraviolet
Balmer	2	3, 4, 5, ...	Visible
Paschen	3	4, 5, 6, ...	Infrared
Brackett	4	5, 6, 7, ...	Infrared
Pfund	5	6, 7, 8, ...	Infrared

gram for the hydrogen atom can be constructed. This diagram and the relation of the spectral series to it are shown in Fig. 11-2. The next step is clearly that of finding some description of how electrons behave in atoms and molecules that leads to an electron behavior consistent with the detailed spectral information like that illustrated by Fig. 11-2 for the hydrogen atom.

11-2 The Bohr Model of the Hydrogen Atom

The quantum restrictions on atoms and molecules or on the electrons of atoms and molecules were treated in Sec. 3-2 in terms of restrictions on angular momentum and in Sec. 3-4 in terms of the wave nature of particles. Now let us consider the picture of the hydrogen atom that emerges when quantum restrictions are applied in these two ways. We begin with the treatment of the hydrogen atom developed by Niels Bohr in 1913. Restrictions on angular momentum provided the basis for Bohr's quantum model of the hydrogen atom. Restrictions on the waves associated with the electron lead, as you will see, to similar results.

The model chosen by Bohr to represent the hydrogen atom is made up of the following postulates:

1. The electron moves about the nucleus in a circular orbit.
2. Only orbits in which the electron has an angular momentum that is an integral multiple of $h/2\pi$ are allowed. (The simple integral multiple should be modified as shown in Sec. 3-2.)
3. The electron does not radiate energy when it is in an allowed orbit. It can gain or lose energy only by jumping from one allowed orbit to another.

On the basis of this model, Bohr calculated the radii and energies of the allowed orbits and showed that the observed spectrum could be predicted theoretically.

The quantized-angular-momentum postulate allows us to write

$$\text{Angular momentum} = I\omega = n\frac{h}{2\pi} \qquad n = 1, 2, 3, \ldots \qquad (11\text{-}5)$$

The moment of inertia of this two-particle electron-proton system is given approximately by $I = mr^2$, where m is the mass of the electron.

With $I = mr^2$ and $\omega = 2\pi \, (v/2\pi r) = v/r$, Eq. (11-5) becomes

$$\text{Angular momentum} = mvr = n\frac{h}{2\pi} \qquad n = 1, 2, 3, \ldots \qquad (11\text{-}6)$$

This quantum restriction, introduced quite arbitrarily by Bohr, can also be arrived at by considering the wave nature of the electron of the atom, as shown in Sec. 3-4.

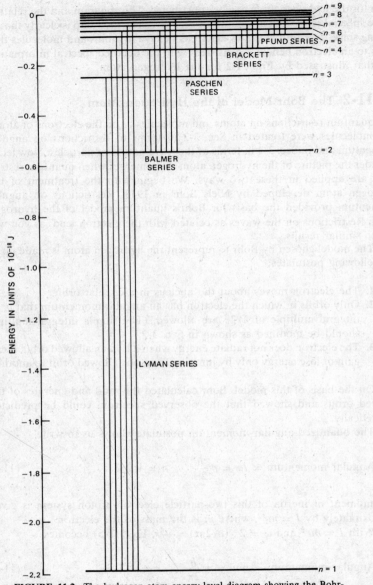

FIGURE 11-2 The hydrogen-atom energy-level diagram showing the Bohr-atom quantum-number designations and the spectral series.

The size of the orbits the electron is allowed to be in, according to Bohr, can be calculated by requiring that the centrifugal force of the rotation be balanced by the electrical attraction to the nucleus. The centrifugal force is given by $f = ma$, where a, the acceleration toward the nucleus, is equal to v^2/r. The coulombic force of attraction between the nucleus of charge $+e$ and the electron of charge $-e$ is $e^2/(4\pi\epsilon_0)r^2$. Thus

$$\frac{mv^2}{r} = \frac{e^2}{(4\pi\epsilon_0)r^2} \tag{11-7}$$

Rearranging this expression and introducing the quantum condition of Eq. (11-6), one gets

$$r = n^2 \frac{(4\pi\epsilon_0)h^2}{4\pi^2 me^2} \qquad \text{where } n = 1, 2, 3, \dots \tag{11-8}$$

The radii of the allowed orbits are found to depend, therefore, on the quantum number n and on known constants. Substitution of numerical values for these constants gives

$$r = n^2 (0.529 \times 10^{-10} \text{ m}) = n^2 (0.529 \text{ Å}) \tag{11-9}$$

Although no experimental values are available for direct comparison with this result, it is apparent that, at least for small values of n, the size of the allowed orbits is quite reasonable compared with the molecular dimensions deduced from the kinetic-molecular theory, as shown, for example, in Tables 2-2 and 2-4. The size of the allowed orbits and the angular momentum of an electron in the first three orbits is shown diagrammatically in Fig. 11-3.

A critical test of Bohr's theory is provided by the calculation of the energies of the allowed orbits. It is the energy differences of an electron in these orbits which must explain the energies of the quanta, or the frequencies, of the emitted radiation. The kinetic energy of the electron in an orbit is given by $\frac{1}{2}mv^2$. The potential energy of the electron as a function of its distance from the nucleus is given by Coulomb's law as

$$\text{Potential energy} = -\frac{e^2}{(4\pi\epsilon_0)r} \tag{11-10}$$

The choice of a zero potential energy at infinite separation of the electron and the nucleus makes the potential energy negative for all finite distances. The total energy of the electron-proton system is

$$\epsilon = \frac{1}{2}mv^2 - \frac{e^2}{(4\pi\epsilon_0)r} \tag{11-11}$$

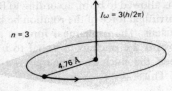

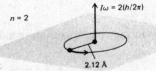

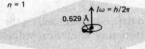

FIGURE 11-3
The radii and angular-momentum vectors of the first three hydrogen-atom orbits according to the Bohr theory.

The previous expression for balanced forces gives the relation $\frac{1}{2}mv^2 = e^2/2(4\pi\epsilon_0)r$. With this relation Eq. (11-11) can be reduced to

$$\epsilon = \frac{e^2}{2(4\pi\epsilon_0)r} - \frac{e^2}{(4\pi\epsilon_0)r} = -\frac{e^2}{2(4\pi\epsilon_0)r} \tag{11-12}$$

(The fact that the potential energy is negative and twice the magnitude of the kinetic-energy term is an illustration of a quite general result stated by the virial theorem. It will be shown in Sec. 13-4 that this relation is obeyed by all systems of the type we consider here in their equilibrium state.) Substitution for r from Eq. (11-8) now gives

$$\epsilon = -\frac{2\pi^2 me^4}{(4\pi\epsilon_0)^2 h^2 n^2} \qquad \text{where } n = 1, 2, 3, \ldots \tag{11-13}$$

If numerical values are inserted for all the constant terms, we obtain

$$\epsilon \text{ (J)} = -\frac{2.1799 \times 10^{-18}}{n^2} \qquad \text{where } n = 1, 2, 3, \ldots \tag{11-14}$$

Conversion to cm^{-1} units, in which the related spectroscopic expressions are often given, yields

$$\bar{\nu}\,(\mathrm{cm}^{-1}) = -\frac{109{,}737}{n^2} \qquad n = 1, 2, 3, \ldots \tag{11-15}$$

The corresponding expression obtained with the correct moment-of-inertia expression, $I = \mu r^2$, where μ is the reduced mass, is

$$\bar{\nu}\,(\mathrm{cm}^{-1}) = -\frac{109{,}677}{n^2} \qquad n = 1, 2, 3, \ldots \tag{11-16}$$

Each allowed orbit, according to the Bohr model of the hydrogen atom, is characterized by a value of the quantum number n and has a definite energy and radius. The orbit with the lowest energy is that with $n = 1$, and it is this orbit which the electron normally occupies at room temperature. Other orbits have large quantum numbers and, according to Eq. (11-14), higher, i.e., less negative, energies. The results produce an energy pattern like that deduced from empirical studies of the hydrogen-atom spectra and shown in Fig. 11-2.

The Bohr theory can therefore claim the considerable achievement of having provided a model for the hydrogen atom which is consistent with the hydrogen-atom spectral data; however, all attempts to extend the approach to atoms with more than one electron were unsuccessful. Furthermore, no explanation was provided for the fact that atoms combine to form molecules.

These difficulties are overcome by the methods of quantum mechanics, developed independently in 1926 by Erwin Schrödinger and W. Heisenberg. We have already made use of a form of the Schrödinger wave equation. Now let us explore it further so that we can apply it to the hydrogen-atom problem and to a variety of other atomic and molecular problems.

11-3 Operators and the Schrödinger Equation

The time-independent Schrödinger equation for a particle of mass m confined to one dimension and subject to a potential energy $U(x)$ was written in Sec. 3-4 as

$$-\frac{h^2}{8\pi^2 m}\frac{d^2\psi(x)}{dx^2} + U(x)\psi(x) = \epsilon\psi(x) \tag{11-17}$$

If there is a function $\psi(x)$ which satisfies this equation, the quantity ϵ that is given when this function is inserted into the equation is the energy of the particle.

This expression, which allows the energy to be calculated, is just one of a number of equations that can be set up to calculate properties of quantum-mechanical systems. All these expressions can be looked on as *operator* equations. Equation (11-17) can be displayed to show this feature by writing it as

$$\left[-\frac{h^2}{8\pi^2 m} \frac{d}{dx^2} + U(x) \right] \psi(k) = \epsilon\psi(x) \qquad (11\text{-}18)$$

The expression in the square brackets is an example of an *operator*. This particular operator is known as the one-dimensional *hamiltonian,* and it or its three-dimensional counterpart is given the symbol $\mathcal{H}$. With this notation Eq. (11-18) can be written as

$$\mathcal{H}\psi = \epsilon\psi \qquad (11\text{-}19)$$

Previously we said that a function that solves the Schrödinger equation (11-17) gives a value for ϵ that is the energy of the particle. The corresponding statement phrased in terms of Eq. (11-19) is that if there is a function ψ which when acted on by the operator $\mathcal{H}$ gives back a constant times the ψ function, that constant is the energy of the particle. Functions that behave in this way are known as *eigenfunctions,* and the constant values ϵ of Eq. (11-19) are *eigenvalues*.

The energies of the system are identified as the eigenvalues for the hamiltonian operator. Any other observable quantity has its own operator. The operator approach is therefore quite general. When an operator for an observable quantity operates on the wave function for the system and gives a result which is a constant times the wave function, that constant is the value of the observable quantity.

An additional generalization, beyond the wave-function examples of Secs. 3-5 to 3-8, allows wave function to be imaginary or complex, i.e., to involve $i = \sqrt{-1}$. Let us now allow ψ to be such a function. Its complex conjugate, obtained by replacing i wherever it appears by $-i$, will be denoted by ψ^*. A complex ψ is normalized if

$$\int \psi^*\psi \, d\tau = 1 \qquad (11\text{-}20)$$

Let us assume that we deal with normalized wave functions.

Now, since it illustrates a very useful formulation, let us consider

$$\int \psi^*\mathcal{H}\psi \, d\tau$$

where $d\tau$ is an element in the coordinate system that is used. Suppose we insert a function for ψ that is an eigenfunction for the operator $\mathcal{H}$; that is, ψ is a function such that $\mathcal{H}\psi$ gives $\epsilon\psi$, where ϵ is just a quantity, or constant, not a function. The above integral becomes

$$\int \psi^*\epsilon\psi \, d\tau = \epsilon \int \psi^*\psi \, d\tau \qquad (11\text{-}21)$$

If, furthermore, ψ is normalized, the integral on the right is unity and the original integral gives

$$\int \psi^* \mathfrak{K} \psi \, d\tau = \epsilon \tag{11-22}$$

Expressions of the type $\int \psi^* \mathfrak{K} \psi \, d\tau$ can be formed with any operator. Some, like the hamiltonian operator $\mathfrak{K}$, can lead (because eigenfunctions of that operator exist) to eigenvalues as in Eq. (11-22).

The eigenfunctions established with the $\mathfrak{K}$ operator may not be eigenfunctions of some other operator. A formulation like that of Eq. (11-22) then yields an average value, or *expectation* value, for the property of the system associated with the operator. The position operator for a one-dimensional system, for example, is the coordinate itself. Thus the expectation value for the position of a particle in a one-dimensional system, which we write as $\langle x \rangle$, is

$$\int \psi^* x \psi \, dx = \langle x \rangle \tag{11-23}$$

Operators for angular momentum constitute an important set. They can be deduced from the operator that leads in the quantum-mechanical treatment to the linear momentum in a one-dimensional system. This operator, written for the x coordinate, is

$$\widehat{p}_x = \frac{h}{2\pi i} \frac{\partial}{\partial x} \tag{11-24}$$

First let us see that this operator is related to the hamiltonian of Eqs. (11-18) and (11-19). Kinetic energy, usually expressed by $\frac{1}{2}mv^2$, can be written in terms of momentum as

$$\text{KE} = \frac{1}{2} \frac{(mv)^2}{m} \tag{11-25}$$

This classical expression can be used to obtain the relation between the quantum-mechanical operators for kinetic energy and momentum. If we interpret the squared-momentum term in Eq. (11-25) as meaning the momentum operator acting on itself, we can write for the kinetic-energy operator the expression

$$\frac{1}{2} \frac{(mv)^2}{m} = \frac{1}{2m} \left(\frac{h}{2\pi i} \frac{h}{2\pi i} \frac{\partial^2}{\partial x^2} \right) = -\frac{h^2}{8\pi^2 m} \frac{\partial^2}{\partial x^2} \tag{11-26}$$

Thus we deduce the kinetic-energy operator to be $-(h^2/8\pi^2 m)(\partial^2/\partial x^2)$. Notice that this is just the first term of the hamiltonian operator. The operator $\mathfrak{K}$ consists of a kinetic-energy operator and a potential-energy operator. It thus is the exact operator counterpart of the classical hamiltonian, which is the sum of the kinetic and potential energies.

Angular-momentum operators, like that for kinetic energy, can also be deduced from the linear-momentum operator of Eq. (11-24). The procedure is suggested in Fig. 11-4. For most atomic and molecular problems angular-

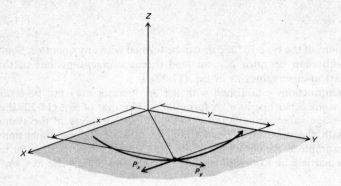

ANGULAR MOMENTUM ABOUT z AXIS $= xP_y - yP_x$
OPERATOR FOR ANGULAR MOMENTUM ABOUT z AXIS $= L_z$

$$= x\left(-i\,\frac{h}{2\pi}\,\frac{\partial}{\partial y}\right) - y\left(-i\,\frac{h}{2\pi}\,\frac{\partial}{\partial x}\right)$$

$$= -i\,\frac{h}{2\pi}\left(x\,\frac{\partial}{\partial y} - y\,\frac{\partial}{\partial x}\right)$$

FIGURE 11-4 The relations between the cartesian momentum components p_x and p_y and the quantum-mechanical angular-momentum operators.

momentum operators expressed in polar rather than cartesian coordinates are used. Two of these operators are of special importance. The operator for the component of angular momentum along an axis, say the z axis, is

$$\widehat{L}_z = \frac{h}{2\pi i}\,\frac{\partial}{\partial \phi} \tag{11-27}$$

The other useful operator is that for the square of the total angular momentum. It is

$$(\widehat{L})^2 = -\,\frac{h^2}{4\pi^2}\left[\frac{1}{\sin\theta}\,\frac{\partial}{\partial\theta}\left(\sin\theta\,\frac{\partial}{\partial\theta}\right) + \frac{1}{\sin^2\theta}\,\frac{\partial}{\partial\phi^2}\right] \tag{11-28}$$

The use of these operators will be illustrated in our studies of the hydrogen atom in the following sections, where you will see that, for atoms, the eigenfunctions for the operator $\mathcal{3C}$ are also eigenfunctions for these two angular-momentum operators.

11-4 The Hydrogen-Atom Problem: The Angular-Momentum Component along a Direction

Now let us use the methods of quantum mechanics to attack the hydrogen-atom problem. The Schrödinger equation, i.e., the energy-operator equation, will lead us to the eigenfunctions and to the corresponding eigenvalues, which we identify with the energies of the atom. The angular-momentum operators will let us see the angular-momentum implications of the eigenfunctions we obtain.

The hamiltonian for an electron moving in the central radius-dependent field of the nucleus is

$$\mathcal{H} = \left[-\frac{h^2}{8\pi^2 m} \left(\frac{\partial^2}{\partial x^2} + \frac{\partial^2}{\partial y^2} + \frac{\partial^2}{\partial z^2} \right) + U(r) \right] \tag{11-29}$$

The system really consists, however, of the two particles, the electron and the nucleus, moving about the center of gravity of the system. The equations of motion are the same as those for a single particle moving about a fixed point if we use the reduced mass μ, as in Sec. 3-1, in place of the mass m of the particle. (Here again, μ will be very nearly the mass of the electron. Replacement of m by μ is worthwhile, however, because it frees the symbol m for later use as a quantum number.) With μ in place of m, and the hamiltonian written above, the Schrödinger equation for the hydrogen atom, or any central-force system, is

$$-\frac{h^2}{8\pi^2 \mu} \left(\frac{\partial^2 \psi}{\partial x^2} + \frac{\partial^2 \psi}{\partial y^2} + \frac{\partial^2 \psi}{\partial z^2} \right) + U(r)\psi = \epsilon\psi \tag{11-30}$$

After considerable manipulation, this expression can be recast in terms of polar coordinates (Fig. 3-2). The result is

$$-\frac{h^2}{8\pi^2 \mu} \frac{1}{r^2 \sin\theta} \left[\sin\theta \frac{\partial}{\partial r} \left(r^2 \frac{\partial \psi}{\partial r} \right) + \frac{\partial}{\partial \theta} \left(\sin\theta \frac{\partial \psi}{\partial \theta} \right) + \frac{1}{\sin\theta} \frac{\partial^2 \psi}{\partial \phi^2} \right]$$
$$+ U(r)\psi = \epsilon\psi \tag{11-31}$$

Let us attempt to separate the equation into factors involving separately the variables r, θ, and ϕ. We investigate functions of the form

$$\psi = R(r)\,\Theta(\theta)\Phi(\phi) \tag{11-32}$$

Insertion of this expression in Eq. (11-31) gives, again after some rearrangement

$$\frac{\sin^2\theta}{R} \frac{d}{dr} \left(r^2 \frac{dR}{dr} \right) + \frac{\sin\theta}{\Theta} \frac{d}{d\theta} \left(\sin\theta \frac{d\Theta}{d\theta} \right) + \frac{1}{\Phi} \frac{d^2\Phi}{d\phi^2}$$
$$+ \frac{8\pi^2 \mu r^2 \sin^2\theta}{h^2} \left[\epsilon - U(r) \right] = 0 \tag{11-33}$$

Some helpful separation of the equation has been accomplished. In particular, the third term involves the variable ϕ, and this variable occurs in no other terms. The equation can be satisfied for all values of ϕ, therefore, only if this third term is a constant. Thus we can set

$$\frac{d^2\Phi/d\phi^2}{\Phi} = \text{const} \tag{11-34}$$

We want for Φ a function that when differentiated twice gives us back the original function, perhaps multiplied by a constant. A suitable function is

$$\Phi = Ae^{im\phi} \tag{11-35}$$

for which

$$\frac{d\Phi}{d\phi} = imAe^{im\phi} \tag{11-36}$$

and

$$\frac{d^2\Phi}{d\phi^2} = -m^2Ae^{im\phi} = -m^2\Phi \tag{11-37}$$

Thus, if Φ has the form of Eq. (11-35), the constant term of Eq. (11-34) is $-m^2$.

We can characterize m by noticing that we want Φ to have the same value at a particular value of ϕ regardless of how many rotations about the z axis have brought the system to that value of ϕ. We want, for example,

$$\Phi = Ae^{im\phi} = Ae^{im(\phi + 2\pi)} = Ae^{im\phi}e^{2m(i\pi)} \tag{11-38}$$

Thus $e^{2m(i\pi)}$, which can be written $(e^{i\pi})^{2m}$, must be unity. If you recall that $e^{i\pi} = -1$, you see that this can be accomplished only if

$$m = 0, \pm1, \pm2, \ldots \tag{11-39}$$

Now let us see the significance of this ϕ-dependent part of the solution to the hydrogen-atom type of problem. We apply the angular-momentum operator $\hat{L}_z$ shown as Eq. (11-27) to the eigenfunction of Eq. (11-32). The only variable this operator affects is ϕ, and thus we can apply it to the partial solution function Φ. We have

$$\hat{L}_z\Phi = \left(\frac{h}{2\pi i}\frac{\partial}{\partial\phi}\right)\left(Ae^{im\phi}\right) = m\frac{h}{2\pi}\Phi \tag{11-40}$$

Thus the eigenfunctions for $\mathcal{H}$ are also eigenfunctions for $\hat{L}_z$. Furthermore, the eigenvalues for the angular-momentum component along the z direction are $m\,h/2\pi$ with $m = 0, \pm1, \pm2, \ldots$.

Notice that from this elaborate treatment we have been led to a result similar to the postulate used by Bohr. Although he did not make the distinction between total angular momentum and the component along a direction, he did, as discussed in Sec. 11-2, postulate that the angular momentum was a multiple of $h/2\pi$.

11-5 The Hydrogen-Atom Problem: The Total Angular Momentum

With the results for Φ from the preceding section, the third term of Eq. (11-33) can be replaced by $-m^2$, and the equation can be rearranged to

$$\frac{1}{\Theta \sin \theta} \frac{d}{d\theta} \left(\sin \theta \frac{d\Theta}{d\theta} \right) - \frac{m^2}{\sin^2 \theta} = -\frac{1}{R} \frac{d}{dr} \left(r^2 \frac{dR}{dr} \right)$$

$$+ \frac{8\pi^2 \mu r^2}{h^2} \left[\epsilon - U(r) \right] \quad (11\text{-}41)$$

The right side does not vary with θ. The equality can hold for all values of θ only if the left side is also independent of θ. Let β be the constant to which each side is equal as θ varies. The equation that the function Θ must satisfy is

$$\frac{1}{\sin \theta} \frac{d}{d\theta} \left(\sin \theta \frac{d\Theta}{d\theta} \right) - \frac{m^2}{\sin^2 \theta} \Theta + \beta \Theta = 0 \quad (11\text{-}42)$$

Solution functions are not as easily found as for the corresponding Φ equation (11-34). Those which occur, some of which are shown in Table 11-2, do so only if β is equal to $l(l + 1)$, where l is a positive integer greater than, or equal to, m. This stipulation is usually expressed as

$$m = 0, \pm 1, \pm 2, \ldots, \pm l \quad (11\text{-}43)$$

We could see the implications of the various Θ functions, each specified by an l and an m value, by applying the total-angular-momentum operator of Sec. 11-3 to the $\Theta\Phi$ function of Eq. (11-32). We would then find that this function is an eigenfunction of the total-angular-momentum operator. The eigenvalues, the values of the total angular momenta, are given by

$$\text{Angular momentum} = \frac{h}{2\pi} \sqrt{l(l + 1)} \qquad l = 0, 1, 2, \ldots \quad (11\text{-}44)$$

Now we see that the *total* angular momentum is quantized and the quantization is expressed in terms of the quantum number l.

11-6 The Hydrogen-Atom Problem: The Radial Factor

We have now, finally, worked Eq. (11-33) down to one involving the single remaining variable r. This single-variable equation is obtained by setting the right side of Eq. (11-41) equal to $\beta = l(l + 1)$. We have

TABLE 11-2 Examples of the Angular Factor $\Theta(\theta)$

l	m	Θ
0 (s orbitals)	0	$\dfrac{1}{\sqrt{2}}$
1 (p orbitals)	0	$\sqrt{\dfrac{3}{2}}\cos\theta$
	± 1	$\dfrac{\sqrt{3}}{2}\sin\theta$
2 (d orbitals)	0	$\dfrac{1}{2}\sqrt{\dfrac{15}{2}}(3\cos^2\theta - 1)$
	± 1	$\dfrac{\sqrt{15}}{2}\sin\theta\cos\theta$
	± 2	$\dfrac{\sqrt{15}}{4}\sin^2\theta$
3 (f orbitals)	0	$\dfrac{3}{2}\sqrt{\dfrac{7}{2}}\left(\dfrac{5}{3}\cos^3\theta - \cos\theta\right)$
	± 1	$\dfrac{1}{4}\sqrt{\dfrac{21}{2}}\sin\theta(5\cos^2\theta - 1)$
	± 2	$\dfrac{\sqrt{105}}{4}\sin^2\theta\cos\theta$
	± 3	$\dfrac{1}{4}\sqrt{\dfrac{35}{2}}\sin^3\theta$

$$-\frac{1}{R}\frac{d}{dr}\left(r^2\frac{dR}{dr}\right) + \frac{8\pi^2\mu r^2}{h^2}\left[\epsilon - U(r)\right] = l(l+1) \tag{11-45}$$

To proceed we must insert a function for $U(r)$. [Notice that up to now it was enough to know that U was a function only of r. The angular factors and their angular-momentum implications are therefore independent of the form of $U(r)$.]

Now let us think specifically about a one-electron atom H or a one-electron ion such as He$^+$ or Li^{2+}. The nuclear charge is $+Ze$, where Z is the atomic number of the atom or ion and $-e$ is the charge of an electron. The potential energy of an electron at a distance r from such a nucleus is $-Ze^2/4\pi\epsilon_0 r$. With this expression for $U(r)$, the radial equation, from Eq. (11-45), can be rearranged to

$$\frac{1}{r^2}\frac{d}{dr}\left(r^2\frac{dR}{dr}\right) + \left\{\frac{8\pi^2\mu}{h^2}\left[\epsilon + \frac{Ze^2}{(4\pi\epsilon_0)r}\right] - \frac{l(l+1)}{r^2}\right\}R = 0 \tag{11-46}$$

TABLE 11-3 Examples of the Radial Function $R(r)$

n	l	$R(r)$
1	0	$R_{1s} = 2\left(\dfrac{Z}{a_0}\right)^{3/2} e^{-Zr/a_0}$
2	0	$R_{2s} = \left(\dfrac{Z}{2a_0}\right)^{3/2}\left(2 - \dfrac{Zr}{a_0}\right) e^{-Zr/2a_0}$
	1	$R_{2p} = \dfrac{1}{\sqrt{3}}\left(\dfrac{Z}{2a_0}\right)^{3/2}\dfrac{Zr}{a_0}\, e^{-Zr/2a_0}$
3	0	$R_{3s} = \dfrac{2}{27}\left(\dfrac{Z}{3a_0}\right)^{3/2}\left(27 - \dfrac{18Zr}{a_0} + \dfrac{2Z^2 r^2}{a_0^2}\right) e^{-Zr/3a_0}$
	1	$R_{3p} = \dfrac{1}{81\sqrt{3}}\left(\dfrac{2Z}{a_0}\right)^{3/2}\left(6 - \dfrac{Zr}{a_0}\right)\dfrac{Zr}{a_0}\, e^{-Zr/3a_0}$
	2	$R_{3d} = \dfrac{1}{81\sqrt{15}}\left(\dfrac{2Z}{a_0}\right)^{3/2}\dfrac{Z^2 r^2}{a_0^2}\, e^{-Zr/3a_0}$

Again we have an expression for which the solution functions are not easily recognized. Some examples, which can be verified to satisfy Eq. (11-46), are given in Table 11-3. Each of these radial functions is specified by the value of the quantum number n, the *principal* quantum number. Solutions to Eq. (11-46) exist only for n an integer with value at least one unit greater than l. This restriction is usually expressed as

$$l = 0, 1, 2, \ldots, n - 1 \qquad (11\text{-}47)$$

As substitution of the solution functions of Table 11-3 in Eq. (11-46) would show, the energy ϵ is given by

$$\epsilon = -\frac{2\pi^2 \mu Z^2 e^4}{(4\pi\epsilon_0)^2 h^2 n^2} \qquad n = 1, 2, \ldots \qquad (11\text{-}48)$$

This result is identical to that produced by the Bohr treatment of Sec. 11-2. Thus we again arrive at an expression for the energies of the states of hydrogenlike atoms that agrees with spectral results, as summarized by the Rydberg equation. In so doing, however, we have developed a much more detailed and valid picture of the behavior of the electron of the atom.

The radial distribution of the wave functions is controlled primarily by the quantum number n. The principal factor affecting the radial extent of a wave function is the exponential factor. This factor has the form e^{-Zr/na_0} where a_0 is written for the collection of constants $h^2(4\pi\epsilon_0)/4\pi^2\mu e^2$. The value of a_0 is 0.529×10^{-10} m, or 0.529 Å. This exponential term is such that for larger values of the principal quantum number n, the wave function falls off less rapidly with

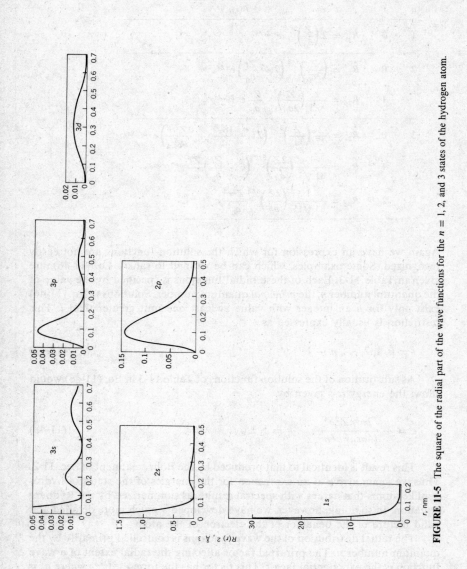

FIGURE 11-5 The square of the radial part of the wave functions for the $n = 1$, 2, and 3 states of the hydrogen atom.

the distance from the nucleus. With larger nuclear charges, which are encountered when atoms other than hydrogen are considered, the falloff is more rapid, and the electron is held more closely to the nucleus. The squares of the radial part of the wave functions are shown by graphs for the three lowest energy orbitals $n = 1$, $n = 2$, and $n = 3$ in Fig. 11-5. The detailed form is seen to depend on l but the overall extension on n. Notice from Fig. 11-5 that the s orbits, those with $l = 0$, have a finite probability of the electron's being at $r = 0$, at the nucleus.

A better picture, for some purposes, of the radial distribution of the electron orbitals is obtained by showing the relative probabilities of the electron's being at various distances from the nucleus. The volume of an annular element a distance r from the nucleus is proportional to the area, $4\pi r^2$, of a sphere of radius r. The probability of the electron's being at a distance between r and $r + dr$ from the nucleus is therefore given by $4\pi r^2 \, dr$ times the probability of its being in a unit volume at a distance r from the nucleus. (A similar situation, it will be recalled, was encountered in studies of molecular velocities in Sec. 2-6, and there also we were led to consider spherical-shell elements.)

Figure 11-6 shows the radial-distribution functions $r^2 R^2(r)$. It is interesting to note that the distance of the electron from the nucleus at the maximum in the radial-distribution curves for 1s, 2p, 3d, etc., where there are single maxima, is exactly equal to the radius of the corresponding orbit calculated by the Bohr theory.

The radial-distribution curves of Fig. 11-6 have been arranged to suggest the energy relationships, namely, that the greater the value of n the higher and less negative the energy, as shown by Eq. (11-48). In a vertical column, e.g., that through 1s, 2s, 3s, there is no change in angular momentum. The increase in energy correlates with the increasing number of nodes in the radial-distribution function, just as it did in the one-dimensional square-well example of Sec. 3-5. Along a diagonal line, e.g., that through 1s, 2p, 3d, the number of nodes does not change. Now the increase in energy is not dependent on radial behavior but is to be attributed to the increasing angular momentum. Thus although they are expressed by an equation that contains only the principal quantum number, the energies of the orbits contain radial and angular components and depend on both radial and angular behaviors.

11-7 The Angular Distribution of Orbitals

The description of the electron in a hydrogenlike atom is given, according to Eq. (11-32), as the product of the radial and the angular factors. The Φ factor was deduced in Sec. 11-4 and the Θ factor in Sec. 11-5. If we put these factors together, we can investigate the net angular factor which must be multiplied by the radial factor to give a complete description of the electron of the atom. We shall also investigate the product of the angular factor and its complex conjugate, a product which reveals the angular dependence of the probability, or electron density.

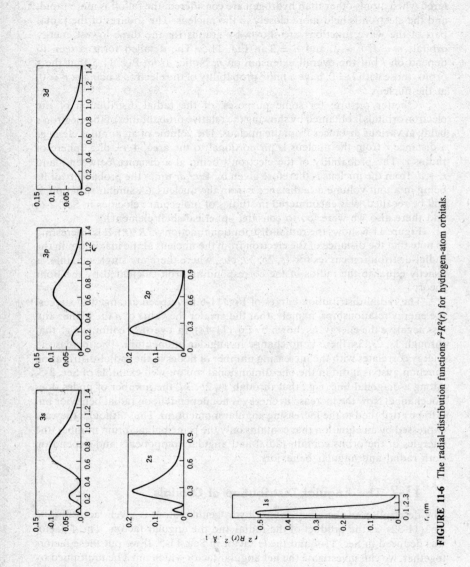

FIGURE 11-6 The radial-distribution functions $r^2R^2(r)$ for hydrogen-atom orbitals.

TABLE 11-4 Angular Factors of the Hydrogen-Atom Functions in the Form Directly Related to the Angular Momentum

l	m	$\Theta\Phi$	$\Theta^*\Theta\Phi^*\Phi$	Diagram
0	0	$\dfrac{1}{2\sqrt{\pi}}$	$\dfrac{1}{4\pi}$	
1	0	$\dfrac{1}{2}\sqrt{\dfrac{3}{\pi}}\cos\theta$	$\dfrac{3}{4\pi}\cos^2\theta$	
	+1	$\dfrac{1}{2}\sqrt{\dfrac{3}{2\pi}}\sin\theta\, e^{i\phi}$	$\dfrac{3}{4\pi}\sin^2\theta$	
	−1	$\dfrac{1}{2}\sqrt{\dfrac{3}{2\pi}}\sin\theta\, e^{-i\phi}$	$\dfrac{3}{4\pi}\sin^2\theta$	
2	0	$\dfrac{1}{4}\sqrt{\dfrac{5}{\pi}}(3\cos^2\theta - 1)$	$\dfrac{5}{16\pi}(3\cos^2\theta - 1)$	
	+1	$\dfrac{1}{2}\sqrt{\dfrac{15}{2\pi}}\sin\theta\cos\theta\, e^{i\phi}$	$\dfrac{15}{8\pi}\sin^2\theta\cos^2\theta$	
	−1	$\dfrac{1}{2}\sqrt{\dfrac{15}{2\pi}}\sin\theta\cos\theta\, e^{-i\phi}$	$\dfrac{15}{8\pi}\sin^2\theta\cos^2\theta$	
	+2	$\dfrac{1}{4}\sqrt{\dfrac{15}{2\pi}}\sin^2\theta\, e^{2i\phi}$	$\dfrac{15}{32\pi}\sin^4\theta$	
	−2	$\dfrac{1}{4}\sqrt{\dfrac{15}{2\pi}}\sin^2\theta\, e^{-2i\phi}$	$\dfrac{15}{32\pi}\sin^4\theta$	

Using the results of Secs. 11-4 and 11-5, we show the angular factors in the third column of Table 11-4. The next column gives the product of these and their complex conjugates. The diagrams in the final column are surfaces that show by the distance from the origin to the surface the value of $\Theta^*\Phi^*\Theta\Phi$ for any angle. You can see, especially in the case of d orbitals, that the lower the value of m the more concentrated the probability function in the z direction. The higher the value of m the more concentrated it is in the xy plane. These are the

TABLE 11-5 Real Angular Factors of the Hydrogen-Atom Functions in Polar and Cartesian Coordinates

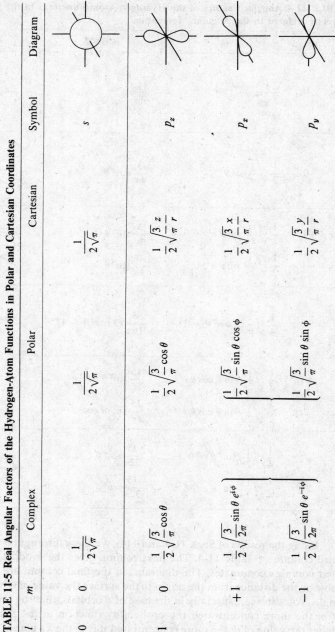

l	m	Complex	Polar	Cartesian	Symbol	Diagram
0	0	$\dfrac{1}{2\sqrt{\pi}}$	$\dfrac{1}{2\sqrt{\pi}}$	$\dfrac{1}{2\sqrt{\pi}}$	s	
1	0	$\dfrac{1}{2}\sqrt{\dfrac{3}{\pi}}\cos\theta$	$\dfrac{1}{2}\sqrt{\dfrac{3}{\pi}}\cos\theta$	$\dfrac{1}{2}\sqrt{\dfrac{3}{\pi}}\dfrac{z}{r}$	p_z	
	$+1$	$\dfrac{1}{2}\sqrt{\dfrac{3}{2\pi}}\sin\theta\, e^{i\phi}$	$\dfrac{1}{2}\sqrt{\dfrac{3}{\pi}}\sin\theta\cos\phi$	$\dfrac{1}{2}\sqrt{\dfrac{3}{\pi}}\dfrac{x}{r}$	p_x	
	-1	$\dfrac{1}{2}\sqrt{\dfrac{3}{2\pi}}\sin\theta\, e^{-i\phi}$	$\dfrac{1}{2}\sqrt{\dfrac{3}{\pi}}\sin\theta\sin\phi$	$\dfrac{1}{2}\sqrt{\dfrac{3}{\pi}}\dfrac{y}{r}$	p_y	

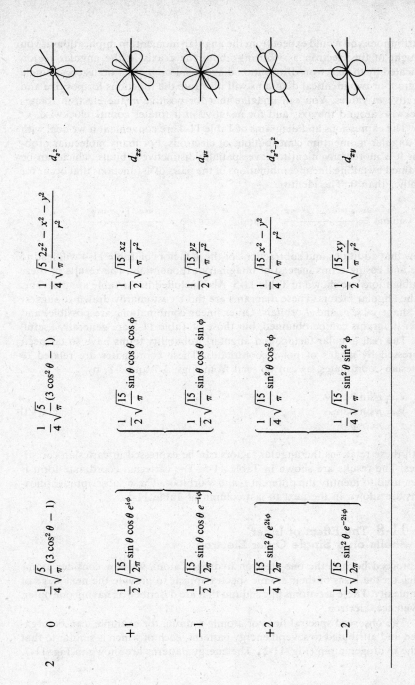

	d_{z^2}	d_{xz}	d_{yz}	$d_{x^2-y^2}$	d_{xy}
	$\dfrac{1}{4}\sqrt{\dfrac{5}{\pi}}\,\dfrac{2z^2-x^2-y^2}{r^2}$	$\dfrac{1}{2}\sqrt{\dfrac{15}{\pi}}\,\dfrac{xz}{r^2}$	$\dfrac{1}{2}\sqrt{\dfrac{15}{\pi}}\,\dfrac{yz}{r^2}$	$\dfrac{1}{4}\sqrt{\dfrac{15}{\pi}}\,\dfrac{x^2-y^2}{r^2}$	$\dfrac{1}{2}\sqrt{\dfrac{15}{\pi}}\,\dfrac{xy}{r^2}$
	$\dfrac{1}{4}\sqrt{\dfrac{5}{\pi}}\,(3\cos^2\theta-1)$	$\dfrac{1}{2}\sqrt{\dfrac{15}{\pi}}\,\sin\theta\cos\theta\cos\phi$	$\dfrac{1}{2}\sqrt{\dfrac{15}{\pi}}\,\sin\theta\cos\theta\sin\phi$	$\dfrac{1}{4}\sqrt{\dfrac{15}{\pi}}\,\sin^2\theta\cos^2\phi$	$\dfrac{1}{4}\sqrt{\dfrac{15}{\pi}}\,\sin^2\theta\sin^2\phi$
2 0	$\dfrac{1}{4}\sqrt{\dfrac{5}{\pi}}\,(3\cos^2\theta-1)$				
$+1$		$\dfrac{1}{2}\sqrt{\dfrac{15}{2\pi}}\,\sin\theta\cos\theta\,e^{i\phi}$			
-1			$\dfrac{1}{2}\sqrt{\dfrac{15}{2\pi}}\,\sin\theta\cos\theta\,e^{-i\phi}$		
$+2$				$\dfrac{1}{4}\sqrt{\dfrac{15}{2\pi}}\,\sin^2\theta\,e^{2i\phi}$	
-2					$\dfrac{1}{4}\sqrt{\dfrac{15}{2\pi}}\,\sin^2\theta\,e^{-2i\phi}$

distributions you would expect from the angular-momentum implications if you thought of the electron as whirring about the z axis in the angular region indicated by the electron-distribution diagrams. For m other than zero, a single diagram or two identical diagrams will illustrate the functions for positive and negative m values. You can imagine that for positive m the electron rotates clockwise around the axis and for negative m it rotates counterclockwise.

The expressions and diagrams of Table 11-4 are convenient if we deal with the angular-momentum contributions of electrons. For many molecular problems it is more convenient to have spatially distinctive orbitals, which can be obtained by taking linear combinations of the pairs of Φ functions that occur for m other than 0. The identities

$$\sin m\phi = \frac{e^{im\phi} - e^{-im\phi}}{2i} \quad \text{and} \quad \cos m\phi = \frac{e^{im\phi} + e^{-im\phi}}{2}$$

show that additions and subtractions of the Φ factors of Table 11-4 will lead to sine and cosine terms instead of imaginary exponentials. The results of these combinations are shown in Table 11-5. Also included in the table are diagrams of the angular factors. These diagrams are those customarily drawn to suggest the shape of s, p, and d orbitals. Other linear combinations are possible, and other diagrams can be obtained, but those of Table 11-5 are generally useful.

The real angular factors and angular-probability terms have so far been expressed by means of polar coordinates. These coordinates are related to cartesian coordinates, as can be seen from Figs. 3-7 and 3-8, by

$$
\begin{aligned}
x &= r \sin \theta \cos \phi \\
y &= r \sin \theta \sin \phi \\
z &= r \cos \theta
\end{aligned}
\tag{11-49}
$$

With these relations the angular factors can be expressed in cartesian coordinates. The results are shown in Table 11-5. The cartesian coordinate form is often used to identify the different p and d orbitals. These subscript identifications are shown in the next to last column of Table 11-5.

11-8 The Effect of Inner Shells on a Single Outer Electron

To proceed beyond the one-electron hydrogen atom, we now consider atoms which on the basis of their atomic spectra appear to provide the next stage of complexity. These are atoms like sodium that are described as having one outer, or valence, electron.

The observed spectral lines of atomic sodium, for example, can be organized and attributed to several energy patterns, each of which is similar to that of the hydrogen atom (Fig. 11-2). The energy patterns are shown in Fig. 11-7.

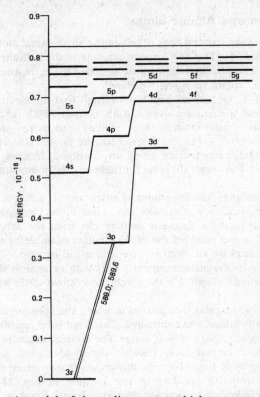

FIGURE 11-7
The energies of the sodium atom and the orbital designations for the single-valence electron. (The wavelengths, in nm, for the transitions corresponding to the sodium D lines are shown.) (1 electron-volt = 0.16022 × 10⁻¹⁸ J molecule⁻¹)

A model of the sodium atom which accounts for the energy patterns of Fig. 11-7 consists of a single outer electron exposed to the central field produced by the nucleus and the filled inner shells of electrons. Wave functions like those deduced for the hydrogenlike atoms in the preceding sections are applicable to the outer electron.

The angular momentum of an electron of an atom is subject to the quantum restrictions worked out in Secs. 11-4 and 11-5. There, you recall, the quantum numbers m for the angular momentum along any imposed direction and l for the total angular momentum appeared in the treatment before the nature of $U(r)$ was specified. Thus these quantum numbers are completely applicable to the present case.

The energy and the radial distribution, however, are affected by the filled inner shells of electrons. An orbital with a low value of l for a given value of n will bring the electron close to the nucleus, as inspection of Figs. 11-5 and 11-6 shows. An electron in such an orbital is less "screened" from the nucleus than electrons in orbitals with higher values of l. Thus the energy of an outer electron of an atom that has filled inner shells depends upon l as well as on n.

11-9 Electron Spin and Atomic States

Close observation of some of the spectral lines of any of the alkali-metal atoms shows these lines to be *doublets*. The best-known example is the sodium D doublet lines at 589.0 and 589.6 nm. Something must be added to the treatment of the preceding section to explain such *fine structure*.

It was suggested by G. E. Uhlenbeck and S. Goudsmit that the electron itself has an intrinsic angular momentum over and above that which results from its orbital motion. This angular momentum is referred to as *spin angular momentum*. Its magnitude is $\sqrt{s(s+1)}\,h/2\pi$, where s has the single value of $\frac{1}{2}$. The component of this angular momentum along any imposed direction is $m_s h/2\pi$, where m_s is $+\frac{1}{2}$ or $-\frac{1}{2}$. A vector diagram for these angular momenta is shown in Fig. 11-8.

Associated with the spin angular momentum of an electron is a magnetic moment which describes the tendency of the electron to line up in a magnetic field. In a free alkali-metal atom, a magnetic field results from the orbital motion of the electron. (You can think of the more familiar example of the magnetic field that is produced by an electric current in a coil of wire.) The electron can line up so that its magnetic moment points with or against this field. The result of this *spin-orbit coupling* is the production of two states with different energies.

For an s orbit there is no angular momentum to which the spin angular momentum can be vectorially added and subtracted. Thus spin-orbit coupling does not produce a doubling of s, that is, $l = 0$, states. The doublet structure of sodium spectral lines results from transitions between energy levels split as a result of spin-orbit coupling as in Fig. 11-8. The transitions that produce the doublet at 589 nm result from the splitting of the $3p$ state of Fig. 11-7.

In anticipation of the following section we here introduce a notation in which the state of an atom is distinguished from the description given to any one electron of the atom. Both descriptions depend on statements or symbols for angular momenta. The symbols for the state of the atom will be given capital letters; those for individual electrons of the atom will be given lowercase letters.

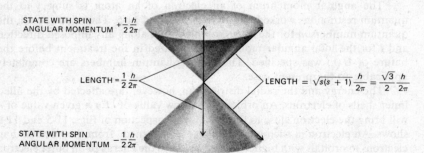

STATE WITH SPIN ANGULAR MOMENTUM $+\frac{1}{2}\frac{h}{2\pi}$

LENGTH $= \frac{1}{2}\frac{h}{2\pi}$

LENGTH $= \sqrt{s(s+1)}\frac{h}{2\pi} = \frac{\sqrt{3}}{2}\frac{h}{2\pi}$

STATE WITH SPIN ANGULAR MOMENTUM $-\frac{1}{2}\frac{h}{2\pi}$

FIGURE 11-8 The angular-momentum vector of a spinning electron and the angular momentum along the direction of an imposed field for the two possible states.

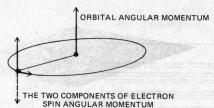

ORBITAL ANGULAR MOMENTUM

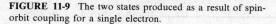

THE TWO COMPONENTS OF ELECTRON
SPIN ANGULAR MOMENTUM

FIGURE 11-9 The two states produced as a result of spin-orbit coupling for a single electron.

The orbital angular momentum of an electron of an atom is given the general symbol l, as in Sec. 11-5. The net orbital angular momentum of all the electrons of an atom is given the general symbol L. Likewise the symbols s, p, d, ... for the amount of angular momentum of a single electron become the symbols S, P, D, ... for the atom.

The spin quantum number of a single electron has the value $\frac{1}{2}$. The spin quantum number, symbol S, for an atom is indicated by the value of $2S + 1$, the *multiplicity* of the atomic state. (Multiplicity is a particular case of degeneracy. The $2S + 1$ expression is to be understood like the $2J + 1$ expression of Sec. 3-2.) For a sodium atom, with $S = \frac{1}{2}$, the multiplicity $2S + 1$ has the value 2, corresponding to the two directions, "up" or "down" that the spin vector of a one-electron atom could adopt along an imposed direction.

The individual members of the two states of a sodium atom that arise from a given value of L and different values of S are shown by a label that gives the total angular momentum. The total-angular-momentum quantum number for the sum of the orbital and spin angular momenta is designated as J. Any state of an atom is described by a symbol of the general form

$$^{2S+1}L_J$$

Some of the states of the sodium atom are so described in Fig. 11-10.

11-10 Electron Configurations and Electronic States

Atomic spectral studies lead us, as shown in Sec. 11-9, to descriptions of the ground and excited states of atoms. The symbols used to designate these states show the net orbital and spin angular momenta produced by the many electrons of the atom. These results can be interpreted in terms of contributions made by each of the electrons of the atom. When this is done, we obtain a description of the electrons of the atom. Such descriptions, known as *electron configurations,* provide the basis for theoretical studies of the chemistry of the atoms of the elements.

The roles of the electrons, summarized by the electron configuration for the atom, are obtained by assigning the electrons of the atom to the lowest available

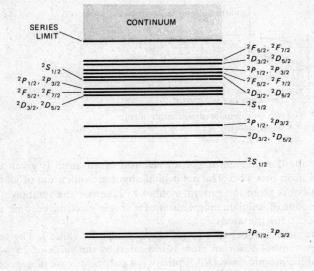

SERIES
LIMIT

CONTINUUM

$^2S_{1/2}$

$^2P_{1/2}, ^2P_{3/2}$

$^2F_{5/2}, ^2F_{7/2}$

$^2D_{3/2}, ^2D_{5/2}$

$^2F_{5/2}, ^2F_{7/2}$

$^2D_{3/2}, ^2D_{5/2}$

$^2P_{1/2}, ^2P_{3/2}$

$^2F_{5/2}, ^2F_{7/2}$

$^2D_{3/2}, ^2D_{5/2}$

$^2S_{1/2}$

$^2P_{1/2}, ^2P_{3/2}$

$^2D_{3/2}, ^2D_{5/2}$

$^2S_{1/2}$

$^2P_{1/2}, ^2P_{3/2}$

$^2S_{1/2}$

FIGURE 11-10 Electronic-state descriptions of some of the energy levels of the sodium atom.

orbitals. The pattern of available orbitals is inferred from those deduced in easily analyzed cases such as the hydrogen atom and the alkali-metal atoms. The assumed orbital energy pattern is verified or modified when the angular-momentum implication of the electron configuration is compared with that of the electronic ground-state symbol.

To proceed we need a rule for assigning electrons to the atomic orbitals. In 1924 Wolfgang Pauli recognized a way in which this assignment could be done so that electronic structures of the atoms that were in accord with the chemistry or periodic-table position of the elements could be deduced. This rule, known as the *Pauli exclusion principle,* states that *in a single atom no two electrons can have the same values for the four quantum numbers n, l, m, and m_s.* Thus, two electrons at most can be assigned to an orbital, which is specified by a particular set of *n, l,* and *m* values.

The electron configurations of the ground states of the atoms of the elements are shown in Table 11-6. The superscripts indicate the number of

Filled orbital sets, enclosed in parentheses, are present in the electronic configurations of all succeeding elements

#	El	Config	Term	#	El	Config	Term	#	El	Config	Term
1	H	$1s$	$^2S_{1/2}$	33	As	$4s^24p^3$	$^4S_{3/2}$	65	Tb	$4f^96s^2$	$^6H_{15/2}$
2	He	$(1s^2)$	$^1S_0$	34	Se	$4s^24p^4$	$^3P_2$	66	Dy	$4f^{10}6s^2$	$^5I_8$
3	Li	$2s$	$^2S_{1/2}$	35	Br	$4s^24p^5$	$^2P_{3/2}$	67	Ho	$4f^{11}6s^2$	$^4I_{15/2}$
4	Be	$2s^2$	$^1S_0$	36	Kr	$(4s^24p^6)$	$^1S_0$	68	Er	$4f^{12}6s^2$	$^3H_6$
5	B	$2s^22p$	$^2P_{1/2}$	37	Rb	$5s$	$^2S_{1/2}$	69	Tm	$4f^{13}6s^2$	$^2F_{7/2}$
6	C	$2s^22p^2$	$^3P_0$	38	Sr	$5s^2$	$^1S_0$	70	Yb	$(4f^{14})6s^2$	$^1S_0$
7	N	$2s^22p^3$	$^4S_{3/2}$	39	Y	$4d5s^2$	$^2D_{3/2}$	71	Lu	$5d4s^2$	$^2D_{3/2}$
8	O	$2s^22p^4$	$^3P_2$	40	Zr	$4d^25s^2$	$^3F_2$	72	Hf	$5d^26s^2$	$^3F_2$
9	F	$2s^22p^5$	$^2P_{3/2}$	41	Nb	$4d^45s$	$^6D_{1/2}$	73	Ta	$5d^36s^2$	$^4F_{3/2}$
10	Ne	$(2s^22p^6)$	$^1S_0$	42	Mo	$4d^55s$	$^7S_3$	74	W	$5d^46s^2$	$^5D_0$
11	Na	$3s$	$^2S_{1/2}$	43	Tc	$4d^55s^2$	$^6S_{5/2}$	75	Re	$5d^56s^2$	$^6S_{5/2}$
12	Mg	$3s^2$	$^1S_0$	44	Ru	$4d^75s$	$^5F_5$	76	Os	$5d^66s^2$	$^5D_4$
13	Al	$3s^23p$	$^2P_{1/2}$	45	Rh	$4d^85s$	$^4F_{9/2}$	77	Ir	$5d^76s^2$	$^4F_{9/2}$
14	Si	$3s^23p^2$	$^3P_0$	46	Pd	$(4d^{10})$	$^1S_0$	78	Pt	$5d^96s$	$^3D_3$
15	P	$3s^23p^3$	$^4S_{3/2}$	47	Ag	$5s$	$^2S_{1/2}$	79	Au	$(5d^{10})6s$	$^2S_{1/2}$
16	S	$3s^23p^4$	$^3P_2$	48	Cd	$5s^2$	$^1S_0$	80	Hg	$6s^2$	$^1S_0$
17	Cl	$3s^23p^5$	$^2P_{3/2}$	49	In	$5s^25p$	$^2P_{1/2}$	81	Tl	$6s^26p$	$^2P_{1/2}$
18	A	$(3s^23p^6)$	$^1S_0$	50	Sn	$5s^25p^2$	$^3P_0$	82	Pb	$6s^26p^2$	$^3P_0$
19	K	$4s$	$^2S_{1/2}$	51	Sb	$5s^25p^3$	$^6D_{1/2}$	83	Bi	$6s^26p^3$	$^4F_{3/2}$
20	Ca	$4s^2$	$^1S_0$	52	Te	$5s^25p^4$	$^3P_2$	84	Po	$6s^26p^4$	$^3P_2$
21	Sc	$3d4s^2$	$^2D_{3/2}$	53	I	$5s^25p^5$	$^2P_{3/2}$	85	At	$6s^26p^5(?)$	?
22	Ti	$3d^24s^2$	$^3F_2$	54	Xe	$(5s^25p^6)$	$^1S_0$	86	Rn	$(6s^26p^6)$	$^1S_0$
23	V	$3d^34s^2$	$^4F_{3/2}$	55	Cs	$6s$	$^2S_{1/2}$	87	Fe	$7s(?)$	?
24	Cr	$3d^54s$	$^7S_3$	56	Ba	$6s^2$	$^1S_0$	88	Ru	$7s^2$	$^1S_0$
25	Mn	$3d^54s^2$	$^6S_{5/2}$	57	La	$5d6s^2$	$^2D_{3/2}$	89	Ac	$6d7s^2$	$^2D_{3/2}$
26	Fe	$3d^64s^2$	$^5D_4$	58	Ce	$4f5d6s^2$	$^1G_4$	90	Th	$6d^27s^2$	$^3F_2$
27	Co	$3d^74s^2$	$^4F_{9/2}$	59	Pr	$4f^36s^2$	$^4I_{9/2}$	91	Pa	$5f^26d7s^2$	$^4K_{11/2}$
28	Ni	$3d^84s^2$	$^3F_4$	60	Nd	$4f^46s^2$	$^5I_4$	92	U	$5f^36d7s^2$	$^5L_6$
29	Cu	$(3d^{10})4s$	$^2S_{1/2}$	61	Pm	$4f^56s^2$	$^6H_{5/2}$	93	Np	$5f^46d7s^2$	$^6L_{11/2}$
30	Zn	$4s^2$	$^1S_0$	62	Sm	$4f^66s^2$	$^7F_0$	94	Pu	$5f^67s^2$	$^7F_0$
31	Ga	$4s^24p$	$^2P_{1/2}$	63	Eu	$4f^76s^2$	$^8S_{7/2}$	95	Am	$5f^77s^2$	$^8S_{7/2}$
32	Ge	$4s^24p^2$	$^3P_0$	64	Gd	$4f^75d6s^2$	$^9D_2$	96	Cm	$5f^76d7s^2$	$^9D_2$

electrons with a particular n, l value. The overall relation of these electron configurations to the periodic-table pattern is evident in the periodic occurrence of filled shells at the noble gases.

Irregularities in the buildup of these electron configurations, e.g., after strontium, atomic number 38, occur. These can be attributed to variations in the orbital energy pattern produced by two effects. One, important at low atomic numbers, is the dependence of the energy on the orbital quantum number l produced by filled inner shells. The other factor is the tendency at high atomic numbers for the nuclear charge to overwhelm the inner-shell effect. Then the

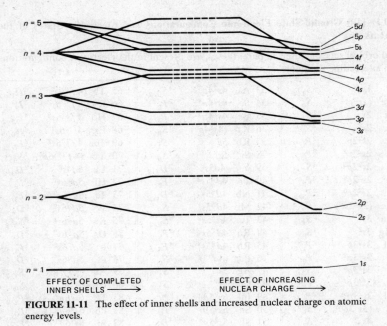

FIGURE 11-11 The effect of inner shells and increased nuclear charge on atomic energy levels.

dependence of the energy on l is diminished. The interplay of these two factors is suggested in Fig. 11-11. Calculations, which will be treated in Sec. 11-13 show the results of the operation of these two factors in more detail.

It is an easy matter, we saw in Sec. 11-9, in the case of an atom with a single outer, or valence, electron to go from an electron configuration to the description of the state of the atom. The atomic-orbital angular momentum L is equal to the contribution l of the single outer electron. The atomic spin angular momentum S is the $s = \frac{1}{2}$ value of the outer electron. The possible values of J that appear as a right subscript are then obtained by the vector sums of L and S.

For an atom with two or more outer electrons, a number of different atomic states can result from a given electron configuration. These arise from occupation of different equivalent orbitals and from different orientations of the electron spins. Rules, known as *Hund's rules*, suggest which of the possible states for any electron configuration will have the lowest energy. The assignment of a ground-state electron configuration for the atoms of an element is supported if the expected lowest-energy atomic state is the same as that deduced from spectral studies.

The variety of states arising from a given electron configuration can be seen by considering a particular example. The ground-state electron configuration of the carbon atom is expected to be $1s^2 2s^2 2p^2$. The two electrons in the p orbitals can occupy the same or different orbitals of the set of three equivalent $2p$ orbitals. Furthermore, if they occupy different orbitals, they can have their spins in the same or in opposite directions. A detailed analysis shows that the atomic states that can arise are $^1S_0$, $^1D_2$, $^3P_0$, and $^3P_1$.

Two simplified statements of Hund's rules suggest that the $^3P_0$ state will be the lowest energy state:

1. *States with higher S values, i.e., higher multiplicities, have lower energies: or electrons tend not to occupy orbitals in a way that requires their spins to be paired.*
2. *For a given multiplicity, states with higher L values have lower energies.*

Spectroscopic studies show that the ground state of the carbon atom is $^3P_0$. This is consistent with the expected electron configuration $1s^2 2s^2 2p^2$. In a similar way, experimental spectroscopic studies are used to establish the electronic states of the atoms of the other elements of Table 11-6. Each indicated electron configuration is consistent with the given electronic state.

11-11 The Variation Theorem and the Helium Atom

In the preceding sections, spectral results have been used in the deduction of atomic state symbols and electron configurations. Quantum mechanics has been a guide to the characteristics, principally that of quantization of angular momentum, of a central-force system. Complex atoms can also be studied by an extension of the quantum-mechanical treatment of the hydrogen atom. As a first step, we consider the helium atom.

To simplify the notation let us now introduce the symbol ∇^2, according to

$$\nabla^2 = \frac{\partial^2}{\partial x^2} + \frac{\partial^2}{\partial y^2} + \frac{\partial^2}{\partial z^2} \tag{11-50}$$

This symbol, known as the *laplacian*, can also imply the corresponding operator in polar coordinates.

With the Laplace symbol, the general three-dimensional Schrödinger equation of Eq. (11-30) or (11-31) can be rewritten for a single particle of mass m experiencing a potential-energy function U as

$$\left(-\frac{h^2}{8\pi^2 m} \nabla^2 + U \right) \psi = \epsilon \psi$$

Here this form of the Schrödinger equation will be developed to apply to the two electrons of the helium atom. If we assume that U encompasses all the potential-energy terms needed to describe this two-electron atom and that ϵ is the total energy of the system, we can write the helium-atom Schrödinger equation as

$$\left[-\frac{h^2}{8\pi^2 m} (\nabla_1^2 + \nabla_2^2) + U \right] \psi = \epsilon \psi \tag{11-51}$$

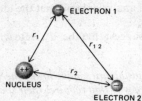

ELECTRON 1

r_1

r_{12}

r_2

++ NUCLEUS

ELECTRON 2

FIGURE 11-12
The coulombic interactions in
the helium atom.

where ∇_1 and ∇_2 are the laplacians for the electrons labeled 1 and 2, as in Fig. 11-12.

The potential-energy expression must include the three coulombic-interaction terms suggested by Fig. 11-12. When these are used for the potential-energy term U, we have the helium-atom Schrödinger equation

$$\left[-\frac{h^2}{8\pi^2 m}(\nabla_1{}^2 + \nabla_2{}^2) + \frac{e^2}{4\pi\epsilon_0}\left(-\frac{2}{r_1{}^2} - \frac{2}{r_2{}^2} + \frac{1}{r_{12}{}^2}\right)\right]\psi = \epsilon\psi \qquad (11\text{-}52)$$

The usual procedure in solving such problems is to try a solution function in which the variables appear in separate factors. Here it would be convenient to deal with a solution function of the form $\psi(1)\psi(2)$, where the first factor involves only the coordinates of electron 1 and the second only the coordinates of electron 2. But the r_{12} term depends on the coordinates of the two electrons in a way that does not allow this separation. As a result, we cannot use this approach to find an eigenfunction for Eq. (11-52), and therefore we cannot solve Eq. (11-52) to obtain the value of ϵ.

This inability to find a function that solves the Schrödinger equation is typical of all but the simplest atomic problems. There is, fortunately, a way of obtaining an approximate solution. Often the approximate solution can be refined so that it is close enough to the exact solution to be of value.

The energy of a quantum-mechanical system is obtained from $\mathcal{H}\psi = \epsilon\psi$ when ψ is an eigenfunction. Alternatively we could write this in the expectation-value form

$$\epsilon = \frac{\int \psi^* \mathcal{H}\psi \, d\tau}{\int \psi^*\psi \, d\tau} \qquad (11\text{-}53)$$

If $\mathcal{H}\psi = \epsilon\psi$, the right side reduces to the eigenvalue ϵ. Suppose, however, that we cannot find a function that satisfies $\mathcal{H}\psi = \epsilon\psi$. We could still use any well-behaved function ϕ to carry out the operations required for the evaluation of the integrals of

$$\frac{\int \phi^* \mathcal{H}\phi \, d\tau}{\int \phi^*\phi \, d\tau}$$

It seems reasonable that the more closely a trial function ϕ approximates the true but unknown solution function ψ, the more closely the result obtained from this expression will approximate the correct energy. We thus write

$$\epsilon_{approx} = \frac{\int \phi^* \mathcal{H} \phi \, d\tau}{\int \phi^* \phi \, d\tau} \tag{11-54}$$

But if the solution function is unknown, we do not know which trial function most closely approximates it and we do not know which calculated energy is close to the correct energy. An important theorem, known as the *variation theorem,* provides the necessary guide.

The theorem, stated without proof, is that the value of the energy calculated from the expression of Eq. (11-54) is less negative, i.e., the system seems less stable, than the value that would be obtained from a function that satisfies $\mathcal{H}\psi = \epsilon\psi$. Thus the best energy that can be obtained from various trial functions is the lowest value produced when these functions are used in Eq. (11-54).

For systems for which an exact solution cannot be found, the procedure is to guess a trial function that is expected to be like the solution function. An energy corresponding to this trial function is calculated. The trial function is then modified, and another energy is calculated. If this energy is lower than the previous one, the trial function has been improved. The process is repeated until a trial function is found which gives the lowest possible energy. This energy is the best approximation to the exact energy, and the corresponding trial function is, in this regard, the best approximation to the true eigenfunction.

One trial function for the helium-atom problem consists of describing each electron as a $1s$ electron. This is acceptable, in view of the Pauli exclusion principle, if the electron spins are opposite. Then, from Tables 11-3 and 11-4 and with $Z = 2$, we write

$$\phi = \frac{8}{\pi a_0^3} e^{-2r_1/a_0} e^{-2r_2/a_0} \tag{11-55}$$

This trial function can be used with Eq. (11-54) and the hamiltonian of Eq. (11-52) to obtain an approximate energy. (The integration involving the r_{12} term causes some difficulty, but the integration can be carried out.) The result gives the energy of the helium atom compared with that of two free electrons and a helium nucleus as $-7218 \text{ kJ mol}^{-1}$, or -74.81 eV. The experimental value is $-7622 \text{ kJ mol}^{-1}$, or -78.99 eV.

The trial function of Eq. (11-55) can be improved in various ways. For example, the idea that each electron screens the nucleus so that the other sees an average nuclear charge of less than 2 suggests that we use $Z < 2$ in Eq. (11-55). If Z is interpreted as Z_{eff} and treated as a variable, it can be adjusted to minimize the energy. The lowest energy that is calculated is -77.47 eV. This value is obtained for $Z = \frac{27}{16} = 1.69$.

Another improvement is made by including a term that reflects the tendency of the electrons to avoid each other. This can be done by including a factor $1 + cr_{12}$ in Eq. (11-55). Then, if c is positive, the trial function will have relatively greater values where r_{12} is large and diminished values where r_{12} is small. When both Z and c are varied to obtain a minimum energy, an energy value of -78.64 eV, close to the experimental value of -78.99 eV, is obtained.

11-12 Electron-Spin Functions

The treatments of the helium atom of the preceding section are all based on the idea that the two electrons of the helium atom occupy identical orbitals. They can do so, according to the statement of the Pauli exclusion principle given in Sec. 11-10, if the spin states of the two electrons are opposed. Now let us explore the total function which describes both the orbital behavior and the spin behavior of the two electrons of the helium atom.

We are interested in the general form of this total function, and we can use the simple approximate designation $1s$ for the orbital description. The spin possibilities, which can be imagined as implying an electron pointing "up" or "down," can be indicated by spin functions α or β.

The hamiltonian for the helium atom involves only the coordinates that appear in the orbital functions. There is no intermingling of the orbital and spin coordinates. The orbital and spin components of the total description are therefore separable, and we can write a total description as

$$\psi = \psi_{\text{orb}}\,\psi_{\text{spin}}$$

As illustrated by Eq. (11-55), ψ_{orb} for the ground state of the helium atom can be written as $1s(1)1s(2)$. We might try, similarly, to satisfy the Pauli exclusion principle by writing ψ_{spin} as $\alpha(1)\beta(2)$. Then

$$\psi = 1s(1)1s(2)\alpha(1)\beta(2) \tag{11-56}$$

Although this expression would be satisfactory in the variation treatment, it is unacceptable on other grounds. Equation (11-56) implies that we can distinguish the spin roles of the two electrons and say that electron 1 points "up," or behaves according to the α spin state, and electron 2 points "down," or behaves according to the β spin state. But the electrons are indistinguishable. Any expression that properly describes the system will be unchanged or at most change sign when the roles of these identical particles are interchanged.

Spin functions for two-electron systems that take proper account of the fact that electrons are indistinguishable are

$$\alpha(1)\alpha(2) \qquad \beta(1)\beta(2) \qquad \alpha(1)\beta(2) + \beta(1)\alpha(2) \tag{11-57}$$

and

$$\alpha(1)\beta(2) - \beta(1)\alpha(2) \tag{11-58}$$

These four possibilities have been grouped into a set of three functions that remain unchanged when the roles, or identifying numbers, of the two electrons are changed and a single function which changes sign for this interchange of roles.

An alternative statement of the Pauli exclusion principle to that introduced in Sec. 11-10 now guides us to a suitable spin function to combine with an orbital function. According to this statement, a total wave function describes the behavior of electrons only if the *wave function changes sign, i.e., is "antisymmetric," when the roles of any two electrons are interchanged.*

In the ground state of the helium atom the orbital part, $1s(1)1s(2)$, of the total wave function is unchanged by an interchange of electrons. Thus, the spin part must change sign. An acceptable wave function for the ground state of the helium atom is therefore

$$\psi = 1s(1)1s(2)[\alpha(1)\beta(2) - \beta(1)\alpha(2)] \tag{11-59}$$

Notice that there is only one acceptable ground-state wave function. The ground state is a singlet. (The same conclusion is reached by the application of the earlier statement of the Pauli exclusion principle, which requires the spins to be opposite to give an $S = 0$ and thus a $2S + 1 = 1$ singlet state.)

Consideration of the excited $1s2s$ configuration further illustrates the equivalence of the two ways of applying the Pauli exclusion principle. Now we can write an antisymmetric orbital function and combine it with a symmetric spin function to give the triplet members

$$[1s(1)2s(2) - 2s(1)1s(2)] \begin{cases} \alpha(1)\alpha(2) \\ \beta(1)\beta(2) \\ [\alpha(1)\beta(2) + \beta(1)\alpha(2)] \end{cases} \tag{11-60}$$

We can also write a symmetric orbital function and an antisymmetric spin function to give the singlet member

$$[1s(1)2s(2) + 2s(1)1s(2)][\alpha(1)\beta(2) - \beta(1)\alpha(2)] \tag{11-61}$$

The first of these functions correspond to the ^3S state expected for spins in the same direction, the second to the ^1S state for spins opposed.

The energies of the $1s2s$ configuration of the helium atom could be obtained by using Eq. (11-60) or (11-61) in a variation treatment. Since the hamiltonian involves only the orbital coordinates, the spin factors would not affect the result directly. The plus and minus signs in the orbital factors, however, do affect the results of the variation calculation. Inspection of the integrals that arise suggests that the energy calculated for the triplet-state orbital function of Eq. (11-60) is lower than that for the singlet-state orbital function of Eq. (11-61). This conclusion is consistent with the empirical Hund rule that states of higher multiplicity lie lower.

The formulation of the Pauli exclusion principle in terms of the required antisymmetry, or change of sign, of wave functions for electrons leads to particular orbital functions. Those of Eqs. (11-60) and (11-61) are examples. Thus, this form of the Pauli exclusion principle guides us to functions that can be used in variation-type calculations. The idea that two electrons can occupy the same orbital only if their spins are opposed does not provide such a guide.

11-13 The Self-consistent Field Method for Many-Electron Atoms

Just as an exact wave function could not be obtained for the two-electron system of the helium atom, so also exact solution functions cannot be found for atoms with more than two electrons. Furthermore, the hamiltonian for such atoms contain many troublesome r_{12}-type terms. In response to these difficulties, D. R. Hartree and, later, V. A. Fock developed a variation treatment described as a *self-consistent field (SCF) method*.

An approximate hamiltonian is set up so that specific coordinates of the r_{12} type which describe the distance between electrons are absent. Each electron is treated as moving in a potential field that is due to the nucleus and the averaged spherically symmetric charge distribution due to all the other electrons of the atom. This charge distribution is initially not known, but trial functions can be used to calculate the probability function for each electron. The electron density corresponding to the trial function is then calculated.

This electron density contributes, along with the nuclear charge, a potential term that can be used to construct a hamiltonian for any one, selected electron. Now the variation method can be used (numerical rather than analytical integration being necessary) to improve the wave function for this single selected electron. This improved trial function can be used to calculate an improved charge-density contribution of this electron.

Next a second electron is selected, and its trial function is similarly improved. As this process is repeated, the improved wave functions and electron densities are fed back into the calculation. After enough cycles, the calculated energies and the trial functions will not change significantly, and we say that we have arrived at a self-consistent field.

The method fails to take into account the specific electron-electron interactions. The positions and motions of the electrons are not "correlated" with each other. The determination of the *correlation energy* is an extremely difficult step still to be accomplished. Nevertheless, the SCF results are valuable, if approximate, guides to the orbitals and energies of many-electron atoms.

The orbital energies that are obtained add detail to the schematic diagram of Fig. 11-11. An example of the results that are obtained is shown in Fig. 11-13. The orbitals that accommodate the outer, or valence, electrons in each periodic table are now clearly shown.

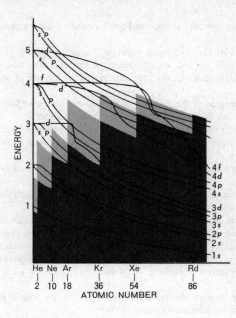

FIGURE 11-13
Orbital energies showing the effects of nuclear charge and the presence of electrons in inner shells. Darker areas indicate filled orbitals; lighter areas indicate partially filled orbitals. (This figure should be compared with Table 11-6.)

PROBLEMS

11-1. Calculate (a) the frequency, (b) the wave number (in cm^{-1}), (c) the wavelength (in nanometers), and (d) the energy (in joules) associated with the first three lines of the Balmer series of the hydrogen-atom spectrum.

11-2. (a) What quantum number values for n_1 and n_2 specify the Lyman series? (b) Calculate the frequency and wavelength of the first member of the Lyman series. (c) In what electromagnetic spectral region does this spectral line occur?

11-3. According to the Rydberg equation, what is the ionization energy of hydrogen atoms? Express your answer in joules per atom, kilojoules per mole of atoms, and electronvolts.

11-4. What is the wavelength at the limit of the Balmer series of atomic hydrogen?

11-5. Ionization energies can be determined (Sec. 14-7) by measuring the energy carried away by a dissociated electron when the ionization process is produced by the interaction of an atom or molecule with a very high energy quantum. If radiation of wavelength 584 Å, or 58.4 nm, from a helium-discharge tube produces ionization of hydrogen atoms, how much kinetic energy will be carried off by the electrons, assuming that they, rather than the proton, account for the bulk of the excess energy? Express the result in electronvolts.

11-6. Calculate the energy that is required to excite an electron of a hydrogen atom from its $n = 1$ to $n = 2$ state. At what temperature is the average translational energy of a gas molecule equal to this hydrogen-atom excitation energy?

11-7. (a) What fraction of hydrogen atoms at 25°C are in the $n = 2$ state at a temperature of 25°C? (b) What temperature is required for 1 percent of the atoms to be in the $n = 2$ state?

11-8. The moment of inertia of the hydrogen atom is $I = \mu r^2$, where μ is the reduced mass $m_e m_p/(m_e + m_p)$ with m_e and m_p the mass of the electron and the proton. What percentage error is introduced in the calculation of I by the use of m, as in Sec. 11-2, instead of μ?

11-9. (a) Calculate the wavelengths of the first line of the Balmer series for atomic hydrogen and atomic deuterium. (b) What is the separation in nanometers?

11-10. Use the Bohr-atom derivation procedure of Sec. 11-2 to obtain an expression for the allowed energies of a hydrogenlike atom, i.e., an atomic ion with a single electron but with a nuclear charge Z.

11-11. What orbit, if any, of a helium atom has the same radius as the $n = 1$ orbit of a hydrogen atom?

11-12. (a) What are the kinetic, potential, and total energies of a hydrogen atom in the $n = 1$ state? (b) What are the values for an $n = 2$ state?

11-13. The Bohr theory of the hydrogen atom gives definite values for familiar, easily conceived quantities. (a) According to this theory, how many times per second does an electron in the ground state of a hydrogen atom complete an orbit about the nucleus? (b) How long does it take to complete a revolution? (c) How fast, in meters per second and miles per hour, is the electron traveling? (d) Compare this speed with the speed of light.

11-14. Stellar hydrogen-atom spectra show longer series, i.e., terms with higher values of n, than spectra obtained by laboratory sources. Why?

11-15. What would the Bohr treatment yield for the hydrogen atom if the attractive potential between the electron and the proton was given by $-e^2/(4\pi\epsilon_0)r^2$ instead of the coulombic potential $-e^2/(4\pi\epsilon_0)r$? [The force of attraction, $-dU/dr$, would then be $2e^2/(4\pi\epsilon_0)r^3$ instead of the inverse-square force $e^2/(4\pi\epsilon_0)r^2$.]

11-16. A hydrogen atom is in a state described, in part, by the total angular momentum of about $2h/2\pi$. (a) What is the value of l? (b) What letter is used to indicate this l value? (c) What are the possible m values for this state? (d) What would be necessary for the states with different m values to be significantly different in energy? (e) Draw an angular-momentum vector diagram to show the magnitude of the total angular momentum and the magnitudes and relative directions of the angular momenta for the states specified by the different m values.

11-17. Use the angular-momentum operator $\widehat{L}_z$ of Eq. (11-27) and the angular factors of Table 11-4 to deduce the angular momentum along the z axis for d orbitals with (a) $m = 0$, (b) $m = +1$, (c) $m = -2$.

11-18. Apply the $\widehat{L}_z$ angular-momentum operator to the real polar forms of the angular factors of Table 11-5 for a d orbital with $m = +1$. How do you interpret the result?

11-19. Using the square of the total-angular-momentum operator given in Eq. (11-28) and the angular factors $\Theta\Phi$ of Table 11-4 deduce the total angular momentum for (a) any p orbital, (b) any d orbital.

11-20. Verify that the $l = 1$, $m = 0$ and the $l = 2$, $m = +1$ angular factors of Table 11-2 are solutions of Eq. (11-42) if $\beta = l(l + 1)$.

11-21. Verify that the $n = 1$, $l = 0$, that is, $1s$, and the $n = 3$, $l = 1$ that is, $3p$, functions of Table 11-3 are solutions of Eq. (11-46).

11-22. (a) What is the total eigenfunction for the $1s$ state of a hydrogen atom? (b) Verify that the function is normalized; i.e., the total probability for the electron of the atom is unity. (The differential-volume element at a distance r from the nucleus is $4\pi r^2\, dr$. You can use the integral $\displaystyle\int_0^\infty x^n e^{-ax}\, dx = n!/a^{n+1}$.)

11-23. What is the average distance of an electron in a $1s$ orbital of a hydrogen atom from the nucleus? (The integral of Prob. 11-22 is again helpful.)

11-24. What is the most probable distance of an electron in a $1s$ orbital of a hydrogen atom from the nucleus?

11-25. (*a*) Write the total eigenfunction of a $2p$ state of a hydrogen atom. (*b*) Calculate the average and most probable distances of the electron from the nucleus.

11-26. Find a general expression for the most probable distance between the electron of a hydrogenlike atom and the nucleus for the orbital with the highest value of l for each value of n. (Use the radial factors of Table 11-3 as a guide to the general form of the radial factor.) Is your result consistent with Fig. 11-5?

11-27. Calculate Z_{eff} for argon and for potassium, given the ionization potentials of 15.68 and 4.318 eV., respectively. Why are the values so different?

11-28. An excited state of the calcium atom has the electron configuration $1s^2 2s^2 2p^6 3s^2 3p^6 4s\, 4d$. (*a*) What is the angular momentum of the state? (*b*) What atomic symbols with superscripts and subscripts could describe the state?

11-29. In the p^2 electron configuration treated in Sec. 11-10 both electrons were assumed to have the same value of n. What would the possible electronic states be if, for example, one of these outer electrons was a $2p$ electron and the other was a $3p$ electron?

11-30. Make a diagram that illustrates the angular-momentum vectors for an atomic state described as $^2D_{3/2}$.

11-31. Angular momentum is contributed to the zirconium atom in its ground state by two $4d$ electrons. Two equivalent d electrons can produce the states ^1S, ^1D, ^1G, ^3P, and ^3F. Which would you expect to be the ground state?

11-32. The ground state of the nitrogen atom is described by the electron state symbol $^4S_{3/2}$. (*a*) What must be the values of m for each of the $3p$ electrons? (*b*) How are the spin-angular-momentum vectors of each of these three $2p$ electrons related?

11-33. The outer electrons of the ground state of the chromium atom are described as $3d^5 4s^1$. What do you think the ground-state electronic symbol might be?

11-34. Write the hamiltonian for a particle in a one-dimensional region of uniform potential of length a bounded by regions of infinitely high potential energy.

11-35. Find the expectation value for x, the position of a particle in a one-dimensional square well of length a when the particle is in the lowest energy state.

11-36. Use the exact solution, $\psi = A \sin(n\pi x/a)$ or $\sqrt{2/a}\sin(n\pi x/a)$ for the particle in a one-dimensional square well in the expression of Eq. (11-53) to obtain the energy corresponding to these eigenfunctions.

11-37. Suppose the solution function $\sqrt{2/a}\sin(\pi x/a)$ for the lowest energy state of the one-dimensional square well problem was not known. (Maybe trigonometric functions had not been studied!) A well-behaved function that could be used to calculate an approximate lowest energy is $Bx(a - x)$. (*a*) Use this function to obtain an expression for the energy of a particle of mass m in a square well of length a. (*b*) Does comparison of this result and that obtained with the eigenfunction illustrate the variation theorem?

11-38. Evaluate B in the expression $Bx(a - x)$ of Prob. 11-37 so this trial function is normalized. Graphically display this normalized function along with $\sqrt{2/a}\sin(\pi x/a)$ and compare the corresponding probability functions.

11-39. (*a*) Set up an acceptable approximate total wave function, including both spatial and spin factors, for two electrons in a one-dimensional square-well potential. (*b*) What is the hamiltonian for this system? (*c*) Why does the wave function that you have written not satisfy $\mathcal{H}\psi = \epsilon\psi$? (*d*) Describe an approximate method of taking into account the electron-electron repulsion effect without introducing difficult integrals.

11-40. (*a*) Write approximate total wave functions, including spatial and spin factors, for the first excited electron configuration of two electrons in a one-dimensional square well. (*b*) State the multiplicity of each state corresponding to this configuration. (*c*) If the rules for atomic systems carry over, which state would be at lower energy?

REFERENCES

The references at the end of Chap. 13 include additional treatments of the methods of quantum mechanics and the application of these methods to atoms.

SLATER, J. C.: "Quantum Theory of Atomic Structure," McGraw-Hill Book Company, New York, 1960.

HYDE, K. E.: Methods for Obtaining Russell-Saunders Term Symbols from Electronic Configurations, *J. Chem. Educ.*, **52:**87 (1975).

BORDASS, W. T., and J. W. LINNETT: A New Way of Presenting Atomic Orbitals, *J. Chem. Educ.*, **47:**672 (1970). Very effective three-dimensional-appearing, computer-generated contour diagrams for atomic orbitals.

12 SYMMETRY AND GROUP THEORY

Many of the molecules to which we apply the methods of quantum mechanics are *symmetric,* a familiar term that will be refined in Sec. 12-1. Examples of simple symmetric molecules are CO_2, H_2O, CH_4, C_6H_6, and SF_6. Many inorganic coordination compounds, e.g., the tetrahedral and octahedral complexes of the transition metals, are also symmetric.

Studies of symmetry are quite unlike any of the other studies that help us organize the macroscopic and molecular worlds of physical chemistry. For this reason, it often seems to be difficult to enter into studies of symmetry and the related theory of groups. The subject seems abstract and far removed from the relatively more familiar quantum-mechanical treatments and experimental studies of molecular properties. Once over the initial obstacle, you will find that ideas about symmetry lead with surprisingly little effort to information about molecules that is of immediate value.

The introduction to symmetry and group theory is presented in this chapter in a way that attempts to minimize the entry problem. The development of the ideas of symmetry and group theory is illustrated by frequent references to the simple, real example of the H_2O molecule. Furthermore, the development is pushed toward practical results so that the usefulness of the methods can be appreciated at an early stage.

The studies of this chapter will lead you to an understanding of the basis and use of *character tables* like those of Appendix C. These tables provide useful summaries of the symmetry and symmetry consequences for molecules of various types of symmetry. In this chapter, the use of character tables will be illustrated by studies of atoms in symmetric environments. In Chap. 13 further use will be made in studies of chemical bonding in molecules. Then, in Chap. 14, the symmetry properties of the vibrations of molecules will make further use of the information provided by character tables and will allow the symmetry properties of the vibrations of molecules to be deduced.

12-1 The Symmetry of Molecules

It is apparent that some molecules, like H_2O and CH_4, are symmetric. Now we shall develop a clear and precise way of describing such symmetries. Consider,

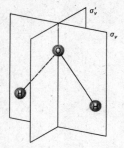

FIGURE 12-1
The two planes of symmetry σ_v and σ_v', of the H_2O molecule.

for example, the plane containing the H_2O molecule and the perpendicular plane shown in Fig. 12-1. These planes are examples of *planes of symmetry*. You can test, what is here quite obvious, that the molecule is symmetric with respect to each plane by "reflecting" the molecule through the plane. This operation consists of treating the plane as a mirror which gives an image behind the mirror that is identical to the scene in front of the mirror. This reflection through the mirror, in both directions, produces a result that is indistinguishable from that existing originally. The reflection process is an example of a *symmetry operation*. It is the symmetry operation associated with a plane of symmetry. The plane of symmetry is an example of an *element of symmetry*.

As this example suggests, we can describe the symmetry of a molecule in terms of the elements of symmetry of the molecule. That a molecule has any particular element of symmetry can be checked by carrying out the symmetry operation associated with each symmetry element. If the operation does nothing more than leave the positions of atoms unchanged or carries one atom of a set of identical atoms into a position of another atom of the set, the result will be indistinguishable from that existing initially. When this is the result of the symmetry operation, the molecule does indeed have the corresponding symmetry element.

The general symbol for a plane of symmetry is σ. If we draw the planes vertically, as in Fig. 12-1, we refer to them as *vertical planes of symmetry*. Such planes are given the symbol σ_v. If, as in the case of the H_2O molecule, there are two vertical planes of symmetry, one is given the label σ_v, the other σ_v', as in Fig. 12-1. If the plane of symmetry is drawn horizontally, we refer to it as a horizontal plane and label it σ_h. If it is drawn in a way that can be described as diagonal, it is labeled σ_d.

Now let us consider some other elements of symmetry and the symmetry operations associated with them. A molecule is said to have a *center of symmetry* if the operation of *inversion* through the center produces a result indistinguishable from that occurring originally. The symbol for a center of symmetry is i. Some examples of molecules with a center of symmetry are shown in Fig. 12-2.

A molecule is said to have an *axis of symmetry* if rotation of the molecule about that axis gives us back our initial situation. A twofold axis is one for which a rotation by $\frac{360}{2}$ degrees, or half a revolution, produces a result like that

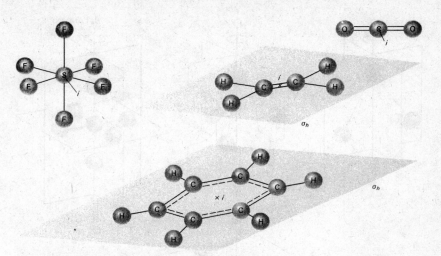

FIGURE 12-2 Examples of centers of symmetry.

occurring originally. As Fig. 12-3*a* shows, the H_2O molecule has a twofold axis of rotation denoted by C_2. A threefold axis is one for which a rotation by $\frac{360}{3}$, or $\frac{1}{3}$ revolution, produces a result identical to that occurring originally. The NH_3 molecule, illustrated in Fig. 12-3*b*, has such an axis. The symbol for it is C_3. There actually are two symmetry *operations* associated with a C_3 axis. One is a rotation, say clockwise, by a $\frac{1}{3}$ revolution. The other then is a clockwise rotation by $\frac{2}{3}$ revolution or a counterclockwise rotation by $\frac{1}{3}$ revolution.

The element of symmetry described as a fourfold axis is illustrated in Fig. 12-3*c*. The symmetry operations corresponding to this element of symmetry consist of rotations by $\frac{1}{4}$, $2(\frac{1}{4})$, and $3(\frac{1}{4})$ of a revolution. A C_4 axis implies a C_2 axis since the operation consisting of a rotation by two quarters revolution is equivalent to rotation by half a revolution.

A sixfold axis of symmetry is illustrated in Fig. 12-3*d*. As the discussion of the fourfold axis suggests, a sixfold axis implies coincident twofold and threefold axes.

If a molecule has a single axis of rotation, we agree to draw the molecule so that this axis is in the vertical direction. If a molecule has more than one axis of rotation, we draw the molecule so that the highest-order axis is vertical. The axes of rotation of the benzene molecule, drawn in accordance with this rule, are shown in Fig. 12-3*d*.

With only one additional type of symmetry element the symmetry of any molecule can be completely described. This element, a *rotation-reflection axis of symmetry,* is illustrated for the allene molecule in Fig. 12-4. In this example the rotation-reflection axis is a fourfold axis. It is given the symbol S_4. The operation corresponding to the S_4 element of symmetry is a rotation by $\frac{1}{4}$ revolution followed by reflection through a plane perpendicular to the axis. You can see

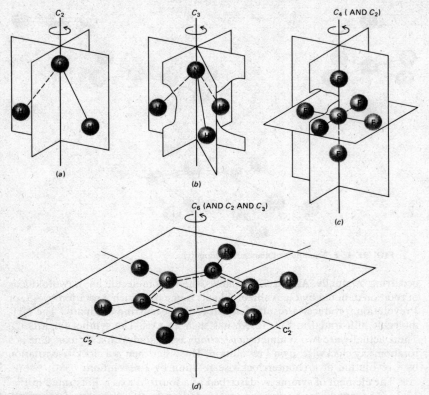

FIGURE 12-3 Examples of axes of symmetry.

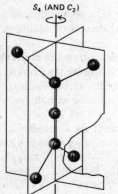

FIGURE 12-4
An example for the molecule allene of an S_4 fourfold rotation-reflection axis.

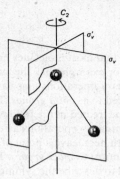

FIGURE 12-5
The three symmetry elements which, together with the identity element E, describe the symmetry of the H_2O molecule.

from Fig. 12-4 that the net result is indistinguishable from that existing originally. (You can also see from Fig. 12-4 that a C_2 axis is coincident with an S_4 axis.)

The symmetry of a molecule is completely and precisely indicated by stating the number and relative orientations of the four kinds of symmetry elements that have been described. Thus instead of saying, for example, that H_2O is a symmetric molecule, we now can draw the diagram of Fig. 12-5 to show the elements of symmetry of the H_2O molecule.

One additional element of symmetry, which adds nothing to a description of the symmetry of a molecule but is helpful for an organized treatment of the consequences of this symmetry, should now be added. This symmetry element is called the *identity* and is given the symbol E. The symmetry operation associated with this symmetry element can be said to consist of no change. (Alternatively the operation can be described as a rotation about any axis by 360°.) Thus all molecules have the symmetry element E. (You will see that inclusion of this identity element is not as frivolous as it seems.) A summary of elements of symmetry and the symmetry operations is given in Table 12-1.

TABLE 12-1 Elements of Symmetry and Symmetry Operations

Elements of symmetry		
Symbol	Description	Symmetry operations
E	Identity	No change
σ	Plane of symmetry	Reflection through the plane
i	Center of symmetry	Inversion through the center
C_p	Axis of symmetry	Rotation about the axis by $(360/p)°$
S_p	Rotation-reflection axis of symmetry	Rotation about the axis by $(360/p)°$ followed by reflection through the plane perpendicular to the axis

12-2 Collections of Symmetry Elements: The Point Groups

It is clear from the examples of the preceding section that most molecules have several elements of symmetry. The H_2O molecule, for example, has the symmetry elements E, C_2, σ_v, and σ_v'. The sets of symmetry operations associated with such collections of symmetry elements are referred to as *point groups*. The mathematical implications of the word "group" will be treated in the following section. The adjective "point" is used because the symmetry operations associated with all the symmetry elements that are dealt with here leave a point of, or in, the molecule fixed in space. (Point groups are in contrast to *space groups*. The latter are the collections of symmetry operations used to describe the symmetry of a crystal. These groups include symmetry operations for which the operation consists of a translation of a molecule or a unit cell to a new location in the crystal.)

Now let us sample the variety of collections of symmetry elements and their associated symmetry operations that can occur. Each collection of symmetry operations constitutes a point group, and each point group is given a symbol. The symbol, usually written in boldface type, is based on the principal elements of symmetry of that point group.

We begin by mentioning two point groups that are found when molecules with minimal symmetry are considered. For example, the bent molecule NOCl has only a plane of symmetry and the staggered molecule H_2O_2 has only a C_2 axis of symmetry. Each, of course, has the identity symmetry element. The point groups which these examples suggest include, as shown in Table 12-2, only the identity operation and one other symmetry operation.

Next we come to five collections of symmetry operations found when we consider molecules with a single axis of symmetry. (This axis might have several rotational symmetry operations associated with it.) The symbols for the point groups suggested by these molecules and the symmetry operations that constitute these groups are shown in Table 12-2. In each of these point groups, as Table 12-2 shows, the axis of rotation is taken to be the z axis. For a twofold axis the associated symmetry operation is a rotation by half a revolution. Since a threefold axis has two symmetry operations associated with it, Table 12-2 includes the entry $2C_3(z)$ whenever there is a threefold axis. The symmetry operations associated with a C_4 axis of symmetry are given as $2C_4(z)$ and $C_2(z)$. Sometimes such C_2 axes are indicated by $C_4{}^2(z)$ to indicate successive rotations by a quarter of a revolution. The planes associated with the symmetry operations of reflections are identified by the v, h, and d subscripts and, where appropriate, reference to the x, y, z coordinate system.

Next, in Table 12-2 is a set of rather more complex point groups, which will not be dealt with in detail. Each has the principal point-group symbol **D**. The symmetry elements on which these point groups are based include axes that lie perpendicular to each other. The point groups for these collections of symmetry operations are referred to as the *dihedral groups*. Each point-group symbol **D**

TABLE 12-2 Examples of Point-Group Symbols and the Symmetry Operations, Other Than the Identity E, Included in These Point Groups

The z axis is assumed to be in the vertical direction

C_s	NOCl	σ_h
C_2	H_2O_2	C_2
C_{2v}	H_2O	$C_2(z)$, $\sigma_v(xz)$, $\sigma_v'(yz)$
C_{2h}	$trans\text{-}C_2H_2Cl_2$	$C_2(z)$, $\sigma_h(xy)$, i
C_{3v}	NH_3	$2C_3(z)$, $3\sigma_v$
C_{4v}	B_5H_9	$2C_4(z)$, $C_2(z)$, $2\sigma_v$, $2\sigma_d$
C_{6v}		$2C_6(z)$, $2C_3(z)$, $C_2(z)$, $3\sigma_v$, $3\sigma_d$
D_{2d}	Allene	$C_2(z)$, $2S_4(z)$, $2C_2(x \text{ and } y)$, $2\sigma_d$
D_{2h}	Ethylene	$C_2(x)$, $C_2(y)$, $C_2(z)$, i, σ_{xy}, σ_{xz}, σ_{yz}
D_{3d}	Cyclohexane	$2C_3(z)$, $2S_6(z)$, $3C_2(\perp \text{ to } z)$, i, $3\sigma_d$
D_{3h}	Cyclopropane	$2C_3(z)$, $2S_3(z)$, $3C_2(\perp \text{ to } z)$, $3C_2'(\perp \text{ to } z)$, σ_h, $3\sigma_v$
D_{4h}	Cyclobutane	$2C_4(z)$, $C_2(z)$, $2S_4(z)$, $2C_2(\perp \text{ to } z)$, $2C_2'(\perp \text{ to } z)$, i, $2\sigma_v$, σ_d
D_{6h}	Benzene	$2C_6(z)$, $2C_3(z)$, $C_2(z)$, $2S_6(z)$, $2S_3(z)$, $3C_2(\perp \text{ to } z)$, $3C_2'(\perp \text{ to } z)$, i, σ_h, $3\sigma_v$, $3\sigma_d$
T_d	Methane	$8C_2$, $6S_4$, $3C_2(=3S_4{}^2)$, $6\sigma_d$
O_h	SF_6	$6C_4(x,y,z)$, $3C_2(x,y,z)$, $6S_4(x,y,z)$, $8C_3(\text{diag})$, $8S_6(\text{diag})$, $6C_2$, $3\sigma_h$, $6\sigma_d$

has a subscript that shows the highest-order rotation axis and suggests the types of planes of symmetry that are present.

The very symmetric tetrahedral molecules, such as CH_4, and the octahedral molecules and ions, such as SF_6, suggest two additional point groups, which, in spite of their complexity, should be introduced. Illustrations of the symmetry elements of such molecules are given in Fig. 12-6. The symmetry operations of

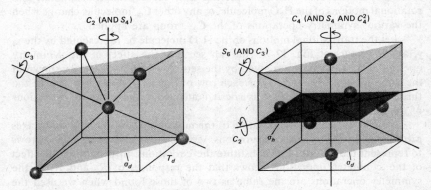

FIGURE 12-6 Representative symmetry elements of the tetrahedral T_d and the octahedral O_h point groups.

the tetrahedral point group $\mathbf{T}_d$ and the octahedral point group $\mathbf{O}_h$, suggested by the collections of symmetry elements of Fig. 12-6, are included in Table 12-2.

A total of about 27 point groups are found if the symmetry of all important molecular structures are investigated. Thus Table 12-2 provides only a sampling of important point groups. Some of the information of Table 12-2 will be called on as individual molecules are studied. You need not attempt to master the table in advance of these studies.

The symmetry of a molecule can be described by specifying the symmetry elements of the molecule. Alternatively, and more simply, one can state the point group to which the molecule belongs. Thus, the entire symmetry of the H_2O molecule is indicated by stating that the H_2O molecule belongs to the $\mathbf{C}_{2v}$ point group. The symmetry of the CH_4 molecule is indicated by saying that it belongs to the $\mathbf{T}_d$ point group, and so forth.

Point groups have not been introduced simply for such compact statements. Point groups are special combinations of symmetry operations, as you will see in·the following section. By exploring the special nature of these combinations we shall be able to learn about the symmetry features of the wave functions of the atoms of the molecules, the wave functions of the molecules, and the vibrations of the molecules of molecules belonging to any point group.

12-3 Transformation Matrices and Symmetry Species

You have seen what happens when a molecule is subjected to the symmetry operation that corresponds to any of the symmetry elements of the point group to which the molecule belongs. The molecule is simply transformed into itself. But the properties of the molecule in which we are interested are not necessarily so simply affected.

All properties, or motions, of a molecule, obtained perhaps as eigenfunctions of the corresponding operator, are related to the symmetry of the molecule. Let us illustrate this by exploring how the overall translational and rotational motions of the H_2O molecule, or any other $\mathbf{C}_{2v}$ molecule, change when the various symmetry operations of the $\mathbf{C}_{2v}$ group are applied.

Let the translational motions of the H_2O molecule be represented by the $\mathbf{x}$, $\mathbf{y}$, and $\mathbf{z}$ vectors of Fig. 12-7. You can see that the effect of the symmetry operations on $\mathbf{x}$, $\mathbf{y}$, and $\mathbf{z}$ are given by the sets of $+1$ and -1 entries shown in the three rows of Fig. 12-7. Thus each row of Fig. 12-7 shows how one of the three vectors, that we have used as a *basis*, is affected by the symmetry operations of the group.

Now let us see how the rotation of the molecule about the x, y, and z axes are affected by the symmetry operations. We can do so by drawing curly arrows to represent the motions that constitute these rotations. Inspection of the effect of the symmetry operations shows that the responses of R_x and R_y to the symmetry operations are the same as two of those found when we used the vectors that represent translational motions as our basis. The effect on R_z, as illustrated in Fig. 12-8, leads to a new, fourth, set of $+1$ and -1 terms.

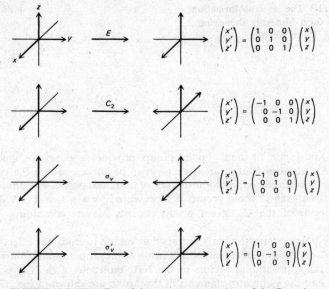

$$\begin{pmatrix} x' \\ y' \\ z' \end{pmatrix} = \begin{pmatrix} 1 & 0 & 0 \\ 0 & 1 & 0 \\ 0 & 0 & 1 \end{pmatrix} \begin{pmatrix} x \\ y \\ z \end{pmatrix}$$

$$\begin{pmatrix} x' \\ y' \\ z' \end{pmatrix} = \begin{pmatrix} -1 & 0 & 0 \\ 0 & -1 & 0 \\ 0 & 0 & 1 \end{pmatrix} \begin{pmatrix} x \\ y \\ z \end{pmatrix}$$

$$\begin{pmatrix} x' \\ y' \\ z' \end{pmatrix} = \begin{pmatrix} -1 & 0 & 0 \\ 0 & 1 & 0 \\ 0 & 0 & 1 \end{pmatrix} \begin{pmatrix} x \\ y \\ z \end{pmatrix}$$

$$\begin{pmatrix} x' \\ y' \\ z \end{pmatrix} = \begin{pmatrix} 1 & 0 & 0 \\ 0 & -1 & 0 \\ 0 & 0 & 1 \end{pmatrix} \begin{pmatrix} x \\ y \\ z \end{pmatrix}$$

FIGURE 12-7 The effect of the symmetry operations of the C_{2v} point group on vectors representing the translational motion of the molecule.

The four different types of symmetry behavior that have been discovered are collected in Table 12-3. Each row represents a *symmetry species*. Each symmetry species is given an identifying label. We use the symbol A to indicate a symmetry species that is symmetric with respect to the axis of rotation, i.e., a species for which $+1$ is the entry under the symbol for the rotation operation. We use the symbol B to indicate a symmetry species that is antisymmetric, and has a -1 entry, for this rotation operation. Here we use additional subscript labels, choosing the subscript 1 for the more symmetric species, 2 for the less symmetric species.

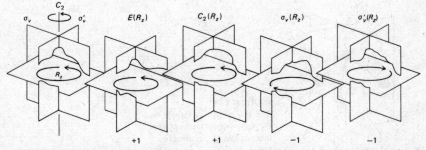

FIGURE 12-8 The effect of the symmetry operations of the C_{2v} point group on the rotational motion of the molecule about the x, y, and z axes.

TABLE 12-3 The $|x|$ Transformation Matrices for a Molecule Belonging to the C_{2v} Point Group

	E	C_2	σ_v	σ_v'
A_1	1	1	1	1
A_2	1	1	-1	-1
B_1	1	-1	1	-1
B_2	1	-1	-1	1

The H_2O molecule, or the C_{2v} point group, provides a somewhat special example. The translation and rotation vectors can be chosen so that the symmetry operations change each vector into itself or into its opposite. The effect of the operations on each of these vectors is represented by a $+1$ or a -1. The symmetry species of the C_{2v} point group consists of sets containing $+1$ and -1 terms.

For some point groups the basis vectors that we use to study the effects of the symmetry operations become mixed as a result of these operations. Consider the three overall translational vectors of the NH_3 molecule of the C_{3v} point group. These and the symmetry elements of this group are shown in Fig. 12-9. Nothing new enters when we consider the effects of the symmetry operations on the z vector of Fig. 12-9. This vector is unchanged by each and every symmetry operation. Thus a set of $+1$'s shows how the z translation vector is transformed.

Now consider the effect of a C_3 rotation, i.e., rotation by a third of a revolution on the x and y vectors. The results are shown by the projection view of Fig. 12-10. The new position of x, that is, the vector x', is related to the original vectors by

$$x' = -\tfrac{1}{2}x - \frac{\sqrt{3}}{2}y$$

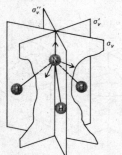

FIGURE 12-9
The symmetry operations and the x, y, z displacement vectors for the C_{3v} molecule NH_3.

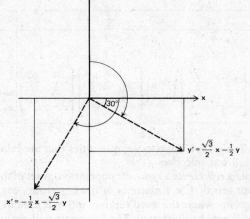

$$x' = -\frac{1}{2}x - \frac{\sqrt{3}}{2}y$$

$$y' = \frac{\sqrt{3}}{2}x - \frac{1}{2}y$$

FIGURE 12-10
The effect of the C_3 operation on the $\mathbf{x}$ and $\mathbf{y}$ vectors of Fig. 12-9 seen in projection.

Similarly

$$\mathbf{y}' = +\frac{\sqrt{3}}{2}\mathbf{x} - \tfrac{1}{2}\mathbf{y}$$

The net effect of the operation C_2 on the set of vectors $\mathbf{x}$ and $\mathbf{y}$ can be shown by the matrix equation

$$\begin{pmatrix} \mathbf{x}' \\ \mathbf{y}' \end{pmatrix} = \begin{pmatrix} -\dfrac{1}{2} & -\dfrac{\sqrt{3}}{2} \\ \dfrac{\sqrt{3}}{2} & -\dfrac{1}{2} \end{pmatrix} \begin{pmatrix} \mathbf{x} \\ \mathbf{y} \end{pmatrix}$$

Thus the effect of the symmetry operation cannot be shown by treating $\mathbf{x}$ and $\mathbf{y}$ separately. We must deal with both together. The transformation properties of the set is shown by a matrix. In a similar way 2×2 transformation matrices are needed to describe the effect of the C_2^2, σ_v, σ_v', and σ_v'' symmetry operations. A summary of the transformation matrices that would be found by considering the translations and rotations of any $\mathbf{C}_{3v}$ molecule is given in Table 12-4.

The symmetry species, i.e., the rows in tables such as Tables 12-3 and 12-4, for any point group can now be recognized as being, in general, a set of transformation matrices. Often, as in the case of the $\mathbf{C}_{2v}$ point group and the first two rows of Table 12-4, these are 1×1 matrices, or simply numbers. Fortunately we shall not need to deal with the higher-order matrices, such as the

TABLE 12-4 Transformation Matrices for the Translations and Rotations of the Point Group C_{3v}

C_{3v}	E	C_3	$C_3{}^2$	σ_v	σ_v'	σ_v''	
	1	1	1	1	1	1	T_z
	1	1	1	-1	-1	-1	R_z
	$\begin{bmatrix} 1 & 0 \\ 0 & 1 \end{bmatrix}$	$\begin{bmatrix} -\frac{1}{2} & -\frac{\sqrt{3}}{2} \\ \frac{\sqrt{3}}{2} & -\frac{1}{2} \end{bmatrix}$	$\begin{bmatrix} -\frac{1}{2} & \frac{\sqrt{3}}{2} \\ -\frac{\sqrt{3}}{2} & -\frac{1}{2} \end{bmatrix}$	$\begin{bmatrix} 1 & 0 \\ 0 & 1 \end{bmatrix}$	$\begin{bmatrix} -\frac{1}{2} & -\frac{\sqrt{3}}{2} \\ -\frac{3}{2} & \frac{1}{2} \end{bmatrix}$	$\begin{bmatrix} -\frac{1}{2} & \frac{\sqrt{3}}{2} \\ \frac{\sqrt{3}}{2} & \frac{1}{2} \end{bmatrix}$	T_x, T_y and R_x, R_y

2×2 matrices displayed in Table 12-4. Easy-to-use quantities that are related to these matrices will serve all our purposes.

Each transformation matrix *represents* a symmetry operation. A set of these matrices, like each of the four sets of 1×1 matrices of the C_{2v} group, constitutes a *representation* of the group, where the word representation is used in the mathematical sense, which will now be illustrated. The C_{2v} group will again be used as an example.

Consider successive operation of any two of the operations of the group, e.g., the combination $\sigma_v'\sigma_v$. As shown in Fig. 12-11, where the **x** vector is used as a basis for the symmetry operations, this combination is equivalent to C_2. We can write

$$C_2 = \sigma_v'\sigma_v$$

If now for any of the rows of Table 12-3 we multiply the matrix, or number, under the σ_v operation by the number under the σ_v', we obtain the number

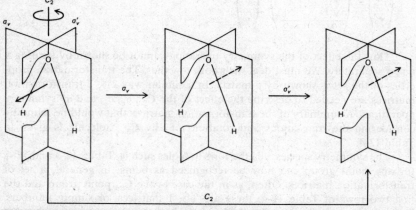

FIGURE 12-11 Successive operation by any two operations of the C_{2v} point group is equivalent to an operation of the group.

under the C_2 operation. In this sense, each of the sets of numbers, or transformation matrices, that describes a symmetry species is a representation of the group. The four representations of Table 12-3 are the only 1×1 matrix representations of the $\mathbf{C}_{2v}$ group.

In a similar way the matrices of Table 12-4 can be shown to represent the operations of the $\mathbf{C}_{3v}$ point group.

12-4 The Symmetry Species of Molecular Properties

Examples of the special ways in which vectors or functions can be affected by the symmetry operations of a point group were illustrated in Sec. 12-3. All eigenfunctions for an atom or molecule transform according to one or another of the special symmetry species. These symmetry species are known for each point group and are listed, as will be described in Sec. 12-5, for a number of point groups in Appendix C. We thus have a very powerful guide to the form of any vector or function that describes the properties or behavior of a symmetric molecule. Each vector or function must transform according to one of the symmetry species of the point group to which the molecule belongs.

Typically, in dealing with molecular properties, we proceed from simple and easily pictured or easily described functions or vectors associated with the atoms of a molecule. We use these to build up functions or vectors appropriate to the whole molecule. Thus, to describe the translational, rotational, and vibrational motion of a molecule we might start with the three cartesian displacement coordinates of each atom of the molecule. To describe the orbitals of a molecule we often adopt a linear-combination-of-atomic-orbitals (LCAO) approach.

Now we will see that we can use the easy-to-deal-with vectors or functions to deduce the symmetry species of the molecular vectors or functions that we are trying to build.

Suppose you were to construct transformation matrices, as in Sec. 12-3, for a set of basis vectors or functions and these functions were themselves linear combinations of some other set of functions or vectors. You would find that the sums of the diagonal elements of the matrices would be the same for the old and the new basis vectors or functions.

The sum of the diagonal elements of a transformation matrix of a representation is known as the *character* of the matrix. Thus, the characters of the transformation matrices that represent a group will be the same for all basis vectors that are or could be formed from each other by linear combinations.

We generally will need large matrices to show the effect of each symmetry operation on the molecule. For example, if we use the three cartesian displacement coordinates on each atom of an n-atom molecule as our basis, we shall generally need matrices of order $3n$ to describe the effects of the operations. If we use bond orbitals as a basis, we shall generally need transformation matrices with an order equal to the number of bonds. These large matrices can be converted, or *reduced*, to sets of smaller matrices by forming linear combinations of the original basis vectors. The original set of large matrices constitute a reducible representation. The smallest matrix representations obtained by appropriate linear combinations of the basis vectors are called *irreducible representations*. The characters of the reducible representation are the same as the sum of the characters of the various smaller irreducible representations.

12-5 Character Tables

In Sec. 12-4 it was shown that the symmetry of molecular eigenfunctions or properties can be worked out by bringing together two sets of representations. One is the reducible representation obtained by inspecting the effect of symmetry operations on the basis vectors or functions; the other is the set of irreducible representations of the point group to which the molecule belongs. These irreducible representations are available in character tables for all the point groups that will be encountered. Some of the important ones are given in Appendix C. Here features of these character tables, particularly features not revealed by that for the C_{2v} point group, will be described.

In most point groups, symmetry operations can be organized into *classes*. The members of a class are always operations of the same type, rotations or reflections, and all members of the class have the same character. The two rotations by $\frac{1}{3}$ and $\frac{2}{3}$ revolution of the NH_3 molecule about its C_3 axis have the same character. So also do the reflections through each of the three σ_v planes. In character tables, as that for the C_{3v} point group in Appendix C illustrates, the symmetry operations for the different classes are shown and the number of operations in each class is given at the head of each column. (In the C_{2v} point group each symmetry operation is in its own class.)

A second feature common to most point groups (but not the C_{2v} point group) is the presence of doubly and triply degenerate symmetry species. The C_{3v} point group again provides a specific example. For this group one of the irreducible representations consists of 2×2 matrices. The symmetry species for such a doubly degenerate representation are labeled E, not to be confused with the same symbol used for the identity operation. Triply degenerate representations have the symbol T (or sometimes F).

The characters of a doubly degenerate E representation are the sums of the two diagonal elements of the representation matrices. The matrix for the identity operation is a 2×2 unit matrix with 1's on the diagonals and 0's off the diagonals. The character for the identity operation for a doubly degenerate E symmetry species is thus always 2. That for a T symmetry species is always 3.

By now some of the labels used for the various symmetry species have been introduced. The symbol A is used for species that are symmetric with respect to the principal axis. B is used for those antisymmetric with respect to this axis. Usually additional identifying subscripts are necessary. These can simply be numbers as in the C_{2v} point group, but if there is a center of symmetry, the subscript g (for German *gerade*, "even") is used for symmetry species symmetric with respect to inversion through the center. The subscript u (for German *ungerade,* "uneven") is used for species antisymmetric with respect to inversion through the center. You now should be able to read the main body of character tables like those of Appendix C.

Character tables display the symmetry type of cartesian vectors and squares and cross products of these coordinates. These often directly reveal the symmetry type of the properties of a molecule in which we are interested.

The symmetry type of the **x**, **y**, and **z** vectors were worked out for the C_{2v} group in Sec. 12-2. The symmetry types to which these vectors belong are often shown in the right-hand region of the character tables, as they are in those of Appendix C.

The atomic p_x, p_y, and p_z orbitals were shown in Table 11-5 to be such that they transform like the **x**, **y**, and **z** vectors. Thus the way in which p orbitals transform can be seen immediately by seeing the symmetry types of **x**, **y**, and **z** as given in the character table for the point group of the symmetry surrounding the atom.

The **x**, **y**, and **z** entries also show the symmetry types for the translation of the molecule in these directions. The entries R_x, R_y and R_z show the symmetry types of rotations of molecules about these axes. These entries will be helpful when, as in Sec. 14-3, we analyze the vibrations of symmetric molecules.

The angular factors of d orbitals were shown in Table 11-4. As for the p orbitals, these can be expressed in terms of cartesian coordinates. These coordinates were shown as subscripts in the display of the d-orbital angular factors in Table 11-5. Character tables usually also include the symmetry types for the cartesian coordinate expressions that describe the angular features of d orbitals.

12-6 The Vectorlike Properties of Character Tables

The set of characters along any row in a character table behaves like the components of a vector in space with dimensions equal to the number of operations in the group. This general statement can be illustrated by turning, first, to the C_{2v} point group. You can see that (1) the sum of the squares of the entries for each symmetry species is equal to 4, the number of operations, of the group; (2) the sum of the term-by-term products over all the operations for any two different symmetry species is zero. The rows act like the components of orthogonal vectors.

These two factors can be expressed mathematically. Let i refer to one row of the character table and j to another row. Let R represent any column of a character table. Thus R is a symmetry operation of any of the classes of symmetry operations. Let n_R be the number of operations in the class. (This number is given in the first row of the character table.) You can verify for any of the character tables of Appendix C that

$$\sum_{\text{all classes}} n_R \chi_i(R) \chi_j(R) = \begin{cases} g & i = j \\ 0 & i \neq j \end{cases} \tag{12-1}$$

where g is the number of symmetry operations in the group. The number g is known as the *order* of the group. These vectorlike properties let us derive an expression that gives the number of times each of the irreducible representations occurs in any reducible representation.

The idea that the characters $\chi(R)$ of any reducible representation are made up of the characters of some of the irreducible representations can be expressed by

$$\chi(R) = \sum_j a_j \chi_j(R) \qquad (12\text{-}2)$$

where $\chi(R)$ represents the character for the class containing the Rth symmetry operation for a reducible representation and $\chi_j(R)$ represents the character for the jth irreducible operation. The a_j's of Eq. (12-2) are the number of times the jth irreducible representation, that in the jth row of the character table, occurs in the reducible representation.

Now let us try to find out how many times each irreducible representation, or each row of the character table, occurs in a reducible representation. We focus on the ith row, and we attempt to find the value of a_i. First we multiply both sides of Eq. (12-2) by $n_R \chi_i(R)$, and then we sum over all classes of symmetry operations. We obtain

$$\sum_{\text{all classes}} n_R \chi_i(R) \chi(R) = \sum_{\text{all classes}} \left[n_R \chi_i(R) \sum_j a_j \chi_j(R) \right] \qquad (12\text{-}3)$$

According to Eq. (12-1), the right side will give zero contributions except when $j = i$. Then the value of the right side is a_i times g, where g is the order of the group. Thus

$$\sum_{\text{all classes}} n_R \chi_i(R) \chi(R) = a_i g$$

or

$$a_i = \frac{1}{g} \sum_{\text{all classes}} n_R \chi_i(R) \chi(R) \qquad (12\text{-}4)$$

Thus, if the characters $\chi(R)$ of a reducible representation are known and the characters of each irreducible representation $\chi_i(R)$ are available from a character table, the number of times each irreducible representation occurs in the reducible representation can readily be calculated.

Equation (12-4) is an often used and important result. It allows us to determine the number of times each of the irreducible representations occurs in any reducible representation.

12-7 Introduction to the Deduction of the Symmetry Properties of Orbitals and Vibrations of Molecules

Let us continue to use the C_{2v} point group and the H_2O molecule to illustrate how the procedure developed in the preceding sections can be used to deduce the symmetry of molecular properties.

Suppose, as in Fig. 12-12, that the electrons in one bond of an H_2O molecule are described by a bond orbital ϕ_1 and those in the other bond by a bond orbital ϕ_2. These provide the basis for the construction, by taking linear combinations, of molecular bonding orbitals. The transformation matrices that describe the effect of the various symmetry operations are

$$
\begin{array}{cc}
E & C_2 \\
\begin{bmatrix} \phi_1' \\ \phi_2' \end{bmatrix} = \begin{bmatrix} 1 & 0 \\ 0 & 1 \end{bmatrix} \begin{bmatrix} \phi_1 \\ \phi_2 \end{bmatrix} & \begin{bmatrix} \phi_1' \\ \phi_2' \end{bmatrix} = \begin{bmatrix} 0 & 1 \\ 1 & 0 \end{bmatrix} \begin{bmatrix} \phi_1 \\ \phi_2 \end{bmatrix}
\end{array}
$$

$$
\begin{array}{cc}
\sigma_v & \sigma_v' \\
\begin{bmatrix} \phi_1' \\ \phi_2' \end{bmatrix} = \begin{bmatrix} 1 & 0 \\ 0 & 1 \end{bmatrix} \begin{bmatrix} \phi_1 \\ \phi_2 \end{bmatrix} & \begin{bmatrix} \phi_1' \\ \phi_2' \end{bmatrix} = \begin{bmatrix} 0 & 1 \\ 1 & 0 \end{bmatrix} \begin{bmatrix} \phi_1 \\ \phi_2 \end{bmatrix}
\end{array}
$$

The characters of the representation provided by these transformation matrices are the sums of the diagonal elements. If we write χ to represent the characters, we have

	E	C_2	σ_v	σ_v'
χ	2	0	2	0

According to the deduction of the preceding section these are also the characters that would have been obtained if we had used molecular orbitals as a basis. But the characters for each molecular orbital must be drawn from those for the irreducible representations of the point group C_{2v} shown in Table 12-3 or Appendix C. By inspection you can see that we can write

$$\chi = \chi_{A_1} + \chi_{B_1} \tag{12-5}$$

Thus we have discovered that the molecular orbitals, the eigenfunctions for the

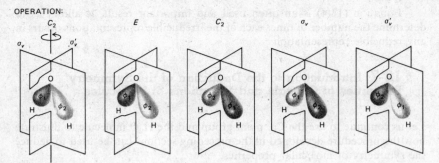

FIGURE 12-12 The effect of the symmetry operations of the C_{2v} point group on the bond orbitals of the H_2O molecule.

H_2O molecule that are constructed from orbitals along the individual bonds, must be of the symmetry types A_1 and B_1.

The transformation matrices do not have to be written to obtain the characters 2, 0, 2, 0 shown above. A diagonal element occurs only if the bond is turned into itself or in other cases turned into the opposite of itself. Bonds (or vectors or orbitals) shifted from one to another equivalent atom do not generate any diagonal elements. Thus, with Fig. 12-12, for each symmetry operation we write a contribution of $+1$ for each unshifted bond orbital. The result 2, 0, 2, 0 for the characters of the E, C_2, σ_v, and σ'_v operations can be written down immediately. (In this simple H_2O bond example you can easily go one more step and describe the bond-orbital combinations that transform as each of the irreducible representations A_1 and B_1. The combination $\phi_1 + \phi_2$ transform as A_1, and the combination $\phi_1 - \phi_2$ transforms as B_1.)

Now let us see whether we can classify the overall translational and rotational motions and the vibrational motions of the H_2O molecule according to symmetry. We begin as in the analysis of the number of degrees of freedom in Sec. 3-1 by treating these motions in terms of the three displacement coordinates on each atom, as shown in Fig. 12-13. These $3n$ vectors provide a basis on which the symmetry operation of the C_{2v} group, to which the H_2O molecule belongs, can act.

We need not work out the 9×9 transformation matrices that describe the effect of E, C_2, σ_v, and σ'_v on the nine displacement vectors. We need only deduce the characters, i.e., the sum of the diagonal elements, of these matrices.

An entry occurs along the diagonal of a transformation matrix only for an atom that does not exchange places with another atom as a result of the symmetry operation. Thus for each symmetry operation we need deal only with the displacement vectors on the atoms that stay put. The effect of each symmetry operation will be to leave each of these vectors unchanged or to reverse them. In the former case a $+1$ will be contributed to the diagonal terms; in the

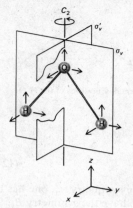

FIGURE 12-13
The nine atomic displacement coordinates and the symmetry elements of the H_2O molecule.

latter case a -1 will be contributed. Inspection of the effect of the symmetry operations on the nine displacement vectors that provide a basis for the translations, rotations, and vibrations of the molecule gives the result

	E	C_2	σ_v	σ_v'
χ	9	-1	3	1

Now, in principle, a change in coordinates could be found such that the nine displacement coordinates of Fig. 12-13 would combine to give coordinates for the three translational motions and the three rotational motions of the molecule as a whole and the three vibrational motions of the atoms of the molecule. (Such a transformation was worked through for diatomic molecules in Sec. 3-1.)

The transformation matrices that describe the effects of the symmetry operations on these new displacement sets would be different from those describing the effects on the displacement vectors of Fig. 12-13. But the sum of the diagonal elements of these transformation matrices would be unaffected. Thus we can treat the set of numbers 9, -1, 3, 1 as being the characters for the three translational, three rotational, and three vibrational motions.

The number of times a particular irreducible representation is contained in the reducible representation can be calculated by applying Eq. (12-4):

$$a_{A_1} = \tfrac{1}{4}[1(9) + (1)(-1) + (1)(3) + (1)(1)] = 3$$
$$a_{A_2} = \tfrac{1}{4}[1(9) + (1)(-1) + (-1)(3) + (-1)(1)] = 1$$
$$a_{B_1} = \tfrac{1}{4}[1(9) + (-1)(-1) + (1)(3) + (-1)(1)] = 3$$
$$a_{B_2} = \tfrac{1}{4}[1(9) + (-1)(-1) + (-1)(3) + (1)(1)] = 2$$

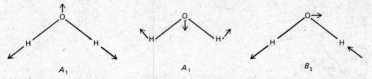

FIGURE 12-14 The symmetry of the three natural, or normal, vibrations of the H_2O molecule.

We can express this result by writing

$$\chi = 3\chi_{A_1} + \chi_{A_2} + 3\chi_{B_1} + 2\chi_{B_2} \tag{12-6}$$

Thus of the nine molecular motions, three have the symmetry A_1, one has the symmetry A_2, three have the symmetry B_1, and two have the symmetry B_2. We have already showed (Sec. 12-3) that the translational motions have the symmetries A_1, B_1, and B_2. We also saw that rotations have the symmetries A_2, B_1, and B_2. It follows from these results and Eq. (12-6) that

$$\chi_{\text{vib}} = 2\chi_{A_1} + \chi_{B_1} \tag{12-7}$$

Of the three vibrations of the water molecule two must be of the totally symmetric A_1 symmetry type, and one must be of the antisymmetric B_1 type.

The above treatment leads to important and not initially obvious results about the nature of the vibrations of the molecule. Vibrations with these symmetries are shown in Fig. 12-14.

The diagonal terms, which lead to values for the characters of the reducible representations, were easily found in the two examples of this section. Often, as in the second example, we look at the effect on the three cartesian vectors on each unshifted atom. In the symmetry operations of the C_{2v} group these vectors are either unchanged or reversed, and the corresponding transformation matrices have $+1$ or -1 diagonal entries.

Other point groups include operations which produce a mixing of the x, y, and z vectors of unshifted atoms. An example is provided by a rotation of $\frac{1}{3}$

TABLE 12-5 Contributions to the Character Made by the Three Cartesian Coordinates on an Unshifted Atom

Operation	Character contribution	Operation	Character contribution
E	3	C_4	1
σ	1	S_3	-2
i	-3	S_4	-1
C_2	-1	S_6	0
C_3	0		

revolution, one of the operations of the C_{3v} group. The transformation matrices can then be worked out and the sum of the diagonal elements can be obtained. Alternatively, the recipes of Table 12-5 can be used. You can recognize or easily verify some of the values listed there.

12-8 The Effect of a Symmetric Field on an Atom or Ion

In Chap. 11 atoms were studied to illustrate how quantum mechanics can be applied to systems of chemical interest. In a similar way, atoms and atomic ions can be used to illustrate a chemically important use of symmetry and group theory.

Let us see how symmetry and group theory help us describe an atom or ion that is subjected to fields of various symmetries. Such fields are exerted by surrounding ions or molecules. Studies of such effects on ions in crystals were made by Hans Bethe in 1929. The term *crystal field,* which stems from Bethe's work, is now usually applied to an approach used in studies of transition-metal ions surrounded by *ligand* molecules or ions. In the crystal-field approach the effect of the ligands is that of producing at the central ion a field with a symmetry that depends on the structural arrangement of the ligands about the ion.

Let us first describe the effect of a crystal field on orbitals, i.e., on the descriptions we use for individual electrons. Then, as in the free-atom systems of Sec. 11-10, we shall use these descriptions to develop atomic state terms. To be specific we consider the effect of an octahedral field on the atomic orbitals of a central atom. Such a field, with symmetry corresponding to the O_h point group, occurs in many coordination compounds of the transition metals. The orbitals of a free atom are characterized, in part, by the angular properties of the wave function. We recognize, for example for a given value of n, one s orbital, three p orbitals, and five d orbitals. These (and higher orbitals if necessary) provide a basis for the construction or classification of orbitals that conform to the symmetry of the imposed octahedral field.

An s orbital is spherically symmetric and thus will transform according to the totally symmetric representation for the symmetry of the imposed field. For an O_h field this symmetry species has the designation A_{1g}. Thus when an atom is subjected to an octahedral field, the s orbitals can be given the symmetry designation a_{1g}.

The behavior of p orbitals in a symmetric field can be recognized from their relation to x, y, and z coordinates, as pointed out in Table 11-5. The location of these cartesian coordinates alongside the characters of the O_h table shows that the set of p orbitals remains triply degenerate in a field of O_h symmetry. The symmetry species of this set is T_{1u}.

The d orbitals, as is shown in Table 11-5, transform according to the squares and cross terms of the x, y, and z coordinates. The location of these terms in the O_h character table shows that in a field of O_h symmetry the five d

**TABLE 12-6 Symmetry Properties
of Atomic Orbitals, or Atomic
States, in an Octahedral Field,
Point Group O_h**

$$s \rightarrow a_1$$
$$p \rightarrow t_1$$
$$d \rightarrow e + t_2$$
$$f \rightarrow a_2 + t_1 + t_2$$
$$g \rightarrow a_1 + e + t_1 + t_2$$
$$h \rightarrow e + 2t_1 + t_2$$

orbitals break up into two sets. One set $d_{x^2-y^2}$ and $d_{2z-x^2-y^2}$, transforms as E_g; the other set, d_{xy}, d_{xz}, and d_{yz}, transforms as T_{2g}.

Although corresponding descriptions for f and g orbitals have not been given, they can be worked out. The results are included in the list of orbital symmetries for the O_h group in Table 12-6.

Now consider the effect of the imposition of a field of O_h symmetry on the orbitals of an atom. As the field becomes important, the sets of orbitals of each symmetry type will take on a particular energy. One effect is the splitting of the initially fivefold-degenerate d-orbital set into a set of three t_{2g} and two e_g orbitals.

Symmetry arguments alone do not indicate the relative energies of the sets of symmetry orbitals that stem from a given set of free-atom orbitals. However, qualitative arguments can be made for fields of particular symmetries. Suppose, for example, that an ion is surrounded by a set of six electron-rich sites located along the cartesian coordinates to form an octahedral field. An electron in an e_g orbital will, as Fig. 12-15 shows, be "pointed" at these electron-repelling sites, whereas one in a t_{2g} orbital will avoid these sites. We expect the e_g orbitals to be at a higher energy than the t_{2g} orbitals.

Now let us consider the *electron states* that arise when a crystal field is applied to a free ion. We consider first an ion with closed shells and a single d valence electron. The Ti^{3+} ion is an example. The electron configuration of the free ion is described as [inner shells]d^1. The atomic state is described as ^2D.

In a strong octahedral field the electron will be in the lower-energy t_{2g} orbital, producing a $^2T_{2g}$ state, or a higher-energy e_g orbital, producing a higher-energy ^2E_g state. A schematic *correlation diagram* showing the development of the symmetry-based states from the free-atom states is shown in Fig. 12-16.

The energy details of a diagram like that of Fig. 12-16 can be obtained only by quantum-mechanical calculations or on an empirical basis from spectral studies. In aqueous solution the Ti^{3+} ion is present as the octahedral $[Ti(H_2O)_6]^{3+}$ ion. It shows a weak absorption in the visible region with a maximum at about $20,400 \ cm^{-1}$. This absorption can be attributed to the transition from the $^2T_{2g}$ ground state to the excited ^2E_g state. Thus, for the

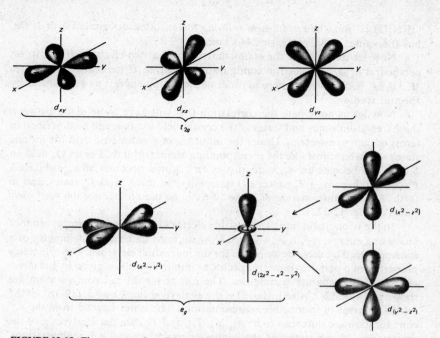

FIGURE 12-15 The concentration of the $t_{2g}d$ orbitals away from the coordinate axes, along which the ligands of an octahedral species are assumed to lie, and the concentration of the e_g orbitals along these directions.

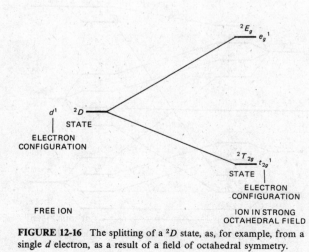

FIGURE 12-16 The splitting of a ^2D state, as, for example, from a single d electron, as a result of a field of octahedral symmetry.

$[Ti(H_2O)_6]^{3+}$ ion, the *crystal-field splitting factor,* often designated Δ or $10Dq$, has the value $20,400$ cm^{-1}, or 244 kJ mol^{-1}.

Now let us consider the states that arise in a two-electron d^2 ion in an octahedral field. The electron configuration of a free d^2 ion leads to the states ^3F, ^1D, ^3P, ^1G, ^1S, written here in order of increasing energy, as determined by spectral studies.

Now let us anticipate the correlation that will have to be made between these free-atom states and states of the crystal-field ion that will be described in terms of their symmetries. Under the influence of a symmetric field the atomic states will behave just like the corresponding atomic orbitals. For an $\mathbf{O}_h$ field an S state will become an A_{1g} state, just as an s orbital becomes an a_{1g} orbital. A P state will become a T_{1u} state, a D state will split into E_g and T_{2g} states, and so forth. Thus the information of Table 12-6 can be used to deduce the *weak-field* states of Fig. 12-17.

In the strong-field limit, the possible electron configurations are, in order of increasing energy, t_{2g}^2, $t_{2g}e_g$, and e_g^2. Now we must find the net symmetry of a state produced by these descriptions for the individual electrons. The symmetry properties of a pair of symmetry species, as implied by t_{2g}^2, is given by the *direct product* of the separate symmetries. The results for the t_{2g}^2 configuration are shown in Table 12-7. Also included is the analysis, guided by Eq. (12-18), of the results in terms of irreducible representations. The states formed from the t_{2g}^2 configuration are thus seen to be A_{1g}, E_g, T_{1g}, and T_{2g}. Similar analyses give the symmetries of the states of the higher-energy $t_{2g}e_g$ and e_g^2 configurations.

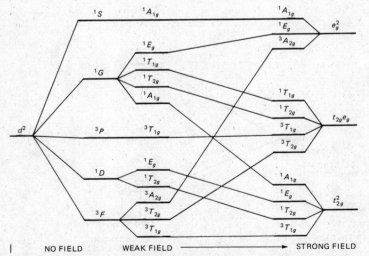

FIGURE 12-17 The splitting of the states of a d^2 configuration as a result of an octahedral field.

TABLE 12-7 Illustration of the Determination of the Electronic States Arising from the Configuration $(t_{2g})^2$

O_h	E	$8C_3$	$6C_2$	$6C_4$	$3C_4{}^2$	i	$6S_4$	$8S_6$	$3\sigma_h$	$6\sigma_d$
Formation of direct product:										
$\chi_{T_{2g}}$	3	0	1	−1	−1	3	−1	0	−1	1
$\chi_{T_{2g}} \times \chi_{T_{2g}}$	9	0	1	1	1	9	1	0	1	1
Analysis in terms of characters of irreducible representations:										
$\chi_{A_{1g}}$	1	1	1	1	1	1	1	1	1	1
χ_{E_g}	2	−1	0	0	2	2	0	−1	2	0
$\chi_{T_{1g}}$	3	0	−1	1	−1	3	1	0	−1	−1
$\chi_{T_{2g}}$	3	0	1	−1	−1	3	−1	0	−1	1
Total	9	0	1	1	1	9	1	0	1	1

Considerations of electron spins would give the multiplicities shown in the results for the three different electron configurations to the right of Fig. 12-17.

Finally, in the construction of Fig. 12-17, correlation lines can be drawn connecting states of the same symmetry and the same multiplicity. We thus have a complete display of the states of a d^2 atom or ion from the limit of a free atom or ion to one exposed to a strong octahedral field. Such a diagram provides the basis for organizing spectral studies or quantum-mechanical studies that deal with the energies of the states of a d^2 atom or ion in an octahedral field.

PROBLEMS

12-1. (a) Label the hydrogen atoms as H_a and H_b in the water molecule of Fig. 12-1 and describe where H_a ends up, i.e., at H_a or at H_b, as a result of each of the four symmetry operations E, C_2, σ_v, and σ_v'. (b) What happens to the oxygen atom as a result of each of these symmetry operations?

12-2. List at least one additional molecule that has the symmetries of each point group of Table 12-2.

12-3. To what point groups do the following molecules belong: (a) PCl_3 (pyramidal), (b) S_2Cl_2 (nonplanar), (c) $C_{10}H_8$, naphthalene, (d) N_2, (e) H_2CO, formaldehyde, (f) CH_2FCl, (g) $CO_3{}^{2-}$?

12-4. The S_8 molecule is said to have $\mathbf{D}_{4d}$ symmetry. Make a diagram of the molecule indicating some of its symmetry elements.

12-5. The molecule SF_5Cl has approximately the same shape as an SF_6 molecule. What is the point group of SF_5Cl?

12-6. Carry out the matrix multiplications

(a) $\begin{bmatrix} 1 & 0 & 0 \\ 0 & -1 & 0 \\ 0 & 0 & 1 \end{bmatrix} \begin{bmatrix} 1 \\ -1 \\ -1 \end{bmatrix}$
(b) $\begin{bmatrix} 2 & 3 \\ 1 & 4 \end{bmatrix} \begin{bmatrix} 1 & 2 \\ 3 & 4 \end{bmatrix}$

(c) $\begin{bmatrix} 1 & 0 & 2 \end{bmatrix} \begin{bmatrix} 1 & 0 & 0 \\ 0 & -1 & 0 \\ 0 & 0 & 1 \end{bmatrix}$
(d) $\begin{bmatrix} a & 0 & 0 \\ 0 & b & 0 \\ 0 & 0 & c \end{bmatrix} \begin{bmatrix} x \\ y \\ z \end{bmatrix}$

(e) $\begin{bmatrix} 1 & -1 & 0 \\ -1 & 1 & 0 \\ 0 & 0 & 2 \end{bmatrix} \begin{bmatrix} x \\ y \\ z \end{bmatrix}$

12-7. How many symmetry operations and how many classes of symmetry operations are there in (a) the C_{2v} point group and (b) the C_{3v} point group?

12-8. Refer to the character tables of Appendix C and state the number of symmetry operations and the number of classes of symmetry operations in (a) the point group D_{2h}, which describes the symmetry, for example, of the ethylene molecule; (b) the tetrahedral point group T_d, which describes the symmetry, for example, of methane; and (c) the octahedral point group O_h which describes the symmetry, for example, of SF_6 and octahedral transition-metal complexes.

12-9. What is the relation between the number of symmetry species and the number of classes of symmetry operations?

12-10. Why is the character under the identity operation always $+1$ for A or B symmetry species, $+2$ for doubly degenerate E symmetry species, and $+3$ for triply degenerate T (sometimes called F) symmetry species?

12-11. Show for any three pairs of symmetry elements of the C_{3v} point group that carrying out the operation corresponding to one of these symmetry elements and then the other is equivalent to the operation associated with a symmetry element of the group. Include in at least one of your pairs both a rotation and a reflection. You can use the x, y, z arrows as in the C_{2v} example of Fig. 12-15 as a basis on which the operations can act.

12-12. For the point group C_{3v} is it true, as it was for the C_{2v} point group, that each symmetry operation is its own reverse? Give examples.

12-13. In the C_{2v} group, successive operations $\sigma_v \sigma_v'$ are equivalent to C_2. Show that all the symmetry species of Table 12-3 properly represent this combination of symmetry operations.

12-14. Repeat Prob. 12-13 for any other two combinations of symmetry operations.

12-15. The matrices of the doubly degenerate representation of the C_{3v} group are given in Table 12-4. Show that these matrices properly represent the fact that (a) successive operations by C_3 are equivalent to the operation $C_3{}^2$, (b) that operation by C_3 and then by $C_3{}^2$, or vice versa, corresponds to the identity operation, (c) that successive reflections through any of the planes of symmetry correspond to the identity operation.

12-16. The character table for the tetrahedral T_d point group is given in Appendix C. (a) Verify that the characters of the symmetry species A_1 and A_2, A_1 and E, E and T_2 behave like the components of orthogonal vectors. (b) Verify that the characters of each of the symmetry species behave like the components of a vector in space with as many dimensions as there are symmetry operations in the group. (c) Verify that the sum of the squares of the characters for the identity symmetry element over all the representations equals the order of the group.

12-17. Repeat Prob. 12-16 for the O_h group, using any pairs of symmetry species to verify the orthogonality property.

12-18. The translational, rotational, and vibrational motion of a water molecule can be described on the basis of three cartesian coordinate vectors that describe the motion or position of each of the atoms. Suppose a column matrix $[x_H \ y_H \ z_H \ x_{H'} \ y_{H'} \ z_{H'} \ x_O \ y_O \ z_O]$ is constructed from these displacement vectors. The effect of the symmetry operations on these vectors is then given by the following transformation matrices.

$$E = \begin{bmatrix} 1 & 0 & 0 & 0 & 0 & 0 & 0 & 0 & 0 \\ 0 & 1 & 0 & 0 & 0 & 0 & 0 & 0 & 0 \\ 0 & 0 & 1 & 0 & 0 & 0 & 0 & 0 & 0 \\ 0 & 0 & 0 & 1 & 0 & 0 & 0 & 0 & 0 \\ 0 & 0 & 0 & 0 & 1 & 0 & 0 & 0 & 0 \\ 0 & 0 & 0 & 0 & 0 & 1 & 0 & 0 & 0 \\ 0 & 0 & 0 & 0 & 0 & 0 & 1 & 0 & 0 \\ 0 & 0 & 0 & 0 & 0 & 0 & 0 & 1 & 0 \\ 0 & 0 & 0 & 0 & 0 & 0 & 0 & 0 & 1 \end{bmatrix}$$

$$C_2 = \begin{bmatrix} 0 & 0 & 0 & -1 & 0 & 0 & 0 & 0 & 0 \\ 0 & 0 & 0 & 0 & -1 & 0 & 0 & 0 & 0 \\ 0 & 0 & 0 & 0 & 0 & 1 & 0 & 0 & 0 \\ -1 & 0 & 0 & 0 & 0 & 0 & 0 & 0 & 0 \\ 0 & -1 & 0 & 0 & 0 & 0 & 0 & 0 & 0 \\ 0 & 0 & 1 & 0 & 0 & 0 & 0 & 0 & 0 \\ 0 & 0 & 0 & 0 & 0 & 0 & -1 & 0 & 0 \\ 0 & 0 & 0 & 0 & 0 & 0 & 0 & -1 & 0 \\ 0 & 0 & 0 & 0 & 0 & 0 & 0 & 0 & 1 \end{bmatrix}$$

$$\sigma_v = \begin{bmatrix} -1 & 0 & 0 & 0 & 0 & 0 & 0 & 0 & 0 \\ 0 & 1 & 0 & 0 & 0 & 0 & 0 & 0 & 0 \\ 0 & 0 & 1 & 0 & 0 & 0 & 0 & 0 & 0 \\ 0 & 0 & 0 & -1 & 0 & 0 & 0 & 0 & 0 \\ 0 & 0 & 0 & 0 & 1 & 0 & 0 & 0 & 0 \\ 0 & 0 & 0 & 0 & 0 & 1 & 0 & 0 & 0 \\ 0 & 0 & 0 & 0 & 0 & 0 & -1 & 0 & 0 \\ 0 & 0 & 0 & 0 & 0 & 0 & 0 & 1 & 0 \\ 0 & 0 & 0 & 0 & 0 & 0 & 0 & 0 & 1 \end{bmatrix}$$

$$\sigma_v' = \begin{bmatrix} 0 & 0 & 0 & 1 & 0 & 0 & 0 & 0 & 0 \\ 0 & 0 & 0 & 0 & -1 & 0 & 0 & 0 & 0 \\ 0 & 0 & 0 & 0 & 0 & 1 & 0 & 0 & 0 \\ 1 & 0 & 0 & 0 & 0 & 0 & 0 & 0 & 0 \\ 0 & -1 & 0 & 0 & 0 & 0 & 0 & 0 & 0 \\ 0 & 0 & 1 & 0 & 0 & 0 & 0 & 0 & 0 \\ 0 & 0 & 0 & 0 & 0 & 0 & 1 & 0 & 0 \\ 0 & 0 & 0 & 0 & 0 & 0 & 0 & -1 & 0 \\ 0 & 0 & 0 & 0 & 0 & 0 & 0 & 0 & 1 \end{bmatrix}$$

(a) Make a diagram of a water molecule showing three atomic displacement vectors centered on each of the three atoms. (b) By drawing new vectors that are the result of the symmetry operations verify that these new vectors are given by the product of the transformation matrix and the column matrix $[x_H \ y_H \ z_H \ x_{H'} \ y_{H'} \ z_{H'} \ x_O \ y_O \ z_O]$. (Notice that the oxygen-atom vectors remain centered on the oxygen atom but that for C_2 and σ_v the hydrogen-atom vectors move to the other equivalent atom.) (c) What are the characters of the reducible matrices? (d) Use Eq. (12-4) and the character table for the C_{2v} group to find the irreducible representations that together have the same characters as the reducible representation.

12-19. Suppose an atom is placed in an environment that has tetrahedral symmetry. (a) What would be the characters of the reducible representation that describes the effect of the symmetry operations on the p_x, p_y, and p_z orbitals? (b) What would be the characters and the symbol for the symmetry species for an s orbital? (c) What would be the symmetry species for the d orbitals? (d) Show that your answer for the d orbitals accounts for the five orbitals that make up the d set.

12-20. Repeat Prob. 12-19 for an atom in an octahedral field.

12-21. Draw s orbitals, or blobs, at each of the three hydrogen atoms of ammonia. (a) What are the characters of the reducible representation that describes the effect of symmetry operations on these orbitals? (b) What irreducible representations together give the same characters? (c) What would be the symmetry types of eigenfunctions for the molecule that are constructed from these atomic s-type orbitals?

12-22. Repeat Prob. 12-21 including an s-type orbital on the nitrogen atom.

12-23. Verify that the electron configurations e_g^2 and $t_{2g}e_g$ of Fig. 12-17 give rise to the states indicated in that figure.

*12-24. Develop a correlation diagram like that of Fig. 12-17 for a d^2 configuration in a tetrahedral field. In such a field, inspection of the relation of the d orbitals to the location of electron-repelling ligands at tetrahedral sites suggests that the e_g orbitals will be at lower energy than the t_{2g} orbitals.

*12-25. Prepare a diagram like Fig. 12-16 to show the effect of a $\mathbf{D}_{4h}$ field on the states of an atom with a single outer d electron. ($\mathbf{D}_{4h}$ symmetry results if an octahedron is distorted along one of its fourfold axes.)

REFERENCES

HERMAN, M., and J. LEIVIN: Group Theory: From Common Objects to Molecules, *J. Chem. Educ.*, **54**:597 (1977).

The following books develop and extend the material of this chapter:

BISHOP, D. M.: "Group Theory and Chemistry," Oxford University Press, London, 1973.

COTTON, F. A.: "Chemical Applications of Group Theory," John Wiley & Sons, Inc., New York, 1963.

HALL, L. H.: "Group Theory and Symmetry in Chemistry," McGraw-Hill Book Company, New York, 1969.

JAFFE, H. H., and M. ORCHIN: "Symmetry in Chemistry," John Wiley & Sons, Inc., New York, 1965.

NUSSBAUM, A.: "Applied Group Theory for Chemists, Physicists, and Engineers," Prentice-Hall, Inc., Englewood Cliffs, N.J., 1971.

ORCHIN, M., and H. H. JAFFE: "Symmetry, Orbitals, and Spectra (S.O.S.)," Wiley-Interscience, New York, 1971.

Examples of specialized applications of group theory:

HSU, CHAO-YANG, and M. ORCHIN: Ligand Group Orbitals and Normal Molecular Vibrations: Symmetry Simplifications, *J. Chem. Educ.*, **51**:725 (1974).

FORD, D. I.: Molecular Term Symbols by Group Theory, *J. Chem. Educ.*, **49**:336 (1972).

PEARSON, R. G.: "Symmetry Rules for Chemical Reactions: Orbital Topology and Elementary Processes," John Wiley & Sons, Inc., New York, 1976.

13 THE THEORY OF CHEMICAL BONDING

An understanding of atomic structure and of the methods of wave mechanics provides the means for tackling one of the fundamental questions of chemistry: What binds atoms together into molecules? This question has existed since the beginnings of chemistry, and a clear answer would be a culmination of much of the theoretical work of chemistry.

The quantum-mechanical approach to covalent bonding will be introduced by a consideration (except for the evaluation of some integrals) of the bonding in the hydrogen-molecule ion and the hydrogen molecule. From these very simple systems it will be possible to extend the theory of chemical bonding in a semiquantitative and semiempirical way. It is this extension which has become a basic and necessary part of the approaches and language in all branches of chemistry.

13-1 The Hydrogen-Molecule Ion

The simplest, though certainly not the most familiar, example of a covalent chemical bond is provided by the H_2^+ ion. Some properties of this ion, consisting of two protons held together by a single electron, can be deduced from spectroscopic observations of highly excited H_2 molecules. The equilibrium bond length of this molecule ion and the variation of its potential energy with internuclear distance derived from such spectroscopic measurements and from refined theoretical calculations are illustrated by the dashed curve in the potential-energy diagram of Fig. 13-1. Now we must see whether we can reach some understanding of the source of the binding energy of this system. A number of approaches are available; the one to be used here is chosen because it leads most naturally into the methods used for other molecules.

We can begin by making use of our knowledge that for an electron bound to a proton the lowest-energy wave function is designated as a $1s$ orbital. If A designates one of the two nuclei with which we now deal, this function, as shown in Tables 11-3 and 11-4, will have the form

$$1s_A = \frac{1}{\sqrt{\pi}} \left(\frac{1}{a_0} \right)^{3/2} e^{-r_A/a_0} \tag{13-1}$$

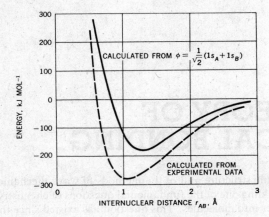

FIGURE 13-1
Calculated and experimental potential-energy curves for the hydrogen-molecule ion.

The corresponding wave function centered on nucleus B will be

$$1s_B = \frac{1}{\sqrt{\pi}} \left(\frac{1}{a_0}\right)^{3/2} e^{-r_B/a_0} \tag{13-2}$$

A suitable trial function for the behavior of an electron associated with two nuclei, as represented in Fig. 13-2, can be based on these two mathematical functions. We can combine the descriptions for the electron in the two separate nuclei to give an expression that may be a satisfactory approximation for the system involving both nuclei and the one electron. A linear combination, as will be checked, turns out to give an expression of the right form. We can write the trial function

$$\phi = \frac{1}{\sqrt{2}} (1s_A + 1s_B) \tag{13-3}$$

where the factor $1/\sqrt{2}$ normalizes the function to the extent that for large separations between nucleus A and nucleus B the total probability of the system containing one electron is unity.

To proceed to the use of Eq. (11-54) to calculate an energy corresponding to the trial function, we must first write down the hamiltonian operator $\mathcal{H}$. In view of the potential-energy interactions, which can be recognized in Fig. 13-2, and leaving the internuclear repulsion to be included later, $\mathcal{H}$ can be written

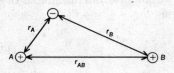

FIGURE 13-2
Coordinates of the two electrons of the hydrogen-molecule ion.

$$\mathcal{H} = -\frac{h^2}{8\pi^2 m}\nabla^2 - \frac{e^2}{4\pi\epsilon_0 r_A} - \frac{e^2}{4\pi\epsilon_0 r_B} \tag{13-4}$$

Now the variation-method energy can be calculated from

$$\epsilon = \frac{\int \phi^* \mathcal{H}\phi \, d\tau}{\int \phi^2 \, d\tau}$$

$$= \frac{\frac{1}{2}\int(1s_A + 1s_B)\left(-\dfrac{h^2}{8\pi^2 m}\nabla^2 - \dfrac{e^2}{4\pi\epsilon_0 r_A} - \dfrac{e^2}{4\pi\epsilon_0 r_B}\right)(1s_A + 1s_B)\, d\tau}{\frac{1}{2}\int(1s_A + 1s_B)^2 \, d\tau}$$

The equivalence of $1s_A$ and $1s_B$ lets us pair up and reduce the total number of terms. Recognizing that

$$\epsilon_H = \int 1s_A\left(-\frac{h^2}{8\pi^2 m}\nabla^2 - \frac{e^2}{4\pi\epsilon_0 r_A}\right)1s_A\, d\tau$$

we obtain the result

$$\epsilon = \frac{\epsilon_H + \displaystyle\int 1s_A\left(-\dfrac{e^2}{4\pi\epsilon_0 r_B}\right)1s_A\, d\tau + \int 1s_A\left(-\dfrac{h^2}{8\pi^2 m}\nabla^2 - \dfrac{e^2}{4\pi\epsilon_0 r_A}\right)1s_B\, d\tau}{1 + \displaystyle\int 1s_A\, 1s_B\, d\tau}$$

$$\tag{13-5}$$

The evaluation of the remaining integrals presents some difficulties, which are most severe in the case of the two-center type of integrals, e.g., such as the second one in the numerator and that in the denominator of Eq. (13-5). These integrals involve functions measured from both nucleus A and nucleus B. Such integrals take on a nonzero value only because the $1s_A$ and $1s_B$ functions have finite values in the same regions, particularly in the region between the nuclei. We say that the functions *overlap*. Without this overlap, Eq. (13-5) would consist of only the first two terms, which would give the energy of a hydrogen atom modified by the effect of an additional nearby proton.

When the internuclear repulsion $e^2/4\pi\epsilon_0 r_{AB}$ is subtracted from the energy obtained by evaluation of the integrals of Eq. (13-5), a potential-energy curve for the hydrogen-molecule ion is found that does have a minimum. This minimum occurs at an internuclear distance of 1.32×10^{-10} m, or 1.32 Å, and has a depth of 171 kJ mol^{-1}, or 1.77 eV. Comparison with the experimental curve of Fig. 13-1 shows that although the approach has some success, it is not able to provide energies in good agreement with the experimental potential-energy curve.

The variation approach can now be followed to see whether the simple approximate function of Eq. (13-3) can be varied so that it approximates the behavior of the electron of the H_2^+ system more closely. Any changes that accomplish this will lead to better agreement with the observed equilibrium bond length and bond energy. The simplest procedure consists in treating the orbital exponent corresponding to the nuclear charge as a variable parameter. This parameter can be adjusted at each internuclear distance to give the lowest possible energy. With this procedure the greatest binding energy occurs at an internuclear distance of 1.06 $\times$ 10^{-10} m, at which distance the effective nuclear charge is 1.23. The dissociation energy is 217 kJ mol^{-1}, or 2.25 eV. Substantial improvement has occurred.

A further type of modification that is important in many modern calculations depends on the recognition that the atomic orbitals used in the trial function need not be restricted to those of lowest energy for the atoms; i.e., the trial function need not be based on $1s$ functions. In principle one can add in contributions from the complete set of atomic orbitals, relying on the variation theorem to decide how much of a contribution leads to an improved wave function. The best wave function and the observed dissociation energy can then be approached as closely as computational facilities permit.

We have seen now that the simplest covalently bound system can be treated by an approximate method, making use of trial functions that are linear combinations of atomic orbitals (LCAO). Although in its simplest form this LCAO method leads to results that are in rather poor agreement with the observed binding energy, methods are available for improving the wave function. Thus satisfactory values for the properties of molecules are often obtained, even if the binding energy is in relatively poor agreement with the experimentally obtained value.

13-2 The Hydrogen Molecule: The Electron-Pair Bond

The procedure of Sec. 13-1 can be extended to describe how two electrons are accommodated between the bonded atoms, as in the simplest molecular example, H_2. We can easily describe the system when the two nuclei are far apart. It then consists of two hydrogen atoms. The correct wave function, as you can verify by substituting in Eq. (11-54), is

$$\phi = 1s_A(1)1s_B(2) \tag{13-6}$$

This function, which places electron 1 on nucleus A and electron 2 on nucleus B, can be used as a trial function at internuclear distances where the system is described as an H_2 molecule rather than two H atoms. The calculated binding energies for the trial function of Eq. (13-6) are shown in Fig. 13-3. You see that $1s_A(1)1s_B(2)$ is a poor approximation to the correct description for the system. The principal fault, as W. Heitler and F. London recognized, is that since electrons are indistinguishable particles, different roles cannot be ascribed to the two electrons. This situation has already been dealt with in the case of the

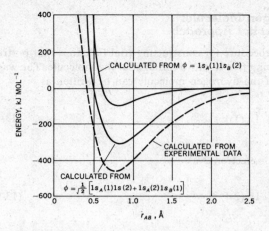

FIGURE 13-3
The binding energy of the H_2 molecule based on the approximate wave functions.

helium atom in Sec. 11-12. The Heitler-London approximation to the wave function for the electrons of the hydrogen molecule is

$$\phi = \frac{1}{\sqrt{2}}[1s_A(1)1s_B(2) + 1s_A(2)1s_B(1)] \qquad (13\text{-}7)$$

where $1/\sqrt{2}$ is a factor that ensures that the wave function is normalized at infinite r_{AB}.

You should note that, as in the study of the helium atom Sec. 11-12, it is acceptable to label electrons in the construction of a trial wave function. The resulting function must, however, attribute identical roles to each of the electrons of the system.

When this trial function is used in Eq. (11-54) and the repulsion of the nuclei is allowed for, the potential minimum, as shown in Fig. 13-3, is found to be 300 kJ mol^{-1} below that of the independent hydrogen atoms. Furthermore, this minimum occurs at an internuclear distance of 0.80 Å. Comparison of these results with the corresponding experimental values of 458 kJ mol^{-1} and 0.740 Å shows that the relatively simple Heitler-London wave function has been successful in accounting for much of the observed bonding.

In this approach the chemical bond can be largely attributed to the fact that the electrons are not confined to one or the other atoms of the bond, as they are in the less satisfactory function $1s_A(1)1s_B(2)$, but rather, as is said, can *exchange*.

As in the treatment of the helium atom, functions for singlet and triplet states are found when electron spins and the Pauli exclusion principle are recognized. The function of Eq. (13-7), together with a spin function that changes sign on electron interchange, is the bonding singlet-state function. A corresponding, antibonding triplet-state function is obtained when a minus sign is used in the orbital part of the orbit-spin function.

13-3 The Hydrogen Molecule: The Molecular-Orbital Approach

There is an alternative procedure for constructing trial functions that portray the pair of electrons as being free to move throughout the molecule. The wave function for electron 1 of the hydrogen molecule can be written as

$$\phi(1) = \frac{1}{\sqrt{2}}[1s_A(1) + 1s_B(1)] \tag{13-8}$$

and the wave function for electron 2 as

$$\phi(2) = \frac{1}{\sqrt{2}}[1s_A(2) + 1s_B(2)] \tag{13-9}$$

The wave function for the pair of electrons in the molecule is then

$$
\begin{aligned}
\phi &= \phi(1)\phi(2) \\
&= \tfrac{1}{2}[1s_A(1) + 1s_B(1)][1s_A(2) + 1s_B(2)] \\
&= \tfrac{1}{2}[1s_A(1)1s_A(2) + 1s_B(1)1s_B(2)] \\
&\quad + \tfrac{1}{2}[1s_A(1)1s_B(2) + 1s_A(2)1s_B(1)]
\end{aligned}
\tag{13-10}
$$

The terms have been collected in the expanded form to show the comparison with the Heitler-London function dealt with in the preceding section. The final two terms are just those used by the Heitler-London function. The first two represent the possibility of both electrons' being on the same atom at the same time. Although it seems reasonable that such configurations should be allowed for, further calculation shows that this approach, in giving them equal importance with Heitler-London terms, rather overdoes it.

This is particularly clear in the limit as r_{AB} approaches infinity. Then the "ionic" terms, which give a probability of both electrons' being on the same nucleus, should not occur in the description of the system. A better approximation, of course, could be obtained by inserting variable coefficients before the factors of Eq. (13-10) and using the variation method to evaluate the relative importance of the two terms in the total wave function at each internuclear distance.

In the molecular-orbital procedure orbitals are formed that can be filled (subject to some important restrictions treated in Sec. 13-5) with the available electrons of the system. Thus, for H_2^+, one electron occupies the $1s_A + 1s_B$ molecular orbital, whereas for H_2, two electrons are placed in this orbital.

In some circumstances it is important to have a more complete set of molecular orbitals. Molecular orbitals can be written with a subtraction between the two atomic orbitals. Thus one can write

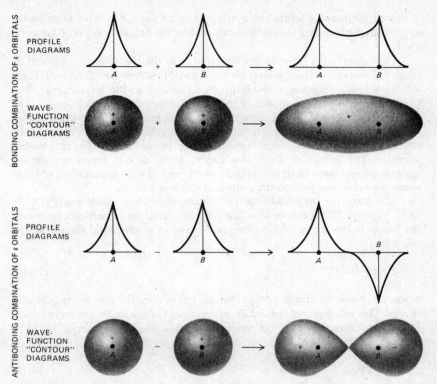

FIGURE 13-4 Diagrams of the low-energy bonding orbital and the high-energy antibonding orbital that can be constructed from overlapping atomic *s* orbitals.

$$\phi = \frac{1}{\sqrt{2}}(1s_A - 1s_B) \tag{13-11}$$

and can use this orbital expression in the variation method to obtain the energy of the system. One finds that the minus sign leads to an *antibonding* orbital. At all finite internuclear distances the energy of the system, H_2 for example, is calculated as greater than that for two separate hydrogen atoms if such orbitals are used. We shall see later that such antibonding orbitals play an important role in some aspects of chemical-bond theory. Here, however, we shall go no farther than Fig. 13-4, which suggests the shapes of the bonding and antibonding molecular orbitals that could be constructed from $1s$ functions.

13-4 The Nature of Chemical Bonds: The Virial Theorem

You have now seen the mechanics by which the bond energy and the distribution of the electrons in a covalent bond can be calculated. Such calculations lead to the introduction of terms like overlap and exchange, but these describe the approximate procedure that is used rather than the nature or basis of the bond itself.

The terms in the Schrödinger equation or in the Hamiltonian operator $\mathcal{H}$ suggest, however, that no matter how the wave functions are described, there will be kinetic- and potential-energy contributions to the total energy. The kinetic energy is a consequence of the wave nature of the particle, and as the one-dimensional square-well example showed, the kinetic energy corresponding to a given wave function is greater the smaller the region of available space. The potential energy arises from the coulombic interactions between charged particles. The nature of these two energy terms is not dependent on the approximations used in describing the bond, and as a result, analysis of these terms provides insight into the nature of the bond itself.

One basis for unscrambling the contributions to the total energy is the *virial theorem*. The theorem says that for any collection of particles for which the forces follow an inverse-square force law, as electrostatic forces do, the relation

$$2(\text{KE}) = -U \tag{13-12}$$

holds; i.e., twice the kinetic energy is equal but of opposite sign to the potential energy. This relation was noticed in the treatment of the hydrogen atom in Sec. 11-2. The total energy of the collection of particles, which, for example, could be the two protons and the one or two electrons of the H_2^+ or H_2 species, is

$$\epsilon = \text{KE} + U \tag{13-13}$$

which, with $2(\text{KE}) = -U$, becomes

$$\epsilon = \tfrac{1}{2}U$$

or

$$\epsilon = -\text{KE} \tag{13-14}$$

These remarkable and simple relations can be applied immediately to the equilibrium condition of an atom or of a molecule. For H_2, for example, the net value of ϵ is -458 kJ mol^{-1}, as illustrated in Fig. 13-3. Thus, at this equilibrium position $(\text{KE})_{H_2} = +458$ kJ mol^{-1} and $U_{H_2} = -916$ kJ mol^{-1}, both relative to two hydrogen atoms. We see that the bond energy in H_2 results from the very large decrease in potential energy. This effect more than compensates for the increase in kinetic energy that results from the confinement of the electrons to these relatively small regions. Similar insights can be gained by applying the virial theorem to other systems in their equilibrium configuration.

Now let us see how we can interpret the energy of a chemical bond at internuclear separations other than that for the minimum in the binding-energy curve. Again H_2 will serve as an example. Consider a coordinate system centered on one atom of an H_2 molecule. The second atom will be at some distance r, the internuclear separation. For this distance to be other than the equilibrium one, some external force must act, and in acting, it contributes an additional potential-energy term to the molecule. The force that must be exerted is just the derivative of the total energy with respect to internuclear distance; i.e., it is the slope of the experimentally based curve such as that of Fig. 13-3. The potential energy corresponding to this force is just $r\, d\epsilon/dr$, and thus the virial theorem becomes

$$2(\text{KE}) = -U - r\frac{d\epsilon}{dr} \tag{13-15}$$

The kinetic- and potential-energy contributions to the total energy ϵ are now deduced from $\epsilon = \text{KE} + U$ and Eq. (13-15) as

$$\text{KE} = -\epsilon - r\frac{d\epsilon}{dr} \tag{13-16}$$

and

$$U = 2\epsilon + r\frac{d\epsilon}{dr} \tag{13-17}$$

Since experimental ϵ versus r curves like that of Fig. 13-3 can be deduced, as will be shown in Chap. 14, the derivative terms can be evaluated. Thus KE-versus-r and U-versus-r curves can be constructed. Examples are shown for H_2 in Fig. 13-5. Now you see that as the bond begins to form at relatively large internuclear distances, it is the kinetic energy that contributes to the binding, a result of the somewhat greater region in which the electrons can move. At this stage additional electron-electron and proton-proton repulsions work to oppose the bonding. Only at shorter internuclear distances does the reverse occur.

13-5 Bonding in Homonuclear Diatomic Molecules

The general ideas that have been developed with regard to the bonding in the $H_2{}^+$ molecule ion and the H_2 molecule can be extended to other homonuclear diatomic molecules. To do this, we must first expand our investigation of linear combinations of the orbitals of the two atoms that will give orbitals for the molecule. In the jargon of quantum mechanics, we want to use the MO-LCAO method, i.e., molecular orbitals approximated by linear combinations of atomic orbitals. Once these orbitals that provide approximate descriptions of the

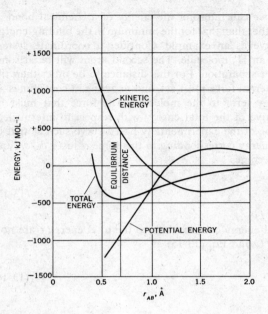

FIGURE 13-5
Average kinetic, potential, and total energies for H_2 as a function of internuclear distance. The difference between the value for the molecule and that for the separated atoms is given for each energy. (*From K. S. Pitzer, "Quantum Chemistry," Prentice-Hall, Inc., Englewood Cliffs, N.J., 1953.*)

behavic. of the electrons in the molecule are constructed, electrons can be assigned to the orbitals in a way that is consistent with the Pauli exclusion principle.

Molecular orbitals of diatomic molecules, both bonding and antibonding orbitals, are characterized by the electron's angular momentum along an imposed direction, which is that of the internuclear line, and the symmetry of the orbital. Since electrons in s orbitals have zero angular momentum, an electron in a molecular orbital made from these orbitals has zero angular momentum. The symbol σ, the Greek counterpart of s, is used to describe molecular orbitals which impart no angular momentum along the internuclear direction.

The symmetry property of orbitals of diatomic molecules that is of importance is the behavior on inversion of the molecular orbital through the center of symmetry. As in Sec. 12-5, the subscript g is used for orbitals that are symmetric in this regard and u for orbitals that are antisymmetric.

With this notation, a bonding, $1s_A + 1s_B$ molecular orbital is identified as σ_g or, to show its origin in $1s$ orbitals, as $1s\sigma_g$. Sometimes the σ_g orbitals are numbered sequentially, the first being $1\sigma_g$. The antibonding $1s_A - 1s_B$ molecular orbital is σ_u, $1s\sigma_u$, or $1\sigma_u$. Also, to emphasize the antibonding nature of the σ_u orbital a superscript asterisk is sometimes added, giving the notation σ_u^*.

The two combinations that can be made from $1s$ atomic orbitals can accommodate a total of four electrons and thus can be used to describe any bonding in species like H_2^+, H_2, He_2^+, and He_2. From the assignment of

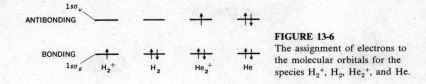

FIGURE 13-6
The assignment of electrons to the molecular orbitals for the species H_2^+, H_2, He_2^+, and He.

electrons to the orbital diagrams, as shown in Fig. 13-6, the net number of bonding electrons, 1, 2, 1, and 0, in these four species, can be deduced. We thus come on a simple qualitative guide to the bonding in such species.

The description of bonding of atoms that have electrons in the $2s$ atomic orbitals, Li and Be, requires molecular orbitals to be constructed from the $2s$ as well as the $1s$ atomic orbitals. This is shown pictorially in Fig. 13-7. The presence of pairs of $1s$ electrons on each atom leads, as you see, to equal numbers of bonding and antibonding electrons, and thus such inner shells produce no net bonding effect in this approximation.

For diatomic molecules of other second-row elements, molecular orbitals must be constructed from atomic p orbitals to develop enough molecular orbitals to accommodate the electrons. With p orbitals, two different situations occur.

Atomic p orbitals that lie along the molecular axis and, as mentioned in Sec. 11-7, give an electron no angular momentum along this axis can be combined, i.e., added or subtracted, to form molecular orbitals, as shown diagrammatically in Fig. 13-8. They are comparable with the orbitals obtained from atomic s orbitals in that they have no additional nodes perpendicular to the molecular axis and give an electron no angular momentum about the axis. Such orbitals are designated as σ molecular orbitals or more specifically as $p\sigma$ orbitals.

Atomic p orbitals that project perpendicular to the molecular axis lead to bonding and antibonding molecular orbitals, as Fig. 13-9 shows. An electron in such an orbital, which is related to the $l = 1, m = \pm 1$ atomic p orbitals of Table 11-4, is designated as a π orbital.

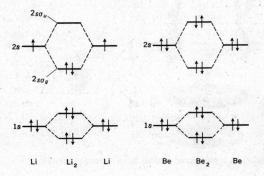

FIGURE 13-7
Molecular-orbital descriptions for Li_2 and Be_2 showing a net pair of bonding electrons for Li_2 but no net bonding electrons for Be_2.

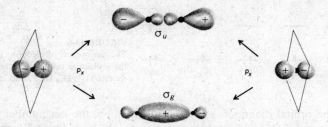

FIGURE 13-8 The formation of σ molecular orbitals from atomic p orbitals.

The molecular orbitals of homonuclear diatomic molecules based on p atomic orbitals, e.g., those shown in Figs. 13-8 and 13-9, can also be characterized by the effect of inverting the function through the center of symmetry of the molecule, i.e., through the midpoint of the bond. If this operation leaves the function unchanged, the orbital is labeled g. If it changes the sign of the function the orbital is labeled u.

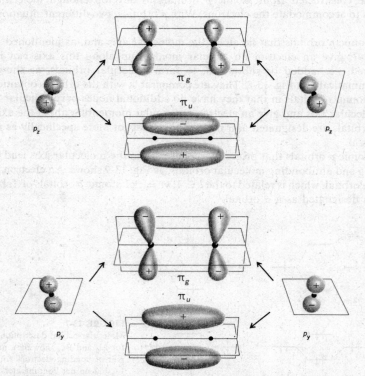

FIGURE 13-9 The formation of π molecular orbitals from atomic p orbitals.

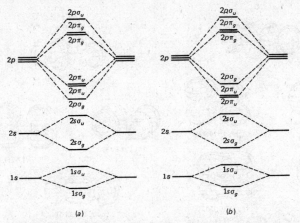

FIGURE 13-10 Molecular-orbital energy patterns for homonuclear diatomic molecules.

Just as the orbital energy diagram for atoms, shown in Fig. 11-25, became complex because of the subtleties that determine the energies of the orbitals, so is the energy pattern of the molecular orbitals of diatomic molecules somewhat uncertain. In particular the σ_g and π_u orbitals resulting from the $2p$ orbitals have nearly the same energy. Some calculations show that in N_2 and O_2 the σ_g orbital is of lower energy and the molecular-orbital energy diagram of Fig. 13-10a is appropriate. For F_2, however, the π orbitals are of lower energy, and the diagram of Fig. 13-10b is appropriate. The SCF calculations that provide these orbital energy results also produce orbital diagrams. Examples are shown in Fig. 13-11. An experimental method for determining the energies of the orbitals of atoms and molecules will be described in Sec. 14-7.

13-6 The Ionic Bond in Diatomic Molecules

For some diatomic molecules we take quite a different approach from that used in the preceding sections to describe the bonding. *Ionic bonds* are interpreted in terms of the coulombic attraction between ions. Since the electronic details of these ions are not dealt with, the approach does not require quantum-mechanical calculations. The treatment is easier but, as you will see, less satisfying than those in which a complete quantum-mechanical description is set up and, with various recognized simplifications, solved.

Let us consider, to be specific, the NaCl molecule. The molecule exists in the high-temperature vapor and its bonding energy and equilibrium bond length and some features of its energy–versus–internuclear-distance curve are known. These are shown by the solid curve of Fig. 13-12. The products of dissociation of an NaCl molecule are the gas-phase Na and Cl atoms.

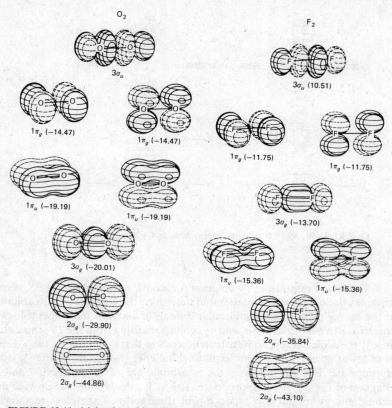

FIGURE 13-11 Molecular-orbital shapes and energies for O_2 and F_2 calculated by an SCF method. Each orbital type is numbered sequentially, but the $1\sigma_g$ and $1\sigma_u$ orbitals from the atomic $1s$ orbitals are not shown. Energies are given in atomic units (u); $1\ u = 27.21\ eV = 2620\ kJ\ mol^{-1}$. The parts of the orbitals shown as full and as dashed lines are of opposite sign. (*From W. L. Jorgensen and L. Salem, "The Organic Chemist's Book of Orbitals," Academic Press, Inc., New York, 1973.*)

Now let us attempt to develop an energy–internuclear-distance curve using the ionic-bonding model. The energy required to convert Na atoms into Na^+ ions and Cl atoms into Cl^- ions, all in the gas state, can be calculated from ionization-energy and electron-affinity data. We write

$$Na \rightarrow Na^+ + e^- \qquad \Delta E = +496\ kJ\ mol^{-1}$$
$$Cl + e^- \rightarrow Cl^- \qquad \Delta E = -349\ kJ\ mol^{-1}$$

and thus

$$Na + Cl \rightarrow Na^+ + Cl^- \qquad \Delta E = +147\ kJ\ mol^{-1} \qquad (13\text{-}18)$$

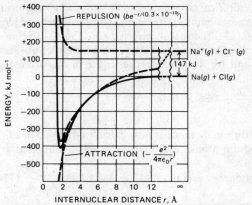

FIGURE 13-12
Calculated (dashed line) and experimentally based (solid line) energy curves for the gas-phase NaCl molecule.

Infinitely separated gas-phase Na^+ and Cl^- ions lie at an energy 147 kJ mol^{-1} higher than separate Na and Cl atoms.

As Na^+ and Cl^- ions approach each other, the potential energy becomes more negative. If we treat the ions as point charges, this potential energy is given by the coulombic term

$$U_{coul} = -\frac{e^2}{(4\pi\epsilon_0)r} \tag{13-19}$$

where r is the internuclear distance. A curve for this function, based on the energies of separate Na^+ and Cl^- ions has been added to Fig. 13-12.

An opposing effect exists in the form of a repulsion between the nuclei each with its closed shell of electrons. This repulsion term cannot easily be deduced, and it is satisfactory here to use an empirical expression, as in Sec. 6-13, to represent the repulsion that sets in at small internuclear distances. The variation of this repulsive-energy contribution with internuclear distance is satisfactorily represented by an empirical equation of the form

$$U_{rep} = be^{-r/\rho} \tag{13-20}$$

where ρ and b are empirical constants. Furthermore, to a quite good approximation, the constant ρ can be taken, as in Sec. 6-13, to be the same for all ionic molecules and equal to 0.30×10^{-10} m $= 0.30$ Å. Thus

$$U_{rep} = be^{-r/(0.30\times10^{-10})} \tag{13-21}$$

The total potential energy can now be written as

$$U = -\frac{e^2}{4\pi\epsilon_0 r} + be^{-r/(0.30\times10^{-10})} \tag{13-22}$$

The value of the remaining empirical constant b can be deduced by requiring U to have a minimum at the experimentally determined equilibrium bond length. Setting the derivative of Eq. (13-22) equal to zero for $r = 2.36 \times 10^{-10}$ m, the equilibrium bond length for NaCl, gives $b = 1.95 \times 10^5$ kJ mol^{-1}. Substitution of numerical values for e and for $4\pi\epsilon_0$ and expressing r in angstroms gives

$$U(\text{kJ mol}^{-1}) = -\frac{138.9}{r(\text{Å})} + 1.95 \times 10^5 e^{-r(\text{Å})/0.30} \tag{13-23}$$

The value of U at the equilibrium distance is now calculated as -514 kJ. The dissociation energy into sodium atoms and chlorine atoms is obtained as

$$\text{Calculated dissociation energy} = 514 - 147 = 367 \text{ kJ mol}^{-1} \tag{13-24}$$

The result is in satisfactory agreement with the experimental value of 406 kJ mol^{-1}.

The repulsion-energy curve, from the second term of Eq. (13-23), and the total-energy curve are included in Fig. 13-12. The ionic model describes the system satisfactorily up to an internuclear separation of about 10 Å. Then the bond description must change so that at complete separation the products released from each other are atoms rather than ions.

13-7 Electronegativities

In Sec. 13-5 homonuclear diatomic molecules, in which the electrons of the molecule are distributed equally between the two atoms, were dealt with. In Sec. 13-6 we considered the NaCl molecule, in which the bonding can be described in terms of the ions produced by the transfer of an electron. The result of electron transfers can also be described as arising from the limit of unequal sharing of a pair of bonding electrons.

The bonding in many heteronuclear diatomic molecules is intermediate between the equally shared and ionic extremes.

In view of this unequal sharing of bond electrons it seems desirable to try to assign to each atom a number which measures the tendency of the bonding electrons to be drawn toward that atom. *Electronegativity* is the name given to the index that attempts to represent this electron-attracting tendency. A large number of methods of arriving at electronegativity values have been suggested but only two need be mentioned.

A rather direct, but somewhat limited, method due to R. S. Mulliken makes use of the ionization potential and the electron-affinity data. The attraction that an atom, or really the ion, exerts on a pair of electrons in a bond between that atom and another atom can be expected to be some average of the attraction of the free ion for an electron, i.e., the ionization potential, and the attraction of the neutral atom for an electron, i.e., the electron affinity. Numerical values are obtained that coincide with values from other methods if electronegativities, designated as x, are calculated from

$$x = \frac{I + A}{5.6} \tag{13-25}$$

where I and A are the ionization potential and electron affinity, in electronvolts. The factor of 5.6 is an arbitrary scale factor. In this way, for example, one calculates

$$x_{Cl} = \frac{13.01 + 3.61}{5.6} = 3.0 \tag{13-26}$$

Similarly, values can be obtained for other elements for which ionization-potential and electron-affinity data are available.

An alternative method, due to Pauling, makes use of bond energies and a treatment of bond energies that is influenced by the variation theorem.

A description of the bonding in a heteronuclear bond, which allows for the ionic character of the bond, is expected, in view of the variation theorem, to lead to a better, i.e., greater, calculated bond energy than would an incomplete pure covalent-bond description.

An important step was made by Pauling in suggesting that the extra energy corresponding to the better description of the bonding electrons could be deduced from bond energies. In this method, the energy a bond would have if the electrons were equally distributed between the nuclei is calculated from the average of the covalent-bond energies of the atoms of the bond. Thus this hypothetical covalent-bond energy is calculated for HCl, as the average of the H_2 and Cl_2 bond energies. The actual bond energy is identified with the more complete description.

Comparison of the values that are established, 432 and 325 kJ, confirms our ideas that a pure covalent description for the bond of a heteronuclear molecule is inadequate and that a good description of a heteronuclear chemical bond must include an ionic term. For almost all heteronuclear bonds a similar result is found, namely, that the actual energy is greater than the calculated covalent value. The calculated energy difference is represented by Δ.

Pauling found that a self-consistent set of electronegativities could best be deduced if one used the relation

$$x_B - x_A = \sqrt{\Delta} \tag{13-27}$$

where Δ is expressed in electronvolts. The use of the square root is quite arbitrary but leads, for example, to essentially the same value for $x_{Cl} - x_I$ from the data for ICl as from the data for HCl and HI.

Pauling's method allows differences in electronegativities to be deduced

TABLE 13-1 Electronegativity Differences and Electronegativities According to the Methods of Pauling and of Mulliken

| Bond | Bond energies, kJ mol^{-1} | | Δ | | |
	Hypothetical covalent (geometric mean of covalent-bond energies)	Observed	kJ	eV	$\sqrt{\Delta} = x_B - x_A$
H—F	262	563	301	3.1	1.7
H—Cl	326	432	105	1.1	1.0
H—Br	290	366	76	0.8	0.9
H—I	256	299	43	0.4	0.6
O—H	250	463	213	2.3	1.5
N—H	264	391	127	1.3	1.1
C—H	387	415	28	0.3	0.5
C—O	222	350	128	1.4	1.2
C—F	234	441	207	2.1	1.4

| Atom | x | |
	Pauling	Mulliken
H	(2.2)	2.5
F	3.9	3.8
Cl	3.2	3.0
Br	3.1	2.7
I	2.8	2.4

from bond-energy data, as shown in Table 13-1. To obtain values for the individual atoms, it is necessary to pick an arbitrary reference point. If x_H is taken as 2.2, electronegativity values range from about 1.0 to 4.0, and this is considered a convenient range. Results obtained in this way are compared in Table 13-1 with values from Mulliken's method, and general agreement is noticed.

13-8 Bonding in Polyatomic Molecules: Valence-Bond Descriptions

Descriptions of the bonding in CH_4 can be used to illustrate the *valence-bond* procedure.

We must arrive at four bonds projecting from the carbon atom in tetrahedral directions. Linus Pauling pointed out that the $2s$ and $2p$ orbitals of the carbon atom could be used to describe these bonds. First, new orbitals that are better suited to the description of the four tetrahedrally oriented bonds are formed. This procedure of combining orbitals to form new ones is called *hybridization,* and the new sets are called *hybrid orbitals.* The most suitable set,

TABLE 13-2 Some Hybridizations Used in Describing σ Bonding

Number of orbitals	Shape	Atomic-orbital combinations	Example
2	Linear	sp	$CH{\equiv}CH$
3	Trigonal	sp^2	$CH_2{=}CH_2$, BF_3
4	Tetrahedral	sp^3 or sd^3	CH_4, MnO_4^-
	Square planar	dsp^2	$PtCl_4^{2-}$, $Ni(CN)_4^{2-}$
5	Trigonal bipyramid	dsp^3	PCl_5, $Fe(CO)_5$
6	Octahedron	d^2sp^3	PtF_6, CoF_6^{2-}

according to Pauling, consists of those wave functions which *project out farthest from the central atom* and can therefore concentrate in the region between two nuclei. When the four orbitals that project farthest are constructed from the $2s$ and $2p$ orbitals, one finds, in fact, that they are concentrated along tetrahedral directions. Thus the sp^3 hybrid orbitals are suitable for describing the bonding in CH_4.

Other combinations of s, p, and d orbitals can be constructed to provide orbitals suitable for bonding in molecules of other shapes. Hybrid orbitals that project in linear, trigonal, tetrahedral, and octahedral directions are produced by the combinations shown in Table 13-2. The trigonal and linear hybrids, which leave one p and two p orbitals of the atom unchanged, are the basis for descriptions of double and triple bonds. The p orbitals form π bonds and supplement the σ bonds, as illustrated in Fig. 13-13. Notice that σ and π components are similar to those constructed in Sec. 13-5 for homonuclear diatomic molecules.

The hybrid orbitals were constructed by Pauling to fit the geometry, or symmetry, of particular molecules. In fact, the various hybrids can be deduced from symmetry considerations alone. Consider the four tetrahedrally arranged carbon-atom orbitals needed in this approach to describe the bonding in methane. For these orbitals the characters for the various symmetry operations of the $\mathbf{T}_d$ group can be seen (Fig. 13-14) by calculating the number of unchanged bond orbitals, or bond lines, for each operation. We obtain

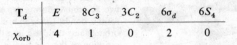

$\mathbf{T}_d$	E	$8C_3$	$3C_2$	$6\sigma_d$	$6S_4$
χ_{orb}	4	1	0	2	0

By inspection of the characters of the irreducible representations of the $\mathbf{T}_d$ character table or by application of Eq. (12-4) we see that

$$\chi_{orb} = \chi_{A_1} + \chi_{T_2} \tag{13-28}$$

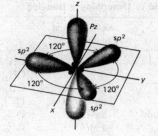

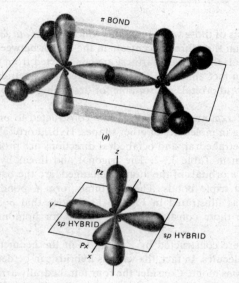

(a)

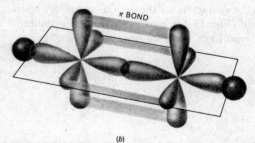

(b)

FIGURE 13-13
(a) sp^2 trigonal hybrids and their use in a description of the bonding in ethylene, $H_2C{=}CH_2$. (The distorted orbitals fail to show that the two p_z orbitals do overlap and form a bond.) (b) sp hybrid orbitals and their use in a description of the bonding in acetylene, $H{-}C{\equiv}C{-}H$.

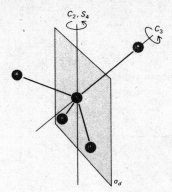

FIGURE 13-14
Representative symmetry elements of the T_d point group and lines representing the four bond orbitals of CH_4.

Thus we need atomic orbitals that transform as A_1 and T_2 to provide the basis for the tetrahedrally directed hybrid orbitals. Inspection of the cartesian coordinate entries in the T_d character table shows that the combination s and p_x, p_y, p_z provides a suitable basis. Thus sp^3 hybrid orbitals make symmetry-suitable orbitals for a tetrahedral molecule. Notice that the d-orbital set d_{xy}, d_{xz}, d_{yz}, along with s, also provides a basis for tetrahedral orbitals. Energy considerations are needed to decide whether sp^3 or sd^3 or a combination of both is most appropriate for a given molecule. In a similar way, the hybrid combinations of Table 13-2 can be deduced from the symmetry of the bonding situation for which they are to be used.

Bond orbitals, based on atomic or hybrid orbitals, provide a quantum-mechanical basis for the shared electron pairs of Lewis diagrams and the bond lines of the standard diagrams of organic molecules.

13-9 Molecular Orbitals for Polyatomic Molecules

If it is to be an eigenfunction of the hamiltonian operator for the molecule, an orbital of a molecule must transform as one of the irreducible representations for the symmetry group to which the molecule belongs. This statement provides a basis for the description of molecular orbitals of polyatomic molecules.

In the MO-LCAO approach we take the atomic orbitals we believe to be involved in the molecular orbitals and we make linear combinations of them. Symmetry considerations lead us to the symmetry of the molecular orbitals that are to be constructed. SCF calculations provide information on the energy ordering of these orbitals and on their detailed shapes.

It is convenient to describe the molecular orbitals by showing them as combinations of central-atom orbitals and attached-atom orbitals. If we take the symmetry of the molecule as given, the symmetry species of the central-atom orbitals and the symmetry of appropriate combinations of the attached-atom orbitals can be shown. The results for the atomic orbitals of the H_2O molecule are shown in Fig. 13-15. The combinations of the two hydrogen-atom orbitals

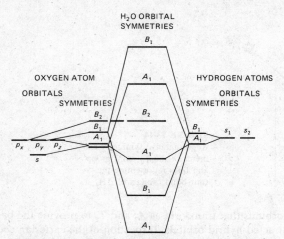

FIGURE 13-15 The symmetries of the molecular orbitals of the H_2O molecule derived from the $2s$ and $2p$ orbitals of the O atom and the $1s$ orbitals of the two H atoms.

that are appropriate to C_{2v} symmetry were worked out in Sec. 12-7. (There we dealt with bond orbitals, but we could just as well have centered the ϕ_1 and ϕ_2 orbitals on the hydrogen atoms.) The symmetry of the central-atom p orbitals are given by the location of x, y, and z in the character table.

If one orbital of a given symmetry type is produced by the central atom and one of this type by the attached atoms, bonding and antibonding orbitals will be formed and the two orbitals will correlate like the B_1 orbitals in Fig. 13-15. The interaction splits the orbitals into high- and low-energy orbitals; it does not change the number of orbitals. If the central atom produces two orbitals of a given symmetry type and the attached atoms produce only one, interaction will produce three molecular orbitals of that symmetry type, as suggested for the A_1 orbitals in Fig. 13-15.

Now the correlation lines and the pattern of molecular orbitals for the H_2O molecule in Fig. 13-15 can be appreciated. The molecular orbitals that correspond to each of these energy lines are also given. The lower A_1 and B_1 orbitals are clearly the molecular bonding orbitals, and the upper A_1 and B_1 orbitals are clearly their antibonding counterparts. The intermediate A_1 orbital might be described as nonbonding. The remaining B_2 orbital is necessarily a nonbonding orbital. Its symmetry is such that it cannot mix with any combination of the attached-atom orbitals. The same procedure can be carried out for the other small molecules.

The C_{3v} example of the NH_3 molecule illustrates the treatment when the point group includes a two-by-two doubly degenerate irreducible representation. To obtain the symmetry types for the attached-atom orbitals we look for hydrogen-atom orbitals that are not shifted by symmetry operations. With the aid of Fig. 12-9 and imagining orbitals on each of the hydrogen atoms, we obtain

C_{3v}	E	$2C_3$	$3\sigma_v$
χ_{red}	3	0	1

Application of Eq. (12-4) gives

$$\chi_{\text{red}} = \chi_{A_1} + \chi_E \tag{13-29}$$

The three attached-atom orbitals thus can be combined in a way that produces an A_1 combination and a doubly degenerate E combination. These attached-atom combinations can then be connected with the central-atom orbitals to form the molecular-orbital pattern for NH_3 given in Fig. 13-16.

In a similar way the molecular-orbital diagram of Fig. 13-17 for CH_4 can be constructed.

Molecular-orbital calculations provide detailed orbital shapes and orbital energies to go along with the qualitative results from symmetry considerations. Examples for H_2O, NH_3, and CH_4 are shown in Fig. 13-18.

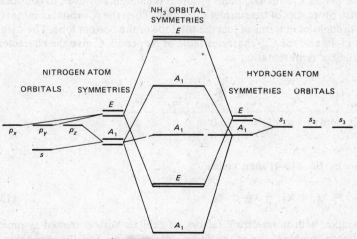

FIGURE 13-16 The symmetries of the molecular orbitals of the NH_3 molecule derived from the $2s$ and $2p$ orbitals of the N atom and the $1s$ orbitals of the three H atoms.

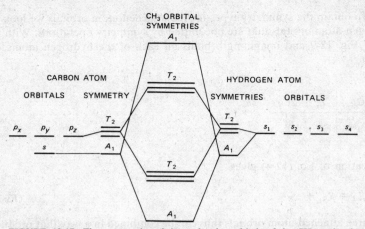

FIGURE 13-17 The symmetries of the molecular orbitals of the CH_4 molecule derived from the $2s$ and $2p$ orbitals of the C atom and the $1s$ orbitals of the four H atoms.

13-10 Molecular π Orbitals of Benzene

The construction of molecular orbitals from the p_z orbitals of an aromatic molecule like benzene requires combinations that are appropriate to the regular-hexagon symmetry of the molecule. The full symmetry of the benzene molecule places it in the $\mathbf{D}_{6h}$ point group. It is enough, however, to consider the symmetry properties of the simpler $\mathbf{C}_{6v}$ group. Then the p_z orbital combinations can be thought of in terms of just the top lobe or the bottom lobe. The diagram of Fig. 13-19 and the $\mathbf{C}_{6v}$ character table of Appendix C give the characters of the reducible representation as

$\mathbf{C}_{6v}$	E	C_2	$2C_3$	$2C_6$	$3\sigma_d$	$3\sigma_v$
χ_{red}	6	0	0	0	0	2

Analysis by Eq. (12-4) then yields

$$\chi_{red} = \chi_{A_1} + \chi_{B_1} + \chi_{E_1} + \chi_{E_2} \tag{13-30}$$

An example, with normalizing factors, of orbitals with corrected symmetries (other linear combinations of the degenerate pairs are equally acceptable) are

$$\psi_{A_1} = \frac{1}{\sqrt{6}}(\phi_1 + \phi_2 + \phi_3 + \phi_4 + \phi_5 + \phi_6)$$

434 THE THEORY OF CHEMICAL BONDING

$$\psi_{B_1} = \frac{1}{\sqrt{6}}(\phi_1 - \phi_2 + \phi_3 - \phi_4 + \phi_5 - \phi_6)$$

$$\psi_{E_1} = \begin{cases} \dfrac{1}{2\sqrt{3}}(2\phi_1 + \phi_2 - \phi_3 - 2\phi_4 - \phi_5 + \phi_6) \\ \frac{1}{2}(\phi_2 + \phi_3 - \phi_5 - \phi_6) \end{cases}$$

$$\psi_{E_2} = \begin{cases} \dfrac{1}{2\sqrt{3}}(2\phi_1 - \phi_2 - \phi_3 + 2\phi_4 - \phi_5 - \phi_6) \\ \frac{1}{2}(\phi_2 - \phi_3 + \phi_5 - \phi_6) \end{cases}$$

The shape of the molecular orbitals corresponding to these functions is displayed according to the energies that would be calculated for these orbitals in Fig. 13-20.

Now, with this simple LCAO-MO description, the ground state of benzene can be described by assigning the six p_z electrons to the A_1 and E_1 orbitals. Notice that all electrons are paired and that the configuration is similar to an atomic filled shell. Other aromatics share these features.

Molecular orbitals like those deduced for benzene can be used as a basis for treating the electronic spectra and for the simplification of the calculation of the energies of π-orbital systems, but computer calculations can readily be made without the previous formation of symmetry MOs from the p_z orbitals.

13-11 Bonding in Coordination Compounds

The largest class of compounds in which d orbitals are involved in bonding is that of coordination compounds of transition-metal ions. Compounds like these consist of a central transition-metal ion with attached electron-rich groups called *ligands*. Transition elements are characterized by incompletely filled $3d$, $4d$, or $5d$ orbitals. It is the role of these d orbitals, along with s and p orbitals, that now must be treated if the bonding in coordination compounds is to be described. Two quite different approaches have been used. The earlier one, due primarily to the work of Pauling, has its origins in the valence-bond approach and the later one, the ligand-field method, in the molecular-orbital approach.

The molecular-orbital approach, which since its development has steadily gained favor over the Pauling valence-bond treatment, requires the development of a set of molecular orbitals that will accommodate the involved electrons of the metal ion and of the ligands.

Let us continue to use complexes of octahedral symmetry as examples. This symmetry, described by the point group $\mathbf{O}_h$, will dictate the form of the molecular orbitals. These orbitals can be constructed by making combinations of central-atom and ligand orbitals that have the same symmetries. The central-atom s orbital belongs to the completely symmetric A_{1g} species. The p orbitals, as the location of x, y, and z in the $\mathbf{O}_h$ character table of Appendix C

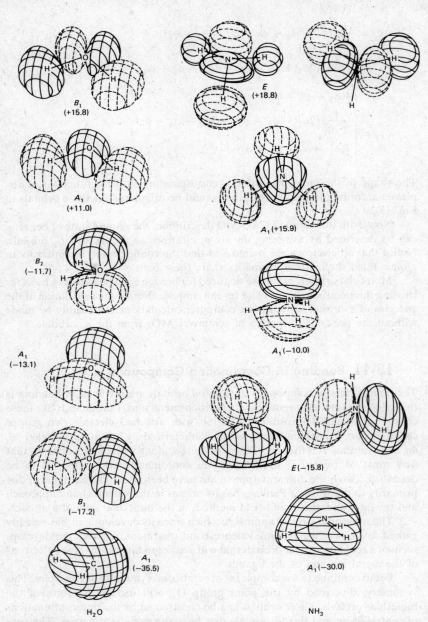

FIGURE 13-18 The molecular-orbital shapes and energies, in electronvolts. (*Calculated by W. L. Jorgensen and L. Salem, "The Organic Chemist's Book of Orbitals," Academic Press, Inc., New York, 1973.*)

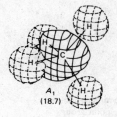

A_1
(18.7)

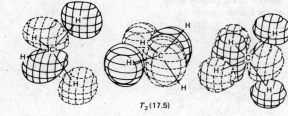

$T_2 (17.5)$

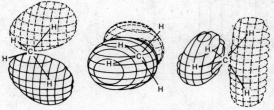

$T_2 (-14.7)$

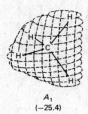

A_1
(−25.4)

CH_4

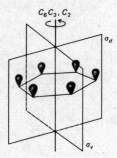

$C_6 C_3, C_2$

σ_d

σ_v

FIGURE 13-19
Representative symmetry elements of the C_{6v} point group and single lobes of the p_z orbitals of the carbon atoms of the benzene molecule.

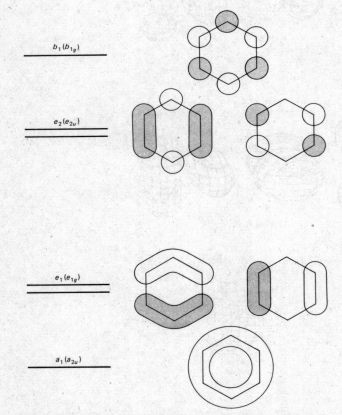

$b_1(b_{1g})$

$e_2(e_{2u})$

$e_1(e_{1g})$

$a_1(a_{2u})$

FIGURE 13-20   The π molecular orbitals and their energy pattern for the benzene molecule.

shows, have T_{1u} symmetry. The d orbitals, as shown by the placement of squares and cross products, have symmetries E_g and T_{2g}.

The orbitals supplied by the octahedrally placed ligands will here be assumed to form σ bonds. (Ligand orbitals that can form π bonds with the central atom are often important, but they will not be considered.) For symmetry purposes the orbital of each ligand behaves like the six octahedrally placed circles of Fig. 12-6b. The contributions these make to the reducible representation can easily be deduced by seeing the circles that do not change places during each of the symmetry operations. The result is

O_h	E	$8C_3$	$6C_2$	$6C_4$	$3C_4{}^2$	i	$6S_4$	$8S_6$	$3\sigma_h$	$3\sigma_d$
χ_{red}	6	0	0	2	2	0	0	0	4	2

Analysis by Eq. (12-4) gives

$$\chi_{\text{red}} = \chi_{A_{1g}} + \chi_{E_g} + \chi_{T_{1u}} \tag{13-31}$$

We now can complete the central-atom–attached-atom correlation diagram of Fig. 13-21. The molecular orbitals in the middle of the diagram are usually called *ligand-field orbitals,* and this particular molecular-orbital development procedure is called the *ligand-field method.*

The result of this entire orbital-construction procedure is the set of molecular-orbital energies for octahedral complexes shown in Fig. 13-21. You should recognize that this diagram is the counterpart of the atomic-orbital diagram of Fig. 11-13. Now we have a basic orbital diagram that can be modified to describe the orbitals of any σ-bonded octahedral coordination compound.

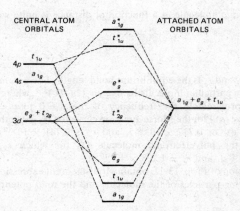

FIGURE 13-21
The symmetry and a representative energy pattern of the molecular orbitals of a central atom surrounded octahedrally by six attached atoms.

PROBLEMS

13-1. Show that Eq. (13-3) is the correct description of the hydrogen-molecule ion at infinite nuclear separation by using it as a trial function with the hamiltonian of Eq. (13-4).

13-2. (a) Plot the trial wave function of Eq. (13-3) for the hydrogen-molecule ion along the internuclear axis for an internuclear distance of 1.06 Å. (b) On a separate diagram plot the probability, according to Eq. (13-3), of the electron's being in various volume elements along the internuclear axis. (c) Add a curve for $\frac{1}{2}(s_A{}^2 + s_B{}^2)$ that corresponds to a hydrogen atom evenly distributed between the two nuclear sites.

13-3. Verify that at infinite nuclear separation the Heitler-London trial function of Eq. (13-7) is normalized.

13-4. Compare the electron-distribution implications of Eqs. (13-6) and (13-7) by plotting the probability function for the electrons of the H_2 molecule along the internuclear axis for the internuclear separation of 0.740 Å.

13-5. Write the hamiltonian for the electrons of the H_2 molecule. (A guide to hamiltonians for two electrons was given by the treatment of the helium atom in Sec. 11-11.)

13-6. Using the result of Prob. 13-5, deduce the energy of the hydrogen molecule at infinite internuclear separation for (a) the bonding Heitler-London function of Eq. (13-7) and (b) the antibonding Heitler-London function.

13-7. What approximate wave functions can be written to describe an H_2 molecule for which one electron is in a bonding molecular orbital and the other is in an antibonding molecular orbital?

13-8. (a) Describe the behavior of the functions of Prob. 13-7 for interchange of electrons. (b) What spin functions must go along with them?

13-9. Plot the probability functions along the internuclear axis, assuming an internuclear distance of 0.740 Å, for the bonding molecular orbital of Eq. (13-8) and the antibonding orbital of Eq. (13-11).

13-10. What energy is given for the hydrogen molecule in the limit of infinite internuclear distance if (a) each electron is described by the bonding molecular orbital of Eq. (13-8) and (b) if one electron is in this orbital and the other is described by an antibonding orbital?

13-11. The energy of a diatomic molecule as a function of distance is quite well represented by a *Morse* function

$$\epsilon = D_e(-2e^{-\beta(r-r_e)} + e^{-2\beta(r-r_e)})$$

where D_e is the dissociation energy and r_e is the equilibrium bond length. The parameter β is related to the properties of a particular molecule by $\beta = \pi\nu_e(2\mu/D_e)^{1/2}$, where ν_e is the vibrational frequency, approximately the frequency of the $v = 0$ to $v = 1$ transition and μ is the reduced mass. (a) Plot the Morse-function curve for H_2 given that $\nu_e = 1.32 \times 10^{14}$ Hz, D_e is 4.476 eV or 0.717×10^{-18} J, and r_e is 0.741×10^{-10} m. (b) Plot the Morse curve for the polyelectronic molecule O_2 for which $\nu_e = 4.74 \times 10^{14}$ Hz, $D_e = 0.814 \times 10^{-18}$ J, and $r_e = 1.208 \times 10^{-10}$ m.

13-12. Using the Morse function of Prob. 13-11, obtain virial-theorem expressions for the total kinetic energy of all the particles of the molecule and the total potential energy as a result of their interactions with each other as a function of internuclear distance.

13-13. Using the results of Probs. 13-11 and 13-12, prepare graphs showing the total energy, the kinetic energy, and the potential energy as a function of internuclear distance for (a) H_2 and (b) O_2. (The expressions obtained for KE and U are very sensitive to the shape of the total energy–internuclear distance function. Use of expressions other than the Morse function will lead to somewhat different results.)

13-14. Write the lowest-energy electronic configurations for He_2^+, C_2, N_2, and O_2.

13-15. A gas consisting of B_2 molecules is found to be paramagnetic. What pattern of molecular orbitals must apply in this case?

13-16. (a) What is the predicted bond order in B_2, C_2, N_2, O_2, and F_2? (b) In which, if any of these, does the bond-order prediction depend on whether the orbital pattern is that of Fig. 13-10a or b? (c) In which, if any, do the magnetic properties depend on the orbital pattern?

13-17. Explain why the dissociation energy of O_2^+ is greater than that of O_2 whereas the reverse is true for N_2^+ and N_2.

13-18. Assuming that the potential-energy function of Eq. (13-22) is satisfactory, (a) evaluate the constant b for KCl so that the minimum in the potential-energy curve occurs at the observed equilibrium internuclear distance of 2.79 Å; (b) prepare a plot of this potential-versus-internuclear separation. (c) What energy does this potential function predict for the separation of KCl from its equilibrium internuclear distance into the ions K^+ and Cl^-? (d) According to the ionization-potential and electron-affinity values of Table 6-5, how much energy is required for the reaction $K + Cl \rightarrow K^+ + Cl^-$ for infinitely separated particles? (e) What are the energetically favored products of the dissociation of KCl? (f) Compare the value calculated for the dissociation to stable products from the results of part (c) or (d) with the observed value of 4.42 eV = 426 kJ mol^{-1}.

13-19. (a) Using the bond-energy data of Table 6-4 calculate, according to the Pauling method, the electronegativity difference between H and Br and between H and C. (b) Assuming a value of 2.2 for H, calculate electronegativity values for Br and for C and compare with the values given in Table 13-1. (c) Calculate the difference in the electronegativities of Br and C directly from bond-energy data.

13-20. Represent the bonding in the molecules NH_3, BF_3, H_2CO, and HCN by (a) Lewis diagrams; (b) diagrams which indicate the angular factor in the wave function and therefore something of the position in space occupied by the electrons.

13-21. The hybridization of atomic orbitals to provide new functions that are a more suitable base for the description of bonding can be illustrated by a similar combination of wave functions of the one-dimensional particle-in-a-box model. (a) Form functions that are the sum and the difference of the two lowest-energy solution functions. (b) Plot these new hybrid functions and the probability functions to which they correspond. (c) Use each hybrid function in a variation-method treatment and obtain the energy to which it corresponds. (d) Plot these energies along with those of the original solution functions and compare the two sets of values.

13-22. Use the D_{3h} character table of Appendix C to verify that phosphorus orbitals directed toward the fluorine atoms in PF_5 can be constructed from a dsp^3 set of orbitals, as indicated in Table 13-2. (Remember that contributions are made to the character of the reducible representation only when the orbital, or whatever, resulting from an operation is described in terms of the original orbital.)

13-23. Use the O_h character table of Appendix C to verify octahedrally directed hybrid orbitals can be constructed from the d^2sp^3 set, as shown in Table 13-2.

13-24. The heat liberated when 1 mol of hydrogen is added to 1 mol of cyclohexene is 120 kJ mol^{-1}. The heat liberated when 3 mol of hydrogen is added to 1 mol of benzene is 208 kJ. What value do these data suggest for the resonance energy of benzene?

13-25. (a) Use a stick-model diagram to show the σ bonds in butadiene. (b) Draw in the additional p orbitals on each carbon atom and show how resonance requires the planarity of the molecule. (c) Indicate how the orbitals are occupied in each of the three most important resonance descriptions.

13-26. Using a stick-model diagram of the σ bonds, draw the most important resonance structures and indicate the expected geometry for CO_2, CH_3COOH, $CH_3CO_2^-$, and phenol.

13-27. The butadiene molecule has a planar zigzag carbon skeleton with symmetry elements that put it in the C_{2h} point group. Draw the four-carbon-atom skeleton and add a p orbital, with $+$ and $-$ lobes at each carbon atom. (a) What are the characters of the reducible representation based on these four carbon-atom p orbitals? (b) What irreducible representations make up the reducible representation of part (a)? (c) Form molecular π orbitals, each containing all four atomic p orbitals, consistent with the required symmetry. (d) Draw a diagram showing the nature of the molecular orbitals and arrange them on a qualitative energy scale on the basis of the number of nodes. (e) Use the diagrams of part (d) to check that each molecular orbital has the intended symmetry.

13-28. The symmetry nature of the π molecular orbitals of cyclobutadiene can be deduced by treating the molecule as belonging to the C_{4v} point group. (a) Find the symmetries of the molecular orbitals. (b) Express these orbitals in terms of the p_z orbitals on each carbon atom. (c) Sketch each orbital and arrange according to the expected energy pattern.

13-29. trans-$Co(NH_3)_4Cl_2$ has the symmetry of the point group D_{4h}. (a) Prepare a molecular-orbital diagram like that for an O_h complex given in Fig. 13-21. (b) Compare the two figures and point out the result of the change in symmetry from O_h to D_{4h}.

REFERENCES

Any of the following fairly short books will provide suitable introductions to the general area of chemical quantum mechanics:

ANDERSON, J. M.: "Introduction to Quantum Chemistry," W. A. Benjamin Inc., New York, 1969.

AVERY, J.: "The Quantum Theory of Atoms, Molecules, and Photons," McGraw-Hill Book Company (UK), Maidenhead, 1972.

GATZ, C. R.: "Introduction to Quantum Chemistry," Charles E. Merrill Publishing Company, Columbus, Ohio, 1971.

GEORGE, D. V.: "Principles of Quantum Chemistry," Pergamon Press Inc., New York, 1972.

HANNA, M. W.: "Quantum Mechanics in Chemistry," W. A. Benjamin, New York, 1969.

KARPLUS, M., and R. N. PORTER: "Atoms and Molecules: An Introduction for Students of Physical Chemistry," W. A. Benjamin, Inc., New York, 1970.
LEVINE, I. N.: "Quantum Chemistry," vol. I, "Quantum Mechanics and Molecular Electronic Structure," Allyn and Bacon, Boston, 1970.

Older classic texts on quantum mechanics in chemistry:

PITZER, K. S.: "Quantum Chemistry," Prentice-Hall, Inc., Englewood Cliffs, N.J., 1953.
PAULING, L., and E. B. WILSON, JR.: "Introduction to Quantum Mechanics," McGraw-Hill Book Company, New York, 1935.
EYRING, J., J. WALTER, and G. E. KIMBALL: "Quantum Chemistry," John Wiley & Sons, Inc., New York, 1944.
SLATER, J. C.: "Quantum Theory of Molecules and Solids," vol. 1, "Electronics of Molecules," McGraw-Hill Book Company, New York, 1963.
LINNETT, J. W.: "Wave Mechanics and Valency," Methuen & Co., Ltd., London, 1960. A short account of some of the principles of quantum mechanics, followed by clear, careful treatments of the hydrogen atom, the helium atom, and the hydrogen-molecule ion and the hydrogen molecule. Some discussion of more complex systems is also included.
COULSON, C. W.: "Valence," 2d ed., Oxford University Press, New York, 1961. A treatment of chemical bonding that avoids much of the mathematical developments and emphasizes the qualitative aspects of chemical-bond theory that are of value for chemical considerations.

Two treatments dealing specifically with molecular orbitals:

DAVIDSON, R. B.: Back-of-the-Envelope Molecular Orbital "Calculations" Using Bond Orbitals and Group Theory, *J. Chem. Educ.*, **54**:531 (1977).
STREITWIESER, A. JR., and P. H. OWENS: "Orbital and Electron Density Diagrams: An Application of Computer Graphics," The Macmillan Company, New York, 1975.
JORGENSEN, W. L., and L. SALEM: "The Organic Chemist's Book of Orbitals," Academic Press, Inc., New York, 1973.

EXPERIMENTAL STUDY OF MOLECULAR STRUCTURE: SPECTROSCOPIC METHODS

Grouped together here and in the following two chapters are treatments of various experimental methods that give information on the geometry and electronic structures of molecules. The difficulties encountered in the application of a completely theoretical approach to molecular bonding and structure lead one to refer frequently to experimentally determined properties in order to understand molecular phenomena. Knowledge of the size, shape, rigidity, and electronic structure of molecules deduced from the experimental methods treated here goes hand in hand with the theoretical approaches of the preceding chapters.

Spectroscopy is the measurement and interpretation of electromagnetic radiation absorbed or emitted when the molecules, atoms, or ions of a sample move from one allowed energy to another. These allowed energies have been used throughout Chaps. 3 to 8 in our interpretation of the thermodynamic properties of materials. Now the origin of the values used there for the spacing of some of the energy levels will be seen. Our principal concern will be with the areas of molecular spectroscopy that stem from changes in the rotational, vibrational, and electronic energies. In addition, energies not considered in our thermodynamic studies, resulting from energy differences that arise when a sample is placed in a magnetic or electric field, are susceptible to spectroscopic studies. Nuclear-magnetic-resonance (nmr) spectroscopy and electron-spin-resonance (esr) spectroscopy will illustrate such studies.

14-1 Rotational Spectra of Diatomic and Other Linear Molecules

The rotational energies of a linear gas-phase molecule were shown in Sec. 3-3 to be given by the expression

$$\epsilon_{\text{rot}} = \frac{h^2}{8\pi^2 I} J(J+1) \qquad J = 0, 1, 2, \ldots \tag{14-1}$$

and the degeneracies of the rotational levels by $g_J = 2J + 1$. Since the collections of terms $h^2/8\pi^2 I$ will occur frequently, it is convenient to introduce the *rotational constant B* such that

$$B = \frac{h^2}{8\pi^2 I} \tag{14-2}$$

Since B is a measure of energy, it will have the units of joules. With Eq. (14-2) we can rewrite Eq. (14-1) as

$$\epsilon_{rot} = BJ(J + 1) \qquad J = 0, 1, 2, \ldots \tag{14-3}$$

In spectroscopy, energies are often expressed in the reciprocal-wavelength, or wave-number, units of cm^{-1}. The rotational constant in these units is written as $\bar{B}$. The rotational energies are then given by

$$\bar{\epsilon}_{rot}\,(cm^{-1}) = \bar{B}J(J + 1) \tag{14-4}$$

Quantities, such as $\bar{B}$, expressed in terms of cm^{-1} can be returned to the SI system by first multiplying by 10^2 cm/m to obtain reciprocal wavelengths in m^{-1} units. Then multiplication by c, as suggested by $\nu = c/\lambda$, gives hertz. Finally multiplication by h, according to $\epsilon = h\nu$, gives back B in joules. Thus

$$B\,(\text{joules}) = (10^2 hc)\bar{B} \tag{14-5}$$

Now let us see how studies of electromagnetic radiation yield information on the energy spacing of rotational states and thus on the energy factor $B = h^2/8\pi^2 I$.

A representative value of the rotational energy spacing factor $\bar{B}$ for small molecules is 1 cm^{-1}. Transitions between rotational levels can be expected to have wave-number values of this order of magnitude. The frequency ν corresponding to a $\bar{\nu}$ value of 1 cm^{-1} is $(3 \times 10^{10}$ cm s$^{-1})(1$ cm$^{-1}) = 3 \times 10^{10}$ s^{-1}, or 30,000 MHz. Radiation with such frequencies occurs in the microwave or far-infrared spectral regions.

Investigation of the absorption of radiation in the microwave and far-infrared regions shows, however, that for gas samples containing molecules like H_2, N_2, or CO_2, no absorption of radiation that can be attributed to changes in the rotational energy of the free molecules of the gas occurs; however, all molecules with permanent dipoles do show extensive, often complex, patterns of absorptions. Linear polar molecules provide regular patterns of nearly equispaced absorption lines, as is illustrated in Fig. 14-1. The basis for the requirement of a polar molecule and the relative simplicity of the rotational spectra of linear molecules can now be given.

A rotating molecule of a gas can withdraw energy from electromagnetic radiation or give up energy to the radiation through electric field–dipole

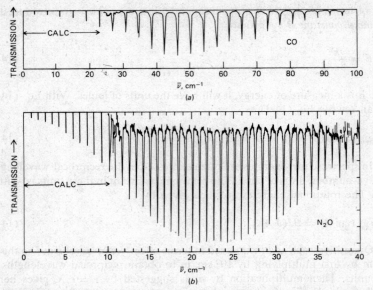

FIGURE 14-1 The far-infrared absorption spectra of (*a*) CO(*g*) (*courtesy of Dr. D. Oepts, University of Amsterdam*) and (*b*) N₂O(*g*) (*courtesy of Dr. John Fleming, National Physical Laboratory, Teddington, England*).

interaction if the molecule has a dipole. The rotating dipole provides a "coupling" with the oscillating electric field of the radiation. The transitions between rotational states that can occur as a result of this coupling are those for which

$$\Delta J = \pm 1 \tag{14-6}$$

(This restriction can also be understood in terms of the spin of radiation photons and the principle of the conservation of angular momentum, or its existence can be easily recognized from the nature of the observed rotation spectra.)

Rotational spectra are always studied by observing the radiation that is absorbed, rather than emitted, by the sample. For such absorption spectra, the only part of the selection rule that is of interest is $\Delta J = +1$.

The transitions between rotational energy levels in dipole-based absorption is shown in Fig. 14-2. Since the rotational energy levels are closely spaced compared with kT, the molecules will be distributed throughout many of the lower allowed levels. The transitions which can occur are therefore between the many levels of Fig. 14-2. These energy differences correspond to the energies of quanta of radiation that bring about $\Delta J = +1$ transitions.

We thus expect absorptions of radiation, due to $\Delta J = +1$ changes in the rotational energy of the molecules of the sample, to occur at energies given by

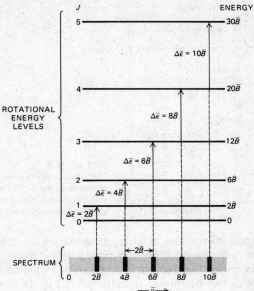

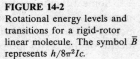

FIGURE 14-2
Rotational energy levels and transitions for a rigid-rotor linear molecule. The symbol $\bar{B}$ represents $h/8\pi^2 Ic$.

$$\Delta\epsilon_{\text{rot}} = B[(J + 1)(J + 2) - J(J + 1)]$$
$$= 2B(J + 1) \qquad J = 0, 1, 2, \ldots \quad (14\text{-}7)$$

or at wave numbers given by

$$\Delta\bar{\epsilon}_{\text{rot}} = \bar{\nu}_{\text{rot}} = 2\bar{B}(J + 1) \qquad J = 0, 1, 2, \ldots \qquad (14\text{-}8)$$

Thus we expect a pattern of spectral lines corresponding to the wave-number values $2\bar{B}$, $4\bar{B}$, $6\bar{B}$. If only a part of such a series is observed, it will show adjacent spectral lines spaced by a constant amount, an amount that can be identified with $2\bar{B}$.

With this analysis we can use the measured spacing between adjacent rotational levels to deduce a value of the rotational constant $\bar{B}$ of the molecule. Then with the relations of Eqs. (14-5) and (14-2), the moment of inertia of the molecule can be calculated. Finally, for diatomic molecules we can use the relation $I = \mu r^2$, where μ is the reduced mass, to obtain a value for the internuclear distance, or bond length, of the molecule.

Linear molecules, other than diatomics, can be treated similarly. Their rotational spectra also consist of a set of nearly equally spaced absorption lines in the microwave, or far-infrared, region. An example is provided by the spectrum of N_2O in Fig. 14-1. From such spectra, a value of $\bar{B}$ is obtained and a value of I can be calculated.

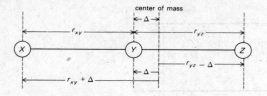

center of mass

CENTER OF GRAVITY RELATION:

$$m_x(r_{xy} + \Delta) + m_y \Delta = m_z(r_{yz} - \Delta)$$

$$\Delta = \frac{m_z r_{yz} - m_x r_{xy}}{m_x + m_y + m_z}$$

MOMENT OF INERTIA:

$$I = mx(r_{xy} + \Delta)^2 + m_y \Delta^2 + m_z(r_{yz} - \Delta)^2$$

$$= \frac{m_x m_y r_{xy}^2 + m_x m_z(r_{xy} + r_{yz})^2 + m_y m_z r_{yz}^2}{m_x + m_y + m_z}$$

FIGURE 14-3
The relation of the moment of inertia to the bond lengths and atomic masses for a linear triatomic molecule.

Some difficulty now arises in extracting bond-length data from the deduced moment of inertia. These difficulties can be illustrated for the linear N_2O molecule. The relation between the bond lengths, atom masses, and moment of inertia of the NNO molecule can be shown, as indicated in Fig. 14-3, to be

$$I = \frac{m_N m_N r_{NN}^2 + m_N m_O(r_{NN} + r_{NO})^2 + m_N m_O m_{NO} r_{NO}^2}{m_N + m_N + m_O} \qquad (14\text{-}9)$$

The masses are known, and the value of I is obtained spectroscopically. When these values are substituted, Eq. (14-9) becomes an equation in the two unknowns r_{NN} and r_{NO}. These two unknowns cannot be evaluated from the single equation. Such difficulties occur in attempts to obtain bond-length and bond-angle values from moment-of-inertia data in all molecules other than diatomics.

Data for other isotopic forms of the molecule provide additional relations. Spectral studies of, for example, $^{14}N^{14}N^{16}O$ and $^{14}N^{14}N^{18}O$ would yield values for the moments of inertia for these species. Use of Eq. (14-9) for each species then produces two simultaneous equations in the unknowns r_{NN} and r_{NO}. The not entirely justified assumption that the bond lengths are not changed by isotopic substitution is now made. The equations can then be solved for the two unknowns. The validity of the treatment can be checked by similar analyses with other isotopic pairs.

Rotational energy changes can also be studied by means of a scattering technique known as *Raman spectroscopy*. The sample is irradiated with a monochromatic beam of, usually, visible radiation. Laser beams (treated in Sec. 20-7) are especially suitable. The wavelength of the beam is chosen so that the beam is not absorbed by the sample. The beam does produce an induced dipole in the molecule and this allows transfer of energy between the molecules of the sample and the beam.

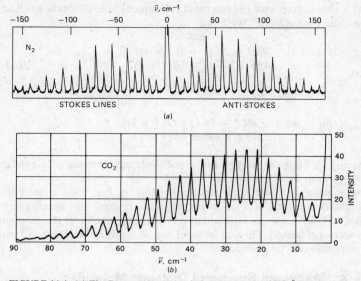

FIGURE 14-4 (*a*) The Raman spectrum of N_2 gas using the 6328-Å He–Ne laser line. The spectral lines are due to changes in the rotational energy of the N_2 molecules. (The intensity alternation is due to the different degeneracies of the even and odd rotational levels, as occurs for like atoms with unit nuclear spin.) (*From H. W. Kroto, "Molecular Rotation Spectra," John Wiley & Sons, Inc., New York, 1975.*) (*b*) The Raman spectrum of CO_2 gas.

For all gaseous samples, the scattered light contains components shifted to frequencies both higher and lower than that of the exciting line. The components near the exciting line, such as those of Fig. 14-4, are due to the transfer of energy from the beam to the rotational motion of the molecules or from the rotational motion of the molecules to the beam.

The scattering, or Raman, interaction depends on the formation of an induced dipole by the incident light. This dipole is formed in any molecule that is polarizable. Since all molecules are polarizable, all molecules of gases show rotational Raman spectra.

The selection rules for rotational Raman spectra are

$$\Delta J = \pm 2 \tag{14-10}$$

In Raman spectra both the $+2$ and -2 possibilities lead to observed spectral lines. Those corresponding to the -2 possibility are at frequencies or energies less than that of the exciting line. Such Raman spectral lines are called *Stokes lines*. Those for which ΔJ is $+2$ occur at higher frequencies or energies than that of the exciting line. These lines are called *anti-Stokes* lines.

For Raman spectra we express the displacement of each rotational Raman line from the exciting line. We have

$$\Delta\epsilon_{\text{rot}} \text{ (Stokes)} = -B[(J + 2)(J) - J(J + 1)]$$
$$= -4BJ + 6B = -4B(J + \tfrac{3}{2}) \tag{14-11}$$

and

$$\Delta\epsilon_{\text{rot}} \text{ (anti-Stokes)} = B[(J + 2)(J) - J(J + 1)]$$
$$= 4BJ + 6B = 4B(J + \tfrac{3}{2})$$

The spacing in both the Stokes and anti-Stokes components of a rotational Raman spectrum can be identified with $4B$ or $4\bar{B}$.

The spacing between adjacent components in Fig. 14-4 is seen to be approximately constant. If a wave-number scale is used, this spacing can be identified with $4\bar{B}$. From an estimate of this quantity, a value of the moment of inertia can be calculated. Then, at least for diatomic molecules, the bond length of the molecule can be deduced.

14-2 Vibrational Spectra of Diatomic Molecules

The molecular motion that has the next larger energy-level spacing after the rotation of molecules is the vibration of the atoms of the molecule with respect to each other.

The allowed energies for a single particle of mass m vibrating against a spring with force constant k, that is, experiencing a potential energy $U = \tfrac{1}{2}kx^2$, where x is the displacement from equilibrium, were shown in Sec. 3-7 to be given by the expression

$$\epsilon_{\text{vib}} = (v + \tfrac{1}{2}) \frac{h}{2\pi} \sqrt{\frac{k}{m}} = (v + \tfrac{1}{2})h\nu_{\text{vib}} \qquad v = 0, 1, 2, \ldots \tag{14-12}$$

where ν_{vib}, the frequency of the classical oscillator, represents the term $(1/2\pi)\sqrt{k/m}$. This quantum-mechanical result indicates a pattern of energy levels with a constant spacing $(h/2\pi)\sqrt{k/m}$. It is this result that was used in Sec. 4-7 for the calculation of the average vibrational energy per degree of freedom.

Now let us investigate the details of the vibrational motion of the atoms of a molecule. The simplest case of a diatomic molecule will be our initial concern.

The *harmonic-oscillator* treatment results when we assume that the potential energy of the bond can be described by the function

$$U = \tfrac{1}{2}k(r - r_e)^2 \tag{14-13}$$

where r is the distance between the bonded atoms or their nuclei and r_e is the value of r at the equilibrium internuclear distance. The constant k enters as a proportionality constant, the force constant. It is a measure of the stiffness of the bond.

The classical solution for a vibrating two-particle diatomic-molecule system can again be obtained from Newton's $f = ma$ relation. If the bond is distorted from its equilibrium length r_e to a new length r, the restoring forces on each atom are $-k(r - r_e)$. These forces can be equated to the ma terms for each atom as

$$m_1 \frac{d^2 r_1}{dt^2} = -k(r - r_e) \quad \text{and} \quad m_2 \frac{d^2 r_2}{dt^2} = -k(r - r_e) \tag{14-14}$$

where r_1 and r_2 are the positions of atoms 1 and 2 relative to the center of gravity of the molecule. The relations between r_1, r_2, and r that keep the center of gravity fixed give, for example,

$$r_1 = \frac{m_1 m_2}{m_1 + m_2} r = \mu r \tag{14-15}$$

Substitution in the $f = ma$ equation for particle 1 gives

$$\frac{m_1 m_2}{m_1 + m_2} \frac{d^2 r}{dt^2} = -k(r - r_e)$$

which, since r_e is a constant, can also be written

$$\frac{m_1 m_2}{m_1 + m_2} \frac{d^2(r - r_e)}{dt^2} = -k(r - r_e) \tag{14-16}$$

The term $r - r_e$ is the displacement of the bond length from its equilibrium position, and if the symbol x is introduced as $x = r - r_e$ and the reduced mass of μ is inserted for the mass term, Eq. (14-16) becomes

$$\mu \frac{d^2 x}{dt^2} = -kx \tag{14-17}$$

This expression is identical with the corresponding equation for a single particle, except for the replacement of the mass m by the reduced mass. It follows that the classical vibrational frequency for a two-particle system is given by

$$\nu_{\text{vib}} = \frac{1}{2\pi} \sqrt{\frac{k}{\mu}} \tag{14-18}$$

and that the quantum-mechanical vibrational-energy-level result is

$$\epsilon_{vib} = (v + \tfrac{1}{2}) \frac{h}{2\pi} \sqrt{\frac{k}{\mu}} \qquad v = 0, 1, 2, \ldots \tag{14-19}$$

or

$$\epsilon_{vib} = (v + \tfrac{1}{2}) h \nu_{vib} \qquad v = 0, 1, 2, \ldots \tag{14-20}$$

If the molecule can be treated as a harmonic oscillator, the vibrational energies of a diatomic molecule consist of a set of levels, as shown with the potential-energy functions in Fig. 14-5.

The spacing of these levels, according to the harmonic-oscillator, or parabolic-potential, approximation is a constant energy amount

$$\Delta\epsilon_{vib} = \frac{h}{2\pi} \sqrt{\frac{k}{\mu}} \tag{14-21}$$

At room temperature the value of kT is sufficiently small compared with typical values of $\Delta\epsilon_{vib}$ for most of the molecules to be in the lowest allowed vibrational state. In a spectroscopic study, therefore, one investigates the absorption of radiation by these $v = 0$ state molecules.

Coupling with electromagnetic radiation can occur if the vibrating molecule produces an oscillating dipole moment that can interact with the electric field of the radiation. It follows that homonuclear diatomic molecules like H_2, N_2, and O_2, which necessarily have a zero dipole moment for any bond length, will fail to interact. The dipole moment of molecules such as HCl, on the other hand, can be expected to be some function, usually unknown, of the internuclear distance. The vibration of such molecules leads to an oscillating dipole moment, and a vibrational spectrum can be expected.

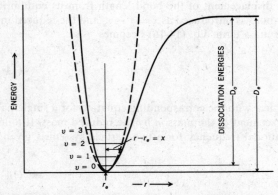

FIGURE 14-5 The approximation of a potential-energy curve (solid line) by a Hooke's-law parabola.

Even when interaction between vibrating molecule and the radiation occurs, a further selection rule applies. This rule restricts transitions resulting from the absorption or emission of a quantum of radiation by the relation

$$\Delta v = \pm 1 \tag{14-22}$$

Vibrational spectra are usually determined by absorption spectroscopy, and then $\Delta v = +1$ is the only part of this selection rule which is pertinent.

Raman scattering shows the effect of molecular vibrations if the polarizability of the molecule varies as the molecule vibrates. This can generally be expected to be the case for diatomic molecules, even homonuclear diatomic molecules. The selection rule is the same as that for oscillating-dipole-based transitions, namely $\Delta v = \pm 1$.

For a sample containing heteronuclear diatomic molecules we thus expect a single absorption line, or band, in the infrared spectral region. For a sample containing *any* type of diatomic molecule we expect Raman spectra showing a single Stokes and a single anti-Stokes line corresponding to the $\Delta v = +1$ and $\Delta v = -1$ transitions on either side of the exciting line. These expectations are generally borne out. (We do, however, also find much weaker lines at approximately 2, 3, ... times the frequency, or energy of the *fundamental* $v = 0$ to $v = 1$ absorption. These *overtone* absorptions can be identified with $v = 0$ to $v = 2$, $v = 0$ to $v = 3$, ... transitions. They occur in violation of the $\Delta v = \pm 1$ selection rule. This rule applies strictly to a harmonic oscillator, and, as Fig. 14-5 suggests, the actual potential-energy curve is not identical to the parabola required for a true harmonic oscillator.)

The calculation of the molecular property, the force constant k, can be illustrated by working from the infrared absorption band of HCl observed at $\bar{v} = 1/\lambda$ (cm) $= 2885$ cm^{-1}. As for the rotational constant expressed in these wave-number units, conversion to SI energy units is accomplished by multiplication by $10^2 ch$. Thus

$$\Delta \epsilon = 10^2 ch \bar{v} \, (\text{cm}^{-1}) \tag{14-23}$$

From $\bar{v} = 2885$ cm^{-1} and Eq. (14-23) we obtain

$$\Delta \epsilon_{\text{vib}} = 5.74 \times 10^{-20} \, \text{J} \tag{14-24}$$

The observed HCl absorption can be assigned to the vibrational transition from $v = 0$ to $v = 1$, and $\Delta \epsilon$ can be equated to $(h/2\pi)\sqrt{k/\mu}$. With $\mu = 1.628 \times 10^{-27}$ kg, this yields

$$k = 483 \, \text{N m}^{-1} \tag{14-25}$$

The theory of vibrational spectra, together with the observed absorption, has now led to a value for the force constant of a chemical bond. The force constant, it will be recalled, measures the force required to stretch a bond by a

TABLE 14-1 Fundamental Frequencies and Force Constants for Some Diatomic Molecules and the Bonds of Polyatomic Molecules

Molecule	$\bar{\nu}$, cm^{-1}	k, N m^{-1}	Molecule	$\bar{\nu}$, cm^{-1}	k, N m^{-1}	Bond	$\bar{\nu}$, cm^{-1}	k, N m^{-1}
KCl	278	80	F_2	892	450	$-C-Cl$	650	360
NaCl	360	120	HCl	2885	480			
Na_2	158	170	H_2	4162	510	$-C-H$	2960	480
I_2	213	170	HF	3958	880			
Br_2	321	240	O_2	1556	1140	$O-H$	3680	770
HI	2230	290	NO	1876	1550			
Cl_2	554	320	CO	2143	1860	$C=C$	1650	960
HBr	2560	380	N_2	2331	2240			
						$C=O$	1700	1210
						$-C\equiv C-$	2050	1560
						$-C\equiv N$	2100	1770

given distance. The qualitative feature to be appreciated from results such as that worked out for HCl is that molecules are flexible. Although it is at first difficult to appreciate the significance of the numerical values obtained for bond-force constants, one can make interesting comparisons of the stiffness of different bonds. Some results for diatomic molecules and for bonds of polyatomic molecules are shown in Table 14-1. The increased stiffness of multiple bonds compared with single bonds is apparent and is in line with the greater strength of multiple bonds. It should be noticed from the data of the table that the observed frequency, being determined by both the reduced mass and the force constant according to Eq. (14-21), is not itself a simple measure of the bond stiffness.

14-3 The Vibrations and Vibrational Absorption Spectra of Polyatomic Molecules

Polyatomic molecules have absorption spectra in the infrared region and Raman spectra that can be interpreted as arising from transitions within each of a number of vibrational-energy-level patterns. Each energy-level pattern corresponds to one of the $3n - 6$ (or $3n - 5$ for linear molecules) characteristic, or normal, vibrations of the molecule. One finds, for example, for H_2O vapor, absorptions centered at 1595, 3657, and 3756 cm^{-1}. For molecules with many atoms, $3n - 6$ becomes large, and one expects very many vibrational transitions and a very complicated infrared-region spectral pattern.

The presence of any amount of symmetry in a molecule often simplifies the vibrational spectrum. Recognition of this symmetry correspondingly simplifies the study of the vibrational modes and vibrational spectra.

Motions of the atoms of a molecule produce net molecular effects that we describe as translations, rotations, or vibrations of the molecule. Such descriptions correspond to the eigenfunctions that would be obtained if we applied the Schrödinger equation, $\mathcal{H}\psi = \epsilon\psi$, to the atoms, each treated as a particle, of the molecule. These eigenfunctions, as stated in Chap. 12, must transform according to one or another of the symmetry types for the molecule.

The characters of the transformation matrices for all $3n$ translation-rotation-vibration motions of a molecule can be deduced by using the three cartesian coordinates at each atom as a basis, as illustrated in Sec. 12-7. The characters deduced from this $3n$ cartesian coordinate basis will be the same as those of the sum of the characters for the irreducible representations that describe the translational, rotational, and vibrational motions of the molecule.

The H_2O example worked out in Sec. 12-7 led us to expect two vibrations of symmetry A_1 and one of symmetry B_2. Diagrams corresponding to vibrations of these types are repeated and shown, along with the vibrational-energy pattern to which each corresponds, in Fig. 14-6.

As in the electronic applications of group theory in Chaps. 12 and 13, additional information or calculations must be called on to describe the eigenfunctions, here the nature of the vibrations, in more detail. Assumption of force constants for bond stretching and angle bending can lead to more detailed descriptions of the vibrational motions than are given in Fig. 14-6. The correctness of the force-constant assumptions and the deduced displacement diagrams is determined by the match between the calculated frequencies and the positions of the observed vibrational absorptions. Such calculations show that the description of vibrational motions as bond stretchings and angle bendings, each with suitable symmetry, is generally satisfactory.

As a second example, we consider the symmetric-top molecule, CH_3Cl. The number of vibrations is $3n - 6 = 9$. The symmetry of the molecule is C_{3v}. The

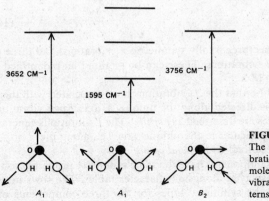

FIGURE 14-6
The symmetry of the three vibrational modes of the water molecule and the associated vibrational-energy-level patterns.

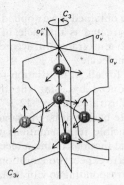

FIGURE 14-7
The $3n$ cartesian displacement coordinates of the CH_3Cl molecule.

$3n$ cartesian displacement vectors are shown in Fig. 14-7. With the recipes for the characters given in Table 12-5 we can write

C_{3v}	E	$2C_3$	$3\sigma_v$
χ_{red}	15	0	3

Analysis in terms of irreducible representations gives

$$\chi_{red} = 4\chi_{A_1} + \chi_{A_2} + 5\chi_E \qquad (14\text{-}26)$$

From the C_{3v} character table we have

$$\chi_{trans} = \chi_{A_1} + \chi_E / \chi_{rot} = \chi_{A_2} + \chi_E \qquad (14\text{-}27)$$

Thus

$$\chi_{vib} = 3\chi_{A_1} + 3\chi_E \qquad (14\text{-}28)$$

The CH_3Cl molecule has three totally symmetric A_1 vibrations and three pairs of doubly degenerate E vibrations. These can be pictured and identified with absorptions, as in Fig. 14-8.

Notice from Fig. 14-8 that the A_1 vibrations have associated with them an oscillating dipole that is directed along the unique, z, axis. Such vibrations of symmetric-top molecules are described as *parallel*. The E vibrations generate an oscillating dipole perpendicular to the unique axis, i.e., along the x or y axis. Such vibrations are described as *perpendicular*.

Oscillating dipole components have the same symmetry properties as the **x**, **y**, **z** vectors that are displayed alongside character tables. The rows in which **x**, **y**, and **z** occur give the symmetry types for the three components of the

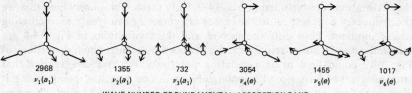

2968	1355	732	3054	1455	1017
$\nu_1(a_1)$	$\nu_2(a_1)$	$\nu_3(a_1)$	$\nu_4(e)$	$\nu_5(e)$	$\nu_6(e)$

WAVE NUMBER OF FUNDAMENTAL ABSORPTION BAND

FIGURE 14-8 The normal vibrations, shown schematically, for the CH_3Cl molecule. Only one member of each degenerate pair is shown.

oscillating dipole. Only vibrations that have the symmetry corresponding to that of **x**, **y**, or **z** can have an oscillating dipole moment. Since absorption spectra depend on interaction of radiation with an oscillating dipole, only the vibrations that belong to symmetry types that correspond to the rows containing the **x**, **y**, or **z** vectors can be *infrared-active*. In both the H_2O and CH_3Cl examples all vibrations are infrared-active. In more symmetric molecules some vibrations will have a symmetry type other than those corresponding to the rows containing the **x**, **y**, or **z** vectors. Such vibrations will be *infrared-inactive;* they will produce no absorption of radiation.

Symmetry considerations also lead to conclusions about the vibrations of symmetric molecules that are *Raman-active*. The distinction between Raman and infrared activity can most easily be seen by considering a molecule with a center of symmetry. A simple example is provided by the CO_2 molecule of Fig. 14-9. The vibrations of the molecule are of three types, and diagrams suggesting

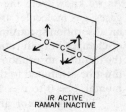

FIGURE 14-9
The infrared-active and Raman-active vibrations of the linear CO_2 molecule.

IR INACTIVE
RAMAN ACTIVE

IR ACTIVE
RAMAN INACTIVE

IR ACTIVE
RAMAN INACTIVE

these vibrations are included in Fig. 14-9. Only those vibrations which remove the symmetry with respect to the center of symmetry can create an oscillating dipole moment. Thus only the second and third vibrations of Fig. 14-9 are infrared-active. Raman activity can be deduced by seeing which distortions of Fig. 14-9 could lead to an oscillating polarizability. You can assume that stretching a bond changes the polarizability in one way and compressing it changes the polarizability to the same extent but in the opposite way. Then you expect only the first vibration of Fig. 14-9 to be Raman-active.

This deduction illustrates a general rule. If a molecule has a center of symmetry, only those vibrations which are antisymmetric with respect to the center can be infrared-active and only those which are symmetric with respect to the center can be Raman-active.

A more detailed analysis of the dependence of polarizability on molecular distortions would show that Raman activity occurs only for vibrations with the symmetry of any of the square or cross-product terms of x, y, and z, shown in character tables. You can use this guide and the character tables of Appendix C to confirm the deductions made about infrared and Raman activity for molecules with a center of symmetry.

In a practical use of great value, particularly in the field of organic chemistry, the infrared absorption spectrum of a large molecule is used to identify the compound or to indicate the presence of certain groups in the molecule. Bonds or groups within a molecule sometimes vibrate with a frequency, i.e., have an energy-level pattern with a spacing, that is little affected by the rest of the molecule. Absorption at a frequency that is characteristic of a particular group can then be taken as an indication of the presence of that group in the compound being studied. Table 14-1 includes a few of the groups that have useful *characteristic frequencies*.

An even simpler use of vibrational spectra consists in verifying the identity of a compound by matching its infrared spectrum to that of a known sample. Large molecules have such complicated spectra, as shown in Fig. 14-10, for example, that identical spectra can be taken as a sure indication of identical compounds. Thus, although for large molecules the complete vibrational spectrum can seldom be understood in terms of the nature of the $3n - 6$ vibrations, there are many uses to which such spectra can be put.

14-4 Rotation-Vibration Spectra of Diatomic Molecules

As we know from the interpretations given to thermodynamic properties of gases, gas molecules are simultaneously rotating and vibrating. It follows that an absorption spectrum or the Raman spectrum of a gas might show the effects of changes in both rotational and vibrational energies. The expanded view of the infrared absorption band of HCl in Fig. 14-11 shows the band structure that must be attributed to the rotational-energy changes accompanying this fundamental, $v = 0$ to $v = 1$ vibrational transition.

The rigid-rotor and harmonic-oscillator expressions of Eqs. (14-3) and

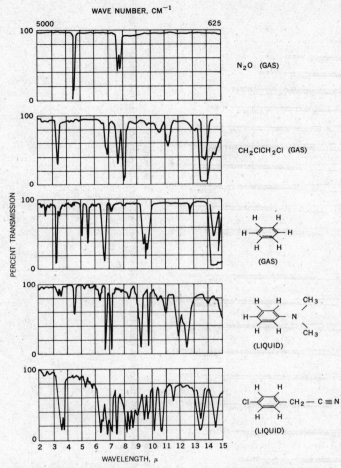

WAVE NUMBER, CM^{-1}

N_2O (GAS)

CH_2ClCH_2Cl (GAS)

(GAS)

(LIQUID)

(LIQUID)

PERCENT TRANSMISSION

WAVELENGTH, μ

FIGURE 14-10 The infrared absorption spectra of simple and complex molecules.

(14-20) can be combined to give the rotation-vibration allowed-energy expression

$$\epsilon_{\text{rot-vib}} = (v + \tfrac{1}{2})h\nu_{\text{vib}} + BJ(J + 1) \qquad \begin{array}{l} v = 0, 1, 2, \ldots \\ J = 0, 1, 2, \ldots \end{array} \qquad (14\text{-}29)$$

The energy pattern that includes only the $v = 0$ and $v = 1$ levels and a few of the rotational levels for each vibrational state is shown in Fig. 14-12.

Analysis of the absorption spectrum for gas-phase molecules for which the energy expression of Eq. (14-29) applies can be made on the basis of this energy

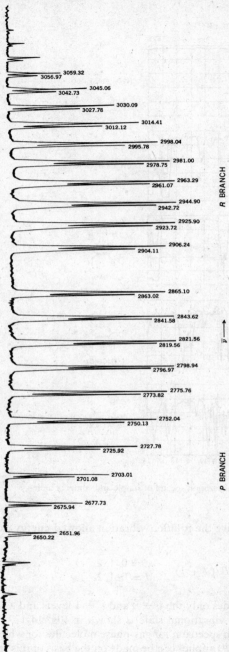
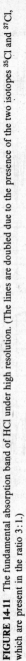

FIGURE 14-11 The fundamental absorption band of HCl under high resolution. (The lines are doubled due to the presence of the two isotopes ^{35}Cl and ^{37}Cl, which are present in the ratio 3:1.)

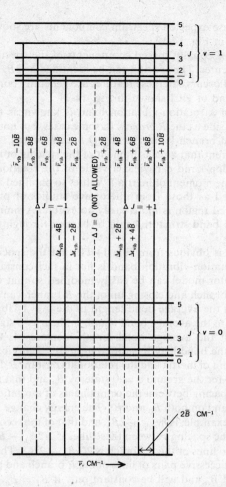

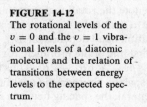

FIGURE 14-12
The rotational levels of the $v = 0$ and the $v = 1$ vibrational levels of a diatomic molecule and the relation of transitions between energy levels to the expected spectrum.

pattern and the selection rules that govern the transitions. Again the rules $\Delta v = \pm 1$ and $\Delta J = \pm 1$ hold, and while only $\Delta v = +1$ applies, both $\Delta J = +1$ and $\Delta J = -1$ are now possible. Transitions allowed by these rules are included in Fig. 14-12.

The energies of the various transitions of Fig. 14-12 are determined by means of the rotation-vibration energy expression of Eq. (14-29). In each case the vibrational contribution is given by $h\nu_{vib}$. The rotational contributions are obtained from Eq. (14-29) and the J value in the $v = 1$ state compared with the J value in the $v = 0$ state. Expressions for the energies of the components of an HCl-type rotation-vibration band are given in Fig. 14-12. Now you can see that the transition lines have been placed on the diagram in order of increasing ϵ, or $\bar{\nu}$, going from left to right. They thus are ordered like the expected components of a rotation-vibration band. These expected spectrum components are shown below the energy-level diagram in Fig. 14-12.

This analysis leads to a set of equally spaced components of the spectral band at either side of the band center. The spacing can be identified as $2\bar{B}$. At the band center a gap equal to $4\bar{B}$ occurs. All these features are generally borne out by the rotation-vibration band of HCl shown in Fig. 14-11.

The lower-frequency side of a rotation-vibration band is known as the *P branch* and the high-frequency side as the *R branch*. In some cases, but not in the HCl-type spectrum, a central branch known as the *Q branch* occurs.

From this analysis it is apparent that a measurement of the spacing of the components of a rotation-vibration band can yield a value of the rotational constant B and thus a value for the moment of inertia I. Values so obtained are often not as precisely determined as those from microwave studies of pure rotational spectra, but the infrared region is more easily accessible. A similar analysis of the rotation-vibration band structure could be carried through for Raman bands.

Now it is time to admit, as is obvious from Fig. 14-11, that the spacing between the components of a rotation-vibration band is not in fact constant. The rigid rotor–harmonic oscillator model can be easily modified so that the observed spreading out of the P branch and closing up of the R branch can be accounted for. We recognize that the average bond length in the $v = 1$ vibrational state need not be identical to the average bond length in the $v = 0$ state. (You might even anticipate that the average bond length increases as the vibrational energy increases.) If the bond length is different in different vibrational states, so also are the moment of inertia and the rotational constant B. Let us denote the rotational constant for the ground $v = 0$ state by B_0 and that for the $v = 1$ state by B_1. Now the spacing between the components of a rotation-vibration band depends on $h\nu_{vib}$ and on both B_0 and B_1. The energy change for the first line of the R branch, for example, is $h\nu_{vib} + 2B_1$, and that of the second line is $h\nu_{vib} + 6B_1 - 2B_0$. Thus the spacing between these lines is $2(2B_1 - B_0)$. The spacing between the next two lines of the R branch is $2(3B_1 - 2B_0)$. Thus, in general, the spacing between successive pairs of lines of the R branch and the P branch will depend on B_1 and B_0 and will be constant only if $B_1 = B_0$. In spite of this added complexity, the values of B_1 and B_0 can easily be obtained by modifying the graphical treatment of Fig. 14-12.

The energy difference between pairs of transitions that start at the same J level of the $v = 0$ state can be used to deduce B_1, the rotational constant for the $v = 1$ state. The energy difference between pairs of transitions that end at the same J level of the $v = 1$ state can be used to deduce B_0, the rotational constant of the $v = 0$ state. Examples of pairs of states that give results for B_1 and pairs that give results for B_0 are shown in Fig. 14-13. Additional pairs can be treated, and average values of B_1 and B_0 can be obtained for all suitable component pairs. The validity of the model is determined by the constancy of the values for B_1 and B_0 obtained from the various component pairs.

The values of B for various vibrational states can be extrapolated to the

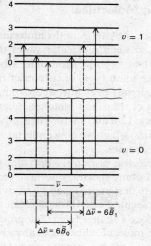

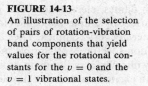

FIGURE 14-13
An illustration of the selection
of pairs of rotation-vibration
band components that yield
values for the rotational constants for the $v = 0$ and the
$v = 1$ vibrational states.

$v = -\frac{1}{2}$ "state" that corresponds to the molecule's being at its equilibrium configuration corresponding to the minimum of the potential-energy curve, such as that of Fig. 14-5. Values of moments of inertia and of bond lengths can thus be deduced for various vibrational states and also for the equilibrium state. Some results, which illustrate the power of the spectroscopic method in revealing intimate details of molecules, are given in Table 14-2. (The results of Table 14-2 illustrate the basis for the difficulties, met in Sec. 14-1, in using different isotopic species to deduce bond lengths from moment-of-inertia data. Bond lengths for $v = 0$ state molecules do change with isotopic substitution. Only the equilibrium bond lengths are unaffected. Microwave studies of pure rotational spectra generally give data for the $v = 0$ state.)

TABLE 14-2 Dependence of $\bar{B}$ and the Bond Distance on the Vibrational State of a Molecule

The subscript equil indicates values for the equilibrium $v = -\frac{1}{2}$ "state," corresponding to the minimum in the potential-energy curve

Molecule	$\bar{B}_{equil}$, cm^{-1}	r_{equil}, Å	$r_{v=0}$, Å	$r_{v=1}$, Å
H$_2$	60.809	0.7412	0.7510	0.7702
HD	45.655	0.7414	0.7495	0.7668
D$_2$	30.429	0.7414	0.7481	0.7616
HCl	10.5909	1.27460	1.2838	1.3028
DCl	5.445	1.275	1.282	1.295
CO	1.9314	1.1282	1.1307	1.1359
N$_2$	1.998	1.098	1.100	1.105

14-5 Electronic Spectra of Diatomic Molecules

If the electron arrangement in a molecule changes, the energy of the molecule is generally changed. Spectra due to transitions between molecular states that differ in electron arrangement are called *electronic spectra*. Electronic, vibrational, and rotational spectra constitute the three main types of spectra of free molecules. The electronic spectra of atoms have already been introduced (Chap. 11), and some features of the electronic spectra of transition-metal complexes and aromatic molecules have been studied in Secs. 12-8 and 13-10. The study of the electronic spectra of small gas-phase molecules, which we now undertake, is in keeping with the preceding sections of this chapter.

The light from flames, electric arcs, and electric discharges provides the basis for a great variety of simple-molecule electronic spectra, but these emission spectra are generally very complex. They are best approached by studying the simpler absorption spectra. Most simple molecules, e.g., those of clean air, require high-energy ultraviolet radiation to produce a change from their ground electronic state to an excited state. A few simple-molecule substances absorb in the visible region, i.e., are colored. One of these, I_2, often is used to provide an introduction to the electronic absorption spectra.

When iodine is dissolved in a solvent like carbon tetrachloride, a violet solution is formed. Iodine vapor also absorbs in the visible region. The absorption band, as shown in Fig. 14-14, is made up of a large number of lines followed, on the short-wavelength side, by a continuum. The lines are produced by the vibrational-energy changes that accompany the energy change due to the electronic rearrangement. The basis of the vibrational structure of electronic bands can be seen by inspecting the potential-energy curves, and the vibrational levels involved in the transition. The I_2 spectrum of Fig. 14-14 can be interpreted in terms of a diagram like that of Fig. 14-15.

Two features of Fig. 14-15 must be pointed out. First we must recognize that since molecules vibrate, at any instant there will be molecules with a range of internuclear distances. The probabilities of various internuclear distances are given by the square of the vibrational wave function. In the lowest vibrational state, contrary to classical ideas, the most probable internuclear distance is that corresponding to the midpoint of the vibrational range. For the higher-energy states, on the other hand, the quantum-mechanical result is more like the classical result that the most probable configuration is at the ends of the vibration, where the atoms must stop and reverse their direction. The probability curves are added to the energy levels that are important in the I_2 absorption-spectrum example of Fig. 14-14.

The observed spectral transitions are related to an energy diagram such as that of Fig. 14-15 on the basis of the Franck-Condon principle, which stems from the idea that electrons move and rearrange themselves much faster than the nuclei of molecules can. For example, the time for an electron to circle a hydrogen nucleus can be calculated from Bohr's model to be about 10^{-16} s, whereas a typical period of vibration of a molecule is about 10^{-13} s, 1000 times

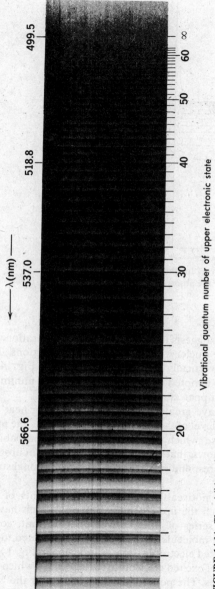

FIGURE 14-14 The visible-region absorption spectrum of $I_2(g)$.

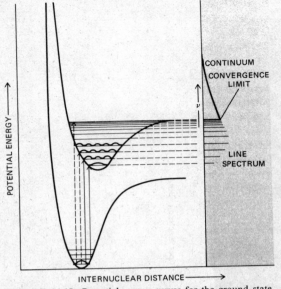

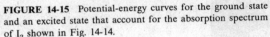

FIGURE 14-15 Potential-energy curves for the ground state and an excited state that account for the absorption spectrum of I_2 shown in Fig. 14-14.

longer. Comparison of these times suggests that an electronic configuration will change in a time so short that the nuclei will not change their positions. The spectral transitions must be drawn vertically in diagrams like those of Fig. 14-15 and not, as one might otherwise be tempted to do, from the potential minimum of the lower curve to that of the upper curve.

Transitions are expected to have greater probability of starting near the midpoint of the lowest vibrational level of the ground electronic state. The most probable transitions will be those which go vertically to high-probability regions. It follows, as Fig. 14-14 shows, that an electronic transition, in absorption, may show a series of lines corresponding to the different vibrational states that are reached.

In the I_2 example the most noticeable vibrational components of the absorption band are those in which the upper-state vibrational levels have v values between 20 and 50. The series of lines converges to a limit, corresponding to the dissociation of the molecule. This limit, which is related to the dissociation energy of I_2 in the excited electronic state, is indicated in Fig. 14-14.

Generally there are a variety of excited electronic states, some of which can be reached by absorption processes. The potential-energy curves for the well-studied states of O_2, for example, are shown in Fig. 14-16. The first two excited

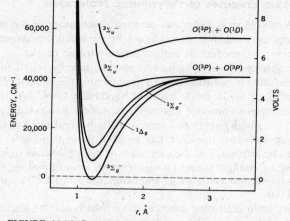

FIGURE 14-16 Potential-energy curves for some of the electronic states of the O_2 molecule. (*From G. Herzberg, "Molecular Spectra and Molecular Structure," vol. 1, "Spectra of Diatomic Molecules," D. Van Nostrand Company, Inc., Princeton, N.J., 1950.*)

states, $^1\Delta_g$ and $^1\Sigma_g{}^+$, are responsible for absorption of solar radiation by the earth's atmosphere. The absorption bands occur in the infrared and in the visible at about 760 nm. Obviously, and fortunately, only a fraction of the incident sunlight around this wavelength is removed. The weakness of the absorption illustrates the selection rule, which is here violated, that transitions occur between states of like multiplicity, i.e., states with equal numbers of unpaired electrons. The ground state of oxygen, in which there are two unpaired electrons, is $^3\Sigma_g$. The two lowest-lying excited electronic states are both singlets, as Fig. 14-16 shows. The entire earth's atmosphere is not enough to cause appreciable absorption by the two transitions that violate this rule. Only for molecules exposed to strong magnetic fields or containing a high-atomic-number atom whose nucleus exerts such a field is this selection rule easily broken.

Electronic emission spectra generally consist of many often overlapping bands, each with a complexity at least as great as that of the I_2 absorption band of Fig. 14-14. The variety of bands results from the variety of different electronic states that can be adopted by an excited high-energy molecule. Transitions, subject to the selection rules, can occur from one excited state to another or from an excited state to the ground state.

Each emission band has, in general, a rich vibrational and rotational substructure. Now, in contrast to absorption bands, a variety of vibrational levels of the initial excited electronic state can be populated. Transitions can occur to various vibrational states of the lower energy electronic state that is reached.

14-6 Electronic Energies of Polyatomic Molecules

For larger and generally shaped molecules detailed descriptions of the states involved in an electronic transition often cannot be achieved. Spectroscopic techniques still provide a considerable insight into electronic properties.

The electronic absorptions of organic compounds, usually found in the ultraviolet region, can often be identified with a group within the molecule. First it is recognized that electrons in single covalent bonds like C—C and C—H require very large energies to produce electronic excitation. Saturated hydrocarbons absorb only very high energy radiation, usually beyond 160 nm, far in the ultraviolet. A simple olefin, however, has an absorption band at around 170 nm, and this can be attributed to the excitation of the π electrons from the electron-paired bonding configuration to a high-energy, or antibonding, state. Such a transition is referred to as a $\pi \rightarrow \pi^*$ transition, the asterisk (*) implying an antibonding orbital.

Some molecules have electronic configurations which can be altered in different ways to lead to an excited, or high-energy, electronic state. This situation arises, for example, with compounds containing a carbonyl group $C{=}\ddot{O}{:}$. For such a group the possibility of exciting the π electrons to the excited π^* state exists, as with an olefin, to give a $\pi \rightarrow \pi^*$ transition. Alternatively, the nonbonding electrons of the oxygen might be excited to the higher-energy π^* electron state, and the absorption would then be characterized as an $n \rightarrow \pi^*$ transition, where the n signifies a nonbonding electron. The two types of transitions are represented in Fig. 14-17.

It should also be pointed out that not all electronic transitions of organic compounds occur in the ultraviolet region. The occurrence of colored compounds indicates absorption of radiation in the visible spectrum. Such absorption requires the electronic energy levels to be more closely spaced than in most molecules. The most common type of organic molecule that absorbs in the visible region, i.e., is colored, consists of a conjugated system, frequently involving aromatic rings. The qualitative explanation for the closer spacing that results from the delocalization of the conjugated electrons is most easily given by regarding such electrons as being free particles within the potential box of the molecule. For sufficiently long "boxes" the spacing is small enough to bring the absorption of radiation into the visible part of the spectrum.

Consider a fairly long conjugated system like β-carotene:

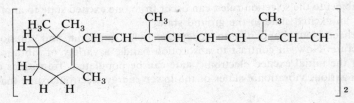

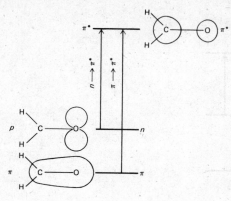

FIGURE 14-17
The orbital transitions of the
formaldehyde molecule that
are responsible for absorptions in the ultraviolet region.

If resonance structures are drawn, it will be noticed that each carbon-carbon bond along the chain has appreciable double-bond character. The π electrons are therefore not localized in one bond but are relatively free to move throughout the whole carbon skeleton. This suggests that the skeleton be considered as a roughly uniform region of low potential bounded at the ends of the molecule by regions of infinitely high potential. The resulting square potential well is to be the receptacle of the 22 π electrons. An expression for the allowed energies of these electrons, electron-electron repulsions being ignored, has been obtained in Sec. 3-5. The energies are given by the expression

$$\epsilon = \frac{n^2 h^2}{8ma^2} \qquad n = 1, 2, 3, \ldots \tag{14-30}$$

where a is the effective length of the molecule. Two electrons, one with each spin direction, can be placed in each square-well orbital. The electron energies described by this molecular-orbital approach are shown in Fig. 14-18.

The chief merit of this treatment of conjugated systems is that it offers an easy approach to relating the calculation of the wavelength of light absorbed to the length of the conjugated system. The visible-region absorption of carotene consists of a band that is centered at 451 nm. Absorption at this wavelength implies the absorption of quanta of energy 4.41×10^{-19} J. According to the free-electron model for the π-electron system, this result can be related to the energy difference

$$\epsilon_{12} - \epsilon_{11} = (12^2 - 11^2)\frac{h^2}{8ma^2} \tag{14-31}$$

Substitution of numerical values leads to the deduction of a, the length of the region in which the electrons are free to move, as

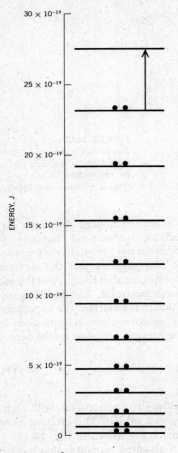

FIGURE 14-18
The energy levels and the observed spectroscopic transition for the 22 π electrons of carotene according to the free-electron or square-well model.

$$a = 17.7 \text{ Å} \tag{14-32}$$

This value, as we shall see when experimental methods for determining molecular dimensions are developed in the following chapters, is very close to that which would be expected for the extended conjugated carbon chain of the β-carotene molecule.

This molecular-orbital approach, generally making use of linear combinations of atomic orbitals, is the one most often used when quantitative quantum-mechanical treatments of conjugated systems are made.

14-7 Experimental Determination of Orbital Energies

In the preceding two sections, energy changes of the outermost, or highest-energy, electron of molecules were dealt with. The energies of other outer, valence-shell, electrons and even of inner electrons can also be determined. For such studies high-energy quanta of the far ultraviolet or of the x-ray region are required. Two techniques that are similar in principle but somewhat different in instrumentation and application have been developed.

One approach, known as *photoelectron spectroscopy,* makes use of the far-ultraviolet radiation from a helium discharge tube to expel an electron from the atom or molecule under study. This discharge tube provides an intense source of 584-Å (58.4-nm) radiation. Such radiation has quanta of energy 2046 kJ mol^{-1}, or 21.21 eV. With such an ionizing beam, the electrons of the outermost electron shell of most atoms and molecules can be expelled. These are the electrons that are most directly involved in the chemical, or bonding, characteristics of molecules. Thus photoelectron spectroscopy provides experimental results that are valuable adjuncts to the theoretical studies described in Chap. 13.

A second experimental approach makes use of low-energy, or "soft," x-rays. Various x-ray targets provide radiation with energies of several thousand electronvolts. Such radiation can expel even the innermost $1s$ electrons of atoms of molecules. Such electrons are bound with an energy that depends primarily on the nuclear charge of the atom to which they are held. The $1s$ electrons of the carbon atoms in any type of molecule, for example, have an ionization energy of about 1200 eV. However, this value depends somewhat on the chemical environment of the carbon atoms. Measurement of the ionization potentials of such inner electrons thus reveals the various chemical environments of the atoms of a given type in the molecules of the sample under study. The results are therefore a guide to the nature of the molecule. As a result, this approach has many analytical applications. It is known as *electron spectroscopy for chemical analysis* (ESCA).

With either of the above two approaches, the sample is irradiated with high-energy radiation, and electrons are expelled. Some of the energy of the incident radiation is carried off as kinetic energy of the expelled electrons. The energy required to produce a particular ionization is equal to the energy of the incident quanta less the kinetic energy of the expelled electrons. We can describe this by the expression

$$I = h\nu - \epsilon_{kin} \tag{14-33}$$

where I is one of the ionization energies and $h\nu$ is the energy of the incident radiation. When high-energy ultraviolet or x-ray ionizing radiation is used, atoms and molecules have a variety of ionization energies. Ionizations that require a large energy will leave the expelled electrons with little kinetic energy. Those requiring a smaller amount of energy will leave the expelled electrons with more kinetic energy. The pattern of electron kinetic energies thus yields a display of the various ionization energies of the atoms or molecules of the sample.

A variety of ionization energies are found for the atoms or molecules, A, of

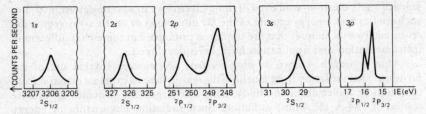

FIGURE 14-19 The photoelectron spectrum of argon. [*From H. Bock and P. Mollère, J. Chem. Educ.,* **51**:*506 (1974)*.]

the sample. Although each state of A^+, the product of the ionization process, can be described by an atomic or molecular state symbol, these states are satisfactorily and more fruitfully described in terms of orbitals, the descriptions of the individual electrons.

Each ionization energy is a measure of the energy required to expel an electron from one of the orbitals of the atomic or molecular species A. Or we can think of it as the energy released when an electron with zero kinetic energy is "dropped" into the empty orbital of the A^+ species. Thus the ionization energies can be taken to be measures of orbital energies.

The ionization spectrum of argon given in Fig. 14-19 illustrates the results obtained for free atoms. The ionizations can be described by the atomic symbols for the Ar^+ ions that are formed. More helpful are the designations of the orbitals of the parent argon atoms from which an electron has been expelled. The pattern of the orbital energies can be compared with the SCF values of Fig. 11-13. (Notice that only the outermost orbital, $3p$, has a low enough ionization energy to be studied by 584-Å helium discharge radiation.)

Now let us turn to the results obtained when the ionization energies of molecules are measured. We must be prepared for the excited A^+ state to be produced in the ground state or various excited vibrational states. These possibilities can again be treated in terms of the potential-energy curves for the electronic states that are involved and the Frank-Condon principle.

The three types of situation are expected. If the ionized electron comes from a nonbonding or an inner orbital, the potential-energy curve for A^+ should be little different from that of A. We expect $v = 0$ to $v = 0$ transitions to occur. A single ionization line would be expected. If a bonding electron is removed, the bonding in A^+ is expected to be weaker than in A. The A^+ potential-energy curve will be shifted in the direction of longer equilibrium bonds. The weaker bonding will produce a more open potential-energy curve. A relatively small vibrational spacing in the spectra band is expected. If an electron of an antibonding orbital is expelled, the opposite effect is expected. The nature of the ionization bands produced for the ejection of nonbonding, bonding, and antibonding electrons serves as a guide to the assignment of ionization bonds to orbitals when the vibrational structure of the bonds are resolved.

The ionization-energy spectrum of N_2 is shown in Fig. 14-20. Alongside the

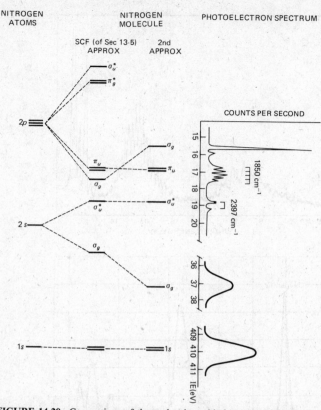

FIGURE 14-20 Comparison of the molecular-orbital energy pattern of N_2 deduced from the photoelectron spectrum with that calculated by the methods of Sec. 13-7. [*From H. Bock and P. D. Mollère, J. Chem. Educ.,* **51**:506 (1974).]

spectrum is the molecular-orbital pattern and orbital designations, developed in Sec. 13-5. The vibrational structure of the upper three bonds is in keeping with the assignment.

The center, or most prominent peak, of a band gives the *vertical ionization energy*. The ionization energies, or orbital energies obtained from SCF calculations, are also for the molecule with the equilibrium structure of the parent molecule. Thus the SCF orbital energies are to be compared with the energies at the centers of the ionization bonds. (For other purposes, the energies of the first, lowest-energy component, which might correspond to $v = 0$ to $v = 0$ transitions might be considered.) The SCF orbital energy results are, as shown in Fig. 14-20, in reasonably good agreement with the experimentally deduced energies. The energies of the uppermost occupied orbitals, σ_g and π_u, are almost identical in the SCF procedure described in Sec. 13-5. In fact, the σ_g orbital is of somewhat

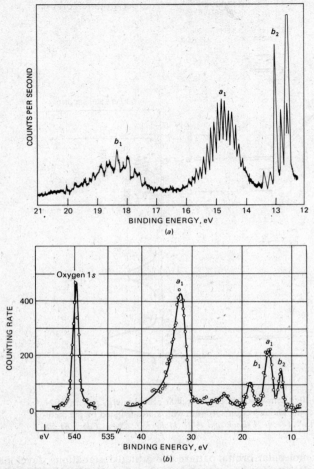

FIGURE 14-21 The photoelectron-spectrum pattern for the H_2O molecule: (*a*) attained with 584-Å helium discharge radiation (*from D. W. Turner et al., "Molecular Photoelectron Spectroscopy," Wiley-Interscience, New York, 1970*); (*b*) obtained with Mg K_α x-rays (*from K. Siegbahn et al., "ECSA Applied to Free Molecules," North-Holland Publishing Company, Amsterdam, 1969*). The symmetries of the orbitals, based on the symmetry elements of Fig. 12-5, from which the electron is removed are indicated.

higher energy than the π_u orbital. This result can be reached by a refinement of the simple SCF treatment.

In a similar way the ionization-energy spectrum for H_2O in Fig. 14-21 can be compared with the molecular orbitals obtained by symmetry considerations in Fig. 13-15. The correlation of theoretical and experimental orbital energies

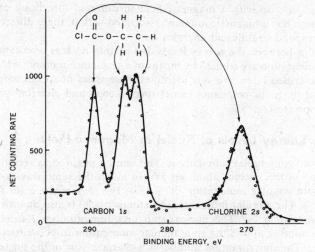

FIGURE 14-22 Part of the photoelectron spectrum of ethyl chloroformate. [*From T. L. James, J. Chem. Educ.,* **48**:*712 (1971).*]

emphasizes the reality of the symmetrized molecular orbitals treated in Sec. 13-9. Similar experimental results for the energies of molecular orbitals of a great variety of molecules are now becoming available.

One illustration (Fig. 14-22) is shown to suggest the use of inner-orbital-ionization energies in providing a "fingerprint" of a molecule. Notice that each carbon atom with a different environment reveals itself through the chemical shift of its 1s ionization energy.

ELECTRON AND NUCLEAR MAGNETIC SPECTROSCOPY

The spectroscopic methods treated earlier in the chapter dealt with the study of transitions between energy levels of free, or nearly free, molecules. The spacing between such molecular energy levels is a characteristic of the electronic structure and atomic makeup of the molecule. The spectroscopic methods now to be studied treat transitions between energy levels whose spacing depend on the magnetic field applied to the sample. Present-day studies make use of energy levels that arise in two different ways. The first type of energy level, and the transitions between such energy levels, to be discussed arises because the nuclei of some atoms have a magnetic moment, and different orientations of such nuclear magnets relative to the applied field have different energies. The second type of energy level to be dealt with arises from the magnetic moment of the electron. An electron that does not have a counterpart with opposite spin direction can also line up with a magnetic field in different directions, and because the electron has a magnetic moment associated with it, these different orientations correspond to different energies.

The transitions between the energy levels due both to nuclear orientation and to electron orientation are studied by means of a resonance method, which will be briefly described later, and one identifies these types of spectroscopic studies as nuclear-magnetic-resonance (nmr) spectroscopy and electron-spin-resonance (esr) spectroscopy.

14-8 The Energy Levels of Nuclei in Magnetic Fields

Many nuclei have spin angular momentum. This can be pictured as resulting from the spinning of the nucleus about an axis in much the same way as an electron has a spin angular momentum of $\sqrt{s(s+1)}(h/2\pi)$, where s for the electron must be $\frac{1}{2}$. The angular momentum of atomic nuclei is also quantized and comes in units of $h/2\pi$. The nuclear-spin quantum number I can be introduced. This number allows the spin angular momentum to be written as $\sqrt{I(I+1)}(h/2\pi)$. The spin quantum number is a characteristic of the nucleus and can be zero or can have various integral or half-integral values. These values can to some extent be correlated with the neutron and proton makeup of the nucleus. Most nmr studies have been concerned with the hydrogen nucleus, which has $I = \frac{1}{2}$, and the method of nmr spectroscopy can be satisfactorily illustrated by restricting our attention to this nucleus.

Along any defined direction in space, and now the applied magnetic field will specify this direction, the angular momentum of the spinning nucleus must present quantized components. A nucleus with an angular momentum $\sqrt{\frac{1}{2}(\frac{1}{2}+1)}(h/2\pi)$ must therefore line itself up, as indicated in Fig. 14-23, in such a way that the angular momentum in the direction of the magnetic field is $+\frac{1}{2}(h/2\pi)$ or $-\frac{1}{2}(h/2\pi)$. The allowed orientations of a nucleus with spin quantum number $\frac{3}{2}$ are also shown in Fig. 14-23 to illustrate the more general case.

The number of different allowed orientations of the nuclear-spin direction is seen from Fig. 14-23 to be determined by the nuclear-spin quantum number. The difference in the energies of these different orientations depends on the interaction of the nuclear magnetic moment with the magnetic field. A nucleus, which is a charged particle, can be pictured as spinning on its axis and can be expected to have a magnetic moment in a manner analogous to the way a coil of wire carrying a current, according to Ampère's law, has a magnetic moment. Our lack of understanding of the details of the charge distribution in a nucleus prevents us from obtaining a theoretical value for the nuclear magnetic moment by this approach.

If, however, the magnetic moment of the nucleus of the hydrogen atom is denoted by μ_H and the magnetic field acting on the proton by $\mathcal{H}$, lining up the nuclear moments with and against the magnetic field will produce the energy levels indicated in Fig. 14-23. These values are calculated from the energy of a

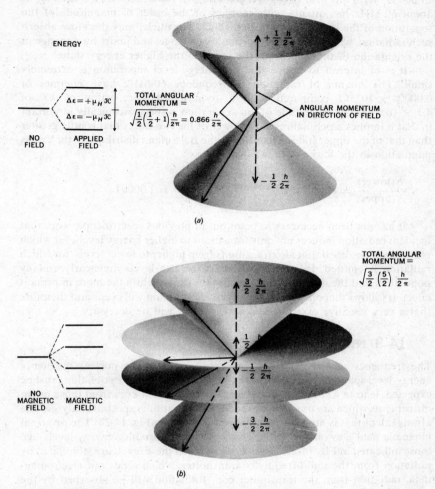

ANGULAR MOMENTUM

ENERGY

$\Delta \epsilon = + \mu_H \mathcal{H}$

$\Delta \epsilon = - \mu_H \mathcal{H}$

NO FIELD

APPLIED FIELD

TOTAL ANGULAR MOMENTUM = $\sqrt{\frac{1}{2}\left(\frac{1}{2}+1\right)}\frac{h}{2\pi} = 0.866\frac{h}{2\pi}$

ANGULAR MOMENTUM IN DIRECTION OF FIELD

$+\frac{1}{2}\frac{h}{2\pi}$

$-\frac{1}{2}\frac{h}{2\pi}$

(a)

TOTAL ANGULAR MOMENTUM = $\sqrt{\frac{3}{2}\left(\frac{5}{2}\right)}\frac{h}{2\pi}$

$\frac{3}{2}\frac{h}{2\pi}$

$\frac{1}{2}\frac{h}{2\pi}$

$-\frac{1}{2}\frac{h}{2\pi}$

$-\frac{3}{2}\frac{h}{2\pi}$

NO MAGNETIC FIELD

MAGNETIC FIELD

(b)

FIGURE 14-23 The allowed orientations of the angular-momentum vector in a magnetic field and the corresponding energy levels. (a) The hydrogen-atom nucleus with $I = \frac{1}{2}$ and magnetic moment μH. (b) A nucleus with $I = \frac{3}{2}$.

magnet lined up at various directions to the magnetic field and the quantum stipulation that the spin be lined up with or opposed to the field. Before proceeding to a more detailed treatment of the method used to study transitions between these energy levels and the complications that arise when the nuclei being studied are part of a molecule, a few general features will be reported.

Magnetic fields used in nmr spectroscopy usually have values of about

14,000 G. With this field strength it is found that radiation with a frequency of about 60 MHz has quanta with energies of the order of magnitude of the separation of the levels shown in Fig. 14-23. The nuclei may therefore absorb such radiation, which is in the radio-frequency range, and jump, by a change in the orientation of the spin, from the lower to the higher energy state.

It is of interest to notice that the energy-level separation is extremely small. The quanta of radiation of frequency 60 MHz have energies of 0.00004×10^{-21} J compared with a room-temperature value of kT of 4.1×10^{-21} J. The magnitude of this separation is spectroscopically important in that it implies a population in the lower of the two states that is little greater than that of the upper state. According to the Boltzmann distribution, the excess population in the lower state is calculated as

$$\frac{N(\text{lower})}{N(\text{upper})} = e^{\Delta\epsilon/kT} = e^{(0.00004 \times 10^{-21})/(4.1 \times 10^{-21})} = 1.00001$$

It has not been necessary to point out in previous spectroscopic work that incident radiation induces not only transitions to higher energy levels, for which radiation is absorbed, but also transitions from higher to lower levels, for which radiation is emitted. In nmr experiments the two levels are nearly equally populated, and the absorption of radiation is only slightly the more important effect. It follows that only weak absorption of radiation will occur and therefore that a very sensitive experimental arrangement will be necessary.

14-9 NMR Spectroscopy

The frequency of the radiation that corresponds to the nuclear magnetic-energy-level spacings and the weakness of the radiation absorption that must be expected, lead to a spectrometer of a radically different kind from those prism instruments which are used for electronic and vibrational spectral analyses. The arrangement that is most frequently used is shown in Fig. 14-24. The principal magnetic field acts on the nuclei of the sample to produce energy levels like those indicated in Fig. 14-23. Transitions between these levels are stimulated by radiation from the radio-frequency transmitter, which sends out electromagnetic radiation from the transmitter coil. Radiation will be absorbed by the sample if the frequency of the radiation is such that the quanta of radiation have an energy matching the nuclear energy-level spacing. When such radiation is absorbed, it can be thought of as producing nuclei in the excited state, which will then tend to reemit the radiation in order to approach the Boltzmann distribution ratio. It is this emitted radiation that is detected by the receiver coil, which, being oriented at right angles to the transmitter, receives no signal unless the sample provides this coupling with the transmitter. The signal from the receiver coil can be displayed on an oscilloscope or a recorder.

This indication of the operation of an nmr spectrometer implies that a fixed magnetic field is imposed on the sample and that the frequency of the radiation

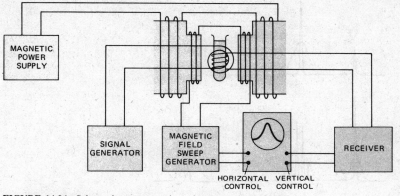

FIGURE 14-24 Schematic representation of an nmr spectrometer.

is varied. Thus, if the energy spacing is $2\mu_H \mathcal{H}$, as indicated in Fig. 14-23, and the radiation has frequency ν and quanta with energy $h\nu$, absorption of radiation can occur when

$$2\mu_H \mathcal{H} = h\nu \tag{14-34}$$

Since it is here possible to control the energy-level spacing by manipulating $\mathcal{H}$, the equality of Eq. (14-34) can be brought about either by adjusting ν after some fixed value of $\mathcal{H}$ is chosen or by adjusting $\mathcal{H}$ after some fixed value of ν has been selected. The latter procedure turns out to be experimentally more satisfactory. A fixed frequency, usually about 60 MHz, is supplied by the transmitter, and the magnetic field is varied through a small range until Eq. (14-34) is satisfied. At this point the sample absorbs radiation, the transmitter and receiver are coupled, the circuit can be said to be in resonance, and a signal is produced from the receiver circuit.

The signal that is obtained as a function of magnetic field for a fixed frequency of 60 MHz is shown in Fig. 14-25a and b for several simple compounds. The identification of the hydrogen atom or groups of hydrogen atoms that produce a given signal can be made by a simple comparison of these spectra or can be more definitely established by the use of deuterium-substituted derivatives. If spectra are obtained at higher resolution, a considerable complexity appears, as is shown by the solid curves of Fig. 14-25a and the lower curve of Fig. 14-25b.

The nuclear energy-level splitting depends on the nuclear magnetic moment and the magnetic field strength. The experimental results indicate that even if the absorption of only hydrogen atoms is studied, a number of closely spaced absorptions are observed. It is now necessary to see whether or not these finer details of nmr spectroscopy, which contain the information of principal interest to the chemist, can be understood.

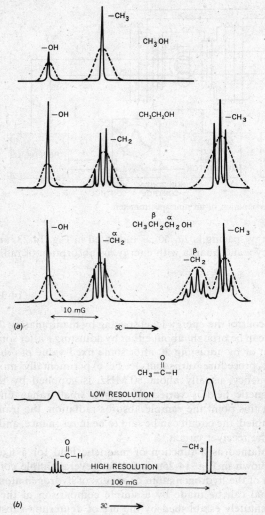

FIGURE 14-25
The nmr spectra of several simple compounds at a frequency of 60 MHz and a magnetic field of 14,000 G. In (*a*) the solid lines give the high-resolution spectra. The dashed lines show the appearance of the spectra at low resolution, where the splitting arising from the interactions of the nuclei would not be observed.

14-10 Chemical Shifts and Nuclear Magnetic Interactions

The factors that lead to the different absorptions of Fig. 14-25 can often be treated separately from the factors that lead to the finer splittings indicated there. The separation in the positions of the spectral lines associated with hydrogen atoms in different chemical environments is called the *chemical shift*. These shifts can be conveniently reported by means of the difference in magnetic field necessary for absorption compared with that necessary for absorption by some reference. This difference is usually reported as the chemical shift δ, defined as

$$\delta = \frac{\mathcal{H}_{\text{ref}} - \mathcal{H}_{\text{sample}}}{\mathcal{H}_{\text{ref}}} \times 10^6 \qquad (14\text{-}35)$$

The reference chosen is now usually tetramethylsilane, $(CH_3)_4Si$, because of the conveniently located, well-defined absorption it produces. Since hydrogen atoms in different samples show absorption, or resonance, at fields that differ by the order of milligauss when the magnetic field is 14,000 G, the values of δ are made of convenient size by the inclusion of the factor 10^6 in Eq. (14-35).

The existence of the chemical shift can be attributed to the screening effect exerted by the electrons about a nucleus. Thus, although the external magnetic field is the same for all hydrogen atoms of a sample of CH_3OH, for example, the electron distribution in the C—H and O—H bonds screens the nuclei from the applied field to different extents. Some correlations have succeeded in showing that the more the electrons of the bond to hydrogen are drawn to the bonding atom, the more exposed the nucleus of the hydrogen atom is. Such exposed nuclei generally absorb at lower magnetic fields than well-shielded nuclei.

As a result of chemical shifts the nmr spectrum is a portrayal of the chemical environment of the various hydrogen atoms of the material. It follows that an analysis of a spectrum of an unknown material can lead to information on the types of bonding to hydrogen atoms and often to the molecular structure of the sample. In this respect nmr complements infrared and ultraviolet spectroscopy in the elucidation of the structures of large molecules. Some of the characteristic chemical shifts used in such analyses are shown in Table 14-3.

The high-resolution detail, as shown schematically in Fig. 14-26, is also characteristic of the hydrogen-atom arrangement of the molecule and is therefore also helpful in structural determinations. Only some features of the source of these additional splittings can be given.

The magnetic field at a nucleus in a molecule is determined not only by the external magnetic field as modified by the shielding electrons but also by the presence and orientation of the other nuclei in the molecule that behave as magnets, i.e., have magnetic moments. Since both ^{16}O and ^{12}C have zero spin and zero magnetic moment, the magnetic nuclei of many organic compounds consist only of the hydrogen atoms. It is the interaction between the nuclei of these atoms that leads to the additional splitting beyond that of the chemical shifts.

The nature and effect of these interactions can be illustrated by reference to

$$\text{O}$$
$$\|$$

the spectrum of acetaldehyde, $CH_3—C—H$. The hydrogen atoms of the methyl group experience a magnetic field that depends on the applied field, on the chemical-shift effect of the shielding electrons, and on the influence of the

TABLE 14-3 Characteristic Values for the Chemical Shift δ for Hydrogen in Organic Compounds

Tetramethylsilane is the reference compound

(CH₃)₄Si
CH₃—CH₂—, (CH₃)₃CH—, (CH₃)₄C
CH₃CH₂—
R—SH
—CH₂— in a ring
(CH₃)₃CH
—CH₂— in ring ketones
(CH₃CO)₂O
CH₃CN
—CH₂—NH₂
CH₃Ph
CH₃CH₂Ph, PhCH₂CH₂Ph,(CH₃)₂CHPh
HC≡C—
CH₃—X ⎫
—CH₂—X ⎬ F, Cl, Br, I
＼CH—X ⎭
PhSH
CH₃NO₂, —CH₂NO₂, ＼CHNO₂
PhNH₂
—CH=CH— conjugated ⎫ olefins
—CH=CH— nonconjugated ⎭
CH₂=C terminal
CH₂=C(CH₃)₂
(CH₃)₂C=CHCH₃

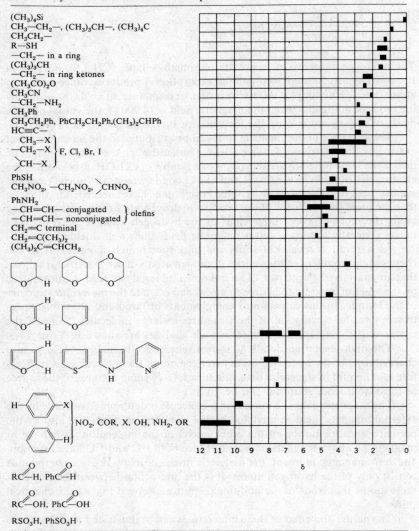

δ
12 11 10 9 8 7 6 5 4 3 2 1 0

RC(=O)—H, PhC(=O)—H

RC(=O)—OH, PhC(=O)—OH

RSO₃H, PhSO₃H

Source: E. Mokacsi, *J. Chem. Educ.*, **41**:38 (1964).

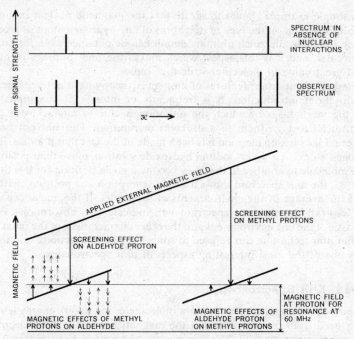

FIGURE 14-26 A schematic representation of the nmr spectrum of acetaldehyde, CH_3—C—H, and its interpretation in terms of the screening effects and nuclear interactions.

magnetic field of the nucleus of the hydrogen atom adjacent to the carbonyl group. This nucleus, as Fig. 14-26 indicates, can line up with or against the principal magnetic field. The methyl hydrogen atoms will therefore experience a slightly greater or lesser magnetic field, depending on the orientation of the lone hydrogen atom. The methyl absorption will therefore be split into a doublet.

The single hydrogen atom also experiences a magnetic field that depends on the applied field, on the shielding provided by its bonding electrons, and on the influence of the three magnetic nuclei in the methyl group. The four different ways in which the three magnets can arrange themselves relative to the applied field are shown in Fig. 14-26, where it is indicated that two of the ways are 3 times as probable as the other two. The lone hydrogen atom can therefore experience four slightly different magnetic fields, depending on the orientation of the spins of the methyl hydrogen nuclei. Four different resonance frequencies would be expected for the lone hydrogen nucleus or, in view of the experimental arrangement, four slightly different applied fields at a fixed radiation frequency. The spectrum of Fig. 14-25 bears out these analyses.

This simple example should illustrate that the magnetic nuclear interactions give information on the type of neighbors of any hydrogen atom or group of atoms in the molecule. Such intimate details can be obtained even for quite large molecules, and it is this aspect which makes the fine splittings of nmr spectra of great value in molecular-structure studies.

A number of important features of nmr spectroscopy have not been dealt with in this brief introduction. It is frequently of interest, for example, to examine the mechanism by which the radiation is able to interact with the magnetic nuclei to turn them to a different orientation. This has not been treated here. Likewise, no mention has been made of the fact that if atoms, like the hydrogen atoms of a water–sodium hydroxide solution, move their position from one molecule to another so that they occupy a given position for less than about 10^{-2} s, the nmr spectrum shows a single absorption at a position characteristic of the average of the environments of the nuclei. If the nuclei change position less rapidly, the nmr spectrum will indicate two absorptions, one characteristic of the one environment and the other characteristic of the other. It follows that nmr technique can be used to study the rate of reactions, and this, in fact, is one of the most interesting aspects of nmr spectroscopy.

14-11 ESR Spectroscopy

The presence of an unpaired electron in a molecule or ion allows energy levels to be produced from the interaction of the magnetic moment of the electron with an applied magnetic field. The electron, like the proton, has a half unit of spin angular momentum, and the spin angular momentum is quantized along the direction defined by the magnetic field if the component in this direction is $+\frac{1}{2}(h/2\pi)$ or $-\frac{1}{2}(h/2\pi)$. These two states will have energies that are separated from the original state with no applied field by the amounts $+\mu_e\mathcal{H}$ and $-\mu_e\mathcal{H}$, where μ_e is the magnetic moment of the spinning electron and $\mathcal{H}$ is the magnetic field acting on the unpaired electron.

The electron-spin magnetic moment, however, is about 1000 times greater than a typical nuclear magnetic moment. The energy of interaction of the magnetic moment of the unpaired electron with the applied field will be greater than the corresponding interaction between the nuclear magnetic moment and the applied field. It is found that when a magnetic field of 3000 G is used, the energy spacing between the levels with different spin orientation relative to this field is such that transitions are caused by radiation of about 30 mm wavelength, a wavelength of the microwave region. The energy separation, even in the relatively low field of 3000 G, is therefore

$$\frac{3 \times 10^8}{0.03}(0.66 \times 10^{-33}) = 0.007 \times 10^{-21} \text{ J}$$

a value to be compared with nuclear-energy spacings of about 0.00004×10^{-21} J in a field of 14,000 G.

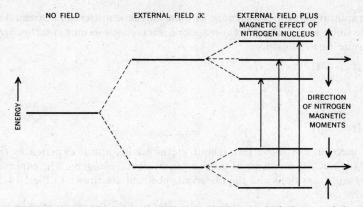

NO FIELD | EXTERNAL FIELD $\mathcal{H}$ | EXTERNAL FIELD PLUS MAGNETIC EFFECT OF NITROGEN NUCLEUS

ENERGY →

DIRECTION OF NITROGEN MAGNETIC MOMENTS

FIGURE 14-27 The energy-level diagram for the unpaired electron of the radical ion $(SO_3)_2NO^-$, showing the splitting of the two electron-spin states by the magnetic moment of the nitrogen nucleus.

The most prominent and revealing feature of esr spectra is the splitting caused in the transition between the two electron-orientation states by the interaction of the magnetic moment of the spinning electron with the magnetic moments of those nuclei in the molecule which have magnetic moments. The electron-spin energies and the splitting of these energies due to the nitrogen nucleus, which has one unit of spin, are shown for the ion $(SO_3)_2NO^-$ in Fig. 14-27. Transitions occur which change the orientation of the electron spin relative to the applied magnetic field. The interaction between the electron and the magnetic nucleus is sufficiently small to ensure that the transitions do not also change the magnetic-moment direction. With this selection rule the transitions of Fig. 14-27 can be drawn. The observed spectrum does in fact show three absorption bands. It should be mentioned that because of the experimental arrangement used in esr, the derivative of the usual spectral absorption or emission curve is often shown. Figure 14-28 shows this presentation of the recorded spectrum.

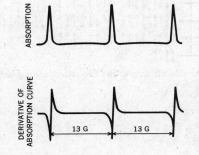

ABSORPTION

DERIVATIVE OF ABSORPTION CURVE

13 G   13 G

FIGURE 14-28
The esr spectrum of the radical ion $(SO_3)_2NO^-$ at a frequency of 9500 MHz and a magnetic field of about 3400 G.

The splittings due to interactions with the magnetic nuclei can be treated in much the same way as the nuclear magnetic interactions in nmr spectroscopy. Thus, in the free-radical ion

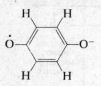

the odd electron can move throughout the molecule, and it experiences the effect of the nuclear moments of the four equivalent hydrogens. The expected splittings and transitions and the observed spectrum are shown in Figs. 14-29 and 14-30.

Thus esr spectroscopy provides a powerful tool for the study of chemical species with unpaired electrons. It gives information not only on the presence and number of such electrons, as measurements of paramagnetism often do, but also on the distribution of the electron in the molecule. The splitting due to interactions with a nuclear magnetic moment depends on the odd electron's being distributed throughout the molecule so that it is to some extent near that nucleus. Such details of electronic configuration in free-radical-type molecules are one of the important features treated by esr.

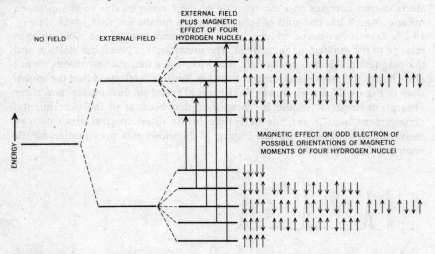

FIGURE 14-29 The energy-level diagram for the odd electron of the free-radical ion 1,4-benzosemiquinone,

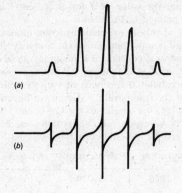

(a)

(b)

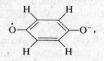

FIGURE 14-30
The esr spectrum (a) integral and (b) differential of 1,4-benzosemiquinone,

at a frequency of 9500 MHz and a magnetic field of about 3400 G.

PROBLEMS

14-1. The wave number of the microwave radiation absorbed in the $J = 0$ to $J = 1$ transition of carbon monoxide has been measured as 3.842 cm^{-1}. (a) What is the value of $\bar{B}$? (b) What is the value of B, the rotational constant, in joules? (c) What is the moment of inertia of the CO molecule? (d) If the absorption is attributed to CO molecules containing the isotopes ^{12}C and ^{16}O, what is the bond length of the molecule?

14-2. Tables of bond lengths give the value 0.93 Å for the HF molecule. (a) What is the moment of inertia of the HF molecule? (b) What are the values of the rotational constants B in joules and $\bar{B}$ in cm^{-1}? (c) What are the wave-number values at which the first, lowest-frequency, four rotational absorptions are expected? (d) Describe the spectral region in which these absorptions occur.

14-3. The high-temperature microwave spectrum of KCl vapor shows an absorption at a frequency of 7687.94 MHz that can be identified with the $J = 0$ to $J = 1$ transition of $^{39}K^{35}Cl$ molecules in the $v = 0$ vibrational state. What are the values of B and I and the bond length of the KCl molecule?

14-4. The microwave spectrum of the CN radical shows a series of lines spaced by a nearly constant amount of 3.798 cm^{-1}. What is the bond length of CN?

14-5. The observed rotational spectrum of HF shows a first absorption at 41.11 cm^{-1} followed by additional absorptions each at about this wave-number amount beyond the preceding one. More precisely, the spacing between adjacent absorptions decreases, being 40.08 cm^{-1} for the $J = 5$ to $J = 6$ transitions and 37.81 cm^{-1} for the $J = 10$ to $J = 11$ transition. (a) Calculate B values and I values from these three given data. (b) What explanation can you give for the variation?

14-6. (a) For a rotational constant $\bar{B}$ of 2 cm^{-1} calculate the population of the rotational states up to J values of about 10 at a temperature of 25°C. (b) Plot the results versus J and also versus rotational energy. (J values up to about 10 are needed for $\bar{B} = 10$ cm^{-1} and to about twice this value for $\bar{B} = 2$ cm^{-1}. In the latter case it will be adequate to calculate the population of every second rotational level.)

*14-7. (a) Obtain an expression for the J level with the maximum population as a function of the rotational constant $\bar{B}$ and the temperature. (Assume that the rotational spacings are small compared with kT so that a derivative can be taken to obtain the maximum.) (b) From this expression calculate the value of J for $\bar{B} = 2$ cm^{-1} and $\bar{B} = 10$ cm^{-1} and compare with the graphs obtained in Prob. 14-6.

*14-8. (a) From the result of Prob. 14-7 obtain an expression for the rotational energy at which the allowed rotational energy is most populated. (b) Simplify your result for the customary case in which the rotational constant B is much less than kT. (c) Explain why the dependence on T and B, or $\bar{B}$, is that shown by this expression.

*14-9. From the tabulated data for the rotational constants of various isotopic forms of OCS (W. Gordy, W. V. Smith, and R. F. Trambarulo, "Microwave Spectroscopy," John Wiley & Sons, Inc., New York, 1953) the lengths of the O—C and C—S bonds have been deduced to be 1.164 and 1.558 Å, respectively. Verify that these bond lengths are generally consistent with the observed rotational constants.

Isotope	$^{16}O^{12}C^{32}S$	$^{16}O^{12}C^{34}S$	$^{16}O^{14}C^{32}S$	$^{18}O^{12}C^{32}S$	$^{18}O^{12}C^{34}S$
$\bar{B}$, cm^{-1}	0.20286	0.19790	0.2016	0.19029	0.18546

From the tabulated data for the rotational constants of various isotopic forms of OCS the lengths of the O—C and C—S bonds have been deduced to be 1.164 and 1.558 Å, respectively. Verify that these bond lengths are generally consistent with the observed rotational constants.

14-10. (a) From the Raman spectrum of CO_2 shown in Fig. 14-4b estimate the rotational constants $\bar{B}$ and B. (b) What is the moment of inertia of the molecule? (c) What is the C—O bond length?

14-11. The bond length of the N_2 molecule has been determined from Raman spectra to be 1.097×10^{-10} m. Work back to find how far, in cm^{-1} from the exciting Raman line, the first three lines of the N_2 rotational Raman spectrum are. Compare with the spectrum of Fig. 14-4a.

14-12. The low-resolution infrared spectrum of CO shows an absorption band centered at 2143 cm^{-1}. What is the force constant of the molecule?

14-13. The force constant of HF is listed as 880 N m^{-1}. (a) At what wave number is the fundamental, $v = 0$ to $v = 1$, vibrational absorption expected? (b) Where would the corresponding absorption of DF be expected?

14-14. Assume that the contribution of the $v = 0$ to $v = 1$ and the $v = 1$ to $v = 2$ transitions to the fundamental absorption band depends simply on the number of molecules in the initial state. Calculate the percentage to which the $1 \rightarrow 2$ transition contributes to the CO fundamental at 2143 cm^{-1} if the temperature is 25°C.

14-15. A typical chemical bond has a force constant of 500 N m^{-1}, an equilibrium bond length of 1.5 Å, and a dissociation energy D_e of 5 eV. (a) On the basis of the harmonic-oscillator approximation plot the potential energy as a function of internuclear distance. Put the minimum at an energy corresponding to -5 eV and extend the potential-energy curves up to the zero energy value. (b) What else must be known before the $v = 0$, $v = 1$, and $v = 2$ energy levels can be drawn in? Select a reasonable value of what is required and add these levels. Also locate $\frac{1}{2}kT$ for $T = 298$ K on the graph.

14-16. Because it does not include the vibrational kinetic energy, the Morse function is said to represent the potential energy of a diatomic molecule and is given, as in Prob. 13-11, by $U(r) = D_e(-2e^{-\beta(r-r_e)} + e^{-2\beta(r-r_e)})$. By forming the second derivative of $U(r)$ with respect to r show that $\beta = \sqrt{k/2D_e}$, where k is the force constant.

14-17. Add to the graph of Prob. 14-15 the Morse-function curve for the example with $k = 500$ N m^{-1}, $r_e = 1.5$ Å, and $D_e = 5$ eV.

14-18. Ordinary HCl consists of 75 percent $H^{35}Cl$ and 25 percent $H^{37}Cl$. A spectrum of HCl might show distinct absorptions due to these isotopic species. (*a*) Calculate the difference in wave numbers for the $v = 0$ to $v = 1$ vibrational transition of $H^{35}Cl$ and $H^{37}Cl$, assuming that the force constants of the two molecules are identical and equal to 484 N m^{-1}. (*b*) Compare this calculated difference with the splitting of the vibration-rotation lines of Fig. 14-11. (*c*) Identify the components due to $H^{35}Cl$ and $H^{37}Cl$.

14-19. Using the procedure suggested in Sec. 14-4, obtain $\bar{B}_1$ and $\bar{B}_0$ for $H^{35}Cl$ or $H^{37}Cl$ from the data of Fig. 14-11.

14-20. Rotational constants for various vibrational levels are often fitted to a linear equation $\bar{B} = \bar{B}_e - \bar{\alpha}_e (v + \frac{1}{2})$. (*a*) From the data of Prob. 14-19 deduce $\bar{\alpha}_e$ and $\bar{B}_e$ for HCl. (*b*) Calculate r_e, r_0, and r_1. (*c*) Which of these is strictly identical for $H^{35}Cl$ and $H^{37}Cl$?

14-21. Describe the symmetries of the vibrations of the formaldehyde molecule. (*a*) How many absorption bands in the infrared spectral region are expected? (*b*) With the idea that each vibration is approximately a bond stretching or bond bending, depict each of the vibrational nodes of the molecule.

14-22. (*a*) Deduce the symmetry types of each of the vibrations of the ethylene molecule. (*b*) Draw sketches showing displacement vectors to depict these vibrations.

14-23. (*a*) Classify according to symmetry the translations, rotations, and vibrations of the NH_3 molecule. (*b*) The infrared spectrum of NH_3 shows four absorption bands that can be attributed to fundamental vibrational transitions. Is your analysis consistent with this observation?

14-24. (*a*) Classify according to symmetry the translations, rotations, and vibrations of carbon tetrachloride. (*b*) Which of the vibrations could give rise to an infrared absorption bond?

*****14-25.** The molecule BF_3 is planar and belongs to the point group $\mathbf{D}_{3h}$. (*a*) Classify the vibrations of the molecule according to their symmetry. (*b*) Which will be infrared-active? (*c*) Which of the infrared-active vibrations will be of the parallel type and which of the perpendicular type?

14-26. For molecules with a center of symmetry, a convenient rule is that vibrations symmetric with respect to the center of symmetry are Raman-active and infrared-inactive; vibrations antisymmetric with respect to the center of symmetry are Raman-inactive and infrared-active. (*a*) To which of the following molecules is this rule applicable: N_2, CCl_4, CO_2, BF_3 (planar), acetylene, ethylene, PCl_5 (trigonal bipyramid), SF_6 (octahedral)? (*b*) Classify the vibrations of an octahedral molecule, like SF_6, and state how many are infrared-active and how many are Raman-active.

14-27. The effective length of the conjugated molecule $CH_3-(CH{=}CH-)_4CH_3$ is about 9.8 Å. (*a*) Calculate and plot the energies of the first five allowed states, using a one-dimensional square-well potential to represent the molecular skeleton. (*b*) Place the eight π electrons in the energy levels that would normally be occupied. (*c*) Indicate the transition that would correspond to the absorption of radiation, and calculate the energy of quanta necessary to cause this excitation. (*d*) Compare the wavelength of the radiation that has quanta of this energy with the wavelength of 300 nm, which is the wavelength of the observed absorption band.

14-28. (*a*) The distinction between D_0, the dissociation energy for a molecule in the $v = 0$ state, and D_e the dissociation energy for a molecule in at the equilibrium position corresponding to $v = -\frac{1}{2}$, is greatest for the molecule H_2. Why is this and what property of the molecule affects this distinction? (b) Raman spectra of H_2 show that the $v = 0$ to $v = 1$ transition requires an energy equivalent to 4162 cm^{-1}. Electronic spectral studies show that for H_2, $D_0 = 4.476$ eV. What is the value of D_e?

14-29. The value of D_0 for the deuterium molecule D_2 is listed as 4.554 eV (G. Herzberg, "Molecular Spectra and Molecular Structure," vol. 1, "Spectra of Diatomic Molecules," D. Van Nostrand & Co., Inc., Princeton, N.J., 1950). Is this value consistent with the value of D_0 of 4.476 eV given for H_2? (Notice that the use of the large energy unit electronvolts tends to obscure small energy differences.)

14-30. An electronic transition in CO is responsible for an absorption band around 140 nm in the ultraviolet. A photograph of this band shows that it consists, in part, of a series of lines, expressed in wave numbers, at 64,703, 66,231, 67,675, 69,088, 70,470 cm^{-1}, and so forth. From the fact that these are absorption lines and are observed at fairly low temperatures, they can be assumed to arise from CO molecules in the lowest vibrational state. The abrupt beginning of the series at 64,703 cm^{-1} suggests that this transition leads to the $v = 0$ level of the excited electronic state. (a) Draw a diagram like Fig. 14-15 to illustrate these transitions. (b) The assumption of Hooke's law for chemical bonds leads to Eq. (14-12), which implies that vibrational levels have a constant spacing. Thus electronic spectra allow this expression to be checked. (c) Calculate a force constant from the $v = 0$, $v = 1$ spacing of the excited electronic state of the CO molecule and compare it with the force constant for the normal, or ground, electronic state.

14-31. The ionization energies of argon are shown in Fig. 14-20. If they were obtained using x-rays of wavelength 2.291 Å from a Cr K_α target as the ionizing radiation, what peaks must have been observed in the kinetic energy of the expelled electrons? Give your answers in joules and in electronvolts.

14-32. Using radiation of wavelength 584 Å from a helium discharge tube, which of the ionizations of argon, shown in Fig. 14-20, and which of those of N_2, shown in Fig. 14-22, could be studied?

14-33. Compare the experimentally determined orbital energy diagram for H_2O of Fig. 14-23 with the orbital diagrams discussed in Sec. 13-9.

REFERENCES

Several general introductions to the principles of spectroscopy and applications to studies of the rotational, vibrational, and electronic energies of molecules:

BARROW, G. M.: "Introduction to Molecular Spectroscopy," McGraw-Hill Book Company, New York, 1962.

BAUMAN, R. P.: "Absorption Spectroscopy," John Wiley & Sons, Inc., New York, 1962.

BULLAIN, E. F. H., W. O. GEORGE, and C. H. J. WELLS: "Introduction to Molecular Spectroscopy," Academic Press, Inc., New York, 1970.

CHANG, R.: "Principles of Spectroscopy," McGraw-Hill Book Company, New York, 1971.

DUNFORD, H. B.: "Elements of Diatomic Molecular Spectra," Addison-Wesley Publishing Company, Reading, Mass., 1968.

HARMONY, M. D.: "Introduction to Molecular Energies and Spectra," Holt, Reinhart and Winston, Inc., New York, 1972.

KING, G. W.: "Spectroscopy and Molecular Structure," Holt, Rinehart and Winston, Inc., New York, 1964. (More detailed and more advanced than the preceding books.)

More specialized books on one or more areas or one or more techniques of molecular spectroscopy:

HERZBERG, G.: "Spectra of Diatomic Molecules," "Infrared and Raman Spectra of Polyatomic Molecules," and "Electronic Spectra of Polyatomic Molecules," D. Van Nostrand Company, Inc., Princeton, N.J., 1950, 1955, and 1967.

WILSON, E. B., JR., J. C. DECIUS, and P. C. CROSS: "Molecular Vibrations," McGraw-Hill Book Company, New York, 1955.

JAFFE, H. H., and M. ORCHIN: "Theory and Applications of Ultraviolet Spectroscopy," John Wiley & Sons, Inc., New York, 1962. An introduction to the theoretical expressions for the electronic energies of organic molecules and consideration of the correlation of experimental results with ideas on electronic structure.

HERZBERG, G.: "The Spectra and Structure of Simple Free Radicals: An Introduction to Molecular Spectroscopy," Cornell University Press, Ithaca, N.Y., 1971. An excellent, short treatment.

LONG, D. A.: "Raman Spectroscopy," McGraw-Hill Book Company, New York, 1977.

Treatments of photoelectron spectroscopy:

ELAND, J. H. D.: "Photoelectron Spectroscopy: An Introduction to Ultraviolet Photoelectron Spectroscopy in the Gas Phase," Butterworths, London, 1974.

TURNER, D. W., C. BAKER, A. D. BAKER, and C. R. BRUNDLE: "Molecular Photoelectron Spectroscopy," Wiley-Interscience, New York, 1970.

BAKER, A. D., and D. BETTERIDGE: "Photoelectron Spectroscopy: Chemical and Analytical Aspects," Pergamon Press, Oxford, 1972.

SIEGBAHN, K., et al: "ESCA Applied to Free Molecules," North Holland Publishing Company, Amsterdam, 1969.

Books on nmr spectroscopy, arranged in order of increasing detail and difficulty:

ROBERTS, J. D.: "Nuclear Magnetic Resonance," McGraw-Hill Book Company, New York, 1959, and "An Introduction to Spin-Spin Splittings in High Resolution Nuclear Magnetic Resonance Spectra," W. A. Benjamin, Inc., New York, 1961. Two nonmathematical introductions to the use of nmr spectroscopy in the elucidation of the structures of organic molecules.

PAUDLER, W. W.,: "Nuclear Magnetic Resonance," Allyn and Bacon, Inc., Boston, 1971.

BECKER, E.: "High Resolution NMR," Academic Press, Inc., New York, 1969.

BOVEY, F. A.: "Nuclear Magnetic Resonance Spectroscopy," Academic Press, Inc., New York, 1969. A brief theoretical introduction followed by a clear and comprehensive treatment of high-resolution nuclear magnetic spectroscopy.

POPLE, J. A., W. G. SCHNEIDER, and H. J. BERNSTEIN: "High-Resolution Nuclear Magnetic Resonance," McGraw-Hill Book Company, New York, 1959.

CARRINGTON, A., and A. D. McLACHLAN: "Introduction to Magnetic Resonance with Applications to Chemistry and Chemical Physics," Harper & Row, Incorporated, New York, 1967.

Recent spectroscopy articles:

THOMAS, C. H.: The Use of Group Theory to Determine Molecular Symmetry from IR Spectra, *J. Chem. Educ.*, **51**:91 (1974).

ASHBY, R. A.: Flames: A Study in Molecular Spectroscopy, *J. Chem. Educ.*, **52**:632 (1975).

HOSKINS, L. C.: Pure Rotational Raman Spectroscopy of Diatomic Molecules, *J. Chem. Educ.*, **52**:568 (1975).

BOCK, H., and P. D. MOLLERE: Photoelectron Spectra: An Experimental Approach to Teaching Molecular Orbital Models, *J. Chem. Educ.*, **51**:506 (1974).

ELLISON, F. O., and M. G. WHITE: X-Ray Photoelectron Spectroscopy and the Role of Relaxation Energy in Understanding Chemical Shifts, *J. Chem. Educ.*, **53**:430 (1976).

15 EXPERIMENTAL STUDIES OF CRYSTAL AND MOLECULAR STRUCTURE: DIFFRACTION METHODS

Except for the relatively simple molecules that can be well treated spectroscopically, much of our information about the angles and distances within and between molecules comes from diffraction experiments. Diffraction occurs when beams of various types are scattered by gaseous or crystalline samples. The experimental methods studied here depend on the constructive and destructive interference that occurs when an x-ray beam or an electron beam is scattered by the sample. We shall see that some features of the analyses are common to all diffraction experiments. The different types of beams and the different states of the sample, however, will lead to appreciable differences in the way the data are analyzed.

Scattering by crystalline materials will be studied first. Most such work makes use of a beam of x-rays. Bond lengths and angles for the molecules or ions of the crystal are obtained. How these units pack together is also a product of the analysis. In the analysis of diffractions of x-rays by crystals, consideration of the ordered array of atoms or ions is basic to an understanding of the results. The study of diffraction by crystals will therefore be preceded by treatments of the classification of crystals, the classification of ordered arrays of points, molecules, or ions, and the ways in which these ordered arrangements can be described.

15-1 Crystal Shapes

A close look at well-formed single crystals, as occur in natural minerals and occasionally from laboratory crystallizations, shows that crystals are characterized by well-defined and to some extent symmetrically arranged planes. A closer look at a number of crystals of a given type shows that although the shape may depend on the details of the crystallization process, the angles between the planes that are observed remain the same.

The shapes of a number of crystals are shown in Fig. 15-1. These drawings idealize the actual shape that would be observed in a particular specimen, which might be longer and more needlelike or flatter and more platelike, but the crystal faces that would be observed would be oriented with respect to each

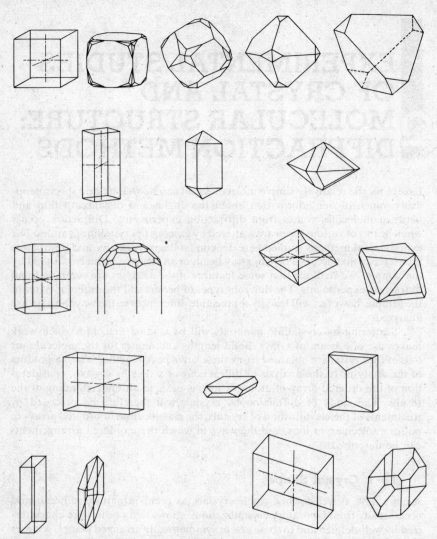

FIGURE 15-1 Some idealized crystals. (*From W. E. Ford, "Dana's Textbook of Mineralogy," 4th ed., John Wiley & Sons, Inc., New York, 1942.*)

other as they are in the illustrations. The great variety of crystalline shapes that can occur leads one to attempt to classify crystals.

The flat faces on crystals, inclined in various ways to each other, are a principal feature of real or idealized crystals. The inclinations of these planes can be described by reporting their intercepts on an "appropriate" set of axes. Such

TABLE 15-1 The Seven Crystal Systems

The axes of symmetry may be either rotation or rotation-reflection axes in all systems except the cubic

System	Axes and intercepts	Minimum symmetry
Cubic	$a = b = c$ $\alpha = \beta = \gamma = 90°$	Four threefold axes (along the diagonals of the cube)
Tetragonal	$a = b \neq c$ $\alpha = \beta = \gamma = 90°$	One fourfold axis
Hexagonal	$a = b \neq c$ $\alpha = \beta = 90°, \gamma = 120°$	One sixfold axis
Trigonal	$a = b = c$ $\alpha = \beta = 90°, \gamma = 120°$ or $a = b = c$ $\alpha = \beta = \gamma$	One threefold axis
Orthorhombic	$a \neq b \neq c$ $\alpha = \beta = \gamma = 90°$	Three twofold axes
Monoclinic	$a = b \neq c$ $\alpha = \gamma = 90°, \beta \neq 90°$	One twofold axis
Triclinic	$a \neq b \neq c$ $\alpha \neq \beta \neq \gamma \neq 90°$	None

a treatment, by René Haüy in 1784, led to the empirical generalization known as the *law of rational indices*. The law states that the intercepts of the planes of the various faces of a crystal on a set of axes suitable for that crystal can be expressed by small integral multiples of unit distances along the three axes.

For any given crystal the suitable set of axes is one of seven types. The types of axes that can be used to describe the crystal planes and (as you will see) other internal features establish the *crystal systems*. The characteristics of the axes for these systems are shown in Table 15-1. (Sometimes only six systems are recognized, the hexagonal and trigonal systems being treated as a single system.) The relation of the crystal systems to each other is illustrated in Fig. 15-2.

Inspection of the crystals or models of them shows that those belonging to any crystal system share certain symmetry properties. Thus any crystal whose faces can conveniently be described by the cubic-system axes will be found to have at least the four threefold axes of symmetry shown in Fig. 15-3. In fact this symmetry provides a better basis for establishing the cubic class than the three equal perpendicular axes that are established by cubic symmetry. As shown in Table 15-1, each crystal system can be characterized by a minimum symmetry as well as by convenient axes.

A crystal or crystal model can be inspected for elements of symmetry just as molecules were inspected in Sec. 12-1. Each idealized crystal will be found to

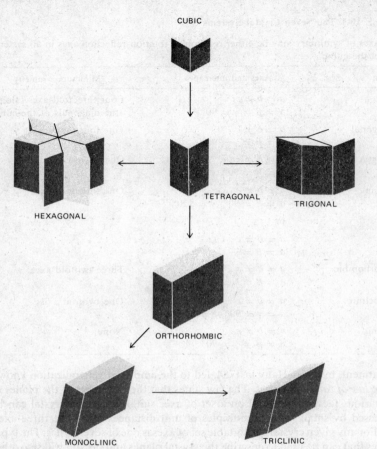

FIGURE 15-2 The seven crystal systems, showing the symmetry hierarchy. (*From Allen Nussbaum, "Applied Group Theory for Chemists, Physicists, and Engineers," Prentice-Hall, Inc., Englewood Cliffs, N.J., 1971.*)

have certain elements of symmetry. Each crystal can be assigned to one of just 32 point groups like those described in Chap. 12 in connection with our studies of molecular symmetry.

The seven crystal systems of Table 15-1 are groupings of these point groups according to certain minimum symmetries. You could verify from the character tables of Appendix C that, for example, the $\mathbf{T}_d$ and $\mathbf{O}_h$ point groups have the minimum symmetry required for the cubic crystal system.

Any crystal can be assigned to one of the 32 point groups. These 32 represent only a fraction of the possible point groups. Noticeably absent are point groups with fivefold and sevenfold axes. As you can see from two-dimensional systems, the absent symmetries are those of objects, or *tiles,* which cannot

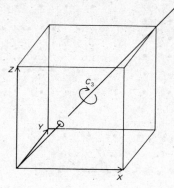

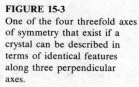

FIGURE 15-3
One of the four threefold axes of symmetry that exist if a crystal can be described in terms of identical features along three perpendicular axes.

be fitted together to form a continuous pattern. The symmetries of crystals reflect the symmetries of smaller units that fit together to produce the crystal.

Assignment of a crystal to a crystal system can sometimes be made, as has been assumed here, on the basis of its external characteristics. The importance for us of the assignment to a crystal system is the fact that the external symmetry of a crystal depends on the symmetry of the arrangement of the molecules or ions that make up the crystal. Therefore we must now investigate the relation between the internal structure of a crystal and the planes and symmetry that constitute its external characteristics.

15-2 Lattices and Unit Cells

It was apparent very early in the study of crystals, that the shapes of crystals stem from an ordered array of smaller structural units. Although we now know a great deal about the nature of these units, it remains very profitable to consider the ways in which points, each with identical surroundings, that are not further characterized can be arranged to give a repeating array.

The limitations on the types of arrangements that can give a repeating pattern in which each point has identical surroundings in the same orientation can best be appreciated from the two-dimensional patterns in Fig. 15-4. Only these five essentially different patterns can be constructed. One can verify that any other two-dimensional pattern that one attempts to draw is identical, except for the relative magnitudes of the spacings a and b and the angle α, with those shown here.

In a similar way there are, as A. Bravais showed in 1848, only 14 different types of lattices that can be drawn in three dimensions. Units of these lattices, which when repeated in three dimensions produce the lattice, are shown in Fig. 15-5. Any three-dimensional array, such as real crystal, must have an internal structure that corresponds to one of the 14 Bravais lattices.

Each real crystal, although made up of atoms or simple or complex ions or molecules, must correspond in internal structure to one of the 14 Bravais

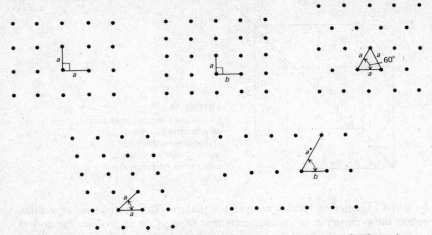

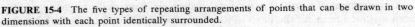

FIGURE 15-4 The five types of repeating arrangements of points that can be drawn in two dimensions with each point identically surrounded.

lattices. This does not mean that atoms, ions, or molecules need be positioned like the lattice points of Fig. 15-5. They must, however, be arranged so that points with identical environments are arranged in the pattern of one of the Bravais lattices.

One of the features of the different Bravais lattices that shows that they are indeed different is the number and arrangement of *nearest neighbors* of each lattice point. Thus the three cubic lattices shown in Fig. 15-5 give to each lattice point 6, 8, and 12 nearest-neighbor lattice points. No other arrangements that produce an extended array with cubic symmetry are possible.

We have already seen that any crystal can be assigned to one of the seven crystal systems on the basis of its symmetry. The repeating units that one constructs to describe the internal patterns of crystals must also have symmetry characteristics that allow them also to be associated with the crystal systems. This has, in fact, been done in Fig. 15-5, where one sees, for example, that the three lattices at the top of the figure have at least four threefold axes of symmetry. They therefore belong to the cubic system. Just as one assigns crystals to crystal systems on the basis of symmetry, so also can one assign the 14 possible lattice arrangements of these systems.

Such assignments, and a number of other features, are most easily done if a unit of the lattice is outlined. Although such outlines are not really pertinent to the nature of the lattice, they are more easily dealt with than the infinite array. The three cubes at the top of the figure, for example, clearly show the cubic symmetry of these three lattices. Such units of the lattice are known as *unit cells*. There is some freedom in the choice of the unit cell for a particular lattice, and the selection is made primarily to exhibit the symmetry of the lattice.

The simplest type of unit cell has lattice points, i.e., points with identical

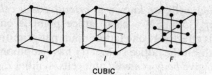

P
I
F
CUBIC
P
I
TETRAGONAL
P
HEXAGONAL
TRIGONAL
P
C
I
F
ORTHORHOMBIC
P
C
MONOCLINIC
P
TRICLINIC

FIGURE 15-5
The 14 Bravais lattices. [*From J. C. D. Brand and J. C. Speakman, "Molecular Structure," Edward Arnold (Publishers) Ltd., London, 1950.*]

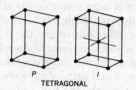

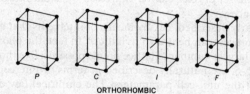

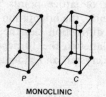

surroundings, only at the corners. Such cells are known as *primitive unit cells*. These cells are labeled *P*, as in Fig. 15-5. Since each lattice point is only one-eighth in a particular cell, there is effectively one lattice point per primitive unit cell. Other unit cells drawn to exhibit the lattice symmetry have additional lattice points either within the cell, to give *body-centered* unit cells, symbol *I*, or on the faces, to give, for example, *face-centered* unit cells, symbol *F*, and *end-centered* unit cells, symbol *C*.

The concept of unit cells suggests also the characterization of lattices not only by the symmetry and the primitive, face-centered, or body-centered nature of the unit cell but also by the type of axes that would most conveniently allow points within the unit cell to be located and planes through various lattice points to be described. Thus, in the cubic system, it is convenient to use the usual orthogonal axes and to measure distances along each axis in terms of the same unit of length. In fact, the unit-cell dimensions provide the most convenient units of length. In the tetragonal system, however, while orthogonal axes are again suitable, lengths in terms of the units $a = b \neq c$ along the x, y, and z axes will be more convenient. The conveniently inclined axes and unit lengths tabulated for the different crystal systems in Table 15-1, can be seen to be related to the unit cells of Fig. 15-5.

The concept of lattices, the existence of only 14 types, and the association of these lattices, with the help of unit cells, to the symmetry-based crystal systems provide a valuable connection between internal structure and crystal form. This connection can be further shown by relating planes in the lattices to planes or faces of actual crystals.

15-3 Crystal Planes

The law of rational indices states that the intercepts of the planes of the various faces of a crystal on a suitable set of axes can be expressed by small integral multiples of three unit distances.

Planes that can be similarly described, i.e., by means of intercepts that are integral multiples of unit distances, can be drawn in lattices. In fact, the planes that are drawn to include the largest number of lattice points possible, like those shown in end view in Fig. 15-6, are naturally described in terms of intercepts that are integral multiples of the unit-cell parameters. The empirical law describing the arrangement of the faces of a crystal is thus understandable if the internal structure of the crystal corresponds to an array of points that constitute a lattice. The important planes of the crystal then correspond to the planes that can be drawn to include a relatively large number of lattice points. The orientation of the faces of a crystal and, more importantly, the orientation and spacing of the planes that are responsible for x-ray diffraction can then be compared with the orientation and spacing of the planes in the 14 possible Bravais lattices. In this way the internal structure of the crystal can be identified with a particular lattice.

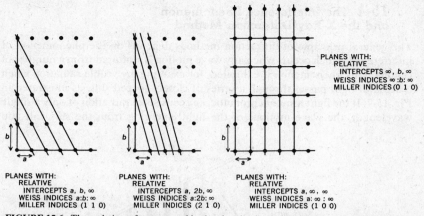

PLANES WITH:
RELATIVE
   INTERCEPTS a, b, ∞
WEISS INDICES $a:b:\infty$
MILLER INDICES (1 1 0)

PLANES WITH:
RELATIVE
   INTERCEPTS a, $2b$, ∞
WEISS INDICES $a:2b:\infty$
MILLER INDICES (2 1 0)

PLANES WITH:
RELATIVE
   INTERCEPTS a, ∞, ∞
WEISS INDICES $a:\infty:\infty$
MILLER INDICES (1 0 0)

PLANES WITH:
RELATIVE
   INTERCEPTS ∞, b, ∞
WEISS INDICES $\infty:b:\infty$
MILLER INDICES (0 1 0)

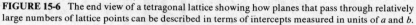

FIGURE 15-6 The end view of a tetragonal lattice showing how planes that pass through relatively large numbers of lattice points can be described in terms of intercepts measured in units of a and b.

The relative orientation of crystal or lattice planes is of great importance in crystal-structure analysis, and a convenient method for describing these planes is needed. The important planes of a lattice, as Fig. 15-6 suggests, can be described in terms of intercepts that are multiples of the unit-cell dimensions. Since crystal planes will be similarly oriented, they can be similarly described. In this way what are called *Weiss indices* are used, and planes are described by their relative intercepts on the x, y, and z axes as $a:b:c$, or $a:2b:\infty c$, and so forth.

Much more convenient, particularly in the analysis of diffraction data, are sets of numbers called *Miller indices*. These are obtained by taking the reciprocals of the coefficients of the Weiss indices. These three reciprocals are then cleared of fractions and reduced to the smallest set of integers. The plane $a:b:c$ becomes a (111) plane; the $a:2b:c$ plane becomes a (212) plane; the $a:b:\infty c$ plane becomes a (110) plane. The Miller indices, referred to in general by (hkl), describe the relative directions of the crystal planes. Information on the coordinate system and the values of the three unit distances is given separately.

A feeling for these indices can soon be acquired if one remembers their reciprocal nature. A low first number means an intercept at a large distance on the x axis; a low second number means a large intercept on the y axis; and so forth. A plane parallel to an axis now has a zero term corresponding to the reciprocal of its intercept on that axis.

The Miller indices provide a convenient way of expressing a particular plane, i.e., a particular direction in a crystal. It should be pointed out that as far as direction is concerned, which is sometimes all that is important, the planes (220) and (110) would be the same and the latter notation would be used.

15-4 The Interference Phenomenon and the X-Ray Diffraction Method

The general principle of diffraction methods depends on the phenomenon of interference, which occurs when any wave motion is scattered from a number of centers. This phenomenon is exhibited, for example, by visible radiation when a beam of light passes through a series of closely spaced slits, as illustrated in Fig. 15-7. If the light is monochromatic, i.e., consists of radiation of only a single wavelength, the wave motions of the light emerging from the slits will add

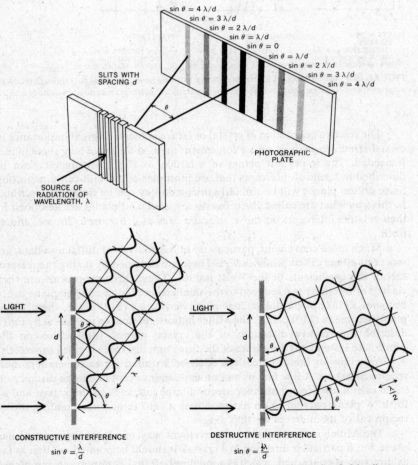

FIGURE 15-7 By measuring the angles for constructive interference the spacing d of the slit system can be deduced. (If $\lambda \approx d$, a number of diffraction lines will be observed on the photographic plate for reasonable values of $\sin \theta = n\lambda/d$.)

together in only certain directions. In these directions *constructive interference* is said to occur, and at these directions a beam of diffracted light will appear. At other directions the diffracted waves will be out of phase to various extents, *destructive interference* will occur, and less light will be seen. For the pattern of scattering units provided by the slits of Fig. 15-7 it is easy to see, as shown in the figure, that constructive interference occurs in directions defined by the angle θ, which are related to the spacing d between the slits and the wavelength λ of the light by the relation

$$\sin \theta = \frac{n\lambda}{d} \qquad (15\text{-}1)$$

where n is an integer. One sees from this, furthermore, that d and λ must be of the same order of magnitude if $n\lambda/d$ is to take on a number of values between 0 and 1 when n assumes various small integral values. Under these conditions Eq. (15-1) yields several values of θ at which constructive interference will occur. When such is the case, the angles for constructive interference can be measured, and if λ is known, Eq. (15-1) can be turned around to give

$$d = \frac{n\lambda}{\sin \theta} \qquad (15\text{-}2)$$

An experiment suggested by Fig. 15-7 could thus be used to deduce the value of the slit spacing d. We have come, therefore, with this very simple example, to see the principle on which the determination of structure by diffraction is based.

Studies of the internal structure of crystals depend upon a penetrating radiation that will enter the crystal and will display interference effects as a result of scattering from the ordered array of scattering centers. X-rays have the necessary penetrating power and show interference effects since they have wavelengths of the same order of magnitude as the spacing of crystal planes.

In the Bragg method the phenomenon is observed when nearly monochromatic x-rays are reflected from a crystal. A beam of x-rays is passed into a crystal, which in Fig. 15-8 is represented by layers of particles. The x-rays are scattered by interaction with the electrons of the atoms or ions of the crystal. Since x-rays are known to be quite penetrating, each layer of atoms can be expected to scatter only a small part of the x-ray beam. If the crystal particles did not have a spacing which was of the same order of magnitude as the wavelength of the x-rays, simple reflections and scattering of the x-rays would occur. The reflection is, in fact, not simple and is greatly disturbed by the interference effect.

The incoming beam of x-rays can be represented as in Fig. 15-8 with all the waves in phase. The nature of the outgoing beams must be investigated. Let us deal with the particular set of crystal planes, with spacing d, shown in Fig. 15-8*a* and x-rays with some particular wavelength λ. For a general angle of incidence θ the x-rays would penetrate the crystal, and no reflection would be observed.

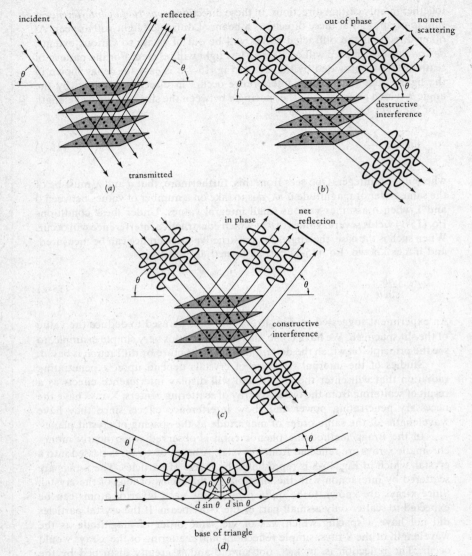

FIGURE 15-8 Reflection of x-rays from the reflecting layers of a crystal. (*a*) The mirrorlike reflection expected for all angles of incidence if interference effects are not considered. (*b*) With interference effects most values of the angle θ will lead to no reflection. (*c*) At certain values of θ reflections will "flash out." (*d*) The basis for the Bragg scattering condition $n\lambda = 2d \sin \theta$.

We can understand this general result by seeing the relation between the individual waves that can be drawn for the reflected waves from each crystal plane. As Fig. 15-8b shows, these waves are, in general, out of phase with each other. The summation of such waves for the many planes that would contribute to the resultant reflected beam gives a zero-amplitude wave. Thus we expect, in general, destructive interference, in line with the observed absence of a reflected beam.

For some special angles, assuming a particular plane spacing d and a particular x-ray wavelength λ, as in Fig. 15-8c, the waves we draw from successive planes will be in phase. The waves then will add together to give a net resultant wave. *Constructive interference* occurs at these special angles. We expect, and find, that at certain angles a reflected beam occurs. *Constructive interference* occurs whenever the phase of beams scattered from successive layers is shifted by an integral multiple of wavelengths. Reference to Fig. 15-8d shows that this happens when the relation

$$n\lambda = 2d \sin \theta \qquad n = 1, 2, 3, \ldots \tag{15-3}$$

holds. This important equation is known as *Bragg's diffraction law*.

This basic equation shows that for a given value of the x-ray wavelength λ, measurement of the angle θ or of the term $\sin \theta$ gives the information on the spacing between planes through the scattering centers that make up the crystal.

For a crystal arranged as in Fig. 15-9 and subjected to a rotation about one of the axes, the a axis, the various crystal planes parallel to the a axis will satisfy Bragg's law and will produce reflections along the "equatorial" plane shown as $h = 0$ in Fig. 15-9. Planes tilted with respect to the a axis will produce

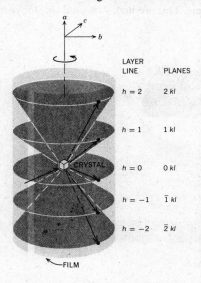

FIGURE 15-9
The single-crystal photographic x-ray technique. One representative point in each of the layers is shown; each layer is made up of a large number of such diffraction spots.

reflection spots along *layer lines* above and below the equatorial plane. The degree of tilt is given by the index h, and the layer lines can be described as in Fig. 15-9.

Arrangement of the Bragg expression to

$$\lambda = 2\frac{d}{n}\sin\theta = 2d_{hkl}\sin\theta \tag{15-4}$$

shows that the higher-order reflections from planes with a spacing d can be treated as if they were due to first-order reflections from planes with spacing $d_{hkl} = d/n$. Thus each reflection can be labeled with a value of hkl corresponding to the Miller indices (hkl) of the planes that give rise to the reflection. Furthermore a spacing d_{hkl} can be associated with each hkl reflection.

A reflection that is labeled, or *indexed,* as 200, for example, would have associated with it a spacing half that of the (100) planes. This procedure is more satisfactory than treating the reflection as a second-order reflection from planes with the (100) spacing. Instead, therefore, of recognizing reflections of various orders of the $(0kl)$ planes in the equatorial layer line, for example, we shall label, or index, the reflections as 010, 020, 030 and 011, 022, 033, and so forth.

Similar indexing of the reflections in the other layer lines can be done, and all these reflections may need to be considered to deduce the nature of the internal structure of the crystal.

For detailed studies of all but the very simplest crystals one must make use of a single crystal and one of a variety of single-crystal instruments that have evolved from the simple arrangement shown in Fig. 15-9. For some purposes, however, it is possible to make use of a simpler technique that uses a crystalline material ground to a powder as a sample. This method, first used by Debye and Scherrer, is illustrated in Fig. 15-10.

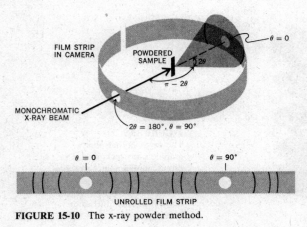

FIGURE 15-10 The x-ray powder method.

The crystals in the sample will present all possible orientations to the x-ray beam. The diffraction obtained will be just like that which would result from mounting a single crystal and turning it through all possible angles. For each crystal plane there will be some one angle at which the Bragg law will be satisfied, and some of the crystals will have this orientation; therefore a diffracted beam will result at the suitable angle, as is depicted in Fig. 15-10. Since there are quite a few crystal planes with a fairly high density of particles, there will be reflections from each of these, and the pattern will show scattering at a large number of angles.

For relatively simple crystals the powder pattern can be used in the study of the crystal structure. For more complex systems, particularly those of low symmetry, many planes in the crystal will happen to have equal or nearly equal spacing, and even if these planes have different directions in the crystal, the powder method will superimpose the reflections from these planes. For this reason, in all but relatively simple cases, one must make use of the more complete display of reflections provided by the single-crystal technique.

The most widespread application of the powder method, which is far more easily used than the single-crystal method, is in the qualitative analysis of solid samples. The spacings between crystal planes, and therefore the position of the line of a powder photograph, are characteristic of a given crystal. The components of a solid mixture can therefore often be rapidly identified from a powder pattern.

15-5 The Determination of the Lattice Type and Unit-Cell Dimensions

The use to which such diffraction patterns can be put in the analysis of a crystal structure can be introduced by seeing the relation of the structure of a cubic crystal to its x-ray powder pattern. The specific example of the NaCl crystal is convenient for our purpose. It can be assumed, as suggested by the external characteristics of the crystal, that NaCl forms a cubic crystal, and in a way analogous to that adopted in a general crystal-structure problem this assignment to the cubic system will later be verified.

The powder pattern of NaCl is shown in Fig. 15-11. Each reflection corresponds, according to Eq. (15-4), to a plane (hkl) with a spacing d_{hkl}. The angles and values of $d_{hkl} = \lambda(2 \sin \theta)$ are given in Table 15-2. The next step in the use

$\theta = 0$ $\theta = 90°$

FIGURE 15-11 The x-ray powder pattern of NaCl taken with Cr K_α x-rays of wavelength 2.291 Å.

TABLE 15-2 Values of d_{hkl} for the NaCl Powder-Pattern Diffraction Lines of Fig. 15-11

The x-ray wavelength for this pattern is 2.291 Å

θ	$\sin \theta$	$d_{hkl} = \dfrac{2.291 \text{ Å}}{2 \sin \theta}$
20°36′	0.3518	3.256
23°58′	0.4062	2.820
35°4′	0.5745	1.994
42°21′	0.6736	1.701
44°43′	0.7036	1.628
54°20′	0.8124	1.410
62°17′	0.8853	1.294
65°16′	0.9083	1.261
84°16′	0.9950	1.151

of a powder pattern (and for a single-crystal pattern) is the assignment of values of hkl for the observed reflections, i.e., the *indexing* of the observed reflections.

This can be done by recognizing that a general expression for the pattern of spacings between the planes of a particular lattice type can be set up. The observed reflections can then be compared with this expression, and the desired identification of the reflections can be accomplished.

The spacing d_{hkl} depends on the set of planes, indicated by the values of hkl, and on the unit-cell dimensions. Let us work out this relation for any of the crystal systems with orthogonal axes. Consider the view, suggested in Fig. 15-12, along the c axis. In Fig. 15-12a (210) planes and in Fig. 15-12b (310) planes are shown. The plane at the lower left goes through a lattice point. The next plane is displaced an amount a/h along the x, or a, axis and b/k along the y, or b, axis. In three dimensions, the general displacements of one (hkl) plane from the next are a/h, b/k, and c/l along the x, y, and z directions, respectively.

An enlargement of the left corner of Fig. 15-12 is shown in Fig. 15-13. One hkl plane passes through the origin. The next hkl plane is shown with the intercepts deduced above. The distance between planes is obtained, and extension to three dimensions gives

$$d_{hkl}^2 = \frac{1}{(h/a)^2 + (k/b)^2 + (l/c)^2} \tag{15-5}$$

This relation for orthogonal systems simplifies in the tetragonal system, for which $b = c$, and in the cubic system, for which $a = b = c$. The cubic-system expression can be written as

$$d_{hkl} = \frac{a}{\sqrt{h^2 + k^2 + l^2}} \tag{15-6}$$

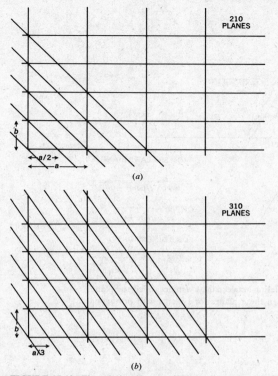

(a)

(b)

FIGURE 15-12 The relation between (210) and (310) planes and the crystal lattice.

Values of d_{hkl} can be calculated from the angle of diffraction and the x-ray wavelength. If values for h, k, and l for each diffraction could be assigned, the unit-cell dimensions, a for the cubic system, could be deduced. Let us see how Eq. (15-5) or (15-6) helps us index diffraction lines like those of Fig. 15-11.

To proceed we must recognize that in fact not all hkl planes will produce a diffraction line. Consider the (100), (110), and (111) planes of primitive, face-centered, and body-centered cubic lattices shown in Fig. 15-14. In the face-centered lattices the (100) and (110) planes sandwich planes with the same number of lattice points. The same is true for the (100) and (111) planes of the body-centered lattice. Reflections from these planes will be destructively interfered with by reflections from the intervening planes. It follows that only in crystals with a structure based on the primitive lattice will all three of these planes, the (100), (110), and (111), produce diffraction lines.

As in the examples of Fig. 15-14, we must be prepared for the first observed diffraction line to be other than that for the indices 100. We can proceed, using a trial-and-error method, to index the lines of Fig. 15-11 or Table 15-2. As a first step, we see whether indexing the first line as 100 leads to a value for the

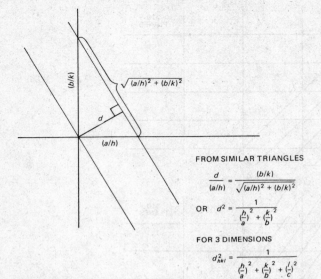

FROM SIMILAR TRIANGLES

$$\frac{d}{(a/h)} = \frac{(b/k)}{\sqrt{(a/h)^2 + (b/k)^2}}$$

OR $\quad d^2 = \dfrac{1}{\left(\dfrac{h}{a}\right)^2 + \left(\dfrac{k}{b}\right)^2}$

FOR 3 DIMENSIONS

$$d_{hkl}^2 = \frac{1}{\left(\dfrac{h}{a}\right)^2 + \left(\dfrac{k}{b}\right)^2 + \left(\dfrac{l}{c}\right)^2}$$

FIGURE 15-13 The relation between the *hkl* indices of crystal planes and the spacing between these planes for systems with orthogonal axes.

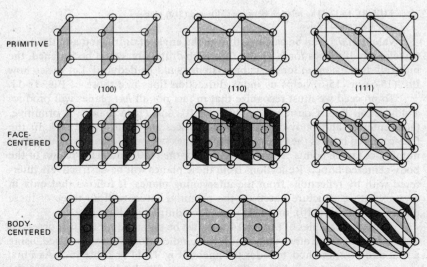

FIGURE 15-14 Planes in primitive, face-centered, and body-centered cubic lattices. The planes that interfere with reflections from (100), (110), and (111) are shown by darker shading.

unit-cell dimension a that allows the second line to be indexed. From Eq. (15-5) we obtain

$$a_{trial} = 3.26 \sqrt{1^2 + 0^2 + 0^2} = 3.26 \text{ Å}$$

Then the next line would have the index hkl such that

$$\sqrt{h^2 + k^2 + l^2} = \frac{a_{trial}}{d_{hkl}} = \frac{3.26}{2.82} = 1.156$$

or $h^2 + k^2 + l^2 = 1.336$

No set of integers gives this result. Our trial indexing of the first line as 100 must be in error.

A similar attempt with the first line indexed as 110 would also fail. Our next try would be 111 for the first line; then

$$a = 3.26 \sqrt{1^2 + 1^2 + 1^2} = 5.64 \text{ Å}$$

The second line would then have to have h, k, and l such that

$$\sqrt{h^2 + k^2 + l^2} = \frac{5.64}{2.82} = 2$$

This equation now can be satisfied with $hkl = 200$, or, of course, 020 or 002.

With this start, which suggests that $a = 5.64$ Å, Eq. (15-6) can be used to obtain hkl values for all the observed lines. The initial indexing and the deduced value of a are substantiated if all subsequent diffractions can be accounted for by integral values of h, k, and l. Indices are added to the NaCl diffraction lines in Fig. 15-15.

Once diffraction lines have been indexed, their values of d_{hkl} can be used with Eq. (15-6) to obtain additional measures of the unit-cell spacings. Thus the

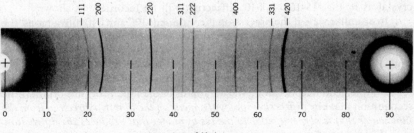

FIGURE 15-15 The NaCl powder pattern of Fig. 15-11 with the diffraction lines indexed.

unit-cell dimensions can be based on the position of many, or all, of the diffraction lines rather than on the first line.

Extension of the examples of Fig. 15-14 shows that crystals based on primitive cubic lattices have diffraction lines corresponding to all *hkl* planes. Those with face-centered cubic lattices only have diffraction lines for which the three *hkl* integers are all odd or all even. Those with body-centered lattices only have lines for which the sum of *h*, *k*, and *l* is even. On this basis, and the indexing of Fig. 15-15, we see that NaCl has a structure that is based on a face-centered cubic lattice.

Note that lines can be indexed, the lattice type can be deduced, and the dimensions of the unit cell can be determined without using the variation in the intensity of the diffraction lines, which is obvious in Fig. 15-15. This variation depends on the position of the Na^+ and Cl^- ions in the unit cell. (Although we have deduced that the NaCl crystal is face-centered cubic, we have not actually located the ions in the unit cell.) We postpone consideration of the intensities of diffractions and positions of atoms or ions in unit cells until Sec. 15-8.

15-6 Indexing Reflections: The Precession Technique

One method, now widely used in crystal-structure studies, is the *precession technique*. The crystal is moved in a precession motion in the x-ray beam. The precession method spreads out all the diffraction spots, having a selected value of one of the indices *h*, *k*, or *l* over the film. The values of the remaining two indices can be determined. Thus the diffraction spots that result can be assigned all three indices *h*, *k*, and *l*. Then the shape and complete dimensions of the unit cell can be deduced.

Consider a crystal mounted in an x-ray beam as in Fig. 15-16*a* and then tilted relative to the beam so that the $l = 0$ diffractions, i.e., all those which would be indexed as *hk*0, can be produced. If the crystal has $a = b$, that is, is cubic or tetragonal, and it is positioned as in Fig. 15-16*b*, diffraction from the (100) could occur and would form the indicated spot.

Now, suppose that the crystal is precessed so that the x-ray beam impinges on the crystal with the same angle as before but now strikes the side of the crystal as in Fig. 15-16*c*. A 010 diffraction will be recorded, as shown.

In a similar way, if the precession is continued, $\overline{1}00$ and $0\overline{1}0$ diffractions, the bar implying minus values, will form spots at the bottom and at the side to form the four-spot pattern produced by this set of planes. Many more diffractions would be observed with the complete range of precession implied by Fig. 15-16*d*. The additional spots can also be related to crystal planes. The (110) planes, for example, lead to spots along the diagonals of the film. Most important is the recognition that *any diffraction spot will appear on the film in a direction from the film center that is perpendicular to the set of planes that produces the diffraction.*

When rows of spots can be recognized in a precession photograph, they can be associated with sets of planes that have a common degree of tilt relative to a given direction. Thus, the 0*k*0 diffractions are found to be in an equatorial-

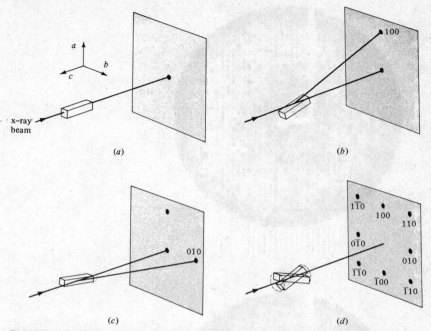

x-ray beam

(a)

100

(b)

010

(c)

$1\bar{1}0$ 100   110

$0\bar{1}0$ 010

$\bar{1}\bar{1}0$ $\bar{1}00$ $\bar{1}\bar{1}0$

(d)

FIGURE 15-16 The relation of the crystal orientation to the diffraction pattern in the precession method. Illustration of the development of reflections from the (100)- and (110)-type planes.

layer-line array of spots. The planes that produce these spots have no tilt relative to the a axis. Other lines of spots due to planes with various amounts of tilt relative to this axis are $1k0$, $2k0$, $3k0$, and so forth. Similar indexing of spots due to amounts of tilt relative to the b axis give the arrays $h10$, $h20$, ... Complete indices of the spots on the interlocking layer lines is then achieved. Thus the diffraction spots on a precession photograph like Fig. 15-17 can easily be indexed for cubic and tetragonal crystals.

The procedure is a little less obvious when, as in other crystal types, the a and b axes are not orthogonal. But the diffraction spot from a set of planes still occurs in a direction perpendicular to the plane directions. An illustration of the nonorthogonal features of the diffraction pattern that must then be dealt with is given in Fig. 15-18.

So far we have not used the information provided by the distance of the diffraction spots from the center of the film. The precession method again introduces a mechanically complicated procedure that leads to an easy interpretation of these distances. The construction of Fig. 15-19 shows that if a tilt is given the film or other detector and this tilt is synchronized with the crystal precession, the distance from the film center to an hkl diffraction spot is inversely proportional to d_{hkl}. Thus the film obtained in the precession method

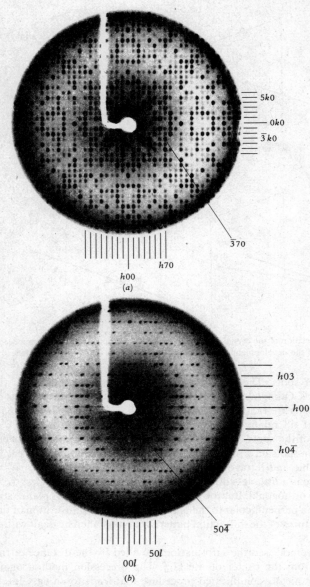

FIGURE 15-17 The precession diffraction patterns formed by the lysozyme chloride crystal and a Cu K_α x-ray beam: (*a*) all spots are $hk0$; (*b*) the crystal is mounted so that the spots are $h0l$. Some of the indexing is indicated. [*J. R. Knox, J. Chem. Educ.,* **49**:476 (1972), *courtesy of Professor Knox.*]

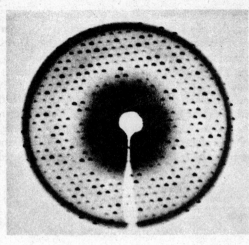

FIGURE 15-18
Precession photograph showing the $hk0$ diffractions of the trigonal ribonuclease-S crystal. [*J. R. Knox, J. Chem. Educ.,* **49**:*476 (1972), courtesy of Professor Knox.*]

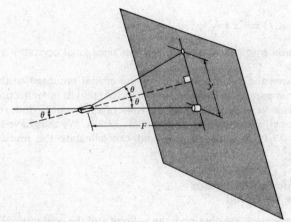

FIGURE 15-19 The relation between the position of a diffraction spot on a precession photograph and the spacing of the planes to which it corresponds. The movement of the photographic plate is synchronized with that of the crystal so that the plate remains perpendicular to the crystal axis.

$$\sin \theta = \frac{y/2}{F} \quad \text{or} \quad 2 \sin \theta = \frac{y}{F}$$

Then $\lambda = 2d_{hkl} \sin \theta$ gives

$$d_{hkl} = \frac{\lambda}{2 \sin \theta} = \frac{\lambda F}{y}$$

Thus, given λ, the wavelength of the x-rays, and F, the distance from crystal to photographic plate, measurement of y for an hkl spot leads to a value of d_{hkl}. Note also that $y \propto 1/d_{hkl}$.

is a display of the orientation of the crystal planes and their spacing. The orientation depends on the fact that the *direction* of the diffraction spot from the center of the film is the direction perpendicular to the plane. The spacing results because the *distance* of the spot from the film center is proportional to the reciprocal of the plane spacing. The precession-method film is said to exhibit the *reciprocal lattice* of the crystal.

Determining the unit-cell shape and dimensions from a precession-method photograph can be illustrated using the results of Fig. 15-17a. The wavelength of the Cu K_α x-rays is 1.542 Å, and the focal length F is 100 mm. On the original photograph the distance, for example, between the $h\bar{7}0$ and $h70$ columns of diffraction spots was found to be equal to 27.3 mm. Thus y of Fig. 15-19 is equal to 13.65 mm, and

$$d_{070} = \frac{F}{y} = \frac{1.542 \text{ Å } (100 \text{ mm})}{13.65 \text{ mm}} = 11.29 \text{ Å}$$

thus

$$d_{010} = (11.29 \text{ Å} \times 7) = 79.1 \text{ Å}$$

The unit-cell dimension b is 79.1 Å, and so, for this tetragonal crystal, is the unit-cell dimension a.

Figure 15-17 shows the pattern for a lysozyme crystal mounted so that diffractions from planes parallel to the b axis are detected; that is, $h0l$ reflections are shown. The c axis is vertical, and again the rows of spots can be indexed. The value of the unit-cell parameter c is obtained as 37.9 Å. We thus have the unit-cell dimensions 79.1, 79.1, and 37.9 Å and can calculate the unit-cell volume as 237,100 Å³.

15-7 The Ionic or Molecular Content of the Unit Cell

Once the unit-cell dimensions are obtained, the volume and the contents of the unit cell can be deduced. For orthogonal systems the unit-cell volume is the product of the three dimensions of the unit cell. This is a special case of the general expression for a cell with dimensions a, b, and c inclined at angles α, β, and γ. The general expression is

$$V = abc \, (1 - \cos^2 \alpha - \cos^2 \beta - \cos^2 \gamma + 2 \cos \alpha \cos \beta \cos \gamma)^{1/2} \quad (15\text{-}7)$$

Let us introduce Z as the number of molecules or specified particles in the unit cell. This number is calculated by dividing the mass of the unit cell ρV, where ρ is the density, by $M/\mathfrak{N}$, the mass of a molecule or specified particle. Thus

$$Z = \frac{\rho V \mathfrak{N}}{M} \tag{15-8}$$

For the NaCl crystal we use $\rho = 2.165$ g/cm^3 and $M = 58.45$ g. With $a = b = c = 5.64$ Å and $V = 179.4$ Å$^3 = 179.4 \times 10^{-24}$ cm^3 we obtain, from Eq. (15-8), the value of 4.00 for Z. Thus there are four NaCl "molecules," or four Na$^+$ and four Cl$^-$ ions, in the unit cell. We know, furthermore, that they are arranged according to the face-centered cubic lattice.

15-8 Intensities of Diffractions and the Structure within the Unit Cell

The crystal symmetry and the unit-cell dimensions sometimes give enough information to determine the exact structure of a simple crystal. For most crystals, however, the problem of determining the arrangement of the atoms or ions within each unit cell remains. The information necessary for deducing these atomic positions is contained in the *intensities* of the diffraction spots.

Let us now consider a crystal that could belong to any of the classes with orthogonal axes, and let us indicate the unit-cell dimensions along the x, y, and z axes as a, b, and c.

To simplify, let us again consider a two-dimensional view in which planes are considered to be parallel to the z axis, as in Fig. 15-12, the z axis being taken perpendicular to the plane of the paper. Such planes have indices ($hk0$), and the edges of the two planes shown are for the (210) and (310) planes. Now let us find the effect of the B atoms of Fig. 15-20, which are displaced from the A atoms by distances x and y, measured in units of the unit-cell dimensions a and b, on the intensities of the diffraction lines.

Waves scattered by the planes of B atoms will interfere with any waves that are scattered by the planes through the A atoms. The scattering from the successive A planes in Fig. 15-20 is displaced by exactly 2π and leads to constructive interference. Now, however, the planes of B atoms interfere with the scattering from the planes of A atoms by providing scattered beams that are out of phase by an amount that depends on the positions of the B atoms. For the 210 reflections the B atoms provide waves that are out of phase by $(x/\frac{1}{2})2\pi$ along the x axis and $(y/\frac{1}{1})2\pi$ along the y axis. Consideration of the 310 reflections shows, as Fig. 15-20 suggests, that for these reflections the B-atom contributions would be out of phase by $(x/\frac{1}{3})2\pi$ and $(y/\frac{1}{1})2\pi$ along the x and y axes. In general, the phase difference of the beam resulting from the displacement of the B atoms from the origin is

$$2\pi \left(\frac{x}{1/h} + \frac{y}{1/k} \right) = 2\pi(hx + ky)$$

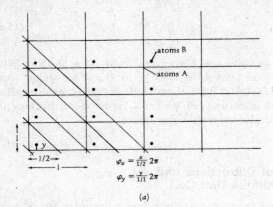

$$\varphi_x = \frac{x}{1/2} 2\pi$$
$$\varphi_y = \frac{y}{1/1} 2\pi$$

(a)

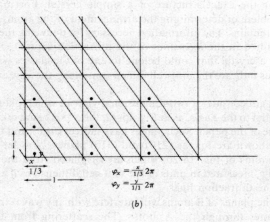

$$\varphi_x = \frac{x}{1/3} 2\pi$$
$$\varphi_y = \frac{y}{1/1} 2\pi$$

(b)

FIGURE 15-20
Phase shifts ϕ_x and ϕ_y (shown as φ_x and φ_y) for B atoms when the origins of the unit cells are oriented for constructive interference from (a) 210 and (b) 310 planes. Distances are reported in terms of a along the horizontal x axis and in terms of b along the vertical y axis.

For a general plane in three dimensions, this phase difference would be

$$2\pi(hx + ky + lz)$$

It should be remembered that h, k, and l are the Miller indices of the reflection planes and of the diffraction spot being considered and that x, y, and z are the coordinates of the atom B expressed as fractions of the unit cell of dimensions a, b, and c.

The net scattering from an hkl plane requires the summing up, allowing for the phase differences, of the scattering amplitudes from all atoms in the unit cell. The summation of waves, all with the same frequency but with different amplitudes and phases, can be accomplished by representing the amplitude and phase of each wave by the diagrams of Fig. 15-21.

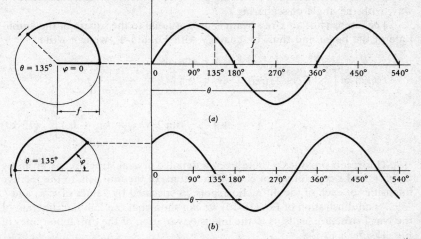

FIGURE 15-21 The generation of a wave by the rotation of a point at a radius equal to the amplitude of the wave for (a) phase angle zero and (b) phase angle φ (shown as φ).

If two scattered waves are considered, as in Fig. 15-22, the square of the amplitude of the resultant wave is obtained as

$$(f_1 \cos \phi_1 + f_2 \cos \phi_2)^2 + (f_1 \sin \phi_1 + f_2 \sin \phi_2)^2 \qquad (15\text{-}9)$$

A similar expression can be written when the effect of more than two atoms must be shown. Then we let j be an index for the atoms of the unit cell. According to the phase-difference expression $2\pi(hx + ky + lz)$, the jth atom contributes to the hkl diffraction a scattered wave with phase $\phi_j = 2\pi(hx_j + ky_j + lz_j)$. The amplitude factor f_j can be taken as being approximately proportional to the number of electrons of the atom, i.e., to the

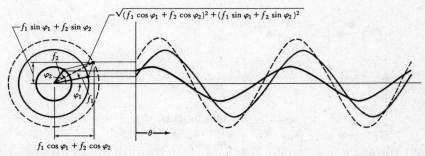

FIGURE 15-22 The addition of waves of different amplitudes and wavelengths (shown as φ).

atomic number. (In fact, the scattering power of an atom varies, but in a known way, with the angle of scattering.)

The intensity of an x-ray beam is proportional to the square of the amplitude of the beam and thus, by analogy with Eq. (15-9), we can write

$$I(hkl) \propto \left[\sum_j f_j \cos 2\pi(hx_j + ky_j + lz_j) \right]^2$$

$$+ \left[\sum_j f_j \sin 2\pi(hx_j + ky_j + lz_j) \right]^2 \quad (15\text{-}10)$$

This result provides a route from a detailed crystal structure, as given by the x, y, and z coordinates of each of the atoms of the unit cell, to the relative intensities of each of the diffraction spots, as specified by values of h, k, and l.

As an illustration of Eq. (15-10) we can show that the familiar diagram of the NaCl structure leads us to the intensity variation of the diffraction lines of Fig. 15-15.

If, arbitrarily, the Cl⁻ ions are given the positions $0, 0, 0; \frac{1}{2}, \frac{1}{2}, 0; \frac{1}{2}, 0, \frac{1}{2}; 0,$ $\frac{1}{2}, \frac{1}{2}$; then, as in Fig. 15-23, the Na⁺ ions occupy the positions $\frac{1}{2}, \frac{1}{2}, \frac{1}{2}; \frac{1}{2}, 0, 0; 0,$ $\frac{1}{2}, 0; 0, 0, \frac{1}{2}$. These coordinates can now be entered into Eq. (15-10). The sine term will involve only sines of multiples of π and can be eliminated at the outset. The intensity result obtained by summing Eq. (15-10) over all the atoms of the unit cell is then

$$I(hkl) \propto [f_{Cl} + f_{Cl} \cos \pi(h + k) + f_{Cl} \cos \pi(h + l)$$
$$+ f_{Cl} \cos \pi(k + l) + f_{Na} \cos \pi(h + k + l) + f_{Na} \cos \pi h$$
$$+ f_{Na} \cos \pi k + f_{Na} \cos \pi l]^2 \quad (15\text{-}11)$$

By trying a few examples you will recognize that unless hkl are all even or all odd, the calculated intensity is zero. This result arises from the relation of the NaCl structure to the face-centered cubic lattice and does not depend on the specific positioning of the Na⁺ and Cl⁻ ions.

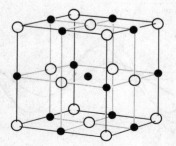

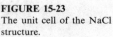

FIGURE 15-23
The unit cell of the NaCl structure.

Next you might notice, that for *hkl* all even, the terms that make up $I(hkl)$ are all positive and

$$I(hkl) \propto (f_{Cl^-} + f_{Na^+})^2 \qquad hkl \text{ all even} \tag{15-12}$$

On the other hand, if *hkl* are all odd, the cosine factors for the Na^+ terms are negative and

$$I(hkl) \propto (f_{Cl^-} - f_{Na^+})^2 \qquad hkl \text{ all odd} \tag{15-13}$$

These results are consistent with the intensities of the diffraction lines of Fig. 15-15.

15-9 The Fourier Synthesis

A method has now been obtained for going from a crystal structure to a calculated x-ray pattern. One can be content with this result, which shows that with sufficient trial-and-error steps a structure for a molecule in a crystal can be obtained. There are, furthermore, very many diffraction spots that can be measured, and a structure which leads to a correct intensity calculation for all the observed spots is almost unquestionably the correct structure.

It is of course desirable (and for large organic molecules almost necessary) that a method be available for deducing a molecular structure from the observed diffraction pattern more directly without having to resort entirely to this trial-and-error procedure. An indication of the problems that arise when this is attempted and some of the methods that are adopted to overcome these difficulties can now be given.

First a convenient expression for the amplitude of the x-rays scattered by the contents of the unit cell is needed. To develop it we recall the general relation

$$e^{i\theta} = \cos\theta + i\sin\theta \tag{15-14}$$

and

$$|e^{i\theta}|^2 = (\cos\theta + i\sin\theta)(\cos\theta - i\sin\theta) \\ = \cos^2\theta + \sin^2\theta \tag{15-15}$$

Comparison of the form of this equation with the squared-amplitude and intensity expressions given in Eqs. (15-9) and (15-10) suggests that the desired complex-number amplitude expression, known as the *structure factor* $F(hkl)$, can be written as

$$F(hkl) = \sum_j f_j e^{2\pi i(hx_j + ky_j + lz_j)} \tag{15-16}$$

In view of Eq. (15-15) this yields

$$|F(hkl)|^2 = \left[\sum_j f_j \cos 2\pi(hx_j + ky_j + lz_j) \right]^2$$

$$+ \left[\sum_j f_j \sin 2\pi(hx_j + ky_j + lz_j) \right]^2$$

The square of the structure factor correctly gives the intensity of the scattered beam obtained above as Eq. (15-10). Thus the complex-number expression of Eq. (15-16) does represent the amplitude of the x-ray beam scattered by the contents of the unit cell.

The structure-factor summation is over all the atoms of the unit cell. If the positions of these atoms were known, a value of the structure factor could be deduced for each hkl reflection. In practice we must proceed not *from* but *to* the atomic positions.

The procedure used depends upon Bragg's suggestion that the crystal be looked upon not as a set of discrete scattering points but as a three-dimensional distribution of varying electron densities. X-rays are, in fact, affected by atoms because they are regions of high electron density and therefore high scattering power compared with that of the surrounding regions. Instead of attempting to deduce the coordinates of the atoms in the crystal, one can look for an electron-density function $\rho(xyz)$ that represents the electron-density distribution in the crystal.

The electron-density function $\rho(xyz)$ is quite complicated if the molecules of the crystal are large. Even in such cases, however, we know that the function will be periodic, repeating itself just as the crystal as a whole repeats the unit cell. Periodic functions, no matter how complex, can be represented by sums, or series, of appropriate sine and cosine terms known as *Fourier series*. A simple illustration of a periodic function and its approximation by a series of such terms is given in Fig. 15-24. More generally we need to use both sine and cosine terms, and a general periodic function $f(x)$ can be then represented as

$$f(x) = \sum_{n=0}^{\infty} (a_n \cos 2\pi nx + b_n \sin 2\pi nx) \tag{15-17}$$

Adjustment of the many constants a_n and b_n can produce a series with the same form as the original function $f(x)$.

In view of the relation of Eq. (15-14), this Fourier-series representation can also be expressed in complex-number form. The counterpart of Eq. (15-17) is then

$$f(x) = \sum_{n=-\infty}^{+\infty} c_n e^{2\pi i n x} \tag{15-18}$$

Again, adjustment of sufficient constants c_n makes it possible to describe the periodic function $f(x)$.

Thanks to the periodic nature of any crystal, with periodicities a, b, and c, the electron-density function can be formally represented by a Fourier series according to

$$\rho(xyz) = \sum_{p,q,r=-\infty}^{+\infty} A(pqr)e^{2\pi i(px+qy+rz)} \tag{15-19}$$

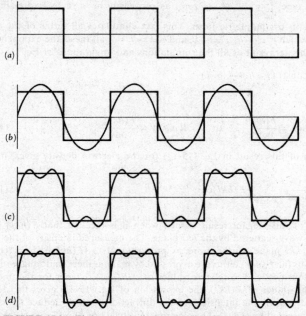

FIGURE 15-24 Fitting a periodic function by a Fourier series: (a) a square periodic function; (b) the first approximation using a single sine function; (c) a second approximation using the sum of two sine terms; (d) a third approximation using the sum of three sine terms.

where p, q, and r take on all integral values from $-\infty$ to $+\infty$ and $A(pqr)$ are the coefficients (to be determined) of the many Fourier-series terms. Finding the coefficients $A(pqr)$ is the goal of the derivation. If these coefficients were known, it would be possible to use Eq. (15-19) to draw the electron density and thus to locate the atoms in the unit cell.

This interpretation of the unit-cell contents by an electron-density function rather than by atoms occupying various positions can be inserted into the structure-factor expression. Then in place of Eq. (15-16) one has the integral expression

$$F(hkl) = (\text{const}) \int\int\int_0^1 \rho(xyz)e^{2\pi i(hx+ky+lz)}dx\,dy\,dz \tag{15-20}$$

This procedure is useful because now the Fourier-series interpretation of $\rho(xyz)$ given by Eq. (15-19) can be inserted for $\rho(xyz)$ to give

$$F(hkl) = (\text{const}) \int\int\int_0^1 \sum_{p,q,r} A(pqr)e^{2\pi i(px+qy+rz)}e^{2\pi i(hx+ky+lz)}dx\,dy\,dz$$

$$= (\text{const}) \int\int\int_0^1 \sum_{p,q,r} A(pqr)e^{2\pi i[(h+p)x+(k+q)y+(l+r)z]}dx\,dy\,dz \tag{15-21}$$

All terms of the type $\int_0^1 e^{2\pi i\theta}\, d\theta$ are zero, as can easily be seen by expressing the exponential term in trigonometric form. This fact eliminates all terms of the series except those for which $p = -h$, $q = -k$, and $r = -l$. For all these, the exponential is $e^{2\pi i(0)} = 1$, and the net result of all the summations and integrations of Eq. (15-21) is

$$F(hkl) = (\text{const})A(-h, -k, -l)$$

or

$$A(-h,-k,-l) = \frac{F(hkl)}{\text{const}} \quad \text{or} \quad A(p,q,r) = \frac{F(hkl)}{\text{const}} \tag{15-22}$$

Substitution of this result in Eq. (15-19) for the electron density gives, finally,

$$\rho(xyz) = \frac{1}{\text{const}} \sum_{h,k,l=-\infty}^{+\infty} F(hkl)e^{-2\pi i(hx+ky+lz)} \tag{15-23}$$

The power of this elegant result is seen when it is recalled that $F(hkl)$ is the amplitude of the wave scattered by the hkl plane. The measured intensity of the beam scattered by the hkl plane, furthermore, is proportional to $[F(hkl)]^2$. For "centro-symmetric" crystals the $F(hkl)$ terms are expressed by real numbers, and square roots of the measured intensities lead to relative values of $\pm F(hkl)$. Except for the undetermined sign on the values of $F(hkl)$, the expression of Eq. (15-23) gives the desired result, a method for using the intensities of the diffraction spots to deduce the crystal structures, as represented by $\rho(xyz)$. The electron density at any point (x,y,z) in the unit cell can be determined by performing the summation of Eq. (15-23) for the chosen value of x, y, and z over all values of hkl, that is, over all the observed diffraction spots. The more intense diffraction spots correspond to the numerically greater diffraction amplitudes and structure-factor terms, so that at first one need extend the summation only to the more intense diffraction spots. Such summations can be performed for various points, specified by values of x, y, and z, in the unit cell. By determination of the electron density at sufficient points, an electron-density map can be drawn showing the positions of the atoms by regions of high electron density.

The undetermined sign, which results because the intensities and not the amplitudes of the diffraction beams are obtained, turns out to be very troublesome, and a number of techniques have been suggested to make use of Eq. (15-23) in spite of this difficulty. These approaches usually depend on methods for obtaining the approximate shape of the molecule and its approximate position in the unit cell. Some molecules, for instance, contain a heavy atom which has a high scattering probability and can be located, whereas the complexities of the remainder of the molecule can be ignored initially. The signs of the most important structure factors can then be guessed. These few structure-factor values can then be used in Eq. (15-23) to deduce a crude electron-density map. This first-approximation map can help us estimate the position of more atoms. Then the signs of more structure factors can be deduced from Eq. (15-16) or (15-20). In this way, one refines a structure by working in the information from more and more diffraction spots until a structure of the desired detail is obtained.

Complete deduction of the structure of a complicated molecule by the x-ray diffraction technique is a major research problem, but no other method provides such a wealth of reliable structural information.

15-10 Ionic Radii

X-ray diffraction techniques have given us a fund of precise, reliable data on the dimensions of atomic, ionic, and molecular systems. Let us see some of the generalizations that can be drawn from such data. We begin, in this section, by considering the simple ions of salt crystals. Such ions are represented as spheres. The simplest and very useful approach treats the radius of a given ion as a fixed quantity independent of the type and number of ions that surround it in a particular crystal.

Consideration of the contributions to the energy of an ionic crystal, as in Sec. 6-13, suggests that normally anions and cations are in contact with each other. If this is the case, the sum of the anion and cation radii can be deduced from the unit-cell dimensions. Examples of the necessary calculations are given for both AB- and AB_2-type crystals in Fig. 15-25.

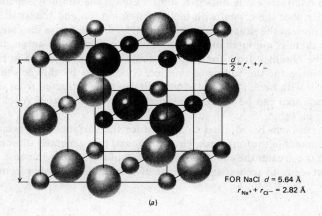

$$\frac{d}{2} = r_+ + r_-$$

FOR NaCl $d = 5.64$ Å
$r_{Na^+} + r_{Cl^-} = 2.82$ Å

(a)

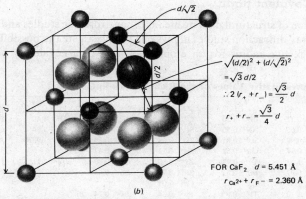

$$\sqrt{(d/2)^2 + (d/\sqrt{2})^2}$$
$$= \sqrt{3}\, d/2$$
$$\therefore 2\,(r_+ + r_-) = \frac{\sqrt{3}}{2} d$$
$$r_+ + r_- = \frac{\sqrt{3}}{4} d$$

FOR CaF_2 $d = 5.451$ Å
$r_{Ca^{2+}} + r_{F^-} = 2.360$ Å

(b)

FIGURE 15-25 Two examples of the relation between unit-cell dimensions and ionic radii: (a) NaCl, (b) CaF_2.

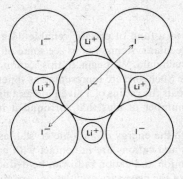

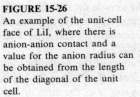

FIGURE 15-26
An example of the unit-cell face of LiI, where there is anion-anion contact and a value for the anion radius can be obtained from the length of the diagonal of the unit cell.

A number of methods have been suggested for obtaining individual ionic radii from these relatively easily obtained sums. Perhaps the simplest depends on the assumption that the crystal with the largest anion, I^-, and the smallest cation, Li^+, will present the situation shown in Fig. 15-26. In this case the cation is so small that there is anion-anion contact and the radius of the anion, the iodide ion, can be obtained from the unit-cell dimensions, as suggested in the figure. Once a value for the radius of one ion is obtained by this or other methods not dealt with here, a table of ionic radii can be constructed from the sums of ionic radii that can be deduced from other crystal structures. A set of values is shown in Table 15-3.

Such ionic radii can be adjusted to account for the variation that occurs when the environment of the ion varies. Thus, it is found that generally the ionic radius is greater the greater the coordination number of the ion. An increase of about 10 percent seems to accompany a change of coordination number from 4 to 8.

15-11 Covalent Radii

The accumulation of structural data by means of spectroscopic studies and both electron and x-ray diffraction studies allows one to investigate the possibility of assigning an effective radius for an atom when it is in a covalently bound

TABLE 15-3 Representative Values of the Radii of Ions in Crystals

						H^- 2.08
Li^+ 0.60	Be^{2+} 0.31	B^{3+} 0.20	C^{4+} 0.15	N^{5+} 0.11	O^{2-} 1.40	F^- 1.36
Na^+ 0.95	Mg^{2+} 0.65	Al^{3+} 0.50	Si^{4+} 0.41	P^{5+} 0.34	S^{2-} 1.84	Cl^- 1.81
K^+ 1.33	Ca^{2+} 0.99	Se^{3+} 0.81	Ti^{4+} 0.68	V^{5+} 0.59	Se^{2-} 1.98	Br^- 1.95
Cu^+ 0.96	Zn^{2+} 0.74	Ga^{3+} 0.62	Ge^{4+} 0.53	As^{5+} 0.47		
Rb^+ 1.48	Sr^{2+} 1.13	Y^{3+} 0.93	Zr^{4+} 0.80	Cb^{5+} 0.70	Te^{2-} 2.21	I^- 2.16
Ag^+ 1.26	Cd^{2+} 0.97	In^{3+} 0.81	Sn^{4+} 0.71	Sb^{5+} 0.62		
Cs^+ 1.69	Ba^{2+} 1.35	La^{3+} 1.15	Ce^{4+} 1.01			
Au^+ 1.37	Hg^{2+} 1.10	Tl^{3+} 0.95	Pb^{4+} 0.84	Bi^{5+} 0.74		

Source: L. Pauling, "The Nature of the Chemical Bond," 3d ed., Cornell University Press, Ithaca, N.Y., 1960.

molecule, i.e., of assigning a *covalent radius* to each atom. One begins by assigning half the length of a homonuclear bond as the covalent radius of the atoms forming the bond. Thus, from the equilibrium bond length of Cl_2 of 1.99 Å, one obtains the value of 1.00 Å for the covalent radius of chlorine. From the carbon-carbon distance of 1.54 Å in ethane, for example, one obtains a value of 0.77 for the covalent radius of carbon and so forth. To proceed one must now establish the extent to which the length of covalent bonds can be treated in terms of the sums of such covalent radii. Some comparisons of calculated and measured bond lengths are shown in Table 15-4.

More extensive treatments of this type show that the bond lengths of many bonds are given within a few hundredths of an angstrom by the sum of assigned atomic covalent radii. This suggests that covalent bonds have lengths sufficiently independent of factors other than the fixed radii for there to be some value in assigning radii to the bonded nuclei. Thus covalent radii are tabulated as illustrated in Table 15-5.

Further comparisons of these values with experimental results indicate, as shown in fact by some of the examples of Table 15-4, that serious discrepancies can occur between simply predicted covalent-bond lengths and those observed. The C—F bond, for example, is calculated from the date of Table 15-5 to have a length of 1.49 Å, whereas microwave spectral results for CH_3F give it as 1.385 Å and electron-diffraction results for CF_4 give 1.32 Å.

Such discrepancies led V. Schomaker and D. P. Stevenson to suggest that a bond length calculated from covalent radii must be adjusted for the difference in electronegativity of the bonded atoms. They suggested the relation

TABLE 15-4 Some Tests of Additivity of Covalent-Bond Radii, Å

Calculated		Observed	
C—C(ethane)	1.54	In CCl_4	1.766
Cl—Cl(Cl_2)	1.99	In $CHCl_3$	1.767
C—Cl	1.77	In CH_3Cl	1.784
N—N(H_2N—NH_2)	1.46	In NF_3	1.37
F—F(F_2)	1.42	In N_2F_4	1.46
N—F	1.44		
H—H	0.741	In H—F	0.917
F—F	1.418		
H—F	1.08		
C—C(ethane)	1.54	In CH_3OH	1.43
O—O(HO—OH)	1.48	In C_2H_5OH	1.48
C—O	1.51	In CH_3—O—CH_3	1.42

Source: Bond-length data given, with references to original sources, in Tables of Interatomic Distances and Configurations on Molecules and Ions, *Chem. Soc. Spec. Pub.* 11, London, 1968.

TABLE 15-5 Covalent Radii for Atoms Involved in Single-Bonded Compounds, Å

H	C	N	0	F
0.37	0.77	0.74	0.74	0.72
	Si	P	S	Cl
	1.17	1.10	1.04	0.99
	Ge	As	Se	Br
	1.22	1.21	1.17	1.14
	Sn	Sb	Te	I
	1.40	1.41	1.37	1.33

Source: From A. F. Wells "Structural Inorganic Chemistry," Oxford University Press, New York, 1962.

$$r_{AB} = r_A + r_B - 0.09(x_A - x_B) \qquad (15\text{-}24)$$

Some, but not all, of the interesting violations of simple covalent radii additivity are removed by this empirical expression. In other cases the Stevenson-Schomaker correction makes the agreement with the observed length poorer than that obtained by a simple addition of the covalent radii. Although a number of factors must be operating to affect the length of a bond between a pair of nuclei in any given molecule, the covalent radii of Table 15-5 are often of value in estimating this bond length.

15-12 Van der Waals Radii

Diffraction studies of crystals give information about how molecules can approach each other and can pack together. Forces, often treated under the name van der Waals forces, provide the attraction and repulsion between molecules that are responsible for the closeness with which molecules can approach each other. The idea of a *van der Waals radius* for each covalently bound atom is introduced. Figure 15-27 shows the shapes attributed to molecules as a result of the introduction of van der Waals radii.

The values of these radii can be deduced from the distances that separate atoms of different molecules in a crystal lattice. In crystalline Br_2, for example, the shortest distance between a bromine atom of one molecule and that of an adjacent molecule is 3.90 Å. Half this value, 1.95 Å, can therefore be assigned as the van der Waals radius of a covalently bound bromine atom. In similar ways, making use of crystal-structure data for many organic compounds, the van der Waals radii given in Table 15-6 can be deduced. These values must be considered reliable to not more than about 0.05 Å, and this uncertainty makes itself evident in the range of values found for a particular element in different compounds and crystals. The values are sufficiently reliable, however, for scale drawings to be constructed and used to see how molecules can fit together. That van der Waals radii can be assigned with some success is attributable to the fact,

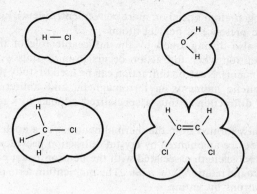

FIGURE 15-27
Examples of molecular structure showing the sizes of the atoms as depicted by van der Waals radii.

mentioned in Sec. 2-16, that the repulsive forces set in very strongly, i.e., the potential-energy curve rises very steeply, as atoms approach each other. It follows that even when rather different attractive forces operate, the closeness of approach will be little affected.

15-13 Neutron Diffraction

An x-ray beam is scattered primarily as a result of interaction with the electrons that surround each atom of an ion or molecule. Thus the atomic scattering factors are approximately proportional to atomic numbers. As a result, it is difficult to locate low-atomic-number atoms in the presence of high-atomic-number atoms. This means that the position of hydrogen atoms can generally not be deduced from x-ray diffraction studies. (A positive attitude to this difficulty is the recognition that the positions of hydrogen atoms are of little consequence and thus do not add to the complexity of many already complex structure determinations.) Within a factor of 3 or 4 all nuclei scatter neutrons to

TABLE 15-6 Van der Waals Radii of Atoms of Covalent Molecules, Å

H	N	O	F
1.2	1.5	1.40	1.35
	P	S	Cl
CH$_3$ group 2.0	1.9	1.85	1.80
	As	Se	Br
Half thickness of	2.0	2.00	1.95
aromatic ring 1.70	Sb	Te	I
	2.2	2.20	2.15

Source: L. Pauling, "The Nature of the Chemical Bond," 3d ed., Cornell University Press, Ithaca, N.Y., 1960.

the same extent. Thus hydrogen-atom nuclei or, more conveniently, deuterium nuclei can be located in the presence of heavier atoms.

Neutron diffraction is also distinguished by the noticeable role of the magnetic moment of the neutron when diffraction occurs from crystals with ordered atomic magnetic moments. Neutron diffraction can be used to study the orientation of atomic magnetic moments in ferromagnetic and antiferromagnetic crystals. Neutron diffraction is thus a specialized adjunct to x-ray diffraction.

A neutron beam is usually formed from the thermal neutrons of a nuclear reactor. A velocity-selector device augmented by crystal diffraction provides a monochromatic beam. The wavelength associated with the neutron beam can be calculated from the de Broglie relation, $\lambda = h/mv$. The momentum term mv is obtained for thermal neutrons by setting

$$\tfrac{1}{2}mv^2 = \tfrac{3}{2}kT$$

and rearranging to give

$$mv = \sqrt{3mkT} \tag{15-25}$$

With appropriate numerical values, including 1.675×10^{-27} kg for the mass of a neutron, we obtain

$$\lambda = 1.46 \times 10^{-10} \text{ m} = 1.46 \text{ Å}$$

A beam of thermal neutrons therefore has a wavelength suitable for diffraction studies of crystals. A diffraction pattern like those obtained for x-ray diffraction, except that a longer-wavelength beam is used, is obtained.

Typically crystals whose structures, except for the positions of hydrogen atoms are known, are studied. The Fourier-transform procedure of Sec. 15-9 is used so that the positions of these remaining nuclei are obtained. The smallness of the nuclei would lead to sharp peaks on a nuclear-density map, but thermal motion produces some spreading of these peaks.

15-14 Electron Diffraction by Gases

Structures can be determined by analyzing the scattering pattern produced when a beam of electrons interacts with a sample. Because of the charge carried by the electron, electron beams interact strongly with the atoms of the sample. Thus electron beams fail to penetrate beyond the surface of solids or liquids. They do, however, penetrate gases and produce diffraction patterns as a result of interaction with the molecules of the gas. An electron beam is produced by drawing electrons out of a cathode plate by means of an applied voltage and directing them to an anode. If such a beam is made to pass across a potential difference of $\mathcal{U}$ volts, each electron acquires kinetic energy as a result of the acceleration in this electric field. The potential difference, or voltage drop, is defined as the energy given to a unit charge when it falls through the potential difference. Thus, if we ignore relativistic effects that begin to be important at the accelerating voltages that are used,

$$\tfrac{1}{2}mv^2 = e\mathcal{V}$$

This relation leads to the momentum expression

$$mv = \sqrt{2me\mathcal{V}}$$

which, for an electron, gives the de Broglie wavelength as

$$\lambda = \frac{h}{mv} = \frac{h}{\sqrt{2me\mathcal{V}}} = \frac{12.25 \times 10^{-10}}{\sqrt{\mathcal{V}}}\ \mathrm{m} = \frac{12.25}{\sqrt{\mathcal{V}}}\ \text{Å} \qquad (15\text{-}26)$$

An accelerating potential of 40 kV therefore corresponds to an electron-beam wavelength of 0.06 Å. Such a wavelength leads one to expect that interference effects will be observed when a beam so accelerated passes through a sample containing scattering centers separated by the distances between the atoms of a molecule.

When a beam of such high-energy electrons passes through a chamber containing gas molecules, the charges of the nuclei (and to some extent the charges of the electrons) of the molecules will interact with the incoming beam. Each of the atoms of the molecules of the gas will act as a radiation-scattering center much as each of the slits of Fig. 15-7 acts as a center of radiation. Since the particles of the electron beam carry a charge, the amount of scattering resulting from the interaction of the electron beam and the gas molecules is relatively large. Few molecules are needed to produce a detectable amount of scattered beam. (With an x-ray beam, on the other hand, the amount of scattering produced by each molecule is much less, and crystals, with their higher concentration of scattering centers, are studied.)

The scattering of an electron beam by the molecules of a gas can be attributed to *coherent scattering,* which implies no exchange of energy between the beam and the scattering centers, and *incoherent scattering,* in which there is energy exchange and a resulting change in the wavelength and phase of the scattered electron beam. Both types of scattering lead to more forward than lateral scattering. A detailed analysis shows that the intensity of such scattered beams falls off from the incident direction according to $1/(\sin^4 \theta)$, where θ is the scattering angle like that in Fig. 15-28.

It is in the coherent, or elastic, scattering, in which the wavelength of the waves is unaffected, that the interference effects show up. These effects are therefore superimposed on a background of scattering that is not dependent on the structure of the molecule. The interference, or diffraction, effects can,

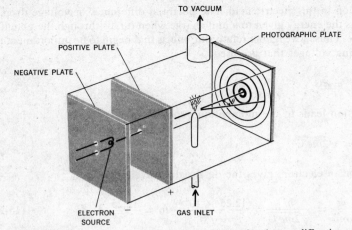

FIGURE 15-28 Arrangement for the study of gases by electron diffraction.

however, be sorted out from the background on the photographic plate, and this part of the scattering, which is here of interest, can be dealt with.

An electron diffraction pattern, as suggested in Fig. 15-28, consists of a pattern of rings of varying intensity. In the simplest and earliest of the methods that have been used, the photographic plate is viewed from the origin outward. The positions of the darkened rings on the photographic plate are estimated visually. For convenient comparison with calculated scattering curves a plot is sketched for the plate darkening as a function of the parameter s defined by

$$s = \frac{4\pi}{\lambda} \sin \frac{\theta}{2} \tag{15-27}$$

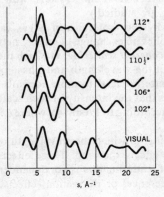

FIGURE 15-29
Comparison of the visual scattering curve for CHF_3 with curves calculated for various F—C—F angles. It is concluded that the angle is between 106 and 110°. (Spectroscopic data give the angle as 108°48′.) (*From L. O. Brockway, in Weissberger, "Physical Methods of Organic Chemistry," 2d ed., pt. II, p. 1123, Interscience, New York, 1960.*)

The curve that is obtained is labeled an *experimental* or *visual scattering curve*. An example is shown for the CHF_3 molecule in Fig. 15-29.

Analysis of how randomly oriented molecules produce a diffraction pattern shows that the intensity at a scattering angle θ can be expressed in terms of the function s. The expression for the scattering by two atoms i and j separated by a distance r_{ij} and randomly oriented in the path of an electron beam is given by

$$I(s) = f_i f_j \left(1 + \frac{\sin sr_{ij}}{sr_{ij}}\right) \tag{15-28}$$

where f_i and f_j are the scattering factors for the atoms i and j. This expression, which will not be derived here, is known as the *Wierl equation*. The scattering curves calculated for two scattering centers with different separations are illustrated in Fig. 15-30.

Equation (15-28) applies directly to a diatomic molecule. It can be extended to a polyatomic molecule by summing over all pairs of atoms to obtain

$$I(s) = \sum_{ij} f_i f_j \frac{\sin sr_{ij}}{sr_{ij}} \tag{15-29}$$

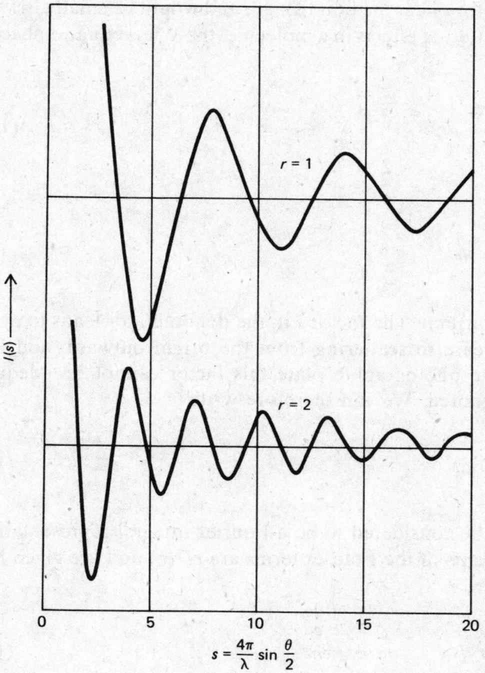

FIGURE 15-30
The calculated variation of $I(s)$ with s for a pair of atoms separated by 1 and 2 Å for an electron beam of wavelength 0.06 Å.

where the summation is over all atoms i and j of the molecule. It can be easily verified that Eq. (15-29) reduces to Eq. (15-28) when a diatomic molecule is treated if it is recalled that $\lim\limits_{x \to 0} [(\sin x)/x] = 1$

For any assumed molecular structure the contributions from all the pairs of atoms can be calculated and a plot of $I(s)$ versus s, called a *theoretical scattering curve*, can be made. The theoretical curves are then compared, as shown in Fig. 15-29, with the experimental curve. The curve most like the experimental curve is taken as being based on the best structure.

A very great aid in using electron diffraction techniques was the suggestion made by L. Pauling and L. O. Brockway that the data on the photographic plate could be used directly to obtain some information about the structure of the sample molecules. This method, known as the *radial-distribution method,* is the counterpart of the Fourier-transform method of Sec. 15-9. The procedure allows the distances between scattering centers of the molecule to be calculated from the experimental scattering results.

The molecule is represented by a continuous distribution in space of regions with varying scattering power. A function $D(r)$, called the *radial-distribution function,* can be introduced such that $D(r)$ represents the product of the scattering powers of unit volumes a distance r apart. The quantity $4\pi r^2 D(r)\, dr$ represents the product of the total scattering powers between a distance r and $r + dr$. For a diatomic molecule, therefore, $D(r)$ would have a large value for r near the bond length and would be small elsewhere. With this description of the scattering effects in a molecule, the Wierl equation becomes the integral equation

$$I(s) \propto \int_0^\infty 4\pi r^2 D(r) \frac{\sin sr}{sr}\, dr \tag{15-30}$$

or

$$I(s) = k \int_0^\infty \frac{rD(r)\sin sr}{s}\, dr \tag{15-31}$$

where k is a proportionality constant. The factor s in the denominator leads to nothing more than a continuous decrease in scattering from the origin outward, and in the simple visual treatment of the photographic plate this factor cannot be adequately handled and was generally ignored. We can therefore write

$$I(s) = k' \int_0^\infty rD(r)\sin sr\, dr \tag{15-32}$$

In this form, the integral can be considered to be a Fourier-integral representation of the function $I(s)$. The coefficients of the Fourier terms are $rD(r)$ and are given by the inverted form as

$$rD(r) = k' \int_0^\infty I(s)\sin sr\, ds \tag{15-33}$$

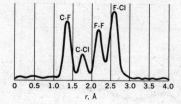

FIGURE 15-31
Radial-distribution function
for CF_3Cl. [*From L. S. Bartell
and L. O. Brockway, J. Chem.
Phys.*, **23**:*1860 (1955)*.]

or

$$D(r) = k'' \int_0^\infty I(s) \frac{\sin sr}{r} \, ds \tag{15-34}$$

This important expression, or ones that treat the smooth fall of intensity with θ or s in somewhat different ways, can be used to convert the experimental data on $I(s)$ as a function of s to a radial-distribution function $D(r)$. Computer integration of the integrals for values of r in the range from r equal to zero to the largest separation of scattering centers expected for the molecule under study gives this function. An example is shown in Fig. 15-31.

One of the chief remaining limitations of the electron diffraction method is that there are a small number of "wiggles" in the experimental curve. These wiggles are really the data provided by the experiment, and with a small number of data, only a few molecular parameters can be determined. A very large molecule cannot be satisfactorily treated unless, as in carbon tetrachloride or benzene, there is some geometric relation which makes several interatomic distances dependent on each other. A second limitation is that the electron beam is not scattered very effectively by hydrogen atoms. It follows that the position of such atoms in a molecule cannot easily be determined by this method. The method of x-ray diffraction studies of crystals overcomes the first difficulty by yielding many scattered beams and therefore much information. The method of neutron diffraction overcomes the second difficulty since protons have a reasonably large scattering cross section for neutrons.

15-15 Diffraction Studies of Liquid Structures

The structure that exists in simple liquids, e.g., liquid metals, can be deduced from diffraction studies. X-rays or neutrons are used so that the structure of the bulk of the liquid rather than the surface is revealed. The long-range disorder of a liquid leads us, however, to an analysis like that applied to the electron diffraction from gases (Sec. 15-14) rather than to one like that for the x-ray diffraction from crystals.

That there is some organization, or structure, in the liquid state has been assumed in the introduction of the cell theory of the liquid state. In fact, even the concept of nearest neighbors assumes that about any one molecule in a liquid certain nearby positions can be distinguished. Thus one is drawn to the supposition that a certain amount of *short-range order* exists in a liquid and that it is the long-range disorder that gives to a liquid its characteristic fluidity.

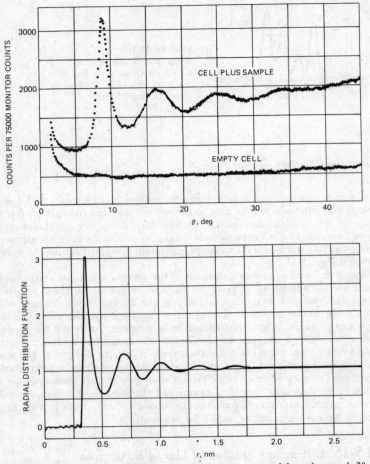

FIGURE 15-32 (*a*) Raw experimental data for neutrons scattered through an angle 2θ by the cell plus the liquid ^{36}Ar sample and by the empty cell. The wavelength of the neutron beam was 0.9782 Å. (*b*) Radial-distribution function for ^{36}Ar at 85 K. [*From Y. L. Yarnell, M. J. Katz, R. G. Wenzel, and S. H. Koenig, Phys. Rev. **A7**:2130 (1973).*]

This supposition is nicely supported by diffraction studies of simple monatomic liquids. The diffraction principle is essentially that which was used to study molecular structure of gas molecules by electron diffraction. It is found that a diffraction pattern is in fact obtained, as shown in Fig. 15-32, when a beam of neutrons or of x-rays passes through a monatomic-liquid sample, and this observation is by itself sufficient for the statement that liquids do exhibit some structure. Liquid diffraction patterns characteristically show one or two nicely formed small-angle diffraction maxima that correspond to the short-range order. They also show rather diffuse diffraction rings corresponding to the farther-removed molecules.

The radial-distribution method introduced in Sec. 15-14 can be used here very effectively. It is only the distance of neighboring molecules from a given central one, and not the angular arrangement, that is of interest. The radial-distribution curve calculated from the scattering curve of Fig. 15-32 is also included in that figure. In this way the layer of nearest neighbors clearly shows up, as does the diffuseness of the longer-range structure.

PROBLEMS

15-1. (a) Show that if additional lattice points in the tetragonal unit cell were placed on the end faces of the primitive lattice, a new body-centered unit cell could be drawn. (b) Suppose that additional lattice points are face-centered on the four side faces of the unit cell of the primitive lattice. Could a new unit cell showing that the lattice is primitive or body-centered be drawn? Which? (c) Suppose all six faces of the primitive tetragonal unit cell are face-centered. To which of the two lattice types of Fig. 15-5 is this lattice equivalent?

15-2. The locations of the atoms of $KMgF_3$ in the cubic unit cell of the crystal are specified by K at $(0, 0, 0)$; Mg at $(\frac{1}{2}, \frac{1}{2}, \frac{1}{2})$, and F at $(0, \frac{1}{2}, \frac{1}{2})$, $(\frac{1}{2}, 0, \frac{1}{2})$, and $(\frac{1}{2}, \frac{1}{2}, 0)$. (a) Draw a unit cell showing the location of all the atoms of the cell. (b) To what type of lattice does this cubic unit cell belong? (c) How many atoms of each type belong to the unit cell? (d) Describe the coordination number of the Mg^{2+} and K^+ ions. (e) Describe the coordination of the F^- ions.

15-3. What are the Miller indices for planes with the following intercepts, each expressed in terms of the unit-cell dimensions (a) $1, \frac{1}{2}, \frac{1}{2}$; (b) $\frac{1}{4}, \frac{1}{2}, \frac{1}{2}$; (c) $1, \infty, \frac{1}{2}$; (d) ∞, $1, \frac{2}{3}$; (e) $-\frac{1}{2}, -\frac{1}{2}, 1$? (f) Sketch a tetragonal unit cell and the orientation of each of these planes relative to the axes of the unit cell.

15-4. A tetragonal crystal has unit-cell dimensions of 12.04, 12.04, and 19.63 Å. The unique axis is taken as the z axis. (a) Prepare sketches showing the planes that have Weiss indices $a : b : \infty c$, $a : b : c$, $a : \infty b : c$, and $a : 2b : 2c$. (b) What are the Miller indices of these planes? (c) Prepare sketches showing the planes that have Miller indices (011), (101), (122), and (021).

15-5. A rotation photograph was taken with Cu K_α x-rays of wavelength 1.542 Å and a film diameter, as in Fig. 15-9, of 30 mm. The distances from the equatorial layer line to the first three layer lines above and below this equatorial line were measured. Average values of 8.25, 18.65, and 37.3 mm were obtained. Calculate the repeat spacing a along the axis about which the crystal was rotated.

15-6. A single-crystal diffraction pattern is taken of a graphite crystal, x-rays of wavelength 1.537 Å being used. The crystal is mounted, as in Fig. 15-9, so that the angle θ is taken as zero when the incoming x-ray beam impinges perpendicularly onto the molecular planes of the crystal. Consider the carbon-atom planes as presenting only continuous planes of high scattering. (a) Plot schematically the signal that will be obtained from the detector as a function of θ, the angle through which the crystal is turned. Label the equatorial-layer diffractions with appropriate indices. The spacing between the molecular planes of graphite is 3.35 Å. (b) Make a scale drawing showing how the waves from different planes add constructively for the first- and second-order diffractions.

15-7. Calculate the necessary angles to enable you to make a scale diagram showing the constructive interference that produces the first- and second-order diffraction of x-rays of wavelength 1.542 Å from crystal planes with a spacing of 2.500 Å.

15-8. In a single-crystal diffraction study using x-rays of wavelength 2.29 Å, as produced by an x-ray tube with a chromium target, a diffracted beam making an angle of 5°27′ with the incident beam is observed. What can be deduced from this single datum?

15-9. Calculate the spacings between (110) planes of KCl viewed as a simple cubic lattice, with the K^+ and Cl^- ions taken as identical and the (100)-plane spacings as 3.152 Å. At what angles would first- and second-order diffraction from the (100) and the (110) planes be observed if x-rays of wavelength 1.537 Å are used?

15-10. The x-rays used to obtain the NaCl powder pattern of Fig. 15-11 have the rather long wavelength (compared with x-rays generally used in diffraction studies) of 2.291 Å. Only a few diffraction lines appear in Fig. 15-11. Why?

15-11. (a) Make two-dimensional drawings showing primitive, body-centered, and face-centered cubic lattices viewed along one of the axes. (b) Add planes so that the basis for extinctions occurring in the body-centered lattice and in the face-centered lattice can be seen.

15-12. (a) Write the numbers that are proportional to the first 10 values of $1/d_{hkl}^2$ for a cubic crystal based on a primitive lattice. Repeat for (b) a body-centered and (c) a face-centered lattice.

15-13. A powder pattern of MgO, which forms cubic crystals, shows diffraction lines at $\sin \theta$ values of 0.1461, 0.1690, 0.2394, 0.2801, 0.2935, 0.3382 and 0.3697. What is the lattice type of MgO?

15-14. (a) Show that with x-rays of wavelength 2.291 Å the last diffraction that would appear as a distinct line is expected to be that observed in Fig. 15-15. (b) What index would the last line probably be given if x-rays with a wavelength of 1.542 Å had been used?

15-15 The following data have been given for the protein ribonuclease-S [J. R. Knox, *J. Chem. Educ.*, **49**:476 (1972)]:

Unit cell volume, 167,000 Å³
Crystal density, 1.282 g cm³
Protein fraction, 0.68%
Molecules per unit cell, 6

What is the mass of a mole of ribonuclease-S?

15-16. Consider a cubic unit cell that has atoms with unit scattering factor at the unit-cell corners. Their effect can most simply be described by placing one such atom at the origin corner with $x = y = z = 0$. (Alternatively you could place one-eighth of such an atom at each of the unit-cell corners.) (a) Introduce a constant factor (const) into the proportionality of Eq. (15-10) and express the intensity of the 100, 200, 110, and 220 diffractions. (b) Now introduce an additional atom, also of unit scattering power, in the center of the unit cell. Since x, y, and z are coordinates expressed in terms of the unit-cell dimensions, its coordinates will be $x = y = z = \frac{1}{2}$. Repeat the calculation of the intensities of the 100, 200, 110, 220 reflections for this body-centered unit cell. Draw the unit cell and the planes and rationalize the intensity results you obtained. (c) Move the central atom so that $x = \frac{3}{4}$, with y and z remaining at $\frac{1}{2}$. What are the intensities of the four diffractions? This should illustrate, in a crude way, that the intensities of diffractions depend on the positions of atoms within the unit cell and can be used to determine them.

15-17. X-ray studies show that $CaTiO_3$, perovskite, crystallizes in a cubic crystal with a unit-cell dimension of 3.80 Å. The density of the crystal is listed as 4.10 g cm^{-3}. (a) What is the content of the unit cell? (b) The x-ray studies also show that the crystal is based on the primitive lattice. What possible positions could be occupied by the Ca^{2+} ion and the Ti^{4+} ion? (c) In view of the structure of $KMgF_3$ described in Prob. 15-2 draw a unit cell that from what you know would describe the $CaTiO_3$ structure.

15-18. List the hkl values in the order which the quantity $h^2 + k^2 + l^2$ increases up to a total of 27. Alongside each hkl show the value of the structure factor for NaCl.

15-19. Cesium chloride forms cubic crystals, but the lattice is primitive. The positions of the ions in the lattice can be described by Cl^- at $(0, 0, 0)$ and Cs at $(\frac{1}{2}, \frac{1}{2}, \frac{1}{2})$. Add structure factors for CsCl alongside those for NaCl obtained in Prob. 15-18.

15-20. Make a table like that of Probs. 15-19 and 15-20 for KCl. What is the pattern of structure factors if $f_{K^+} = f_{Cl^-}$.

15-21. Using Na^+ and Cl^- scattering factors proportional to their atomic number, construct a diagram to suggest the precession pattern that would have been obtained if an NaCl crystal had been used instead of the lysozyme crystal in the study reported in Fig. 15-17.

15-22. Repeat the graphical display of Prob. 15-21 for KCl taking the scattering factors of K^+ and Cl^- to be equal.

15-23. Consider the crystal of Fig. 15-20 to have atoms A, at the origin, and B such that the scattering factor f_B is one-half of f_A. Furthermore, suppose that the unit cell has $a = 5$ Å and that the position of B relative to A is given by $x = 0.4$ and $y = 0.3$ in units of the cell dimension. (a) Calculate for some assumed wavelength of x-rays the angles at which first-order constructive interference from the A planes will occur for the planes (100), (010), (110), (210), and (120). (b) Calculate the relative intensities of the diffraction spots corresponding to each of these planes. (Take $f_A = 1$ and $f_B = 0.5$.) (c) Move atom B to a different position and see that the relative intensities calculated for the different diffractions are changed. In this way various positions of atom B can be assumed until a calculated pattern is obtained that matches an observed pattern.

15-24. Set up the Fourier-series expressions according to Eq. (15-23) for the electron density at atom A, with $x = y = z = 0$, and atom B, with $x = 0.4$, $y = 0.3$, and $z = 0$, as in Prob. 15-23. Obtain expressions for $\rho(000)$ and $\rho(0.4, 0.3, 0)$ in terms of the intensities of the reflections calculated in part (b) of Prob. 15-23. If the signs of the structure factors, which are the square roots of the intensities, are known, the relative electron densities at the two points can be calculated from data obtainable experimentally.

15-25. The unit cell of KCl is face-centered and has the dimension 6.28 Å. To what extent are the ionic radii of Table 15-3 consistent with this value?

15-26. The unit-cell dimension of the CaF_2 crystal is 5.451 Å. How well do the Ca^{2+} and F^- radii of Table 15-3 agree with this value?

15-27. The angle between the C—Cl bonds in CH_2Cl_2 is determined by both electron diffraction and microwave-spectroscopic techniques to be 112°, and the C—Cl bond lengths are found to be 1.77 Å. Calculate the Cl–Cl distance in methylene chloride, and discuss this value in view of the van der Waals radius for chlorine given in Table 15-6.

15-28. For any element for which data are available, compare an ionic radius with a covalent radius and a van der Waals radius.

15-29. Plot underneath each other the theoretical scattering curves that would be obtained for a CO molecule with assumed bond lengths of 1.00 and 1.40 Å. Carry each plot out to a value of s, equal to $(4\pi/\lambda)\sin(\theta/2)$, of about 20.

15-30. Plot underneath each other, the theoretical scattering curves for CCl_4 that would be obtained with an assumed tetrahedral structure and C—Cl bond lengths of 1.7 and 1.8, carrying the curves out to $s = 15$. Compare with the reported results of I. L. Karle and J. Karle, *J. Chem. Phys.*, **17**:1052 (1949) and L. S. Bartell, L. O. Brockway, and R. H. Schwendeman, *J. Chem. Phys.*, **23**:1854 (1955).

15-31. The visual appearance of the photograph of the diffracted electron beam of 40 kV from CO_2 shows maxima at $s = 6.7$, 12.2, 17.8, and 23, shoulders on these maxima at about 8.5, 14, and 19, and minima at 4.4, 10.0, 15.4, and 21. By plotting theoretical scattering curves for assumed values of the bond lengths (assuming a linear symmetric structure), deduce the C=O bond length in CO_2 [see I. L. Karle and J. Karle, *J. Chem. Phys.*, **17**:1052 (1949)].

15-32. (*a*) Compare the position of the first peak of the radial-distribution curve for argon in Fig. 15-32*b* with estimates of the size of argon atoms obtained by other techniques. (*b*) Using a model for the structure of liquid argon, calculate the ratio of the position expected for the second peak to that expected for the first peak and compare with the value from Fig. 15-32*b*.

REFERENCES

Several books that provide introductions to crystals and the use of x-rays to deduce crystal structures:

BUERGER, M. J.: "Contemporary Crystallography," McGraw-Hill Book Company, New York, 1970.

CARPENTER, G. B.: "Principles of Crystal Structure Determination," W. A. Benjamin, Inc., New York, 1969.

SANDS, D. E.: "Introduction to Crystallography," W. A. Benjamin, Inc., New York, 1969.

STOUT, G. H., and L. H. JENSEN: "X-Ray Structure Determination: A Practical Guide," The Macmillan Publishing Company, New York, 1968.

WARREN, B. E.: "X-Ray Diffraction," Addison-Wesley Publishing Company, Inc., Reading, Mass., 1968.

WOOLFSON, M. M.: "An Introduction to X-Ray Crystallography," Cambridge University Press, Cambridge, 1970.

Electron diffraction:

PINSHER, Z. G.: "Electron Diffraction," Butterworth and Company, Ltd., London, 1953.

EXPERIMENTAL STUDIES OF THE ELECTRICAL AND MAGNETIC PROPERTIES OF MOLECULES

The properties of molecules that are deduced from spectroscopic or diffraction methods are electrical in the sense that the molecular binding forces result from forces between electrons and the nuclei of the molecules or ions. Molecules and ions also display electrical and magnetic properties that are more similar to those observed in ordinary-sized systems.

ELECTRICAL PROPERTIES: MOLECULAR DIPOLE MOMENTS

Since molecules are made up of charged units, i.e., electrons and the atomic nuclei, much of the behavior of molecules is understandable in terms of electrical interactions. A detailed theoretical treatment of a molecule by the methods of quantum mechanics would reveal the electron distribution of the molecule and would lead to deductions of how a particular assembly of charges that make up a molecule would interact with other molecules, with a surrounding medium, or with an electric field. It is also possible to learn much about the electric nature of molecules by an experimental approach. In this section the procedure which produces results for the *dipole moment* of a molecule will be dealt with. The goal, however, is not only to obtain such results but also to show how some electrical phenomena in chemical systems are treated.

16-1 Dipole Moments of Molecules

The principal characteristic of the charge distribution in a molecule that can be measured is the extent to which the center of the electron distribution of a molecule fails to coincide with the center of the positive-nuclear-charge distribution. The charge asymmetry is obtained as the dipole moment of the molecule. This charge asymmetry, as we shall see, may result from an unequal sharing of the bonding electrons, the extreme case of which leads to a molecule with positively and negatively charged ions such as a molecule of NaCl vapor. More subtle electron distributions like the apparent slight asymmetry of the

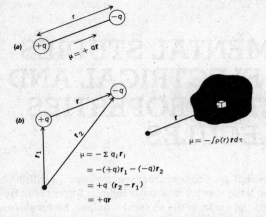

FIGURE 16-1
(a) The dipole moment of
separated equal but opposite
charges. (b) The dipole-
moment deduction, by means
of Eqs. (16-2) and (16-3), for
the two-particle system and a
complex system representing a
molecule.

bonding electrons, as in a C—H bond, or the projection of the nonbonding
electrons of, for example, the nitrogen atom in ammonia, also lead to molecular
dipoles. Dipole-moment results allow such aspects of the electronic configuration of molecules to be discussed.

As Fig. 16-1 indicates, the dipole moment of two equal and opposite
charges is defined as the product of the charges and the distance separating
them. Thus the dipole moment is given by

$$\mu = qr \tag{16-1}$$

Furthermore, the dipole moment has a direction as well as a magnitude; i.e., it
is a *vector* quantity. It is frequently convenient diagrammatically to represent a
dipole moment by an arrow showing the direction from the positive to the
negative charge and the magnitude by the length of the arrow, as in Fig. 16-1a.
In fact, the concept of a dipole arises when, as suggested in Fig. 16-1b, the effect
of an assembly of charges at some distant point is investigated, and with this
approach the dipole moment due to a collection of charges is defined as

$$\mu = - \sum_i q_i r_i \tag{16-2}$$

where q_i and r_i are the charges and vector lengths of the ith charges of the
assembly. For a molecule the distribution of the electrons requires an integral
form of Eq. (16-2)

$$\mu = - \int \rho(\mathbf{r}) \mathbf{r} \, d\tau \tag{16-3}$$

where $\rho(\mathbf{r})$ is the charge density at a position defined by the vector $\mathbf{r}$ and $d\tau$ is
a volume element. The integration over all the electrons and nuclei required by

Eq. (16-3) can, of course, be carried out only for relatively simple molecules, where the electron distribution can be determined by theoretical methods. In general, the detailed electronic distribution is not known, and information is provided by the measurement of the molecular dipole moment by methods that will be developed in this chapter. The determination of this one quantity does not, of course, allow the charge distribution $\rho(\mathbf{r})$ of Eq. (16-3) to be deduced. Usually, one makes use of the measured value of the dipole moment of a molecule by depicting the charge asymmetry which it measures in terms of a model, like that of Fig. 16-1a, of separated, opposite charges that have the dipole moment of that measured for the molecule.

The order of magnitude of molecular dipole moments can be deduced by recognizing that these moments result from charges like that of an electron $(0.1602 \times 10^{-18}$ C) separated by angstrom distances. For one electron separated from an equally charged positive center by a distance of 1 Å, the dipole moment would be

$$\mu = (0.1602 \times 10^{-18})(1 \times 10^{-10}) = 16.02 \times 10^{-30} \text{ C m}$$

In most of the chemical literature, molecular dipole moments are quoted in units of *debyes,* a quantity based on the cgs-esu system. The relation to SI units is

$$1 \text{ debye} = 3.338 \times 10^{-30} \text{ C m}$$

Thus an electronic charge separated from one of opposite sign by a distance of 1 Å has a dipole moment of $(16.02 \times 10^{-30})/(3.338 \times 10^{-30}) = 4.80$ debyes.

In addition to the dipole moment a molecule can have as a result of its asymmetric charge distribution, for all molecules there is the possibility of distorting the electronic distribution in a molecule by applying an electric field. In this way an *induced dipole moment* can be produced. The effectiveness of an applied field in making a molecule polar is determined by the *polarizability* of the molecule. The polarizability, defined as the dipole moment induced by an electric field of unit strength, is the second important electrical property of molecules with which we shall deal. The units and values of this quantity are best left until its determination from measurable quantities is considered. It should be immediately clear, however, that all molecules, symmetric or not, are polarizable and can have an induced dipole moment. On the other hand, symmetric molecules, like H_2, CO_2, and CCl_4, necessarily have zero "permanent" dipole moments.

16-2 Some Basic Electrostatic Ideas

Some basic ideas that enter into the treatment of charged particles in a vacuum (or approximately, in air) must be reviewed. This and the following section, where media other than vacuum are considered, provide the necessary background to the theory of the measurement of molecular dipole moments.

The basic relation in treating the interaction of stationary charges is Coulomb's law, which states that two point charges q_1 and q_2 separated by a distance r in vacuum (or approximately, air) will interact with a force f given by

$$f = \frac{q_1 q_2}{4\pi\epsilon_0 r^2} \tag{16-4}$$

where ϵ_0 is the *permittivity constant* and has a value such that

$$4\pi\epsilon_0 = 1.11264 \times 10^{-10} \, \text{C}^2 \, \text{N}^{-1} \, \text{m}^{-2}$$

For q_1 and q_2 of opposite signs the force is one of attraction; with the same signs, one of repulsion.

The interaction of charges at a distance suggests that an electric field exists around each charge. The intensity of the electric field $\mathcal{E}$ at a point is defined as the force which would be exerted on a unit positive charge placed at that point. Thus the electric field strength about a point charge q is the force on a unit charge, or

$$\mathcal{E} = \frac{f}{q} \tag{16-5}$$

The field strength is measured in newtons per coulomb. The force on the unit test charge has a direction as well as a magnitude. The electric field $\mathcal{E}$ is therefore a vector quantity and has the direction as well as the magnitude of the force on a unit positive test charge. It is frequently helpful to draw *lines of force* to represent the intensity and the direction of an electric field.

Consider, for example, the electric field about a point charge $+q$, as in Fig. 16-2. At a distance r from this charge a unit positive charge would be repelled by a force $q/4\pi\epsilon_0 r^2$. The electric field intensity is therefore $q/4\pi\epsilon_0 r^2$ at a distance r from the $+q$ charge. This electric field can be depicted by drawing lines of force emanating from the point charge. As these lines suggest, the *total* field produced by the charge is independent of the distance from the charge and is given, as suggested by Fig. 16-2, as

$$\frac{q}{4\pi\epsilon_0 r^2} 4\pi r^2 = \frac{q}{\epsilon_0} \tag{16-6}$$

Another important aspect of an electric field is described by the electrical potential $\mathcal{V}$. This quantity represents the potential energy of a unit positive charge in the electric field. A unit positive charge in an electric field of intensity $\mathcal{E}$ experiences a force equal to $\mathcal{E}$, and for a given displacement of the unit charge the work involved is the force, or the field strength, times the distance that the charge is moved. Since the potential energy increases as the unit positive test

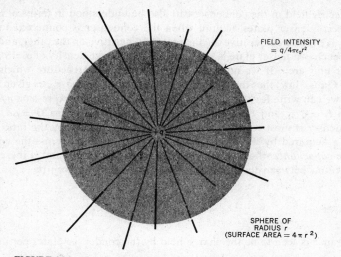

FIELD INTENSITY
= $q/4\pi\epsilon_0 r^2$

SPHERE OF
RADIUS r
(SURFACE AREA = $4\pi r^2$)

FIGURE 16-2 The electric field of a charge $+q$ represented by lines of force. A total of q/ϵ_0 lines emanate from a charge of $+q$.

charge is brought closer to the positive charge q which generates the electric field, the change $d\mathcal{V}$ for an infinitesimal change dr is

$$d\mathcal{V} = -\mathcal{E}\, dr \tag{16-7}$$

Rearrangement of Eq. (16-7) gives a relation that is useful when electric fields are deduced from applied or known potentials. This expression is

$$\mathcal{E} = -\frac{d\mathcal{V}}{dr} \tag{16-8}$$

The example of a plane-parallel condenser with air (or more properly, vacuum) between the plates can now be considered. If, as in Fig. 16-3, the condenser is connected to a battery that produces a potential difference of $\mathcal{V}$ volts, there will be a potential drop of $\mathcal{V}$ volts across the condenser. According to Eq. (16-8), the field between the plates of the condenser will be $\mathcal{V}/d$, where d is the distance between the plates.

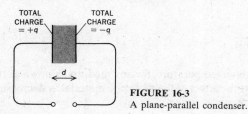

TOTAL
CHARGE
= $+q$

TOTAL
CHARGE
= $-q$

d

FIGURE 16-3
A plane-parallel condenser.

The electric field in the condenser can also be understood in terms of the charges the condenser plates acquire when the condenser is connected to a battery. If q is the charge, positive on one plate and negative on the other, and if the area of each condenser plate is A, there will be a charge density of $\sigma = q/A$ charges per unit area. If we now carry over the idea (a procedure which is justified by Gauss' law) that the electric field of a charge $+q$ is q/ϵ_0, as given by Eq. (16-6), we can write for the field per unit cross section the expression σ/ϵ_0. Then, from $\mathcal{E} = \sigma/\epsilon_0$ and $\mathcal{E} = \mathcal{V}/d$, we have the useful relation $\mathcal{V} = \sigma d/\epsilon_0$.

A condenser is most readily characterized experimentally by the ratio of the charge q acquired by the plates to the voltage $\mathcal{V}$ applied across the condenser. The *capacitance* of a condenser is defined by this ratio, and if there is air or a vacuum between the plates, the capacitance is C_0, given by

$$C_0 = \frac{q}{\mathcal{V}} \tag{16-9}$$

The capacitance is seen to be the charge held by the condenser plates per unit potential.

The capacitance can be related to the geometry of the condenser by substituting the results $q = \sigma A$ and $\mathcal{V} = \sigma d/\epsilon_0$ to give

$$C_0 = \frac{\sigma A}{\sigma d/\epsilon_0} = \frac{\epsilon_0 A}{d} \tag{16-10}$$

The capacitance is thus a property of the geometry of the condenser and for a plane-parallel condenser is large for large A and small d.

16-3 Electrostatics for Dielectric Media

The presence of a nonconducting, or *dielectric,* material around the charges that have been dealt with alters the relations which have been obtained. An understanding of this dielectric effect will be the basis from which the electrical properties of molecules are deduced.

The starting point is again Coulomb's law. When the charges q_1 and q_2 are immersed in a dielectric material, it is found that the force between them is less at any given value of r than when such a dielectric medium is absent. Coulomb's law can be written to apply to both vacuum and dielectric media by writing it in the form

$$f = \frac{q_1 q_2}{4\pi\epsilon r^2} = \frac{q_1 q_2}{(\epsilon/\epsilon_0)(4\pi\epsilon_0 r^2)} \tag{16-11}$$

where ϵ/ϵ_0 is a constant, at a given temperature, for any medium. Known as the *dielectric constant,* it represents the effect of the dielectric material in decreasing the force between the charges.

The definition [Eq. (16-5)] of the electric field as the force exerted on a unit positive charge can now be applied to determine the field of the charge $+q$ when it is immersed in a dielectric material. The force on the unit positive charge at a distance r would be $q/(\epsilon/\epsilon_0)(4\pi\epsilon_0 r^2)$, and the total field for such a surrounded charge would be

$$\frac{q}{(\epsilon/\epsilon_0)(4\pi\epsilon_0 r^2)} 4\pi r^2 = \frac{q}{\epsilon} \qquad (16\text{-}12)$$

The electric field is therefore lowered by the presence of the nonconducting materials by a factor equal to the dielectric constant ϵ/ϵ_0.

Now we can consider the properties of the condenser of Fig. 16-3 which can be measured and which will allow an understanding of the role of the dielectric material. Suppose the condenser is charged until the same charge q as for vacuum accumulates on the plates. The charge per unit area is again $\sigma = q/A$, but in view of Eq. (16-12) the electric field $\mathcal{E}$ is reduced from σ/ϵ_0 to σ/ϵ. Now $\mathcal{V}$ is given by $\mathcal{E} = \mathcal{V}/d$, or $\mathcal{V} = \mathcal{E}d$, as

$$\mathcal{V} = \frac{\sigma d}{\epsilon} \qquad (16\text{-}13)$$

and the capacitance is

$$C = \frac{q}{\mathcal{V}} = \frac{\sigma A}{\sigma d/\epsilon} = \epsilon \frac{A}{d} \qquad (16\text{-}14)$$

By comparison with Eq. (16-10), we see that measured capacitances with and without dielectric material give ϵ/ϵ_0.

$$\frac{C}{C_0} = \frac{\epsilon}{\epsilon_0} \qquad (16\text{-}15)$$

where C_0 is the capacitance of the condenser in vacuum. The dielectric material has therefore increased the capacitance of the condenser. It is this relationship (16-15) that is often used as a more directly operational definition of the dielectric constant, since it is a quite straightforward matter to measure the capacitance of a condenser.

Now it is necessary to investigate the mechanism by which the dielectric material decreases the electric field between the condenser plates when a given charge is placed on the plates. Again consider the condenser to be charged to a suitable potential so that charges $+q$ and $-q$ reside on the two plates. The effect of the dielectric can be understood, without going into the molecular behavior, by supposing that the dielectric material is *polarizable* and that the charges on the plates distort the electric balance within the dielectric material so that it develops an opposing charge arrangement, as shown in Fig. 16-4. This

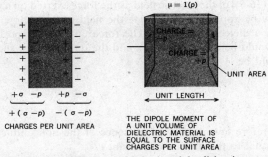

$\mu = 1(p)$

+σ −p   +p −σ

+ (σ −p)   − (σ −p)

CHARGES PER UNIT AREA

THE DIPOLE MOMENT OF
A UNIT VOLUME OF
DIELECTRIC MATERIAL IS
EQUAL TO THE SURFACE
CHARGES PER UNIT AREA

FIGURE 16-4 The electrical behavior of the dielectric material of a condenser.

opposing effect is conveniently described by introducing the term *polarization* and symbol p to represent the dipole moment induced in a unit volume of the dielectric material. Considering such a volume of the dielectric, one sees that its dipole moment p can be described as being due to charges of $+p$ on one end and $-p$ on the other. In the interior of the dielectric material between the condenser plates, such charges cancel out, and one is left with only the charges on the surfaces of the dielectric next to the condenser plates. This situation is represented in Fig. 16-4.

How the dielectric reduces the field between the condenser plates can now be understood. The field $\mathcal{E}_0$ with vacuum between the condenser plates is related to the plate charge density by

$$\mathcal{E}_0 = \frac{\sigma}{\epsilon_0} \tag{16-6}$$

When a dielectric material is present, the charge q on the plates is partially balanced by the charge p on the surface of the dielectric. This interpretation of the factors affecting $\mathcal{E}$ gives

$$\mathcal{E} = \frac{\sigma - p}{\epsilon_0} \quad \text{or} \quad \mathcal{E} = \mathcal{E}_0 - \frac{p}{\epsilon_0} \tag{16-17}$$

Combination of this mechanistic interpretation of the reduction of $\mathcal{E}$ with the expressions $\mathcal{E} = \sigma/\epsilon$ and $\mathcal{E}_0 = \sigma/\epsilon_0$ leads to the desired result

$$\mathcal{E} = \frac{p}{\epsilon - \epsilon_0} \tag{16-18}$$

for the electric field in a dielectric medium in terms of the polarization of the dielectric and the dielectric constant.

16-4 The Molecular Basis for Dielectric Behavior

A molecular explanation of the role of dielectric material in affecting electrical phenomena will now be given. Our attention will at first be restricted to the effect of the induced dipole moment that all molecules possess as a result of the electrical distortions of the electron distribution in a molecule by an applied electric field. All molecules are polarizable and therefore will have contributions from this factor.

Let the dipole moment induced in a molecule be denoted by μ_{ind}. If there are n molecules per unit volume of the dielectric material which has a polarization, or dipole moment per unit volume, of p, then

$$p = n\mu_{ind} \tag{16-19}$$

The nature of the dielectric can therefore be understood in terms of the molecular property μ_{ind}.

The simplest relation that would account for the consequences of the induced dipole moment in a molecule is one in which the induced dipole is proportional to the field acting on the molecule. If this field is $\mathcal{E}_{int}$ and the proportionality constant is α, the relations

$$\mu_{ind} = \alpha\epsilon_0\mathcal{E}_{int} \tag{16-20}$$

and

$$p = n\alpha\epsilon_0\mathcal{E}_{int} \tag{16-21}$$

are obtained when an ϵ_0 term is included explicitly rather than incorporated in α. The polarizability α is one of the molecular properties that will be deduced. It represents the ease with which the electron configuration of the molecule can be distorted by an acting electric field.

The field acting on the molecule results from several contributions. With reference to Fig. 16-5, it can be seen that the charges on the plates, the charges at boundaries of the dielectric adjacent to the plates, and the charges on the surface of a small cavity that is supposed to surround the molecule all contribute to the field on the molecule. The net result of these terms is

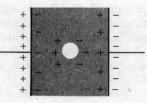

FIGURE 16-5
The charges that contribute to the field $\mathcal{E}$ acting on a molecule which is treated as being in a cavity within the dielectric material.

$$\mathcal{E}_{\text{int}} = \frac{\sigma}{\epsilon_0} - \frac{p}{\epsilon_0} + \frac{p}{3\epsilon_0} \tag{16-22}$$

where the last term is the cavity-charge contribution. It is obtained by integrating, over the surface of the sphere, the effects of the surface charge in generating a field in the direction perpendicular to the condenser plates. Finally, with the help of Eq. (16-17), one eliminates σ and obtains

$$\mathcal{E}_{\text{int}} = \mathcal{E} + \frac{p}{3\epsilon_0} \tag{16-23}$$

The relation of Eq. (16-21) allows the quantity $\mathcal{E}_{\text{int}}$, which is not directly measurable, to be eliminated and gives

$$p = n\alpha\epsilon_0\left(\mathcal{E} + \frac{p}{3\epsilon_0}\right) \tag{16-24}$$

Substitution for $\mathcal{E}$ by the relation of Eq. (16-18) then allows the elimination of $\mathcal{E}$ and p to give, on rearrangement,

$$\tfrac{1}{3}n\alpha = \frac{\epsilon/\epsilon_0 - 1}{\epsilon/\epsilon_0 + 2} \tag{16-25}$$

The more frequently used form of this result is obtained by writing

$$n = \frac{\rho}{M}\mathfrak{N}$$

where ρ is the density, ρ/M is the number of moles per unit volume, and $(\rho/M)\mathfrak{N}$ is the molecules per unit volume, to get

$$\mathcal{P} = \tfrac{1}{3}\mathfrak{N}\alpha = \frac{\epsilon/\epsilon_0 - 1}{\epsilon/\epsilon_0 + 2}\frac{M}{\rho} \tag{16-26}$$

where $\mathcal{P}$, called the molar polarization, has been introduced for the set of quantities $\tfrac{1}{3}\mathfrak{N}\alpha$. The derivation has now led to an expression, known as the *Clausius-Mosotti equation,* that allows the calculation of either the polarizability of a molecule α or the molar distortion polarization $\mathcal{P}$ from measurements of the dielectric constant of the dielectric material. Something of the nature and importance of these molecular properties will be mentioned after the more general case, where a molecule having a permanent dipole moment, as well as being polarizable, is considered.

Consider now, as was done by Debye in 1912, the contribution to the dielectric material of any permanent dipole moment μ of the molecules of the

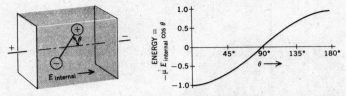

FIGURE 16-6 The energy of a dipole as a function of its orientation in an electric field $\mathcal{E}_{int}$.

material. With no applied field the dipoles will be oriented in all directions and will be ineffective in contributing to the polarization $\mathcal{P}$ of the dielectric. In the presence of a field, however, as Fig. 16-6 illustrates, the molecules will tend to line up with the field so that their dipole moments add to the polarization $\mathcal{P}$. The energy of the dipole varies with the angle with which it is oriented to the acting field direction according to

$$\text{Energy} = -\mu\mathcal{E}_{int}\cos\theta \tag{16-27}$$

The tendency of the molecules to go to the lowest energy position by lining up with the field is opposed, however, by the thermal motions of the molecules. The distribution expression of Boltzmann gives the way in which these two factors operate. Considerable manipulation is necessary for the calculation of the average dipole moment in the direction of the field. It is possible to omit this derivation and proceed with the result shown in Eq. (16-34).

According to the Boltzmann distribution law, the number of molecules dN that are lined up at an angle between θ and $\theta + d\theta$ to the field is given by the expression

$$dN = Ae^{\mu\mathcal{E}_{int}\cos\theta/kT}(2\pi\sin\theta)\,d\theta \tag{16-28}$$

where A is a proportionality constant and, as Fig. 16-7 illustrates, $2\pi\sin\theta\,d\theta$ is the element of solid angle inclined between θ and $\theta + d\theta$ to the field direction. Since the dipole-moment contribution of a molecule so oriented in the direction of the field is $\mu\cos\theta$, the contribution of the molecules in the solid-angle element is

$$\mu\cos\theta\,dN = Ae^{\mu\mathcal{E}_{int}\cos\theta/kT}(\mu\cos\theta)2\pi\sin\theta\,d\theta \tag{16-29}$$

The total dipole contribution in the field direction will therefore be

$$\int_0^{2\pi} Ae^{\mu\mathcal{E}_{int}\cos\theta/kT}(\mu\cos\theta)2\pi\sin\theta\,d\theta \tag{16-30}$$

To obtain the average molecular contribution, this total value is divided by the number of molecules and this number is obtained by integrating dN of Eq. (16-28). The average dipole contribution μ_{av} is then expressed as

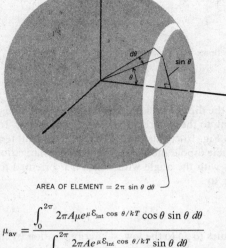

FIGURE 16-7
The solid-angle element for the integration over all molecules with various alignments with respect to the field direction. (Solid angles are equivalent to surface areas on a sphere with unit radius.)

AREA OF ELEMENT = $2\pi \sin\theta \, d\theta$

$$\mu_{av} = \frac{\int_0^{2\pi} 2\pi A\mu e^{\mu \mathcal{E}_{int} \cos\theta/kT} \cos\theta \sin\theta \, d\theta}{\int_0^{2\pi} 2\pi A e^{\mu \mathcal{E}_{int} \cos\theta/kT} \sin\theta \, d\theta}$$

$$= \mu \frac{\int_0^{2\pi} e^{\mu \mathcal{E}_{int} \cos\theta/kT} \cos\theta \sin\theta \, d\theta}{\int_0^{2\pi} e^{\mu \mathcal{E}_{int} \cos\theta/kT} \sin\theta \, d\theta} \qquad (16\text{-}31)$$

These integrals can be simplified by writing $x = \mu \mathcal{E}_{int}/kT$ and $y = \cos\theta$. Then, since $dy = -\sin\theta \, d\theta$, one has

$$\mu_{av} = \frac{\mu \int_{-1}^{+1} y e^{xy} \, dy}{\int_{-1}^{+1} e^{xy} \, dy} \qquad (16\text{-}32)$$

Both integrals are of the exponential type dealt with in Appendix A. Substitution of the limits shown in Eq. (16-32) into these results gives

$$\mu_{av} = \mu \left(\frac{e^x + e^{-x}}{e^x - e^{-x}} - \frac{1}{x} \right) = \mu \left(\coth x - \frac{1}{x} \right) \qquad (16\text{-}33)$$

The resulting function, which also occurs in studies of the magnetic effects of molecules with magnetic moments, was developed in this connection by P. Langevin, and is often referred to by his name. In the present connection, the function simplifies because x, which is the ratio of the energy effect of the dipole in the electric field to kT, is much less than unity. The first two terms of the series expansion of $\tanh x$ can then be kept to give

$$\coth x = \frac{1}{\tanh x} = \frac{1}{x - x^3/3} = \frac{1}{x}\left(1 - \frac{x^2}{3}\right)^{-1}$$

Furthermore, the binomial expansion of $(1 - x^2/3)^{-1}$ can be used to give

$$\left(1 - \frac{x^2}{3}\right)^{-1} = 1 + \frac{x^2}{3}$$

Appropriate substitutions now give the desired quantity, the average dipole moment in the direction of the field, as

$$\mu_{av} = \mu(\tfrac{1}{3}x) = \frac{1}{3}\frac{\mu^2 \mathcal{E}_{int}}{kT} = \frac{\mu^2}{3kT}\mathcal{E}_{int} \qquad (16\text{-}34)$$

Comparison of this result with Eq. (16-20) shows that the factor $\mu^2/3kT$ enters in just the way the term $\alpha\epsilon_0$ did. If the previous derivation were now carried out with the dipole-moment term as well as the polarizability term, it follows that the result, comparable with Eq. (16-26), would be obtained as

$$\mathcal{P} = \frac{\epsilon/\epsilon_0 - 1}{\epsilon/\epsilon_0 + 2}\frac{M}{\rho} = \frac{1}{3}\mathcal{N}\alpha + \frac{\mathcal{N}\mu^2}{9\epsilon_0 k}\frac{1}{T} \qquad (16\text{-}35)$$

This result is known as the *Debye equation*. It shows how the molecular polarizability α and the molecular dipole moment μ contribute to produce a dielectric constant greater than unity in any nonconducting material. Conversely, it suggests that these molecular properties might be deduced from measurement of the dielectric constant.

16-5 Determination of the Dipole Moment and the Molecular Polarizability

The dielectric constant of a material is measured by placing it between the plates of a condenser or, for liquids, filling a cell in which the plates are inserted. This condenser can then be used as one arm of an electric bridge, like a Wheatstone bridge for measuring resistances, and the capacitance of the sample condenser can be balanced against a variable-reference condenser which has no dielectric between its plates. In principle, the capacitance of the reference condenser can be deduced from its geometry. In this way the capacitance of the sample condenser can be obtained, filled and empty, and the dielectric constant of the sample can be deduced.

When the compound of interest is a liquid or solid material, measurements are generally made on solutions of the material in some inert nonpolar substance like CCl_4 or benzene. The Debye equation is based on the independent behavior of the polar molecules. Molecules with dipole moments exert considerable interaction on each other, and it is therefore best to apply the Debye

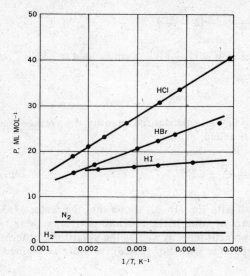

FIGURE 16-8
The molar polarization versus the reciprocal of the absolute temperature. [*From the data of C. T. Zahn, Phys. Rev.,* **24**:*400 (1924).*]

equation to dilute solutions of polar compounds in nonpolar solvents. For gaseous samples the intermolecular distance is usually large enough for these interactions to present no difficulty.

Measurement of the dielectric constant and use of the Debye equation do not directly lead to the separate determination of α and μ. Two principal ways are available for sorting out these two factors.

The first way consists in measuring ϵ and ρ as functions of temperature and using these data to plot $[(\epsilon/\epsilon_0 - 1)/(\epsilon/\epsilon_0 + 2)](M/\rho)$ against $1/T$. The Debye equation leads us to expect such a plot to yield a straight line, and Fig. 16-8 shows that the data for the hydrogen halides do behave in this manner. From such plots the slope of the straight line can be used to obtain the dipole moment μ, and the intercept at $1/T$ can be made to yield the polarizability α. This procedure is quite straightforward and fails only if the molecules are associated to different extents at different temperatures or if the molecular configuration changes with temperature.

The second procedure evaluates the polarizability part of the molar polarization $\mathcal{P}$ by an interesting relation between the dielectric constant and the refractive index given by Maxwell's theory of electromagnetic radiation. The theory cannot be dealt with here, but the basis of the relation can be suggested. The refractive index of a material is the ratio of the velocity of light in a vacuum to the velocity of light in the material. The velocity is always less in dielectric material than it is in vacuum. The slowing down is due to the interaction of the electrons of the polarizable molecules of the medium with the oscillating electric field of the radiation. The permanent dipoles of the molecules would also interfere, but the visible radiation used to measure the refractive index carries such a rapidly alternating electric field, about 10^{15} Hz, that the molecules are unable to orient themselves rapidly enough to keep up with the field. Thus only the polarizability interferes with the passage of the light.

Maxwell's theory shows that for materials composed of molecules with no permanent dipole moment,

$$\epsilon = n_R{}^2 \tag{16-36}$$

where n_R is the refractive index of the material. It is apparent, therefore, that even when the molecules of the dielectric do have dipole moments, the polarizability term of the total molar polarization $\mathcal{P}$ can be calculated as

$$\frac{n_R{}^2 - 1}{n_R{}^2 + 2}\frac{M}{\rho} = \tfrac{1}{3}\mathfrak{N}\alpha \tag{16-37}$$

Refractive-index data therefore provide a value for α that can be used along with the dielectric-constant data to give the molecular dipole moment μ.

Some results for a few simpler molecules are shown in Table 16-1. The information on molecular polarizabilities provided by these experiments finds rather less molecular-structure application than the dipole-moment results. The data of Table 16-1 should show, however, a qualitative correlation of molecular polarizability with the number of electrons in the molecule and the "looseness" with which they are bound. The polarizability data obtained here will be of value when molecular interactions are treated in the study of liquids.

TABLE 16-1 The Dipole Moment and the Polarizability of Some Simple Molecules

Substance	μ, debye†	Substance	μ, debye†	Substance	α, ml
HF	1.8	CH_2Cl_2	1.60	He	0.20×10^{-24}
HCl	1.07	CH_3Cl	1.85	Ne	0.39
HBr	0.79	HCN	2.95	A	1.62
HI	0.38	CH_3NO_2	3.50	H_2	0.80
BrClCO	0.13	CH_3OH	1.71	N_2	1.73
H_2O	1.82	CsF§	7.9	H_2O	1.44
NH_3	1.47	CsCl§	10.5	H_2S	3.64
NF_2	0.23	KF§	7.3	CH_4	2.60
PH_3	0.55	KCl§	10.4	CCl_4	10.5
AsH_3	0.18	KBr§	10.5	C_6H_6	25.1
$CHCl_3$	1.15				

† 1 debye = 3.338×10^{-30} m C.

§ Determined by molecular-beam techniques. N. F. Ramsey, "Molecular Beams," Oxford University Press, New York, 1956.

Source: Except as noted, dipole moments are from A. L. McClellan, "Tables of Experimental Dipole Moments," H. Freeman and Co., San Francisco, 1963.

16-6 Dipole Moments and Ionic Character

In considering at first only diatomic molecules, the measured dipole moment of a molecule gives information on the displacement of the center of negative charge from that of the positive charge. In the past this asymmetry has been interpreted primarily in terms of an unequal sharing of the bonding electrons. The theoretical treatment of heteronuclear molecules in Chap. 13 anticipated such unequal sharing and introduced *percent ionic character* as a measure of such bonding.

The assumption that a dipole moment results from the location of the bonding electrons leads to a calculation of the ionic character from a dipole moment. The example of HCl, with a dipole moment of 1.07 debyes, or 3.57×10^{-30} m C, and a bond length of 1.275 Å, will illustrate the calculation. If the pair of bonding electrons were completely held by the chlorine atom, the molecule would be represented as positively and negatively charged ions separated by the equilibrium bond length. The dipole moment of such a completely ionic structure would be

$$\mu_{ionic} = (0.1602 \times 10^{-18})(1.275 \times 10^{-10})$$
$$= 20.42 \times 10^{-30} \text{ m C} = 6.12 \text{ debyes} \tag{16-38}$$

On the other hand, if the pair of bonding electrons were equally shared, the bonding electrons would be almost symmetrically placed relative to the positive nuclear charges, and the dipole moment would be zero. In fact, the dipole moment is between these two extremes, and the amount of ionic character is calculated as

$$\% \text{ ionic character} = \frac{\mu_{obs}}{\mu_{ionic}}(100\%) = \frac{1.07}{6.12}(100) = 17\% \tag{16-39}$$

Of course, the result does not tell which end of the molecule is positive and which is negative. This detail must be deduced, or inferred, by other means.

The data obtained by the electrical measurements described here can be coupled with the electronegativity results developed in Sec. 13-7 to represent the electron-attracting powers of the atoms. The data for the percent ionic character for diatomic molecules can be obtained from measured dipole moments and bond lengths, as shown for HCl, and these data can be plotted against the electronegativity difference, as is done in Fig. 16-9. For these molecules the dipole moment is generally greater the greater the difference in electronegativity of the bound atoms, as would be expected from a simple interpretation of both factors.

For polyatomic molecules it is customary to try to understand the molecular dipole moment in terms of the contributions of the individual bonds of the molecule in a manner similar to that in which one tried to understand the energy of a molecule in terms of bond energies. With this approach one obtains

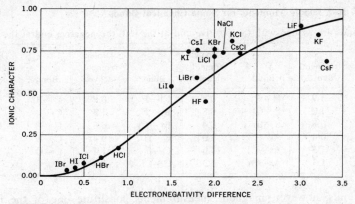

FIGURE 16-9 Curve relating the amount of ionic character of a bond to the electronegativity difference of the two atoms. Experimental points, based upon observed values of the electric dipole moment of diatomic molecules. (*From L. Pauling, "The Nature of the Chemical Bond," 3d ed., Cornell University Press, Ithaca, N.Y., 1960.*)

bond moments. For the water molecule, for example, the measured dipole moment is 1.85 debyes, and, as Fig. 16-10 shows, this quantity can be resolved into two bond moments which are in the directions of the two bonds and which add together, vectorially, to give the observed molecular moment. The procedure implies that the molecular moment arises from within the separate bonds of the molecule. The contribution of any nonbonding electrons to the total dipole moment will of course be resolved and included in the derived bond moments. Table 16-2 includes some results for bonds of diatomic and polyatomic molecules.

MAGNETIC PROPERTIES

Magnetic measurements are a tool for molecular studies that have not been of such general applicability as electrical measurements. For certain types of

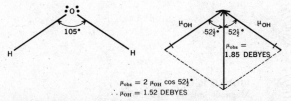

FIGURE 16-10 Resolution of the total dipole moment of the water molecule into O—H bond moments. The dipole direction that indicates that H is positive relative to O is assumed.

TABLE 16-2 Dipole Moments for Some Chemical Bonds

The bonds are written with the positive end at the left, the negative end at the right

Bond	Dipole moment, debyes	Bond	Dipole moment, debyes	Bond	Dipole moment, debyes	Bond	Dipole moment, debyes
H—F	1.9	H—P	0.4	Cl—F	0.9	C—Br	1.4
H—Cl	1.0	P—Cl	0.8	Br—F	1.3	C—I	1.2
H—Br	0.8	P—Br	0.4	Br—Cl	0.6	C—O	0.7
H—I	0.4	As—F	2.0	C—H	(0.4)	C—N	0.2
H—O	1.5	As—Cl	1.6	C—F	1.4	C=O	2.3
H—N	1.3	As—Br	1.3	C—Cl	1.5		

compounds, however, magnetic measurements constitute one of the most powerful approaches to the elucidation of the arrangement of the electrons in the compound. The theory of magnetic studies parallels that of electrical studies so closely that a detailed treatment need not be given. Following some mention of the parallels between electrical and magnetic phenomena, the applications of magnetic studies will be dealt with.

16-7 Determination of Magnetic Molecular Properties

The effect of magnets on each other at a distance suggests the presence of a magnetic field surrounding a magnet, just as electric fields were suggested by the effects between separated electric charges. The intensity of a magnetic field in vacuum is denoted by $\mathcal{H}$, and the field at a point is defined as the force that would be exerted on a unit magnetic pole placed at that point. The magnetic field strength is expressed in oersteds or gauss. Magnetic fields, like electric fields, are represented in magnitude and direction by lines of force. Figure 16-11 illustrates this description of the magnetic field between two magnetic poles.

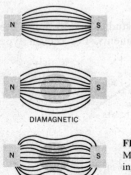

DIAMAGNETIC

PARAMAGNETIC

FIGURE 16-11
Magnetic lines of force showing the effect of diamagnetic and paramagnetic materials on the magnetic field.

When any material is placed between the poles of a magnet, the magnetic field $\mathcal{H}$ is different in the material from what it was in vacuum. The magnetic field in the material is denoted by B. Unlike the case of electric fields and dielectric materials, the magnetic field may be either increased or decreased by the presence of the material. Each of these possibilities is illustrated by the lines-of-force diagrams of Fig. 16-11.

In magnetic measurements the quantity that is obtained experimentally is the intensity of magnetization per unit field strength, that is, $I/\mathcal{H}$. It is convenient, for chemical treatments, to multiply by the molar volume M/ρ and to deal with the quantity

$$\chi_M = \frac{M}{\rho} \frac{I}{\mathcal{H}} \tag{16-40}$$

called the *magnetic susceptibility per mole* or the *molar magnetic susceptibility*.

The molar magnetic susceptibility, being the magnetization per mole induced by unit field strength, can be recognized as the magnetic counterpart, on a molar basis, of the sum of the electrical polarizability α and the molecular-dipole term $\mu^2/3kT$. This parallel does exist, in fact, and it is therefore convenient to deal with the corresponding terms α_M, the magnetic polarizability, and μ_M, the magnetic moment. Without treating the theory in detail, the relation of these quantities is stated as

$$\chi_M = \mathfrak{N} \left(\alpha_M + \frac{\mu_M{}^2}{3kT} \right) \tag{16-41}$$

Several qualitatively different behaviors are recognized. Most organic compounds have only a magnetic-polarizability contribution, and this term acts to reduce the magnetic field in the material; that is, α_M is negative. It follows, since μ_M is zero for these materials, that χ_M and I are also negative. Materials that behave in this manner are said to be *diamagnetic*.

Other materials, which we shall see are characterized by having unpaired electrons, have magnetic moments that correspond to the dipole moments of polar molecules. The magnetic-moment term, when it exists, is almost always much larger than the polarizability term. The magnetic-moment contribution to χ_M is necessarily positive, and this is illustrated by a diagram like that of Fig. 16-12 in which the microscopic magnets tend to line up to draw the magnetic field into the sample. Materials that behave in this manner are said to be *paramagnetic*.

There are, finally, the important classes of ferromagnetic and antiferromagnetic materials in which the magnetic properties depend on cooperative phenomena between many atoms of the sample. These materials will not be dealt with here.

Experimentally, one frequently obtains magnetic-susceptibility data from measurements with a Gouy balance. In this method, as illustrated in Fig. 16-13,

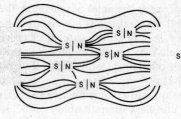

FIGURE 16-12
The microscopic explanation of paramagnetism. The magnetic moments of the sample molecules or ions tend to draw the magnetic field through the sample.

a sample is suspended from one arm of a balance in such a way that it is partly in the magnetic field. An electromagnet is ordinarily used, and when the magnet is turned on, the sample is generally repelled by or attracted into the magnetic field. The force required to maintain the position of the sample is measured by the weight that must be added or removed from the balance pan to maintain equilibrium. If the sample is paramagnetic, the magnetic moments will tend to line up with the field and the sample will have lower energy in the magnetic field and will therefore be drawn into the field. If the sample is diamagnetic, the reverse will be the case and the sample will be repelled by the field.

The relation between the force exerted on a sample by a nonhomogeneous magnetic field and the magnetic susceptibility of the sample can be determined with reference to Fig. 16-14. It is supposed that the sample is paramagnetic, so that the magnetic field lines up the microscopic magnets of the sample. The magnetic moment per unit volume is $(\rho/M)\chi_M \mathcal{H}$, and the magnetic moment of the section of thickness dz and volume $A\,dz$ in Fig. 16-14 which experiences a magnetic field $\mathcal{H}$ is therefore

$$\frac{\rho}{M}\chi_M \mathcal{H} A\,dz \tag{16-42}$$

This induced magnetic moment is in the direction of the applied magnetic field if, as supposed here, the material is paramagnetic. Since the magnetic field increases along the sample toward the center of the magnetic field, the lowering of the potential energy of successive segments will be greater as a result of the lining up of the magnetic moments of expression (16-42) with the greater magnetic fields. The force corresponding to this varying potential energy is the rate of change of the potential with z. If the magnetic field gradient is $d\mathcal{H}/dz$, the force on a sample segment is

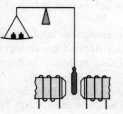

FIGURE 16-13
The Gouy balance for the measurement of magnetic susceptibilities.

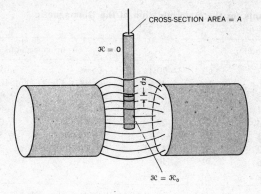

CROSS-SECTION AREA = A

$\mathfrak{K} = 0$

$\mathfrak{K} = \mathfrak{K}_0$

FIGURE 16-14
The effect of a nonhomogeneous magnetic field on a sample.

$$\frac{\rho}{M} \chi_M \mathfrak{K} A \, dz \, \frac{d\mathfrak{K}}{dz} = \frac{\rho}{M} \chi_M A \mathfrak{K} \, d\mathfrak{K} \tag{16-43}$$

and if the segments of the sample extend from the center of the magnetic field, where the magnetic field value is $\mathfrak{K}_0$, to outside the magnetic field, where the value is zero, the total force in the sample is

$$f = \int_0^{\mathfrak{K}_0} \frac{\rho}{M} \chi_M A \mathfrak{K} \, d\mathfrak{K} = \frac{1}{2} \frac{\rho}{M} \chi_M A \mathfrak{K}_0{}^2 \tag{16-44}$$

This result is the basis of the Gouy-balance method and shows that, for an experimental arrangement like that of Fig. 16-13, the measurement of the force exerted on the sample by a known maximum field strength $\mathfrak{K}_0$ can be used to deduce the magnetic susceptibility of the sample. In practice, however, one frequently compares the force on a standard sample with that on an unknown sample instead of evaluating the cross-section sample area and the magnetic field directly.

A typical experiment with a paramagnetic substance or solution might make use of a sample tube of 1 cm^2 cross section and a magnet with $\mathfrak{K}_0$ of 10,000 G. For such an arrangement the force exerted by the magnetic field might be equivalent to a mass of a few tenths of a gram, and for such a value Eq. (16-44) indicates a susceptibility of about 10^{-4}, or, as susceptibilities are usually reported, 100×10^{-6} cgs unit per gram. Diamagnetic susceptibilities are negative and typically are smaller than this value by a factor of about 100.

16-8 Molecular Interpretation of Diamagnetism

All materials affect a magnetic field in which they are inserted as a result of an induced magnetic moment, which produces a diamagnetic effect, just as all compounds show an induced dipole moment in an electric field. This induced magnetic effect is generally of secondary importance and is almost always

TABLE 16-3 Pascal's Constants for the Determination of the Diamagnetic Susceptibility, 10^{-6} cgs Units

Atomic contributions				Group corrections	
H	-2.93	Cl	-20.1	C=C	5.5
C	-6.00	Br	-30.6	C=C—C=C	10.6
N, open chain	-5.55	I	-44.6	N=N	1.85
ring	-4.61	S	-15	C=N	8.15
monomide	-1.54	Se	-23	—C≡N	0.8
O, alcohol, ether	-4.61	B	-7	Benzene	-1.4
carbonyl	1.72	Si	-13	Cyclohexane	-3.0
carboxyl group	-3.36	P	-10		
F	-6.3	As	-21		

Source: P. W. Selwood, "Magnetochemistry," 2d ed., Interscience Publishers, Inc., New York, 1956.

greatly overshadowed by the more interesting permanent-magnetic-moment contribution, when one exists. It is necessary, however, to be able to subtract the induced-moment contribution from the total magnetic susceptibility.

The diamagnetic effect is produced by the orbital motion of the electrons of the atoms, ions, or molecules of the sample. It can be understood qualitatively on the basis of Lenz's law, which states that for an ordinary-sized system of a current flowing in a coil of wire in a magnetic field, the field will induce a current in the coil in such a way as to oppose the applied field. In a similar way, the orbital motion of the electrons is disturbed by the applied field, and the disturbance is such that a magnetic field contribution in opposition to the applied field is produced. The diamagnetic effect is, in fact, temperature-independent and is a function of the quantum numbers of the electrons; i.e., it depends on the nature of the electron orbitals, as these ideas would suggest.

The diamagnetic effect of a given molecule can be estimated from tables that give the contribution of the various atoms within the molecule. Such terms, some of which are shown in Table 16-3, are known as *Pascal's constants*. For good agreement with the observed diamagnetic susceptibilities it is necessary also to include terms for any multiple or unusual bonding situation in which the atoms are involved. Some of these terms are also included in Table 16-3. For most purposes, the diamagnetic term can be satisfactorily estimated from such a table of Pascal's constants.

16-9 Molecular Interpretation of Paramagnetism

The paramagnetic effect can most easily be introduced by considering the introductory problem of the magnetic behavior of an electron revolving about a nucleus. A classical treatment is easily made and yields a result which can then be converted to the correct quantum-mechanical result. The motion of an electron in an orbit corresponds, in this connection, to the passage of a current through a coil of wire. It is known that a current in a coil of wire of ordinary dimensions produces a magnetic field perpendicular to the coil. The magnetic field so produced is equal, according to Ampère's law, to that of a magnet with magnetic moment μ_M given by the product of the current and the cross-section area of the loop of wire. For the magnetic moment produced by a current of i A circulating in a coil of enclosed area A to have the proper electromagnetic units, it is necessary to divide the Ampère's-law terms by the factor c, the velocity of light, to obtain

$$\mu_M = \frac{iA}{c} \tag{16-45}$$

The current corresponding to an electron in orbit is obtained by multiplying the number of times the electron passes any point on the orbit by its electronic charge. Thus, with this classical picture of an electron in an atomic orbit,

$$i = \frac{v}{2\pi r} e \tag{16-46}$$

where the electron velocity is v and the orbit has radius r. The cross-section area is

$$A = \pi r^2 \tag{16-47}$$

Thus the magnetic moment μ_M obtained is

$$\mu_M = \frac{vre}{2c} \tag{16-48}$$

which can be written

$$\mu_M = \frac{mvre}{2mc} \tag{16-49}$$

or

$$\frac{\mu_M}{mvr} = \frac{e}{2mc} \tag{16-50}$$

This final form expresses the result of this classical derivation that can be carried over into quantum-mechanical systems, namely, that the ratio of the magnetic moment to the orbital angular momentum is equal to $e/2mc$.

Since, as stated in Sec. 11-5, the orbital angular momentum of an electron of an atom depends on the quantum number l and is given by the expression

$\sqrt{l(l + 1)}(h/2\pi)$, we can express the magnetic moment due to the orbital motion of the electron as

$$\mu_M = \frac{eh}{4\pi mc} \sqrt{l(l + 1)} \tag{16-51}$$

The constant factor in this equation provides a convenient unit in which to express the magnetic moment of atoms and molecules, and one therefore introduces the symbol μ_0, called the *Bohr magneton,* as

$$\mu_0 = \frac{eh}{4\pi mc}$$

With this unit, the orbital magnetic moment of an electron of an atom is given by

$$\mu_M = \mu_0 \sqrt{l(l + 1)} \tag{16-52}$$

When a similar approach is extended to molecules and ions, rather than free atoms, it would seem reasonable to expect the orbital motions of the electrons to contribute a magnetic moment of the order of a Bohr magneton. This expectation is not generally borne out, and it appears that the orbital motions of the electrons in a polyatomic system are tied into the nuclear configuration of the molecule or the ion so tightly that they are unable to line up with the applied magnetic field and are therefore ineffective. Even for single-atom ions in solution, the interaction of the orbitals of the ion with the solvating molecules is apparently sufficient to prevent the orbitals from being oriented so that their magnetic moment contributes in the direction of the field. Thus the orbital-magnetic-moment contribution to the magnetic susceptibility is generally quite small.

We must look to electron spin to explain the larger part of the magnetic moment of those molecules and ions which have magnetic moments. The association of a spin angular momentum of $\sqrt{s(s + 1)}(h/2\pi)$, where s has the value of $\frac{1}{2}$, leads, according to Eq. (16-50), to the expectation of a spin magnetic moment. Atomic spectral data require, however, a magnetic moment that is twice that expected on the basis of the ratio of the magnetic moment to angular momentum given by Eq. (16-50). Therefore, for the spin magnetic moment due to the electron of an atom or molecule we have

$$\mu_M = 2\mu_0 \sqrt{S(S + 1)} \tag{16-53}$$

where for one, two, three, . . . unpaired electrons, the spin-angular-momentum quantum number S is $\frac{1}{2}, \frac{2}{2}, \frac{3}{2}, \ldots$. With Eq. (16-53) and the assumption that the α_M contribution has been taken care of and that the orbital contribution to x_M is

TABLE 16-4 Contributions of Unpaired Electrons to the Magnetic Susceptibility

No. of unpaired electrons	Total electron-spin quantum number S	Spin magnetic moment $2\sqrt{S(S+1)}\mu_0$	Magnetic susceptibility at 25°C $\chi_M = \dfrac{4\mu_0^2\mathfrak{N}}{3kT}S(S+1)$
1	$\frac{1}{2}$	$1.73\mu_0$	$1{,}260 \times 10^{-6}$
2	$\frac{2}{2}$	$2.83\mu_0$	$3{,}460 \times 10^{-6}$
3	$\frac{3}{2}$	$3.87\mu_0$	$6{,}290 \times 10^{-6}$
4	$\frac{4}{2}$	$4.90\mu_0$	$10{,}100 \times 10^{-6}$
5	$\frac{5}{2}$	$5.92\mu_0$	$14{,}700 \times 10^{-6}$

negligible, the magnetic susceptibility of Eq. (16-41) is related to the total electron spin by the relation

$$\chi_M = \frac{4\mu_0^2\mathfrak{N}}{3kT}S(S+1) \tag{16-54}$$

Thus a measurement of χ_M leads to a value of S, and this value can be interpreted in terms of a number of unpaired electrons. Table 16-4 shows the results to be expected for χ_M for various numbers of unpaired electrons at 25°C.

Equation (16-54) implies that if the magnetic polarizability is not too large, the magnetic susceptibility will vary inversely as the absolute temperature; i.e.,

$$\chi_M = \frac{\text{const}}{T} \tag{16-55}$$

This relation, known as *Curie's law,* is in fact found to be valid over not too large a temperature range.

The best example of a simple molecule for which the magnetic data bear on the electronic structure is provided by oxygen. Over a considerable temperature range the molar magnetic susceptibility, again in cgs units used for reporting such results, is found to be represented by

$$\chi_M = \frac{1.00}{T} \tag{16-56}$$

giving, at 25°C, the value

$$\chi_M = 3360 \times 10^{-6}$$

The values of Table 16-4 show that this susceptibility is to be interpreted as arising from two unpaired electrons. The bonding in O_2 is therefore unusual in that although there is an even number of electrons, they are not all paired. The explanation for this, as seen in Sec. 13-5, can be given in terms of a simple molecular-orbital treatment.

PROBLEMS

16-1. Give the dipole moment of an NaCl molecule at an internuclear separation of 5 Å in SI units and in debyes.

16-2. What is the instantaneous dipole moment of an H_2^+ ion when the nuclei and the electron form an equilateral triangle with sides 1.1 Å long?.

16-3. A potential of 100 V is placed across the plates of a condenser. The area of each plate is 2.4×10^{-4} m², and the distance between the plates is 0.01 m. (a) Calculate the electric field between the plates of the condenser and the force that would be exerted on an electron in this region. What would be the charge density on the condenser plates? (b) If the condenser is filled with CCl_4, which has $\epsilon/\epsilon_0 = 2.238$, and the charge density on the plates is that in part (a), find the charge density on the carbon tetrachloride adjacent to the plates and the electric field in a cavity in the CCl_4. (c) What would be the force exerted on an electron in a cavity in the CCl_4?

16-4. The maximum voltage that can be applied to dielectric materials with dielectric constants of about 2.4 is about 10^8 V m⁻¹. (a) Calculate the energy difference between most favorable and most unfavorable orientations of a molecule with a dipole moment of 1 debye in the dielectric subjected to this applied potential. (b) At 25°C what would the relative population of the two states be? This demonstrates the relative unimportance of applied electric fields in the molecular world.

16-5. The dielectric constant of liquid CCl_4, which has tetrahedral molecules and no permanent dipole moment, is 2.238 at 20°C. The density of CCl_4 is 1.595 g ml⁻¹. Calculate the molar polarization and the polarizability α.

16-6. In the deduction of the molar polarizability of a gas at not too high a pressure, the dielectric effect of the medium is small enough to permit the final term of Eq. (16-22), which is due to the charges on the cavity in the dielectric, to be dropped. Follow through the derivation of an expression for α and $\mathcal{P}$ for a low-pressure gas. Notice that this result is also obtained directly from Eq. (16-25) or (16-26) when the value of ϵ/ϵ_0 approaches unity.

16-7. The dielectric constant of oxygen gas at 0°C and 1 atm pressure is 1.000523. What property of the O_2 molecule can you determine from this datum?

16-8. The molar polarization of ethyl ether, deduced from measurements of the dielectric constant of cyclohexane solutions of ether at 20°C, is 58.5 cm³ mol⁻¹. The molar refraction is 22.48 cm³ mol⁻¹. What is the dipole moment of ethyl ether?

16-9. Measurements of the dielectric constant of SO_2 vapor lead to the molar polarization expression $P = 9.38 + 16{,}830/T$, with units of cm³ mol⁻¹. What are the polarizability and the dipole moment of the SO_2 molecule?

16-10. The following values have been reported for the dielectric constant of BrF_5 vapor at 1 atm pressure by M. T. Rogers, R. D. Pruett, H. B. Thompson, and J. L. Speirs, *J. Am. Chem. Soc.*, **78**:44 (1956):

T, K	345.6	362.6	374.9	388.9	402.4	417.2	430.8
ϵ/ϵ_0	1.006320	1.005824	1.005525	1.005180	1.004910	1.004603	1.004378

(a) Assuming ideal-gas behavior, calculate the molar polarization at each temperature. (b) Deduce α and μ for BrF_5. (c) Suggest a structure for the BrF_5 molecule that is compatible with the dipole-moment value.

16-11. The following values are reported for the dielectric constant of ammonia vapor at 1 atm pressure:

T, K	250	275	300	325	350	375
ϵ/ϵ_0	1.00851	1.00707	1.00606	1.00514	1.00451	1.00397

(a) Calculate the dipole moment μ and the molecular polarizability α. Assume ideal-gas behavior. (b) Nonideality of the gas, particularly at the lower temperatures, should be taken into account to make the most out of the measurements. Calculate the gas density for the lowest temperature, 250 K, and plot this corrected point along with those for which ideal-gas behavior was assumed. Use any of the nonideal-gas expressions dealt with in Chap. 1 or 2.

16-12. The following data have been reported [X. X. Sanger and X. X. Steiger, *Helv. Phys. Acta.*, **1**:369 (1928)] for the dielectric constant of water vapor at a constant density of 4.181×10^{-4} g cm^{-3}:

T, K	393	423	453	483
ϵ/ϵ_0	1.0040020	1.0037167	1.0034881	1.0032873

(a) Calculate molar polarization values from these dielectric-constant values. (b) Plot the data of part (a) versus $1/T$ and obtain an expression of the form $P = a + b/T$. Deduce values of α and μ for the water molecule. (c) The dielectric constant can be simply related to the molar polarization and α and μ only if the vapor consists of monomeric water molecules. It has been suggested that at the lowest temperature, 393 K, appreciable dimers or other polymers are present. If you have access to a computer program, obtain the best values of a and b in $P = a + b/T$ with and without this lowest-temperature point. What changed and presumably improved value of μ for H_2O is obtained if the doubtful point is excluded?

16-13. Measurements of the dielectric constant of a solution of a polar solute in a nonpolar solvent can be used to obtain the molar polarization of the solute. The molar polarization, related to the dielectric constant by Eq. (16-26) is interpreted as $P = x_A P_A + x_B P_B$, where x_A and x_B are the mole fractions of the two solution components. The following data are given for triethylamine in benzene at 25°C:

Mole fraction triethylamine	0	0.0170	0.0222	0.0265	0.0447	0.0580	0.0805
Dielectric constant	2.2725	2.2817	2.2839	2.285	2.2914	2.2949	2.2999

The density of benzene is 0.874 g cm^{-3} at 25°C, and this value can be used in calculating molar polarizabilities since the limit of infinite dilution in benzene is all that is of interest. The refractive index and density of triethylamine are 1.40032 and 1.069 g cm^{-3} at 25°C. What are the molar polarization and the dipole moment of triethylamine?

16-14. The dipole moment of CH_3Cl is 1.86 debyes, and that of $CHCl_3$ is 1.15 debyes. Both molecules are nearly tetrahedral. Assuming that C—H has a bond moment of 0.4 debye with H positive, calculate the C—Cl bond moment for each compound. The disagreement can be understood in terms of the induced dipoles in the three very polarizable chlorine atoms of $CHCl_3$.

16-15. The dipole moment of NH_3 is found to be 1.46 debyes, and the angle between two N—H bonds is $107°$. Calculate the N—H bond moment.

16-16. Compare several of the bond moments given in Table 16-2 with the values that would be obtained using the relation depicted in Fig. 16-9.

16-17. Calculate the ionic character of the five metal halides of Table 16-1 on the basis of point electronic charges separated by the equilibrium bond length. The bond lengths for CsF, CsCl, KF, KCl, and KBr are 2.34, 2.90, 2.55, 2.67, and 2.82 Å, respectively. Compare with the values of Fig. 16-9.

16-18. Compare the frequency of rotation of a representative gas-phase molecule with the frequency of visible light of about 10^{15} Hz. What are the implications of this comparison on the ability of a molecule to rotate so as to affect an index-of-refraction measurement?

16-19. The ion $Co(NH_3)_6^{3+}$ has been shown from magnetic measurements to have no unpaired electrons, whereas the ion CoF_6^{3-} has four unpaired electrons. Considering only the effect of unpaired electrons, calculate the change in apparent weight of a 0.1 M solution of salts of these ions in 1-cm-diameter test tubes suspended in a Gouy balance when a magnetic field of 5000 G is turned on.

16-20. (*a*) Using Table 16-3, calculate the magnetic susceptibility of benzene. (*b*) What would be the apparent weight loss of a sample of benzene ($d_{25} = 0.87$ g cm^{-3}) 1 cm^2 in cross section placed in a magnetic field of 3×10^4 G? (Neglect the susceptibility of the glass. Use cgs units throughout.)

16-21. How sensitive a balance would be needed to measure the magnetic susceptibility of oxygen gas at 1 atm and $25°C$? Assume the tube has a cross-section area of 1 cm^2 and that O_2 is an ideal gas. Make use of Eq. (16-56).

16-22. Calculate the loss of weight for 1 cm^3 of $O_2(l)$ at $-180°C$, $d = 1.14$ g ml^{-1}, assuming that Eq. (16-56) is valid.

REFERENCES

HILL, N. E., W. E. VAUGHAN, A. H. PRICE, and M. DAVIES: "Dielectric Properties and Molecular Behavior," Van Nostrand Reinhold Publishing Company, London, 1969. Theory, experiments, and interpretation of the results in terms of the electric and dynamic properties of molecules.

LEFÈVRE, R. W. J.: "Dipole Moments: Their Measurement and Application in Chemistry," Methuen & Co., Ltd., London, 1953. An introductory account of the measurement of dielectric constants and the deduction of molecular properties from the experimental data.

SMYTH, C. P.: "Dielectric Behavior and Structure," McGraw-Hill Book Company, New York, 1955. The deduction of molecular properties from dielectric-constant measurements and the nature and application of dielectric-loss measurements (not dealt with in this text). The last half of the book contains an extensive and detailed discussion of the relation of dipole moments to molecular structure.

SMITH, J. W.: "Electric Dipole Moments," Butterworth & Co. (Publishers), Ltd., London, 1955. Similar to the book by Smyth in scope and level.

PROCH, A., and G. McCONKEY: "Topics in Chemical Physics: Lectures by P. Debye," chaps. 1 and 3, Elsevier Publishing Company, Amsterdam, 1962. Two very clearly presented treatments are "The Static Electric Field: Dielectric Constant and Polarizability of Gases" and "The Dielectric Properties of Condensed

Phases." Reference can also be made to one of the earliest monographs on dipole moments, P. Debye, "Polar Molecules," Dover Publications, Inc., New York, 1928.

SCHIEBER, M. M.: "Experimental Magnetochemistry," John Wiley & Sons, Inc. (Interscience Publishers Division), New York, 1967. An outline of principles and experimental techniques followed by data, and interpretation, for many types of inorganic compounds.

GOODENOUGH, J. B.: "Magnetism and the Chemical Bond," Interscience Publishers, Inc., New York, 1963. A monograph written for those with some prior knowledge of atomic structure, quantum mechanics, and group theory, dealing with the electronic basis of the magnetic properties of metals and metal-ion systems.

PASS, G., and H. SUTCLIFFE: Measurement of Magnetic Susceptibilities and the Adoption of SI Units, *J. Chem. Educ.*, **48**:180 (1971).

THE NATURE OF ELECTROLYTES IN SOLUTION

Many interesting phenomena, e.g., most occurring in biological systems, involve ions in aqueous solutions. Our knowledge of the behavior of free, independent molecules is not a complete basis for understanding systems in which charged particles are immersed in a medium that is far from inert.

We shall begin, in the first part of this chapter, by seeing the experimental basis that led to the now familiar idea that electrolytes, i.e., acids, bases, and salts, are more or less dissociated in aqueous solution and that the ions that are present act to some extent as free, independent particles. This interpretation of aqueous solutions of electrolytes is akin to the simple kinetic-molecular theory of ideal gases.

Many refinements of this simple theory are necessary if more experimental results are considered and if the finer details of the results on which the simple theory is based are recognized. Thus, in a way that now parallels the van der Waals elaborations of the simple kinetic-molecular theory, two additional aspects of the behavior of ions in solution are introduced. These are concerned with the interaction of the ions with the solvent and the interactions of the ions with each other. The second part of the chapter will be devoted to these refinements of the simple ionic model.

IONS IN AQUEOUS SOLUTION

17-1 Electrical Conductivity of Solutions

The fact that aqueous solutions of certain materials, called *electrolytes,* conduct an electric current provides the most direct evidence for the idea that ions capable of independent motion are present. More detailed studies of the electrical conductivity of such solutions provide information on the number and independence of these ions.

Measurements of the conductivity of aqueous solutions are made with a conductivity cell and an electric circuit like that shown in Fig. 17-1. When an alternating current is used to prevent buildup of charges of opposite sign near the two electrode surfaces so that there is little electric resistance at the metal-

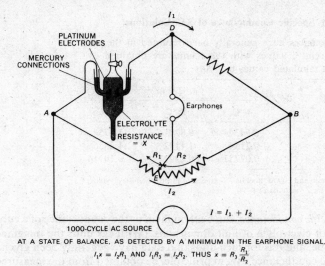

At a state of balance, as detected by a minimum in the earphone signal,

$$I_1 x = I_2 R_1 \text{ AND } I_1 R_3 = I_2 R_2. \text{ THUS } x = R_3 \frac{R_1}{R_2}$$

FIGURE 17-1 Schematic diagram of a conductivity cell in a Wheatstone bridge circuit.

solution interface, it is found that the conductivity cell obeys Ohm's law: the current flowing through the cell is proportional to the voltage across the cell. It is therefore possible to assign a resistance of so many ohms to such a cell just as one assigns a resistance to a metallic conductor.

It is more convenient, however, to focus our attention on the *conductance* of an electrolytic solution than on its *resistance*. These quantities are reciprocally related, and the conductance L is calculated from the measured resistance as

$$L = \frac{1}{R} \tag{17-1}$$

where R is the resistance in ohms, symbol Ω. L therefore has the units of Ω^{-1}. As for metallic conductors, the resistance and therefore the conductance depend on the cross-section area A and the length l of the conductivity cell, i.e., of the region between the electrodes. As for a metallic conductor, one has

$$R = \rho \frac{l}{A} \tag{17-2}$$

where ρ is the *specific resistance* and is the proportionality factor that corresponds to the resistance of a cell of unit cross-section area and unit length. One can also write

$$L = \kappa \frac{A}{l} \tag{17-3}$$

TABLE 17-1 Specific Conductance of KCl Solutions

Such conductances have generally been reported in the cgs unit of Ω^{-1} cm^{-1}; values with these units are obtained by dividing the tabulated values by 100.

Concentration, equiv liter^{-1}	κ, Ω^{-1} m^{-1}		
	0°C	18°C	25°C
1	6.543	9.820	11.173
0.1	0.7154	1.1192	1.2886
0.01	0.07751	0.12227	0.14114

Source: G. Kortum and J. O'M. Bockris, "Textbook of Electrochemistry," vol. 1, Elsevier Press, Inc., Amsterdam, 1951.

where κ, the *specific conductance,* can be thought of as the conductance of a cube of the solution of electrolyte of unit dimensions. (With cgs units the imagined cell is a 1-cm cube, and it is for such units that data have generally been given.)

The specific conductance can, in principle, be obtained from the measured value of R, which gives $L = 1/R$, and of l and A of the cell. In practice, it is more convenient to deduce l and A, or rather the *cell constant* l/A, from a measurement of L when the cell is filled with a solution of known specific conductance. Once this geometric factor has been obtained for a cell, it can be used to deduce κ for an unknown solution from a measured value of L and Eq. (17-3).

The cell constant is almost always determined by using a solution of KCl. Specific conductances of these reference solutions, shown in Table 17-1, have been determined by measurements with rather elaborately designed electrodes which avoid the uncertainty in the effective current-carrying cross section that exists in ordinary cells. Since the strong temperature dependence shown in Table 17-1 is characteristic of all conductance results, it is necessary to make measurements of conductances in well-thermostated cells.

Although the specific conductance is a measure of the ease with which a current flows through a unit cube of solution, it is not a convenient quantity for the discussion of the conduction process of solutions of electrolytes. Solutions of different concentrations, for example, will have very different specific conductances simply because a given volume of the different solutions will contain different amounts of electrolyte. Since it will be of particular interest to compare the current-carrying ability of a given number of electrolyte charges at different concentrations, it is helpful to define yet another measure of conductance.

17-2 Equivalent Conductance

An equivalent mass of an electrolyte is that amount which, for complete dissociation, would lead to ions with total positive and negative charges of $+e\mathfrak{N}$ and $-e\mathfrak{N}$, where e is the electronic charge. Thus an equivalent of NaCl gives an

Avogadro's number of Na^+ ions and of Cl^- ions; an equivalent of $MgSO_4$ gives half an Avogadro's number of Mg^{2+} ions and of SO_4^{2-} ions; and so forth. One equivalent of any electrolyte would, on complete dissociation, provide the same effective number of charge-carrying particles. The conductance that would be conveniently dealt with, therefore, is that which would be given by a conductance cell with electrodes a unit distance apart and of large enough cross sections for the volume of solution containing 1 equiv of the electrolyte to be held between the electrodes. This conductance, known as the *equivalent conductance* Λ, is a measure of the current-carrying ability of an equivalent of solute.

The volume of solution of concentration c equiv liter^{-1}, that is, c equiv in 10^{-3} m^3, that holds 1 equiv is $1/c$ liters, or $10^{-3}/c$ m^3. A cell with this volume and plates separated by 1 m would be equivalent to $10^{-3}/c$ unit cells placed alongside each other, and thus the conductance, which is the equivalent conductance, is given by

$$\Lambda = \frac{10^{-3}}{c}\kappa \qquad (17\text{-}4)$$

This relation defines the equivalent conductance in terms of the specific conductance. The concept of the cell holding solution of volume $10^{-3}/c$ m^3 is introduced only to suggest the definition of Eq. (17-4), and one should recognize that in practice one uses any convenient conductance cell, measures R, and calculates $L = 1/R$. With this datum one obtains $\kappa = (\text{cell const})L$, and finally Λ from Eq. (17-4).

Many precise measurements of equivalent conductances were made by Friedrich Kohlrausch and his coworkers between about 1860 and 1880. The data of Table 17-2 are typical of their results.

On the basis of such data and in the absence of any satisfactory theory about the nature of conduction in these solutions, some valuable empirical relations were deduced. It was recognized that for some electrolytes plotting the equivalent conductance of an electrolyte at a fixed temperature against the

TABLE 17-2 Equivalent Conductances Λ in Ω^{-1} m^2 in Aqueous Solution at 25°C

Values for $c = 0$ are obtained by extrapolation or, for HAc and NH_4OH, by a combination of extrapolated values.

c	NaCl	KCl	HCl	NaAc	CuSO$_4$	H$_2$SO$_4$	HAc	NH$_4$OH
0.000	(0.012645)	(0.014986)	(0.042616)	(0.00910)	(0.0133)	(0.04296)	(0.03907)	(0.02714)
0.0005	0.012450	0.014781	0.042274	0.00892		0.04131	0.00677	0.0047
0.001	0.012374	0.014695	0.042136	0.00885	0.01152	0.03995	0.00492	0.0034
0.010	0.011851	0.014127	0.041200	0.008376	0.00833	0.03364	0.00163	0.00113
0.100	0.010674	0.012896	0.039132	0.007280	0.00505	0.02508		0.00036
1.00		0.01119	0.03328	0.00491	0.00293			

Source: Data mostly from D. A. MacInnes, "The Principles of Electrochemistry." Reinhold Publishing Corporation, New York, 1939.

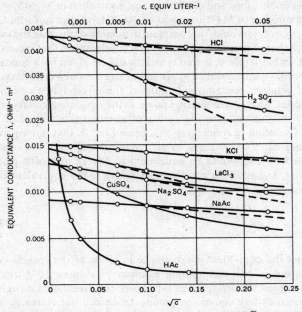

FIGURE 17-2 The equivalent conductance versus $\sqrt{c}$ for some electrolytes in water at 25°C.

square root of the concentration led to plots which conformed very closely at the lower concentrations to straight lines. Such plots for a few electrolytes are shown in Fig. 17-2. It is clear from this figure that two different types of behavior are exhibited. Those electrolytes which lead to essentially linear plots are now classed as *strong electrolytes,* and those which seem to approach the dilute-solution limit almost tangentially are classed as *weak electrolytes.*

An important relation can be deduced from the extrapolations of the strong-electrolyte data to infinite dilution to give what are known as *limiting equivalent conductances.* These conductances, denoted by Λ_0, are the basis for *Kohlrausch's law of the independent migration of ions.* The law is more easily stated and understandable if some later ideas are anticipated and the conductance of an electrolyte at infinite dilution is treated as being made up of contributions from the individual ions of the electrolyte. In this way one introduces *equivalent ionic conductances* and writes for the limit of infinite dilution

$$\Lambda_0 = \lambda_0{}^+ + \lambda_0{}^- \tag{17-5}$$

The law of Kohlrausch now suggests that at infinite dilution the conductance of an electrolyte, NaCl for example, depends on independent contributions from

Na^+ and from Cl^-. The independence of these contributions is judged by a comparison of pairs of electrolytes containing a common ion. The difference between Λ_0 for KCl and LiCl is, for example, the same as that for $KClO_4$ and $LiClO_4$. Each difference can thus be interpreted as the value of $\lambda_0^{K^+} - \lambda_0^{Li^+}$ and $\lambda^{Cl^-} - \lambda_0^{NO_3^-}$, and these differences are seen to be independent of the other ionic species present. Kohlrausch's law, it should be noted, gives no way of deducing the contributions of the individual ions.

The immediate practical application of the idea of the independent contribution of the ions at infinite dilution is a method for deducing the limiting equivalent conductance of weak electrolytes. For acetic acid, for example, one can write

$$\Lambda_0(HAc) = \Lambda_0(NaAc) + \Lambda_0(HCl) - \Lambda_0(NaCl) \tag{17-6}$$

In this way, the value at 25°C of

$$\Lambda_0(HAc) = 0.00910 + 0.04262 - 0.01265 = 0.03907 \tag{17-7}$$

is found, and it is clear from Fig. 17-2 that no reliable value could have been determined by a graphical extrapolation.

The availability of limiting equivalent conductances for all types of electrolytes was a prerequisite for the development of the theory for the nature of electrolytes in solution.

17-3 The Arrhenius Theory of Dissociations

Before the development of the important theory of Arrhenius, about 1887, a number of suggestions had been made to explain the fact that solutions of electrolytes are conductors of electricity. It is difficult for the modern student, who is brought up with the idea that salts and strong acids and bases are completely ionized in water, to appreciate the early difficulties in recognizing that such solutions of ions could exist. In the nineteenth century chemists were very much impressed with the difficulty of breaking apart stable molecules, and they could not accept the idea that a molecule, like HCl, could be dissociated except at a very high temperature. It must also be remembered that at this time solid salts had not been represented as an array of ions in the crystal lattice.

It was Arrhenius who made the then bold postulate that dissolving an electrolyte in an aqueous solution could lead to electrolytic dissociation and, even at ordinary temperatures, the conversion of an appreciable fraction of the electrolyte to free ions. Support for the theory was the explanation offered by Arrhenius for the observed variation of conductance with concentration, as illustrated by the data of Fig. 17-2 and Table 17-2. The increase of equivalent conductance with decreasing concentration, observed in dilute solutions of all electrolytes, was attributed by him to the increasing dissociation of the electrolyte. A chemical equilibrium between undissociated electrolyte molecules and the ions that result from dissociation always leads to an increase of the degree of dissociation for more dilute solutions. Since the conductance depends on the presence of charged species, a qualitative explanation for the concentration variation of the equivalent conductance was immediately reached.

These ideas led to a method for the calculation of the degree of dissociation of an electrolyte from the conductivity data. The supposition of a dissociation equilibrium implies that at infinite dilution all electrolytes are completely dissociated. A comparison of the equivalent conductance at some finite concentration with that at infinite dilution therefore gives a measure of the fraction of electrolyte dissociated at the higher concentration. One introduces α, the *degree of dissociation,* and writes

$$\alpha = \frac{\Lambda}{\Lambda_0} \tag{17-8}$$

In this way results for the degree of dissociation can be calculated. Arrhenius treated strong and weak electrolytes in essentially the same way, the apparent different behavior revealed in Fig. 17-2 being interpreted merely as a difference in degree of dissociation.

The Arrhenius theory and the deduced degrees of dissociation were received with considerable skepticism, and it was still generally held to be unlikely that the mere solution of an electrolyte could break up the molecules into separate ions. At this stage the measurements of colligative properties of solutions of electrolytes by van't Hoff became available. The interpretation of these results by the electrolytic-dissociation theory of Arrhenius swung support almost completely over to this new theory.

17-4 Colligative Properties of Aqueous Solutions of Electrolytes

In Chap. 9 the four colligative properties of solutions were seen to depend only on the molality, which is a measure of the number of solute particles in a given amount of solvent. These colligative properties can be used to "count" the solute particles in a solution. This approach was applied by the great Dutch chemist van't Hoff to solutions of electrolytes.

The molality given by colligative-property measurements can be expressed in terms of the molality m expected on the basis of the formula of the electrolyte. Van't Hoff introduced the factor i and expressed the molality given by the colligative properties as im. Then for solutions of electrolytes, we write

$$\Delta T_{bp} = (im)K_{bp} \qquad \Delta T_{fp} = -(im)K_{fp} \qquad \Pi = i\Pi_0 \tag{17-9}$$

The van't Hoff i factor shows explicitly the enhancement of the colligative properties encountered with electrolytes. The freezing-point depressions of Table 17-3 give the i factors of Table 17-4. These van't Hoff i factors are clearly

TABLE 17-3 Observed Freezing-Point-Depression Terms, $iK_{fp} = -\Delta T_{fp}/m$, for Electrolytes in Water

For nonelectrolytes $K_{fp} = -\Delta T_{fp}/m = 1.86$

m	NaCl	HCl	$CuSO_4$	$MgSO_4$	H_2SO_4	$Pb(NO_3)_2$	$K_3Fe(CN)_6$
0.001	3.66	3.690		3.38		5.368	7.10
0.01	3.604	3.601	2.703	2.85	4.584	4.898	6.26
0.1	3.478	3.523	2.08	2.252	3.940	3.955	5.30
1.0	3.37	3.94	1.72	2.02	4.04	2.435	

in qualitative accord with the view that electrolytes are more or less dissociated in solution. Since, for noninteracting solute particles, the colligative measurements give the number of particles in solution, it is apparent that the strong electrolytes behave as though there were about 2, 3, or 4 times as many particles as might have been expected. The numbers, furthermore, correspond to the number of ions that would be expected to result from the dissociation of the electrolyte molecule. The colligative-property results provided by van't Hoff seemed to give proof to the Arrhenius idea of appreciable dissociation of electrolytes in aqueous solution.

It is necessary, however, to look more closely at the results and to see to what extent the Arrhenius theory can provide an explanation for the fact that the i factors tend to be less than the integer expected for complete dissociation. A quantitative explanation can be attempted in terms of incomplete dissociation.

Consider the general electrolyte $A_a B_b$, which might undergo complete dissociation to form a positive ions and b negative ions according to the equation

$$A_a B_b \rightleftharpoons aA^{(+)} + bB^{(-)}$$

where the parentheses indicate some number of charges. It is necessary to calculate the net number of particles that result from a degree of dissociation α. If the molality of the electrolyte is m and the degree of dissociation is α, the concentration of undissociated electrolyte will be $m - \alpha m = m(1 - \alpha)$. In addition, the concentration of $A^{(+)}$ and $B^{(-)}$ will be $a\alpha m$ and $b\alpha m$, respectively.

TABLE 17-4 Van't Hoff i Factors Calculated from the Data of Table 17-3 and the Freezing-Point-Depression Constant K_{fp} of 1.86 for Water

m	NaCl	HCl	$CuSO_4$	$MgSO_4$	H_2SO_4	$Pb(NO_3)_2$	$K_3Fe(CN)_6$
0.001	1.97	1.98		1.82		2.89	3.82
0.01	1.94	1.94	1.45	1.53	2.46	2.63	3.36
0.1	1.87	1.89	1.12	1.21	2.12	2.13	2.85
1.0	1.81	2.12	0.93	1.09	2.17	1.31	

The concentration of particles, regardless of their kind, is therefore

$$m(1 - \alpha) + a\alpha m + b\alpha m \qquad (17\text{-}10)$$

It is customary to let ν be the total number of ions yielded by complete dissociation of a molecule; i.e.,

$$\nu = a + b \qquad (17\text{-}11)$$

With this notation the molality of particles for the partially dissociated electrolyte is

$$m(1 - \alpha) + \alpha\nu m \qquad (17\text{-}12)$$

rather than the value of m expected for no dissociation.

The definition of the van't Hoff i factor shows that it is to be identified with the ratio

$$i = \frac{m(1 - \alpha) + \alpha\nu m}{m} = 1 - \alpha + \alpha\nu \qquad (17\text{-}13)$$

From this interpretation of i, one obtains

$$\alpha = \frac{i - 1}{\nu - 1} \qquad (17\text{-}14)$$

This relation provides an alternative way to that given by Eq. (17-8) for calculating the degree of dissociation of an electrolyte.

The two methods of calculating α lead to fair agreement, and in the early stages of the theory such agreement could be accepted as support for the interpretation of the conductivity and the i-factor data in terms of incomplete dissociation. The modern view does not accept the idea of only partial dissociation of strong electrolytes under these conditions.

If the equilibria postulated by Arrhenius are, in fact, set up, and if this is the only feature of ionic solutions that need be considered, it should be possible to calculate a good equilibrium constant from the deduced degrees of dissociation.

17-5 Dissociation Equilibria

Electrolytes classed as weak electrolytes on the basis of a very strong dependence of conductance on concentration give quite constant, concentration-independent values of dissociation constants based on α values from measured conductances or colligative properties. Thus partial dissociation is a major factor in determining the properties of solutions of weak electrolytes. For strong electrolytes there is no support from calculated dissociation equilibrium constants for partial dissociation. The concentration dependence of the conductance, shown in Fig. 17-2, and of the van't Hoff i factors, shown in Table 17-4, for strong electrolytes must be attributed to other effects.

The modifications to the theory of dissociations that are necessary to bring the calculated results for strong electrolytes reasonably in line with experiment will be postponed until the second part of this chapter. This is consistent with the historical fact that such unacceptable conclusions from the Arrhenius theory were known but were wisely, if unscientifically, set aside while the acceptable features of the theory were used and developed.

17-6 Electrolysis and the Electrode Process

Much additional information on the properties of the ions in an aqueous solution can be obtained from studies of the passage of a direct current through a cell containing a solution of an electrolyte. Such dc experiments involve chemical reactions at the electrodes, a feature that is avoided in conductivity studies by the use of an alternating current. It is first necessary, therefore, to describe and classify these electrode processes.

When electrodes are inserted in a solution of electrolyte and a sufficient potential, of the order of several volts, is applied, chemical reactions are observed at the electrodes. *Electrolysis* is said to be occurring. The electrode that is charged positively, i.e., having a deficit of electrons, by the applied potential is called the *anode,* and that charged negatively, i.e., having an excess of electrons, is called the *cathode*. The electrodes consist of conductors that introduce the source and sink of electrons into the solution. In classifying the reactions that occur as a result of the charged electrodes, it is convenient to distinguish *inert electrodes,* usually a platinum wire, that serve only to transfer electrons to and from the solution, from *reacting electrodes* that enter chemically into the electrode reaction. Most simply, the reacting electrode is a metal that either contributes metal ions to the solution or accepts discharged metal ions from the solution.

The two major categories of electrode reactions that occur in an electrolysis cell are shown in Fig. 17-3. Of course, cells can be constructed that involve various combinations of these reaction types, consistent with the requirement that at the *cathode* electrons are introduced by the external circuit and *reduction* occurs, whereas at the *anode* electrons are removed and *oxidation* occurs.

More complicated electrode reactions do occur, but the features of electrolytic solutions that are to be studied in this chapter can be dealt with in terms of electrode reactions of these major types.

Electrolyses of the type illustrated here were extensively and quantitatively studied as early as 1820 by Michael Faraday. He was led to the important conclusion, that now can be stated as follows: *one equivalent of product is produced by the passage of* 96,490 C *of charge.* It can be recognized that 96,490 C is the charge of one mole of electrons. Faraday's result is understandable

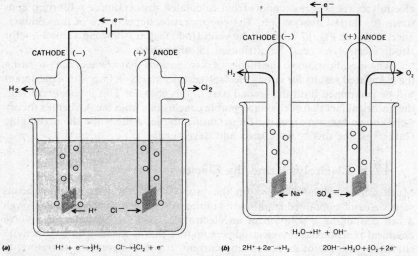

(a) $H^+ + e^- \rightarrow \frac{1}{2}H_2$ $Cl^- \rightarrow \frac{1}{2}Cl_2 + e^-$ (b) $2H^+ + 2e^- \rightarrow H_2$ $2OH^- \rightarrow H_2O + \frac{1}{2}O_2 + 2e^-$

FIGURE 17-3 Types of electrolysis electrode reactions. (a) Current-carrying ions are discharged at the electrodes. (b) Cations and anions that are discharged with difficulty permit the decomposition of water and the consumption of H^+ and of OH^-.

because an Avogadro's number of electrons added to or removed from a reagent will produce an equivalent of product.

The quantity of charge that corresponds to a chemical equivalent is of enough importance to merit a name, and the unit of a *faraday* is introduced as

$$1 \; \mathfrak{F} = \mathfrak{N}(\text{charge of one electron}) = 96,490 \; C$$

17-7 Transference Numbers

Now that the general features of electrode processes have been mentioned, the details of the passage of the electric current through the body of the solution can be investigated. The flow of either the positive or the negative ions, or both, might be responsible for conduction processes, and the first goal is the determination of the fraction of the current carried by each ion in a given electrolyte. For this purpose the *transference numbers* t_+ and t_- are introduced according to the definitions

t_+ = fraction of current carried by cation
t_- = fraction of current carried by anion

such that

$$t_+ + t_- = 1 \tag{17-15}$$

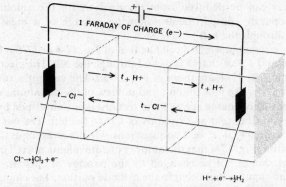

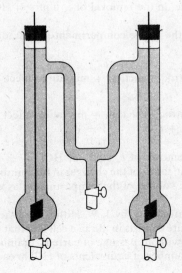

FIGURE 17-4 Transference numbers for HCl by the Hittorf method.

In metal conductors, e.g., a copper wire, all the current is carried by the electrons, and for such conductors one could write $t_- = 1$ and $t_+ = 0$. For solutions of electrolytes it is clearly difficult to guess what fraction of the current is carried past some position in the electrolyte by the cations and what fraction by the anions. One method, known as the *Hittorf method,* for measuring transference numbers will now be illustrated by two examples.

A schematic diagram of a cell marked off into three compartments is shown in Fig. 17-4. In practice, a cell of the type shown in Fig. 17-5 can be used, and the three compartments that can be drained off corrrespond to those marked off by the cross-section lines of Fig. 17-4. The following treatment will show that

FIGURE 17-5
Hittorf transference-number apparatus.

transference numbers can be deduced from the analysis for the amount of electrolyte in the separate compartments following passage of a measured amount of current through the cell.

Consider an experiment in which a cell like that of Fig. 17-4 or 17-5 is filled with an HCl solution and 1 $\mathcal{F}$ of charge is passed through the cell. The electrode processes, indicated in Fig. 17-4, are those of Fig. 17-3a. The current is carried across the cross sections by the flow of ions, and in view of the definitions of t_+ and t_-, the passage of 1 $\mathcal{F}$ of charge across these sections is accomplished by the flow of t_+ equiv of H^+ to the right and t_- equiv of Cl^- to the left. The net flow across these sections is then $t_+ + t_- = 1$ equiv of ions, which corresponds to 1 $\mathcal{F}$ of charge. It is clear from Fig. 17-4 that the number of equivalents of HCl in the central compartment should not be changed by the passage of current.

Consider now the changes that occur in the cathode portion. The change in equivalents of H^+ and Cl^- due to ion migrations is shown by the transfers across the cross-section line. In addition to migration, there is a removal of 1 equiv of H^+ at the electrode by the reaction

$$H^+ + e^- \rightarrow \tfrac{1}{2}H_2$$

The net cathode-compartment changes for the passage of 1 $\mathcal{F}$ are calculated as

Change in equivalents of H^+ = electrode reaction + migration effect
$$= -1 + t_+ = t_+ - 1 = -t_- \text{ equiv}$$

Change in equivalents of Cl^- = electrode reaction + migration effect
$$= 0 - t_- = -t_-$$

Passage of 1 $\mathcal{F}$ of current results, therefore, in the removal of t_- equiv of HCl from the cathode portion.

In a similar manner, the changes in the anode compartment per faraday are calculated as

Change in equivalents of H^+ = electrode reaction + migration effect
$$= 0 - t_+ = -t_+$$

Change in equivalents of Cl^- = electrode reaction + migration effect
$$= -1 + t_- = t_- - 1 = -t_+$$

The net effect around the anode is the removal of t_+ equiv of HCl.

It should be noted that the analysis is in terms of the changes in the number of equivalents, and not concentration. The volume of the compartments, as we shall see, is not critical.

This calculation suggests a method introduced by J. W. Hittorf for determining transference numbers. The procedure consists in filling a cell like that of Fig. 17-5 with the HCl solution and, first, without passage of current, draining the compartments and analyzing for the number of equivalents of HCl in each compartment. The number of equivalents would be calculated from the concentrations and compartment volumes. The cell is then refilled with the same solution, and a measured number of coulombs of current is passed. The compartments are then drained and analyzed to give the number of equivalents in each and, from this, the change in equivalents in each compartment.

If not too large an amount of current is passed and if no mixing of the compartment solutions occurs, it will be found, in accordance with the previous treatment, that the number of equivalents in the central compartment will be unchanged. The changes in the number of equivalents in either of the electrode compartments allow the determination of the transference numbers of H^+ and Cl^-.

In practice, of course, an amount of charge must less than 1 $\mathfrak{F}$ is passed through the cell. The observed changes in the electrode compartments can, however, be used to calculate the change expected per faraday of charge passed through the cell. These data can then be used directly with the type of analysis indicated above to give t_+ and t_-.

The treatment is much the same when other electrode processes occur. The electrolysis of a solution of $CuSO_4$ will illustrate this. Again consider the effect of the passage of 1 $\mathfrak{F}$ of charge. The electrode reactions and transfers between the compartments are shown in Fig. 17-6. Again, if the electrolysis is not carried too far, the middle compartment will experience no net change. The net effect on the electrode compartments as a result of the processes of Fig. 17-6 can be shown as in Table 17-5. The overall effect of the passage of a faraday of charge on the solution of the entire cell is the gain of 1 equiv of H^+ and the loss of 1 equiv of Cu^{2+} or, in terms of electrolytes, the gain of 1 equiv of H_2SO_4 and the loss of 1 equiv of $CuSO_4$. The changes in the electrode compartments, however, involve the transference number, and thus analyses of these compartments allow values of transference numbers to be obtained.

Other methods are available for the determination of transference num-

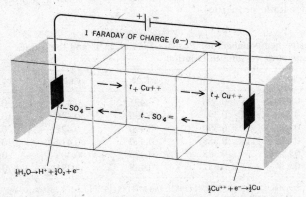

FIGURE 17-6 Transference numbers for $CuSO_4$ by the Hittorf method.

TABLE 17-5 Changes in the Electrode Compartments of a Hittorf Transference-Number Cell for the Passage of 1 $\mathfrak{F}$ of Charge through a $CuSO_4$ Solution, as in Fig. 17-6

	Cathode compartment	Anode compartment
Change due to electrode reactions	-1 equiv of Cu^{2+}	$+1$ equiv of H^+
Change due to migration	$+t_+$ equiv of Cu^{2+} $-t_-$ equiv of SO_4^{2}	$-t_+$ equiv of Cu^{2+} $+t_-$ equiv of SO_4^{2-}
Net electrode compartment changes	Loss of t_- $(= 1 - t_+)$ equiv of $CuSO_4$	Gain of 1 equiv of H_2SO_4 and loss of t_+ equiv of $CuSO_4$
Net cell change	Gain of 1 equiv of H_2SO_4 and loss of 1 equiv of $CuSO_4$	

bers, but the detailed look at the conduction process that the Hittorf method requires makes this method sufficient to illustrate the determination of these quantities.

Table 17-6 shows the transference numbers for several electrolytes at various concentrations. The cation transference numbers t_+ are listed, and the relation $t_+ + t_- = 1$ can be used to give the corresponding anion values. This table shows that both positive and negative ions carry the current through the solution and that they do so to approximately the same extent.

It is important to notice that the transference numbers show some concentration dependence, particularly for electrolytes with highly charged ions. The relative conductance contributions of the ions are therefore a function of concentration.

Knowledge of the values of transference numbers lets us proceed to a discussion of other ionic properties.

TABLE 17-6 Transference Numbers for Positive Ions at 25°C and the Values Obtained by Extrapolation to Infinite Dilution

Normality	HCl	NaCl	KCl	$CaCl_2$	$LaCl_3$
0	0.821	0.396	0.491	0.438	0.477
0.01	0.825	0.392	0.490	0.426	0.462
0.02	0.827	0.390	0.490	0.422	0.458
0.05	0.829	0.388	0.490	0.414	0.448
0.1	0.831	0.385	0.490	0.406	0.438
0.2	0.834	0.382	0.489	0.395	0.423

Source: L. G. Longsworth, *J. Am. Chem. Soc.*, **54**:2741 (1932), and **57**:1185 (1935); L. G. Longsworth and D. A. MacInnes, *J. Am. Chem. Soc.*, **60**:3070 (1938).

17-8 Ionic Conductances

Values can now be obtained from the contributions the individual ions of an electrolyte make to the equivalent conductance. The empirical law of Kohlrausch implies that at infinite dilution the equivalent conductance can be interpreted in terms of such ionic contributions and that the contributions of an ion are independent of the other ion of the electrolyte.

At infinite dilution, therefore, it is profitable to write

$$\Lambda_0 = (\lambda_+)_0 + (\lambda_-)_0 \tag{17-16}$$

where $(\lambda_+)_0$ and $(\lambda_-)_0$ are the *equivalent ionic conductances at infinite dilution*. Since the transference numbers give the fraction of the total current carried by each ion, i.e., the fraction of the total conductance that each ion contributes, we can write

$$\lambda_0^+ = (t_+)_0 \Lambda_0 \quad \text{and} \quad \lambda_0^- = (t_-)_0 \Lambda_0 \tag{17-17}$$

where $(t_+)_0$ and $(t_-)_0$ are the transference numbers extrapolated to infinite dilution. Table 17-7 shows some values for these limiting equivalent ionic conductances. An immediate use of such tabulated values is the calculation of the limiting equivalent conductance of a weak electrolyte without the addition and subtraction procedures of Sec. 17-2.

In a formal manner one can use the data for the equivalent conductance and the transference numbers at concentrations other than that of infinite dilution to obtain values of λ_+ and λ_- at these higher concentrations. At such concentrations, however, the law of independent migration of the ions fails, and the conductance is really a property of the electrolyte rather than of the individual ions of the electrolyte. This means that an ionic conductance calcu-

TABLE 17-7 Equivalent Ionic Conductances and Ionic Mobilities at Infinite Dilution and 25°C

Ion	$(\lambda_+)_0$, $\Omega^{-1}\,m^2$	$(v_+)_0$, $ms^{-1}/(V\,m^{-1})$	Ion	$(\lambda_-)_0$, $\Omega^{-1}\,m^2$	$(v_-)_0$, $ms^{-1}/(V\,m^{-1})$
H^+	0.034982	36.3×10^{-8}	OH^-	0.01980	20.5×10^{-8}
Li^+	0.003869	4.01	Cl^-	0.007634	7.91
Na^+	0.005011	5.19	I^-	0.00768	7.95
K^+	0.007352	7.61	CH_3COO^-	0.00409	4.23
Ag^+	0.006192	6.41	NO_3^-	0.007144	7.41
NH_4^+	0.00734	7.60	SO_4^{2-}	0.00798	8.27
Ca^{2+}	0.005950	6.16			
Ba^{2+}	0.006364	6.60			
La^{3+}	0.00696	7.21			

Source: Data from D. A. MacInnes, "The Principles of Electrochemistry," Reinhold Publishing Corporation, New York, 1939.

lated for a Cl^- ion, for example in a 1 M HCl solution, will be different from that deduced for the Cl^- ion in a 1 M NaCl solution. The concept of ionic conductances is really valuable, therefore, only at infinite dilutions.

Instead of trying to understand the different current-carrying properties of the ions of Table 17-7 in terms of ionic conductances, we proceed now to obtain an even more fundamental ionic property, the velocity with which the ions travel through the solution under the influence of the applied electric field.

17-9 Ionic Mobilities

Consider a cell of the type used to introduce the concept of equivalent conductance. Such a cell, it will be recalled, consists of two electrodes 1 m apart and of cross-section area A such that an amount of solution that contains 1 equiv of electrolyte is held between the electrodes. A distorted picture of such a cell is shown in Fig. 17-7.

For an applied voltage $\mathcal{V}$, a current I will flow through the cell. These electrical quantities are related, since the conductance of such a cell is the equivalent conductance of the electrolyte, by

$$I = \frac{\mathcal{V}}{R} \quad \text{or} \quad I = \Lambda \mathcal{V} \tag{17-18}$$

At infinite dilution the current can be attributed to the independent flow of positive and negative ions, and one can write

$$I = \Lambda_0 \mathcal{V} = [(\lambda_+)_0 + (\lambda_-)_0]\mathcal{V} = (\lambda_+)_0 \mathcal{V} + (\lambda_-)_0 \mathcal{V} = I_+ + I_- \tag{17-19}$$

This flow of current through the cell can also be analyzed in terms of the details of the ion movements in the cell. Since the cell contains 1 equiv of electrolyte, there will be $\mathfrak{N}/Z_+$ positive ions present and $\mathfrak{N}/Z_-$ negative ions

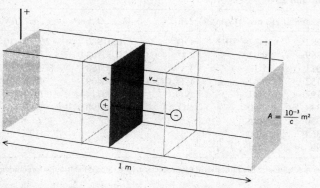

FIGURE 17-7 Diagram for ionic-mobility calculation.

present, where $\mathfrak{N}$ is an Avogadro's number and Z_+ and Z_- are the charges of the ions of the electrolyte. The average velocities with which the ions move to their respective electrodes under the influence of the applied voltage are represented by v_+ and v_-. The current passing a cross section of the cell can now be obtained in terms of these ionic quantities and the applied voltage.

For an ion to cross the shaded cross section of Fig. 17-7 within 1 s, it must start within a distance v_+ or v_- m from the cross section. (The ions travel a distance v_+ or v_- in 1 s.) In 1 s, therefore, all the positive ions in the right rectangular compartment and all the negative ions in the left compartment will have crossed the boundary. Since these rectangular volumes have lengths of v_+ and v_- and the cell has a width of 1 m, the volumes will contain fractions $v_+/1$ and $v_-/1$ of the total number of positive and negative ions in the cell. We can therefore write

$$\text{No. positive ions crossing boundary per second} = \frac{\mathfrak{N}}{Z_+} \frac{v_+}{1} = \frac{\mathfrak{N}v_+}{Z_+}$$

$$\text{No. negative ions crossing boundary per second} = \frac{\mathfrak{N}}{Z_-} \frac{v_-}{1} = \frac{\mathfrak{N}v_-}{Z_-}$$

The current corresponding to these flow rates is obtained by multiplying by the ion charges eZ_+ and eZ_- to give

$$\text{Positive charge crossing per second} = I_+ = eZ_+ \frac{\mathfrak{N}v_+}{Z_+} = e\mathfrak{N}v_+$$

$$\text{Negative charge crossing per second} = I_- = eZ_- \frac{\mathfrak{N}v}{Z_-} = e\mathfrak{N}v_-$$

For an infinitely dilute solution, if the average ionic velocities in the electric field direction are represented as $(v_+)_0$ and $(v_-)_0$, comparison with Eq. (17-19) gives

$$\mathcal{V}(\lambda_+)_0 = e\mathfrak{N}(v_+)_0 \qquad \text{and} \qquad \mathcal{V}(\lambda_-)_0 = e\mathfrak{N}(v_-)_0 \tag{17-20}$$

Furthermore, the substitution $e\mathfrak{N} = \mathfrak{F}$ can be made to yield, finally,

$$(v_+)_0 = \frac{(\lambda_+)_0 \mathcal{V}}{\mathfrak{F}} \qquad \text{and} \qquad (v_-)_0 = \frac{(\lambda_-)_0 \mathcal{V}}{\mathfrak{F}} \tag{17-21}$$

The average velocity with which an ion moves toward an electrode under the influence of a potential of 1 V applied across a 1-m cell is given by $(v_+)_0/\mathcal{V}$ or $(v_-)_0/\mathcal{V}$ and is known as the *ionic mobility*. The ionic mobility is calculated, as Eq. (17-21) shows, by dividing the ionic conductance, as listed in Table 17-7, by the value of the faraday. These mobility results are also shown in Table 17-7.

The most remarkable feature of the data of Table 17-7 is, perhaps, the high values for the mobilities of the H^+ and OH^- ions compared with those of all the other ions. Since the proton is present as an H_3O^+ ion, and since both the H_3O^+ and OH^- ions are expected to be highly solvated, an explanation cannot be given in terms of the size of these ions. A mechanism of the type suggested originally by T. van Grotthuss in 1805 to explain conduction by all electrolytes appears now to be applicable, but only to the H_3O^+ and OH^- ions. Figure 17-8 shows how a series of transfers of protons between neighboring water molecules can have the effect of moving either an H^+ or an OH^- through the solution. The high mobilities of H^+ and OH^- and the fact that they are the dissociation products of the solvent are seen to be related. In other solvents, where such a mechanism could not operate, these ions would show mobilities more in line with those of the other ions.

The values of the mobilities of the other ions in aqueous solution are more difficult to understand. The high degree of solvation expected for the small ions, such as Li^+, and for the highly charged ions, such as La^{3+}, apparently works against the expected dependence of mobility in size and charge.

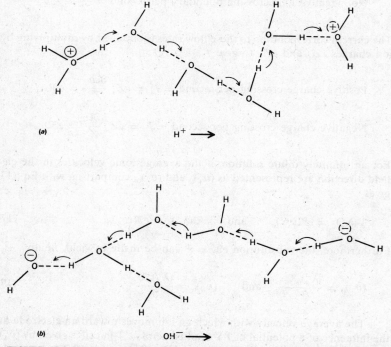

FIGURE 17-8 Movement of (a) H^+ and (b) OH^- by the Grotthuss mechanism. The charges outlined by dashed circles are formed as a result of the series of proton transfers.

It is interesting to compare the mobilities of ions with the speeds previously found for molecules of gases. For a reasonable voltage gradient of 10^4 V m^{-1}, or 100 V cm^{-1}, for instance, ions would migrate according to the mobility data of Table 17-7 with a velocity of about 5×10^{-4} m s^{-1}. It would take a typical ion about 30 min to travel 1 m in the direction of the applied voltage. The electric field that is conveniently applied to a solution is not an overwhelming factor in the affairs of ions. The ions are to be thought of as having only a slight directional component imposed on their random motions.

17-10 The Dependence of Ionic Conductance on Concentration

Around any ion in solution, as will be shown in Sec. 17-15, there exists an *ion atmosphere* containing a preponderance of the ions with charges opposite that of the central ion. The ionic distribution can be looked on as resembling, for example, that in an expanded and loosely held NaCl crystal. The overall arrangement places each ion among nearest neighbors of the opposite charge. This ion atmosphere around each ion is, of course, better formed at higher concentrations.

The application of an electric field, as in a conductance experiment, results initially in the movement of the central ion away from the center of the oppositely charged sphere. The distorted ion atmosphere tends to oppose the applied field, and this decreases the current produced by a given applied electric field. Since the ion atmosphere is more important at higher concentrations, this decrease becomes more important at higher concentrations. Evaluation of this factor by P. Debye and H. Hückel showed that it contributes to the $\sqrt{c}$ dependence of the equivalent conductance displayed in Fig. 17-2. This effect is further enhanced by the tendency of the oppositely charged ions that predominate in the ion atmosphere to move in the opposite direction.

This ionic-atmosphere drag depends on the fact that the atmosphere does not instantaneously adjust itself to the new positions of the central ion. One says that the ionic atmosphere has a *relaxation time;* i.e., when a stress is applied, it takes a finite time for the atmosphere to relax, or to be reestablished. The mechanism by which this occurs, as the central ion moves, is better thought of as a process of building new ions on the front of the atmosphere and dropping some off the back than of maintaining the same set of ions, which move to keep up with the central ion.

The second factor that acts to decrease the conductance at higher concentrations is an enhanced frictional drag that sets in. When an electric field is applied, the ions set off to the oppositely charged electrodes. Each ion moves with a velocity that depends on a balance between the electric force and the viscous drag. The average velocity and therefore the current are concentration-dependent because the ions can be thought of as carrying along with them their many solvating molecules, and at higher concentrations an ion seems to swim against the current produced by the oppositely charged, solvated ions moving in the opposite direction.

The conductivity theory of Debye and Hückel has been used to draw the slopes of the straight dashed lines of Fig. 17-2. It is apparent that the effects considered by the theory are adequate to explain the conductance behavior of strong electrolytes up to concentrations of about 0.01 M. Thus the Arrhenius assumption that a decrease in conductance must be interpreted as a decreased number of conducting particles cannot be maintained. The relation $\alpha = \Lambda/\Lambda_0$ can be applied only when the Debye-Hückel effects are not appreciable or have been corrected for. Only for solutions with low ionic concentrations will these effects be small. For weak electrolytes, therefore, one can still rely on Λ/Λ_0 to give a value that can be interpreted primarily in terms of a degree of dissociation.

17-11 Some Applications of Conductance Measurements

Previously, the results of conductance measurements have been used for the investigation of the nature of electrolytes in solution. There are also a number of direct applications of conductance measurements to chemical problems. The usefulness of conductance arises from its dependence on the ionic concentration and from its special sensitivity to the concentration of H^+ and OH^- ions.

Example 17-1: Conductimetric titrations
An acid-base titration, using HCl and NaOH, for example, can be performed in a conductivity cell, and the change to conductance followed as the base is added to the acid. Results like those shown in Fig. 17-9 are obtained. The net behavior is seen to depend on the high ionic conductances of H^+ and OH^- compared with the ions Na^+ and Cl^-, and the equivalence point can then be conveniently taken as the intersection of the two straight lines that can be drawn.

For titrations involving a weak acid or a weak base the behavior is not quite so simple, but the conductance still provides a useful means for following the titration.

Of particular value is the fact that the conductance is derived from the measured resistance of the cell. The change in resistance as the titration proceeds can be used in an instrumental method for following the course of the titration automatically.

Example 17-2: Degree of ionization of weak electrolytes
For weak electrolytes, for which the ionic concentrations are sometimes very small, the dominant effect on the conductivity is the association of the ions of the weak electrolyte into undissociated molecules. In such cases the Arrhenius relation $\alpha = \Lambda/\Lambda_0$ can be used to deduce the degree of ionization.

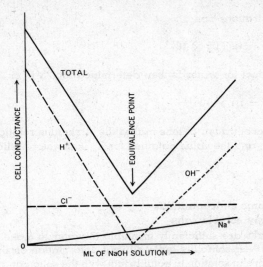

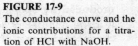

FIGURE 17-9
The conductance curve and the ionic contributions for a titration of HCl with NaOH.

A good, but rather special, illustration of a use of conductance measurements is to be found in the determination of the dissociation constant of water.

$$H_2O \rightleftharpoons H^+ + OH^-$$

At 25°C the lowest specific conductance that can be obtained with the most carefully distilled water is $58 \times 10^{-7}\,\Omega^{-1}\,m^{-1}$, and this conductance must be attributed to the equilibrium concentration of H^+ and OH^-. The molarity of pure water is

$$c = \frac{(1000)(0.997)}{18.02} = 55.3 \text{ mol liter}^{-1}$$

which gives, for the equivalent conductance, the result

$$\Lambda = \frac{10^{-3}\kappa}{c} = 1.05 \times 10^{-10}\,\Omega^{-1}\,m^2$$

The equivalent conductance expected for completely dissociated water is calculated from the data of Table 17-7 as $0.05478\,\Omega^{-1}\,m^2$. The degree of dissociation of water at 25°C is therefore

$$\alpha = \frac{\Lambda}{\Lambda_0} = \frac{1.05 \times 10^{-10}}{0.05478} = 1.9 \times 10^{-9}$$

and the ionic concentrations are

$$[H^+] = [OH^-] = \alpha c = 1.05 \times 10^{-7}$$

The familiar ion product for water is then determined for 25°C as

$$K_w = [H^+][OH^-] = 1.1 \times 10^{-14}$$

The very low concentration of ions makes the Arrhenius relation $\alpha = \Lambda/\Lambda_0$ quite valid, and the value obtained for K_w is therefore reliable.

Example 17-3: The ionic concentrations produced by sparingly soluble salts

A large number of salts are sufficiently insoluble in water to make a chemical analysis of their solubility quite difficult. Information on the concentration of the ions in solution in equilibrium with the solid can be obtained from measurements of the conductance of a saturated solution. For the salt MX, for example, the solubility product $[M^+][X^-]$ can then be deduced. For very insoluble salts the concentration of ions in solution will again be low enough for the conductance to be taken as a measure of ionic concentrations.

The example, frequently referred to, of an insoluble salt that can be studied in this way is AgCl. The specific conductance of a saturated solution at 25°C is given, after subtraction of the specific conductance of the water itself, as

$$\kappa = 2.28 \times 10^{-4} \, \Omega^{-1} \, m^{-1}$$

The conductance of 1 equiv at infinite dilution, obtained from the data of Table 17-7, is $0.01383 \, \Omega^{-1} \, m^2$.

Since the solubility of AgCl is quite low, the equivalent conductance of a saturated solution will be little different from that at infinite dilution. Thus one can use Eq. (17-4) to write for the saturated solution

$$\Lambda = \Lambda_0 = \frac{10^{-3}\kappa}{c} \tag{17-22}$$

or

$$c = \frac{10^{-3}\kappa}{\Lambda_0} = \frac{10^{-3}(2.28 \times 10^{-4})}{0.01382} = 1.65 \times 10^{-5} \tag{17-23}$$

The solubility product is then calculated as

$$K_{sol} = [Ag^+][Cl^-] = (1.65 \times 10^{-5})^2 = 2.72 \times 10^{-10} \qquad (17\text{-}24)$$

Such a treatment is disturbed if, for example, complex ions like Ag_2Cl^+ or $AgCl_2^-$ are present, and if any ion pairs or higher-neutral-association species are important. The solubility of the electrolyte would then not be simply given by the concentrations of the Ag^+ or Cl^- ions deduced in this way.

REFINEMENTS OF THE MODEL
OF IONS IN AQUEOUS SOLUTIONS

The Arrhenius idea of ions in solution in equilibrium with parent molecular species allows many of the properties of ionic solutions to be understood. But a number of difficulties arise. Criticisms ultimately were leveled at the Arrhenius theory for postulating, in such cases, molecules instead of ions, a reversal of the initial criticisms of the Arrhenius equation that attacked it for postulating ions in solution instead of molecules!

Refinements to the simplest ideas of the ionic solutions depend on the recognition of the role of the solvent and on the effect of interactions between the ions.

17-12 The Role of the Solvent: Dielectric Effect

A remarkable feature of the Arrhenius theory is that although it attributes the dissociation process to the solution of the electrolyte, it proceeds to ignore the role of the solvent, or rather treats the solvent as if it were an inert medium. A detailed understanding of the molecular nature of ionic solutions must clearly involve the very important role played by the solvent. It is necessary, for instance, to understand why water is a unique solvent for ionic systems.

Two aspects of solvent behavior can be recognized. Here the dielectric effect will be pointed out. In the following section the *solvation,* or more particularly *hydration,* of ions by the solvent will be considered.

The electrostatic force of attraction between ions of charge Z^+ and Z^- is given by Coulomb's law:

For vacuum: $$f(r) = \frac{e^2 Z^+ Z^-}{(4\pi\epsilon_0)r^2} \qquad (17\text{-}25a)$$

For medium of dielectric ϵ/ϵ_0: $$f(r) = \frac{e^2 Z^+ Z^-}{(\epsilon/\epsilon_0)(4\pi\epsilon_0)r^2} \qquad (17\text{-}25b)$$

With the numerical values $e = 0.1602 \times 10^{-18}$ C and $4\pi\epsilon_0 = 1.1126 \times 10^{-10}$ C^2 N^{-1} m^{-2}, the second of these equations is

$$f(r) = 0.2306 \times 10^{-27} \frac{Z^+Z^-}{(\epsilon/\epsilon_0)r^2} \qquad (17\text{-}26)$$

This force is given in units of newtons. For water, the dielectric-constant factor ϵ/ϵ_0 has the very large value of about 80. The force of interaction and the energy required to overcome coulombic forces are thus smaller by almost two orders of magnitude in water than in vacuum or materials of very low dielectric. The easy dissociation of electrolytes in aqueous solution compared with gas-phase or low-dielectric material is therefore readily understandable in terms of the high dielectric constant of water. The initial criticisms raised against the Arrhenius theory for postulating the dissociation of electrolytes in solution however, remain valid arguments against any theory postulating appreciable dissociation to form free ions in solvents of low dielectric constant.

Although the dielectric effect is a major factor for the formation of ionic species in aqueous solutions, it is not great enough to reduce the intermolecular interaction to the small values found for gas-phase molecules. We must therefore expect that for all but extremely dilute solutions ionic interactions will enter to produce behavior different from the ideal behavior found at infinite dilution.

17-13 Ionic Activity Coefficients and Their Dependence on the Ionic Strength of the Solution

The thermodynamic properties of solutions of electrolytes are treated in terms of the ions of the electrolyte and, in the case of weak electrolytes, the undissociated parent molecule. The ionic concentrations always appear in a combination that corresponds to an uncharged parent electrolyte. Thus, if we deal with dissociation equilibria we obtain, for ideal behavior, equilibrium-constant expressions like $[H^+][Ac^-]/[HAc]$ for acetic acid and $[H^+]^2[SO_4^{2-}]/[H_2SO_4]$ for sulfuric acid.

Because of the large interionic interactions, as suggested in the preceding section, even quite dilute solutions exhibit nonideal behavior. Thermodynamic treatments then require, as in Sec. 8-9, the use of effective concentrations, or activities, in place of concentrations. Generally for aqueous solutions of electrolytes this treatment is necessary only for the charged species.

Treatment of the acetic acid equilibrium, for example, so that a constant equilibrium constant is obtained requires us to write

$$\frac{(a_{H^+})(a_{Ac^-})}{a_{HAc}} \simeq \frac{(a_{H^+})(a_{Ac^-})}{[HAc]} = K_{th}$$

where K_{th} is written to suggest that a correct, or nearly so, thermodynamic expression has been written.

Again, as in Sec. 8-9, it is convenient to introduce activity coefficients to show explicitly the deviation from ideal behavior. We write, for example,

$$a_{H^+} = \gamma_{H^+}[H^+] \quad \text{and} \quad a_{Ac^-} = \gamma_{Ac^-}[Ac^-]$$

Then K_{th} can be expressed as

$$K_{th} = \gamma_{H^+}\gamma_{Ac^-} \frac{[H^+][Ac^-]}{[HAc]}$$

The following sections will show that there are a variety of ways of deducing activity coefficient terms like $\gamma_{H^+}\gamma_{Ac^-}$. None of the thermodynamic methods leads to separate values of terms of the γ_{H^+} and γ_{Ac^-} type. (The Debye-Hückel theory, however, does predict individual activity coefficients, as you will see in Sec. 17-16.) As a result, we often introduce an average, or mean, activity coefficient. In the case of a one-to-one electrolyte this is simply

$$\gamma_{\pm} = \sqrt{\gamma_+\gamma_-} \tag{17-27}$$

A similar treatment of the activities themselves leads, again for one-to-one electrolytes, to the mean activity $a_{\pm}$, which is related to the ionic activities by

$$a_{\pm} = \sqrt{a_+a_-} \tag{17-28}$$

Extension of this procedure lets activities and their coefficients be defined for electrolytes beyond the AB type. An AB_2 electrolyte would dissociate according to

$$AB_2 \rightleftharpoons A^{2+} + 2B^-$$

and the activity term that would appear in all thermodynamic treatments would be of the form

$$(a_{A^{2+}})(a_{B^-})^2$$

The corresponding mean activity $a_{\pm}$ that could be introduced is related by

$$(a_{\pm})^3 = (a_{A^{2+}})(a_{B^-})^2 \quad \text{or} \quad a_{\pm} = [(a_{A^{2+}})(a_{B^-})^2]^{1/3}$$

Similarly, the mean-activity coefficient would be related to the ionic activities by

$$\gamma_{\pm} = (\gamma_{A^{2+}} \gamma_{B^-}^2)^{1/3} \tag{17-29}$$

In general, for an electrolyte A_xB_y,

$$a_\pm = (a_{A(+)}^x a_{B(-)}^y)^{1/(x+y)}$$

and

$$\gamma_\pm = (\gamma_{A(+)}^x \gamma_{B(-)}^y)^{1/(x+y)} \tag{17-30}$$

Mean activities and activity coefficients are a considerable convenience, and their use loses nothing that is of thermodynamic concern. Furthermore, no thermodynamically exact method has been devised that allows the determination of the individual ion activities or activity coefficients.

Evaluation of activity coefficients for many systems, by means that we shall consider later, led Lewis and Randall to recognize that the mean-activity coefficient of the ions of an electrolyte can be related to a function of the concentration of charged particles in the solution. That such a relation exists reflects the fact that it is the ionic interactions that are primarily responsible for the nonideality of ionic solutes. Lewis and Randall introduced the *ionic strength* as a measure of the nonideality that the solution imposes on any dissociated electrolyte in the solution. Recognition of this function, as we shall see, will simplify our thermodynamic determinations of activity coefficients.

The ionic strength μ is a characteristic of the solution and is defined as

$$\mu = \frac{1}{2} \sum_i c_i Z_i^2 \tag{17-31}$$

where c_i is the concentration of the ith ion, Z_i is its charge, and the summation extends over all the ions in the solution. It has been found empirically and substantiated for dilute solutions by the theory of Debye and Hückel that the ionic strength is a good measure of the nonideality imposed by all the ions of a solution on the ions produced by a given electrolyte in the solution.

It is important to keep in mind that the ionic strength is a property of the solution and not of any particular ion in the solution.

Lewis and Randall were able to generalize their determinations of activity coefficients of ions of electrolytes into the following empirical statement: *in dilute aqueous solutions the activity coefficient of a given strong electrolyte is the same in all solutions of the same ionic strength.* In view of the tremendous number of different electrolyte solutions one might deal with, this rule is of great help. Thermodynamic results for activity coefficients confirm this statement. This thermodynamic deduction of activity coefficients is greatly simplified by a theoretical treatment of ionic solution by P. Debye and E. Hückel although it does not depend on that treatment. (This theory will be taken up in Secs. 17-15 and 17-16.)

The Debye-Hückel theory recognizes the existence of a stabilizing effect on a particular ion due to the excess of oppositely charged ions that tend, in spite of the random movement of the ions, to surround that ion preferentially. The net result of the analysis for dilute solutions, less than about 0.01 M, is the important expression for the mean-activity coefficient at 25°C of an electrolyte with anion charge Z_- and cation charge Z_+,

$$\log \gamma_\pm = 0.5091 Z_+ Z_- \sqrt{\mu} \tag{17-32}$$

where Z_- is to be written as a negative number. Thus the Debye-Hückel theory predicts that $\log \gamma_\pm$ is negative and therefore that $\gamma_\pm$ is less than unity. For solutions of sufficiently low ionic strength the experimental results are in good agreement with this theoretical expression. This limiting-law prediction of the Debye-Hückel theory provides, as you will see, a convenient guide to the extrapolations that enter into the thermodynamic deduction of activity coefficients.

17-14 Activity Coefficients from the Dissociation of a Weak Electrolyte

Studies of chemical equilibria can be used to deduce thermodynamic properties of nonideal systems. Acid-base equilibria provide many illustrations. The traditional example is the equilibrium set up by the dissociation of acetic acid, CH_3COOH, here abbreviated HAc,

$$HAc \rightleftharpoons H^+ + Ac^-$$

The thermodynamic equilibrium constant K_{th} is

$$K_{th} = \frac{(a_{H^+})(a_{Ac^-})}{a_{HAc}}$$

which can also be written

$$K_{th} = \frac{\gamma_+ \gamma_-}{\gamma_{HAc}} \frac{[H^+][Ac^-]}{[HAc]} \tag{17-33}$$

This expression is simplified when it is realized that the electrostatic interactions are primarily responsible for the nonideality which produces activity coefficients different from unity. The uncharged HAc molecule should therefore behave relatively ideally, and we can set $\gamma_{HAc} = 1$. Introduction of the mean-activity coefficient $\gamma_\pm = \sqrt{\gamma_+ \gamma_-}$ and rearrangement gives

$$\log \frac{[H^+][Ac^-]}{[HAc]} = \log K_{th} - 2 \log \gamma_\pm \tag{17-34}$$

The concentration expression is that for the equilibrium constant in terms of concentrations and can be written in terms of the degree of dissociation. Then

Eq. (17-34) can be written as

$$\log \frac{c\alpha^2}{1-\alpha} = \log K_{\text{th}} - 2 \log \gamma_\pm \tag{17-35}$$

For solutions that are very dilute in ions one can still use the Arrhenius expression

$$\alpha = \frac{\Lambda}{\Lambda_0} \tag{17-36}$$

to obtain the degree of dissociation from the conductivity. (More accurately, one can correct for the effect of ion concentration on conductance.) The left side of Eq. (17-35) can be determined for various acetic acid concentrations from conductivity measurements. The right side consists of a constant term $\log K_{\text{th}}$ and a term which, in view of the discussion of the preceding section, can be expected to be a function of μ, the ionic strength. If the solution contains only the H^+ and Ac^- ions from the dissociation of HAc, one has

$$\mu = \tfrac{1}{2}[(c\alpha)(1)^2 + (c\alpha)(-1)^2] = c\alpha \tag{17-37}$$

The theory of Debye and Hückel, to be developed in Sec. 17-16, suggests that in the low-ionic-concentration range $\log \gamma_\pm$ is proportional to $\sqrt{\mu}$. It might therefore be informative to plot the left side of Eq. (17-35) against $\sqrt{c\alpha}$, as in Fig. 17-10. At low concentrations the points do seem to fall along a straight line,

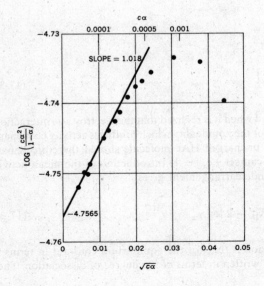

FIGURE 17-10
The extrapolation of the logarithm of the concentration equilibrium-constant expression, $\log [c\alpha^2/(1-\alpha)]$, for acetic acid to zero ionic strength, according to the plot suggested by the Debye-Hückel theory.

in agreement with the prediction of the Debye-Hückel theory. The theory predicts, furthermore, that the last term of Eq. (17-35) should be

$$-2 \log \gamma_\pm = +(2)(0.5091) \sqrt{c\alpha} = 1.018 \sqrt{c\alpha}$$

The line of Fig. 17-10, drawn with slope $+1.018$, fits the data satisfactorily. Extrapolation to zero ionic strength, where $\gamma_\pm = 1$ and $\log \gamma_\pm = 0$, gives

$$\log K_{th} = -4.7565$$

and

$$K_{th} = 1.752 \times 10^{-5} \tag{17-38}$$

Equation (17-35) can also now be rearranged to give

$$\log \gamma_\pm = \tfrac{1}{2} \log K_{th} - \tfrac{1}{2} \log \frac{c\alpha^2}{1-\alpha} = -2.3782 - \tfrac{1}{2} \log \frac{c\alpha^2}{1-\alpha} \tag{17-39}$$

From this equation we can determine $\gamma_\pm$ for the dissociation products of HAc at any concentrations for which values of α can be obtained.

For example, at an acetic acid concentration of 0.01 mol liter^{-1}, the degree of dissociation from the data of Table 17-2 is 0.0417. We obtain

$$\log \gamma_\pm = -2.3782 + \tfrac{1}{2}(4.7409) \quad \text{and} \quad \gamma_\pm = 0.982$$

17-15 The Debye-Hückel Theory of Interionic Interactions

Except at infinite dilution, electrostatic interaction between ions alters the properties of the solution from those expected from the free-ion model.

The treatment of ion-ion interactions by Debye and Hückel in 1923 and 1924 led to an explanation of the properties of relatively dilute solutions, less than about 0.01 M. Even this limited success has proved valuable in that a way to extrapolate available experimental data to the limit of infinite dilution was provided. Also provided was a base for more empirical extensions to higher concentrations. It is worthwhile, therefore, to follow through the Debye-Hückel derivation in some detail.

Consider one of the ions, a positive ion to be specific, of an aqueous solution of an electrolyte. It will be affected by coulombic interactions with the other ions of the solution. These interactions are described by a potential-energy term that is proportional to the product of the charges and inversely proportional to the distance between them. Thus a nearby ion will have a greater effect on the reference ion than a far-off ion will. But the number of such distant ions increases as the volume of a spherical shell, i.e., as r^2, and thus these more distant ions, and therefore the bulk of the solution, might appear to require our attention in the deduction of the effect on the reference ion. Fortunately, ions of opposite charge can be expected to distribute themselves uniformly at some distance away from a given ion to produce an electrical neutrality well removed from a given ion.

The Debye-Hückel treatment deals with the distribution of ions around a given ion and the net effect these neighboring ions have on the ions of the solution.

It is necessary to present here only a very condensed version that takes in the important features of the theory but ignores many of the subtleties involved. Even so, the treatment presented here is somewhat lengthy, due to the use of simple steps rather than some more compact but rather advanced mathematical relationships.

Consider first how the ions in a solution distribute themselves relative to each other. The two factors that play roles are the thermal jostlings and the electrical interactions between charged particles. Suppose that on the average there are n_i ions of the i type per unit volume. Around any positive ion there will be an increase in the concentration of negative ions and a decrease in the concentration of positive ions. These changes result from the ions moving to the energetically more favored regions, i.e., those in which their potential energy is low. The tendency for this movement must compete with the random thermal motion.

Boltzmann's equation can be used to give the number of ions that on the average are a distance r from the positive charge. The energy of ions of charge $Z_i e$ in a potential of value $\mathcal{U}$ is $(eZ_i)\mathcal{U}$. If Z_i is positive, the energy is higher near the reference positive charge, and if Z_i is negative, the energy is lower. Boltzmann's equation gives

$$n_i(r) = n_i e^{-(eZ_i\mathcal{U})/kT} \qquad (17\text{-}40)$$

where $n_i(r)$ is the number of ith ions per unit volume at a distance r from the reference positive charge and n_i is the average number per unit volume in the solution.

This expression cannot be used directly to calculate the density of ions of each type in the neighborhood of the reference positive ion because the neighboring ions, as well as the reference ion, determine the potential $\mathcal{U}$. Some manipulation of expressions for charge densities and potentials is necessary to get around this difficulty.

To provide a reference for this more complex situation let us first calculate what the density of ions about the reference positive ion would be if only the reference charge affected the distribution. Then we could write

$$\mathcal{U} = \frac{e}{(\epsilon/\epsilon_0)4\pi\epsilon_0 r} = \frac{e}{4\pi\epsilon r}$$

where e is the charge of the reference ion, and thus

$$n_i(r) = n_i e^{-e^2 Z_i/4\pi\epsilon rkT}$$

or

$$\frac{n_i(r)}{n_i} = e^{-e^2 Z_i/4\pi\epsilon rkT} \qquad (17\text{-}41)$$

This comparison of the number of ions per unit volume at some distance r from the reference charge compared with the average number in the bulk of the solution is shown for various ions in Fig. 17-11.

To correct the data of Fig. 17-11 to allow for the effects the various types of ions that surround the reference ion have on each other, we must first develop an expression for the charge density about a reference ion.

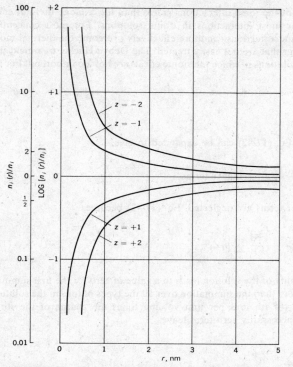

FIGURE 17-11 The variation in the ratio of the density of ions to the average ion density in the neighborhood of a charge of $+e$ according to Eq. (17-41), which takes into account only the effect of the reference charge.

The charge density at a distance r from the unit positive charge can be written as the ion density times the ion charges. The charge density, is a function of r, is

$$\rho(r) = \sum (eZ_i)n_i(r) \tag{17-40}$$

If the potential at a distance r is $\mathcal{V}$, Eq. (17-40) can be used to write

$$\rho(r) = e \sum_i n_i Z_i e^{-eZ_i\mathcal{V}/kT} \tag{17-42}$$

The treatment is mathematically tractable and the development is physically reasonable only if it is assumed that

$$eZ_i\mathcal{V} \ll kT \tag{17-43}$$

i.e., that the energy of the ionic interactions is less than the average thermal energy. Such is the case for most interactions in dilute solutions. For most concentrated solutions the interionic attractions can more effectively overcome the thermal motion, and associations occur that are not easily treated. The Debye-Hückel treatment therefore applies only to solutions in which interionic effects are not too important. For these solutions

$$\frac{eZ_i \mathcal{U}}{kT} \ll 1 \tag{17-44}$$

The exponential of Eq. (17-42) can be expanded to give

$$e^{-ez_i \mathcal{U}/kT} = 1 - \frac{ez_i \mathcal{U}}{kT} + \text{higher terms} \tag{17-45}$$

If all the higher terms are neglected, Eq. (17-42) becomes

$$\rho(r) = e \sum_i n_i Z_i - \frac{e^2 \mathcal{U}}{kT} \sum_i n_i Z_i^2 \tag{17-46}$$

The electrical neutrality of the solution leads to a value of zero for the first summation since it is nothing more than the summation over all the types of ions in the solution of the average number of ith ions per unit volume times the charge of the ith ion. Elimination of this necessarily zero term leaves

$$\rho(r) = -\frac{e^2 \mathcal{U}}{kT} \sum_i n_i Z_i^2 \tag{17-47}$$

The expression $\sum_i n_i Z_i^2$ is very similar to the *ionic strength* introduced by Lewis and Randall on an empirical basis and can be related to it. This useful quantity is expressed in terms of the molar concentrations of the ions rather than in SI units of ions per cubic meter. Since the number of ions of the ith type per cubic meter is related to the number of moles per liter c_i by the relation

$$n_i = 10^3 \mathfrak{N} c_i \tag{17-48}$$

where $\mathfrak{N}$ is Avogadro's number, we have

$$\sum_i n_i Z_i^2 = 10^3 \mathfrak{N} \sum c_i Z_i^2 = 2 \times 10^3 \mathfrak{N} \mu \tag{17-49}$$

where μ, the customary symbol for the ionic strength, is

$$\mu = \frac{1}{2} \sum_i c_i Z_i^2 \tag{17-50}$$

With this notation the charge distribution about the central positive-reference ion is written from Eq. (17-47), as

$$\rho(r) = \frac{-2 \times 10^2 \mathfrak{N} e^2 \mu \mho}{kT} \tag{17-51}$$

The charge density near a reference ion thus is seen to be proportional to the ionic strength μ of the solution. You can see the basis of this in Fig. 17-11. The highly charged negative ions have a great tendency to occupy regions close to a reference positive ion, and the highly charged positive ions have a corresponding tendency to avoid this region.

Equation (17-51) is a complicated one because the charge density $\rho(r)$ depends upon the potential $\mho$ and $\mho$ itself depends on both the charge of the reference ion and on the charge density around this ion. The net effect of these two factors on $\mho$ can be obtained by using a theorem from electrostatics summarized by the Poisson equation. You can go directly to this relation (17-57), or follow through the following simplified derivation of it.

The rate of change, or gradient, of the potential $\mho$ is related to the electric field by

$$\mathcal{E} = -\frac{d\mho}{dr} \tag{17-52}$$

The electric field at the surface of a sphere of radius r that encloses a charge q is thus

$$\mathcal{E} = -\frac{d}{dr}\left(\frac{q}{4\pi\epsilon r}\right) = \frac{q}{4\pi\epsilon r^2} \tag{17-53}$$

A more detailed treatment shows that a similar result is obtained for the electric field at the surface of the sphere even if the charge q, instead of being at the center of the sphere, is spread out or dispersed within the sphere of radius r. Therefore, for any spherically symmetric arrangements, one can express the electric field at a distance r from a central point as

$$\mathcal{E} = \frac{\text{enclosed charge}}{4\pi\epsilon r^2} \tag{17-54}$$

If a uniform charge density ρ is assumed, the enclosed charge is $\frac{4}{3}\pi r^3 \rho$ and the electric field intensity at r is

$$\mathcal{E} = \frac{\frac{4}{3}\pi r^3 \rho}{4\pi\epsilon r^2} = \frac{1}{3}\frac{r\rho}{\epsilon} \tag{17-55}$$

A desired relation is obtained by multiplying both sides by r^2 and differentiating with respect to r to obtain

$$\frac{d}{dr}(r^2 \mathcal{E}) = \frac{d}{dr}\left(\frac{r^3 \rho}{3\epsilon}\right) = \frac{r^2 \rho}{\epsilon}$$

or

$$\frac{1}{r^2}\frac{d}{dr}(r^2\mathcal{E}) = \frac{\rho}{\epsilon} \tag{17-56}$$

Now the relation $\mathcal{E} = -d\mho/dr$ can be used again to give the electrical potential $\mho$ as a function of r and the charge density, i.e.,

$$\frac{1}{r^2}\frac{d}{dr}\left(r^2\frac{d\mho}{dr}\right) = -\frac{\rho}{\epsilon} \tag{17-57}$$

This expression, which in fact is valid for any charge distribution $\rho(r)$, can be recognized as the form of the Poisson equation appropriate to a spherically symmetric problem. Now $\rho(r)$ of Eq. (17-51) can be inserted into Eq. (17-57) to give

$$\frac{1}{r^2}\frac{d}{dr}\left(r^2\frac{d\mho}{dr}\right) = \frac{2\times10^3\mathfrak{N}e^2\mu\mho}{\epsilon kT} \tag{17-58}$$

or

$$\frac{d}{dr}\left(r^2\frac{d\mho}{dr}\right) = \frac{2\times10^3\mathfrak{N}e^2\mu}{\epsilon kT}r^2\mho \tag{17-59}$$

To simplify the notation let us restrict ourselves to aqueous solutions and a temperature of 25°C and introduce a symbol β such that β^2 represents the constant terms in Eq. (17-59). Then

$$\beta^2 = \frac{2\times10^3\mathfrak{N}e^2}{\epsilon kT} \tag{17-60}$$

With $\epsilon/\epsilon_0 = 78.54$ for water and $T = 298.15$, insertion of values for the remaining constants gives

$$\beta^2 = 1.080 \times 10^{17} \quad\text{and}\quad \beta = 3.29 \times 10^8$$

In terms of the constant β, defined by Eq. (17-60), Eq. (17-59) becomes

$$\frac{d}{dr}\left(r^2\frac{d\mho}{dr}\right) = (\beta^2\mu)r^2\mho \tag{17-61}$$

Equation (17-61), known as the *Poisson-Boltzmann equation,* is a differential equation that can be solved to give $\mho$ as a function of r. A certain amount of manipulation is necessary to put Eq. (17-61) into an easily solved form. The solution, as can readily be verified by substitution in Eq. (17-61), is

$$\mho = \frac{Ze}{4\pi\epsilon r}\exp(-\beta\sqrt{\mu}r) \tag{17-62}$$

Thus, in place of the potential function $Ze/4\pi\epsilon r$ that is contributed by a reference charge Ze, we have a modification that depends, for aqueous solutions at 25°C, on the ionic strength μ. Illustrations of the effect this factor produces are shown in Fig. 17-12.

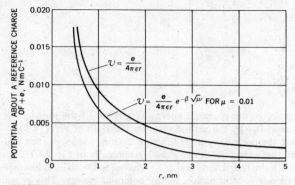

FIGURE 17-12 Illustration of the potential about a reference charge $+1$ according to Eq. (17-62) for the case of an aqueous solution at 25°C with ionic strength 0.01.

We can now return to the question of the ion atmosphere that surrounds a reference ion of charge Ze. Although analytically more convenient expressions will be needed later, we can substitute Eq. (17-62) into Eq. (17-40) to calculate the ratio $n_i(r)/n_i$ for ions of various types that are contributors to the ionic strength μ of the solution. Some examples are shown in Fig. 17-13. Notice that the ion atmosphere works against itself and does not build up to the extent shown in Fig. 17-11.

A more convenient expression than Eq. (17-62) is obtained if we restrict our attention to solutions and regions for which $\beta\sqrt{\mu}r \ll 1$, which occurs for low ionic strengths and regions not too far removed from the reference ion. Then the exponential of Eq. (17-62) can be expanded to give

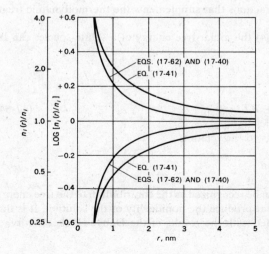

FIGURE 17-13
Variation in ion densities about a reference ion of charge $+e$ according to the Debye-Hückel treatment compared with that which ignores the effect of the neighboring ions.

$$\mathcal{V} = \frac{Ze}{4\pi\epsilon r}(1 - \beta\sqrt{\mu}r + \cdots)$$

or

$$\mathcal{V} \approx \frac{Ze}{4\pi\epsilon r} - \frac{\beta\sqrt{\mu}Ze}{4\pi\epsilon} \tag{17-63}$$

In this form the difference in the potential energy as a result of the ions in the ion atmosphere is shown explicitly by the second term on the right of Eq. (17-63).

The contribution to the potential-energy function $\mathcal{V}$ from a reference ion and the ions of the atmosphere that surrounds it are shown graphically in Fig. 17-13. Notice from Eq. (17-63) that with the restrictions that led to this equation the ion atmosphere makes a distance-independent contribution to the potential energy. This potential-energy component acts even on the reference ion which produced the ion atmosphere. Thus, the potential energy of a positive reference ion is reduced by the amount $(\beta Ze/4\pi\epsilon)\sqrt{\mu}$ as a result of the ion atmosphere it develops. A negative reference ion builds up a positively charged ion atmosphere, and its potential energy is reduced by a term of the same form.

In the following section we shall see how the potential-energy lowering, or stabilization, of ions that result from their ion atmospheres affects the activity of the ions.

17-16 The Debye-Hückel Theory of Ionic Activity Coefficients

The deduction of activity coefficients by the method of Sec. 17-14 is helped by the Debye-Hückel theory guide but does not depend on it. The theory, however, not only provides this aid but also yields values for the activity coefficients of ions in the very dilute solution region. As such it provides an approach based on theories of molecular interactions that supplements the thermodynamic treatments.

According to Eq. (9-34) the molar free energy of a solute species can be expressed by the relation

$$\begin{aligned}\overline{G} &= \overline{G}^\circ + RT\ln a \\ &= \overline{G}^\circ + RT\ln\gamma m \\ &= \overline{G}^\circ + RT\ln m + RT\ln\gamma \end{aligned} \tag{17-64}$$

Ideal behavior corresponds to the relation

$$\overline{G}_{\text{ideal}} = \overline{G}^\circ + RT\ln m \tag{17-65}$$

The added $RT\ln\gamma$ term can be recognized as the contribution to the free energy as a result of the effects that produce the nonideality of the solution. It is this term that can be interpreted with the results of the Debye-Hückel theory.

The nonideal contribution to the free energy of ions in solution can be interpreted as the difference between the energy required to create the ions in a solution in which there is no interionic interactions and that required where there are such interactions. The energy required to perform the hypothetical creation of a charge depends on the potential it experiences.

If we imagine the growth of an ionic charge Ze, either by a growth of Z or the value of the electronic charge, we can write

$$\text{Energy} = \int_0^{Ze} \mathcal{V}\, d(Ze) \tag{17-66}$$

With $\mathcal{V} = Ze/4\pi\epsilon r$ for an ion in a dielectric with no interfering ions, this becomes

$$\text{Energy} = \frac{1}{4\pi\epsilon r} \int_0^{Ze} Ze\, d(Ze) = \frac{1}{4\pi\epsilon r} \frac{(Ze)^2}{2} \tag{17-67}$$

If interionic interactions are recognized, as in the Debye-Hückel treatment of the preceding section, the potential is given by Eq. (17-62) or more conveniently by Eq. (17-63) as

$$\mathcal{V} = \frac{Ze}{4\pi\epsilon r} - \frac{\beta\sqrt{\mu}Ze}{4\pi\epsilon}$$

With this expression we obtain for an integration like that of Eq. (17-66)

$$\text{Energy} = \frac{1}{2}\frac{Ze}{4\pi\epsilon r}Ze - \frac{1}{2}\frac{\beta\sqrt{\mu}Ze}{4\pi\epsilon}Ze \tag{17-68}$$

The additional energy term, which is to be identified with the nonideal contribution $RT\ln\gamma$, is the final term of Eq. (17-68) multiplied by the number of ions $\mathfrak{N}$. Thus we write

$$-\frac{1}{2}\frac{\beta\sqrt{\mu}Ze}{4\pi\epsilon}Ze\mathfrak{N} = RT\ln\gamma$$

or

$$\ln\gamma = -\frac{Z^2 e^2 \beta \mathfrak{N} \sqrt{\mu}}{(2RT \times 4\pi\epsilon)} \tag{17-69}$$

On substitution of the expression for β from Sec. 17-15, we obtain

$$\ln \gamma = -\frac{e^3 (2 \times 10^3 \pi \mathfrak{N})^{1/2}}{(4\pi\epsilon_0 kT)^{3/2}} \frac{Z^2 \sqrt{\mu}}{(\epsilon/\epsilon_0)^{3/2}} \tag{17-70}$$

This is the important limiting law, i.e., for dilute solutions, obtained by Debye and Hückel in 1923. It shows how the activity coefficient of an ion of charge Z can be calculated. It should be mentioned that our derivation has assumed a positive reference charge. The same result is obtained for a negative charge. Thus a positive or a negative value of Z can be used in Eq. (17-70), and the same calculated value of the activity coefficient of the positive or negative ion will be obtained.

As in the preceding section, it is convenient to put numerical values in Eq. (17-70) for the special case of aqueous solutions at 25°C. Substituting values for the constants and 78.54 for ϵ/ϵ_0 for water and converting to logarithms to the base 10 gives

$$\log \gamma = -0.5091 Z^2 \sqrt{\mu} \tag{17-71}$$

More explicitly, one writes the important results

$$\log \gamma_+ = -0.5091 Z_+^2 \sqrt{\mu} \quad \text{and} \quad \log \gamma_- = -0.5091 Z_-^2 \sqrt{\mu} \tag{17-72}$$

The thermodynamic expressions have been set up in terms of the mean-activity coefficient, however, and it is therefore necessary to have the Debye-Hückel prediction of the mean-activity coefficient as well as the predictions for individual ions.

The mean-activity coefficient for a general electrolyte $A_x B_y$ is

$$\gamma_\pm = (\gamma_+^x \gamma_-^y)^{1/(x+y)} \tag{17-73}$$

If the charge of A is Z_+ and that of B is Z_-, it can be shown that Eqs. (17-72) for γ_+ and γ_- yield

$$\log \gamma_\pm = 0.5091 Z_+ Z_- \sqrt{\mu} \tag{17-74}$$

where the value of Z_- is entered with its minus sign. You can verify the correctness of Eq. (17-74) by applying Eqs. (17-72) and (17-73) to various types of electrolytes.

Equation (17-74) is the frequently useful limiting-law result of the Debye-Hückel theory. It is used, as illustrated in Sec. 17-14, as a guide to graphical and extrapolation procedures. It provides useful values of mean-activity coefficients only for very dilute solutions, those with ionic strengths less than 0.01, for example. Comparison of the predictions of Eq. (17-74) with data like those of Table 17-8 are shown in Fig. 17-14. Major deviations, which extend into the low-ionic-strength region, indicate that effects other than the electro-static ones dealt with in the Debye-Hückel theory are operating. It has been

TABLE 17-8 Mean Molal Activity Coefficients $\gamma_\pm$ for Electrolytes in Water at 25°C

	Molality								
	0.001	0.005	0.01	0.05	0.10	0.50	1.0	2.0	4.0
HCl	0.965	0.928	0.904	0.830	0.796	0.757	0.809	1.009	1.762
NaCl	0.966	0.929	0.904	0.823	0.778	0.682	0.658	0.671	0.783
KCl	0.965	0.927	0.901	0.815	0.769	0.650	0.605	0.575	0.582
HNO$_3$	0.965	0.927	0.902	0.823	0.785	0.715	0.720	0.783	0.982
NaOH			0.899	0.818	0.766	0.693	0.679	0.700	0.890
CaCl$_2$	0.887	0.783	0.724	0.574	0.518	0.448	0.500	0.792	2.934
K$_2$SO$_4$	0.89	0.78	0.71	0.52	0.43				
H$_2$SO$_4$	0.830	0.639	0.544	0.340	0.265	0.154	0.130	0.124	0.171
CdCl$_2$	0.819	0.623	0.524	0.304	0.228	0.100	0.066	0.044	
BaCl$_2$	0.88	0.77	0.72	0.56	0.49	0.39	0.39		
CuSO$_4$	0.74	0.53	0.41	0.21	0.16	0.068	0.047		
ZnSO$_4$	0.734	0.477	0.387	0.202	0.148	0.063	0.043	0.035	

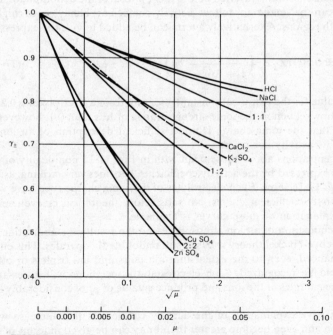

FIGURE 17-14 Comparison of mean-activity coefficients of one-to-one, two-to-one, and two-to-two electrolytes with the Debye-Hückel limiting law of Eq. (17-74), (For one-to-one electrolytes the molality m equals the ionic strength μ. For two-to-one electrolytes, $m = \frac{1}{3}\mu$, and for two-to-two electrolytes $m = \frac{1}{4}\mu$.)

suggested, for example, that the Zn^{2+}–SO_4^{2-} ion pair is responsible for the marked deviation of the $ZnSO_4$ activity-coefficient line from the Debye-Hückel limiting-law line in Fig. 17-14.

17-17 Activity Coefficients in More Concentrated Solutions

If attention is paid to solutions with ionic strengths greater than about 0.01 but less than about 0.1, a similar pattern of activity-coefficient behavior for different electrolytes is noticed, as Fig. 17-14 suggests. These data and such curves can be fitted by an extension of the Debye-Hückel limiting law

$$\log \gamma_{\pm} = 0.5091 Z_+ Z_- \frac{\sqrt{\mu}}{1 + \sqrt{\mu}} \tag{17-75}$$

If an adjustable constant is inserted before the $\sqrt{\mu}$ term of the denominator, this expression can be made to follow activity-coefficient behavior to higher ionic-strength regions. Alternatively a term can be added to give the expression

$$\log \gamma_{\pm} = 0.5091 Z_+ Z_- \left(\frac{\sqrt{\mu}}{1 + \sqrt{\mu}} - b\mu \right) \tag{17-76}$$

A suitable value for the empirical constant b for one-to-one electrolytes is 0.2, as Fig. 17-15 shows. Even in the ionic-strength range of less than 0.1, however, it is apparent that the ionic charge is not a sufficient description of an ion to account for its activity coefficient.

At concentrations above those dealt with in Fig. 17-15 nonideality of the solutions, as expressed by the activity coefficients, becomes very striking, as the curves of Fig. 17-16 show. Even electrolytes of the same charge type have very different activity-coefficient curves. No satisfactory theoretical or even semi-empirical explanation of these curves is available.

The phenomenon of an ion atmosphere and the resultant stabilization on which the Debye-Hückel theory is based still undoubtedly operates. This effect is much enhanced, even to the extent that ion pairs and ion triplets or other species should be recognized. Such electrostatic associations will necessarily lower the free energies of the ions and produce a value of $\gamma_{\pm}$ of considerably less than unit.

A qualitative explanation of the activity coefficients that increase with concentration and even become greater than unity can be given in terms of the solvation of the ions. As the ions tie up solvent molecules, the effective concentration, i.e., the moles solute per mole of free solvent, becomes greater than the concentration calculated as moles of solute per mole of solvent. The solute in

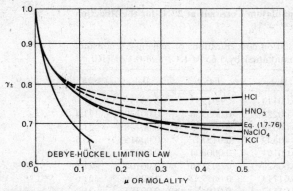

FIGURE 17-15 The mean-activity coefficient of some one-to-one electrolytes compared with the Debye-Hückel limiting law and with Eq. (17-76).

the apparently more concentrated solution has a higher free energy than would be expected, and this shows up as an increased activity coefficient.

A quantitative explanation for data like those of Fig. 17-16, however, is as yet nonexistent. In solution chemistry, one of the principal goals of research is that of clearly recognizing the factors that are involved and fitting the data like those in Fig. 17-16 into a quantitative theory.

Since the activity coefficients for ions in solutions of high ionic strengths depart very appreciably from unity, the study of any equilibrium involving ions under these conditions cannot be made simply in terms of concentrations, as one always seems to do in practice problems dealing with ionic equilibria. The activities of the ions should be used, but it is frequently difficult to obtain the

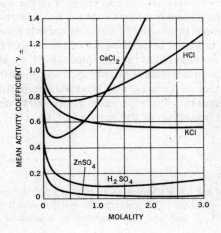

FIGURE 17-16
The mean-activity coefficient of some electrolytes in the concentration range up to 3 M. (*Adopted from L. P. Hammett, "Introduction to the Study of Physical Chemistry." Copyright 1952 by McGraw-Hill, Inc. Used by permission of McGraw-Hill Book Company.*)

TABLE 17-9 Equilibrium Constant at 25°C for the Reaction
$Fe^{3+} + I^- \rightarrow Fe^{2+} + \frac{1}{2}I_2$

Values for K based on concentrations of reagents; a constant
ionic strength maintained by 1.65 M KCl and 0.1 M HCl

$[Fe^{3+}]$	$[I^-]$	$[Fe^{2+}]$	$[I_2]$	K
0.001223	0.00114	0.001257	0.0053	21
0.002644	0.00224	0.003536	0.00129	21.4
0.00483	0.00358	0.007535	0.00238	21.3
0.00900	0.00549	0.01574	0.00415	20.5
0.00436	0.00161	0.000804	0.00032	20.5
0.001104	0.00526	0.003856	0.00104	21.4
0.00043	0.01713	0.005752	0.00076	21.6
0.00192	0.01117	0.01045	0.00185	21.0

Source: From J. N. Brönsted and K. Pedersen, *Z. Phy. Chem.*, **103**:307 (1923).

activity coefficients that are necessary for the calculation of activities from concentrations.

A common approach that attempts to avoid this difficulty arranges to keep the ionic strength at a high but essentially constant value by the addition of a relatively large amount of nonreacting electrolyte. Although this procedure makes all the activity coefficients very different from unity, it is intended to keep the activity coefficients of any participating ion constant regardless of the variation in the amount of the other reacting ions. The activity coefficients of the ions in the equilibrium

$$Fe^{3+} + I^- \rightleftharpoons Fe^{2+} + \tfrac{1}{2}I_2 \tag{17-77}$$

for example, would be expected to be very sensitive to changes in the ionic strength of the system. That this equilibrium is set up would not be apparent if one attempted to use the concentrations in an equilibrium-constant expression. As the data of Table 17-9 indicate, however, in the presence of 1.65 M KCl the activity coefficients apparently are not changed as the amounts of Fe^{3+}, I^-, and Fe^{2+} are varied and a quite constant equilibrium constant based on concentrations results. It must be recognized that this constant may be very different from the thermodynamic equilibrium constant. The experiment really shows only that an equilibrium is established according to the reaction of Eq. (17-77).

PROBLEMS

17-1. The specific conductance of a 0.1 M KCl solution at 25°C is 1.289 Ω^{-1} m^{-1}. What are the conductance and the resistance of a conductance cell for which the electrodes have an effective area of 2.037 cm^2 and are separated by a distance of 0.531 cm?

17-2. The resistance of a conductance cell filled with a 0.01 M KCl solution is found to be 8.30 Ω at 25°C. What is the cell constant l/A for the cell?

17-3. The resistance of a cell is 192.3 Ω when it is filled with 0.1 M KCl. Its resistance is 6363 Ω when it is filled with 0.003186 M NaCl solution. Both measurements are at 25°C. What are the specific and the equivalent and conductances of the NaCl solution?

17-4. The limiting equivalent conductances of NH_4Cl, NaCl, and NaOH in aqueous solution at 25°C are 0.01497, 0.012645, and 0.02478 Ω^{-1} m², respectively. Calculate the limiting equivalent conductance of NH_4OH and compare with the value reported in Table 17-2.

17-5. The limiting equivalent conductance of NaOH is 0.02478. With this datum and the results of Table 17-2 calculate the equivalent conductance of a completely ionized mole of water at infinite dilution in the solvent water at 25°C.

17-6. Using the data of Table 17-2, calculate according to the Arrhenius treatment of the dissociation of electrolytes the dissociation constant for (a) HCl, (b) acetic acid, and (c) NH_4OH at the concentrations for which the conductance data are given.

17-7. The rapid falloff in equivalent conductance with concentration displayed by $CuSO_4$ (Table 17-2) might suggest that it is a weak electrolyte. Calculate degrees of dissociation and dissociation constants, but do not overinterpret the results.

17-8. The following equivalent conductances of sodium propionate at 25°C have been reported by D. Belcher, *J. Am. Chem. Soc.*, **60**:2746 (1938):

Conc. mol liter⁻¹	0.002178	0.004180	0.007870	0.01427	0.02597
Λ, Ω^{-1} m²	0.008253	0.008127	0.007972	0.007788	0.007564

(a) What is the limiting conductance of sodium propionate? (b) What, in view of the data of Table 17-2, is the limiting conductance of propionic acid? (c) At a concentration of 1 M the equivalent conductance of propionic acid is 1.4×10^{-4} Ω^{-1} m². What is the degree of dissociation of propionic acid in this solution? (d) From the curves of Fig. 17-2 or the data of Table 17-2 estimate what effect the interionic interaction would have on this conductance measurement. (e) Deduce a dissociation constant for propionic acid.

17-9. (a) Interpret the variation in the van't Hoff i factors for $CuSO_4$ in Table 17-4 from the expected limiting value as being due to the partial association of the ions. (b) On this basis calculate the degree of dissociations and the dissociation constant values for $CuSO_4$ and compare with the values obtained in Prob. 17-7.

17-10. At low concentrations the freezing-point-depression constant $-\Delta T_{fp}/m$ for one-to-one electrolytes in water approaches the limiting value of 3.72. At higher concentrations the values of $-\Delta T_{fp}/m$ deviate from this limit. (a) Calculate the value that would be expected for a 1 m solution as a result of the removal of water molecules from the solvent by solvation of each of the ions by six water molecules. (b) In view of the results shown in Table 17-3 for NaCl, would such an explanation be able to account for the observed variation in $\Delta T_{fp}/m$?

17-11. Diagram the process by which current is carried through a solution of NaCl and show the electrode reactions that carry the current between the solutions and the electrode when an aqueous solution of NaCl is electrolyzed.

17-12. (a) Diagram the conduction within an aqueous solution and at the electrodes when an aqueous solution of Na_2SO_4 is electrolyzed between inert electrodes. (b) Write the electrode reactions. (c) If 0.342 A is passed through such a cell for 4.80 min, how many equivalents and how many moles of the products of electrolysis will be obtained?

17-13. What volumes of gases, measured at 1 atm pressure and 0°C, will be obtained at the electrodes when 1000 C of charge is passed through an aqueous NaOH solution?

17-14. What weight of copper will be deposited at the cathode by the passage of 0.473 A of current through a solution of copper sulfate for 5 min?

17-15. A determination of the transference numbers of cadmium and iodide ions by Hittorf gave the following data. A stock solution of CdI_2 was prepared, and by precipitation of iodide as AgI its concentration was determined to be 0.002763 g of CdI_2 per gram of solution. Another sample of this solution was placed in a Hittorf transference-number cell, and current was passed through the cell. It was found that 0.03462 g of cadmium was deposited at the cathode by the passage of the current. Furthermore, analysis of the anode-compartment solution, which weighed 152.643 g, indicated the presence of 0.3718 g of cadmium iodide. (a) What are the electrode reactions? (b) Indicate diagrammatically, using t_+ and t_- to represent the transference numbers, the changes in the amounts of the ions in the anode and cathode compartments as a result of migration and electrode reactions. (c) How many coulombs of charge were passed through the cell in the experiment? (d) What are the transference numbers of Cd^{2+} and I^- in this CdI_2 solution? (e) What was the change in the equivalents of CdI_2 in the cathode compartment?

17-16. A solution is prepared so that it is 0.01 M in HCl and 0.1 M in NaCl. (a) Can the fraction of current carried by the various ions of this solution be rigorously deduced from any of the data given in this chapter? (b) Estimate a value for the fraction of the current carried by each of the ions.

17-17. Calculate the ionic mobility of the Cl^- ion at an ionic concentration of 0.1 gram ion per liter from the transference numbers for the electrolytes HCl, NaCl, and KCl of Table 17-6 and the equivalent conductances of Table 17-2. Note that only at infinite dilution is the ionic conductance a property of the ion rather than the electrolyte.

17-18. The specific conductance, at 18°C, of a saturated silver iodate solution is $1.19 \times 10^{-3} \Omega^{-1} m^{-1}$ more than the water used to prepare the solution. The sum of the limiting equivalent conductances of Ag^+ and IO_3^- is found from measurements on more soluble salts to be $0.00873 \Omega^{-1} m^2$. (a) Calculate the solubility product $[Ag^+][IO_3^-]$ at 18°C. (b) What value of the solubility is obtained if it is assumed that no species other than Ag^+ and IO_3^- are present in the solution?

17-19. At 18°C the specific conductance of water saturated with CaF_2 is 3.86×10^{-3}, and that of the water used in the preparation of this solution is 0.15×10^{-3}. The equivalent ionic conductances at infinite dilution of Ca^{2+} and F^- are 0.00510 and $0.00470 \Omega^{-1} m^2$, respectively. Calculate the solubility product for CaF_2 and, assuming only Ca^{2+} and F^- ions in solution, the solubility of CaF_2.

17-20. The specific conductance of a saturated barium sulfate solution at 25°C is reported as $3.590 \times 10^{-4} \Omega^{-1} m^{-1}$. The water from which the solution was made had a specific conductance of $0.618 \times 10^{-4} \Omega^{-1} m^{-1}$. What is the solubility product of barium sulfate at 25°C?

17-21. In aqueous solutions chlorine is hydrolyzed, to some extent, according to the reaction $Cl_2 + H_2O \rightleftharpoons H^+ + Cl^- + HOCl$. The hypochlorous acid is not appreciably dissociated in this solution. At 25°C the specific conductance of a 0.0246 M chlorine solution was found to be $0.68 \Omega^{-1} m^{-1}$. What fraction of Cl_2 has been hydrolyzed?

17-22. (a) Calculate the energy required to dissociate 1 mol of NaCl in the solvents acetonitrile and benzene, which have dielectric constants 39 and 2.3, respectively. Ignoring the entropy change accompanying dissociation and the solvation of the ions (which is in fact very important in the polar solvents), use Boltzmann's distribution to deduce the relative amounts of dissociated and undissociated NaCl in (b) benzene, (c) acetonitrile, and (d) water at 25°C.

17-23. Calculate the ionic strengths of solutions that contain (a) 0.30 M $CaCl_2$, (b) 0.30 M Na_3PO_4, (c) 0.10 M Na_2SO_4 and 0.2 M NaCl, (d) 0.0078 M acetic acid, which is 4.8 percent dissociated, and 0.5 M dioxane.

17-24. What is the ionic strength of an 0.0078 M aqueous solution of acetic acid?

17-25. If the mean-activity coefficient of the ions formed from the dissociation of Na_3PO_4 is 0.887 in a certain solution, what is the activity coefficient $\gamma_+^3\gamma_-$ of the salt?

17-26. If the activity coefficient for $CaCl_2$ in a 0.1 M solution is 0.515, what is the mean-activity coefficient for the ions?

17-27. For 1 M solutions at 25°C the activities a_+a_- of the electrolytes NaCl, $NaNO_3$, HNO_3, and HCl are 0.657, 0.548, 0.724, and 0.809, respectively. Show that these data are such that the activities of electrolytes could not be broken down into contributions from the separate ions, as was done, for example, for conductivities at infinite dilution.

17-28. According to the limiting law of the Debye-Hückel theory, calculate the activity coefficient of Ba^{2+} and of Cl^- and the mean-activity coefficient of $BaCl_2$ in a 0.0050 M aqueous solution at 25°C.

17-29. According to the limiting form of the Debye-Hückel theory, calculate the activity coefficients of each of the ions Na^+, SO_4^{2-}, OH^-, and H^+ in a solution that contains both 0.003 M Na_2SO_4 and 0.001 M NaOH.

17-30. Calculate the activity coefficients for the hydrogen and the acetate ion in a solution which is 0.0078 M in acetic acid. The degree of dissociation at this concentration is 4.8 percent.

17-31. From the conductance data of Table 17-2 and the limiting law of the Debye-Hückel theory, deduce the mean-activity coefficient of the ions of NH_4OH in the concentration range for which data are given.

17-32. Do the following data support the idea that the activity coefficients of ions are functions of the ionic strength of the solutions containing the ions?

Solubility of TlCl in Solutions Containing K_2SO_4 and Solutions Containing KNO_3 at 25°C

K_2SO_4, mol liter^{-1}	TlCl, mol liter^{-1}	KNO_3, mol liter^{-1}	TlCl, mole liter^{-1}
0	0.01607	0	0.01607
0.01	0.01779	0.02	0.01716
0.025	0.01942	0.05	0.01826
0.050	0.02137	0.10	0.01961
0.015	0.02600	0.30	0.02313
0.50	0.03417	1.00	0.03072

Source: W. C. Bray and W. J. Winninghoff, *J. Am. Chem. Soc.*, **33**:1663 (1911).

17-33. Using the data of Prob. 17-32, calculate the thermodynamic solubility product of TlCl at 25°C and the mean-activity coefficient of the Tl^+ and Cl^- in K_2SO_4 and KNO_3.

17-34. (a) Using the data of Prob. 17-33, plot $\log \gamma_+$ versus $\sqrt{\mu}$ for K_2SO_4 and for KNO_3 solutions. (b) Add the curves for the Debye-Hückel limiting law and for the relation of Eq. (17-75).

17-35. The following data are given (C. W. Davies, *J. Chem. Soc.*, **1930**: 2410) for the solubility of thallous iodate at 25°C in solutions containing various amounts of KCl:

KCl, mol liter^{-1}	0	0.01	0.02	0.05	0.10
$TlIO_3$, mol liter^{-1}	1.844×10^{-3}	2.005×10^{-3}	2.107×10^{-3}	2.335×10^{-3}	2.625×10^{-3}

Assuming that $TlIO_3$ is completely dissociated, calculate the mean-activity coefficient of $TlIO_3$ in each of the solutions. Compare the dependence of the activity coefficient on ionic strength with the limiting Debye-Hückel law and with the higher-ionic-strength behaviors of Figs. 17-14 and 17-15.

17-36. Use the data of Appendix Table B-2 and the Debye-Hückel limiting law to estimate the solubility at 25°C of calcium fluoride in a 0.01 M potassium chloride solution and compare with the solubility in pure water.

17-37. How would you interpret the tabulated data for the equivalent conductance of sodium iodide in acetone at 25°C?

NaI	Equivalent	NaI	Equivalent
0.0001	0.01736	0.0050	0.01245
0.0002	0.01717	0.0100	0.01097
0.0005	0.01646	0.0200	0.00950
0.0010	0.01550	0.0500	0.00761
0.0020	0.01432	0.1000	0.00641

REFERENCES

Some of the references listed here include discussion of electrochemical cells and activities and coefficients. These are not dealt with in this text until Chap. 18.

GURNEY, R. W.: "Ionic Processes in Solution," McGraw-Hill Book Company, New York, 1953.

ROBINSON, R. A., and R. H. STOKES: "Electrolyte Solutions," Butterworth & Co., Ltd., London, 1959.

MONK, C. B.: "Electrolytic Dissociation," Academic Press, Inc., New York, 1961.

DAVIES, C. W.: "Ion Association," Butterworth & Co., Ltd., London, 1962.

FUOSS, R. M.: "Electrolytic Conductance," Interscience Publishers, Inc., New York, 1959.

KORTUM, G.: "Treatise on Electrochemistry," 2d ed., Elsevier Publishing Company, Amsterdam, 1965. A revised edition of a comprehensive treatment of electrochemistry.

HARNED, H. S., and B. B. OWEN: "The Physical Chemistry of Electrolytic Solutions," Reinhold Publishing Corporation, New York, 1958.

VINCENT, C. A.: The Motion of Ions in Solution under the Influence of an Electric Field, *J. Chem. Educ.*, **53**:490 (1976).

THE ELECTROMOTIVE FORCE OF CHEMICAL CELLS

In previous treatments of the thermodynamics of chemical reactions, quantitative use could not be made of the fact that the useful work which can theoretically be obtained from the reaction is a measure of the free-energy change accompanying the reaction. It was necessary to develop devious ways of determining free-energy changes from measurable thermal quantities.

In this chapter arrangements are considered whereby the work done during a reversible chemical change can be determined. The procedure leads to a direct and frequently very accurate measurement of the free-energy change of the system. The arrangement consists in allowing the reaction to proceed at a state of balance in an electrochemical cell and determining the work electrically.

The balanced, or reversible, state of the electrochemical cell can easily be upset by varying the voltage applied to the cell. Then an appreciable current, corresponding to a net reaction in the cell, flows through the cell and the external electric circuit. In studying such systems we are introduced to the subject of electrokinetics, an example of the larger field of chemical kinetics to be dealt with in the following chapter.

As in other thermodynamic and kinetic studies, we need not necessarily be concerned with theories of the molecular and ionic behavior of the system being studied. Both the thermodynamic and kinetic data, however, can be used to explore the nature of ionic solutions and solid-solution interfaces.

18-1 Types of Electrodes

Although an electrochemical cell requires two electrodes for an electrochemical reaction to occur and its electrical consequences to be measured, the nature of the cells that can be constructed is best introduced in terms of the individual electrodes. The electrode, including the electrode itself and the reagents that are involved with it, is called the *half-cell*, and the component of the total chemical reaction that occurs in the half-cell is the *half reaction*, or *electrode reaction*.

Gas electrodes A gas can be induced to participate in an electrochemical reaction by means of an electrode like that of Fig. 18-1. An example that is important in the development of electrochemical data is the hydrogen electrode illustrated. The electrode is such that on the surface of the inert-metal electrode

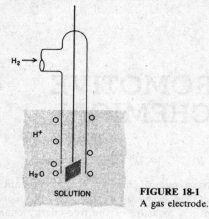

FIGURE 18-1
A gas electrode.

the reagents $H_2(g)$, $H^+(aq)$, or $H_3O^+(aq)$ and e^-, the latter in the metallic conductor, can be accommodated. The electrode reaction that can then proceed is

$$H^+ + e^- \rightleftharpoons \tfrac{1}{2}H_2 \tag{18-1}$$

written, as is the convention, as a reduction reaction. The electrode assembly in which this reaction can proceed is indicated, without producing a diagram like Fig. 18-1, by

$$Pt|H_2(P \text{ atm})|H^+(c \text{ mol liter}^{-1}) \tag{18-2}$$

The vertical lines indicate interfaces between physical states, and the significant features of these states are indicated. The symbol Pt is more restricted than necessary, being used here to imply any inert-metal electrode.

Oxidation-reduction electrodes Although all electrodes involve oxidation-reduction reactions in the sense that electrons are being gained or lost at the electrode, this term is generally used for electrodes consisting of an inert metal dipping into a solution containing two different oxidation states of a species. An example consists of a platinum wire dipping into a solution containing ferrous and ferric ions. Such a cell is described by

$$Pt|Fe^{2+}(c_1), \ Fe^{3+}(c_2)$$

The comma is used to separate the two chemical species which are in the same solution. These electrodes are similar to the gas electrodes except that the two species involved in the electrode reaction are ions. The electrode reaction in the example is

$$Fe^{3+} + e^- \rightleftharpoons Fe^{2+} \tag{18-3}$$

and there is the possibility of the electrode's either donating or accepting electrons.

Oxidation-reduction electrodes can also be made with organic molecules that can exist in two different oxidation states. A generally used material of this type that is related to important biochemical oxidation-reduction reagents is the system of hydroquinone and quinone, which can form the oxidation-reduction system

$$\text{(structure)} + 2H^+ + 2e^- \rightleftharpoons \text{(structure)} \tag{18-4}$$

The presence of a platinum electrode in a solution containing these two species again clearly provides an electrode that can donate or accept electrons. One usually represents hydroquinone by QH_2 and quinone by Q, and the electrode is then abbreviated as

$$Pt|QH_2, Q, H^+(c)$$

The occurrence of H^+ as a reagent in Eq. (18-4) makes it necessary also to state its concentration in the system. This electrode is generally known as the *quinhydrone* electrode, from the name of the crystalline compound $QH_2 \cdot Q$, in which form the material is added to the solution.

Metal–metal-ion electrodes The simplest of the electrodes in which the electrode material plays a chemical role is one in which a metal electrode dips into a solution containing ions of the metal. An example is that of a metallic silver electrode in a silver nitrate solution. The electrode is represented as

$$Ag|Ag^+(c)$$

and the electrode reaction is

$$Ag^+ + e^- \rightleftharpoons Ag \tag{18-5}$$

Such an electrode can be set up with any metal that is of intermediate activity. Very active metals react directly with the water itself and cannot be used for such an electrode.

Amalgam electrodes A variation of the previous electrode is one in which the metal is in the form of an amalgam, i.e., is dissolved in mercury, rather than in the pure form. Electrical contact is made by a platinum wire dipping into the amalgam pool. The reaction is the same as in the metal–metal-ion electrode, the mercury playing no chemical role.

The particular value of amalgam electrodes is that active metals like sodium can be used in such electrodes. A sodium-amalgam electrode is represented as

$$\text{Na(in Hg at } c_1)|\text{Na}^+(c_2)$$

where the concentration of the sodium metal in the mercury as well as that of the sodium ion in the solution must be given. In addition to allowing the study of active metals, the amalgam electrode illustrates some of the thermodynamic relations which will be obtained for electrochemical cells.

Metal–insoluble-salt electrodes A more elaborate but usually satisfactory and frequently used electrode consists of a metal in contact with an insoluble salt of the metal, which in turn is in contact with a solution containing the anion of the salt. An example is represented as

$$\text{Ag}|\text{AgCl}|\text{Cl}^-(c)$$

The electrode process at such an electrode is

$$
\begin{aligned}
\text{Ag}^+ + e^- &\rightleftharpoons \text{Ag} \\
\text{AgCl}(s) &\rightleftharpoons \text{Ag}^+ + \text{Cl}^- \\
\hline
\text{AgCl}(s) + e^- &\rightleftharpoons \text{Ag} + \text{Cl}^-
\end{aligned}
\tag{18-6}
$$

The electrode reaction involves only the concentration of Cl^- as a variable, in contrast with the $\text{Ag}|\text{Ag}^+$ electrode, which has the Ag^+ concentration as a variable.

The most frequently used electrode of this type, the *calomel electrode,* consists of metallic mercury in contact with calomel, Hg_2Cl_2, which is in contact with a chloride solution. Figure 18-2 shows the usual arrangement of this electrode. The electrode reaction is

$$
\begin{aligned}
\text{Hg}^+ + e^- &\rightleftharpoons \text{Hg} \\
\tfrac{1}{2}\text{Hg}_2\text{Cl}_2 &\rightleftharpoons \text{Hg}^+ + \text{Cl}^- \\
\hline
\tfrac{1}{2}\text{Hg}_2\text{Cl}_2 + e^- &\rightleftharpoons \text{Hg} + \text{Cl}^-
\end{aligned}
\tag{18-7}
$$

The calomel electrode is quite easily prepared and is frequently used. The electrode is generally made with a chloride solution of 0.1 M, 1.0 M, or saturated KCl. The saturated calomel electrode is the most common, and for this electrode the calomel is ground up with solid KCl, and the solution is a saturated KCl solution. For this electrode the concentration of the chloride is therefore

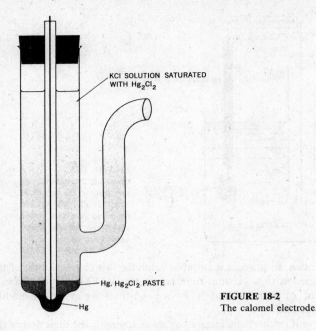

KCl SOLUTION SATURATED
WITH Hg_2Cl_2

Hg, Hg_2Cl_2 PASTE

Hg

FIGURE 18-2
The calomel electrode.

fixed at a given temperature, and one has an electrode whose emf is completely determined. This, as we shall see, is sometimes convenient.

18-2 Electrochemical Cells, EMFs, and Cell Reactions

When pairs of electrodes like those of Sec. 18-1 are combined and are connected by an external electrical conductor, an electric current will flow and chemical reactions will occur in the two half-cells. Combining electrodes is done without complication if both electrodes can operate in the same solution, as in the example of Fig. 18-3. When this is not tolerated, a connection must be made between the solutions that allows ionic conduction to occur between the half-cells but prevents mixing of the two half-cell solutions. A KCl *salt bridge*, illustrated in the assembly of Fig. 18-4, is often used. Such a coupling device, indicated by a double vertical line in a cell diagram, has no net influence on the cell reaction, and although some difficulties are introduced into the quantitative interpretation of the cell voltage, or *electromotive force* (emf), we shall set these problems aside for the time being.

The voltage, or emf, of a cell like that of Fig. 18-3 or 18-4 can be measured by placing a voltmeter across the terminals. However, it would be found that the measured voltage would depend on the current that is drawn off by the voltmeter. The maximum voltage is found to be that produced in the limit as

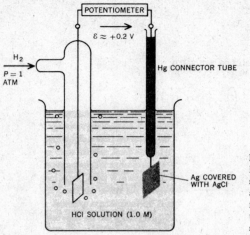

FIGURE 18-3
Electrode arrangement corresponding to the cell $Pt|H_2(1 atm)|HCl(1.0 M)|AgCl|Ag$ for a cell in which both electrodes can operate in the same solution.

zero current is drawn. In practice a suitable value for this characteristic of the cell can be obtained with a vacuum-tube voltmeter (VTVM), which draws a very small current, or more accurately, by a potentiometer arrangement like that shown in Fig. 18-5.

In reporting emf results from laboratory measurements the direction of the electron flow would be given, as well as the numerical value of the emf. This direction can be indicated along with the diagram of the electrochemical cell by agreeing that *the emf will be called positive if there is a tendency for electrons to*

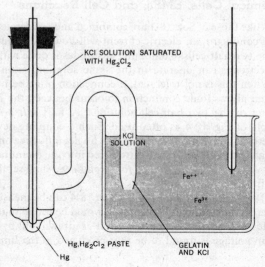

FIGURE 18-4
A cell composed of two electrodes whose solutions cannot be mixed.

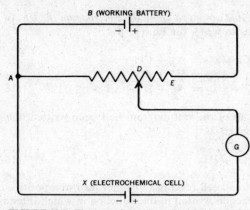

FIGURE 18-5 The potentiometric method for measuring the voltage produced by an electrochemical cell operating at a state of balance. A fraction AD/AE of the working battery can be picked off to produce a voltage that drives a current in the lower circuit in the direction opposite that in which the electrochemical cell drives the current. When position D is such that no current flows in the lower circuit, as determined by the galvanometer, the voltage of the electrochemical cell at a state of balance is obtained as AD/AE times the voltage of the working battery.

be driven through the external circuit from the electrode written on the left to the electrode written on the right. For example, the electrochemical cell of Fig. 18-3 is found to drive electrons from the hydrogen electrode to the silver electrode with an emf of about 0.2 V. This could be reported by writing the cell as

$$Pt|H_2(1 \text{ atm})|HCl(1.0 \text{ } M)|AgCl|Ag \qquad (18\text{-}8)$$

and giving the emf as $+0.2$ V. If the cell were described as

$$Ag|AgCl|HCl(1.0 \text{ } M)|H_2(1 \text{ atm})|Pt \qquad (18\text{-}9)$$

the emf would be reported as -0.2 V. In either case the emf values show that there is a tendency for electrons to be driven through the external circuit from the hydrogen to the silver electrode is shown.

Under balanced, reversible conditions a cell reaction can proceed in either direction, and we must therefore agree on a procedure for writing the cell reaction so that when a free-energy change is deduced from the electrical work the cell can perform, the free-energy change will be of appropriate sign for the direction in which the reaction is written.

It is the convention that once a diagram of a cell is written, *the cell reaction will be written so that electrons are accepted from the external circuit by the electrode written on the right and are given up by the electrode on the left.* In the above example, this leads us to write, for Eq. (18-8),

Right electrode: $\quad AgCl + e^- \rightleftharpoons Ag + Cl^-$
Left electrode: $\quad\quad\quad \frac{1}{2}H_2 \rightleftharpoons H^+ + e^-$
Cell reaction: $\quad\overline{AgCl + \frac{1}{2}H_2 \rightleftharpoons Ag + H^+ + Cl^-}$ $\qquad$ (18-10)

If the second form, Eq. (18-9) of the cell diagram had been written, the cell reaction would have to be given as

$$Ag + H^+ + Cl^- \rightleftharpoons AgCl + \frac{1}{2}H_2 \qquad\qquad (18\text{-}11)$$

The conventions on cell emf and cell reactions together lead to a positive emf being associated with the reaction written in the direction in which it tends to proceed.

18-3 Free-Energy Changes for Cell Reactions

When the emf of a cell is measured with the reaction proceeding at a state of balance, or reversibly, the work that can be obtained from the cell current is the maximum work, over and above any PV work, that can be delivered to the mechanical reservoir. Thus, in view of the analysis of free energy in Sec. 8-1, this work is equal to the free-energy change accompanying the cell reaction.

The electrical work done by a cell as it drives an Avogadro's number of electrons through an opposing voltage, as imposed, for example, by a potentiometer arrangement, is equal to the product of the total charge of these electrons and the voltage through which this charge is driven. We have already seen that this charge, 96,490 C, of a mole of electrons is the faraday $\mathcal{F}$. With this notation, the work produced as n mol of electrons is driven by the cell emf $\mathcal{E}$ through a nearly equal balancing voltage is

$$\Delta E_{\text{mech res}} = n\mathcal{F}\mathcal{E} \qquad\qquad (18\text{-}12)$$

This mechanical energy, being the maximum useful work the reaction can produce, is equal to the *decrease* in the free energy of the reacting system as a result of the process described by the cell reaction. Thus we have

$$\Delta G = -n\mathcal{F}\mathcal{E} \qquad\qquad (18\text{-}13)$$

where $\mathcal{E}$ is the reversible emf of the cell. Note that the sign of $\Delta E_{\text{mech res}}$, and thus of ΔG, is such that for the spontaneous direction of reaction, which is associated with a positive emf, we do obtain the necessary negative ΔG.

Thus, for the cell reaction of Eq. (18-10) and the $\mathcal{E}$ value of $+0.2$ V, we obtain

$$AgCl + \tfrac{1}{2}H_2 \rightleftharpoons Ag + H^+Cl^-$$
$$\Delta G = -(1)(96{,}490)(+0.2) = -20 \text{ kJ} \qquad (18\text{-}14)$$

18-4 Standard EMFs and Electrode Potentials

A method for the presentation of the data obtained from measurements of the equilibrium emf of electrochemical cells must now be developed. One expects (a thermodynamic proof of this will be given in Sec. 18-5) that varying the concentration of any reagents involved in the electrode process will affect the emf of the cell. In view of this, the emfs of cells with the reagents at standard states are reported. In keeping with the standard states introduced in Chap. 8, these standard-state conditions are again chosen to consist of gases at unit activity, implying for most gases approximately 1 atm pressure, and solutes also at unit activity. For solutes, which for electrochemical cells are frequently ions, the activities can be quite appreciably different from molar concentrations. How activity coefficients can be determined from emf measurements will shortly be explained. For the present it is sufficient to recognize that a standard state is chosen and that the emfs that cells would have for their variable reagents at unit activity are tabulated.

It is impractical, however, to list the emfs of all possible combinations of electrodes. It would be much more convenient to have some means of tabulating the relative electron-accepting powers of the individual electrodes. This can be done by tabulating the emfs of cells composed of a selected reference electrode and a variety of other electrodes. Quite arbitrarily, it is agreed that the hydrogen electrode, with a hydrogen pressure of 1 atm and a unit hydrogen-ion activity in the solution, be used as the reference electrode.

Tabulations like that of Table 18-1 can then be given of the emfs measured for cells with the standard hydrogen electrode on the left and another electrode on the right. For example,

$$Pt|H_2(1 \text{ atm})|HCl(a = 1)|Cl_2(1 \text{ atm})|Pt \qquad (18\text{-}15)$$

The emf of this particular cell is found to be $+1.3595$ V, and it is this value which is given in Table 18-1 for the $Pt|Cl_2|Cl^-$ electrode.

Such tabulated values can also be interpreted as electrode emfs based on a zero emf being assigned to the reference hydrogen electrode. If the value is that which would occur for all reagents at unit activity, such electrode emfs are known as *standard electrode potentials,* indicated by the symbol $\mathcal{U}^\circ$. The hydrogen-chlorine cell data can now be interpreted as

Right electrode:	$\tfrac{1}{2}Cl_2 + e^- \rightleftharpoons Cl^-$	$\mathcal{U}^\circ = +1.3595$ V
Left electrode:	$\tfrac{1}{2}H_2 \rightleftharpoons H^+ + e^-$	$\mathcal{U}^\circ = \quad 0$
Cell reaction:	$\tfrac{1}{2}Cl_2 + \tfrac{1}{2}H_2 \rightleftharpoons Cl^- + H^+$	$\mathcal{E}^\circ = +1.3595$ V

$$(18\text{-}16)$$

TABLE 18-1 Some Standard Electrode Potentials for Aqueous Solutions at 25°C

Electrode	Electrode reaction	$\mathcal{U}°$, V
	Acid solution ($a_{H^+} = 1$)	
$Pt\|F_2\|F^-$	$F_2(g) + 2e^- = 2F^-$	$+2.87$
$Pt\|H_2O_2\|H^+$	$H_2O_2 + 2H^+ + 2e^- = 2H_2O$	$+1.77$
$Pt\|Mn^{2+}, MnO_4^-$	$MnO_4^- + 8H^+ + 5e^- = Mn^{2+} + 4H_2O$	$+1.51$
$Pt\|Cl_2\|Cl^-$	$Cl_2 + 2e^- = 2Cl^-$	$+1.3595$
$Pt\|Tl^+, Tl^{3+}$	$Tl^{3+} + 2e^- = Tl^+$	$+1.25$
$Pt\|Br_2\|Br^-$	$Br_2 + 2e^- = 2Br^-$	$+1.065$
$Ag\|Ag^+$	$Ag^+ + e^- = Ag$	$+0.7991$
$Pt\|Fe^{2+}, Fe^{3+}$	$Fe^{3+} + e^- = Fe^{2+}$	$+0.771$
$Pt\|O_2\|H_2O_2$	$O_2 + 2H^+ + 2e^- = H_2O_2$	$+0.682$
$Pt\|I_2\|I^-$	$I_3^- + 2e^- = 3I^-$	$+0.536$
$Cu\|Cu^{2+}$	$Cu^{2+} + 2e^- = Cu$	$+0.337$
$Pt\|Hg\|Hg_2Cl_2\|Cl^-$	$Hg_2Cl_2 + 2e^- = 2Cl^- + 2Hg$	$+0.2676$
$Ag\|AgCl\|Cl^-$	$AgCl + e^- = Ag + Cl^-$	$+0.2225$
$Pt\|Cu^+, Cu^{2+}$	$Cu^{2+} + e^- = Cu^+$	$+0.153$
$Cu\|CuCl\|Cl^-$	$CuCl + e^- = Cu + Cl^-$	$+0.137$
$Ag\|AgBr\|Br^-$	$AgBr + e^- = Ag + Br^-$	$+0.0713$
$Pt\|H_2\|H^+$	$2H^+ + 2e^- = H_2$	0.0000
$Pb\|Pb^{2+}$	$Pb^{2+} + 2e^- = Pb$	-0.126
$Ag\|AgI\|I^-$	$AgI + e^- = Ag + I^-$	-0.1518
$Cu\|CuI\|I^-$	$CuI + e^- = Cu + I^-$	-0.1852
$Pb\|PbSO_4\|SO_4^{2-}$	$PbSO_4 + 2e^- = Pb + SO_4^{2-}$	-0.3588
$Pt\|Ti^{2+}, Ti^{3+}$	$Ti^{3+} + e^- = Ti^{2+}$	-0.369
$Cd\|Cd^{2+}$	$Cd^{2+} + 2e^- = Cd$	-0.403
$Fe\|Fe^{2+}$	$Fe^{2+} + 2e^- = Fe$	-0.4402
$Cr\|Cr^{3+}$	$Cr^{3+} + 3e^- = Cr$	-0.744
$Zn\|Zn^{2+}$	$Zn^{2+} + 2e^- = Zn$	-0.7628
$Mn\|Mn^{2+}$	$Mn^{2+} + 2e^- = Mn$	-1.180
$Al\|Al^{3+}$	$Al^{3-} + 3e^- = Al$	-1.662
$Mg\|Mg^{2+}$	$Mg^{2+} + 2e^- = Mg$	-2.363
$Na\|Na^+$	$Na^+ + e^- = Na$	-2.7142
$Ca\|Ca^{2+}$	$Ca^{2+} + 2e^- = Ca$	-2.866
$Ba\|Ba^{2+}$	$Ba^{2+} + 2e^- = Ba$	-2.906
$K\|K^+$	$K^+ + e^- = K$	-2.925
$Li\|Li^+$	$Li^+ + e^- = Li$	-3.045
	Basic solution ($a_{OH^-} = 1$)	
$Pt\|MnO_2\|MnO_4^-$	$MnO_4^- + 2H_2O + 3e^- = MnO_2 + 4OH^-$	$+0.588$
$Pt\|O_2\|OH^-$	$O_2 + 2H_2O + 4e^- = 4OH^-$	$+0.401$
$Pt\|S\|S^{2-}$	$S + 2e^- = S^{2-}$	-0.447
$Pt\|H_2\|OH^-$	$2H_2O + 2e^- = H_2 + 2OH^-$	-0.82806
$Pt\|SO_3^{2-}, SO_4^{2-}$	$SO_4^{2-} + H_2O + 2e^- = SO_3^- + 2OH^-$	-0.93

Source: Mostly from a compilation by A. J. deBethune, T. S. Licht, and N. Swendeman, *J. Electrochem. Soc.*, **106**:616 (1959).

The emf of any cell with the reagents in their standard states, not necessarily involving the hydrogen electrode, can be used to obtain data for the standard electrode potentials listed in Table 18-1. Thus the cell

$$Pt|Cl_2(1 \text{ atm})|HCl(a = 1)|AgCl(s)|Ag$$

is found to have an $\mathcal{E}°$ value of -1.1370 V. This cell emf can be interpreted in terms of the standard *electrode potentials* $\mathcal{V}°$ as

$$\text{Cell emf} = \mathcal{V}°(\text{right electrode}) - \mathcal{V}°(\text{left electrode})$$

or

$$-1.1370 = \mathcal{V}°_{Ag,AgCl} - (+1.3595)$$

and

$$\mathcal{V}°_{Ag,AgCl} = 0.2225 \text{ V} \tag{18-17}$$

By such means, convenient pairs of electrodes can be selected and electrode potentials determined. Table 18-1 shows the results that are obtained for the more common electrodes. These standard electrode potentials can be called reduction potentials because the listed numbers give the relative tendency for the electrode reaction to proceed with the gain of electrons, i.e., for reduction to occur. The electrodes at the top of the table, with the most positive values of $\mathcal{V}°$, have a high tendency to accept electrons. Those low down in the table have a relatively greater tendency to donate electrons.

The use of this table in calculating a cell emf can be illustrated by the example of the cell

$$Pt|Tl^+(a = 1), Tl^{3+}(a = 1)||Cl^-(a = 1)|Hg_2Cl_2(s)|Hg$$

The electrode reactions and the emfs due to the electrodes can be combined to give

Right electrode:
$$\tfrac{1}{2}Hg_2Cl_2 + e^- \rightleftharpoons Hg + Cl^- \qquad\qquad \mathcal{V}°_{Hg|Hg_2Cl_2|Cl^-} = +0.2676$$
Left electrode:
$$\tfrac{1}{2}Tl^+ \rightleftharpoons \tfrac{1}{2}Tl^{3+} + e^- \qquad\qquad -\mathcal{V}°_{Tl^+,Tl^{3+}} = -1.25$$

Overall reaction:
$$\tfrac{1}{2}Tl^+ + \tfrac{1}{2}Hg_2Cl_2 \rightleftharpoons \tfrac{1}{2}Tl^{3+} + Hg + Cl^- \qquad\qquad \mathcal{E}° = -0.98 \text{ V} \tag{18-18}$$

Furthermore, for the overall reaction

$$\Delta G^\circ = -n\mathcal{F}\mathcal{E}^\circ = -(1)(96{,}500)(-0.98) = 94{,}500 \text{ J} \qquad (18\text{-}19)$$

The calculation tells us that the current will tend to flow through the external circuit from the electrode written on the right to that written on the left and that the reaction will tend to proceed spontaneously in the direction opposite that in which it is written in Eq. (18-18).

A point that should be mentioned is that one can write the reactions, such as those in the example, with one or two electrons exhibited. If two electrons are shown, this corresponds to 2 equiv of reactants, and the free-energy change will be twice as much as for 1 equiv. The emf, of course, will not be altered by a change in the amount of material involved. We can therefore write

$$
\begin{array}{ll}
Hg_2Cl_2 + 2e^- \rightleftharpoons 2Hg + 2Cl^- & \mathcal{V}^\circ_{Hg|Hg_2Cl_2|Cl^-} = +0.2676 \\
Tl^+ \rightleftharpoons Tl^{3+} + 2e^- & -\mathcal{V}^\circ_{Tl^{3+},Tl^+} = -1.25 \\
\hline
Tl^+ + Hg_2Cl_2 \rightleftharpoons Tl^{3+} + 2Hg + 2Cl^- & \mathcal{E}^\circ = -0.98 \text{ V}
\end{array}
$$
$$(18\text{-}20)$$

For the overall reaction as written, we calculate

$$\Delta G^\circ = -n\mathcal{F}\mathcal{E}^\circ = -(2)(96{,}500)(-0.98) = +189{,}000 \text{ J} \qquad (18\text{-}21)$$

Equations (18-20) and (18-21) show that the free-energy change as a result of the consumption of 1 mol, that is, 472 g, of mercurous chloride in this way is 189,000 J. Equations (18-18) and (18-19) show that for the consumption of $\frac{1}{2}$ mol, or 236 g, the free-energy change is 94,500 J. The free-energy change depends, as is seen by the n in the equation, $\Delta G^\circ = -n\mathcal{F}\mathcal{E}^\circ$, on the amount of reagents being dealt with. The cell emf is independent of the amounts of reagents.

Calculations using the data of Table 18-1 yield only the emfs that electrochemical cells will have if all the reagents are at unit activity. It is now necessary to see how these emfs are related to actual experimental conditions.

18-5 The Concentration and Activity Dependence of the EMF

The dependence of the emf of a cell on the concentration, or more directly on the activity, of the variable reagents can be calculated from our knowledge of the relation between the free energy and the activity.

Consider an electrochemical cell for which the overall chemical reaction is

$$a\text{A} + b\text{B} \rightleftharpoons c\text{C} + d\text{D} \qquad (18\text{-}22)$$

Further, suppose that A, B, C, and D are reagents whose concentration can be varied; i.e., they are gases, or solutes in aqueous solution. If, in addition, there are solids involved in the reaction, they will contribute only a constant term to the results, as we shall see.

For species A the free energy of 1 mol can be written

$$\bar{G}_A = G_A^\circ + RT \ln a_A \tag{18-23}$$

and for a mol of reagent A, the free energy is

$$a\bar{G}_A = aG_A^\circ + aRT \ln a_A = aG_A^\circ + RT \ln (a_A)^a \tag{18-24}$$

From expressions like these for all four reagents, the free-energy change for the overall cell reaction can be deduced, as was done in Chap. 8, and it gives

$$\Delta G = \Delta G^\circ + RT \ln \frac{(a_C)^c (a_D)^d}{(a_A)^a (a_B)^b} \tag{18-25}$$

where ΔG° is the difference in free energy of the products and the reactants when all reagents are in their standard states. Furthermore, according to the discussion of Sec. 18-3,

$$\Delta G = -n\mathcal{F}\mathcal{E} \qquad \text{and} \qquad \Delta G^\circ = -n\mathcal{F}\mathcal{E}^\circ$$

which gives

$$\mathcal{E} = \mathcal{E}^\circ - \frac{RT}{n\mathcal{F}} \ln \frac{(a_C)^c (a_D)^d}{(a_A)^a (a_B)^b} \tag{18-26}$$

This expression for the activity dependence, or approximately the concentration dependence, of emf is known as the *Nernst equation*.

This important equation shows how the emf of a cell can be calculated from the emf for all reagents in their standard states and the activities of the reagents. It is clear that when the activities of all the reagents are unity, the logarithmic term drops out and $\mathcal{E} = \mathcal{E}^\circ$, that is, the emf for the standard states.

At 25°C, the temperature at which most standard electrode potentials are reported, the factor before the logarithm term can be explicitly worked out and gives

$$\mathcal{E} = \mathcal{E}^\circ - \frac{0.05915}{n} \log \frac{(a_C)^c (a_D)^d}{(a_A)^a (a_B)^b} \tag{18-27}$$

Included in the numerical factor is the term 2.3026 for the conversion from natural logarithms to logarithms to the base 10.

It should be recognized that the activity term has the familiar form of the equilibrium-constant expression. The activities of the reagents, however, have the values that are determined by the solutions used to make up the cell. These are not generally the equilibrium values.

As in the development of the equilibrium-constant expression, the activities of solid or otherwise fixed-concentration reagents are not explicitly included. The contribution to the free energy and the emf of the cell of such reagents is implicitly included in the $\Delta G°$ and $\mathcal{E}°$ terms.

The use of Eq. (18-27) is illustrated by the calculation of the emf of the cell

$$\text{Pt}|\text{H}_2(g)\text{pressure}P\,|\text{HCl,activity}a\,|\text{AgCl}|\text{Ag}$$

The overall reaction and the standard emf are calculated from the reactions and the data of Table 18-1 as follows:

Right electrode:
$$\text{AgCl} + e^- \rightarrow \text{Ag} + \text{Cl}^-(a) \qquad\qquad \mathcal{V}° = +0.2225$$
Left electrode:
$$\tfrac{1}{2}\text{H}_2 \rightarrow \text{H}^+(a) + e^- \qquad\qquad -\mathcal{V}° = \ \ 0$$

Overall reaction:
$$\tfrac{1}{2}\text{H}_2 + \text{AgCl} \rightarrow \text{Ag} + \text{H}^+(a) + \text{Cl}^-(a) \qquad \mathcal{E}° = +0.2225 \text{ V}$$
$$(18\text{-}28)$$

Equation (18-27) now gives

$$\mathcal{E} = \mathcal{E}° - \frac{0.05915}{1} \log \frac{(a_{\text{H}^+})(a_{\text{Cl}^-})}{(a_{\text{H}_2})^{1/2}} \qquad (18\text{-}29)$$

To proceed to a calculated emf we need to know the activities of H^+ and Cl^- for an HCl solution of a given concentration and for H_2 at its given pressure. The methods of Sec. 9-5 yield the necessary solute activities, and those of Sec. 8-8 or 8-9 give the necessary activity-pressure relations for a gas. In practice, however, ionic activities are often determined by the measurement of the cell emf and the deduction, by use of Eq. (18-29), of the activities. The procedure will be shown in the following section.

18-6 Activities from EMF Measurements

The unknowns in an equation like Eq. (18-29) for the emf of a cell are really both the activities of the variable concentration species *and* the standard emf $\mathcal{E}°$. Tabulated values of the latter have already been given, but now we must see how they are determined. This determination can be seen to be related to the measurement of activities since $\mathcal{E}°$ values are defined as the cell emf for reagents at unit activity.

Consider again the cell

$$\text{Pt}|\text{H}_2(1 \text{ atm})|\text{HCl}(c)|\text{AgCl}(s)|\text{Ag}$$

At a pressure of 1 atm, hydrogen will behave ideally, and its activity will be very nearly equal to its pressure. Then Eq. (18-29) becomes

$$\mathcal{E} = \mathcal{E}° - \frac{0.05915}{1} \log \frac{(a_{H^+})(a_{Cl^-})}{(P_{H_2})^{1/2}} \tag{18-30}$$

At a hydrogen pressure of 1 atm this becomes

$$\mathcal{E} = \mathcal{E}° - 0.05915 \log (a_{H^+})(a_{Cl^-}) \tag{18-31}$$

In terms of concentrations and activity coefficients the expression can be written

$$\begin{aligned}\mathcal{E} &= \mathcal{E}° - 0.05915 \log (\gamma_+[H^+]\gamma_-[Cl^-]) \\ &= \mathcal{E}° - 0.05915 \log \gamma_+\gamma_- - 0.05915 \log [H^+][Cl^-]\end{aligned} \tag{18-32}$$

The brackets imply that the concentrations expressed here are molar concentrations. The directly measurable quantities are now rearranged to the left side of the equation to give

$$\mathcal{E} + 0.05915 \log [H^+][Cl^-] = \mathcal{E}° - 0.05915 \log \gamma_+\gamma_- \tag{18-33}$$

Furthermore, for solutions containing appreciable HCl, the concentrations of H^+ and Cl^- are equal and correspond to c, the hydrochloric acid concentration. Let us also introduce the *mean-activity coefficient* $\gamma_\pm$, defined as $\sqrt{\gamma_+\gamma_-}$, for each of these activity coefficients. Then

$$\mathcal{E} + 0.05915 \log c^2 = \mathcal{E}° - 0.05915 \log \gamma_\pm^2 \tag{18-34}$$

and finally

$$\mathcal{E} + 0.11830 \log c = \mathcal{E}° - 0.11830 \log \gamma_\pm \tag{18-35}$$

The right side of the equation is made up of a constant term and the logarithmic term. For solutions in the Debye-Hückel limiting-law region, this term can, according to Eq. (17-74), be expected to be proportional to $c^{1/2}$. The left side of the equation, which can be obtained from measurements of $\mathcal{E}$ and c, is therefore plotted against $c^{1/2}$, as shown in Fig. 18-6.

At $c = 0$ the activity coefficient must go to unity, and the logarithmic term on the right side of the equation will vanish. The extrapolation of the data of Fig. 18-6 to $c^{1/2} = 0$ gives, therefore, a value of $\mathcal{E}°$. In this way one finds

$$\mathcal{E}° = +0.2225 \text{ V} \tag{18-36}$$

The emf of this cell for the reagents in their standard states can be written

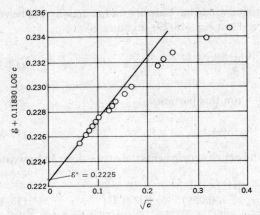

FIGURE 18-6 Determination of $\mathcal{E}°$ for the cell $Pt|H_2$ (1 atm)$|HCl(c)|AgCl(s)|Ag$ from the measured values of $\mathcal{E}$ at various concentrations of HCl. The straight-line extrapolation is drawn with the slope predicted by the Debye-Hückel limiting law. (*In part from L. P. Hammett, "Introduction to the Study of Physical Chemistry." Copyright 1952 by McGraw-Hill, Inc. Used by permission of McGraw-Hill Book Company.*)

$$\mathcal{E}° = \mathcal{V}°_{Ag,AgCl} - \mathcal{V}°_{H_2}$$

which, with $\mathcal{V}°_{H_2}$ taken as zero, yields

$$\mathcal{V}°_{Ag,AgCl} = 0.2225 \text{ V} \tag{18-37}$$

as given in Table 18-1. In a similar way the electrode potentials that other electrodes would have if all reagents were at unit activity can be obtained.

Now it can be shown how activity coefficients of HCl can also be determined from the data of Fig. 18-6. Reference to Eq. (18-35) shows that once a

TABLE 18-2 Mean-Activity Coefficients for HCl from the EMF of the Cell
$Pt|H_2(1 \text{ atm})|HCl(c)|AgCl(s)|Ag$

c_{HCl} mol liter^{-1}	$\mathcal{E}$, V	$\gamma_{\pm}$
0.003215	0.52053	0.942
0.005619	0.49257	0.926
0.009138	0.46860	0.909
0.013407	0.44974	0.895
0.02563	0.41824	0.866
0.1238	0.34199	0.788

value for $\mathcal{E}°$ is obtained, the measured value of the left side of the equation allows the calculation of the only remaining unknown, the $\log \gamma_{\pm}$ term. One obtains, therefore, as shown in Table 18-2, the mean-activity coefficients of HCl at any concentration for which emf data are available.

In a similar way, the activity coefficient of other electrolytes involved in an electrochemical reaction can be determined. As before, no way is found for determining the individual activity coefficients, and so again mean-activity coefficients are all that can be considered.

18-7 Equilibrium Constants and Solubility Products from EMF Data

The data of Table 18-1 constitute a wealth of information on the free energies of inorganic reactions. Although reported as emfs, these data are readily converted into free energies by the expression $\Delta G° = -n\mathcal{F}\mathcal{E}°$. Such free-energy data are of use in determining equilibrium properties and, in particular, the equilibrium constant for the overall cell reaction.

Consider, for example, the possibility of reducing ferric iron to ferrous iron by using metallic zinc as a reducing agent. The reaction in which one would be interested might be performed in the cell

$$Zn|Zn^{2+}||Fe^{3+}, Fe^{2+}|Pt$$

and the reaction would be

$$
\begin{aligned}
Fe^{3+} + e^- &\rightleftharpoons Fe^{2+} & \mathcal{U}°_{Fe^{2+}|Fe^{3+}} &= +0.771 \\
\tfrac{1}{2}Zn &\rightleftharpoons \tfrac{1}{2}Zn^{2+} + e^- & -\mathcal{U}°_{Zn|Zn^{2+}} &= +0.7628 \\
\hline
Fe^{3+} + \tfrac{1}{2}Zn &\rightleftharpoons Fe^{2+} + \tfrac{1}{2}Zn^{2+} & \mathcal{E}° &= +1.534 \text{ V}
\end{aligned}
\tag{18-38}
$$

The cell emf is written

$$\mathcal{E} = 1.534 - \frac{0.05915}{1} \log \frac{a_{Fe^{2+}}(a_{Zn^{2+}})^{1/2}}{a_{Fe^{3+}}} \tag{18-39}$$

At equilibrium the cell would be able to perform no useful work, and its emf must then be zero. For equilibrium activities of the variable reagents of Eq. (18-38) one therefore has $\mathcal{E} = 0$ and

$$1.534 = \frac{0.05915}{1} \log \left[\frac{a_{Fe^{2+}}(a_{Zn^{2+}})^{1/2}}{a_{Fe^{3+}}} \right]_{equil} \tag{18-40}$$

The activity expression is now the familiar equilibrium constant expressed correctly in activities. Thus

$$\left[\frac{a_{Fe^{2+}}(a_{Zn^{2+}})^{1/2}}{a_{Fe^{3+}}}\right]_{equil} = K = 8 \times 10^{25} \tag{18-41}$$

The result shows that essentially all the iron will be reduced to the ferrous state by zinc.

For some cells the overall reaction corresponds to the solution of an insoluble salt. In such cases the equilibrium constant that can be determined is a solubility product. This can be illustrated by the cell

$$Ag|Ag^+|Br^-|AgBr(s)|Ag$$

The electrode reactions and the emfs are

$$
\begin{array}{ll}
AgBr(s) + e^- \rightleftharpoons Ag + Br^- & \mho^\circ_{Ag|AgBr|Br^-} = +0.0713 \\
Ag \rightleftharpoons Ag^+ + e^- & -\mho^\circ_{Ag|Ag^+} = -0.7991 \\
\hline
AgBr(s) \rightleftharpoons Ag^+ + Br^- & \mathcal{E}^\circ = -0.7278 \text{ V}
\end{array}
\tag{18-42}
$$

The cell emf is written

$$\mathcal{E} = -0.7278 - \frac{0.05915}{1} \log (a_{Ag^+})(a_{Br^-}) \tag{18-43}$$

The solubility of silver bromide is very small, and if no other ions are present in appreciable amounts, the activity coefficients will be sufficiently close to unity to allow the activities to be replaced by concentrations. Again at equilibrium the emf of the cell will be zero and

$$0.7278 = -0.05915 \log ([Ag^+][Br^-])_{equil}$$

or

$$([Ag^+][Br^-])_{equil} = K_{solubil} = 4.8 \times 10^{-13} \tag{18-44}$$

The examples of this section are intended to show that the data of Table 18-1 can be used to determine the equilibrium constant for any reaction which is the overall reaction for a cell made from electrodes included in Table 18-1.

18-8 Electrode-Concentration Cells

A particularly simple electrochemical reaction is one that performs the dilution of either the electrode material itself, as studied here, or of the electrolyte, as treated in Sec. 18-9. For the electrode material to be involved in such a process, it must have a variable concentration. Gaseous and amalgam electrodes fall into this classification.

A cell can be constructed from amalgams with two different concentrations of the same metal. The cell

$$Pb\text{-}Hg(a_1)|PbSO_4(soln)|Hg\text{-}Pb(a_2)$$

allows the electrode reactions

$$
\begin{aligned}
Pb^{2+} + 2e^- &\rightleftharpoons Pb(a_2) \\
Pb(a_1) &\rightleftharpoons Pb^{2+} + 2e^- \\
\hline
Pb(a_1) &\rightleftharpoons Pb(a_2)
\end{aligned}
\tag{18-45}
$$

to be written. No chemical change occurs, and the reaction consists of the transfer of lead from an amalgam of one concentration to that of another concentration. The emf of such a cell, which necessarily has $\mathcal{E}° = 0$, is

$$\mathcal{E} = -\frac{0.05915}{2} \log \frac{a_2}{a_1} \tag{18-46}$$

The lead will tend to go spontaneously from the high-activity amalgam to that of low activity. For example, if a_1 is greater than a_2, $\mathcal{E}$ is positive and the reaction proceeds in the direction indicated.

One finds that solutions of metals in mercury constitute fairly ideal solutions and that the emfs are almost correctly calculated by using concentrations instead of activities. Table 18-3 shows some data which illustrate this.

The electrode-concentration cells consisting of gas electrodes can be illustrated by the cell

$$Pt|H_2(P_1)|HCl|H_2(P_2)|Pt$$

At all ordinary pressures hydrogen behaves very nearly ideally, and the emf corresponding to the overall cell reaction

$$H_2(P_1) \rightleftharpoons H_2(P_2) \tag{18-47}$$

TABLE 18-3 EMFs of Cadmium-Amalgam Electrode-Concentration Cells at 25°C

Cd, g per 100 g Hg		emf, V	
Left electrode	Right electrode	Observed	Calculated $= \dfrac{0.05915}{2} \log \dfrac{10}{1}$
1.000	0.1000	0.02966	0.02957
0.1000	0.01000	0.02960	0.02957
0.01000	0.001000	0.02956	0.02957
0.001000	0.0001000	0.02950	0.02957

can be written

$$\varepsilon = -\frac{0.05915}{2} \log \frac{P_2}{P_1} \tag{18-48}$$

For satisfactorily reversible platinum electrodes one finds experimental results in agreement with this expression.

18-9 Electrolyte-Concentration Cells

A second type of cell whose emf is derived only from the free-energy change of a dilution reaction is that in which the electrolyte of the cell is involved in the dilution. If one attempts to construct such a cell by having two solutions of different concentrations in physical contact with each other, complications arise because of the nonequilibrium processes that occur at the liquid-liquid junction. For the present only the simpler *concentration cells without liquid junctions* are considered. Such cells can be illustrated with two cells of the type

$$Pt|H_2|HCl(c)|AgCl(s)|Ag$$

each of which has a reaction

$$\tfrac{1}{2}H_2 + AgCl \rightleftharpoons Ag + H^+(c) + Cl^-(c) \tag{18-49}$$

Consider two such cells electrically connected through their silver electrodes in the opposed manner,

$$Pt|H_2|HCl(c_1)|AgCl|Ag\text{—}Ag|AgCl|HCl(c_2)|H_2|Pt$$

The overall reaction is now the sum of the two simple cell reactions. If the pressure of hydrogen gas is the same for both terminal electrodes, the electrode reactions can be combined to give

Right cell:	$Ag + H^+(c_2) + Cl^-(c_2) \rightleftharpoons \tfrac{1}{2}H_2 + AgCl$
Left cell:	$\tfrac{1}{2}H_2 + AgCl \rightleftharpoons Ag + H^+(c_1) + Cl^-(c_1)$
Overall reaction:	$H^+(c_2) + Cl^-(c_2) \rightleftharpoons H^+(c_1) + Cl^-(c_1)$

$$\tag{18-50}$$

The overall reaction therefore involves no chemical change and consists only of the transfer of HCl from a concentration c_2 to a concentration c_1. The emf of the complete cell is expressed as

$$\varepsilon = -\frac{0.05915}{1} \log \frac{(a_{H^+})_1 (a_{Cl^-})_1}{(a_{H^+})_2 (a_{Cl^-})_2} = -0.05915 \log \frac{[a_\pm]_1^2}{[a_\pm]_2^2}$$

$$= -0.11830 \log \frac{(a_\pm)_1}{(a_\pm)_2} \tag{18-51}$$

Again one can see that the spontaneous process takes HCl from a higher activity, or concentration, to a lower activity, or concentration. If, for example, c_2 is greater than c_1 and therefore $(a_\pm)_2$ is greater than $(a_\pm)_1$, the emf will be positive and the reaction will proceed in the direction in which it is written.

One can clearly use such concentration cells to determine the activity of an electrolyte at one concentration or in a solution containing other ions compared with the activity of an electrolyte in another solution.

The principal purpose in presenting these concentration cells here, however, is to provide a contrast to the situation that arises when concentration cells with liquid junctions are dealt with.

18-10 Electrolyte-Concentration Cells with Liquid Junctions

The treatment of emfs has so far ignored the problem that arises if one seeks to couple two electrodes which operate in different solutions. If, for instance, one studies the cell consisting of a $Zn|Zn^{2+}$ electrode and a $Cu|Cu^{2+}$ electrode, one must separate the two solutions, probably $ZnSO_4$ and $CuSO_4$, so that they cannot mix with each other. If the solutions do mix, copper will plate out directly onto the zinc electrode and no emf will be obtained. We are therefore forced to form a liquid junction between the solutions, and, as we shall see, this gives rise to a *junction potential*. Since the direct contact between solutions of different concentrations is not a balanced state, as required for reversible processes, the system is not directly susceptible to thermodynamic analysis. The source of the junction potential will be seen, however, if the cell reaction of a concentration cell is treated in detail.

The dilution of HCl was studied in Sec. 18-9. It can also be accomplished in a cell with a liquid junction, as illustrated in Fig. 18-7. Assume that two HCl solutions of different concentration can be brought together and prevented from mixing. The flowing of two streams of solution together sometimes accomplishes this. One then can set up the cell

$$Pt|H_2|HCl(c_1)|HCl(c_2)|H_2|Pt$$

The emf of the cell can be related to the overall reaction that occurs when 1 $\mathfrak{F}$ of current flows. The reactions which occur at the electrodes and those which occur at the liquid junction can be written separately. The electrode reactions are

At right electrode:	$H^+(c_2) + e^- \rightarrow \frac{1}{2}H_2$
At left electrode:	$\frac{1}{2}H_2 \rightarrow H^+(c_1) + e^-$
Overall electrode reaction:	$H^+(c_2) \rightarrow H^+(c_1)$

$$(18\text{-}52)$$

The junction reaction is understood by reference to Fig. 18-7. As the current flows according to our convention, 1 $\mathfrak{F}$ of positive charge must pass through the cell and therefore across the junction. The fraction of current

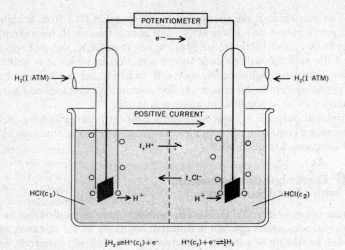

FIGURE 8-7 An electrochemical cell with a liquid junction.

carried by the ions is expressed in terms of their transference numbers, and t_+ equiv of H^+ moves to the right whereas t_- equiv of Cl^- moves to the left. The junction reactions are therefore

$$t_+H^+(c_1) \rightarrow t_+H^+(c_2) \quad \text{or} \quad (1 - t_-)H^+(c_1) \rightarrow (1 - t_-)H^+(c_2)$$

and

$$t_-Cl^-(c_2) \rightarrow t_-Cl^-(c_1) \tag{18-53}$$

The electrode reaction and the junction reactions are now combined to give the overall cell reaction. Thus

Electrode reaction: $H^+(c_2) \rightarrow H^+(c_1)$
Junction reactions: $H^+(c_1) - t_-H^+(c_1) \rightarrow H^+(c_2) - t_-H^+(c_2)$
                       $t_-Cl^-(c_2) \rightarrow t_-Cl^-(c_1)$

Overall cell reaction: $t_-[H^+(c_2) + Cl^-(c_2)] \rightarrow t_-[H^+(c_1) + Cl^-(c_1)]$
$$\tag{18-54}$$

The emf of this cell, which has $\mathcal{E}° = 0$, can now be written

$$\mathcal{E} = -\frac{0.05915}{1} \log \frac{[(a_{H^+})_1(a_{Cl^-})_1]^{t_-}}{[(a_{H^+})_2(a_{Cl^-})_2]^{t_-}} = -0.05915 t_- \log \frac{[a_\pm]_1^2}{[a_\pm]_2^2}$$

$$= -0.11830 t_- \log \frac{(a_\pm)_1}{(a_\pm)_2} \tag{18-55}$$

TABLE 18-4 Calculated and Experimental Potentials for an NaCl Concentration Cell with Transference

The cell is $Ag|AgCl|NaCl(c_1)|NaCl\ (c_2)|AgCl|Ag$, and the potential is calculated from $\mathcal{E} = -0.11830t_+ \log[(a_\pm)_1/(a_\pm)_2]$ with $t_+ = 0.39$; the concentration c_1 is constant at 0.0498 mol liter^{-1}, and the activity coefficient of NaCl in this solution is 0.822

		$\mathcal{E}$, mV	
c_2	$(\gamma_\pm)_2$	Calculated	Observed
0.00996	0.904	30.4	30.39
0.01996	0.871	17.2	17.11
0.02998	0.852	9.47	9.44
0.07933	0.792	−8.59	−8.58
0.09987	0.778	−12.81	−12.72

Source: Data from G. J. Janz and A. R. Gordon, *J. Am. Chem. Soc.*, **65**:218 (1943), simplified and abbreviated.

The emf of the cell, unlike that without a liquid junction, depends on the transference numbers. Such cells are frequently described as *concentration cells with transference.*

If the activities of HCl at the two concentrations are known, the measured emf allows the determination of the transference number. The method is satisfactory, and the results compare well with those obtained by the Hittorf method. The difficulties with the method arise through the experimental problem of obtaining a liquid junction that prevents mixing of the two solutions. Reproducible and meaningful emfs are not always easily obtained. The assumption has been made, furthermore, that the transference numbers are independent of concentration in the concentration range c_1 to c_2.

The success of a simple treatment of transference cells is illustrated by the agreement between the calculated and experimental potentials for an NaCl cell with transference as shown in Table 18-4.

18-11 The Salt Bridge

It has already been mentioned that one attempts to circumvent the liquid-junction problem by connecting the different solutions by means of a bridge containing a saturated KCl solution. One then assumes that no junction potential exists. The use of such a device can best be justified by the empirical result that emfs so obtained are generally in satisfactory agreement with results from cells without liquid junctions.

The success of the salt bridge can be attributed to the high concentration of KCl at the solution junction. The effect of the difference between the two electrode solutions is thereby swamped out by the conduction due to the K^+ and

Cl$^-$ ions. The fact that the ions of KCl have about equal transference numbers and diffusibilities is also said to be important. The mechanism of the salt bridge, however, is difficult to analyze, and only with a detailed understanding of its operation (it is not a thermodynamic device) can the role of these quantities be understood. The salt bridge is often used as a convenient device for constructing an electrode, as in the assembly of Fig. 18-4. Such an electrode can dip into the solution of another electrode to form an electrochemical cell. When the two electrode solutions could have been mixed and have not been mixed only because of cell-construction convenience, the cell is susceptible to thermodynamic treatment, and thermodynamic functions enter into the cell emf expression; i.e., the activity of an electrolyte will occur, but an individual ion activity will not. The cell

$$Pt|H_2(1 \text{ atm})|HCl|KCl(1\ N)|Hg_2Cl_2(s)|Hg$$

might be constructed, for example, and the cell reaction

$$Hg_2Cl_2 + H_2 \rightleftharpoons 2Hg + 2Cl^- + 2H^+ \tag{18-56}$$

would be written. The cell emf expression is then

$$\mathcal{E} = \mathcal{E}^\circ - \frac{(2)(0.05915)}{2} \log a_{Cl^-} a_{H^+} \tag{18-57}$$

A typical thermodynamic-activity expression, $a_{Cl^-} a_{H^+}$ or $a_\pm{}^2$, occurs.

The nonthermodynamic nature of the salt bridge is illustrated when the electrode solutions must be separated for an emf to be produced. The cell

$$Pt|H_2(1 \text{ atm})|HCl(c = 0.01)\|HCl(c = 0.1)|H_2(1 \text{ atm})|Pt$$

can be constructed, and an emf obtained. The electrode reactions are

Right electrode: $\quad H^+(0.1) + e^- \rightleftharpoons \tfrac{1}{2}H_2$
Left electrode: $\qquad\qquad\quad \tfrac{1}{2}H_2 \rightleftharpoons H^+(0.01) + e^-$ $\qquad$ (18-58)

The net reaction, on the assumption that no junction reaction need be considered, is

$$H^+(0.10) \rightleftharpoons H^+(0.01) \tag{18-59}$$

Since the $\mathcal{E}^\circ$ value is zero, the cell emf can be written

$$\mathcal{E} = -0.05915 \log \frac{a_{0.01H^+}}{a_{0.10H^+}} \tag{18-60}$$

This apparent approach to the activities of individual ions of an electrolyte, however, is upset by the assumptions made concerning the effectiveness of the salt bridge.

Although a cell making use of a salt bridge is not one that can be analyzed by strict thermodynamic arguments, in a practical way the salt bridge is effective and allows cells to be studied that consist of electrodes requiring different solutions.

18-12 Ion-Selective Membrane Electrodes

Before proceeding to an important application of emf measurements, brief mention should be made of a component of the most common electrochemical instrument, the *glass electrode*. Figure 18-8 indicates the electrode assembly of a pH meter, which includes a typical glass electrode. The electrode, not the cell, usually consists of the arrangement

$$Ag|AgCl(s)|HCl(c = 1)|glass$$

The value of the electrode stems from the fact that when it is placed in a solution of given acidity and the cell is completed by use of another electrode, the emf of the cell appears to depend primarily on the difference in the concentration or activity of the hydrogen ions on either side of the glass.

The glass membrane of the glass electrode separates two different solutions, as does the KCl salt bridge. Unlike the salt bridge, which provides for electrical

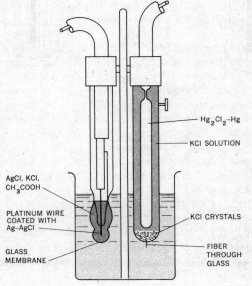

AgCl, KCl,
CH$_3$COOH

PLATINUM WIRE
COATED WITH
Ag–AgCl

GLASS
MEMBRANE

Hg$_2$Cl$_2$–Hg

KCl SOLUTION

KCl CRYSTALS

FIBER
THROUGH
GLASS

FIGURE 18-8
The glass electrode and calomel electrode of a pH meter. (*From F. Daniels, J. W. Williams, P. Bender, R. A. Alberty, C. D. Cornwell, and J. E. Harriman, "Experimental Physical Chemistry," 7th ed. Copyright 1970 by McGraw-Hill, Inc. Used by permission of McGraw-Hill Book Company.*)

conduction across the liquid junction, the glass membrane most often used leads to a cell whose emf is primarily responsive to hydrogen ions. Glasses can be made that allow passage of only one type of ion, in this case the hydrogen ion, and thus the electrode can be constructed to be sensitive to this ion only.

Much of the importance of the glass electrode stems from its lack of response to various oxidizing and reducing agents and to a large variety of ionic species. Difficulties may occur, however, if the glass electrode is used in solutions of high sodium-ion concentration or in solution sufficiently alkaline to attack the glass membrane.

The glass electrode that responds to variations in the hydrogen activity is just one member of a growing list of practical electrode devices known as *ion-selective-membrane electrodes*. The three general types of membranes used are illustrated in Fig. 18-9.

Modifications of the glass membrane of a glass electrode can make the membrane permeable and the electrode responsive to a variety of ions. Glass electrodes have been prepared that are sensitive to each of the ions of the alkali-metal family and to other ions such as NH_4^+, Ag^+, and Cu^+ as well as H^+.

Solid-state membranes are best represented by the fluoride-ion electrode. The membrane material is the sparingly soluble crystalline substance LaF_3. Fluoride ions are conducted through the crystal with ease while other ions are

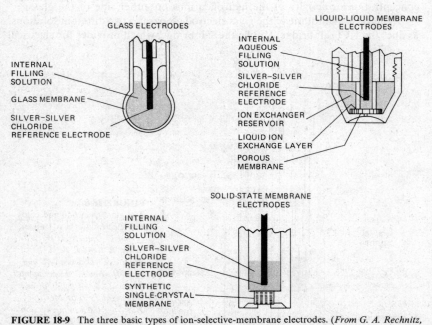

FIGURE 18-9 The three basic types of ion-selective-membrane electrodes. (*From G. A. Rechnitz, Chem. Eng. News, January 1975, p. 35.*)

rejected. The fluoride-ion electrode is highly specific and rugged, and thus is a valuable analytical tool.

Liquid-membrane electrodes can be varied by the choice of liquid, which can be organic or inorganic, and by the presence of dissolved ion-exchange substances. Liquid membranes have been developed for electrodes selective for Ca^{2+}, Mg^{2+}, NO_3^-, Cl^-, and many others.

When supplemented with a reference electrode, all such electrodes produce a potential that more or less conforms to the equation

$$\mathcal{E} = \text{const} + \frac{RT}{n\mathcal{F}} \ln a_M \tag{18-61}$$

where a_M is the activity of the ion to which the electrode is selective. In practice, measurements must be made of known solutions containing potentially interfering ions, to judge the conformity to this Nernst-type expression.

18-13 Thermodynamic Data from EMF Measurements

The emf data of electrochemical cells provide not only activity-coefficient data but also much valuable information on the thermodynamic properties of ions in aqueous solution at the standard state of unit activity.

The standard electrode potentials of Table 18-1, for example, through the relation $\Delta G° = -n\mathcal{F}\mathcal{E}°$ give values for the free-energy change accompanying the cell reaction. With the added arbitrary assignment of a zero value for the free energy of formation of H^+ at unit activity, values for the standard free energies of individual ionic species, as listed in Appendix B-2, are obtained.

Additional information is obtained from measurements of the temperature dependence of the emfs of electrochemical cells.

The thermodynamic relation

$$\left[\frac{\partial(\Delta G)}{\partial T}\right]_P = -\Delta S \quad \text{or} \quad \left[\frac{\partial(\Delta G°)}{\partial T}\right]_P = -\Delta S° \tag{18-62}$$

becomes, with the substitution of

$$\Delta G° = -n\mathcal{F}\mathcal{E}°$$

the entropy-determining relation

$$-n\mathcal{F}\left(\frac{\partial \mathcal{E}°}{\partial T}\right)_P = -\Delta S° \quad \text{or} \quad \Delta S° = n\mathcal{F}\left(\frac{\partial \mathcal{E}°}{\partial T}\right)_P \tag{18-63}$$

By this expression the entropy change for the cell reaction can be determined from the temperature coefficient of the cell emf.

Furthermore, this entropy value can be inserted into the expression, for a given temperature,

$$\Delta H = \Delta G + T \Delta S$$

to give the enthalpy change for the reaction as

$$\Delta H^\circ = -n \mathfrak{F} \mathcal{E}^\circ + n \mathfrak{F} T \left(\frac{\partial \mathcal{E}^\circ}{\partial T} \right)_P \tag{18-64}$$

Thus ΔG, ΔH, and ΔS can be evaluated for the cell reaction from measurements of the emf and the temperature coefficient of the emf. Since this procedure is often a more convenient way of obtaining these thermodynamic properties than direct calorimetric measurements, emf studies provide an appreciable amount of thermodynamic information for systems involving ions in aqueous solution.

For example, the cell

$$\text{Pt}|\text{H}_2|\text{HCl(soln)}|\text{AgCl}|\text{Ag}$$

has a standard emf, i.e., with variable reagents at unit activity, of 0.2224 V at 25°C and a temperature coefficient of -0.000645 V K^{-1}. The cell reaction is

$$
\begin{array}{l}
\text{AgCl} + e^- \rightleftharpoons \text{Ag} + \text{Cl}^- \\
\underline{\tfrac{1}{2}\text{H}_2 \rightleftharpoons \text{H}^+ + e^-} \\
\text{AgCl} + \tfrac{1}{2}\text{H}_2 \rightleftharpoons \text{Ag} + \text{H}^+(a = 1) + \text{Cl}^-(a = 1)
\end{array}
\tag{18-65}
$$

and for this reaction one obtains the thermodynamic results

$$\Delta G^\circ = -n \mathfrak{F} \mathcal{E}^\circ = -(1)(96{,}490)(0.2224) = -21{,}460 \text{ J} \tag{18-66}$$

$$\Delta S^\circ = n \mathfrak{F} \left(\frac{\partial \mathcal{E}^\circ}{\partial T} \right)_P = (1)(96{,}490)(-0.000645) = -62.2 \text{ J K}^{-1} \tag{18-67}$$

and

$$\Delta H^\circ = \Delta G^\circ + T \Delta S^\circ = -21{,}460 + 298(-62.2) = -40{,}000 \text{ J} \tag{18-68}$$

Thus measurements of the emf of cells and the temperature dependence of the emf give thermodynamic data for reactions in which solutions of ions are formed. Such measurements, along with direct calorimetric determinations of the heats of solutions of electrolytes and of the temperature coefficient of the solubilities of electrolytes, provide much of the data of Appendix B-2.

18-14 Overpotential and Electrode Currents

The electrochemical cell provides a marvelous device for measuring the work that can be obtained, and thus the free-energy change that accompanies, a reaction proceeding at a state of balance, i.e., reversibly. At a state of balance forward and reverse reactions do occur, but they do so to equal extents. A very reasonable, if easily overlooked question is: To what extent do each of these reactions occur when a particular cell is at a state of balance? At either of the electrodes, one reaction deposits electrons at the electrode and the other removes electrons from the electrode. At equilibrium both reactions occur. The zero net current results from the equal anodic and cathodic currents, shown in Fig. 18-10.

Nothing in what we have done so far in this chapter suggests the magnitude of these two opposing currents. These magnitudes depend on the rates with which the two opposing electrode reactions occur. Thus, in dealing with these currents or these reactions we anticipate the more extensive treatment of the following chapter and enter upon the subject of chemical kinetics. We sample this subject here by dealing with reactions at electrodes, a subject called *electrode kinetics*.

In dealing with the rates of the opposing anodic and cathodic reactions we are of course not restricted to the special reversible situation in which the rates of these reactions are equal. The rates can be made unequal by raising or lowering the applied voltage. Then either the anodic or the cathodic reaction occurs more rapidly than under reversible conditions. The study of the rates of electrode reactions begins with an analysis of the effect of the potential on the net current.

The relation of the potential between an electrode and the solution in which it is immersed and the current produced by this potential can be measured by means of the electrode arrangement of Fig. 18-11. The net current, which is related to the rate of reaction at the electrodes of the principal cell, is

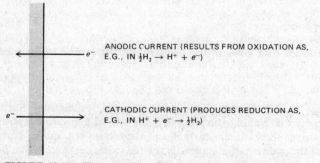

ANODIC CURRENT (RESULTS FROM OXIDATION AS, E.G., IN $\frac{1}{2}H_2 \rightarrow H^+ + e^-$)

CATHODIC CURRENT (PRODUCES REDUCTION AS, E.G., IN $H^+ + e^- \rightarrow \frac{1}{2}H_2$)

FIGURE 18-10 The opposing currents at an electrode-solution interface.

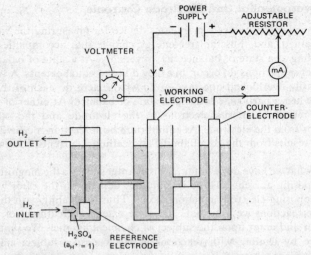

FIGURE 18-11 The experimental arrangement for measuring the overpotential-current relation at an electrode, the electrode shown as the working electrode. [*From J. O' M. Bockris, N. Bonciocat, and F. Gutmann, "An Introduction to Electrochemical Science," Wykeham Publications (London), Ltd., London, 1974.*]

shown by the ammeter reading. The potential between the solution of the electrode under study and the working electrode is given by the potentiometer reading in the auxiliary circuit. When the principal circuit is adjusted to its reversible, equilibrium state, the auxiliary circuit will indicate some potential difference $\Delta\Phi_{rev}$. If the voltage applied to the principal circuit is changed so that a net current flows, the potential shown by the auxiliary circuit will change to some value indicated as $\Delta\Phi$. It is convenient to introduce the term *overpotential* η, defined as

$$\eta = \Delta\Phi - \Delta\Phi_{rev} \qquad (18\text{-}69)$$

The net current that flows in the principal circuit can be interpreted as

$$i = i_c - i_a \qquad (18\text{-}70)$$

where subscripts c and a stand for cathodic and anodic, respectively. Furthermore, the overpotential is said to be positive if it is such as to produce a positive i, that is, if it drives the cathodic current and suppresses the anodic current.

Notice that the overpotential is directly related to the net current that flows to or from the electrode under study and the solution in which it is immersed. Or we can say that the net current, and thus the net rate of electrode reaction, is directly related to the value of the overpotential.

The dependence of the net current i on the overpotential often conforms to the empirical *Tafel equation,*

$$\eta = a + b \ln i \tag{18-71}$$

The Tafel equation suggests that the net electrode current increases exponentially with the overpotential, as seen by writing the equation in the form

$$i = (\text{const})(e^{\eta/b}) \tag{18-72}$$

Notice that this current-potential relation is very different from that which describes the behavior in a metallic conductor. Then the current rises linearly, not exponentially, with the potential difference.

In the following section we shall see the basis for the form of the Tafel equation and in so doing we shall be introduced to the rates and mechanisms of electrode reactions.

18-15 Electrode Currents and Electrode Reactions

At a solid electrode immersed in a well-stirred electrolyte a stationary electrolyte layer about a 0.1 to 0.01 mm thick lies along the electrode. Various models of the double layer that occurs at the electrode-electrolyte interface have been put forward. A recent model is illustrated in Fig. 18-12.

For moderate currents and a well-stirred electrolyte the current is limited by the rate of the reactions within the double layer on or near the electrode

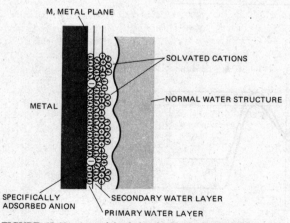

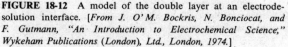

FIGURE 18-12 A model of the double layer at an electrode-solution interface. [*From J. O'M. Bockris, N. Bonciocat, and F. Gutmann, "An Introduction to Electrochemical Science," Wykeham Publications (London), Ltd., London, 1974.*]

surface. The reactions are those which are involved in one or more stages of the transfer of electrons between the electrode and ionic or molecular species in the electrolyte. We can describe some features of reactions which involve the transfer of electrons, or electron carriers, between the electrode and the adjacent solution.

Rates of chemical reactions will be treated in Chap. 19 by assuming that some "awkward" high-energy intermediate stage blocks the transition from reactants to products. With this view, the energy profile for the transfer of electrons between the electrode itself and the electron-gaining (reducible) or electron-losing (oxidizable) species in solution can be described by Fig. 18-13a. The potentials of an electron in the metal electrode and in the oxidizable species produce the electrode-solution potential difference $\Delta\Phi$, or for reversible conditions $\Delta\Phi_{rev}$. The work involved in moving an electron from one potential to another is $e\,\Delta\Phi$ or $e\,\Delta\Phi_{rev}$. For 1 mol of electrons or singly charged particles the work is $\mathfrak{F}\,\Delta\Phi$ or $\mathfrak{F}\,\Delta\Phi_{rev}$.

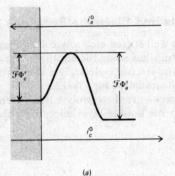

(a)

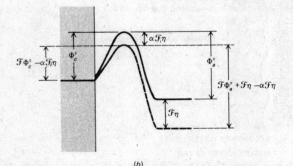

(b)

FIGURE 18-13 The barrier to the cathodic and anodic currents (a) under reversible, $\eta = 0$, conditions and (b) at an overpotential η.

The potential in the solution layer adjacent to the electrode depends on the molecular and ionic details in this layer. Here it is enough to treat this layer as constituting a region across which the electron or an electron-carrying species must travel in electrode reactions. As in Fig. 18-13a, the energy maximum within the double layer can be indicated by the symbol $\mathcal{F}\Phi^{\ddagger}$.

The Boltzmann distribution expression or the related equilibrium expressions of Chap. 8 suggest that the fraction of electrons or electron carriers that can surmount the barrier at the electrode surface will be proportional to an exponential term of the form $e^{-\mathcal{F}\Phi^{\ddagger}/RT}$.

From Fig. 18-13a we can now express the dependence on $\mathcal{F}\Phi^{\ddagger}$ of the electrode currents when the cell is operating reversibly. Then $i_c^{\circ} = i_a^{\circ}$, but each can be described by

$$i_c^{\circ} = k_c\, e^{-\mathcal{F}\Phi_c^{\ddagger}/RT} \qquad i_a^{\circ} = k_a\, e^{-\mathcal{F}\Phi_a^{\ddagger}/RT} \tag{18-73}$$

where k_c and k_a are proportionality constants.

Now let us see how these currents are changed at an overpotential η. The difference between the potential of an electron in the electrode and in the electron receiver in the solution is changed as shown in Fig. 18-13b. The barrier height will be affected in some intermediate way that is not easy to deduce. The *symmetry factor* α is usually introduced to express the fraction of the overvoltage that is effective in lowering the energy barrier. The effect on the cathodic process (Fig. 18-13b) is to change the barrier from $\mathcal{F}\Phi_c^{\ddagger}$ to $\mathcal{F}\Phi_c^{\ddagger} - \alpha\mathcal{F}\eta$. The effect on the anodic process is to change the barrier from $\mathcal{F}\Phi_a^{\ddagger}$ to $\mathcal{F}\Phi_a^{\ddagger} + \mathcal{F}\eta - \alpha\mathcal{F}\eta$, or $\mathcal{F}\Phi_a^{\ddagger} + (1 - \alpha)\mathcal{F}\eta$. We now can express the cathodic and anodic currents by

$$i_c = k_c e^{-(\mathcal{F}\Phi_c^{\ddagger} - \alpha\mathcal{F}\eta)/RT} \qquad i_a = k_a e^{-[\mathcal{F}\Phi_a^{\ddagger} + (1 - \alpha)\mathcal{F}\eta]/RT} \tag{18-74}$$

Expressions for the cathodic and anodic currents in terms of the reversible currents $i_c^0 = i_a^0 = i_0$ can be obtained from Eqs. (18-73) and (18-74) as

$$i_c = i_0 e^{+\alpha\mathcal{F}\eta/RT} \qquad i_a = i_0 e^{-(1-\alpha)\mathcal{F}\eta/RT} \tag{18-75}$$

The net current is given by

$$i = i_c - i_a = i_0(e^{+\alpha\mathcal{F}\eta/RT} - e^{-(1-\alpha)\mathcal{F}\eta/RT}) \tag{18-76}$$

This result is known as the *Butler-Volmer equation*.

The factor α in the equations for i_c, i_a, and i can be deduced, as will be shown, from η-versus-i measurements. Values near $\alpha = \frac{1}{2}$ are commonly found. The variation of i, i_c, and i_a with η for $\alpha = \frac{1}{2}$ is shown in Fig. 18-14.

For overvoltages that are large, positively or negatively, the net current is given by one or the other of the terms of Eq. (18-76). Then only the cathodic or the anodic current is the significant contributor to the total current, and we can write:

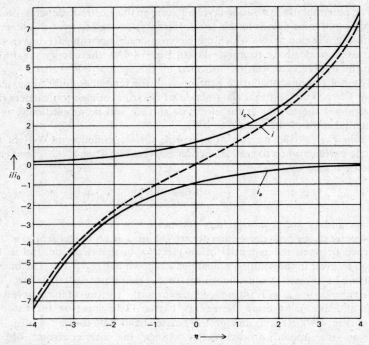

FIGURE 18-14 The variation of i, i_c, and i_a with the overpotential in units of $\mathfrak{F}/RT$, according to Eq. (18-76).

For large positive η:

$$i \approx i_c = i_0 e^{+\alpha \mathfrak{F} \eta / RT} \quad \text{and} \quad \ln i = \ln i_0 + \frac{\alpha \mathfrak{F}}{RT}\eta \quad (18\text{-}77)$$

For large negative η:

$$i \approx i_a = i_0 e^{-(1-\alpha)\mathfrak{F}\eta/RT} \quad \text{and} \quad \ln i = \ln i_0 - \frac{(1-\alpha)\mathfrak{F}}{RT}\eta \quad (18\text{-}78)$$

These equations are of the form of the empirical Tafel equation (18-71). According to the model for electrode reactions that we have developed, we can identify the coefficient b of Eq. (18-71) with

$$b = \begin{cases} \dfrac{RT}{\alpha \mathfrak{F}} & \text{for cathodic currents} \\[3mm] \dfrac{-RT}{(1-\alpha)\mathfrak{F}} & \text{for anodic current} \end{cases} \quad (18\text{-}79)$$

TABLE 18-5 Values of $i_0 = i_c = i_a$ for the Hydrogen-Evolution Reaction on Various Metals in $1\,M\,H_2SO_4$

Metal	i_0, A m^{-2}
Pd, Pt	8
Rh, Ir	2
W	1×10^{-2}
Ni	3×10^{-2}
Nb	1×10^{-3}
Ti	6×10^{-5}
Cd	1×10^{-7}
Hg	6×10^{-9}

Source: J. O'M. Bockris, N. Bonciocal, and F. Gutmann, "An Introduction to Electrochemical Science," Wykeham Publications (London), Ltd., London, 1974.

Under certain current-overpotential conditions, a linear portion occurs on graphs of log i versus η. From such results and Eq. (18-77) or (18-78) values of i_0 can be deduced. Some representative results are shown in Table 18-5. Notice the remarkable range of values and particularly the small reversible current for hydrogen evolution on mercury and the large current for hydrogen evolution on, for example, platinum. The difficulty with which hydrogen is discharged at a mercury surface allows many ions which have a larger electrode potential than the hydrogen ion to be discharged in polarographic studies. The large reversible current at a platinum electrode makes this electrode particularly suitable for studies of electrochemical cells under reversible conditions.

For a number of electrode processes, the value of the Tafel slope b is about 0.051, corresponding to an α value of $\frac{1}{2}$. This suggests that the diagram of Fig. 18-13 does describe the rate-limiting step of the electrode reaction. This step is thus the passage of an electron or a singly charged electron carrier or receiver from the solution to the electrode surface. This conclusion, however, clearly leaves many of the details of the electrode reaction mechanism unsettled.

Different values of the Tafel slope b can be interpreted in terms of different mechanisms of the electrode reaction. Thus, although the b value corresponding to $\alpha = \frac{1}{2}$ is found for hydrogen evolution at mercury electrodes, a value only about one-fourth as large is found for hydrogen evolution at platinum or palladium electrodes. A mechanism that fits this observation was suggested by Tafel.

Suppose that H$^+$ ions easily and rapidly reach the electrode and are discharged to produce an attached M—H species. Suppose further, that the reverse of this reaction is also easy and rapid. The currents for the two processes, which are assumed to be large compared with that corresponding to net hydrogen evolution, are given by

$$i_a = k_a[\text{H}^+] \qquad \text{and} \qquad i_c = k_c[\text{M—H}] \tag{18-80}$$

The ratio of the two currents can be formed and rearranged to give

$$[\text{M—H}] = \frac{k_a}{k_c} \frac{i_c}{i_a} [\text{H}^+] \tag{18-81}$$

Further, if we assume the mechanism described in Fig. 18-13 is appropriate to the forward and reverse electrode reactions, we can write

$$[\text{M—H}] = \frac{k_a}{k_c} \frac{e^{+\alpha\eta\mathfrak{F}/RT}}{e^{-(1-\alpha)\eta\mathfrak{F}/RT}} [\text{H}^+] = \frac{k_a}{k_c} e^{+\eta\mathfrak{F}/RT} [\text{H}^+] \tag{18-82}$$

In the mechanism proposed by Tafel, the rate-controlling step is the interaction of two attached hydrogen atoms, described as M—H, to form an H_2 molecule. The rate of such a process, as you will see in Sec. 19-2, is proportional to the square of the M—H concentration. The rate of this reaction is equal to the rate of hydrogen evolution, and thus it is proportional to the net electrode current. We can write, with Eq. (18-82),

$$i = k[\text{M—H}]^2 = k \frac{k_a^2}{k_c^2} e^{2\eta\mathfrak{F}/RT} \tag{18-83}$$

Rearrangement to Tafel-equation form, for solutions of constant pH, gives

$$\eta = \text{const} + \frac{RT}{2\mathfrak{F}} \ln i \tag{18-84}$$

The Tafel slope b is, according to this mechanism, about 0.013 and is in agreement with the value found from studies of the evolution of hydrogen from platinum and palladium.

Seldom can the observed η-versus-i behavior be so neatly explained by a mechanism. More typically additional studies, such as pH, temperature, and isotope dependence of the current-overpotential relationships, must be made to achieve a well-supported mechanism. As you will see in the following chapter, even then one comes to a description of a reaction which perhaps is acceptable but is never proved.

PROBLEMS

18-1. Write the cell reactions for the following cells and use Table 18-1 to determine the emfs of the cells under standard conditions:

(a) $Cd|Cd^{2+}||KCl|Hg_2Cl_2|Hg$
(b) $Pt|Tl^+, Tl^{3+}||Cu^{2+}|Cu$
(c) $Pb|PbSO_4(s)|SO_4^{2-}||Cu^{2+}|Cu$

18-2. By writing electrochemical cells and calculating their emfs deduce the standard free-energy changes for the following reactions:

(a) $\frac{1}{2}Br_2 + Ag \rightleftharpoons AgBr(s)$
(b) $H_2 + Cu^{2+} \rightleftharpoons 2H^+ + Cu$
(c) $\frac{1}{2}Cl_2 + Br^- \rightleftharpoons Cl^- + \frac{1}{2}Br_2$
(d) $Ca^{2+} + 2Na \rightleftharpoons Ca + 2Na^+$
(e) $Hg_2Cl_2 \rightleftharpoons 2Hg + Cl_2$

18-3. Calculate the emf of the cell and $\Delta G°$ for the cell reaction of $Pt|Cl_2(1 \text{ atm})|ZnCl_2(a = 1)|ZnCl_2(a = 1)|Zn$ using the electrode potentials of Table 18-1.

18-4. In what direction would the concentrations of the variable reagents in each of the reactions of Prob. 18-2 be changed to attain cells with zero emf?

18-5. The emf of the cell $Pt|H_2(1 \text{ atm})|HBr(c)|AgBr(s)|Ag$ has the tabulated values at $25°C$ [A. S. Keston, *J. Am. Chem. Soc.*, **57**:1671 (1935)]. By a suitable graphical method deduce (a) $\mathcal{E}°$ for the cell and (b) the activity coefficients for HBr at each of the reported concentrations.

c, mol liter^{-1}	0.0003198	0.0004042	0.0008444	0.001355	0.001850	0.002396	0.003719
$\mathcal{E}$, volts	0.48469	0.47381	0.43636	0.41243	0.39667	0.38383	0.36173

18-6. The emf of the cell in which the reaction $H_2 + Hg_2Cl_2 \rightarrow 2Hg + 2HCl$ occurs has been studied by G. N. Lewis and M. Randall [*J. Am. Chem. Soc.*, **36**:1969 (1944)] as a function of pressure at $25°C$. The pressure was obtained by allowing the hydrogen gas to escape against a hydrostatic head measured in centimeters of water. Their results are:

P, cmH$_2$O in excess of 1 atm	0	37	63	84
$\mathcal{E}$, V	0.40088	0.40137	0.40163	0.40190

Compare the pressure dependence of these results with the thermodynamic predictions.

18-7. The cell $Zn|ZnCl_2(c)|AgCl(s)|Ag$ has been studied by G. N. Lewis and M. Randall ("Thermodynamics," p. 420, McGraw-Hill Book Company, New York 1923). They report, for $25°C$:

c, mol liter^{-1}	0.000772	0.001253	0.001453	0.003112	0.006022	0.01021
$\mathcal{E}$, V	1.2475	1.2289	1.2219	1.1953	1.1742	1.1558

(a) Using a Debye-Hückel limiting-law extrapolation, deduce, as well as possible from these data, the value of $\mathcal{E}°$ and the activity coefficients of $ZnCl_2$ at each concentration.

(b) Compare the value deduced for $\mathcal{E}°$ from these data with that obtained from the data of Table 18-1.

18-8. (a) Calculate the reversible standard emf of the lead storage cell. The overall reaction is

$$Pb(s) + PbO_2(s) + 2H_2SO_4(aq) \rightleftharpoons 2PbSO_4(s) + 2H_2O(l)$$

(b) According to this result, in which direction does the reaction go when the cell is being used to do work? (c) In fact the acid concentration is generally such that the solution has a specific gravity of 1.15 and contains 20 percent sulfuric acid. Would the reversible emf of such a cell be more or less than that calculated for the standard cell?

18-9. The emf of the lead storage cell depends on the temperature and on the sulfuric acid content of the solution. At 25°C the emf is 1.90 V when the solution is 7.4 percent sulfuric acid, 2.00 V when the solution is 21.4 percent, and 2.14 V when the solution is 39.2 percent. With the help of these data, what can you deduce about the activity or the activity coefficient of the sulfuric acid?

18-10. The emf of the cell $Zn(s)|ZnCl_2(m = 0.01021)$, $AgCl(s)|Ag$ is 1.1566 V at 25°C. What is the mean-activity coefficient of $ZnCl_2$?

18-11. A cell with zinc and lead amalgam electrodes, the latter supplied with solid $PbSO_4$, is described by $Zn(Hg)|ZnSO_4(m)$, $PbSO_4(s)|Pb(Hg)$ where (m) refers to tabulated values of molality. When the amalgams are such that the standard emf of the cell $\mathcal{E}°$ is 0.4109 V, the following data were obtained [Cowperthwaite and LaMer, *J. Am. Chem. Soc.*, **53**:4333 (1931)]:

Molality of $ZnSO_4$	0.0005	0.002	0.01	0.05
emf, V	0.61144	0.58319	0.55353	0.52867

Calculate the mean-activity coefficient of $ZnSO_4$ from each of these data and compare with the curves of Figs. 17-14 and 17-16.

18-12. The emf of the cell $Ag(s)|AgCl(satd)$, $KCl(m = 0.05)|AgNO_3(m = 0.1)|Ag(s)$ is 0.4312 V at 25°C. The mean-activity coefficients of KCl and $AgNO_3$ at these concentrations are estimated to be 0.817 and 0.723, respectively. What is the solubility product of AgCl?

18-13. If the cell used in Sec. 18-6 to obtain the standard emf of the $Ag|AgCl(s)$ electrode is operated in basic solution with the hydroxide-ion concentration known, the ionization constant of water can be deduced. Studies of the cell $H_2(1 \text{ atm})|Ba(OH)_2(m = 0.005)$, $BaCl_2(m_1)$, $AgCl(s)|Ag$ give the tabulated results at 25°C.

m_1, mol liter^{-1}	0.00500	0.01166	0.01833	0.02833
$\mathcal{E}$, V	1.04983	1.02783	1.01597	1.00444

(a) Modify the equation for the cell emf shown in Eq. (18-31) by replacing a_{H^+} by $a_{OH^-} = K_w/a_{H^+}$. Then replace activities by activity-coefficient–concentration products, introduce the known value of $\mathcal{E}°$ for the cell, and rearrange the equation so that all known or measurable quantities are on the left side. [A value of $\mathcal{E}°$ for the $Ag|AgCl(s)$ electrode that is consistent with these data is $+0.22239$ V.] (b) From a suitable plot of the left side of the equation obtained in part (a) against the ionic strength deduce K_w. Can you also deduce anything about any activity coefficients?

18-14. From the data of Table 18-1, calculate the solubility product of $PbSO_4$ at 25°C.

18-15. Calculate the emf of the zinc amalgam cell with electrodes containing an 0.001 m amalgam of zinc as one electrode and 0.003 m zinc as the other electrode. The electrolyte is 0.1 m aqueous $ZnCl_2$. Assume that the amalgams behave ideally.

18-16. The emf of the liquid-junction concentration cell

$$Ag(s) \quad AgCl(sat), \quad HCl(m = 0.10) \| HCl(m = 0.020), \quad AgCl(sat) \quad Ag(s)$$

is 0.0645 V at 25°C. The emf of the corresponding cell without a liquid junction

$$Ag(s)|AgCl(s), \quad HCl(m = 0.10)|H_2—H_2|HCl(m = 0.020), \quad AgCl(s)|Ag(s)$$

is 0.0778 V. What can you learn about transference numbers from these data?

18-17. The emf of the cell

$$H_2(1 \text{ atm})|HCl(m = 0.01), \ AgCl(s)|Ag$$

at various temperatures is:

t, °C	0	15	25	35
emf, V	0.45780	0.46207	0.46419	0.46565

What value do these data give for the heat of formation of HCl in an 0.01 m aqueous solution? Compare with the value for HCl(aq) in Appendix B-2.

18-18. At 25°C the emf $\mathcal{E}$ and the derivative $(\partial \mathcal{E}/\partial T)_P$ of the cell $Pb|PbCl_2(s)$, KCl, $AgCl(s)|Ag$ are 0.4902 V and $-0.000\ 186$ V K^{-1}, respectively. The silver electrode is positive. Calculate ΔG and ΔH for the reaction

$$Pb(s) + 2AgCl(s) \rightarrow PbCl_2(s) + 2Ag(s)$$

Compare with the value obtained from the data of Appendix B-1.

18-19. The ion product for water is 1.008×10^{-14} at 25°C. Use the data of Appendix B to estimate the ionization constant at 0 and at 60°C. The experimental values are 0.115×10^{-14} and 9.614×10^{-14}, respectively.

18-20. The solubility of AgCl in water has been deduced from conductivity data to be:

Temperature, °C	1.55	4.68	9.97	17.51	25.86	34.12
Solubility, g AgCl/1000 g H_2O	0.0056	0.0066	0.0089	0.0131	0.0194	0.0274

(a) Calculate the solubility product from these data, and by a suitable graphical treatment estimate the heat of solution of AgCl at 25°C from the temperature dependence of the solubility product. (b) Deduce the free energy of AgCl in its standard hypothetical state of unit activity in water at 25°C. (c) Calculate the entropy of solution of AgCl to its standard unit-activity state in water at 25°C, and with the absolute entropy of AgCl(s) of 96.11 J K^{-1} mol^{-1} obtain a value for the entropy of AgCl in aqueous solution.

REFERENCES

MACINNES, D. A.: "The Principles of Electrochemistry," Dover Publications, Inc., 1961. A new edition of an important earlier work, originally published in 1939, on electrochemistry. Excellent treatment is given not only of the material on emfs, but also on conductance, transference numbers, and so forth.

CONWAY, B. E.: "Electrochemical Data," Elsevier Publishing Company, Amsterdam, 1952. Included along with other data relevant to electrochemical studies are tables of the emfs of a variety of cells and electrodes.

DE BETHUNE, A. J., and N. A. S. LOND: "Standard Aqueous Electrode Potentials and Temperature Coefficients at 25°," C. A. Hampel, Skokie, Ill., 1964.

BIEGLER, T., and R. WOODS: The Standard Hydrogen Electrode: A Misrepresented Concept, *J. Chem. Educ.*, **50**:604 (1973).

IVES, D. J. G., and G. J. JANZ: "Reference Electrodes," Academic Press, Inc., New York, 1961. Detailed discussions of the theory and use of different types of electrodes, including the hydrogen electrode, the calomel electrode, the silver-silver halide electrodes, the glass electrode, and so forth.

ROBBINS, O., JR.: The Proper Definition of Standard Electromotive Force, *J. Chem. Educ.*, **48**:737 (1971).

EISENMAN, G., R. BATES, G. MATLOCK, and S. M. FRIEDMAN: "The Glass Electrode," Interscience Publishers, Inc., New York, 1965. A reprint volume of articles by the authors on glass electrodes, pH measurements, and sodium- and potassium-sensitive electrodes.

EISENMAN, G. (ed.): "Glass Electrodes for Hydrogen and Other Cations: Principles and Practice," Marcel Dekker, Inc., New York, 1967. Similar in goals and scope to the preceding listing.

DURST, R. A. (ed.): Ion-Selective Electrodes, *Nat. Bur. Stand. (U.S.) Spec. Pub.* 314, 1969. A collection of 11 discussions of the theory and application of ion-selective electrodes.

FISCHER, R. B.: Ion-Selective Electrodes, *J. Chem. Educ.*, **51**:387 (1974).

BOCKRIS, J. O'M., N. BONCIOCAT, and F. GUTMANN: "An Introduction to Electrochemical Science," The Wykeham Publishers, Ltd., London, 1974. An excellent introduction to electrode processes.

GILEADI, E., E. KIROWA-EISNER, and J. PENCINER: "Interfacial Electrochemistry: An Experimental Approach," Addison-Wesley Publishing Company, Inc., Reading, Mass., 1975. Treatment of double-layer theory, electrode kinetics, and related phenomena, followed by a set of experiments on these subjects.

LAIDLER, K. J.: The Kinetics of Electrode Processes, *J. Chem. Educ.*, **47**:600 (1970).

BOCKRIS, J. O'M., and Z. NAGY: Symmetry Factor and Transfer Coefficient: A Source of Confusion in Electrode Kinetics, *J. Chem. Educ.*, **50**:839 (1973).

RATES AND MECHANISMS OF CHEMICAL REACTIONS

Our study of the molecular world has so far been concerned with only one of the two broad aspects which interest chemists. Chemical systems at equilibrium have been treated, and the nature of chemical compounds, which may be reactants or products in a chemical reaction, has been studied. Now the actual process of chemical reactions is investigated, and our attention is focused not only on the reactants and the products but also on the details of the transformation from one set of chemical species to another. That this aspect has previously been neglected or avoided is emphasized by recognizing that the time variable has so far been absent and that it will now play a major role.

The question of how reactants are converted into products in some particular chemical reaction calls for an answer in terms of molecular-level happenings. Two phases of the question and the answer can be recognized. One focuses on the molecular details of what are called *elementary reactions,* e.g., the collision of two molecules to produce one or more new species and the decay of some highly energetic molecule. The second phase is the sequence of elementary reactions that constitutes the overall chemical transformation. Information comes from a variety of experimental approaches but principally from measurements of how the rate of the reaction depends on the concentrations of any reagents that are effective. Such experimental results are usually expressed analytically by what is known as the *rate equation,* which describes the dependence of the rate of reaction at a given temperature on the concentration of the reagents.

RATES AND RATE EQUATIONS FOR CHEMICAL REACTIONS

Most reactions appear to be the result of a succession of molecular events, e.g., collisions or rearrangements. Before we tackle the details of the elementary process, let us see how we deduce the sequences of the steps, or *mechanism,* for a particular reaction. The unraveling of these steps is based primarily on the dependence of the rate of the reaction on the concentration of various reactants and products. Therefore we begin by turning our attention to the study of the rates of chemical reactions and the concentration dependence of these rates.

19-1 Introduction to Rate Equations

Studies of the rate of a reaction usually give information on the decrease in the amount of one of the reactants or on the increase in the amount of a product that occurs in some time interval. If the reaction system is one of constant or near-constant volume, the change in the amount of reagent will correspond to a change in the concentration of that reagent. For liquid systems the rate of a reaction is often expressed in terms of the rate of change of the molar concentration of a reagent. For constant-volume gaseous systems it is generally more convenient to deal with the partial pressure of the reagent. For ideal gases, as is seen from $P = (n/V)RT$, the partial pressure is proportional to the concentration n/V.

The rate of a reaction can be defined as the derivative with respect to time of the extent of the reaction ξ, introduced in Sec. 8-4. Consider again a generalized reaction

$$a\text{A} + b\text{B} \rightarrow c\text{C} + d\text{D} \tag{19-1}$$

The number of moles of a product, C for example, is given as the reaction proceeds by $n_C = c\xi$. The number of moles of a reactant, A for example, is given by $n_A = a(1 - \xi)$. In view of such relations, the rate of the reaction can be expressed as

$$\text{Rate of reaction} = \frac{d\xi}{dt} = \frac{1}{c}\frac{dn_C}{dt} = \frac{1}{d}\frac{dn_D}{dt} = -\frac{1}{a}\frac{dn_A}{dt} = -\frac{1}{b}\frac{dn_B}{dt}$$

This definition is often modified, but the name rate of reaction is retained when changes in concentration rather than changes in numbers of moles are used. Thus, we generally use

$$\text{Rate of reaction} = \frac{1}{c}\frac{d[\text{C}]}{dt} = \frac{1}{d}\frac{d[\text{D}]}{dt} = -\frac{1}{a}\frac{d[\text{A}]}{dt} = -\frac{1}{b}\frac{d[\text{B}]}{dt}$$

In practice, the rate is generally determined by following the rate with which the concentration of one or more of the reactants is used up. In special cases, however, the presence and amount of a product might be the best indication of the extent of the reaction.

It is found that a large number of reactions have rates that, at a given temperature, are proportional to the concentration of one or two of the reactants, with each reactant raised to a small integral power. If reactions are considered in which A and B represent possible reactants, the rate equations for reactions with such concentration dependence would be of the form

$$\text{Rate} = k[A] \qquad\qquad\qquad \text{first order}$$
$$\text{Rate} = k[A]^2 \quad \text{or} \quad k[A][B] \qquad \text{second order} \qquad\qquad (19\text{-}2)$$

Reactions that proceed according to such simple rate equations are said to be reactions of the first or second order, as indicated. As we shall see, not all reactions have such simple rate laws. Some involve concentrations raised to nonintegral powers; others consist of more elaborate algebraic expressions. There are, however, enough reactions that are simple first- or second-order at least under certain conditions to make the idea of the order of a reaction useful.

It is very important to realize that the order of a reaction and the rate equation are summaries of experimental results. Later, when attempts are made to devise mechanisms that are consistent with the rate equations, it will be necessary to keep in mind that mechanisms are theoretical but that the rate equation is an analytical portrayal of the experimental data.

19-2 Fitting Rate Data to First- and Second-Order Rate Equations

A first-order reaction is one for which, at a given temperature, the rate of the reaction depends only on the first power of the concentration of a single reacting species. If the concentration of this species is represented by c (for solutions the units of moles per liter are ordinarily used), and if the volume of the system remains essentially constant during the course of the reaction, the first-order rate law can be written

$$-\frac{dc}{dt} = kc \qquad\qquad (19\text{-}3)$$

The rate constant k is then a positive quantity and has the units of the reciprocal of time.

The experimental results obtained in a study of the rate of a reaction are usually values of c or some quantity related to c at various times. Such data can best be compared with the integrated form of the first-order rate law. If the initial concentration at time $t = 0$ is c_0, and if at some later time t the concentration has fallen to c, the integration gives

$$-\int_{c_0}^{c} \frac{dc}{c} = k \int_{0}^{t} dt \qquad\qquad (19\text{-}4)$$

and

$$-\ln \frac{c}{c_0} = \ln \frac{c_0}{c} = kt \qquad\qquad (19\text{-}5)$$

or

$$\log \frac{c_0}{c} = \frac{k}{2.303} t \qquad (19\text{-}6)$$

Sometimes more convenient is the form

$$\log c = -\frac{k}{2.303} t + \log c_0 \qquad (19\text{-}7)$$

A reaction can therefore be said to be first-order if a plot of $\log (c_0/c)$ or $\log c$ against t gives a straight line. If a straight line is obtained, the slope of the line can be used to give the value of the rate constant k. An alternative to this graphical procedure is the calculation of a value of k from the individual measurements of c at the various times t, from Eq. (19-6), for example. The reaction is classified as first-order if all the data lead to essentially the same values for k, that is, if Eq. (19-6) is satisfied with k a constant.

These equations can be illustrated by a reaction which is found to be first-order, under certain conditions and whose mechanism is of some interest. The conversion of *tert*-butyl bromide to *tert*-butanol in a solvent containing 90 percent acetone and 10 percent (5 M) water has been studied by L. C. Bateman, E. D. Hughes, and C. K. Ingold. The overall reaction is

$$(CH_3)_3CBr + H_2O \rightarrow (CH_3)_3COH + HBr$$

and the reaction is slow enough for its progress to be followed by the titration of

TABLE 19-1 The Concentration of *tert*-Butyl Bromide as a Function of Time for the Reaction $(CH_3)_3CBr + H_2O \rightarrow (CH_3)_3COH + HBr$ in a 10 Percent Water–90 Percent Acetone Solvent

At 25°C		At 50°C	
Time, h	$(CH_3)_3CBr$ mol liter^{-1}	Time, min	$(CH_3)_3CBr,$ mol liter^{-1}
0	0.1039	0	0.1056
3.15	0.0896	9	0.0961
6.20	0.0776	18	0.0856
10.0	0.0639	27	0.0767
13.5	0.0529	40	0.0645
18.3	0.0353	54	0.0536
26.0	0.0270	72	0.0432
30.8	0.0207	105	0.0270
37.3	0.0142	135	0.0174
43.8	0.0101	180	0.0089

Source: From the data of L. C. Bateman, E. D. Hughes, and C. K. Ingold, *J. Chem. Soc.*, p. 960, 1940.

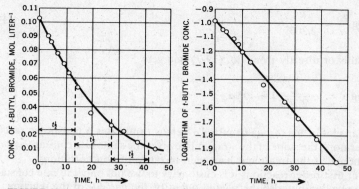

FIGURE 19-1 Graphical representation of the 25°C rate of Table 19-1 showing that for the conditions used the reaction $(CH_3)_3CBr + H_2O \rightarrow (CH_3)_3COH +$ HBr is first-order with respect to $(CH_3)_3CBr$. The rate constant is found to be 1.44×10^{-5} s^{-1}, and the half-life 0.48×10^5 s, or 13.4 h.

samples for their HBr content. Some of the data that were obtained are shown in Table 19•1. Figure 19-1 shows the concentration of the *tert*-butyl bromide plotted against time and also the plot of the logarithm of these concentrations versus time. The linearity of this second plot shows that in this water-acetone system the reaction follows first-order kinetics. The rate equation for the reaction is therefore

$$-\frac{d[(CH_3)_3CBr]}{dt} = k[(CH_3)_3CBr]$$

and the slope of the line of Fig. 19-1 leads to a value for k of 1.4×10^{-5} s^{-1}.

It is characteristic of first-order reactions that, as Eq. (19-6) shows, all that need be measured to see whether or not a reaction is first-order is the ratio of the concentrations of the reagent at various times to the concentration at some initial time. The measurement of any quantity that is proportional to the concentration of the reagent can therefore be used, and the actual concentrations need not be calculated. Thus if some quantity α, perhaps the absorption of some wavelength of light by the reagent, is related to the concentration by the proportionality equations

$$c = (\text{const})\alpha$$

and

$$c_0 = (\text{const})\alpha_0 \tag{19-8}$$

then Eq. (19-6) becomes

$$\log \frac{\alpha_0}{\alpha} = \frac{k}{2.303} t \tag{19-9}$$

From this or directly from Eq. (19-7) one gets

$$\log \alpha = -\frac{k}{2.303} t + \log \alpha_0 \tag{19-10}$$

A linear plot of $\log (\alpha_0/\alpha)$ or of $\log \alpha$ versus t indicates a first-order reaction. Furthermore, the slope of the straight line gives the same rate constant as would be obtained if the treatment had been in terms of concentrations.

For first-order reactions it is customary to use not only the rate constant k for the reaction but also the related quantity, the *half-life* of the reaction. The half-life is the time required for the concentration or amount of the reagent to decrease to half its initial value. For a first-order reaction the relation of the half-life $t_{1/2}$ to the rate constant can be found from Eq. (19-6) by inserting the requirement that at $t = t_{1/2}$ the concentration is $c = \frac{1}{2}c_0$. In this way one obtains

$$\log \frac{c_0}{\frac{1}{2}c_0} = \log 2 = \frac{k}{2.303} t_{1/2}$$

or

$$t_{1/2} = \frac{0.693}{k} \tag{19-11}$$

This result shows that for a first-order reaction there is a simple reciprocal relation between k and $t_{1/2}$. Furthermore, since the expression involves no term for the concentration or amount of material, the time required for half the reactant to be used up is independent of the initial concentration or amount of the reactant. This can be seen graphically in Fig. 19-1, where dashed lines have been drawn to show that the time intervals for the amount of *tert*-butyl bromide to decrease to half its value are all equal. It is the simple relation of Eq. (19-11) that makes the half-life a useful quantity for first-order reactions. Higher-order reactions, as we shall see, have a half-life that is a function of the initial concentration as well as of the rate constant, and the concept of half-life is then of little value.

A type of reaction which is in some ways outside the realm of chemistry but which conforms beautifully to first-order kinetics is that of radioactive decay. It is found that the rate with which a radioactive species decays is proportional to the amount of that species. The decay is therefore first-order, and one can use a half-life to characterize the decay rate, as is invariably done.

The natural-logarithm expression that led to Eq. (19-6) and to the half-life expression of Eq. (19-11) can be rewritten as

$$c = c_0 e^{-kt} \qquad (19\text{-}12)$$

This form suggests another time measure, like the half-life, to characterize the rate of the reaction. The symbol τ is usually used for $1/k$, and Eq. (19-12) can then be written as

$$c = c_0 e^{-t/\tau} \qquad (19\text{-}13)$$

The value of τ is the time it takes for the concentration to fall to $1/e$ of the original concentration. It is customary to use τ rather than $t_{1/2}$ in relaxation studies, as will be shown in Sec. 19-3.

A reaction is classified as second-order if the rate of the reaction is proportional to the square of the concentration of one of the reagents or to the product of the concentrations of two species of the reagents. The second situation leads to the same equations as the first if the two reactants are used up at the same rate and if their initial concentrations are equal. For these situations, the rate law is

$$-\frac{dc}{dt} = kc^2 \qquad (19\text{-}14)$$

where c is the concentration of the single reagent or of one of the two reagents. Again the kinetic data are usually compared with the integrated form of the equation. One has

$$-\int_{c_0}^{c} \frac{dc}{c^2} = k \int_{0}^{t} dt$$

and

$$\frac{1}{c} - \frac{1}{c_0} = kt \qquad (19\text{-}15)$$

A reaction of the types considered so far is therefore of second-order if a plot of $1/c$ versus t gives a straight line. The slope of the straight line is equal to the rate constant. As Eq. (19-15) shows, this constant involves the units of concentration, differing in this respect from the first-order rate constant that involves only the units of time. Furthermore, the time for the concentration to drop to half its initial value is deduced from Eq. (19-15) to be

$$t_{1/2} = \frac{1}{kc_0} \qquad (19\text{-}16)$$

The half-life therefore depends on the initial concentration and is not a convenient way of expressing the rate constant of second-order reactions.

Experimental rate data can be tested for conformity to a second-order rate law in a number of ways. As an illustration, we consider a case where, instead of working with the concentration of the reacting species, as would be done in using Eq. (19-15), it is more convenient to develop the rate equation by introducing a term for the amount of reaction that has occurred at time t. The overall reaction might, for example, be of the form

$$A + B \rightarrow products$$

If it is inconvenient to arrange to have the initial concentrations of A and B equal, the analysis that led to Eq. (19-15) cannot be used, but the kinetic data can be treated in terms of the following quantities:

a = initial concentration of A
b = initial concentration of B
x = decrease in A or B at time t = amount of product at time t
$a - x$ = concentration of A at time t
$b - x$ = concentration of B at time t

The differential second-order rate equation would then be

$$\frac{dx}{dt} = k[A][B] = k(a - x)(b - x) \tag{19-17}$$

The integration can be performed by using partial fractions. Thus

$$\frac{dx}{(a - x)(b - x)} = k\,dt$$

leads to the integral

$$\frac{1}{a - b} \int_0^x \left(-\frac{dx}{a - x} + \frac{dx}{b - x} \right) = k \int_0^t dt$$

On integration this gives

$$\frac{1}{a - b} \left[\ln (a - x) - \ln (b - x) \right]_0^x = kt$$

Insertion of the limits and rearrangement gives, finally,

$$\frac{1}{a - b} \ln \frac{b(a - x)}{a(b - x)} = kt \tag{19-18}$$

TABLE 19-2 Concentrations of Isobutyl Bromide and Sodium Ethoxide in Ethanol at 95.15°C, mol liter^{-1}

t, min	$b - x =$ [C$_4$H$_9$Br]	$a - x =$ [NaOEt]	$x =$ decrease in [C$_4$H$_9$Br] or [NaOEt]	k from Eq. (19-18)
0	0.0505	0.0762	0.0030	5.6
5	0.0446	0.0703	0.0086	5.8
10	0.0398	0.0655	0.0135	5.8
17	0.0340	0.0596	0.0182	5.7
30	0.0275	0.0532	0.0277	5.5
50	0.0193	0.0451	0.0335	5.5
70	0.0150	0.0407	0.0386	5.4
90	0.0119	0.0376	0.0421	5.4

Source: From the data of I. Dostrovsky and E. D. Hughes, *J. Chem. Soc.*, p. 157, 1946.

The data obtained by Dostrovsky and Hughes for the reaction of isobutyl bromide and sodium ethoxide are shown in Table 19-2. Such data can be compared with the second-order rate equation by calculating the values of k for the various times to get the values listed in Table 19-2 or by making the appropriate plot, as in Fig. 19-2, and observing the linearity of the data. Either test shows that the reaction under these conditions is second-order and has the rate equation

$$-\frac{d[\text{C}_4\text{H}_9\text{Br}]}{dt} = -\frac{d[\text{NaOEt}]}{dt} = 5.5 \times 10^{-3}[\text{C}_4\text{H}_9\text{Br}][\text{NaOEt}] \quad (19\text{-}19)$$

where the concentrations are expressed in moles per liter and the time in seconds.

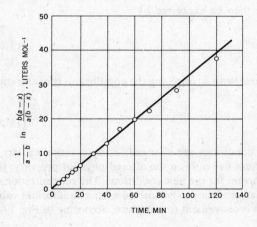

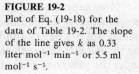

FIGURE 19-2
Plot of Eq. (19-18) for the data of Table 19-2. The slope of the line gives k as 0.33 liter mol^{-1} min^{-1} or 5.5 ml mol^{-1} s^{-1}.

A similar treatment involving the amount of reaction that has occurred at time t can be applied if, for example, the overall reaction follows an equation of the form

$$A + 2B \rightarrow \text{products}$$

The integrated rate equation corresponds to Eq. (19-18) but is different from it.

19-3 Relaxation Methods

In most kinetic studies, the progress of a reaction is followed as the system moves under fixed conditions toward the equilibrium state. An alternate procedure consists of changing the conditions on a system at equilibrium and observing the system as it moves toward the equilibrium appropriate to the new conditions. This approach is particularly useful in the study of fast reactions. New conditions can be applied so rapidly that movement of even very responsive systems to a new state of equilibrium can be followed. A temperature jump of as much as $10\,°C$, for example, can be produced in an aqueous solution by an electric discharge that lasts no more than $1\ \mu s$. If the properties of the system can be recorded following such a change, the rates of reactions that produce a new state of equilibrium, even within a few microseconds, can be measured.

Let us consider a specific example. The dissociation equilibrium for water can be written as

$$H_2O \rightleftharpoons H^+ + OH^- \tag{19-20}$$

Let a be the concentration of water and x the concentration of the H^+ and OH^- ions. Furthermore, let k_1 be the rate constant for the forward reaction and k_{-1} the rate constant for the reverse reaction. The net rate of formation of the ions in an aqueous solution can then be expressed by

$$\frac{dx}{dt} = k_1(a - x) - k_{-1}x^2 \tag{19-21}$$

At equilibrium, $dx/dt = 0$ and, with x_e implying the equilibrium concentration of H^+ and OH^-,

$$k_1(a - x_e) = k_{-1}(x_e)^2 \tag{19-22}$$

Now suppose that the conditions are changed, as by a sudden jump in temperature. If the equilibrium depends on the altered physical property, the system will not be at equilibrium for the new conditions. The concentration of the H^+ and OH^- ions will change as they move toward x_e, the equilibrium value under the new conditions. It is convenient to introduce, according to Fig. 19-3,

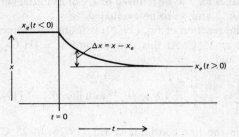

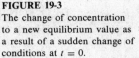

FIGURE 19-3
The change of concentration
to a new equilibrium value as
a result of a sudden change of
conditions at $t = 0$.

$\Delta x = x - x_e$ to show how the concentrations of H^+ and OH^- move away toward their new x_e value.

The rate of change of x, with x now expressed as $x_e + \Delta x$, is given by Eq. (19-21) as

$$\frac{d(x_e + \Delta x)}{dt} = \frac{d(\Delta x)}{dt} = k_1(a - x_e - \Delta x) - k_{-1}(x_e + \Delta x)^2 \qquad (19\text{-}23)$$

If the new equilibrium to which the system is moving is little different from the original equilibrium, Δx will at all times be much less than x_e. Then a $(\Delta x)^2$ term can be neglected compared with an $x_e \Delta x$ term. With this condition and the equilibrium expression of Eq. (19-22), Eq. (19-23) becomes

$$\frac{d(\Delta x)}{dt} = -(k_1 + 2k_{-1}x_e)\,\Delta x \qquad (19\text{-}24)$$

We thus have obtained a first-order type of relation. A solution function for Eq. (19-24) can be written as

$$\Delta x = (\Delta x)_0 e^{-t/\tau} \qquad (19\text{-}25)$$

where $(\Delta x)_0$ is the initial, $t = 0$, value of the displacement from the new equilibrium and τ is the *relaxation time*. Substitution of Eq. (19-24) in Eq. (19-25) gives

$$k_1 + 2k_{-1}x_e = \frac{1}{\tau} \qquad (19\text{-}26)$$

Thus the rate constants and the equilibrium concentration x_e are related to the relaxation time. This time is seen from Eq. (19-25) to be that in which the relaxation process carries the system a fraction $1/e$ toward the equilibrium position. Thus τ is a time interval like the half-life $t_{1/2}$ introduced in Sec. 19-2.

Measurement of τ, the time it takes for x to be reduced to $1/e$ of its initial value, allows the term involving k_1, k_{-1}, and x_e to be evaluated.

The relaxation time for the reaction of Eq. (19-20) is found by temperature-jump studies to be $36\,\mu s$ at $25°C$. At this temperature $x_e = [H_3O^+] = [OH^-]$ is $1 \times 10^{-7}\,mol\,liter^{-1}$ and

$$\frac{k_1}{k_{-1}} = K = \frac{[H_3O^+][OH^-]}{[H_2O]} = \frac{10^{-14}}{55.5} = 1.8 \times 10^{-16}\,mol\,liter^{-1} \qquad (19\text{-}27)$$

With these data we can obtain the rate constants of Eq. (19-26) at $25°C$ as

$$k_1 = 2.5 \times 10^{-5}\,s^{-1} \quad \text{and} \quad k_{-1} = 1.4 \times 10^{11}\,liters\,mol^{-1}\,s^{-1} \qquad (19\text{-}28)$$

Notice that the large value of k_{-1} is to be coupled with the small equilibrium values of $[H^+]$ and $[OH^-]$ to give the rate with which H^+, or H_3O^+, and OH^- associate. This balances the dissociation rate determined by the small value of k_1 but the large value of $[H_2O]$.

19-4 Enzyme Kinetics

Many rate equations that are more complex than the first- and second-order equations of Sec. 19-2 are encountered in chemical-rate studies. Such rate equations can also be illustrated by considering reactions that occur in biological systems, or at least are affected by enzymes occurring in such systems.

The effect of enzymes on the rate with which chemical reactions move toward their equilibrium position provides one of the most dramatic catalytic effects. Much of the current interest in the subject is centered on the details of the interaction between the *enzyme,* which is the catalyst, and the material, known as the *substrate,* whose reaction it affects. But it is important also to understand how an enzyme-catalyzed reaction proceeds in time and how the catalytic activity of the enzyme-substrate pair is evaluated from the measurement of the progress of such reactions.

The experimental data for enzyme-catalyzed reactions show a variety of forms that depend on the enzyme, the substrate, the temperature, the presence of interfering substances, and so forth. Many of the behaviors that are found can be looked on as variations from the "ideal" curve of Fig. 19-4. It is such rate curves for which we shall now develop a rate equation in a form that is conveniently related to the quantities that are measured in enzyme studies.

Inspection of the curve of Fig. 19-4 shows that at high substrate concentrations the rate of the reaction is independent of the substrate concentration. It is, however, proportional to the total amount of enzyme $[E_{tot}]$ in the system. At low substrate concentrations the rate, as shown by the initial straight-line section of the curve of Fig. 19-4, is proportional to the substrate concentration. The rate would also be found to be proportional to the total enzyme concen-

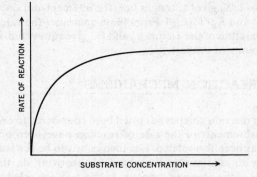

FIGURE 19-4
The form of the rate-versus-substrate-concentration curve for an "ideal" enzyme-catalyzed reaction.

tration. These features can be accounted for by a rate equation, where R denotes the rate of the reaction of the form

$$R = \frac{(\text{const}) [E_{tot}][S]}{\text{const}' + [S]} \tag{19-29}$$

To anticipate the notation that will be introduced when the mechanism of enzyme-catalyzed reactions are dealt with, we introduce the symbols k_2 and K_M for the two constants and thus write the rate equation in the form

$$R = \frac{k_2[E_{tot}][S]}{K_M + [S]} \tag{19-30}$$

Although the parameters k_2 and K_M could be determined so that a function corresponding to the experimental curve on an R-versus-[S] plot is obtained, a more convenient procedure can be found. The initial rate is often obtained by measuring [S] after a time t at which only a small fraction of the substrate has been consumed. If $[S_0]$ is the initial substrate concentration, we can express the initial rate as $([S_0] - [S])/t$. Then Eq. (19-30) becomes

$$[S_0] - [S] = \frac{k_2[E_{tot}][S_0]}{K_M + [S_0]} t \tag{19-31}$$

The "constants" $k_2[E_{tot}]$ and K_M can be evaluated from measurements of the initial rate of reaction. This rate, R_{init}, is approximately $([S_0] - [S])/t$, where $[S_0]$ is the substrate concentration at $t = 0$ and [S] is the concentration after a small time interval t. Values of R_{init} can be obtained for various values of $[S_0]$. A convenient procedure for obtaining the constants of Eq. (19-31) is based on the reciprocal of this equation. We write

$$\frac{1}{R_{init}} = \frac{1}{k_2[E_{tot}]} + \frac{K_M}{k_2[E_{tot}]} \frac{1}{[S_0]} \tag{19-32}$$

Thus, if a plot of $1/R_{init}$ versus $1/S_0$ gives a straight line, the intercept and slope can be used to obtain $k_2[E_{tot}]$ and $K_M/k_2[E_{tot}]$. From these quantities the value of K_M can be calculated. Separation of the factors k_2 and $[E_{tot}]$ requires studies of systems with various amounts of enzyme.

RATE LAWS AND REACTION MECHANISMS

The physical chemist's role in reaction kinetics has often been considered to end when the experimental measurements of the rate of reaction have been obtained and a rate equation has been formulated. For such efforts to be rewarding, however, it is necessary to continue to the phase of theorizing on the molecular behavior that leads to the observed rate law. In this way one is led to consider reaction mechanisms. Since the study of the details of reaction processes could lead to an investigation of all organic and inorganic chemistry, it is necessary that only a few representative reactions be considered and that the approach to an understanding of chemical reactions that comes from reaction kinetics be indicated.

All the features of some reactions can be accounted for by a mechanism that consists of the single step in which all the reactant molecules come together, the atoms and electrons are rearranged in the moment of impact, and the product molecules fly apart. Such a mechanism is said to involve a *concerted* process.

In most reactions, however, such a concerted process would require a complicated and improbable combination of changes to get from reactants to products. It is then more satisfactory to attempt to explain the reaction as proceeding by means of a sequence of steps, each step consisting of simple atomic or electronic moves.

19-5 Reaction Mechanisms and Rate Laws: The Stationary-State Method

Let us here investigate the rate laws that would be expected on the basis of a sequence of elementary reaction steps that appear to enter into the mechanism of many organic and inorganic and ionic and free-radical reactions. We shall make use of the idea, developed in detail in Sec. 19-9, that the rate of an elementary step is proportional to the product of the concentrations of the reactants in that step. Various intermediates may enter into the elementary steps of the mechanism even if they are not obtained as products of the overall reaction.

Let us consider some mechanisms in which the first step is a *reversible* reaction that produces one or more intermediates and one or more final product species. The second step consists in the decay of one of the intermediates, the reaction of one of the intermediates with another intermediate, or the reaction of one of the intermediates with one of the reactant species. The result of the second step may be final products or additional intermediates. In the latter case, for simplicity, we shall assume that all further reactions are relatively very rapid. One example of the many variations is

$$A \rightleftharpoons M + C$$
$$\underline{M + B \rightarrow D}$$
$$A + B \rightarrow C + D$$

where A and B are reactants, M is an intermediate, and C and D are products. Other variations are illustrated by the compilation of suggested mechanisms for reactions in Table 19-3.

The deduction of the rate equation for a reaction that proceeds by one of the mechanisms of this general type can be carried out most easily if we can assume that for most of the period over which the reaction is studied the concentrations of the intermediates are small compared with reactants or products. Failure to detect such intermediates lends support to this assumption. If the concentration of the intermediate fails to build up to an appreciable

TABLE 19-3 Some Reactions for Which Mechanisms Consisting of an Initial Reversible Step Followed by Reaction of One of the Products of This Step Have Been Suggested

Additional mechanistic steps beyond the first two are required to account for the overall reaction

First step:	$Br_2 \rightleftharpoons 2Br$
Second step:	$Br + H_2 \rightarrow HBr + H$
Overall reaction:	$Br_2 + H_2 \rightarrow 2HBr$

First step:	$CHCl_3 + OH^- \rightleftharpoons :CCl_3^- + H_2O$
Second step:	$:CCl_3^- \rightarrow :CCl_2 + Cl^-$
Overall reaction:	$2CHCl_3 + 7OH \rightarrow CO + HCOO^- + 6Cl^- + 4H_2O$

First step:	$Co(CN)_5OH_2{}^{2-} \rightleftharpoons Co(CN)_5{}^{2-} + H_2O$
Second step:	$Co(CN)_5{}^{2-} + I^- \rightarrow Co(CN)_5 I^{3-}$
Overall reaction:	$Co(CN)_5OH_2{}^{2-} + I^- \rightarrow Co(CN)_5 I^{3-} + H_2O$

First step:
$$\underset{\text{O}}{\overset{\text{O}}{\text{CH}_3-\overset{\|}{\text{C}}-\text{CH}_3}} + OH^- \rightleftharpoons CH_3\overset{\|}{\text{C}}CH_2^- + H_2O$$

Second step:
$$CH_3-\overset{\|}{\underset{\text{O}}{\text{C}}}CH_2^- + Br_2 \rightarrow CH_3\overset{\|}{\underset{\text{O}}{\text{C}}}CH_2Br + Br^-$$

Overall reaction:
$$CH_3-\overset{\|}{\underset{\text{O}}{\text{C}}}-CH_3 + 3Br_2 + 4OH^- \rightarrow$$
$$CH_3\overset{\|}{\underset{\text{O}}{\text{C}}}-O^- + CHBr_3 + 3Br^- + 3H_2O$$

value, it follows that except at the initial and final stages of the reaction the rate of change of the intermediate can be set equal to zero. This result, a feature of the *stationary-state method,* is very helpful in the deduction of the rate equation corresponding to a postulated mechanism.

Consider, to be specific,

$$A \underset{k_{-1}}{\overset{k_1}{\rightleftharpoons}} M + C \tag{19-33}$$

$$M + B \xrightarrow{k_2} \text{products} \tag{19-34}$$

The value of [M] increases as a result of the elementary reaction associated with k_1 and decreases as a result of the k_{-1} and k_2 reactions. The rate of formation of M is given as

$$\frac{d[M]}{dt} = k_1[A] - k_{-1}[M][C] - k_2[M][B]$$

Thus the steady-state assumption of $d[M]/dt = 0$ lets us write

$$k_1[A] = k_{-1}[M][C] + k_2[M][B]$$

or

$$[M] = \frac{k_1[A]}{k_{-1}[C] + k_2[B]} \tag{19-35}$$

According to the mechanism, the rate of formation of products, or the rate of consumption of B, which from the overall stoichiometry is also that for A, is equal to the rate of the second reaction, i.e.,

$$\text{Rate} = -\frac{d[A]}{dt} = -\frac{d[B]}{dt} = k_2[M][B] \tag{19-36}$$

The steady-state expression obtained for [M] allows this to be written

$$\text{Rate} = \frac{k_1 k_2 [A][B]}{k_{-1}[C] + k_2[B]} \tag{19-37}$$

Different but related rate equations can be worked out in the same way for the various mechanisms shown in Table 19-3.

That a single mechanism, such as that of Eqs. (19-33) and (19-34), can lead to different rate equations can be illustrated by considering three examples with different relative rate constants.

Example 19-1: For $k_{-1}[C] \gg k_2[B]$

For this case, Eq. (19-37) reduces to

$$\text{Rate} = \frac{k_1 k_2}{k_{-1}} \frac{[A][B]}{[C]} \tag{19-38}$$

A similar result could have been obtained more directly (and without the assumption that [M] is small) by assuming that an equilibrium is established by the first reaction and that the second reaction does not use B up fast enough to upset this equilibrium. Then one would have written

$$k_1[A] = k_{-1}[M][C] \qquad \text{or} \qquad \frac{[M][C]}{[A]} = \frac{k_1}{k_{-1}} = K$$

and

$$\text{Rate} = k_2[M][B] = \frac{k_1 k_2}{k_{-1}} \frac{[A][B]}{[C]} \tag{19-39}$$

An illustration of this situation is the reaction of the iodide ion with hypochlorite according to

$$I^- + OCl^- \rightarrow OI^- + Cl^-$$

The rate of the reaction is influenced by the pH, and the rate law that is deduced from rate data is

$$\text{Rate} = \frac{k[I^-][OCl^-]}{[OH^-]} \tag{19-40}$$

A suitable mechanism for this reaction has an initial rapid equilibrium step

$$OCl^- + H_2O \rightleftharpoons HOCl + OH^-$$

followed by a slow step involving the reagents I^- and HOCl.

Example 19-2: For $k_{-1}[C] \ll k_2[B]$

Equation (19-37) now reduces to

$$\text{Rate} = k_1[A] \tag{19-41}$$

i.e., the rate law would simply be first-order in [A] even though the reaction is still assumed to proceed through the same sequence of steps.

One can recognize that the assumed inequality makes the initial dissociation of A the rate-determining step and the later steps in the mechanism of no consequence.

Example 19-3: For $k_{-1}[C]$ and $k_2[B]$ of comparable magnitudes
An illustration of this situation is provided by the reaction

$$Co(CN)_5OH_2{}^{2-} + I^- \rightarrow Co(CN)_5I^{3-} + H_2O$$

The observed rate law has the form

$$Rate = \frac{a[Co(CN)_5OH_2{}^{2-}][I^-]}{b + c[I^-]} \tag{19-42}$$

A mechanism that is reasonable and leads to an expression of this form is

$$Co(CN)_5OH_2{}^{2-} \underset{k_{-1}}{\overset{k_1}{\rightleftharpoons}} Co(CN)_5{}^{2-} + H_2O$$
$$Co(CN)_5{}^{2-} + I^- \xrightarrow{k_2} Co(CN)_5I^{3-}$$

The analysis that led to Eq. (19-37) would, for this example, lead to the expected rate equation

$$Rate = \frac{k_1 k_2[Co(CN)_5OH_2{}^{2-}][I^-]}{k_{-1}[H_2O] + k_2[I^-]} \tag{19-43}$$

Since the reaction is run in aqueous solution with a large and essentially constant concentration of water, we see that the mechanism is consistent with the empirical rate law.

19-6 A Mechanism for Enzyme-Catalyzed Reactions

A variety of rate laws is required to portray the rates of enzyme-catalyzed reactions for the great variety of enzymes, substrates, and the rate-influencing reagents and physical conditions that are encountered. The rate law of Sec. 19-4, however, is a guide to many of these variations and the mechanism of this section, often called the Michaelis-Menten mechanism, is likewise a base for other variations.

The mechanism that accounts for the rate law of Eq. (19-30) is similar to those dealt with in the preceding section.

With S representing substrate, E the enzyme, and E · S an enzyme-substrate complex, the mechanism of the reaction is presumed to be adequately represented by

$$E + S \rightleftharpoons E \cdot S \tag{19-44}$$

$$E \cdot S \rightarrow E + \text{products} \tag{19-45}$$

As in the preceding section, the steady-state assumption, which, however, is not always clearly applicable in these reactions, leads to

$$k_1[E][S] = k_{-1}[E \cdot S] + k_2[E \cdot S]$$

and

$$[E \cdot S] = \frac{k_1}{k_{-1} + k_2}[E][S] \tag{19-46}$$

To bring these expressions to a form that can be compared with the empirical rate equation, we must recognize that it is only $[E_{tot}] = [E] + [E \cdot S]$, and not $[E]$, that is generally known. Often, in fact, only a quantity proportional to $[E_{tot}]$, and not even values of $[E_{tot}]$, are available.

Replacement of $[E]$ in Eq. (19-46) leads to

$$[E \cdot S] = \frac{k_1[E_{tot}][S]}{(k_{-1} + k_2) + k_1[S]} \tag{19-47}$$

Now this expression for the intermediate $E \cdot S$ can be inserted into the expression for the rate of the net reaction. This rate can be based on the formation of products in the second mechanism step, Eq. (19-45). We have

$$-\frac{d[S]}{dt} = R = k_2[E \cdot S] = \frac{k_1 k_2[E_{tot}][S]}{k_{-1} + k_2 + k_1[S]}$$

$$= \frac{k_2[E_{tot}][S]}{(k_{-1} + k_2)/k_1 + [S]} \tag{19-48}$$

It is customary for the terms $(k_{-1} + k_2)/k_1$ to be indicated by the new symbol K_M, that is,

$$K_M = \frac{k_{-1} + k_2}{k_1} \tag{19-49}$$

to give the rate-law result of this mechanism as

$$R = \frac{k_2[E_{tot}][S]}{K_M + [S]}$$

We have come at this stage to the form of the empirical rate law obtained in Sec. 19-4.

We now are in a position to interpret the values of the parameters K_M and $k_2[E_{tot}]$ in terms of their roles in the steps of the mechanism.

Reference to Eq. (19-46) shows that, as the reaction is proceeding,

$$\frac{[E][S]}{[E \cdot S]} = K_M \tag{19-50}$$

Thus K_M is related to species concentrations, as is the dissociation constant for the species $[E \cdot S]$. The value of K_M, however, is given by $(k_{-1} + k_2)/k_1$, and this is equal to the value of the dissociation constant for $[E \cdot S]$ only to the extent that k_2 is small and can be neglected compared with k_{-1}. Thus, when the breakup of the $E \cdot S$ complex to form original E and S species dominates the process whereby the complex forms products, the value of K_M approaches the dissociation constant for the $E \cdot S$ complex.

What now is the significance of the term $k_2[E_{tot}]$? One first notes that the rate of the overall reaction is

$$R = k_2[E \cdot S] \tag{19-51}$$

It follows that $k_2[E_{tot}]$ is the rate that the reaction would have if all the enzyme was in the form of the enzyme-substrate complex. Thus $k_2[E_{tot}]$ is the maximum rate for a given value of $[E_{tot}]$. The *turnover* rate of an enzyme in a particular enzyme-catalyzed reaction is the rate per mole of enzyme; i.e., the turnover rate is equal to the value of k_2, and this can be calculated from $k_2[E_{tot}]$ if the total enzyme concentration is known.

19-7 Unimolecular Gas-Phase Reactions

One final reaction system that requires a treatment like those of the two preceding sections can be described. A variety of gas-phase reactions are thought of as resulting from the simple, unimolecular falling apart or isomerization of gas-phase molecules. Some fraction of the reactant species has energy high enough to ensure that, depending on how this energy is distributed throughout the different vibrational modes of the molecules, there is a certain chance of these activated molecules decomposing. The rate of reaction would then be proportional to the number or concentration of such activated molecules. At a given temperature, this number is proportional to the total number or concentration of the reactant molecules. With these proportionalities the reaction would conform to a first-order rate law.

A difficulty arises when it is asked how the high-energy molecules accumulate their greater than average thermal energy. They must do so as a result of collisions with other molecules, and these collisions can be assumed to be binary collisions. If the reactant molecules are designated by A and those with rather large thermal energies by A*, we can write the *activation* reaction

$$A + A \rightarrow A + A^*$$

The rate of this reaction and the rate of formation of A* would then be proportional to $[A]^2$.

This activation process seems to imply that the overall reaction would be a second-order one. But we can suppose that in the gas there is an equilibrium reservoir of high-energy molecules, as could be calculated from the Boltzmann distribution, and that the reaction being considered never proceeds fast enough to deplete this reservoir. In this case the reaction rate is proportional to the number of high-energy molecules and not to the rate with which they are formed.

These ideas were first put forward and developed by F. A. Lindemann (later Lord Cherwell). He suggested considering the reaction sequence

$$A + A \underset{k_{-2}}{\overset{k_2}{\rightleftharpoons}} A + A^* \qquad A^* \overset{k_1}{\longrightarrow} \text{products} \tag{19-52}$$

The rate constants for the second-order forward and reverse reactions are indicated by k_2 and k_{-2}. It is this reaction which builds up the reservoir of activated molecules.

A net rate of formation of A* can be written in terms of its formation and destruction in the first reaction and its destruction in the second reaction. Thus

$$\frac{d[A^*]}{dt} = k_2[A]^2 - k_{-2}[A][A^*] - k_1[A^*] \tag{19-53}$$

The rate of the overall reaction, which can be expressed as the rate of formation of products, is given by

$$\text{Rate} = k_1[A^*] \tag{19-54}$$

Application of the steady-state assumption, $d[A^*]/dt = 0$, to Eq. (19-53) gives an expression for $[A^*]$ which can be written as

$$[A^*] = \frac{k_2[A]^2}{k_{-2}[A] + k_1} \tag{19-55}$$

Thus, according to the Lindemann mechanism, the rate law for the reaction is

$$\text{Rate} = \frac{k_1 k_2 [A]^2}{k_{-2}[A] + k_1} \tag{19-56}$$

Measurements of rates of reaction are often compared with this rate law by forming a first-order rate-law expression

$$\text{Rate} = k_{\text{exp}}[\text{A}] \qquad (19\text{-}57)$$

Then, the Lindemann mechanism leads us to interpret k_{exp} according to

$$k_{\text{exp}} = \frac{k_1 k_2 [\text{A}]}{k_{-2}[\text{A}] + k_1} \qquad (19\text{-}58)$$

A number of gas-phase reactions have been studied and have been found to have a k_{exp} term of Eq. (19-57) varying generally as suggested by Eq. (19-58). A logarithmic display is usually necessary to encompass the range of k_{exp} and concentration or pressures. At high pressures or concentrations the k_1 term in the denominator is negligible compared with the $k_{-2}[\text{A}]$ term. Then

$$k_{\text{exp}} = \frac{k_1 k_2}{k_{-2}} \qquad \text{and} \qquad \log k_{\text{exp}} = \log \frac{k_1 k_2}{k_{-2}}$$

At low pressures or concentrations that k_1 term dominates the $k_{-2}[\text{A}]$ term in the denominator. Then

$$k_{\text{exp}} = k_2[\text{A}] \qquad \text{and} \qquad \log k_{\text{exp}} = \log [\text{A}] + \log k_2$$

The isomerization of methyl isocyanide, according to the reaction

$$\text{CH}_3\text{NC} \rightarrow \text{CH}_3\text{CN}$$

provides the data for Fig. 19-5. The limiting expectations are clearly borne out.

Although the Lindemann mechanism is generally satisfactory, it fails to take in some of the subtleties involved. We must explore more carefully the relation between k_{exp} and the expression on the right of Eq. (19-58). The reciprocal gives

$$\frac{1}{k_{\text{exp}}} = \frac{k_{-2}}{k_1 k_2} + \frac{1}{k_2[\text{A}]} \qquad (19\text{-}59)$$

It follows that a plot of $1/k_{\text{exp}}$ versus $1/[\text{A}]$ or $1/P_{\text{A}}$ should give a straight line. Such a plot for some of the data of Fig. 19-5 is shown in Fig. 19-6. Equation (19-59) is not followed, and thus Eq. (19-58) does not properly describe the dependence of k_{exp} on [A].

A variety of refinements of the Lindemann mechanism have been made. They generally recognize that the rate of deactivation of A* and the rate of conversion of A* to products are not simply proportional to the concentration of

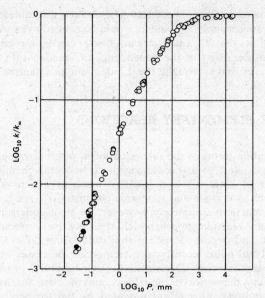

FIGURE 19-5 A plot of log (k/k_∞), where k_∞ is the rate in the high-pressure limit, versus log P for the reaction $CH_3NC \rightarrow CH_3CN$ at 230°C. P is the pressure of CH_3NC. [*From F. W. Schneider and B. S. Rabinovich, J. Am. Chem. Soc.,* **84**:4215 (*1962*).]

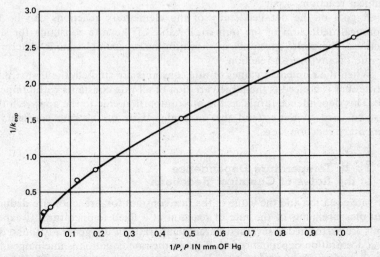

FIGURE 19-6 Some of the data of Fig. 19-5 plotted according to Eq. (19-59).

A*. If, as [A] is varied, the reaction system produces A* molecules with different energy profiles, different rate constants k_{-2} and k_1 would be needed to express the rates of reaction. It follows that k_{-2} and k_1 are not strictly constant, even at a given temperature. Considerations of the dependence of reaction rate on amount of activation energy have brought the Lindemann mechanism in agreement with experiment.

THE NATURE OF ELEMENTARY REACTIONS

The form of the concentration terms of the rate equation is of great value in deducing a sequence of reaction steps that could constitute an overall chemical reaction. It is this aspect of kinetics which leads to much of our present description of the reactions in organic and inorganic chemistry.

To understand these reactions completely, however, we must understand the details of the elementary-reaction steps in which, typically, two molecules come together, rearrange, and depart as species that differ from those that encountered each other. Until quite recently such elementary processes were subject to no direct experimental study. Descriptions of some features in such reactions were developed in a theoretical or model way, and the basis for these ideas was primarily the indirect information provided by the temperature dependence of the rates of chemical reactions. Now very direct and revealing experimental results for elementary reactions are becoming available for some relatively simple reactions through the use of molecular-beam techniques. Although such studies reveal the details of only gas-phase elementary reactions, they provide invaluable data for the answer to the question of how elementary chemical reactions occur.

A goal of the detailed study of the elementary reactions can be the theoretical deduction of the numerical value of the rate constants for such reactions. These rate constants, as shown in the preceding sections, determine the rate of any overall reaction.

When the numerical values of rate constants are studied, the first striking feature that is noticed is the large variation of all rate constants with temperature. This dependence furnishes the most important clue to the approach that must be used to understand the molecular basis of the rate constants of elementary reaction steps.

19-8 Temperature Dependence of the Rates of Chemical Reactions

The rate equation and the value of the rate constant for a reaction are deduced from measurements of the rate of reaction at a fixed temperature. If experiments are performed at several different temperatures, it is generally found that the concentration dependence exhibited in the rate equation is unchanged but that the value of the rate constant is very temperature-dependent.

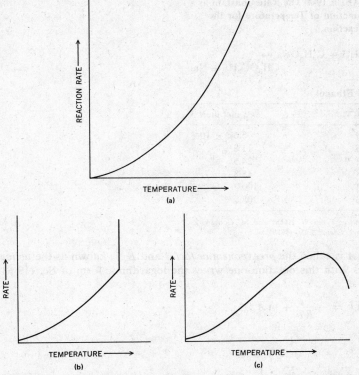

FIGURE 19-7 The shape of rate-versus-temperature curves for (a) most chemical reactions, (b) reactions that reach an explosive stage, (c) reactions that are enzyme-catalyzed.

The temperature dependence of the reaction rate shows up according to

$$\text{Rate} = k(T)(\text{concentration-dependent term}) \qquad (19\text{-}60)$$

in $k(T)$, the rate "constant." Often this term has the temperature dependence shown in Fig. 19-7a. The rate increases rapidly with increasing temperature. Other temperature dependences e.g., those of Fig. 19-7b and c, also show up in special circumstances, but most chemical reactions have the temperature dependence illustrated in Fig. 19-7a.

In 1889 Arrhenius recognized that this typical temperature dependence indicates an exponential increase of the rate, or rate constant, with temperature. This empirical relation can be conveniently written

$$k = Ae^{-E_a/RT} \qquad (19\text{-}61)$$

TABLE 19-4 The Rate Constant as a Function of Temperature for the Reaction

$$CH_3I + C_2H_5ONa \rightarrow CH_3OC_2H_5 + NaI$$

in Ethanol

t, °C	k_2, mol liters^{-1}
0	5.60×10^{-5}
6	11.8
12	24.5
18	48.8
24	100
30	208

Source: From W. Hecht and M. Conrad, *Z. Phys. Chem.*, **3**:450 (1889).

where A is called the *preexponential factor* and E_a is known as the *activation energy*. With this notation one writes the logarithmic form of Eq. (19-61)

$$\ln k = -\frac{E_a}{RT} + \ln A$$

or

$$\log k = -\frac{E_a}{2.303R}\frac{1}{T} + \log A \tag{19-62}$$

The data of Table 19-4 are shown on a logarithmic k-versus-$1/T$ plot in Fig. 19-8. The empirical constants E_a and A can be deduced from the slope and intercept of such a plot.

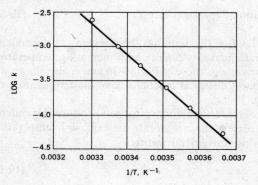

FIGURE 19-8
The Arrhenius plot of Eq. (19-62) for the data of Table 19-4. The straight line is represented by $\log k = -4250/T + 11.38$, or $\log k = -35,300/RT + \log 2.4 \times 10^{11}$, or $\ln k = -81,300/RT + \ln 2.4 \times 10^{11}$. Thus $E_a = 81,380$ J, and $A = 2.4 \times 10^{11}$ mol liter^{-1} s^{-1}.

Most reactions that proceed at a reasonable rate, i.e., have half-lives of minutes or hours, have values of E_a of 50 to 100 kJ. For such reactions one can use Eq. (19-62) to verify the photographer's guide that reactions go 2 or 3 times as fast when the temperature increases by 10°C.

Some reactions that appear to follow the temperature dependence expressed by Eq. (19-61) are found to have a somewhat temperature-dependent A term. If this term contains a power of T as a factor, an equation of the form of Eq. (19-62) will contain a log T term with a coefficient indicating the power to which T is raised in the preexponential A factor. There are only a few reactions for which such a temperature-dependent A term has been established, and in these cases there is no common power-of-T dependence.

19-9 The Collision Theory

The collision theory, as its name implies, focuses attention on the idea that the reaction of molecules can occur only as a result of a coming together, or a collision, of the reactant molecules. A reaction step in which two different gas-phase molecular types come together and produce one or more new species depends on collisions between the two types of molecules. Here let us see on what the rate of such collisions depends. The collision-number expressions deduced in Sec. 2-9 could again be used, but instead let us develop an expression that will be helpful when a more detailed look at reactive molecular collisions is taken.

Consider a single molecule of A moving through a gas that contains N_B^* molecules of B per unit volume and, to begin with, assume that the B molecules are at rest. As shown in Fig. 19-9, the *cross-section area* σ_{AB} for a collision between an A and a B molecule is related to the radii of A and B if they are assumed to be spherical by

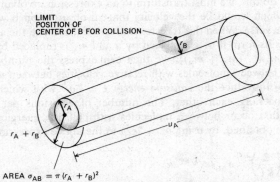

LIMIT
POSITION OF
CENTER OF B FOR COLLISION

r_B

r_A

$r_A + r_B$

u_A

AREA $\sigma_{AB} = \pi (r_A + r_B)^2$

FIGURE 19-9 The collision cross section σ_{AB}. Molecule A will collide with any B molecule whose center is within the volume $u_A \sigma_{AB}$ swept out by the cross-section area σ_{AB}.

$$\sigma_{AB} = \pi(r_A + r_B)^2 \tag{19-63}$$

The volume in which the A molecule can suffer collisions with B molecules in 1 s is that swept out by the A molecule, as shown in Fig. 19-9. If the A molecule travels with velocity u_A, the number of collisions by the A molecule with B molecules per second is $N_B^* u_A \sigma_{AB}$.

The probability, or fraction, of A molecules having a velocity in the range u to $u + du$ is given by the Maxwell-Boltzmann distribution, Eq. (2-28),

$$\frac{dN_A}{N_A} = 4\pi \left(\frac{m_A}{2\pi kT}\right)^{3/2} u_A^2 e^{-(1/2)m u_A^2/kT} \, du_A \tag{19-64}$$

Thus, if there are N_A^* molecules of A per unit volume, the number with speeds in the range u and $u + du$ will be

$$N_A^* \frac{dN_A}{N_A} = N_A^* \left[4\pi \left(\frac{m_A}{2\pi kT}\right)^{3/2} u_A^2 e^{-(1/2)m u_A^2/kT} \, du_A\right] \tag{19-65}$$

The product of the number of collisions an A molecule makes with B molecules, $N_B^* u_A \sigma_{AB}$, and the number of A molecules per unit volume with a speed in the range u_A to $u_A + du_A$, Eq. (19-65), gives the number of A–B collisions per unit volume involving A molecules with speeds in the u_A to $u_A + du_A$ range. This result is

$$N_A^* N_B^* (4\pi) \left(\frac{m_A}{2\pi kT}\right)^{3/2} \sigma_{AB} u_A^3 e^{-(1/2)m u_A^2/kT} \, du_A$$

This A-focused result will be satisfactory if A molecules are very light and fast-moving relative to B molecules. But in general, we must allow for motions of both A and B. To do this, we must transform to an expression involving the *relative velocity u*, which would be the velocity that an observer on B would attribute to A, or vice versa. When this transformation is carried out, the above expression maintains its form if u_A is replaced by u and m_A is replaced by the reduced mass $\mu = [m_A m_B/(m_A + m_B)]$. We then can express the number of collisions that occur between molecules with relative velocities between u and $u + du$. We can also introduce the *collision energy* $\epsilon = \frac{1}{2}\mu u^2$ with which the molecules are approaching each other. The number of collisions per unit volume per second that occur between molecules with collision energies between ϵ and $\epsilon + d\epsilon$ is obtained, by using $u^2 = 2\epsilon/\mu$ in the above expression, as

$$N_A^* N_B^* \left(\frac{1}{\pi\mu}\right)^{1/2} \left(\frac{2}{kT}\right)^{3/2} \sigma_{AB} \epsilon e^{-\epsilon/kT} \, d\epsilon$$

The total number of collisions per unit volume per second between A and B molecules is

$$Z_{AB} = N_A^* N_B^* \left(\frac{1}{\pi\mu}\right)^{1/2} \left(\frac{2}{kT}\right)^{3/2} \int_0^\infty \sigma_{AB}\epsilon e^{-\epsilon/kT}\, d\epsilon \tag{19-66}$$

The simplest approach to the integration, taken in Sec. 2-9, expresses σ_{AB} as $\pi(r_A + r_B)^2$, where r_A and r_B are the fixed radii of the rigid spheres that represent molecules A and B. Then σ_{AB} is assumed to be independent of the collision energy, as suggested in Fig. 19-10a. If the molecules A and B attract each other, however, we might expect this attraction to be effective at low collision energies in drawing the molecules toward each other. We could add such an effect to our collision-number calculation by supposing a dependence of σ_{AB} on ϵ given by the line of Fig. 19-10b. As this suggests, the collision diameter can accommodate some of the subtle features involved in molecular collisions.

If we proceed here with the assumption that σ_{AB} is independent of the collision energy, Eq. (19-66) leads (with the definite integrals of Appendix A) to the result

$$Z_{AB} = 2\sigma_{AB} \left(\frac{2kT}{\pi\mu}\right)^{1/2} N_A^* N_B^* \tag{19-67}$$

With the substitution $\sigma_{AB} = \pi(d_A + d_B)^2/4$ and $d_A = d_B = d$ this result is seen to be related to the collision expressions of Sec. 2-9.

In nonreacting systems this result gives us the number of A–B collisions per unit volume per second. In reacting systems we can expect that only some fraction of these collisions will be effective in producing an elementary reaction step.

Collision theory is straightforward to the stage at which an expression, Eq. (19-66), for the number of collisions between A and B molecules per unit volume per second is obtained. Difficulties arise when we try to deduce the number of reactions occurring rather than the number of collisions. The only factor in the collision theory that can be used to express the distinction between

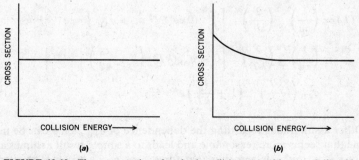

FIGURE 19-10 The cross sections for elastic collisions (a) without and (b) with intermolecular attraction.

collisions and reactive collisions is σ_{AB}. Let $\sigma_{AB,R}$ be a collision-cross-section function which, when used in Eq. (19-66), produces a result giving the number of reactive collisions per unit volume. The rate of the reaction is then given by

$$\text{Rate} = N_A^* N_B^* \left(\frac{1}{\pi\mu}\right)^{1/2} \left(\frac{2}{kT}\right)^{3/2} \int_0^\infty \sigma_{AB,R} \epsilon e^{-\epsilon/kT}\, d\epsilon \tag{19-68}$$

Comparison with the form of the empirical rate equation

$$\text{Rate} = k'(T) N_A^* N_B^* \tag{19-69}$$

then allows us to write, for the rate constant $k'(T)$ expressed in units of (molecules $m^{-3})^{-1}$ s^{-1}, the result

$$k'(T) = \left(\frac{1}{\pi\mu}\right)^{1/2} \left(\frac{2}{kT}\right)^{3/2} \int_0^\infty \sigma_{AB,R} \epsilon e^{-\epsilon/kT}\, d\epsilon \tag{19-70}$$

It only remains for us to deal with $\sigma_{AB,R}$, and, as will become apparent, a great deal of the problem has been assigned to, or submerged in, this quantity.

Our ideas on activation energy suggest that $\sigma_{AB,R}$ is zero for collision energies less than some critical amount, ϵ_0. What happens when molecules collide with collision energies greater than this critical amount ϵ_0? The simplest assumption is that all such collisions are reactive collisions. We express this idea by letting

$$\sigma_{AB,R} = \begin{cases} 0 & \text{for } \epsilon < \epsilon_0 \\ \sigma_{AB} & \text{for } \epsilon > \epsilon_0 \end{cases} \tag{19-71}$$

This assumption corresponds to the step function of Fig. 19-11a.

With the assumption of this step function for $\sigma_{AB,R}$, collision theory gives the rate constant as

$$\begin{aligned}
k'(T) &= \left(\frac{1}{\pi\mu}\right)^{1/2} \left(\frac{2}{kT}\right)^{3/2} \left[\int_0^{\epsilon_0} (0)\epsilon e^{-\epsilon/kT}\, d\epsilon + \sigma_{AB} \int_{\epsilon_0}^\infty \epsilon e^{-\epsilon/kT}\, d\epsilon\right] \\
&= \left(\frac{1}{\pi\mu}\right)^{1/2} \left(\frac{2}{kT}\right)^{3/2} \left[0 + \sigma_{AB}(kT)^2\left(1 + \frac{\epsilon_0}{kT}\right)e^{-\epsilon_0/kT}\right] \\
&= \sigma_{AB}\left(\frac{8kT}{\pi\mu}\right)^{1/2}\left(1 + \frac{\epsilon_0}{kT}\right)e^{-\epsilon_0/kT}
\end{aligned} \tag{19-72}$$

Other assumptions regarding the dependence of $\sigma_{AB,R}$ on ϵ can be made, and one that seems more reasonable and leads to a simple result assumes again that for $\epsilon < \epsilon_0$, $\sigma_{AB,R}$ is zero but that for $\epsilon > \epsilon_0$, $\sigma_{AB,R}$ becomes greater the greater the value of ϵ. One way of developing this idea is to assume that it is not

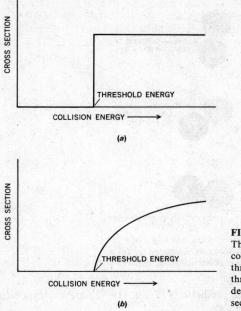

FIGURE 19-11
The cross sections for reactive collisions on the basis of (a) a threshold energy and (b) a threshold energy and a further dependence of reactive cross section on collision energy.

the energy based on the relative velocity of the molecules that matters but the energy component in the direction of the line between the centers. Thus, as Fig. 19-12 suggests, for energies near ϵ_0 only very direct center-to-center collisions can be effective, but for greater values of ϵ even rather glancing collisions can have a line-of-centers energy greater than ϵ_0. This idea leads to the curve of Fig. 19-11b or to the statement

$$\sigma_{AB,R} = \begin{cases} 0 & \text{for } \epsilon < \epsilon_0 \\ \sigma_{AB}\left(1 - \dfrac{\epsilon_0}{\epsilon}\right) & \text{for } \epsilon > \epsilon_0 \end{cases} \tag{19-73}$$

On this basis

$$k'(T) = \left(\frac{1}{\pi\mu}\right)^{1/2}\left(\frac{2}{kT}\right)^{3/2}\int_0^{\epsilon_0}(0)\epsilon e^{-\epsilon/kT}\,d\epsilon + \sigma_{AB}\int_{\epsilon_0}^{\infty}\epsilon\left(1 - \frac{\epsilon_0}{\epsilon}\right)e^{-\epsilon/kT}\,d\epsilon$$

$$= \sigma_{AB}\left(\frac{8kT}{\pi\mu}\right)^{1/2}e^{-\epsilon_0/kT} \tag{19-74}$$

The results of Eqs. (19-73) and (19-74), based on the $\sigma_{AB,R}$ functions of Fig. 19-11a and b, are quite different. Only for a few radical-recombination reactions is the activation energy, which we here identify with ϵ_0, small enough for $1 + \epsilon_0/kT$ to be approximately equal to 1. More typically ϵ_0 is many times

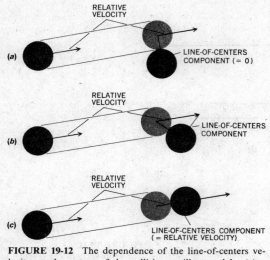

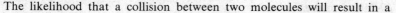

FIGURE 19-12 The dependence of the line-of-centers velocity on the nature of the collision as illustrated by (a) a glancing collision, (b) an intermediate collision, and (c) a direct collision.

greater than kT, and thus the predictions of Eq. (19-72) are correspondingly greater than those of Eq. (19-74).

The sensitivity of the results to the form assumed for the $\sigma_{AB,R}$ function can be understood from the graphical display of the $\sigma_{AB,R}$ and the population, $e^{-\epsilon/kT}$, integrand factors as given in Fig. 19-13. Small changes in the form of the $\sigma_{AB,R}$ function, particularly near ϵ_0, produce large changes in the product function of the integral.

The likelihood that a collision between two molecules will result in a

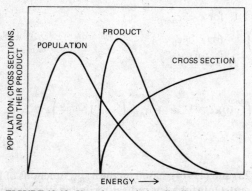

FIGURE 19-13 How the population distribution and the dependence of cross section on energy affect the rate of reaction.

reaction is certain to depend on the detailed nature of the molecules and on the transformation that must occur. In some cases collisions of certain types, e.g., glancing collisions, might begin the distortions that lead to reaction. In some cases collisions of a certain type might cause some of the rotational and vibrational energy to influence the reaction. The best we can hope for from the simple collision theory is the prediction of a typical or representative rate constant. The expression of Eq. (19-74), now known as the *line-of-centers rate constant,* is generally used for this purpose.

The rate constant of Eq. (19-74) is given in the units (molecules m^{-3})$^{-1}$ s^{-1}. Bimolecular rate constants obtained from the studies of the rates of reactions usually are expressed in (mol liter^{-1})$^{-1}$ s^{-1}. To convert Eq. (19-74) into these units, we multiply by $\mathfrak{N}$ molecules mol^{-1} and 10^3 liters m^{-3} and obtain

$$k(T) = 10^3 \mathfrak{N} k'(T)$$
$$= 10^3 \mathfrak{N} \sigma_{AB} \left(\frac{8kT}{\pi \mu} \right)^{1/2} e^{-\epsilon_0/kT}$$

and with $\sigma_{AB} = \pi (r_A + r_B)^2$

$$k(T) = 10^3 \mathfrak{N} \pi (r_A + r_B)^2 \left(\frac{8kT}{\pi \mu} \right)^{1/2} e^{-\epsilon_0/kT} \tag{19-75}$$

With the representative values of $M = 50$ g (and thus $\mu = 4.15 \times 10^{-26}$ kg) and $r_A = r_B = 1.5$ Å, we obtain for units of (mol liter^{-1}) s^{-1} and a temperature of 25°C

$$k(T) = 6 \times 10^{10} e^{-E_0/RT} \tag{19-76}$$

The preexponential factors in Table 19-5 fall mostly around this value. The theory has therefore been successful to some extent. Closer inspection will show that disagreement can become quite appreciable, the empirical values being less

TABLE 19-5 Rate Constants for Second-Order Gas-Phase Reactions According to $k = Ae^{-E_a/RT}$ for R in J K^{-1} mol^{-1}

Reaction	Rate constant (mol liter^{-1} s^{-1})
$H_2 + I_2 \rightarrow 2HI$	$1 \times 10^{11} e^{-167,000/RT}$
$2HI \rightarrow H_2 + I_2$	$6 \times 10^{10} e^{-184,000/RT}$
$2NO_2 \rightarrow 2NO + O_2$	$4.5 \times 10^9 e^{-112,500/RT}$
$2NOCl \rightarrow 2NO + Cl_2$	$9 \times 10^9 e^{-101,000/RT}$
$NO + Cl_2 \rightarrow NOCl + Cl$	$1.7 \times 10^9 e^{-83,000/RT}$
$NO + O_3 \rightarrow NO_2 + O_2$	$8 \times 10^8 e^{-10,500/RT}$
$CH_3I + HI \rightarrow CH_4 + I_2$	$1.6 \times 10^{12} e^{-140,000/RT}$
$2C_2F_4 \rightarrow$ cyclo-C_4F_8	$6.6 \times 10^7 e^{-108,000/RT}$
$2C_2H_4 \rightarrow$ cyclo-C_4H_8	$7.1 \times 10^7 e^{-158,000/RT}$

than expected on the basis of the collision-theory result by a factor of 10 and sometimes by several powers of 10. It seems likely that for a reaction to occur as a result of a collision, there must be not only enough energy but also a suitable orientation of the colliding molecules. For larger molecules this *steric factor* can be expected to be much less than unity because many collisions would not bring the reactive parts of the molecules together. There seems, however, to be no satisfactory quantitative way of allowing for this effect, and all that can be expected is that the observed preexponential factor will be less than that calculated when such geometric considerations are important.

19-10 Elementary Reactions in Liquid Solution: Diffusion-Controlled Reactions

The idea of elementary reaction processes, similar to those recognized for gas-phase reactions, can be carried over to liquid systems, but some significant differences in the molecular model for these steps must be introduced. We begin by deducing the liquid-state counterpart of the gas-phase rate-of-collision expression.

Consider a liquid system consisting of molecular species A and B, which can be identical or different, dissolved in a relatively inert solvent, so as to produce a solution with N_A^* and N_B^* molecules of A and of B per unit volume. What is the rate at which A and B molecules will encounter each other?

To proceed, we must borrow some of the concepts and results that will be dealt with in Sec. 22-5. In particular, we must use the concept of a *diffusion coefficient,* which is a measure of the rate with which a material diffuses across a unit cross-section area as a result of a unit concentration gradient. The relation of the liquid-phase reaction process to diffusion can be recognized by first focusing on a particular A molecule and asking about the rate with which B molecules would diffuse to it.

The result, which seems reasonable and will not be derived here, is that the rate is proportional to the number N_B^* of molecules of B per unit volume, the diffusion coefficient D_B of B, and the distance $r_A + r_B$ within which the center of B must come to that of A for the molecules to be in contact. The derived expression is

$$\text{Rate of B molecules diffusing to A molecule} = 4\pi D_B(r_A + r_B)N_B^*$$

For the total rate of encounters between A and B molecules per unit volume, on this basis, we would write

$$\text{Rate of encounters per unit volume} = 4\pi D_B(r_A + r_B)N_B^*N_A^*$$

In a similar way, if we focused on a B molecule and asked about the rate with which A molecules diffuse toward it, we would obtain

$$\text{Rate of encounters per unit volume} = 4\pi D_A(r_A + r_B)N_A^*N_B^*$$

The encounter rate that we should expect, since in general both A and B will have appreciable diffusion tendencies, can be written as the mean of these results, namely,

$$\text{Rate of encounters} = 4\pi(D_A + D_B)(r_A + r_B)N_A^* N_B^* \qquad (19\text{-}77)$$

We thus have an expression that corresponds to the maximum rate of reaction that could occur in liquid solutions, and we see again the proportionality to the product of the concentration of the reacting species.

To proceed to a numerical value for the rate it is adequate here to anticipate an expression that will be derived in Sec. 22-5 showing that the diffusional coefficient of a sphere in a liquid is related to the coefficient of viscosity η of the liquid and the radius of the sphere by

$$D = \frac{kT}{6\pi r\eta}$$

or

$$D_A = \frac{kT}{6\pi r_A\eta} \quad \text{and} \quad D_B = \frac{kT}{6\pi r_B\eta} \qquad (19\text{-}78)$$

where k is Boltzmann's constant. Substitution of these relations in Eq. (19-77) gives

$$\text{Rate of encounters} = \frac{2kT}{3\eta} \frac{(r_A + r_B)^2}{r_A r_B} N_A^* N_B^* \qquad (19\text{-}79)$$

If r_A and r_B are equal, Eq. (19-79) reduces to

$$\text{Rate of encounters} = \frac{8kT}{3\eta} N_A^* N_B^* \qquad (19\text{-}80)$$

If Eq. (19-80) describes a rate of reaction, the rate constant in (mol liter^{-1})$^{-1}$ s^{-1} is obtained by multiplying the coefficient of $N_A^* N_B^*$ by 10^3 liters m^{-3} and by Avogadro's constant. Thus

$$k(T) = \frac{8 \times 10^3 RT}{3\eta} \qquad (19\text{-}81)$$

For the solvent water at 25°C, for which η is approximately 10^{-3} kg m^{-1} s^{-1}.

$$k(T) = 10^{10} \text{ mol}^{-1} \text{ liter s}^{-1} \qquad (19\text{-}82)$$

Although the model for the calculation of the encounter rate in liquids is very crude and the derivation introduces further uncertainties, the result does seem to correspond to the rates of some very fast solution reactions. In fact, rates nearly equal to that given by Eq. (19-81) are said to imply a *diffusion-controlled* reaction.

The coming together of molecules in the liquid has been called an encounter, and this usage implies some distinction between an encounter and a collision. The principal distinction, as we shall now see, arises from the difficulty with which molecules of a liquid, once adjacent to each other, separate from each other. A similar difficulty stands in the way of the fragments of a decay step escaping from each other. The special character of a liquid system is treated in terms of what is called a *cage effect*.

Consider a pair of molecules that have just encountered each other or (what in this regard is equivalent) a pair of molecules that have just arisen from the decay of a parent molecule. The molecules can become separated from each other only as a result of their diffusional motion through the liquid. Since, on the molecular level, diffusion is pictured as the result of repeated jostlings of the neighboring molecules, we can picture the A–B molecular pair as remaining for some time together in a "cage" formed by the surrounding solvent. The whole process of A and B coming together and remaining together for a number of subsequent collisions is known as an *encounter*. Now let us try to estimate the number of collisions (which, in fact, are not easily defined in a liquid system) that occur during an encounter. A result from the analysis of the net distance a particle moves as a consequence of a series of random steps taken in some time t must be used. This result, from the random-walk problem, is that the average, squared distance is related to the diffusion coefficient by the relation

$$\overline{r^2} = 6Dt \tag{19-83}$$

If we say that a pair of colliding molecules have escaped from each other when they are separated by an additional amount $r_A + r_B$, that is, their average diameter, and if we use 3 Å as a representative value for this diameter and 10^{-9} m^2 s^{-1} as a representative diffusion coefficient, we calculate

$$\text{Time duration of an encounter} \approx \frac{\overline{r^2}}{6D} = \frac{(3 \times 10^{-10})^2}{6 \times 10^{-9}}$$
$$= 1.5 \times 10^{-11} \text{ s} \tag{19-84}$$

By contrast, the time required for gas-phase molecules subject to no retarding force to become separated by this same 3-Å distance is

$$t = \frac{3 \times 10^{-10}}{\overline{u}} = \frac{3 \times 10^{10}}{\sqrt{8kT/\pi m}} \tag{19-85}$$

With representative values, this is calculated to be

$$t = 0.08 \times 10^{-11} \text{ s} \tag{19-86}$$

Thus the encounter lasts some 20 times as long (and other estimates would place this as high as 100 times as long) at it would take the molecules to separate under gas-phase conditions. It follows that in the liquid phase each encounter can be looked upon as consisting of 10 to 100 collisions. This factor makes up for the less frequent liquid-phase encounters than gas-phase collisions and leads us to appreciate the fact that for some of the few simple reactions that have been studied in both phases the rates of the reactions are not greatly different.

The idea of a cage implies also that a decay process cannot be as well defined as in the gas phase. The fragments that are produced have considerable opportunity to react with each other or with the adjacent solvent before they move freely into the bulk of the solution to react with other entities.

19-11 The Transition-State Theory

The collision theory is from the outset tied to the kinetic-molecular theory. The transition-state theory begins in a way that allows some use to be made of the important thermodynamic concepts. The transition-state theory, like the collision theory, falls far short of the goal of a completely theoretical prediction of rate constants. Nevertheless, the approach of the transition-state theory helps us understand not only the molecular features of gas-phase reactions but also some of the molecular features that operate on reactions in solution.

The transition-state theory focuses attention on the species in the reaction process that corresponds to the maximum-energy stage in the reaction process. This species, called the *activated complex* or *transition state,* is in this theory treated formally as a molecule in spite of its ill-defined nature and transitory existence. More specifically, the theory assumes that this species can be treated as a thermodynamic entity.

To be specific let us consider a bimolecular elementary reaction that leads to products. As such a reaction proceeds, there must at all times be a small fraction of the reacting species A and B that are in the process of undergoing the bond rearrangements that ultimately convert them into product species. These transition-state species will be denoted by the symbol $(AB)^{\ddagger}$, and this species will be treated as though it were a well-defined molecule worthy of thermodynamic consideration. The assumption is satisfactory as long as the reacting system does not lurch so violently from reactants to products that the transition-state species cannot establish an equilibrium with the reactants and products.

Now assume that A and B establish an equilibrium concentration of the transition-state species and that this species reacts further to form products. Thus

$$A + B \rightleftharpoons (AB)^{\ddagger} \rightarrow \text{products}$$

The rate of the reaction depends on two factors, the concentration of the transition-state species and the rate with which it breaks up to give products.

The concentration of the activated complex can, at least formally, be written in terms of the equilibrium expression

$$K^{\ddagger} = \frac{[(AB)^{\ddagger}]}{[A][B]}$$

or

$$[(AB)^{\ddagger}] = K^{\ddagger}[A][B] \tag{19-87}$$

Although no value is given for $K^{\ddagger}$, it will be seen that its thermodynamic interpretation is profitable and justifies its introduction.

The rate with which the complex breaks up can be estimated by recognizing that it can fly apart into product molecules when a suitable vibration happens to have a large enough amplitude to break open the complex. The frequency of such a vibration will therefore be something like the rate with which the complex breaks up.

Let us denote the frequency of vibration along the *reaction coordinate* by ν_{RC}. The rate of the reaction is then given by the transition-state theory as

$$\text{Rate} = -\frac{d[A]}{dt} = -\frac{d[B]}{dt} = \nu_{RC}K^{\ddagger}[A][B] \tag{19-88}$$

This expression becomes of value when $K^{\ddagger}$ is given a thermodynamic interpretation.

Since we have no calorimetric-type thermodynamic data for the species $(AB)^{\ddagger}$, it is best to depend now on our understanding of thermodynamic properties in terms of molecular properties. In fact, in view of Sec. 8-5, we can go directly to an interpretation of the equilibrium constant $K^{\ddagger}$ in terms of partition functions and the ground-state energy difference of A and B and the species $(AB)^{\ddagger}$. We write

$$K^{\ddagger} = \frac{[(AB)^{\ddagger}]}{[A][B]} = \frac{q_{(AB)^{\ddagger}}}{q_A q_B} e^{-E_{(AB)^{\ddagger}}/RT} \tag{19-89}$$

where $E_{(AB)^{\ddagger}}$ is the energy difference between A and B, on the one hand, and $(AB)^{\ddagger}$, on the other.

The partition function written to show the contributing degrees of freedom is

$$q = q_{\text{trans}}q_{\text{rot}}q_{\text{vib}}q_{\text{elec}} \tag{19-90}$$

The nature of these partition-function factors is shown again in Table 19-6. It should be clear that, in general, enough data are available for species A and B to permit all factors in q_A and q_B to be calculated.

For the species $(AB)^{\ddagger}$ the factors q_{trans} and q_{elec} generally cause no difficulty. The rotational factor requires an estimate of the size and shape of the

TABLE 19-6 Summary of Partition-Function Expressions and Representative Values for Gases at a Concentration of 1 mol liter^{-1}

Partition function		Partition function per degree of freedom for unit volume	Representative value of partition function per degree of freedom
$q_{trans} = q_{trans}^3$		$q_{trans} = \left(\dfrac{2\pi mkT}{h^2}\right)^{1/2}$	10^{10}
$q_{rot} = \begin{cases} q^3 & \text{nonlinear} \\ q^2 & \text{linear} \end{cases}$		$q_{rot} = \left(\dfrac{8\pi^2 IkT}{h^2}\right)^{1/2}$	$10\text{--}100$
$q_{vib} = \begin{cases} q^{3n-6} & \text{nonlinear} \\ q^{3n-5} & \text{linear} \end{cases}$		$q_{vib} = \dfrac{1}{1 - e^{-hv/kT}}$	$1\text{--}10$

species, and this can be done. Most difficult is an estimate of the vibrational frequencies of the transition-state complex, particularly since, for at least some degrees of freedom, this species will be loosely bound and the corresponding vibrational modes will contribute appreciably to the partition function. One such vibration is that presumed to occur along the reaction coordinate, and it is motion along this coordinate that leads to conversion of the activated complex to product molecules. It is convenient to factor out the term for this degree of freedom from the partition function. If $q_{(AB)^\ddagger}$ denotes the complete partition function for the $(AB)^\ddagger$ species and $q'_{(AB)^\ddagger}$ denotes the partition function with the contribution from the vibrational mode along the reaction coordinate factored out, we can write, in view of Eq. (4-55) for the vibrational-mode partition function,

$$q_{(AB)^\ddagger} = \frac{1}{1 - e^{-hv_{RC}/kT}}\, q'_{(AB)^\ddagger} \tag{19-91}$$

Further, if the molecule is only weakly bound along the reaction coordinate, hv_{RC} will be much less than kT and we can write

$$q'_{(AB)^\ddagger} = \frac{1}{1 - e^{-hv_{RC}/kT}} = \frac{1}{1 - (1 - hv_{RC}/kT + \cdots)} \approx \frac{kT}{hv_{RC}} \tag{19-92}$$

When we combine the above equations, it follows that the rate can be expressed as

$$\begin{aligned} \text{Rate} &= v_{RC}\frac{kT}{hv_{RC}}\frac{q_{(AB)^\ddagger}}{q_A q_B}e^{-E_{(AB)^\ddagger}/RT}[\text{A}][\text{B}] \\ &= \frac{kT}{h}\frac{q'_{(AB)^\ddagger}}{q_A q_B}e^{-E_{(AB)^\ddagger}/RT}[\text{A}][\text{B}] \end{aligned} \tag{19-93}$$

Furthermore, comparison with the rate law for a bimolecular step lets us identify the rate constant k_2 as

$$k_2 = \frac{kT}{h} \frac{q'_{(AB)^{\ddagger}}}{q_A q_B} e^{-E_{(AB)^{\ddagger}}/RT} \tag{19-94}$$

Although for relatively simple species all the partition functions can be calculated and a quantitative result obtained, it seems best to use the transition-state theory to obtain an appreciation of the factors that influence the rate of an elementary reaction step.

We do this by first recalling the representative values of the various partition-function factors in Table 19-6. Then if we seek an order of magnitude for the deduced rate constant, we can apply such values to both the A and B and the $(AB)^{\ddagger}$ species. Let us do so for generally shaped, i.e., not monatomic or linear, A and B molecules with n_A and n_B atoms, respectively, forming a generally shaped $(AB)^{\ddagger}$ complex containing $n_A + n_B$ atoms. Letting q_{trans}, q_{rot}, and q_{vib} imply partition function *per degree of freedom* for the type of motion indicated by the subscript, we can write

$$\begin{aligned} q_A &= (q_{trans})^3 (q_{rot})^3 (q_{vib})^{3n_A - 6} \\ q_B &= (q_{trans})^3 (q_{rot})^3 (q_{vib})^{3n_B - 6} \\ q'_{(AB)^{\ddagger}} &= (q_{trans})^3 (q_{rot})^3 (q_{vib})^{3(n_A + n_B) - 7} \end{aligned} \tag{19-95}$$

(Note that the -7 in the vibration exponent of $q'_{(AB)^{\ddagger}}$ results from the previous separation of the contribution from the reaction-coordinate vibration.)

After appropriate cancellations, we have

$$k_2 = \frac{kT}{h} \frac{(q_{vib})^5}{(q_{trans})^3 (q_{rot})^3} e^{-E_{(AB)^{\ddagger}}/RT} \tag{19-96}$$

Insertion of numerical values gives, for the representative k_2, for the types of molecules being considered,

$$k_2 = 10^{-20} e^{-E_{(AB)^{\ddagger}}/RT} \tag{19-97}$$

where k_2 has the units of (molecules m^{-3}) s^{-1}. Conversion to mole liter units requires multiplication by $10^3 \mathfrak{N}$ to give

$$k_2 = 6 \times 10^6 e^{-E_{(AB)^{\ddagger}}/RT} \quad \text{(mol liter}^{-1})^{-1} \text{ s}^{-1} \tag{19-98}$$

More important than this reasonable value is the recognition that the formation of the activated complex implies the conversion of translational and rotational degrees of freedom, with large partition functions, to vibrational degrees of freedom with small partition functions, as shown by the ratio of partition

TABLE 19-7 Representative Values for the Preexponential Terms of Eq. (19-94) for Various Molecular Types

Type of reaction	Preexponential term	Representative value at 25°C	
		$(molecules\ m^{-3})^{-1}$ s^{-1}	$(mol\ liter^{-1})^{-1}$ s^{-1}
Atom + atom → diatomic	$\dfrac{kT}{h}\dfrac{q_r^{\ 2}}{q_t^{\ 3}}$	10^{-15}	10^{12}
Atom + linear → linear	$\dfrac{kT}{h}\dfrac{q_v^{\ 2}}{q_t^{\ 3}}$	10^{-17}	10^{10}
Atom + linear → nonlinear	$\dfrac{kT}{h}\dfrac{q_v q_r}{q_t^{\ 3}}$	10^{-16}	10^{11}
Atom + nonlinear → nonlinear	$\dfrac{kT}{h}\dfrac{q_v^{\ 2}}{q_t^{\ 3}}$	10^{-17}	10^{10}
Linear + linear → nonlinear	$\dfrac{kT}{h}\dfrac{q_v^{\ 3}}{q_t^{\ 3}q_r}$	10^{-19}	10^{8}
Nonlinear + nonlinear → nonlinear	$\dfrac{kT}{h}\dfrac{q_v^{\ 5}}{q_t^{\ 3}q_r^{\ 3}}$	10^{-20}	10^{7}

Source: After A. A. Frost and R. G. Pearson, "Kinetics and Mechanisms," John Wiley & Sons, Inc., New York, 1961.

functions in Eq. (19-96). This loss of freedom that opposes the formation of the activated complex is most important for the generally shaped molecules that have been considered. For reactions involving monatomic species, with no rotational degrees of freedom, and linear molecules, with only 2 such degrees of freedom, this effect is less severe. Some representative results, collected in Table 19-7, show the consequence for different types of molecules and transition states.

19-12 Comparison of the Results of the Collision and the Transition-State Theories

The theories presented in the preceding sections adopt different approaches, but both succeed in reaching numerical results that are consistent with observed values, at least as regards order of magnitude. Now let us see whether a comparison of the analytical form of these results reveals any common ground over which the theories proceed.

Consider the simplest example of monatomic A and B species colliding to form a diatomic-activated complex with internuclear distance $r_A + r_B$. The transition-state theory requires us to characterize the activated complex by its mass $m_A + m_B$ and its moment of inertia $I = \mu(r_A + r_B)^2$, where μ is the reduced mass $m_A m_B/(m_A + m_B)$. The only vibrational degree of freedom of this species is that along the reaction coordinate, and since this has been given special treatment, there is no remaining contribution to $q'_{AB,vib}$. Thus, according to the transition-state theory,

$$k_2 \text{ (transition-state theory)} = \frac{kT}{h} \frac{q'_{(AB)^{\ddagger}}}{q_A q_B} e^{-E_{(AB)^{\ddagger}}/RT}$$

$$= \frac{kT}{h} \frac{q_{(AB)^{\ddagger},\text{trans}} q_{(AB)^{\ddagger},\text{rot}}}{q_{A,\text{trans}} q_{B,\text{trans}}} e^{-E_{(AB)^{\ddagger}}/RT} \qquad (19\text{-}99)$$

The partition-function expressions that must be used are

$$q_{(AB)^{\ddagger},\text{trans}} = \left[\frac{2\pi(m_A + m_B)kT}{h^2} \right]^{3/2} \qquad q_{(AB)^{\ddagger},\text{rot}} = \frac{8\pi^2(r_A + r_B)^2 \mu kT}{h^2}$$

$$q_{A,\text{trans}} = \left(\frac{2\pi m_A kT}{h^2} \right)^{3/2} \qquad\qquad q_{B,\text{trans}} = \left(\frac{2\pi m_B kT}{h^2} \right)^{3/2}$$

Substitution of these relations in Eq. (19–94), with cancellation of many terms, gives

$$k_2 \text{ (transition-state theory)} = (r_A + r_B)^2 \left(\frac{8\pi kT}{\mu} \right)^{1/2} e^{-E_{(AB)^{\ddagger}}/RT} \qquad (19\text{-}100)$$

The result, with the relation $\sigma_{AB} = \pi(r_A + r_B)^2$, is virtually identical with Eq. (19–74), the principal result of the collision theory. One need only identify $E_{(AB)^{\ddagger}}$ with the molar equivalent of the molecular threshold energy ϵ_0. Thus one sees that the two theories not only lead to similar numerical results but also involve similar molecular features.

19-13 Application of the Transition-State Theory to Reactions in Solution

For reactions occurring in the liquid state, one cannot proceed directly with the collision theory or (in the form developed above) the transition-state theory. But the latter theory can be developed so that it gives a theoretical interpretation to the A and E_a parameters of the Arrhenius equation without demanding detailed molecular data. Here, then, one welcomes the thermodynamic functions with their lack of such demands.

We now proceed by treating the formation of the activated complex $(AB)^{\ddagger}$ and the equilibrium constant $K^{\ddagger}$ in terms of the *free energy of activation,* the *entropy of activation,* and the *enthalpy of activation.* With such terms $K^{\ddagger}$ can be interpreted as

$$(\Delta G^{\circ})^{\ddagger} = -RT \ln K^{\ddagger}$$

or

$$K^{\ddagger} = e^{-(\Delta G^{\circ})^{\ddagger}/RT} \qquad (19\text{-}101)$$

For the reaction at a given temperature the free energy of activation can be interpreted in terms of an entropy and an enthalpy contribution according to

$$(\Delta G^\circ)^\ddagger = (\Delta H^\circ)^\ddagger - T(\Delta S^\circ)^\ddagger$$

Substitution of this relation in Eq. (19-101) yields

$$K^\ddagger = e^{+(\Delta S^\circ)^\ddagger/R} e^{-(\Delta H^\circ)^\ddagger/RT} \qquad (19\text{-}102)$$

This interpretation of $K^\ddagger$ can be inserted into Eq. (19-88). The assumption that the vibrational energy $h\nu_{RC}$ is small compared with kT, leads, as in the derivation of Eq. (19-93), to

$$\text{Rate} = \frac{kT}{h} e^{+(\Delta S^\circ)^\ddagger/R} e^{-(\Delta H^\circ)^\ddagger/RT}[\text{A}][\text{B}] \qquad (19\text{-}103)$$

Then the rate constant is expressed as

$$k_2 = \frac{kT}{h} e^{+(\Delta S^\circ)^\ddagger/R} e^{-(\Delta H^\circ)^\ddagger/RT} \qquad (19\text{-}104)$$

where now the $(\Delta S^\circ)^\ddagger$ term is to be calculated for all degrees of freedom except that along the reaction coordinate.

With the recognition that the variation of the preexponential T term is small compared with that of the exponential term, Eq. (19-104) agrees in form with the empirical Arrhenius expression.

For reactions in condensed phases, the difference between $(\Delta H^\circ)^\ddagger$ and $(\Delta E^\circ)^\ddagger$ will be small. For gases, the difference between these two quantities can be expressed in terms of the change in the number of moles of gas that occur in the reaction. If these features are ignored, we can write the approximate relation

$$A \approx \frac{kT}{h} e^{+(\Delta S^\circ)^\ddagger/R}$$

where A is the empirical preexponential factor.

Since $(\Delta S^\circ)^\ddagger$ is the entropy change in going from the reagents to the activated complex, and since little can easily be said about the properties of the activated complex, the transition-state theory tends to avoid any definite quantitative predictions. In spite of the ill-defined nature of the transition state, a number of conclusions can be drawn concerning $(\Delta S^\circ)^\ddagger$.

In the formation of an activated complex from reactant molecules all gas-phase reactions lead to the conversion of translational and rotational degrees of freedom of the reactants to vibrational degrees of freedom of the transition-state species. The more widely spaced energy level for this latter type of molecular motion implies a smaller entropy and thus a negative value for $(\Delta S)^\ddagger$.

For reactions that occur in solution a similar but smaller, negative $(\Delta S)^\ddagger$

might be expected as the less free translations and rotations are lost and are replaced by vibrations. In addition, however, solvent molecules are involved, and the effect on them can dominate the effect that can be attributed to the reacting molecules themselves. All solutes, and particularly ions, in solvents other than very inert ones, interact with solvent molecules. The solvent molecules are to some extent oriented about the solute, and this orientation imposes a restriction on the motion of some of the solvent molecules. This solvation is an appreciable factor in determining the entropy of the system. Changes in this solvation entropy must therefore be considered in the formation of the activated complex. Therefore the uniformly negative value of $\Delta S^{\ddagger}$ for bimolecular gas-phase reactions, corresponding to a loss of freedom of motion, does not hold for reactions of solvated species in solution.

When oppositely charged ions, for example, react to form a neutral molecule, the extent of solvation is greatly reduced. Even the activated complex, in which the opposite charges will at least be close together, can be expected to be formed with a decrease in solvation and a corresponding positive entropy of activation. An example of such a situation is provided by the displacement of water molecules in the reaction

$$Cr(OH_2)_6{}^{3+} + CNS^- \rightarrow [Cr(OH_2)_5CNS]^{2+} + H_2O$$

which has a value of $\Delta S^{\ddagger}$ of $+120$ J K^{-1} mol^{-1}.

On the other hand, the formation of an activated complex that carries charges when the reagents do not will lead to a large negative value of $\Delta S^{\ddagger}$ corresponding to the additional loss of freedom of motion by the solvating molecules. The displacement of bromide in the reaction step

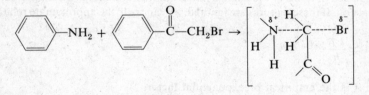

is an example of such a situation. The entropy of activation for this reaction has been reported as -200 J K^{-1} mol^{-1}, a very large negative value.

Although not all entropies of activation-of-solution reactions can be rationalized so easily, this type of argument shows how the transition-state theory gives a valuable framework within which observed rate constants can be understood.

PROBLEMS

19-1. (a) What are the units of the rate constants of first- and second-order reactions if the concentrations are expressed in moles per liter and the time in seconds?

(b) If the rate of a reaction followed the rate law $k[A][B]^{2/3}$, what would the units of k be?

19-2. Using the data of Table 19-1, prepare graphs like those of Fig. 19-1 for the hydrolysis of *tert*-butyl bromide at 50°C. (a) Is the reaction first-order at this temperature? (b) What are the rate constant and half-life at 50°C? (c) Show the half-lives on the plot of c versus t. See that the concentration does fall to half its value in time $t_{1/2}$ regardless of the concentration considered.

19-3. The hydration of ethylene oxide in aqueous solution proceeds according to the overall equation

$$CH_2\!\!-\!\!CH_2 + H_2O \rightarrow CH_2OHCH_2OH$$

The rate of the reaction has been followed by J. N. Brönsted, M. Kilpatrick, and M. Kilpatrick [*J. Am. Chem. Soc.*, **51**:428 (1929)] by measuring the change in volume of the liquid system. (This is done by observing the height of the liquid in the capillary tube of a dilatometer, a large reaction cell resembling a thermometer.) They obtained the following results, at 20°C, using 0.12 M ethylene oxide and 0.007574 M $HClO_4$:

t, min	0	30	60	90	120	240	300	360	390	∞
h, arbitrary units	18.48	1805	17.62	17.25	16.89	15.70	15.22	14.80	14.62	12.3

Confirm that the reaction is first-order with respect to ethylene oxide. What is the rate constant?

19-4. (a) Calculate a first-order rate constant for each concentration datum at 25°C for the reaction of *tert*-butyl bromide given in Table 19-1. (b) Do these results indicate a first-order reaction? (c) Assume that the reaction is second-order in *tert*-butyl bromide. Calculate values for the second-order rate constant at each of the reported times. Does the reaction follow a second-order rate law?

19-5. The gaseous dimerization of butadiene has been followed by measurement of the total gas pressure by W. E. Vaughan, *J. Am. Chem. Soc.*, **54**:3863 (1932). The data tabulated were obtained at 326°C. What is the order of the reaction, and what is the rate constant?

t, min	P, atm	t, min	P, atm	t, min	P, atm
0	(0.8315)	24.55	0.7194	90.05	0.5964
3.25	0.8138	33.00	0.6944	119.00	0.5694
8.02	0.7886	42.50	0.6701	176.67	0.5332
12.18	0.7686	55.08	0.6450	259.50	0.5013
17.30	0.7464	68.05	0.6244	373	0.4698

19-6. The displacement of bromide by thiosulfate ion has been studied at 37.50°C in the reaction

$$n\text{-}C_3H_7Br + S_2O_3^{2-} \rightarrow C_3H_7S_2O_3^- + Br^-$$

by T. I. Crowell and L. P. Hammett, *J. Am. Chem. Soc.*, **70**:3444 (1948). The thiosulfate-ion concentration remaining at various times was determined by titration with iodine. From these data and the known initial concentrations the following data were obtained:

t, s	Concentration, mol liter^{-1}		t, s	Concentration, mol liter^{-1}	
	$S_2O_3^{2-}$	C_3H_7Br		$S_2O_3^{2-}$	C_3H_7Br
0	0.0966	0.0395	5,052	0.0766	0.0196
1,110	0.0904	0.0333	7,380	0.0720	0.0149
2,010	0.0863	0.0292	11,232	0.0668	0.0097
3,192	0.0819	0.0248	78,840	0.0571	0.0000

Derive the rate equation, including a numerical value for the rate constant, for this reaction.

19-7. Benzene diazonium chloride in aqueous solution decomposes according to the equation

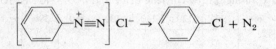

and the reaction can conveniently be followed by the amount of N_2 evolved. Cain and Nicoll, *J. Chem. Soc.,* **81**:1412 (1902) report the following results for 20°C and 35 ml of a solution containing 10 g of diazobenzene chloride per liter:

t, min	116	192	355	481	1282	1429	
N_2 evolved, ml measured at 13°C and 0.987 atm	9.7	16.2	26.3	33.7	51.4	54.3	60.0

What is the order of the reaction, and what is the rate constant?

19-8. The radioactive decay of radium, with half-life 1590 years, leads to the formation of the inert gas radon, which, with a half-life of 3.82 days, decays further. If a sample of radium is kept in a sealed vial, the radon gas collects. (*a*) Derive an expression for the number of radon atoms present as a function of time if a 1-g sample of radium is considered. The expression need be valid only for a time interval of less than about 1 year. (*b*) Plot the number of atoms of radon as a function of time in the time interval 0 to 2 weeks. (*c*) The amount of radon is seen to reach a constant value, and radon is said to be in *secular equilibrium* with radium. Why does this differ from ordinary equilibrium?

19-9. For a reaction of the type

$$C \underset{k_{-1}}{\overset{k_1}{\rightleftharpoons}} A + B$$

that is to be studied by a relaxation technique (*a*) write an expression for the net rate of reaction of C. (*b*) Write an expression for the equilibrium concentrations of A, B, and C. (*c*) Assume that a sudden change in the conditions puts C an amount Δx above its equilibrium value and puts both A and B this amount below their equilibrium values. Write an expression for the rate of change of Δx as the system moves toward equilibrium. [Neglect terms in $(\Delta x)^2$.] (d) Is the return to equilibrium a first-order process? (e) Write an expression for the relaxation time τ.

19-10. The ionization of the indicator ion bromocresol green

$$HIn^- \underset{K_{-1}}{\overset{k_1}{\rightleftharpoons}} H^+ + In^{2-}$$

is a rapid reaction which has been studied by relaxation methods. The following data have been given

$C_{H^+} + C_{In^{2-}}$, mol liter^{-1}	4.30	6.91	50.9	85.7	100.5	129.1	176.0	286.5
Time, μs	0.99	0.86	0.319	0.180	0.151	0.127	0.089	0.058

Problem 19-9 should have suggested the relation $1/\tau = k_{-1}(C_{H^+} + C_{In^{2-}}) + k_1$. Determine k_1, k_{-1} and the equilibrium constant K.

19-11. For aqueous acetic acid solutions at 25°C relaxation studies have yielded the k_1 and k_{-1} values of $7.8 \times 10^5\,s^{-1}$ and $4.5 \times 10^{10}\,m^{-1}\,s^{-1}$ for the reaction

$$CH_3COOH \underset{K_{-1}}{\overset{k_1}{\rightleftharpoons}} CH_3COO^- + H^+$$

Calculate values for the relaxation time for (a) 1 M and (b) 0.01 M solutions.

19-12. The fumarase-catalyzed dehydration of l-malate to yield fumarate has been extensively studied. Data for one set of runs at 25°C in the presence of 5 mmol of phosphate [R. A. Alberty, V. Massey, C. Frieden, and A. R. Fuhlbrigge, *J. Am. Chem. Soc.*, **76**:2485 (1954)] were as follows for a fixed enzyme concentration:

l-malate, mmol liter^{-1}	0.100	0.333	1.000	3.33	10.0	33.3	100
Initial rate	1.9	4.2	6.1	6.5	7.2	7.4	6.9

(a) Do these data fit the form of Eq. (19-30) or (19-32)? (b) To the extent that they do, what are the values of the parameters of the equation?

19-13. The following data [from C. S. Hames, *Biochem. J.*, **26**:1406 (1932)] give the initial rate of reaction, in milligrams of maltose formed in 5 ml of solution per minute as a result of the action of the enzyme *amylase* on starch:

Starch conc. %	0.030	0.040	0.050	0.086	0.129	0.216	0.431	0.647	1.078
Initial rate	0.140	0.165	0.180	0.260	0.305	0.345	0.400	0.435	0.445

Show that the reaction follows the rate law of Sec. 19-4 and deduce the parameters K_m and $k_2[E_{tot}]$.

19-14. In the amylase-catalyzed conversion of starch to sugar, treated in Prob. 19-13, the effect of changes in the amount of enzyme for a fixed initial concentration of starch on the initial rate was studied. The following results were reported:

Relative enzyme conc.	0.125	0.25	0.375	0.50	0.75	1.00
Initial rate	0.167	0.36	0.495	0.70	1.01	1.35

Is this dependence of the initial reaction rate on enzyme concentration consistent with rate law of Sec. 19-4?

19-15. The reaction by which a tertiary chlorine, as in *tert*-butyl chloride, is replaced by a hydroxyl group appears to result from the formation of a carbonium ion, which subsequently adds water or hydroxide. The reaction with $(CH_3)_3CCl$ is quite rapid, whereas that with

is imperceptibly slow. What do these relative rates imply about the preferred geometry of the carbonium ion?

19-16. Consider the schematic hypothetical reaction mechanism

$$A \underset{k_{-1}}{\overset{k_1}{\rightleftharpoons}} M \qquad M + A \xrightarrow{k_2} C$$

(a) Write down expressions for the net rate of change of each of the species A, M, and C. (b) If M is a species that is present in only undetectably small amounts at all times, obtain an expression of M in terms of the concentrations of the major reagents A and C. (c) With the result of part (b) obtain rate equations for the disappearance of A and for the formation of C. (d) What relative values of the rate constants would result in the reaction being first-order with respect to A? What values would make it second-order?

19-17. By what factor would the rate of a reaction for which the activation energy is 159 kJ be increased by a temperature rise of 10°C from 25 to 35°C?

19-18. Under certain conditions the decomposition of nitrogen dioxide according to the equation $2NO_2 \rightarrow 2NO + O_2$ follows the rate law

$$\text{Rate} = k[NO_2]^2$$

The following values of k as a function of temperature have been reported [M. Bodenstein, *Z. Phys. Chem.*, **100**:106 (1922)]:

T, K	592	603.2	627	651.5	656
k, (mol liter^{-1})$^{-1}$ s^{-1}	0.522	0.755	1.700	4.020	5.030

Deduce the values of the parameters in the Arrhenius equation $k = Ae^{-E_a/RT}$.

19-19. The rate constant for the combination of methyl radicals, CH_3, to form ethane has been deduced to have the value 4.5×10^{10} (mol liter^{-1})$^{-1}$ s^{-1} at 125°C. The activation energy appears to be zero, and it can be expected that there will be little steric hindrance to this radical recombination. Using the expression (19-75) from the collision-theory derivation and the values of $r_A = r_B = 1.54/2$ Å from the normal C—C bond length, calculate a value for k and compare with that deduced from experimental data.

19-20. (a) What would be the half-life for a representative gas-phase reaction if each A–B collision were a reactive collision and the pressures of A and B initially were 10^{-9} atm, a pressure readily obtained in a laboratory vacuum system? (b) What would the half-life be at a pressure of 10^{-11} atm and a temperature of 1500 K, as occurs in the earth's atmosphere at an altitude of about 500 km?

19-21. From the rates of diffusion of hemoglobin in water at 20°C, the value deduced for the diffusion coefficient D is 6.5×10^{-11} m^2 s^{-1}. Using the assumption that the molecule can be treated as a sphere with radius of 30 Å, test the validity of Eq. (19-78). The viscosity of water at 20°C is 0.010 P, a value that corresponds to 0.0010 kg m^{-1} s^{-1}.

19-22. The diffusion coefficient of sucrose in water at 20°C is 4.0×10^{-10} m^2 s^{-1}. The viscosity of water is cited in Prob. 19-21. What value of r does this suggest for the sucrose molecule? Does this seem reasonable?

19-23. A low-frequency molecular vibration would absorb quanta at the far end of the infrared spectral region at a wave number of the order of 100 cm^{-1}. Verify that for such a vibration along the reaction coordinate, we can assume that $h\nu_{RC} < kT$ for a room-temperature value of T.

19-24. For a representative molecule verify the values of the partition functions for each degree of freedom shown in Table 19-6.

19-25. For one type of molecular reactants and transition-state species found in Table 19-7 other than the example used in Sec. 19-11, show that the partition-function factor appearing in the transition-state theory of the rate constant is that listed.

19-26. It is customary to attribute deviations from simply calculated rate constants to a steric factor, which depicts how molecular size and shape impede the effectiveness with which molecular collision yields products. The transition-state approach can be used to deduce a comparable term by comparing the partition-function terms, as in Table 19-7, with those for the atom + atom reaction for which there can be no steric hindrance. (a) Tabulate the ratio of the partition-function terms for various reaction types to that for the atom + atom reaction. (b) Insert numerical values and see whether they are compatible with the idea that for more complex molecules steric effects can reduce the reaction rate by as much as several powers of 10.

19-27. Calculate the entropies of activation at 25°C for the reactions of Table 19-5. Does this show that low preexponential factors can be explained by either a steric difficulty, as the collision theory would suggest, or a very unfavorable entropy of activation, as the transition-state theory would express it?

19-28. According to Appendix B-1, the entropy of a fairly simple gas-phase molecule is in the range 150 to 200 J K^{-1} mol^{-1} at room temperature. The entropies of activation obtained in Prob. 19-27 do not correspond to the formation of one firmly bound transition-state complex from two reagent molecules. How can the difference between 150 to 200 and the values of Prob. 19-27 be explained?

REFERENCES

FROST, A. A., and R. G. PEARSON: "Kinetics and Mechanism: A Study of Homogeneous Chemical Reactions," 2d ed., John Wiley & Sons, Inc., New York, 1961. The empirical treatments, experimental studies, and the theories of the rates of chemical reactions are first presented. Then rather detailed treatments of particular reactions or reaction types that serve to illustrate chemical kinetic studies are presented.

BENSON, S. W.: "The Foundations of Chemical Kinetics," McGraw-Hill Book Company, New York, 1960. A rather comprehensive account of the kinetics of chemical reactions. The treatment is somewhat more detailed and more mathematical than that of Frost and Pearson.

WESTON, R. E. JR., and H. A. SCHWARZ: "Chemical Kinetics," Prentice Hall, Inc., Englewood Cliffs, N.J., 1972.

AMDUR, I., and G. G. HAMMES: "Chemical Kinetics," McGraw-Hill Book Company, New York, 1966.

GARDENER, W. C.: "Rates and Mechanisms of Chemical Reactions," W. A. Benjamin, Inc., New York, 1969.

DENCE, J. B., H. B. GRAY, and G. S. HAMMOND: "Chemical Dynamics," W. A. Benjamin, Inc., New York, 1968.

HALPERN, J.: Some Aspects of Chemical Dynamics in Solution, *J. Chem. Educ.*, **45:**372 (1968).

Applications of results from kinetic studies are also found in books dealing with the reactions in a particular branch of chemistry:

EDWARDS, J. O.: "Inorganic Reaction Mechanism," W. A. Benjamin, Inc., New York, 1964.

INGOLD, C. K.: "Structure and Mechanism in Organic Chemistry," G. Bell & Sons, Ltd., London, 1963.

LEFFLER, J. E.: "The Reactive Intermediates of Organic Chemistry," Interscience Publishers, Inc., New York, 1958.

A number of monographs on certain topics in the general area are also available, and these often provide a more satisfactory introduction to a particular aspect than do the more general treatments referred to above. Some articles and monographs of interest:

CRUICKSHANK, F. R., A. J. HYDE, and D. PUGH: Free Energy Surfaces and Transition State Theory, *J. Chem. Educ.*, **54:**289 (1977).

JOHNSON, H. S.: "Gas Phase Reaction Rate Theory," The Ronald Press, New York, 1966.

CALDIN, E. F.: "Fast Reactions in Solution," Blackwell Scientific Publications, Ltd., Oxford, 1964. A treatment of simple classical methods and also relaxation, nmr, and esr techniques.

MELANDER, L: "Isotope Effects on Reaction Rates," The Ronald Press Company, New York, 1960.

LAIDLER, K. J.: "The Chemical Kinetics of Excited States," Oxford University Press, New York, 1955.

TROTMAN-DICKENSON, A. F.: "Gas Kinetics," Butterworth Scientific Publications, London, 1955.

SLATER, N. B.: "Theory of Unimolecular Reactions," Methuen & Co., Ltd., London, 1959.

ROBINSON, P. J., and K. A. HOLBROOK: "Unimolecular Reactions," Wiley-Interscience, New York, 1972.

PATEL, R. C., and R. J. BOE: Fast Reactions: Rapid Mixing and Concentration-Jump Experiments, *J. Chem. Educ.*, **47:**800 (1970).

A special area that has assumed great importance deals with the details of the collisions and reactions of gas-phase molecules. The following references deal in whole or in part with this subject:

GREENE, E. F., and A. KUPPERMAN: Chemical Reaction Cross Sections and Rate Constants, *J. Chem. Educ.*, **45:**361 (1968).

LEVINE, R. D., and R. B. BERNSTEIN: "Molecular Reaction Dynamics," Oxford University Press, New York, 1974.

NORDMAN, C. E., and S. M. BLINDER: Collision Theory of Chemical Reactions, *J. Chem. Educ.*, **51:**790 (1974).

20 Photochemistry

The interaction of radiation with matter has already been used in two ways to explore the details of the atomic-molecular world. Absorption or emission of radiation provided the data for the spectroscopic studies of Chap. 14. Scattering of radiation provided the data for the diffraction studies of Chap. 15. Now the *consequences* of absorbed radiation will provide another avenue into the atomic-molecular world. Such studies also provide the basis for understanding such practical applications as the development of lasers and the varied attempts to harness solar energy.

The absorptions whose consequences we shall deal with are mostly those which excite a molecule or ion to a higher electronic state. Various paths bring such an excited species back to its ground state. The electronic excitation energy can be degraded into thermal energy of the absorbing species and of its neighbors. This path is of no special interest, but it must be recognized. A second energy-loss route consists of the emission of radiation. Two *radiative* processes, *fluorescence* and *phosphorescence,* will be recognized, and an application in lasers will be pointed out. Finally, in a third general energy-dissipation process, the excitation energy goes into breaking or rearranging chemical bonds. A result can be the initiation of chemical reactions. Strictly speaking, only this third route constitutes *photochemistry,* but we have adopted the word for the entire study of the consequences of absorbed radiation.

20-1 Nonradiative Processes

The transition associated with an electronic absorption band produces a higher-energy electron configuration. The molecule is also often left in one of the higher vibrational states of the new electronic state. For molecules in solution molecular collisions are very effective in removing the excess vibrational energy, probably by one vibrational level step at a time. This energy goes into the motion of the molecules of the solvent and is not detected as emitted radiation. A typical time required for the dissipation of excess vibrational energy by such a process is of the order of 10^{-10} s. When this is compared with a typical vibrational period of 10^{-13} s, it is seen that many vibrations, say a thousand, occur while the excess vibrational energy is being lost.

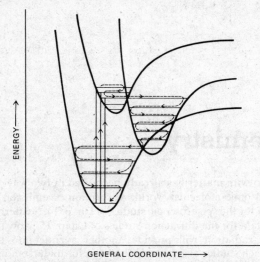

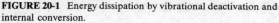

FIGURE 20-1 Energy dissipation by vibrational deactivation and internal conversion.

The potential energy for a given electronic state is a function of all the internal coordinates of the molecule, and for polyatomic molecules the potential energy would have to be represented by a surface in this many-dimensional space. The net effect of these two features is that potential-energy curves or, more properly, surfaces of different electronic states will cross each other. A representative arrangement of potential curves is shown in Fig. 20-1.

The occurrence of a crossing or nearby potential surface with that initially reached by the absorption process allows a second type of radiationless process. This type can lead to the return of the excited molecule to its ground electronic state. When potential surfaces or (to simplify the discussion) two potential curves cross as in Fig. 20-1, it is possible for the molecule, originally in an excited electronic configuration to change over into the configuration corresponding to a different electronic state. The crossing of the potential curves facilitates this process, known as *internal conversion* because at the crossover point the geometry and the potential energies of the two electronic states are equal and the vibrational kinetic energy of the molecule in either state would be zero.

For polyatomic molecules, potential curves often exist with suitable relative positions so that combinations of vibrational deactivations and internal conversions can return the molecule to its ground state before any emission process has had a chance to occur. Other molecules, however, either do not have such crossing potential curves or have electronic states in which the molecule becomes trapped. In such cases emission does occur.

20-2 Radiative Processes

The emission or absorption of radiation can be introduced by considering the molecules of a sample to be within a radiation-filled cavity. The radiation for a cavity at temperature T is described by Planck's radiation law as

$$\rho(\nu) = \frac{8\pi h\nu^3}{c^3} \frac{1}{e^{h\nu/k} - 1} \tag{20-1}$$

Let us deal with just two states of the molecules that are exposed to this radiation, the ground state g and a higher-energy state h.

At equilibrium the ratio of the number of molecules N_h in the higher-energy state to the number N_g in the ground state is given by the Boltzmann distribution

$$\frac{N_h}{N_g} = e^{-h\nu_{gh}/kT} \tag{20-2}$$

In seeing how the radiation establishes this equilibrium we shall be led to useful measures of the interaction of radiation with matter.

Transitions from g to h or h to g can be *induced* by the interaction of the radiation with the molecules. The interaction depends on the nature of the g and h states and on the frequency and density of the radiation. If the *Einstein coefficient of induced absorption* is represented by $B_{g\to h}$ and the *coefficient for induced emission* by $B_{h\to g}$, we can write two transition rates as

$$\text{Rate of induced } g \to h \text{ transitions} = N_g B_{g\to h}\rho(\nu_{gh}) \tag{20-3}$$

and

$$\text{Rate of induced } h \to g \text{ transitions} = N_h B_{h\to g}\rho(\nu_{gh}) \tag{20-4}$$

where $\rho(\nu_{gh})$ is the density of radiation at a frequency ν_{gh} that would be absorbed or emitted in the $g \to h$ or $h \to g$ transitions. These two transitions are shown as solid arrows in Fig. 20-2.

There is, in addition, the possibility of *spontaneous emission*, suggested by the dashed arrow of Fig. 20-2. If A_{gh} is introduced for the *Einstein coefficient of spontaneous emission*, we can write

$$\text{Total rate of } h \to g \text{ transitions} = N_h[B_{h\to g}\rho(\nu_{gh}) + A_{gh}] \tag{20-5}$$

If the forms of $B_{g\to h}$ and $B_{h\to g}$ are investigated, it is found that they depend only on the nature of the g and h states and not on the direction of the transition. Thus

$$B_{g\to h} = B_{h\to g} = B_{gh}$$

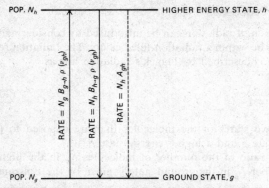

FIGURE 20-2 The induced and spontaneous radiative transition processes between two states.

At equilibrium the net rate of transitions from g to h must be equal to that from h to g. Equating the rates of Eqs. (20-3) and (20-5) gives

$$\frac{N_h}{N_g} = \frac{B_{gh}\rho(\nu_{gh})}{B_{gh}\rho(\nu_{gh}) + A_{gh}} \tag{20-6}$$

Now one can replace N_h/N_g by the Boltzmann expression for this quantity, and one can also replace $\rho(\nu_{gh})$ by the blackbody expression of Eq. (20-1). Rearrangement of the resulting equation gives the relation

$$A_{gh} = \frac{8\pi h(\nu_{gh})^3}{c^3} B_{gh} = 8\pi h(\bar{\nu}_{gh})^3 B_{gh} \tag{20-7}$$

where $\bar{\nu}_{gh}$ is expressed in wave-number units

In the following section it will be shown how studies of the absorption of radiation occurring when a beam passes through a sample provide quantities that let us deduce the values of the coefficients B_{gh} and A_{gh}.

20-3 Measurements of the Absorption of Radiation

The quantities used in reporting the experimental results for the absorption of radiation can be introduced by considering the derivation of Beer's law for an absorbing solute in a nonabsorbing solvent. The decrease in intensity of the radiation as it penetrates a distance dl, as in Fig. 20-3, is, according to Beer's law, proportional to the radiation intensity I, to the molar concentration C, and to the path length dl. Introducing α, the absorption coefficient, as the proportionality constant allows the equation

$$-dI = \alpha I C\, dl \tag{20-8}$$

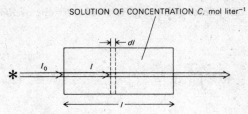
SOLUTION OF CONCENTRATION C, mol liter^{-1}

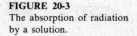

FIGURE 20-3
The absorption of radiation
by a solution.

to be written. The dependence of α on the frequency is sometimes emphasized by writing $\alpha(\nu)$. Integration of this equation over the cell length l allows the absorption coefficient to be expressed in terms of I_0, the incident intensity, or the intensity with no absorbing material, and I, the intensity of the radiation after passing through the cell containing the solution. The integrated form of Beer's law is obtained in this way as

$$\alpha = \frac{1}{Cl} \ln \frac{I_0}{I} \tag{20-9}$$

Absorption due to a liquid or a solute usually occurs over a range of wavelengths or frequencies to produce an absorption band. A measure of the interaction of the absorbing species and the radiation is obtained by integrating α over the band. Often the integration is carried out over a wave-number $\bar{\nu}$ scale.

An approximate result can be obtained by multiplying α_{max}, the maximum value of α, by the width of the band $\Delta\bar{\nu}_{1/2}$ at $\alpha = \frac{1}{2}\alpha_{max}$. Thus

$$\int_{\substack{over \\ band}} \alpha \, d\bar{\nu} \approx \alpha_{max} \, \Delta\bar{\nu}_{1/2} \tag{20-10}$$

In most of the reported literature the concentration, as appears in Eq. (20-9), is in moles per liter, the path length in centimeters, and $\bar{\nu}_{1/2}$ in cm^{-1}. It follows that the units of $\int \alpha \, d\bar{\nu}$ are liters per mole per square centimeter.

A typical strong absorption resulting from an electronic transition that produces an absorption at 300 nm has $\Delta\bar{\nu}_{1/2} = 6000$ cm^{-1} (corresponding to $\Delta\lambda_{1/2} = 50$ nm) and $\alpha_{max} = 20,000$ (mol liter^{-1})$^{-1}$ cm^{-2}. For such a band

$$\int \alpha \, d\bar{\nu} \approx 10^8 \text{ liters mol}^{-1} \text{ cm}^{-2} \tag{20-11}$$

Absorption at the band center is such that I is $\frac{1}{2}I_0$ for a 3.5×10^{-5} M solution in a 1-cm cell.

The total absorption is sometimes compared with that which would result from the interaction of light with a harmonic oscillating electron of an atom. It can be shown that this reference system would give rise to an absorption band with an integrated intensity of 2.31×10^8 liters mol^{-1} cm^{-2}. Comparison of an actual absorption band with this reference band gives a value for the *oscillator strength f* according to

$$f = \frac{\int \alpha \, d\bar{\nu}}{2.31 \times 10^8} = 4.33 \times 10^{-9} \int \alpha \, d\bar{\nu} \tag{20-12}$$

The "typical" absorption with an integrated absorption coefficient of 10^8 has an oscillator strength of 0.433.

The integrated absorption coefficient or the oscillator strength is the experimentally determined measure of the extent to which an absorbing substance interacts with electromagnetic radiation. In the following section the integrated absorption coefficient or the oscillator strength will be related to the coefficients B_{gh} and A_{gh} for induced and spontaneous emission.

20-4 The Half-Life for Spontaneous Emission

In Sec. 20-2 molecules in a radiation-filled cavity were considered. One of the results obtained was

$$\text{No. of absorption transitions per unit time} = N_g B_{gh} \rho(\nu_{gh}) \tag{20-13}$$

In Sec. 20-3 the passage of a beam through a sample was treated, and the effect of absorption was expressed by Beer's law

$$-dI = \alpha I C \, dl$$

The decrease in beam intensity as a result of the entire absorption band can be described by

$$-dI = \left(\int \alpha \, d\nu \right) I C \, dl \tag{20-14}$$

Now we must relate the two situations and the two equations (20-13) and (20-14) so that we can use the results from absorption measurements to evaluate B_{gh}. This will lead us, by means of Eq. (20-7), to values for A_{gh}.

The intensity of a beam can be expressed as the energy which it would bring to a unit cross-section area in a unit time interval. All the energy in a volume of length c, the speed of light, and unit cross section will reach an end cross-section area in unit time. Thus the energy density ρ at any frequency is related to the intensity of a beam at that frequency by

$$I = c\rho$$

or

$$\rho = \frac{I}{c} \tag{20-15}$$

The number of ground-state molecules in a sample of unit cross section and length dl is simply related to the concentration if N_g is very much greater than N_h. Then N_g is equal to the number of solute molecules in the sample volume. If C is the molar concentration,

$$N_g = \frac{\mathfrak{N} C \, dl}{1000} \tag{20-16}$$

Finally the rate of the absorption transitions must be related to the decrease in the beam intensity $-dI$. Multiplication of the number of absorption transitions per unit time by the energy $h\nu$ absorbed in each transition gives $-dI$. Thus

$$-dI = h\nu \times \text{rate of transitions}$$

and, with Eq. (20-13),

$$-dI = h\nu \frac{\mathfrak{N} C \, dl}{1000} B_{gh} \frac{I}{c} = \left(B_{gh} \frac{h\nu}{c} \frac{\mathfrak{N}}{1000} \right) IC \, dl$$

Comparison with Eq. (20-14) lets us write

$$B_{gh} = \frac{1000c}{\mathfrak{N} h\nu_0} \int \alpha \, d\nu$$

or

$$B_{gh} = \frac{1000c}{\mathfrak{N} h\bar{\nu}_0} \int \alpha \, d\bar{\nu} \tag{20-17}$$

where ν_0 and $\bar{\nu}_0$ are the frequency and the wave number of the center of the absorption band.

Here let us proceed to the relation between the coefficient for spontaneous emission A_{gh} and the measurable absorption quantity. By combining Eqs. (20-17) and (20-7) we obtain

$$A_{gh} = \frac{8\pi 1000c(\bar{\nu}_0)^2}{\mathfrak{N}} \int \alpha \, d\bar{\nu} = 1.252 \times 10^{-9}(\bar{\nu}_0)^2 \int \alpha \, d\bar{\nu} \tag{20-18}$$

According to Eq. (20-5), the spontaneous emission process produces the $h \rightarrow g$ transition according to the rate law

$$\left(\frac{dN_h}{dt}\right)_{\text{spont}} = A_{gh} N_h \tag{20-19}$$

The "rate constant" A_{gh} can be related to the half-life for the state h by

$$t_{1/2} = \frac{\ln 2}{A_{gh}} \tag{20-20}$$

Substituting the expression Eq. (20-18) for A_{gh} gives

$$t_{1/2} = \frac{0.55 \times 10^9}{(\bar{\nu}_0)^2 \int \alpha \, d\bar{\nu}} \tag{20-21}$$

The half-life resulting from spontaneous emission by the upper state reached by the typical allowed transition dealt with earlier can now be calculated. We insert the value of 10^8 for $\int \alpha \, d\bar{\nu}$ and 3.3×10^4 cm^{-1}, corresponding to $\lambda = 300$ nm, for $\bar{\nu}_0$ into Eq. (20-21). The result is

$$t_{1/2} = 0.5 \times 10^{-8} \tag{20-22}$$

The relations that have been developed can be used to calculate lifetimes of excited states, as determined by spontaneous emission, for any absorption band for which $\bar{\nu}$ at the band center and $\int \alpha \, d\bar{\nu}$ are known. In general, lifetimes are longer for upper states reached by a more weakly absorbing transition, and they are also longer the smaller the energy separation between the states.

The calculated lifetimes are for states reached directly by the absorption process. The emitting state, however, is often reached by rapid nonradiative processes described in Sec. 20-1. Then the lifetime of the spontaneously emitting state will not be simply related to the intensity of the absorption band. The relation of Eq. (20-21), however, will be a general guide to the lifetime due to the emission process. Such lifetimes are comparable with the typical non-radiative processes treated in Sec. 20-1.

Any decrease in the efficiency of collisional deactivation, e.g., by freezing in a glass or cooling to liquid-nitrogen temperature, will allow the spontaneous emission to occur to a significant extent. Many absorption bands are less intense, i.e., occur with a smaller integrated absorption coefficient, than that cited for typical completely allowed transitions. Emissions corresponding to these bands occur, in view of Eq. (20-21), with a correspondingly longer half-life. One finds in practice that spontaneous emission can be observed with a half-life into the microsecond range or even up to about 10^{-4} s in cases where the value of A_{gh} is small enough and nonradiative processes are relatively ineffective.

20-5 Fluorescence and the Quenching of Fluorescence

If the efficiency of nonradiative processes that return the molecule to its ground state is not too great, various emission processes can occur. One type of process produces an emission band like that of Fig. 20-4a. The observation that the emission band generally appears at longer wavelengths, i.e., lower energy, than the absorption band suggests that vibrational deactivation within the potential curve of the upper electronic state is essentially complete before much emission

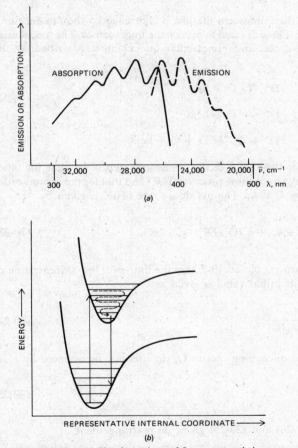

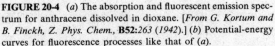

FIGURE 20-4 (a) The absorption and fluorescent emission spectrum for anthracene dissolved in dioxane. [*From G. Kortum and B. Finckh, Z. Phys. Chem.,* **B52**:*263 (1942)*.] (b) Potential-energy curves for fluorescence processes like that of (a).

occurs. The emission transition of Fig. 20-4b, rather than the exact reverse of the absorption transition, is to be drawn.

Most fairly intense absorption bands occur from the ground state to an excited state with the same multiplicity (defined in Sec. 11-9) as the ground state. The emission process of Fig. 20-4 is then a transition with no multiplicity change. The term *fluorescence* is now used for emission transitions that occur between states of the same multiplicity. This definition therefore includes emissions from states reached from the initial excited state by internal conversion as long as the second state has the same multiplicity, usually a singlet state, as the ground state.

It is found that the fluorescent lifetime is shortened by the presence of a variety of substances. These are said to *quench* the fluorescence. The mechanism of excitation, fluorescence, and bimolecular quenching is described by the reactions

$$D + h\nu \rightarrow D^* \qquad D^* \xrightarrow{k_e} D + h\nu$$

$$D^* \xrightarrow{k_q} D + \text{heat}$$

$$D^* + Q \xrightarrow{k_2} D + Q + \text{heat}$$

The rate constant for the radiative, i.e., emission, step is k_e, that for other first-order nonradiative quenching processes is k_q, and that for the second-order quenching process by Q is k_2. The net decay rate of D^* is given by

$$-\frac{d[D^*]}{dt} = (k_e + k_q + k_2[Q])[D^*] \qquad (20\text{-}23)$$

It follows, by the treatment of Sec. 19-2, that the time τ for the concentration of D^* to fall to $1/e$ of its initial value is given as

$$\tau = \frac{1}{k_e + k_q + k_2[Q]} \qquad (20\text{-}24)$$

In the absence of the quenching species Q, the lifetime, represented by τ_0, is

$$\tau_0 = \frac{1}{k_e + k_q} \qquad (20\text{-}25)$$

Combining Eqs. (20-24) and (20-25) gives, on rearrangement,

$$\frac{1}{\tau} = \frac{1}{\tau_0} + k_2[Q] \qquad (20\text{-}26)$$

Thus the analysis presented here suggests that a plot of $1/\tau$ versus [Q] will give

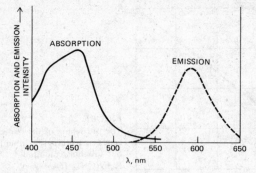

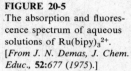

FIGURE 20-5
The absorption and fluorescence spectrum of aqueous solutions of Ru(bipy)$_3^{2+}$. [*From J. N. Demas, J. Chem. Educ.,* **52**:*677 (1975).*]

a straight line of which the intercept can be identified with $1/\tau_0$ and the slope with the quenching rate constant k_2.

The visible-region fluorescent spectrum of the ruthenium complex ion tris(2,2'-bipyridine)ruthenium is shown in Fig. 20-5. The fluorescence is quenched by dissolved oxygen. A plot, according to Eq. (20-26), of the fluorescent lifetimes for oxygen-free, air-saturated, and oxygen-saturated solutions is shown in Fig. 20-6. The value of τ_0 is 0.56 μs, and the slope of the line gives $k_2 = 3.4 \times 10^9$ liters mol^{-1} s^{-1}. Thus the quenching reaction is rapid, and by comparison with the rate constant-value deduced in Sec. 19-10 it can be described as diffusion-controlled.

Information on the action of quenching agents can also be obtained from measurements of the fluorescent intensity as a function of the concentration of the quenching agent.

If the fluorescent cell is continually illuminated with exciting radiation, the concentration of D* can be expressed by assuming a steady state. If the illumination and concentration of D are maintained constant in the absence and in the presence of quencher, constant formation rates of D* require constant decay rates, and thus

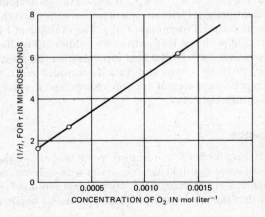

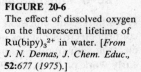

FIGURE 20-6
The effect of dissolved oxygen on the fluorescent lifetime of Ru(bipy)$_3^{2+}$ in water. [*From J. N. Demas, J. Chem. Educ.,* **52**:*677 (1975).*]

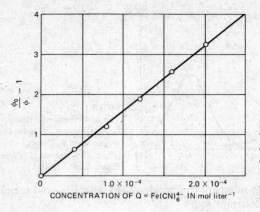

FIGURE 20-7
The quenching of the fluorescence of $Ru(bipy)_3^{2+}$ in aqueous solutions containing $K_4Fe(CN)_6$. [*From J. N. Demas, J. Chem. Educ.,* **52**:*677 (1975).*]

$$(k_e + k_q)[D^*]_{[Q]=0} = (k_e + k_q + k_2[Q])[D^*]_{[Q]} \tag{20-27}$$

The fluorescent signal ϕ (or ϕ_0 in the absence of Q) is proportional to the concentration of D^*. Thus Eq. (20-27) can be rearranged to

$$\frac{\phi_0}{\phi} - 1 = \frac{k_2}{k_e + k_q}[Q] = K_{SV}[Q] \tag{20-28}$$

where K_{SV} is written with subscripts to identify the *Stern-Volmer equation*. As before, we can designate $1/(k_e + k_q)$ by τ_0, and then we have

$$K_{SV} = k_2\tau_0 \tag{20-29}$$

Measurements of ϕ as a function of [Q] allow a plot like that of Fig. 20-7 to be constructed. The slope yields the value of $K_{SV} = k_2\tau_0$. If a value of τ_0 is available from studies of the fluorescent material without quencher or with any other quencher, a value of k_2 can be deduced from that of K_{SV}. The example of Fig. 20-7 yields $K_{SV} = 1.6 \times 10^4$ and, with $\tau = 0.56$ μs from the studies of Fig. 20-6, the result $k_2 = 3 \times 10^{10}$ liters mol^{-1} s^{-1}. Notice that this value is even greater than that calculated in Sec. 19-10 for a typical diffusion-controlled reaction. Here the quenching reaction is between ions of opposite charge, and the rate is enhanced by the coulombic attraction.

20-6 Phosphorescence

Phosphorescent emission is here defined as resulting from transitions that connect electronic states of different multiplicities, i.e., states with different net electron-spin angular momenta. It is now recognized, primarily as a result of the early work of G. N. Lewis, that the most important phosphorescent bands of organic compounds arise from transitions between a triplet excited state and a singlet ground state.

The potential-energy diagram representing a situation that can lead to phosphorescence is shown in Fig. 20-8. Absorption of radiation from the ground singlet to an excited singlet can occur to an appreciable extent; i.e., the transition can be allowed. Collisional deactivation can then drop the energy past the point where the potential curve of the singlet state crosses that of the triplet state. Conversion between states of different multiplicities, a process known as *intersystem crossing,* is apparently not easy. It can occur, however, if the collisional deactivation does not carry the molecule too quickly past the potential crossing point. Once a triplet electronic state is formed, further vibrational energy will be lost and the molecules will occupy the low-lying vibration levels of the triplet electronic state.

Emission from this triplet state to the ground state constitutes phosphorescence. Since such transitions are forbidden by the prohibition against spin changes, the spontaneous-emission process occurs with low probability. According to Eq. (20-18), A_{gh} is very small. The phosphorescent emission can continue over relatively long periods of time. Half-lives for phosphorescence of the order of seconds or longer are not uncommon. Notice that a roundabout mechanism, like that of Fig. 20-8, is required to populate a long-lived excited state.

The process of intersystem crossing between a singlet and a triplet state is sufficiently difficult, even if the potential curves cross, for phosphorescence to be

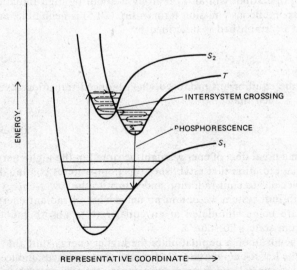

FIGURE 20-8 An energy-diagram representation of absorption followed by intersystem crossing and phosphorescence.

seldom observed in liquids at ordinary temperatures. Again the process of forming a glass with the material as a solute and cooling the system to liquid-nitrogen temperatures is often resorted to. With this procedure many organic compounds undergo appreciable excited-singlet-to-triplet processes and are observed to emit radiation as phosphorescence.

The lifetimes of excited states is a subject of great importance in photochemical studies. The occurrence of a long-lived high-energy species, such as the triplet states that lead to phosphorescence, often provides the means whereby photochemical reactions can occur. In this way the study of electronic spectra, particularly fluorescence and phosphorescence, and photochemistry are intimately related.

20-7 Lasers

An excited-state molecule can move to a lower energy state or return to the ground state by the two different types of radiative process shown in Fig. 20-2. *Spontaneous* emission produces the fluorescence and phosphorescence treated in the preceding sections. Now let us consider the important *induced* emission devices known as *lasers* (*l*ight *a*mplification by *s*timulated *e*mission of *r*adiation).

Consider again the populations of two states, such as those labeled g and h in Fig. 20-2. At equilibrium the ratio N_h/N_g is given by the Boltzmann distribution. The equilibrium population of state h is always less than that of state g, except in the limit of infinite temperature, where the populations become equal. Equalization of the populations can also be brought about by high radiation densities. Then the spontaneous emission term in Eq. (20-5) is negligible, and the equilibrium that is established is described by

$$N_g B_{g \to h} \rho(\nu_{gh}) = N_h B_{h \to g} \rho(\nu_{gh}) \tag{20-30}$$

Since $B_{g \to h} = B_{h \to g}$, the equilibrium produced when induced transitions overwhelm other effects is such that

$$N_g = N_h \tag{20-31}$$

In such a system a great deal of energy might be stored in the high-energy h-state molecules. The radiation that establishes this population is continually inducing h-state molecules to emit radiation and return to the lower-energy g state. For this equilibrium system we obtain no net release of radiant energy because molecules are being stimulated at an equal rate to absorb radiant energy and move from state g to state h.

Laser action depends upon a population of the higher-energy state that is greater than that of the lower-energy state. Under such circumstances, induced, or stimulated, emission can release more radiant energy than is stored by the concurrent induced absorption process. Thus, a *population inversion*, the opposite of that for an equilibrium system at finite temperatures or radiation densities, must be produced if laser action is to occur. Let us see how this can be done.

Three types of energy can be delivered to suitable systems so that a population inversion is produced, namely, radiation energy, collision energy, and chemical energy.

The preceding section on phosphorescence suggests how radiation might establish a population inversion. An indirect approach must circumvent the equality of the coefficients for induced absorption and emission. Two general arrangements of energy levels, known as a *two-level* and a *three-level* laser system, are illustrated in Fig. 20-9. In the former the lower energy state is the ground state, and a large amount of *optical pumping* is necessary to produce a population inversion. In a three-level system population inversion between the two excited states that can produce laser action is more easily attained. The first practical laser device, the ruby laser, corresponds, however, to the two-level system, as shown in Fig. 20-10.

The second excitation procedure, which applies primarily to gas lasers, depends upon collisions. The primary energetic particles are usually electrons produced by an electric discharge. They collide with the molecules which will produce laser action or with an intermediary. In CO_2 lasers the CO_2 molecules are raised to an excited state by collisions with, for example, N_2 or He molecules which have been given large amounts of translational energy by collisions with electrons. The CO_2 laser system, which depends on the laser emission of CO_2 vibrational energy and thus yields infrared laser radiation, is described in Fig. 20-11.

Chemical energy is the basis for laser action when the products of a chemical reaction are produced in an excited state. In most chemical lasers the reaction products appear in high-energy vibrational states. Thus, as for the CO_2

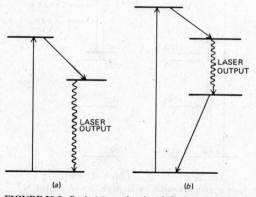

FIGURE 20-9 Basic (*a*) two-level and (*b*) three-level laser systems.

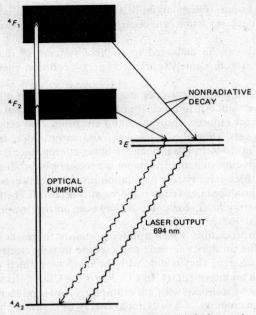

FIGURE 20-10 The processes that lead to the laser action of the Cr^{3+}-ion ruby laser.

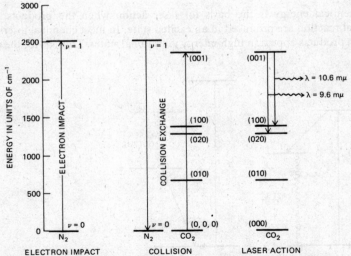

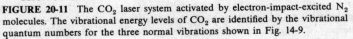

FIGURE 20-11 The CO_2 laser system activated by electron-impact-excited N_2 molecules. The vibrational energy levels of CO_2 are identified by the vibrational quantum numbers for the three normal vibrations shown in Fig. 14-9.

laser of Fig. 20-11, chemical laser action is usually found in the infrared spectral region.

In some cases the excited-state products do not themselves undergo laser action but excite a species that does. Thus the population inversion necessary for CO_2 laser action can be produced by allowing the products of a chemical reaction to interact with the CO_2 molecules and excite them.

Thus, by various means, population inversions can be produced. Suppose that in such a system, a photon enters along a laser tube. Emission in excess of absorption will be stimulated. This additional emission, moreover, will be in phase and in the same direction as the light which stimulated the emission. The augmented light beam will induce additional emissions, all with the same phase and in the same direction as the original beam. It follows that a beam of radiation described as *coherent* will be produced as transitions from the highly populated high-energy state to a lower state are induced. Various optical devices, e.g., reflecting mirrors and pulse arrangements, can be used to enhance the intensity of the laser beam without affecting the chief characteristics of the beam, its coherence and its directionality.

20-8 Photochemical Reactions

In ordinary chemical reactions the energy of activation is supplied by the chance collection in a molecule or a pair of molecules of a large amount of thermal energy. An alternative way in which the necessary activation energy can be acquired is through the absorption of quanta of visible or ultraviolet radiation. Reactions which follow as a result of energy so acquired are classified as *photochemical* reactions. With this description, photochemistry appears as a special branch of kinetics. In practice the theory and the experimental arrangements used in photochemistry set it off as a rather special subject. The goal of these reaction studies, however, is still the elucidation of the mechanism of the reaction.

In all photochemical reactions energy is acquired by a molecule as a result of the absorption of light. The energy of a light quantum is related to the frequency of the light by Planck's law, $\Delta\epsilon = h\nu$. The energy of an Avogadro's number of light quanta is called an *einstein*. The einstein is therefore the energy acquired when each of an Avogadro's number of molecules absorbs one quantum of radiation. The name of the einstein unit of radiation stems from Einstein's photochemical law, which states that each molecule is activated by the absorption of one light quantum.

The amount of energy in an einstein of radiation can be appreciated from a calculation of this quantity for visible light, say of 600 nm wavelength. The frequency of such light is given by c/λ and the energy per quantum by $h\nu = hc/\lambda$. Multiplication by Avogadro's number gives the energy of the einstein. In this way it is found that 1 einstein of yellow light has an energy of 200 kJ. Light of shorter wavelength will have a correspondingly higher energy.

In the ultraviolet, for example, at a wavelength of 200 nm, the energy of 1 einstein is 600 kJ.

From these energy values and the bond energies deduced in the thermo-dynamic studies of Chap. 6 it is seen that the absorption of light in the visible or ultraviolet can be expected to be sufficient to break a chemical bond or at least to produce a high-energy reactive molecule.

The amount of the chemical reaction that occurs in a photochemical experiment is related to the amount of light that is absorbed.

The experimental arrangement for a photochemical experiment is indicated in Fig. 20-12. The data that are obtained using a setup that has been suitably calibrated allow the determination of the number of light quanta that are absorbed in a particular experiment.

A photochemical reaction follows from the absorption of a quantum of radiation by a species in the reaction mixture. The initial consequence of this absorption of radiation is known as the *primary process* in the photochemical reaction.

The excited electronic state may correspond, in contrast to all the states treated so far, to an electronic form in which the electrons of a bond of the absorbing molecule no longer maintain a chemical bond. In such cases the upper-state potential curve shows no minimum, and the absorption of radiation leads to the dissociation of the absorbing molecule. Furthermore, the fragments obtained may be in their lowest or in some excited electronic state. In almost all photochemical studies, when a bond breaks as a result of the absorption of a quantum of radiation, a homolytic cleavage of a chemical bond occurs; i.e., dissociation leads to the formation of free radicals, and the earlier discussions of reaction mechanisms lead us to expect chemical reactions to be initiated by these free radicals.

On the other hand, the absorption of radiation may lead to an excited, but bound, state. Such species have the necessary activation energy for many chemical reactions. The photochemical consequences of such species depend, however, on the lifetime of this species, or some other related high-energy species, compared with the average time between collisions of this species and a molecule with which it can react.

Nonradiative processes (Sec. 20-1) and fluorescence (Sec. 20-5) often quickly remove the excitation energy of a molecule. An excited molecule has a greater chance of initiating a photochemical reaction if intersystem crossing

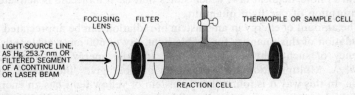

FIGURE 20-12 Apparatus for photochemical studies.

moves it into a triplet state. A photochemical reaction can therefore be expected to occur if the excited state is a repulsive one and free radicals are formed and do not immediately recombine or if the lifetime of a bound excited state is long enough for a collision to occur which forms intermediate or product species.

One can determine the number of quanta absorbed and the number of molecules of reactant used or of a product formed in a given experiment. From these data the quantum yield, or quantum efficiency, defined as the ratio of the number of molecules reacting or produced to the number of quanta absorbed, is determined. Some reactions have quantum yields close to unity. The extremes, however, go from quantum yields of zero for molecules that absorb visible or ultraviolet radiation and show no photochemical reactions to quantum yields as high as 10^6 for chain reactions like that which will be discussed for the reaction of H_2 and Cl_2.

20-9 Flash Photolysis

Often, as for example in studies of the reactions in the ozone layer of the earth's atmosphere, we are interested in the kinetic behavior of species that are not available as on-the-shelf chemicals. The rate constants of reactions involving such species as H atoms, O atoms, OH and HO_2 radicals must be known if the dynamics of complex reaction mixtures are to be understood. Rate-constant data can sometimes be obtained by generating such species by a high-intensity short-duration flash of light and then following their subsequent reaction. This approach is known as *flash photolysis*.

A typical flash used in such studies can generate about 1 μmol of products in the several-microsecond duration of the flash. One or more of the products, formed directly or indirectly, are usually followed by measuring the absorption of light at a suitable wavelength. As an illustration of this technique studies of the formation and reaction of the perhydroxyl radical, HO_2, will be described.

Perhydroxyl radicals are formed by the reaction of H atoms and O_2 molecules in the presence of a third body M. The reaction is

$$H + O_2 + M \rightarrow HO_2 + M \tag{20-32}$$

Hydrogen atoms can be generated by the photolysis of water. In the presence of an H_2 atmosphere, the hydroxyl radicals that are formed react further to produce additional H atoms. These two reactions are

$$H_2O + h\nu \rightarrow OH + H \tag{20-33}$$

$$OH + H_2 \rightarrow H_2O + H \tag{20-34}$$

The formation of HO_2 radicals by this flash-photolysis route and studies of the kinetics of subsequent reactions has been reported.† The reaction system

†C. J. Hochanadel, J. A. Ghormley, and P. J. Ogren, *J. Chem. Phys.*, **56**:4426 (1972).

contained 2.8 percent H_2O, 1.9 percent O_2, and enough H_2 to produce a total pressure of 1 atm. The formation of H atoms and their attachment to O_2 to form HO_2 occurred rapidly. Within about 10 μs the intermediates, H and OH, were largely consumed. The kinetics of the subsequent reactions of HO_2 radicals could then be studied. The optical transmission at 210 nm, where HO_2 absorbs, can be used to follow the decrease of this species.

If, as is expected, the reaction that removes HO_2 is second-order in HO_2, the HO_2 concentration will vary with time according to Eq. (19-15)

$$\frac{1}{c} = \frac{1}{c_0} + kt \qquad (20\text{-}35)$$

That the reaction is indeed second-order is confirmed by the linear relation for $1/\{\log{(I_0/I)}\}$, which is proportional to $1/c$, versus t, as shown in Fig. 20-13. This order and the net product of the reaction, H_2O_2, suggest that the decay of HO_2 occurs by the reaction

$$HO_2 + HO_2 \rightarrow H_2O_2 + O_2 \qquad (20\text{-}36)$$

The rate constant for the reaction can be obtained only if the absorption coefficient of HO_2 at 210 nm is known so that a reciprocal concentration rather than the reciprocal log (I_0/I) plot can be constructed. Estimates of this absorption coefficient lead to a rate constant of 6×10^9 liters mol^{-1} s^{-1} for the reaction of Eq. (20-36).

The reaction following the initial photolysis process can often be changed by changing the reagents in the reaction system. Thus, if the H_2 atmosphere in the above study is replaced by an inert-gas atmosphere, the OH species survives the initial rapid reaction phase. The principal subsequent reaction then is

$$OH + HO_2 \rightarrow H_2O + O_2 \qquad (20\text{-}37)$$

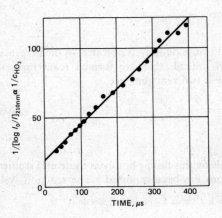

FIGURE 20-13
Illustration that the decay of HO_2 conforms to Eq. (20-35) and thus follows a second-order rate law. [*From C. J. Hochanadel et. al., J. Chem. Phys.*, **56**:4426 (1972).]

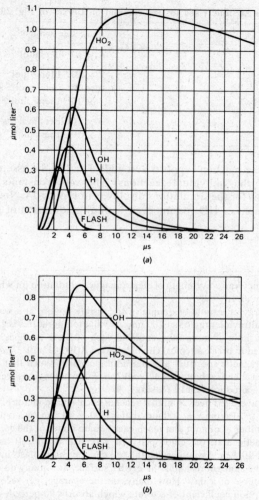

FIGURE 20-14 Computer simulation of the formation and reaction of HO_2 in (*a*) H_2 + 3 percent H_2O + 2 percent O_2 and (*b*) Ar + 3 percent H_2O + 2 percent O_2. Total pressures equal 1 atm, and 0.96 μmol H and OH are produced by the flash. [*From S. M. Koop and P. J. Ogren J. Chem. Educ.,* **53**:*128 (1976).*]

Studies of the decay of HO_2 produced in a photolysis system containing about 3 percent H_2O, 2 percent O_2, and an atmosphere of argon suggest a value of 1.2×10^{11} liters mol^{-1} s^{-1} for the rate constant for this reaction.

In such flash-photolysis studies, computer simulation of the reaction system

TABLE 20-1 The Principal Reactions Used for the Simulation Curves of Fig. 20-14

Reaction	Rate constant
$OH + H_2 \rightarrow H_2O + H$	4×10^6 liters mol^{-1} s^{-1}
$H + O_2 + H_2 \rightarrow HO_2 + H_2$	2×10^{10} liters^2 mol^{-2} s^{-1}
$H + O_2 + Ar \rightarrow HO_2 + Ar$	6×10^9 liters^2 mol^{-2} s^{-1}
$H + O_2 + H_2O \rightarrow HO_2 + H_2O$	1.4×10^{11} liters^2 mol^{-2} s^{-1}
$HO_2 + HO_2 \rightarrow H_2O_2$	6×10^9 liters mol^{-1} s^{-1}
$OH + HO_2 \rightarrow H_2O + O_2$	1.2×10^{11} liters mol^{-1} s^{-1}

throughout the course of the reaction supports and adds detail to the assumptions about the roles of the individual reactions. The rate constants of Table 20-1 provide the basis for the simulations displayed in Fig. 20-14. Notice that appreciable development of HO_2 occurs even within the duration of the flash.

PROBLEMS

20-1. What is the frequency and wavelength of electromagnetic radiation for which each quantum has an energy of 10^{-21} J?

20-2. Calculate the energy of a mole of quanta in the visible region, at a wavelength of 600 nm and in the ultraviolet region at 200 nm. At what temperatures is $\frac{3}{2}RT$, the translational energy of a mole of molecules, equal to each of these energies?

20-3. The energy required to break a typical chemical bond is 300 kJ mol^{-1}. (a) In what regions of the electromagnetic spectrum are the radiation quanta such that if a molecule absorbs a quantum a chemical bond might break? (b) For what regions are the quanta of too little energy to produce bond breaking?

20-4. The solar energy, averaged over 24 h, that reaches each square meter of the earth's surface is about 240 J. (a) Taking $\lambda = 500$ nm, that is, 500×10^{-9} m, as a typical wavelength, calculate the number of quanta that reach each square meter of the earth's surface. (b) The photosynthetic unit, the chloroplast, of a typical plant cell has a diameter of 4 μm, that is, 4×10^{-6} m. Assuming that the cell and the chloroplasts in the cell, are directly exposed to the sunlight reaching the earth's surface, how many quanta reach a chloroplast in the course of a day? How many, on the average, per second?

20-5. What is the absorption coefficient of a solute which absorbs 90 percent of a certain wavelength of light when the beam is passed through a 0.1-m cell containing a 0.25 M solution?

20-6. A 3.4×10^{-5} M solution of cinnamaldehyde, $C_6H_5CH{=}CH{-}HC{=}O$, in cyclohexane has an absorption band centered at 280 nm, at which wavelength the absorbance log (I_0/I) for a 1-cm cell is 0.88. Absorbances of 0.44 occur at about 260 and 300 nm. (a) What is the absorption coefficient at the band maximum? (b) Approximately what is the value of $\int \alpha \, d\overline{\nu}$? (c) What is the oscillator strength? (d) Why might you have expected such a value?

20-7. What would be the half-life for spontaneous emission for the excited state reached by the absorption in Prob. 20-6?

20-8. Fluorescence of the sodium atom from the ^2P state to the ground state, the states involved in the sodium doublet at 589 nm, is reduced to half its intensity by the presence of 0.002 atm of N_2. If the lifetime of the excited Na atom, in the absence of a quencher, is 0.1 μs, what is the rate constant for the quenching process and the quenching cross section for N_2?

20-9. The quenching rate constant k_2, introduced in Sec. 20-3, varies with the particular quenching agent. The effectiveness of gas-phase quenching agents is usually described by assuming zero activation energy for the quenching reaction and assigning a cross section that accounts for the value of the rate constant. Use Eq. (19-75) to obtain, with zero activation energy, a relation between k_2 and the quenching cross section $\sigma_Q = \pi d_Q{}^2/4$.

20-10. The quenching rate constant k_2 is 4×10^{10} (mol liter^{-1})$^{-1}$ s^{-1} for the quenching of mercury phosphorescence by oxygen. In view of the relation obtained in the Prob. 20-9, what is the quenching cross section?

*20-11. An equation that is the counterpart of the Stern-Vollmer equation (20-28) is applicable to some photochemical reactions even when no fluorescence is observed. Cyclohexatriene, C_6H_8, produces H_2 and benzene when irradiated with 253.7-nm ultraviolet radiation. The mechanism that appears to operate is the initial formation of an excited $C_6H_8{}^*$ species. Internal conversion to a vibrationally excited, ground electronic state C_6H_8 rapidly occurs. This species can decompose to the final products, or can be deactivated on collision with any molecule M which acts as a quencher. (a) Use the steady-state approximation to obtain an expression for the rate of formation of H_2. (b) Put this expression in a form permitting data on the rate of formation of H_2 versus pressure of the reaction system to be used to test the mechanism and to evaluate the constants. (c) The following data have been reported by R. Srinivason, *J. Chem. Phys.*, **38**:1039 (1963):

P, mm	0.30	0.85	1.50	2.35	4.75	10.25	23.10
Rate formation of H_2, mol min^{-1}	0.295	0.256	0.214	0.202	0.119	0.072	0.032

Do these data conform to the mechanism described above? If so, deduce all you can about the reaction system. (d) Calculate the quantum yield for hydrogen at each of the experimental points. (e) Derive an expression for the quantum yield as a function of the pressure and see whether the deduced quantum yields follow this relation.

20-12. Photosensitized reactions are often initiated by excited-state mercury atoms produced by the absorption of 253.7-nm radiation by the atoms. (a) Is the energy of these excited Hg* atoms sufficient to produce the reaction

$$Hg^* + H_2 \rightarrow Hg + H + H$$

(b) If so, what might be the electronic states of the hydrogen atoms that are produced?

20-13. What would happen if a sample of hydrogen gas was irradiated with 253.7-nm radiation from a mercury-discharge tube?

20-14. (a) How much energy would 1 mol of acetone acquire if 1 mol absorbed 1 einstein of ultraviolet radiation of wavelength 253.7 nm? (b) How does this compare with the $C{=}O$ bond energy?

20-15. Irradiation of HI vapor with ultraviolet radiation of wavelength 207 nm leads to the formation of H_2 and I_2. It has been observed that for every joule of radiant energy that is absorbed, 0.00044 g of HI is decomposed. How many HI molecules were decomposed per quantum of absorbed radiation?

20-16. At the beginning of a photochemical study a 1-liter reaction vessel contains an amount of Cl_2 to give a partial pressure of 0.5 atm at 25°C and an equal pressure of H_2. Irradiation with 400 nm of radiation results in the absorption of 6.28 J of radiant energy and the decrease in the partial pressure of Cl_2 from 0.5 to 0.013 atm, the temperature being held at 25°C. How many molecules of HCl are formed for each quantum absorbed?

20-17. A 100-W sodium-vapor lamp radiates most of its energy in the yellow D line at 589 nm. How long would such a lamp take to excite more than half the molecules of an absorbing species in a 1-mmol sample if all the radiant energy were absorbed by the sample?

20-18. Hydrogen atoms can be produced by the direct dissociation of H_2 molecules if radiation of a wavelength shorter than 849 Å is used. What might be the electronic state of the atoms so produced? Compare with the answer to Prob. 20-12.

REFERENCES

Excellent introductory treatments of photochemistry:

CUNDALL, R. B., and A. GILBERT: "Photochemistry," Appleton-Century-Crofts, New York, 1970.
TURRO, N. J.: "Molecular Photochemistry," W. A. Benjamin, Inc., New York, 1967.
WAYNE, C. H. J.: "Photochemistry," American Elsevier Publishing Company, Inc., New York, 1970.
WELLS, C. H. J.: "Introduction to Molecular Photochemistry," Chapman and Hall, London, 1972.

More extensive treatments:

CALVERT, J. G., and J. N. PITTS: "Photochemistry," John Wiley & Sons, Inc., New York, 1966.
SIMONS, J. P.: "Photochemistry and Spectroscopy," Wiley-Interscience, New York, 1971.

Two related physical-chemistry laboratory suggestions:

DEMAS, J. N.: Luminescence Spectroscopy and Bimolecular Quenching: A Physical Chemistry Experiment, *J. Chem. Educ.*, **52**:677 (1975).
DEMAS, J. N.: Luminescence Decay Times and Bimolecular Quenching: An Ultrafast Kinetics Experiment, *J. Chem. Educ.*, **53**:657 (1976).

21 SURFACES AND HETEROGENEOUS CATALYSIS

Since molecules on the surface of a liquid have a different environment from those in the bulk of the liquid, the surface has a different free energy from the bulk of the material. In most chemical systems the fraction of the molecules on a surface and the free-energy difference between the surface and the bulk material are relatively small. Now systems are considered in which the surface effects are dominant. Mention will be made of the surface of a liquid and of a liquid droplet and of a liquid film spread out in another liquid but attention will be devoted principally to systems in which the molecules of a gas are concentrated on the surface of a solid. The molecules are said to be *adsorbed* on the solid surface, and this process is distinguished from the penetration of one component throughout the body of a second, called *absorption*. The chapter will begin with a direct study of the adsorption process and the adsorbed layer.

Such studies are now almost always directed toward understanding the chemical reactions that occur at the surface. The surface, it will be shown, enters into reactions as a catalyst. It is interesting that this type of catalysis, called *heterogeneous catalysis,* is understandable only on the basis of some of the information deduced in adsorption studies; on the other hand, conclusions that are drawn from the chemical reactions on a surface help to answer some of the problems unsolved by direct adsorption studies.

The goal of modern physicochemical studies of surface phenomena is the understanding of these phenomena by means of a molecular model. However, systems which have a very thin, often monomolecular layer of gas adsorbed on a complex solid adsorbent resist many of the methods developed to investigate atomic and molecular properties. However, the photoelectron (ESCA) method of Sec. 14-7 can be applied to reveal some of the bonding properties of adsorbed species. Infrared absorption spectra, which reveal the characteristic vibrations of the adsorbed species, can also be obtained by using infrared-transparent materials and a technique that involves total internal reflection. The current theories of surface reactions, however, are still often loosely supported. But some of the background information and treatments on which present ideas are based will be introduced.

It should be pointed out immediately that heterogeneous catalysis is a procedure of great importance in industrial chemistry. This fact and the challenge of the many unexplained phenomena make the study of the adsorbed state one of the most exciting areas of modern physicochemical research.

LIQUID SURFACES

21-1 Surface Tension

The surface tension of liquids can be looked upon as that property which draws a liquid together and forms a liquid-vapor interface, thereby distinguishing liquids from gases.

The molecular basis for this property is indicated in Fig. 21-1, where the unbalanced attractions experienced by the surface molecules are shown to lead to a net drawing together of the liquid. On this basis it can be expected that a small amount of free liquid will pull itself together to form a more or less spherical drop. It is also clear that the surface layer will have properties, such as free energy, that will differ from those of the bulk of the liquid.

The surface tension of a liquid can be defined with reference to Fig. 21-2. Most easily pictured is a wire frame, arranged like a piston, used to expand a soap film. The definition also applies, however, to the mechanically more difficult systems where the film would be replaced by a layer of liquid of appreciable thickness. The force required to stretch the film or liquid layer is found to be proportional to the length l of the piston. Since there are two surfaces to the film, the total length of the film is $2l$ and the proportionality equation

$$f = \gamma(2l) \tag{21-1}$$

can be written. The proportionality constant γ is known as the *surface tension*, and according to Eq. (21-1), it can be looked upon as the force exerted by a surface of unit length.

Of more general use is the relation between surface tension and surface energy. The work required to expand the surfaces in Fig. 21-2 by moving the piston a distance dx is $f\,dx$, or $2l\gamma\,dx$. Since the area of new surface is $2l\,dx$, the result

$$\frac{\text{Work}}{\text{Change of surface area}} = \frac{2l\gamma\,dx}{2l\,dx} = \gamma \tag{21-2}$$

FIGURE 21-1
Interaction forces for a surface molecule compared with one in the body of the liquid.

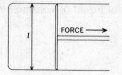

FIGURE 21-2
A wire piston supporting a
soap film.

can be obtained. This expression shows that the surface tension can be interpreted as the energy per unit surface area and that it is a mechanical rather than
thermal energy. In these terms, the tendency of a surface to reduce its area is
just another example of a system tending toward an arrangement of low free
energy.

A number of methods are available for the measurements of surface
tension, but only the *capillary-rise method* will be dealt with here. The arrangement of Fig. 21-3, showing a capillary glass tube inserted into a container of the
liquid to be studied, is all that is necessary. All liquids that wet the glass will rise
in the tube, and it is this capillary rise that can be used to deduce the surface
tension.

The rise of the liquid can be understood if it is assumed that an adsorbed
thin film of liquid exists on the wall of the capillary. To reduce its total surface
area, the liquid rises in the tube. Equilibrium is reached when the free energy is
a minimum; any further rise would expend more free energy in the work to
draw up the liquid column than would be saved by the decrease in surface area.

These ideas can be put in more quantitative form by reference to Fig. 21-3.
The decrease in surface area that results from a rise in liquid by an amount dl
is $2\pi r\, dl$, and the corresponding decrease in surface energy is

$$dG_{\text{surf energy}} = \gamma\, dA = \gamma(2\pi r)\, dl \qquad (21\text{-}3)$$

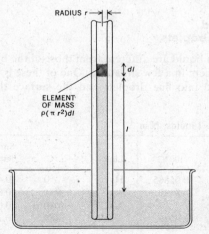

RADIUS r

dl

ELEMENT
OF MASS
$\rho(\pi r^2)dl$

l

FIGURE 21-3
The capillary rise of a liquid
which wets the capillary wall.

The expenditure of free energy in raising an amount of liquid of volume $\pi r^2\, dl$ and density ρ to a height l is

$$dG_{\text{grav}} = (\pi r^2\, dl\, \rho)gl \tag{21-4}$$

When the column of liquid has risen in the capillary to its equilibrium height, these two free energies balance. For this condition

$$2\pi r\gamma\, dl = \pi r^2\rho gl\, dl$$

and

$$\gamma = \frac{r\rho gl}{2} \tag{21-5}$$

Measurement of the quantities on the right side of Eq. (21-5) gives a value of γ.

If the liquid does not adhere to the glass, i.e., does not wet it, a capillary rise does not occur and the phenomenon of a depressed liquid in the tube, as observed with mercury and glass, results. Here the mutual attraction between the mercury atoms is greater than that between mercury and glass, and a minimum glass-mercury area is therefore sought by the mercury withdrawing from the inserted tube.

Table 21-1 shows the results obtained for the surface tension of a number of liquids. The only generalization that can be offered is that liquids, like water, which have very strong cohesive forces tend to have high surface tensions. This can be attributed to a greater tendency for the surface molecules to be pulled into the bulk of the liquid. The molten metals and metal salts provide other examples of high surface tension.

21-2 Surface Tension and Vapor Pressure of Small Droplets

Although the surface properties of a liquid are different from those of the bulk liquid, this effect can be ignored except in a few situations. One of these is the case in which a liquid is dispersed into fine droplets and the surface then

TABLE 21-1 Surface Tension of Some Liquids, N m^{-1}

Liquid	20°C	60°C	100°C	Liquid	t, °C	Surface tension
H_2O	0.07275	0.06618	0.05885	Hg	0	0.480
C_2H_5OH	0.0223	0.0223	0.0190	Ag	970	0.800
C_6H_6	0.0289	0.0237		NaCl	1080	0.094
$(C_2H_5)_2O$	0.0170		0.0080	AgCl	452	0.125

constitutes a large fraction of the total material. A similar situation occurs with finely divided solid material.

Consider the transfer of dn mol of liquid to a droplet of initial radius r. If the normal vapor pressure of the liquid is P_0 and of the droplet is P, the free-energy change for this process can be written, according to Sec. 8-3, as

$$dG = dn \, RT \ln \frac{P}{P_0} \tag{21-6}$$

The free-energy change can also be calculated from the surface-energy change of the droplet that results from the surface-area increase due to the addition of dn mol, or volume $M \, dn/\rho$. This volume adds a spherical shell, whose area is $4\pi r^2$. The thickness dr is given by the relation

$$\frac{M \, dn}{\rho} = 4\pi r^2 \, dr$$

or

$$dr = \frac{M}{4\pi r^2 \rho} \, dn \tag{21-7}$$

The increase in surface energy is γ times the increase in surface area resulting from the increase dr in the droplet radius; i.e.,

$$dG = \gamma \, dA = \gamma[4\pi(r + dr)^2 - 4\pi r^2] = 8\pi\gamma r \, dr \tag{21-8}$$

Substitution of Eq. (21-7) now gives

$$dG = 8\pi\gamma r \frac{M}{4\pi r^2 \rho} \, dn = \frac{2\gamma M}{\rho r} \, dn \tag{21-9}$$

Equating the two calculations for the free-energy change [Eqs. (21-6) and (21-9)] gives

$$dn \, RT \ln \frac{P}{P_0} = \frac{2\gamma M}{\rho r} \, dn$$

and

$$\ln \frac{P}{P_0} = \frac{2\gamma M}{\rho r RT} \tag{21-10}$$

If, as is assumed here, SI units are used, care must be taken to express the

TABLE 21-2 The Vapor Pressure of
Water as a Function of the Radius
of Curvature of the Surface at 25°C

$(P_0 = 0.03126 \text{ atm})$

m	Å	P/P_0
10^{-6}	10^4	1.001
10^{-7}	10^3	1.011
10^{-8}	10^2	1.111
10^{-9}	10^1	2.88

density in units of kilograms per cubic meter instead of the often used units of grams per cubic centimeter. The conversion is ρ (kg m^{-3}) $= 10^3 \rho$ (g cm^{-3}).

This desired result relates the vapor pressure P of a droplet, or really of a liquid element with highly curved surface, to the vapor pressure P_0 of the bulk liquid. The appearance of r in the denominator implies a dependence of vapor pressure on droplet size that is illustrated in Table 21-2.

These data produce something of a dilemma when the condensation of a vapor to a liquid is considered. The formation of an initial small droplet of liquid would lead to a particle with such a high vapor pressure, according to Eq. (21-10), that it would evaporate even if the pressure of the vapor were greater than the vapor pressure of the bulk liquid. It is necessary to imagine the condensation to occur on dust particles or other irregularities so that the equilibrium thermodynamic result can be circumvented by some mechanism that avoids an initial slow equilibrium growth of droplets.

Similar considerations are necessary when the reverse process, the boiling of a liquid, which requires the formation of small vapor nuclei, is treated. Chemically, one also encounters this phenomenon in the difficulty with which some precipitates form and in the tendency for liquids to supercool. Likewise, the digestion of a precipitate makes use of the high free energy of the smaller crystals for their conversion into larger particles.

21-3 Liquid Films on Liquids

The most interesting and easily studied liquid films are formed by allowing a small quantity of a *surface-active* material, e.g., a long-chain organic acid like stearic acid, $CH_3(CH_2)_{16}COOH$, to spread out on the surface of water. Such molecules are suitable because the acid group shows an attraction for water (short-chain acids are, in fact, soluble in water) that makes the material spread out over the water surface, whereas the long hydrocarbon end prevents the material from dissolving. It can now be shown that such films can be made to form a *monomolecular layer* on the water surface.

Modern studies of such films are made on a *surface balance*, developed by

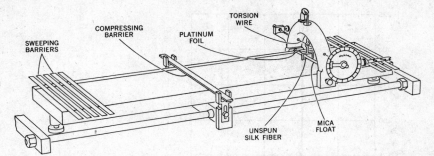

FIGURE 21-4 A Langmuir film-balance apparatus. (*Courtesy of Herman E. Ries, Jr., Standard Oil Company of Indiana, Whiting, Ind.*)

Langmuir in 1917. The apparatus is shown in Fig. 21-4. The trough is filled with water, and a measured amount of the surface-active material is added. The movable barrier is pushed forward, and measurements of the force exerted on the fixed barrier are read off the delicate tension device. It is customary to plot the results as the force on the fixed barrier versus the surface area per molecule of the surface-active agent, i.e., the surface area covered by the surface-active agent divided by the number of molecules in the sample. Typical results for stearic acid are shown in Fig. 21-5.

The initial slow increase in film force with decreasing surface area indicates that the surface is not completely covered by the surface-active film. The beginning of the steep part of the curve is taken to correspond to the completion of the film; further decrease in area must compress the film itself, and a large increase in force is necessary. Finally, the film buckles and folds, and the area can be decreased without any further increase in force.

A calculation can now be made which supports the idea that the onset of the steep part of the curve corresponds to a monomolecular film. For stearic acid this film has, according to Fig. 21-5, an area of about 20.5 Å^2 per molecule. This value can be shown to be about that expected for the cross-section area occupied by a stearic acid molecule.

Some features of these liquid films will be encountered in the study of the adsorption of gases on solids. The concept of a monomolecular layer will be of great importance, but the transition to multiple layers, for gases on solids, will be less easily detected. Likewise, the surface area of the adsorbent will be talked about but will seldom be as definite a concept as in liquid-film systems. Part of this difficulty stems from the nonhomogeneity that must be anticipated for solid adsorbents. Finally, the nature of the attraction of the surface layer for the adsorbent will be studied and will be found to be rather more complicated than the essentially physical, or van der Waals, attractions that act on the surface film on a liquid. It is all these added complexities which make the study of the nature and reactions of gases adsorbed on solids of special interest.

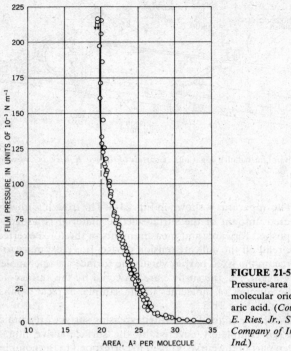

FIGURE 21-5
Pressure-area isotherm and molecular orientation of stearic acid. (*Courtesy of Herman E. Ries, Jr., Standard Oil Company of Indiana, Whiting, Ind.*)

An extension of studies of liquid-surface films could be made to liquid-liquid interfaces. The molecules of stearic acid, for example, would be expected to concentrate at an oil-water interface just as they do at an air-water interface. All such systems are clearly important in studies of lubrication and in the wetting action of water containing soaps or detergents.

ADSORPTION

Although the distinction between *adsorption* and *absorption* is not always clear-cut and the noncommittal word *sorption* is sometimes used, the processes that will be considered here will be essentially surface effects and the word adsorption will be used.

The most important and interesting type of adsorption is certainly that in which gases are adsorbed on a solid. Before treating this subject, however, the much simpler and more easily treated process of the adsorption, or spreading, of a film of one liquid on the surface of another will be dealt with briefly.

21-4 Classifications of Adsorptions of Gases on Solids

It is very convenient in the study of adsorption to recognize that more adsorptions can be placed in one of two categories. These categories are suggested by the possibilities of having essentially physical forces holding the gas molecules to the solid or of having chemical bonds serve the function. The categories of *physical adsorption* and *chemical adsorption,* or more commonly, *chemisorption,* thus arise. The observed characteristics of any adsorption process usually allow it to be placed in one category or the other. Table 21-3 outlines the experimental features that allow a process to be so categorized. The different behaviors of the two types of adsorption should be recognized as having the features of a physical process, such as condensation, or those of a chemical reaction. It should be pointed out that whether or not more than a monolayer is being formed is not directly observable but, as we shall see, can often be deduced from experimental data.

Most interest in adsorption, and in the closely related field of heterogeneous catalysis, is in chemisorption. Two of the items mentioned in Table 21-3 will therefore be dealt with in more detail and with particular emphasis on chemisorption.

21-5 Heat of Adsorption

In all adsorptions heat is given out, and ΔH for the process

$$\text{Gas} \rightarrow \text{adsorbed layer} \tag{21-11}$$

TABLE 21-3 Characteristics of Physical Adsorption and Chemisorption

Physical adsorption	Chemisorption
Heat of adsorption less than about 40 kJ mol^{-1}	Heat of adsorption greater than about 80 kJ mol^{-1}
Adsorption appreciable only at temperatures below the boiling point of the adsorbate	Adsorption can occur at high temperatures
Incremental increase in amount adsorbed increases with each incremental increase in pressure of adsorbate	Incremental increase in amount adsorbed decreases with each incremental increase in pressure of adsorbate
Amount of adsorption on surface a function more of adsorbate than adsorbent	Amount of adsorption characteristic of both adsorbate and adsorbent
No appreciable activation energy involved in adsorption process	Activation energy may be involved in adsorption process
Multilayer adsorption occurs	Adsorption leads to a monolayer, at most

is negative. Heats of adsorptions, however, are generally listed without sign. The necessity for a negative ΔH, in contrast to chemical reactions in general, arises from the fact that the entropy of the ordered, constrained adsorbed layer is always less than that of the gas; i.e., for the reaction of Eq. (21-11), ΔS is invariably negative. It follows that for the process of Eq. (21-11) to be spontaneous and have a negative value for ΔG the value of ΔH must be negative and greater than $T \Delta S$.

For physical adsorption the heats involved are of the order of heats of vaporization, i.e., generally less than 40 kJ mol^{-1}, and in keeping with the idea that physical adsorption may be leading to the formation of multilayers, these heats are more dependent on the nature of the gas than they are on that of the solid adsorbent. Adsorptions classed as chemisorptions, on the other hand, have heats of adsorption that compare with those of ordinary chemical reactions; in other words, they have heats of anywhere up to about 630 kJ mol^{-1}.

The approximate values mentioned for physical and chemical adsorptions are not intended to imply a constancy for these heats as a function of the amount of gas adsorbed. Some of the variations in differential heats of adsorption in the chemisorption region are shown in Fig. 21-6. The frequently observed curve over the region of adsorption from low coverages to multilayer formation has a high initial heat that falls off at large amounts of adsorption. This behavior is taken as indicative of an initial chemisorption, to form something like a monolayer, followed by the formation of multiple layers that are bound by physical forces.

Even within a range attributed to chemisorption, however, the heat of adsorption is usually found to be a function of the amount adsorbed. A number of molecular explanations have been offered for this variation. Active sites can

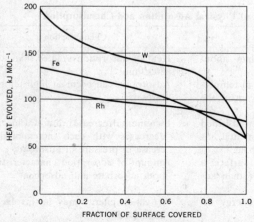

FIGURE 21-6 The heat of adsorption for H_2 on clean metal surfaces. (*From O. Beeck, Discuss. Faraday Soc.,* **1950:***118.*)

be assumed to exist on the adsorbent, and as these are occupied by the first additions of gas, the binding of later additions must occur on less active sites and the strength of binding falls off. Alternatively, the binding of some gas to the solid can occur with electrons being given up to the solid by the adsorbed molecules or with electrons being withdrawn from the solid, and as such processes continue, the solid becomes more and more reluctant to gain or lose more electrons. Such an explanation is particularly appropriate to semiconducting and conducting adsorbents. The final important factor that has been suggested is that the mutual repulsion of the adsorbed molecules, especially if they acquire a net charge when they are adsorbed, operates to oppose the addition of further molecules.

21-6 The Adsorption Isotherm

The most common adsorption experiment is the measurement of the relation between the amount of gas adsorbed by a given amount of adsorbent and the pressure of the gas. Such measurements are usually made at a constant temperature, and the results are generally presented graphically as an *adsorption isotherm*. Experimentally, one measures either the volume of gas taken up by a given amount of adsorbent or the change in weight of the adsorbent when it is exposed to a gas at a given pressure. The apparatus that can be used is shown in Fig. 21-7.

A great variety of adsorption-isotherm shapes are found. Chemisorption is usually accompanied by an initial steeply rising curve that gradually flattens off. The initial rise is taken as corresponding to the strong tendency of the surface to bind the gas molecules, and the leveling off can be attributed to the saturation

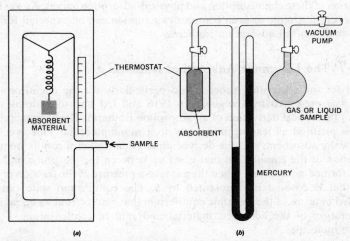

FIGURE 21-7 Adsorption-isotherm apparatus: (*a*) gravimetric; (*b*) volumetric.

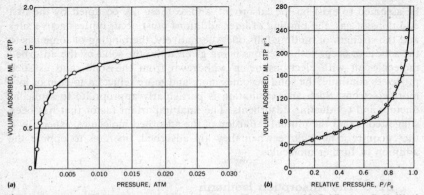

FIGURE 21-8 (*a*) The adsorption isotherm for H_2 on Cu powder at 25°C. [*From A. F. H. Ward, Proc. R. Soc. Lond.,* **A133**:*506 (1931)*.] (*b*) The adsorption of N_2 up to the vapor pressure of N_2, on silica. (*From P. Emmett, "Catalysis," vol. 1, Reinhold Publishing Corporation, New York, 1954.*)

of these forces, perhaps by one or more of the three mechanisms mentioned in Sec. 21-5. Physical adsorption, on the other hand, is accompanied by an adsorption isotherm that tends to have an increasingly positive slope with increasing gas pressure. Each incremental increase in gas pressure produces a larger increase in the amount of gas adsorbed—up to the limit of a pressure equal to the vapor pressure of the material being adsorbed, at which pressure the adsorption isotherm ascends vertically as condensation occurs.

Some adsorption isotherms, as Fig. 21-8 suggests, can be interpreted as a combination of these chemisorption and physical-adsorption curves. As we shall see, however, no simple or even complex explanation can be expected for the detailed shapes of all adsorption isotherms.

21-7 The Langmuir Adsorption Isotherm

A model for the adsorption process, and particularly for the chemisorption process, was presented by Langmuir in 1916 and led him to a simple but important theoretical derivation of an adsorption isotherm. The chemisorption process is pictured as leading ultimately to a monomolecular film over the surface of the adsorbent, and the derived adsorption isotherm results from an investigation of the equilibrium that is set up between the gas phase and the partially formed monolayer. When the gas is at a pressure P, the fraction of the surface that is covered is represented by θ. The equilibrium state can be interpreted in terms of the dynamic equilibrium that results from an equal rate of evaporation of the adsorbed material and rate of condensation of the gas-phase molecules.

The Langmuir theory suggests that the rate of evaporation can be taken to be proportional to the fraction of the surface covered and can therefore be written as $k_1\theta$, where k_1 is some proportionality constant. This simple proportionality assumption ignores the complications that often make the heat of adsorption dependent on the extent of coverage and may well be expected to spoil the simple assumption of an evaporation rate proportional to $k_1\theta$. The rate of condensation, furthermore, is taken to be proportional both to the gas pressure P, which according to the kinetic-molecular theory of Chap. 2 determines the number of molecular collisions per unit area per unit time, and to the fraction of the surface not already covered by adsorbed molecules, i.e., to $1 - \theta$. It is assumed that only collisions with this exposed surface can lead to the sticking of a molecule to the surface. The relation between equilibrium surface coverage and gas pressure is then obtained by equating the expressions deduced for the rate of evaporation and the rate of condensation, i.e.,

$$k_1\theta = k_2 P(1 - \theta) \tag{21-12}$$

where k_2 is another proportionality constant. Rearrangement gives

$$\theta = \frac{k_2 P}{k_1 + k_2 P} \tag{21-13}$$

and introduction of $a = k_1/k_2$ allows this result to be written

$$\theta = \frac{P}{a + P} \tag{21-14}$$

Inspection of Eq. (21-14) shows that a chemisorption-type isotherm is obtained from this theory. At small values of P, where P in the denominator can be neglected compared with a, Eq. (21-14) reduces to a simple proportionality between θ and P, and this behavior is that corresponding to the initial steep rise of the isotherm curve. At higher pressures the value of P in the denominator contributes appreciably, and the increasing denominator leads to values of θ that do not increase proportionally to the increase in P. For sufficiently large values of P, θ approaches the constant value of unity.

Experimental isotherm data consist of the amount of gas adsorbed by a given weight of adsorbent as a function of the gas pressure. For adsorption, up to a monolayer, the amount of gas y adsorbed at some pressure P and the amount of gas y_m needed to form a monolayer are related to θ according to

$$\frac{y}{y_m} = \theta \tag{21-15}$$

and Eq. (21-14) becomes

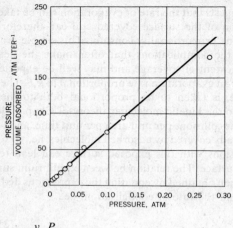

FIGURE 21-9
The Langmuir plot for the adsorption of H_2 on Cu powder at 25°C shown in Fig. 21-8a.

$$y = \frac{y_m P}{a + P} \tag{21-16}$$

Experimental results can be compared with the Langmuir theory most easily if Eq. (21-16) is rearranged to

$$\frac{P}{y} = \frac{a}{y_m} + \frac{P}{y_m} \tag{21-17}$$

If the experimental data are in accord with the Langmuir theory, a plot of P/y versus P will yield a straight line. If such a curve is obtained, the intercept can be identified with a/y_m and the slope with the constant $1/y_m$. For many chemisorptions one finds, as Fig. 21-9 shows, a good linear relationship on the Langmuir suggested plot. For physical adsorption isotherms of S-shaped curves, the Langmuir plot does not yield a straight line, and the theory is clearly not applicable to such cases. The success of Eq. (21-17) in fitting experimental chemisorption-type curves must not, of course, be taken as necessarily confirming the model and assumptions that have been used in the derivation.

Other theories have been developed to explain the more complete adsorption process that leads to multilayer formation. The most important of these treatments is due to S. Brunauer, P. H. Emmett, and E. Teller. Their theory, like that of Langmuir, leads to an isotherm expression, usually abbreviated as the BET isotherm. Although this expression receives considerable attention as a basis for surface-area determinations, which will be dealt with next, it will not be necessary for us to investigate the BET theory.

21-8 Determination of Surface Areas

If one is to obtain a definite picture of the happenings on a surface, it is important to have some way of estimating the surface area. Since many of the solids used in adsorption studies are highly irregular and porous, like charcoal, the area cannot be measured directly and an adsorption method, generally using the BET isotherm, is ordinarily employed. Although the Langmuir isotherm can represent only the chemisorption process, it can be used to show that a surface area can be deduced from adsorption studies.

The specific example of the adsorbent used for the experiments that led to one of the isotherms of Fig. 21-8 can be considered. The Langmuir plot of these data in Fig. 21-9 gives the following, where all liters are at 20°C and 1 atm:

$$\text{Slope} = \frac{1}{y_m} = 735 \text{ liter}^{-1} \tag{21-18}$$

$$\text{Intercept} = \frac{a}{y_m} = 5.3 \text{ atm liter}^{-1} \tag{21-19}$$

The values of y_m and a are calculated as

$$y_m = 0.00136 \text{ liter} \qquad a = 0.0072 \text{ atm} \tag{21-20}$$

and the adsorption isotherm is represented by the equation

$$y = \frac{0.00136P}{0.0072 + P} \text{ liter} \qquad \text{for } P, \text{ atm} \tag{21-21}$$

The result is obtained, therefore, that the surface of 1 g of adsorbent would be covered by an amount of H_2 which occupies a volume of 0.00136 liter at STP, i.e., by $(0.00136/22.4) \times 6.0 \times 10^{23} = 3.6 \times 10^{19}$ molecules.

The surface area is obtained if the area covered by this much H_2 can be estimated. The easiest, if rather crude, method is to make use of the bulk volume of liquid H_2 and to calculate the effective area per molecule as $(V_{\text{liq}}/\mathfrak{N})^{2/3}$, where V_{liq} is the volume of 1 mol of liquid H_2. In this way one estimates, using the density of 0.070 g ml^{-1} for liquid hydrogen, that the area covered by one molecule is

$$\frac{2 \text{ g mol}^{-1}}{(0.070 \text{ g ml}^{-1})(10^{-6} \text{ ml m}^{-3})(6 \times 10^{23} \text{ molecules mol}^{-1})}$$
$$= 13 \times 10^{-20} \text{ m}^2$$

and the area of 1 g of this copper powder adsorbent is therefore

$$(3.6 \times 10^{19})(13 \times 10^{-20}) = 4.7 \text{ m}^2 \tag{21-22}$$

In practice, one relies on the BET isotherm and makes use of physical-adsorption data rather than the chemisorption data used in this Langmuir example. The calculation procedures are equivalent, however.

TABLE 21-4 Estimates of Surface Area of Clean Nickel Films from the Physical Adsorption of Different Gases

Gas	Area per molecule, ($Å^2$)	Amount adsorbed to give monolayer (on 1-g nickel film), 10^{19} molecules	Surface area of 1-g nickel film, m^2
Kr	14.6	6.15	9.0
Kr†	14.6	5.85	8.6
CH_4	15.7	5.40	8.5
n-C_4H_{10}	24.5	3.48	8.5

†On a different film.
Source: O. Beeck and A. W. Ritchie, *Discuss. Faraday Soc.*, **8:**159 (1950).

Surface areas estimated from such adsorption studies can often be accepted as generally reliable but approximate. Table 21-4 shows the type of variation in area estimated from different isotherms, and Table 21-5 shows some typical surface areas of adsorbents.

There may, of course, be a number of subtleties connected with the surface that may lead to puzzling area values. The presence of fine pores or capillaries, for example, may be such as to allow one gas to penetrate whereas another gas with larger molecules finds the pores inaccessible. In this connection it is of interest to note the molecular-sieve materials, which consist of dehydrated zeolites. They appear to have pores that are of sufficiently uniform size to make it possible to obtain an adsorbent which can, for example, accept n-paraffin molecules but not branched-chain molecules.

The use of chemisorption data for surface determinations would introduce the very questionable assumption that the "active" surface area is the same both for the gas with which the area is determined and for any other gas that might be studied. In practice, it is much more satisfactory to use the BET-isotherm

TABLE 21-5 Volumes of Adsorbed Nitrogen to Form a Monolayer and the Surface Areas of a Number of Catalysts

Area covered by an adsorbed nitrogen molecule taken as 16.2 $Å^2$

Material	Monolayer volume, ml g^{-1} at STP	Surface area, $m^2 g^{-1}$
Fused Cu catalyst	0.09	0.39
Fe, K_2O catalyst 930	0.14	0.61
Fe, Al_2O_3, K_2O catalyst 931	0.81	3.5
Fe, Al_2O_3 catalyst 954	2.86	12.4
Cr_2O_3 gel	53.3	230
Silica gel	116.2	500

Source: P. H. Emmett, "Catalysis," vol. 1, Reinhold Publishing Corporation, New York, 1955.

expression to deduce the surface area since the BET isotherm includes adsorption to form multilayers.

21-9 Adsorption from Solution

A very important but little understood process is the adsorption of a solute of a solution onto a solid adsorbent. This procedure is followed, for example, in the decolorizing of solutions using, ordinarily, activated charcoal. The separation technique of chromatography also makes use of the relative adsorption tendencies of the solutes of a solution.

This process of adsorption from solution is even more difficult to treat theoretically than the corresponding gas-on-solid process. It appears, however, that only a monomolecular layer is formed, any further addition being strongly opposed by the solvating power of the solvent.

A fairly satisfactory empirical isotherm, which can be applied to adsorptions of gases with considerable success but has been used principally for adsorption from solution, has been discussed by H. Freundlich. If y is the weight of solute adsorbed per gram of adsorbent and c is the concentration of the solute in the solution, this empirical relation is

$$y = kc^{1/n} \qquad (21\text{-}23)$$

where k and n are empirical constants. The equation is conveniently used in the logarithmic form

$$\log y = \log k + \frac{1}{n} \log c \qquad (21\text{-}24)$$

When applied to gases, y is the amount of gas adsorbed and c is replaced by the pressure of the gas. Experimental results conform to the Freundlich expression if a plot of $\log y$ against $\log c$, or $\log P$, yields a straight line. The constants can then be determined from the slope and intercept. Figure 21-10 shows data treated in terms of the Freundlich expression.

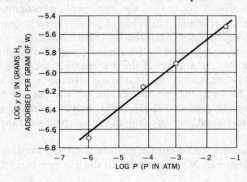

FIGURE 21-10
A Freundlich plot of the isotherm data for H_2 adsorbed on tungsten at 400°C. [*From the more extensive data of W. G. Frankenberg, J. Am. Chem. Soc.,* **66**:*1827 (1944).*]

Many chemical processes occur in the presence of certain surfaces that do not proceed at all in the absence of such surfaces or do so very slowly. Such reactions are said to be exhibiting *heterogeneous catalysis*. The effect of the surface is often so profound that it may be difficult to remember that this effect is that of hastening the approach to an equilibrium state. A catalyst may, and generally will, provide very different accelerations for the approach of different reactions to their equilibrium state. Full use of this important influence in chemical reactions requires a detailed understanding of the reactions that are occurring on the surface of the catalyst.

The most dramatic surface catalytic effects must be attributed to reactions of chemisorbed species. Physical adsorption is effective in raising the local concentration of the reagents and in supplying a reservoir of thermal energy to these reagents. These factors, however, are probably of minor importance in heterogeneous catalysis. Chemisorption, on the other hand, may result in a rather drastic disruption of the bonding in an adsorbed molecule. It is easily seen that such molecules or molecular fragments may enter into reactions in a manner quite different from that in which the unperturbed gas-phase molecules do. In kinetic terms, the molecules on the surface are such that they may react through a state of much lower activation energy than the normal molecules can.

It follows that heterogeneous catalysis can be understood in detail only when the nature of the adsorbed species is so understood. At present, only some features of heterogeneous catalysis can be given a molecular description. It is true, however, that one of the most fruitful approaches to an understanding of the adsorbed state is through studies of the reactions that the molecules of this state undergo.

21-10 Kinetics of Heterogeneous Decompositions

The study of the kinetics of single-phase reactions led (Chap. 19) to a considerable understanding of the details of reaction mechanisms. A similar study of heterogeneously catalyzed reactions leads only to the more explicit recognition that the catalytic effect is a surface reaction. The study of some relatively simple decompositions that are heterogeneously catalyzed will illustrate this.

The kinetics of decomposition can often be accounted for on the assumption that the rate is proportional to the amount of the reagent on the surface. In line with this assumption it is convenient to treat three situations that are distinguished by the relation between the pressure of the gas and the amount adsorbed on the surface. An even greater variety exists, however, in the dependence of rate of reaction on reagent pressure, but all the complexities cannot be considered here.

First, for low surface coverages the amount of gas adsorbed is, according to the Langmuir isotherm, approximately proportional to the gas pressure. The rate of decomposition, if decomposition is indeed a surface reaction, would be expected, no other complication occurring, to be proportional to the gas pressure. The rate with which the gas is decomposed, dn/dt mol s^{-1}, would be given by

$$- \frac{dn}{dt} = kP \tag{21-25}$$

where k is a proportionality constant. For a constant-volume system, dn can be replaced by $(V/RT) \, dP$, so that the rate law would be

$$- \frac{dP}{dt} = \frac{RT}{V} kP$$

or

$$\ln \frac{P_0}{P} = \frac{RTk}{V} t \tag{21-26}$$

where the initial gas pressure is P_0 at time $t = 0$.

The decomposition of phosphine on glass,

$$PH_3 \rightarrow P + \tfrac{3}{2}H_2 \tag{21-27}$$

as shown by the data of Fig. 21-11, conforms to this rate law and therefore presumably proceeds by the decomposition of adsorbed molecules. That the surface is involved is readily shown by increasing the surface area, e.g., by the addition of glass wool, and observing the higher rate constant.

The second decomposition-rate-expression type that will be mentioned here is anticipated for moderate adsorption for which the amount adsorbed can be expected, according to the Langmuir isotherm, to be proportional to the expression $P/(a + P)$. The decomposition might then follow the rate expression

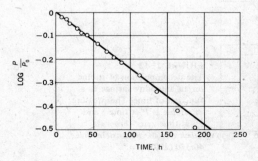

TIME, h

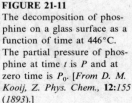

FIGURE 21-11
The decomposition of phosphine on a glass surface as a function of time at 446°C. The partial pressure of phosphine at time t is P and at zero time is P_0. [*From D. M. Kooij, Z. Phys. Chem.,* **12**:*155* (*1893*).]

$$-\frac{dP}{dt} = \frac{RT}{V}\frac{kP}{a+P} \qquad (21\text{-}28)$$

where k is a constant. Separation of variables gives

$$-a\frac{dP}{P} - dP = \frac{RTk}{V}dT$$

and integration between the limits P_0 at time $t = 0$ and P at time t gives

$$a\ln\frac{P_0}{P} + (P_0 - P) = \frac{RTk}{V}t \qquad (21\text{-}29)$$

Finally, conversion to base 10 logarithms, with rearrangement so that pressure ratios rather than pressure appear as variables, gives

$$\log\frac{P_0}{P} + \frac{P_0}{2.303a}\left(1 - \frac{P}{P_0}\right) = \frac{RTk}{2.303aV}t \qquad (21\text{-}30)$$

The experimental results for the decomposition of stibine on an antimony surface,

$$SbH_3 \rightarrow Sb + \tfrac{3}{2}H_2 \qquad (21\text{-}31)$$

fit this rate law. It is necessary to show that for some value of $P_0/2.303a$, a plot of the left side of Eq. (21-30) against t yields a straight line, and, as Fig. 21-12 shows, such a plot can be obtained.

Finally, for a strongly adsorbed gas, the surface coverage is essentially complete, and the amount of adsorbed material is essentially independent of the

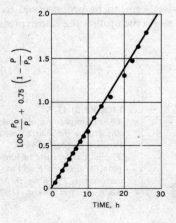

FIGURE 21-12
The decomposition of stibine on an antimony surface as a function of time. The pressure of stibine is P at time t and P_0 at time zero. [*From A. Stock and M. Bodenstein, Ber.,* **40:**570 (1907).]

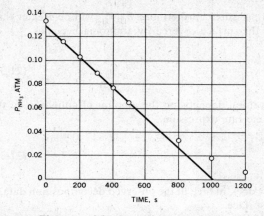

FIGURE 21-13
The decomposition of ammonia on a tungsten surface at 856°C. [*From C. N. Hinshelwood and R. E. Burk, J. Chem. Soc.,* **127**:*1105 (1925)*.]

pressure. The rate of decomposition would then be expected to be independent of P, and the rate law would be written

$$-\frac{dP}{dt} = k \tag{21-32}$$

and

$$P = -kt + \text{const} \tag{21-33}$$

The data for the decomposition of ammonia on a tungsten surface are shown plotted in Fig. 21-13 to illustrate their conformity to this relation.

Even decompositions of the type used in these examples, however, do not necessarily follow such simply explained rate laws. One or more of the decomposition products may be adsorbed on the catalyst. In such cases the products inhibit the reaction by competing with the reagent for the catalyst surface. An example of this situation is provided by the decomposition of ammonia on a platinum filament. The Langmuir-isotherm derivation leads, for the simultaneous adsorption of NH_3 and H_2, to the coverage expressions

$$\theta_{NH_3} = \frac{b_{NH_3} P_{NH_3}}{1 + b_{NH_3} P_{NH_3} + b_{H_2} P_{H_2}}$$

and

$$\tag{21-34}$$

$$\theta_{H_2} = \frac{b_{H_2} P_{H_2}}{1 + b_{NH_3} P_{NH_3} + b_{H_2} P_{H_2}}$$

Adsorption studies of the separate reagents show that hydrogen is adsorbed to a much greater extent than ammonia and therefore that $b_{NH_3} P_{NH_3} \ll b_{H_2} P_{H_2}$.

For appreciable hydrogen pressures, furthermore, $b_{H_2} P_{H_2}$ will be greater than unity, and the fraction of the surface covered by ammonia becomes

$$\theta_{NH_3} = \frac{b_{NH_3} P_{NH_3}}{b_{H_2} P_{H_2}} \tag{21-35}$$

If the rate of the decomposition depends on the amount of ammonia on the surface, the constant-volume rate expression

$$-\frac{dP_{NH_3}}{dt} = k \frac{P_{NH_3}}{P_{H_2}} \tag{21-36}$$

is expected. Such a rate law does, in fact, fit the observed decomposition data of ammonia on a platinum surface.

This type of inhibition is an illustration of the important *catalyst-poison* behavior. The adsorption of a product on a foreign substance can compete for the catalyst surface and thereby inhibit the reaction. The effect of a small amount of such adsorption can be very great and leads to the recognition either that some catalysts have only a few active sites at which reactions can occur or that a small amount of adsorbent can alter the electron content of the catalyst to spoil its activity.

This brief discussion of the kinetics of heterogeneously catalyzed reactions should indicate that studies like those mentioned above can bear out the fact that such reactions are surface reactions. It becomes difficult, however, to study the nature of the surface reaction by kinetic measurements. For a reaction of any complexity the details of the adsorption processes and the details of the surface reaction cannot be deduced from the kinetic data alone.

PROBLEMS

21-1. The surface tension of mercury is 0.52 N m^{-1}, and its density is 13.6 g ml^{-1} at 25°C. Mercury does not wet glass. (a) Derive an expression for the lowering of the surface of mercury that will occur when a glass tube of internal radius r is inserted into the liquid. What will the depression be if r is (b) 1 mm and (c) 5 mm?

21-2. A particle of mist has a mass of about 10^{-12} g. What is its vapor pressure compared with that of water if the temperature is 20°C?

21-3. In view of Eqs. (21-5) and (21-10), consider what will happen as the radius of the capillary tube in which a liquid rises is reduced toward the limit of $r = 0$.

21-4. Suppose that water in a certain container boils when the liquid is at a temperature at which bubbles of 10^{-7} m diameter can be formed by the equilibrium vapor. Estimate from approximate relations and data previously given (a) the vapor pressure that must be reached by the liquid for these vapor bubbles to be formed and (b) the temperature at which boiling will occur at a pressure of 1 atm.

21-5. What is the minimum size of the droplets that could grow spontaneously from a vapor with twice the equilibrium vapor pressure at 20°C if the vapor is (*a*) benzene and (*b*) water?

21-6. Thermodynamic relations apply to systems in which the individualistic behavior of molecules is averaged out. On this basis discuss the applicability of Eq. (21-10) to very small droplets.

21-7. How many molecules would be in a water droplet at 100°C if its vapor pressure, according to Eq. (21-10), is twice the equilibrium vapor pressure of bulk water?

21-8. Sketch the force–versus–total-surface-area curve that would be expected in a Langmuir surface-film experiment when a 0.1-ml sample of a solution containing 0.1 mol liter^{-1} of palmitic acid, $CH_3(CH_2)_{14}COOH$, in the volatile solvent ethanol is placed on the surface of water and compressed in a Langmuir film balance.

21-9. The data of I. Langmuir, *J. Am. Chem. Soc.*, **40**:1361 (1918), for the adsorption of nitrogen on mica at 90 K are as tabulated. (*a*) Show that these data fit a Langmuir-isotherm expression and evaluate the constants in the expression. (*b*) Estimate the area covered by a single nitrogen molecule from the fact that the density of liquid nitrogen is 0.81 g ml^{-1}. (*c*) Estimate the surface area of the mica sample in the Langmuir experiment.

P, atm	2.8	3.4	4.0	4.9	6.0	7.3	9.4	12.8	17.1	23.5	33.5
Amount absorbed (mm^3 at 20°C and 1 atm)	12.0	13.4	15.1	17.0	19.0	21.6	23.9	25.5	28.2	30.8	33.0

21-10. The following data are given for the adsorption of nitrogen on alumina, Al_2O_3, at 77.3 K. (*a*) Do these data conform to the Langmuir isotherm? (*b*) Calculate the amount of nitrogen that would have to be adsorbed to form a monolayer. (*c*) If the area covered by a single nitrogen molecule is taken as 16×10^{-20} m^2, what is the surface area of this sample of alumina?

P_{N_2}, atm	0.0417	0.0849	0.1272	0.223
N_2 absorbed, mmol/g Al_2O_3	83.1	90.3	104.5	111.8

21-11. Suppose the adsorption process leads to the formation of adsorbed H atoms rather than adsorbed H_2 molecules. What would be the significance of the constant in the equation?

21-12. Acetic acid is adsorbed from solution by activated charcoal. The following data have been reported for the amounts y of acetic acid adsorbed as a function of the concentration c of the equilibrium solution:

c, mol liter^{-1}	0.018	0.031	0.062	0.126	0.268	0.471	0.882
y, mol	0.47	0.62	0.80	1.11	1.55	2.04	2.48

Show that these data fit a Freundlich isotherm and determine the constants in the Freundlich-isotherm expression.

21-13. (*a*) Show that at low surface coverages the Langmuir isotherm corresponds to the Freundlich expression with $n = 1$. (*b*) Show also that at high surface coverages the Langmuir equation corresponds to the Freundlich expression with $n = \infty$.

21-14. Obtain Eqs. (20-34) for the fraction of surface covered by each of two adsorbents if the adsorptions follow Langmuir's adsorption isotherm.

21-15. The decomposition of ammonia on a platinum catalyst is inhibited by the presence of hydrogen. The following data give the rate of decrease in ammonia pressure for three different hydrogen pressures at 1138°C:

Pressure of H_2, mmHg	50	100	150
Rate of NH_3 decomp., mmHg s^{-1}	0.275	0.133	0.083

Are these data consistent with the analysis of NH_3 decomposition described in Sec. 21-10?

REFERENCES

Recommended general treatments of surfaces and adsorption:

ADAMSON, A. W.: "Physical Chemistry of Surfaces," 3d ed., Interscience Publishers, Inc., New York, 1976.
GREGG, S., and K. SING: "Adsorption, Surface Area, and Porosity," Academic Press, Inc., New York, 1967.
SOMORJAI, G. A.: "Principles of Surface Chemistry," Prentice-Hall, Inc., Englewood Cliffs, N.J., 1972.

Other books and articles dealing with specific areas or topics:

ROSS, S., and J. P. OLIVIER: "On Physical Adsorption," Interscience Publishers, Inc., New York, 1964. A clear exposition of experimental methods, results, and interpretation in the area of physical adsorption.
HAYWARD, D. O., and M. B. W. TRAPNELL: "Chemisorption," 2d ed., Butterworth & Co., Ltd., London, 1964. An excellent summary of the present state of our knowledge of the rates, equilibrium pressures, heats, and mechanisms involved in the chemisorption of gases on solids.
DAVIES, J. T., and E. K. RIDEAL: "Interfacial Phenomena," Academic Press, Inc., New York, 1963. Studies and properties of surfaces and interfaces in liquid systems.
BOND, G. C.: "Catalysis of Metals," Academic Press, Inc., New York, 1962. A complete account of an important area of heterogeneous catalysis that brings together some of the approaches and much of the recent work on chemisorption and catalytic effects of metals.
HAENSEL, V., and R. L. BURWELL, JR.: Catalysis, *Sci. Am.*, **225** (6): 46 (1971).
DREXHAGE, K. H.: Monomolecular Layers and Light, *Sci. Am.*, **222** (3): 108 (1970).

22 MACROMOLECULES

Many approaches, both theoretical and experimental, to the study of the behavior of chemical systems have already been developed and applied. In these studies a distinction has generally been made between a molecular treatment and a macroscopic one. An important and very interesting class of systems occurs which is, in a way, intermediate between these extremes. These systems often consist of or contain molecules so large that they can be treated either as large molecules or as small macroscopic particles. Most particles of current interest in this size range, about 100 to 10,000 Å, are found to be single molecules, and the term *macromolecule* is convenient.

A number of different physicochemical approaches are required to reveal the nature of these systems. Some of these special techniques have already been mentioned but find their greatest current application in the study of macromolecule systems. Still other techniques must be introduced for these special systems. The deduction of the details of these large and often very complex molecules is one of the current exciting challenges presented to the physical chemist. Many of the systems, as will be seen, have great biological importance. Some of this area of study is often included in biochemistry, but the term *molecular biology* also seems appropriate. In the short study of macromolecules that can be presented here, it is desirable to discuss synthetic and naturally occurring macromolecules side by side. Although the areas of plastics and biological materials may seem little related, it will be found that the physico-chemical study of the basic chemical units of these areas has very much in common. For these studies it is convenient to distinguish between macromolecules in solution and in the solid state. After a more general introduction to the types of systems that occur or can be produced with particles in this size range, these two principal sections, i.e., solutions and the solid state, will be treated so that information on the structure, shape, and behavior of macromolecules can be obtained.

INTRODUCTION TO
MACROMOLECULE MATERIALS

22-1 Types and Sizes of Particles

The existence of particles in the size range that will be dealt with here was suggested by the early observation made by the botanist Robert Brown of the random motion of pollen grains as seen under a microscope. It was later recognized that these particles, though large enough to be seen, were small enough to reveal the effects of random molecular bombardment, the so-called *brownian motion*. By the end of the nineteenth century, study of small-particle systems, called *colloids,* became an important branch of physical chemistry.

The unique behavior of colloids is now recognized to be exhibited by particles in the size range of about 100 to 10,000 Å. One of the most commonly recognized features of such systems is that they scatter light, as is observed for example when a beam of sunlight passes through dusty air or through thin skimmed milk. Furthermore, the particles of a colloidal system do not settle out and (as the chemist has invariably experienced with some silver chloride precipitates) tend to pass through ordinary filter paper. Colloidal systems frequently occur; as Table 22-1 shows, they can be of many different phase types.

A closer look at the chemical world, however, shows that there are particles in this size range of great interest and importance that are not listed in Table 22-1. They stem from the existence of single molecules large enough for individual molecules to have colloidal dimensions. In view of present interest, these macromolecule systems can be classed as synthetic polymers and as the naturally occurring macromolecules. Most interest in the natural materials is now centered on *proteins* and *nucleic acids,* but natural macromolecules also include the *polysaccharides* and the *polyisoprenes,* the latter being the molecules of natural rubber. These categories of macromolecules are outlined in Table 22-2.

In addition to the many types of highly dispersed systems listed in Table 22-1 and the macromolecules, which will be the principal subject in this chapter,

TABLE 22-1 Some Common Types of Colloids Classified by Phase Type

Name	Type	Example
Aerosol	Solid particles in gas	Smoke
Aerosol	Liquid particles in gas	Fog
Sol	Solid particles in liquid	S, Au, AgCl in H_2O
Emulsion	Liquid particles in liquid	Mayonnaise, milk
Foam	Gas bubbles in liquid	Whipped cream
Gels	Liquid in solid matrix	Jellies

TABLE 22-2 Classes of Macromolecules

Class	Example
Synthetic macromolecules:	
Addition polymers	Polyethylene
Condensation polymers	Nylon
Natural macromolecules:	
Proteins:	
Fibrous	Keratin, silk fibroin
Globular	Hemoglobin
Nucleic acids	Deoxyribonucleic acid (DNA)
Polysaccharides	Cellulose
Polyisoprene	Natural rubber

listed in Table 22-2, mention should also be made of the colloidal-sized groups known as *micelles*. The turbidity exhibited by soap or detergent solutions is the best-known indication of micelle formation. Since the molecules of soap or detergent are very small compared with colloidal dimensions, the particles causing the turbidity are groups, or micelles, of these molecules. Their formation is closely analogous to that of monomolecular films studied in the preceding chapter. Most soaps and detergents have a long hydrocarbon "tail" and a polar "head." In the soaps the head is the sodium or potassium salt of the carboxylic acid, that is, $RCOO^-K^+$; in the detergents the head is the salt of a sulfonic acid, i.e., of the type $RSO_3^-Na^+$. A micelle can be expected to form in a manner depicted in Fig. 22-1. It will be seen later that the charged layer around the surface of the particles is important for the stability of the individual micelles.

All out studies will now be directed toward an understanding of macromolecule systems. It will be clear that many of the methods dealt with are applicable to all systems with colloidal-sized particles. No specific treatment of the important system of sols, i.e., solids dispersed in liquids, will be given. Such

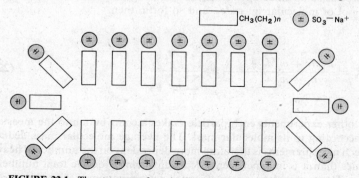

FIGURE 22-1 The structure of a micelle. An actual micelle must consist of hundreds of soap or detergent molecules.

colloids are now studied largely in connection with their role in the precipitation process and therefore are more suitably treated in a study of analytical chemistry.

MACROMOLECULES IN SOLUTION

Much of our information about the size and general shape of macromolecules has been deduced from various properties of solutions containing these molecules. In this section some of the methods used to understand the behavior of solutions of macromolecules will be investigated, and in the process of such studies a number of properties of the macromolecules themselves will be discovered. It is first necessary, however, to discuss the meaning of molecular mass when applied to a polymeric material.

22-2 Molecular Masses of Polymers

Polymerization reactions, both synthetic and natural, can lead to high-molecular-mass compounds. The reaction chain, however, is broken by some termination process that usually occurs in a random manner with respect to the size to which the polymer has already grown. It follows that polymers have a range of molecular masses and that any data for the size or mass of the molecules of a polymer must represent some sort of average value. It will be seen that attempts to deduce molecular masses of polymers lead to *number-average* and *mass-average* molecular masses.

The number average M_n is defined as the mass of sample divided by the total number of moles n in the sample. Any measurement that leads to the number of particles or molecules present in a given mass of sample will allow the calculation of a number-average molecular mass. If the sample can be considered as being made up of fractions consisting of n_1 mol of molecular mass M_1, n_2 mol of molecular mass M_2, and so forth, then

$$M_n = \frac{n_1 M_1 + n_2 M_2 + \cdots}{n_1 + n_2 + \cdots} = \frac{\sum_i n_i M_i}{\sum_i n_i} \tag{22-1}$$

In other experiments each particle makes a contribution to the measured result according to its molecular mass. The average molecular mass deduced from such measurements is therefore more dependent on the number of heavier molecules than it is in experiments depending simply on the total number of particles. The appropriate average for such determinations is the *mass average,* defined as

$$M_w = \frac{\sum\limits_i n_i M_i^2}{\sum\limits_i n_i M_i} \tag{22-2}$$

For an appreciable distribution of molecular sizes in a polymer sample, the two molecular masses M_n and M_w will be appreciably different.

22-3 Osmotic-Pressure Determinations of Molecular Masses

A measurement of any of the colligative properties of a solution of macromolecules leads, essentially, to a value for the number of solute molecules in a given amount of solvent, as discussed in Chap. 9. There it was pointed out that for the solutions of low molality, which are always obtained with macromolecules, the only colligative property that is conveniently measured is the osmotic pressure. Such measurements are one of the most important means of molecular-mass determinations. It should be evident from the nature of colligative properties, i.e., their dependence only on the number and not on the nature of the solute molecule, that a number-average molecular mass is obtained.

The high concentration in terms of mass of solute per weight of solvent, even for low molalities, means that solute interactions will occur and nonideal behavior will result. Therefore, it is almost always necessary to extrapolate the measurements to infinite dilution, as in Chap. 9. Sensitive osmotic-pressure instruments now allow measurements to be made on very dilute solutions, and molecular masses even up to 500 kg can be obtained.

The expressions obtained for the osmotic pressure in Sec. 9-10 have been written in terms of mole fraction or molality. To study the osmotic pressure of a compound of unknown molecular mass, it is convenient to start with Eq. (9-65) and to write it as

$$\Pi = \frac{(n_\mathrm{B})RT}{n_\mathrm{A} v} = \frac{(\text{mass of B})/(\text{mol mass of B})RT}{\text{volume of solution}}$$

Introduction of the concentration unit of grams per milliliter for the factor (mass of B)/(volume of solution), which can be represented by c, allows this expression to be written

$$\frac{\Pi}{c} = \frac{RT}{\text{mol mass of solute}} \tag{22-3}$$

If the osmotic pressure is given in atmospheres and c in grams per milliliter, the gas constant R must be in millimeter atmospheres per kelvin.

Equation (22-3) can be expected to be valid only at infinite dilution. This follows, in addition to the approximations introduced in its derivation, from the

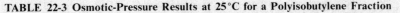

TABLE 22-3 Osmotic-Pressure Results at 25°C for a Polyisobutylene Fraction

	II, atm		II/c, atm ml g⁻¹	
Conc., g ml⁻¹	In benzene	In cyclohexane	In benzene	In cyclohexane
0.0200	0.00208	0.0117	0.104	0.585
0.0150	0.00152	0.0066	0.101	0.44
0.0100	0.00099	0.0030	0.099	0.30
0.0075		0.00173		0.23
0.0050	0.00049	0.00090	0.098	0.18
0.0025		0.00035		0.14

Source: Calculated from the data of P. J. Flory, *J. Am. Chem. Soc.*, **65**:372 (1943).

fact that large-molecular-mass compounds tend to interact with each other at the concentrations at which the measurements are made. The procedure that must be used, therefore, is to measure Π/c as a function of c and to extrapolate these results to infinite dilution. The intercept of Π/c at zero concentration can then be taken as the value of $RT/(\text{mol mass of solute})$. From this value a valid molecular mass for the solute in solution is obtained.

The data of Table 22-3 show the osmotic pressures and concentrations of solutions of a polyisobutylene fraction in two different solvents. The extrapolations of these data in Fig. 22-2 lead to a value of Π/c of 0.097 atm ml g⁻¹ at infinite dilution. With this value and Eq. (22-3) the molecular mass, an average molecular mass in grams, is calculated as

$$\text{Mol mass polyisobutylene} = \lim_{c \to 0} \frac{RT}{\Pi/c} = \frac{(82.05)(298)}{0.097} = 250,000$$

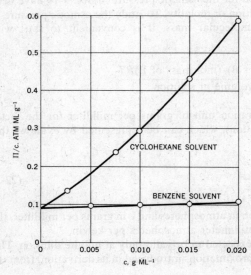

FIGURE 22-2
The extrapolation of the osmotic-pressure–concentration ratio to infinite dilution for a sample of polyisobutylene in cyclohexane and in benzene (data of Table 22-3).

22-4 Viscosities of Solutions of Macromolecules

When the viscosities of solutions are studied so that the properties of the solute molecules can be deduced, viscosities are obtained for the pure solvent and for solutions of various concentrations. At each concentration the effect of the solute can be conveniently shown by calculating

$$\frac{\eta - \eta_0}{\eta_0} \quad \text{or} \quad \frac{\eta}{\eta_0} - 1 \tag{22-4}$$

where η and η_0 are the viscosity of the solution and the solvent, respectively.

The properties of solutions of macromolecules are often affected by the interaction of these large solute particles. Results that reflect the properties of the individual particles rather than their interactions are obtained by extrapolating measured quantities to infinite dilution. Here this is done by introducing the concentration c as *mass per unit volume* rather than as the chemically more common molar concentration. The viscosity effect per unit concentration of the solute can now be expressed as

$$\frac{\eta/\eta_0 - 1}{c} \tag{22-5}$$

and the value extrapolated to infinite dilution is represented by $[\eta]$, where

$$[\eta] = \lim_{c \to 0} \frac{\eta/\eta_0 - 1}{c} \tag{22-6}$$

If c is in grams per milliliter, the values of $[\eta]$ are known as *intrinsic viscosities*. Notice, however, that $[\eta]$ is not really a viscosity. It depends on the ratio η/η_0 and thus does not contain viscosity units. The intrinsic viscosity of a solution of a given macromolecule is used to deduce the shape and sometimes the molecular mass of the molecule.

The addition of a macromolecular solute to a solvent invariably increases the viscosity. This qualitative result seems reasonable in view of the familiar thickening that accompanies the formation of such solutions. This thickening, however, is usually the result of molecular interactions and is not related to the intrinsic-viscosity effect.

The molecular explanation of the increase in viscosity that results from the addition of macromolecules is based on the disruption of the flow pattern or velocity gradient they produce. As Fig. 22-3a attempts to suggest, the fluid in contact with a macromolecule moves with the same velocity as that molecule. The smooth velocity contour of Fig. 22-3b is destroyed, and less efficient flow lines are followed.

When this approach is developed quantitatively, the fraction of the volume of the solution attributable to the solute is most directly related to the viscosity

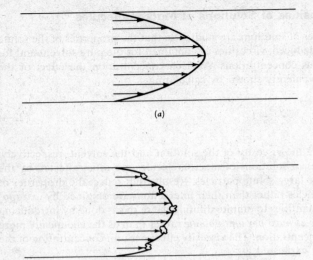

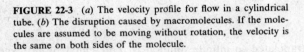

(a)

(b)

FIGURE 22-3 (a) The velocity profile for flow in a cylindrical tube. (b) The disruption caused by macromolecules. If the molecules are assumed to be moving without rotation, the velocity is the same on both sides of the molecule.

effect. If v_{eff} is introduced as the effective specific volume of the macromolecular material in solution, i.e., the volume per unit mass, then since c is the mass of solute per unit volume of solution, cv_{eff} is the effective volume of solute per unit volume of solution.

According to derivations by Einstein and by R. Simha, the extrapolation of viscosities of solutions of molecules that have spherical or ellipsoidal shapes should conform to

$$\lim_{c \to 0} \frac{\eta/\eta_0 - 1}{cv_{eff}} = \nu \tag{22-7}$$

where ν is a shape-dependent parameter shown in Fig. 22-4. If v_{eff} is removed from the extrapolation term and treated separately, we can write

$$\lim_{c \to 0} \frac{\eta/\eta_0 - 1}{c} = \nu v_{eff}$$

or

$$[\eta] = \nu v_{eff} \tag{22-8}$$

Thus, the intrinsic viscosity of a macromolecular substance depends on the

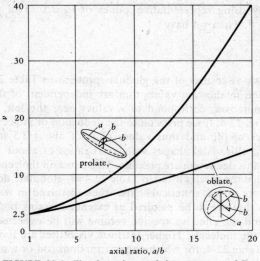

FIGURE 22-4 The dependence of the parameter of Eq. (22-7) on the shape of the macromolecule.

shape of its molecules and on its specific volume. (Additional factors must be taken into account if viscosities deduced from high flow-rate studies are considered. In such cases the flow is said to be nonnewtonian, implying that the proportionality between driving force and flow rate does not hold. The molecular interpretation of viscosities obtained under such conditions must allow for an alignment of molecules with the flow lines. Here such effects will not be considered.)

The effective specific-volume term v_{eff} raises some difficulties. The specific volume of the dry solute, which we denote by v_2, is nothing more than the reciprocal of the density of the dry solute and can be measured. But in solution many types of macromolecules hold solvent molecules in their cavities and on their surface. If we introduce δ to represent the mass of solvent that is bound in this way per unit mass of solute and v_1 to represent the specific volume of the solvent, we can write

$$v_{\text{eff}} = v_2 + \delta v_1 \qquad (22\text{-}9)$$

Then Eq. (22-8) can be written as

$$[\eta] = \nu(v_2 + \delta v_1) \qquad (22\text{-}10)$$

Application of this result is awkward because of the two unknowns ν and δ. A variety of procedures can be followed.

For example, we can consider a particular class of compounds, say proteins.

Then we can proceed by using representative values of $v_2 = 0.75$ ml g^{-1}, $\delta = 0.2$, and $v_1 = 1$ ml g^{-1}. Then we have

$$[\eta] = \nu(0.95) \approx \nu$$

The values for the intrinsic viscosities of the globular proteins in Table 22-4 conform to this expectation in showing values that are independent of their molecular masses and, moreover, correspond to ν values near the left, the spherical-shape side, of Fig. 22-4. If we press on to the deduction of molecular shape, we see that values of $[\eta]$, and thus values of ν, of about 3.5 lead, according to Fig. 22-4, to ellipsoidal shapes with axial ratios of about 3:1.

Some refinements to this deduction are possible. These sustain the general conclusion reached here that the species listed in Table 22-4 as "globular" do, in fact, have a balled-up more or less spherical shape when dissolved in water.

For macromolecules that are to be pictured as extended chains both ν, according to Fig. 22-4, and the effective specific volume will be expected to increase with the size of the molecule. Higher intrinsic viscosities are indeed found for the species of Table 22-4, for which either a random coil or a more rigid extended rod shape is expected.

For many synthetic polymers the dependence of the intrinsic viscosity on molecular mass is represented for a given molecular type in a given solvent by an empirical equation of the form

$$[\eta] = KM^a \tag{22-11}$$

where M is the molecular mass and K and a are empirical constants. Once these parameters have been determined by measurements on polymer fractions with known molecular masses, the equation can be used to obtain such mass data from the easily obtained intrinsic-viscosity results.

TABLE 22-4 Intrinsic Viscosities of Biologically Important Macromolecules

Shape	Substance	Molecular mass, g amu	$[\eta]$, ml g^{-1}
Globular	Ribonuclease	13,680	3.4
	Serum albumin	67,500	3.7
	Ribosomes (*E. coli*)	900.000	8.1
	Bushy stunt virus	10,700,000	3.4
Random coils	Insulin	2,970	6.1
	Ribonuclease	13,680	16.0
	Serum albumin	68,000	52
	Myosin subunit	197,000	93
Rods	Fibrinogen	330,000	27
	Myosin	440,000	217
	Poly-α-benzyl-L-glutamate	340,000	720

22-5 Diffusion

In chemical kinetics we dealt with the change of chemical species in a reaction mixture with time. In diffusion studies, we deal with the change in the location of solute with time. The conceptually simplest (but not experimentally the most convenient) illustration of the nature of this time dependence is given by the changes exhibited by an initially thin sheet of solute (Fig. 22-5). As time progresses, the concentration of the solute would correspond to the curves that are shown. The rate at which these curves develop, i.e., the rate of spreading out of the solute, depends, for a given solvent and temperature, on the nature of the solute.

The driving force for diffusion at any time is the rate of change of concentration along the diffusion direction, i.e., the concentration gradient $\partial c/\partial x$ or $(\partial c/\partial x)_t$, where c is the concentration and x the one dimension we deal with here.

Experimental studies of diffusion show that a proportionality exists between the rate of flow across any cross section with area A and the concentration gradient $\partial c/\partial x$ at that cross section. Thus we write

$$\text{Rate of diffusion in } x \text{ direction} \propto A\,\frac{\partial c}{\partial x}$$

The diffusion direction is that in which the concentration decreases, i.e., in

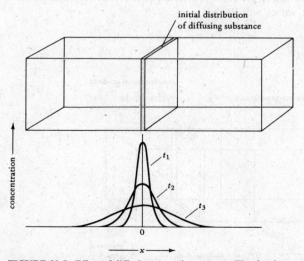

FIGURE 22-5 Effect of diffusion on a plane source. The development of the concentration profile after three time intervals is shown.

which $\partial c/\partial x$ is negative. This proportionality can be written as an equality by the introduction of the proportionality constant D as

$$\text{Rate of diffusion in } x \text{ direction} = -DA\frac{\partial c}{\partial x} \qquad (22\text{-}12)$$

The negative sign allows D, the *diffusion coefficient*, to take on positive values. Equation (22-12) is based on observations of diffusion processes and is known as *Fick's first law of diffusion*. The proportionality constant D depends on the nature of both the diffusing solute and the solvent. If the rate of diffusion is expressed in terms of the same quantity measure that is used in c, such as grams, molecules, or moles, suitable units for D are seen to be square centimeters per second.

If diffusion through a *unit* cross-section area is considered, Eq. (22-12) becomes simply

$$\text{Rate of diffusion} = -D\frac{\partial c}{\partial x} \qquad (22\text{-}13)$$

It is often more convenient to have a description of the effect of diffusion on the concentration in a volume element, as in Fig. 22-6. For this we need to calculate the net rate with which the diffusing substance accumulates in the volume element $A\,dx$. This can be done by calculating the rate with which the substance enters the volume element at x and the rate with which it leaves at $x + dx$. The concentration gradient $\partial c/\partial x$, in general, will vary along x, and the rate with which it varies will be

$$\frac{\partial}{\partial x}\left(\frac{\partial c}{\partial x}\right) = \frac{\partial^2 c}{\partial x^2}$$

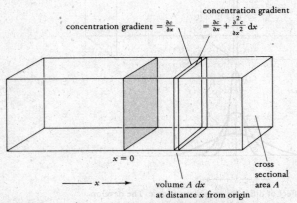

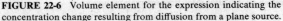

concentration gradient $= \dfrac{\partial c}{\partial x}$

concentration gradient $= \dfrac{\partial c}{\partial x} + \dfrac{\partial^2 c}{\partial x^2}\,dx$

$x = 0$

$x \longrightarrow$

volume $A\,dx$ at distance x from origin

cross sectional area A

FIGURE 22-6 Volume element for the expression indicating the concentration change resulting from diffusion from a plane source.

Now

Rate of entry at $x = -DA \frac{\partial c}{\partial x}$

Rate of leaving at $x + dx = -DA \left(\frac{\partial c}{\partial x} + \frac{\partial^2 c}{\partial x^2} dx \right)$

Subtraction of these two rates gives

Rate of accumulation $= -DA \frac{\partial c}{\partial x} - \left[-DA \left(\frac{\partial c}{\partial x} + \frac{\partial^2 c}{\partial x^2} dx \right) \right]$

$$= DA \frac{\partial^2 c}{\partial x^2} dx$$

Division of the rate of accumulation, i.e., the rate with which the amount changes in the volume element, by the volume $A\,dx$ of the element gives the rate of change of concentration $\partial c / \partial t$ as

$$\frac{\partial c}{\partial t} = D \frac{\partial^2 c}{\partial x^2} \tag{22-14}$$

This relation is known as *Fick's second law*. Equation (22-14) is the basis for the deduction of most of the consequences of diffusion.

Let us return to the effect of diffusion on the plane source of Fig. 22-5 and develop an analytical expression that shows how the dissolved material spreads out with time. You can verify by substitution back into Eq. (22-14) that a solution for Eq. (22-14) for this situation is given by

$$c = \frac{\text{const}}{t^{1/2}} e^{-x^2/4Dt} \tag{22-15}$$

This equation indicates a curve that is symmetric in x and falls off to small values at large x. Furthermore, the coefficient of x^2 in the exponential is such that the smaller the value of t the more rapid the falloff.

The proportionality constant can be evaluated if we stipulate that the total amount of diffusing substance in the plane source is N. Then we have

$$N = \int_{-\infty}^{+\infty} c \, dx = \frac{\text{const}}{t^{1/2}} \int_{-\infty}^{+\infty} e^{-x^2/4Dt} \, dx$$

Definite integrals of this type are tabulated in Appendix A-1 and give

$$N = 2 \text{ const } (\pi D)^{1/2}$$

or

$$c = \frac{N}{2(\pi Dt)^{1/2}} e^{-x^2/4Dt} \qquad (22\text{-}16)$$

Given the initial amount N of the substance set at $x = 0$ and the value of the diffusion coefficient, one can calculate the amount in any volume element, i.e., the concentration, at any position at a later time. Curves with the shape of those of Fig. 22-5 are obtained.

A simple and revealing measure of the tendency of particles to move as a result of this diffusion process is given by the average squared net distance the particles travel in a one-dimensional diffusion process. (The average net distance is not helpful. The particles are just as likely to move to the right as to the left, so that the average net distance is always zero. In the average of the net *squared* distance, movements to the right and left add up rather than cancel out.)

The amount of diffusion substance that after time t has reached an element dx at x will be $c\, dx$. The squared net distance traveled by the molecules of the diffusing substance is x^2. The average squared net distance is calculated by adding up, by means of an integration, the x^2 values contributed by the molecules of the sample and dividing by the total number of molecules. Thus

$$\overline{x^2} = \frac{\int_{-\infty}^{+\infty} x^2 c\, dx}{N} = \frac{1}{2(\pi Dt)^{1/2}} \int_{-\infty}^{+\infty} x^2 e^{-x^2/4Dt}\, dx \qquad (22\text{-}17)$$

Substitution of this integral value from Appendix A-1 gives

$$\overline{x^2} = 2Dt$$

and

$$\sqrt{\overline{x^2}} = \sqrt{2Dt} \qquad (22\text{-}18)$$

This simple result can be used to estimate the extent of movement that can be accomplished by a diffusion motion. For example, the value of D for sucrose in water at 25°C is reported to be $4.0 \times 10^{-6}\,\mathrm{cm^2\ s^{-1}}$ or $4.0 \times 10^{-10}\,\mathrm{m^2\ s^{-1}}$. Thus

$$\overline{x^2} = 8.0 \times 10^{-10} t$$

and

$$\sqrt{\overline{x^2}} = 2.83 \times 10^{-5} \sqrt{t}$$

For example, in 1 h, or 3600 s, the value of $\sqrt{\overline{x^2}}$ is $1.7 \times 10^{-3}\,\mathrm{m}$, or 1.7 mm; this is a measure of the average net distance that sucrose molecules travel in a 1-h one-dimensional diffusion experiment.

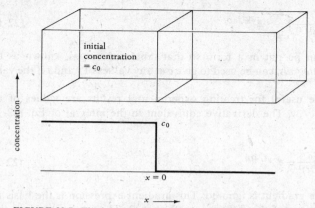

FIGURE 22-7 The initial concentration in an extended source.

Experimental studies that lead to values of the diffusion coefficient are not made by starting with the planar source of Fig. 22-5. Instead a solution is brought in contact with the solvent, as in Fig. 22-7. Furthermore, the progress of the solute into the solvent is not measured, but optical methods are used to reveal the *gradient*, i.e., the rate of change, of the concentration in the neighborhood of the initial boundary.

The development of this concentration gradient can be deduced from an expression for the concentration as a function of time. This concentration-versus-time relation is obtained by recognizing that the solute of each dx element of the solution will diffuse in the same manner as in the plane-source treatment, i.e., will follow Eq. (22-16). To find the concentration at some point P as in Fig. 22-8, it is only necessary to integrate over all such planar elements. If y locates the point P and x locates a representative element of the diffusing solution, as in Fig. 22-8, the integration is over all values of x from y to ∞. This development, with the assumption of an initial solute concentration of c_0 and an amount of diffusing substance in the volume element dx of $c_0\, dx$, leads to

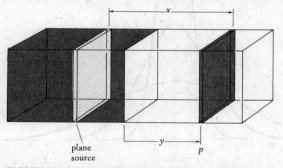

FIGURE 22-8 Diffusion from an extended source treated in terms of diffusion from plane sources.

$$c = \frac{c_0}{2(\pi Dt)^{1/2}} \int_{x=y}^{x=\infty} e^{-x^2/4Dt} \tag{22-19}$$

The integral can be put in a form so that tabulated values, known as the *error-function integrals,* can be used to give c at any values of y and t if the value of D is known.

Often more useful for treating experimental results are values of the magnitude of $\partial c/\partial y$. The derivative equivalent to the integral of Eq. (22-17) leads to

$$\frac{\partial c}{\partial y} = \frac{c_0}{2(\pi Dt)^{1/2}} e^{-y^2/4Dt} \tag{22-20}$$

if the sign of the gradient is ignored. This gradient expression is the basis for most determinations of the diffusion coefficient D. The gradient curves that develop according to this expression are illustrated in Fig. 22-9.

With the commonest optical system one measures the gradient of the refractive index. This can be taken to be proportional to the concentration gradient. One way to proceed is to recognize that the maximum in the gradient curve, which occurs at $y = 0$, has $\partial c/\partial y = c_0/2(\pi Dt^{1/2})$ and thus

$$\frac{dn}{dy} = (\text{const}) \frac{c_0}{2(\pi Dt)^{1/2}} \tag{22-21}$$

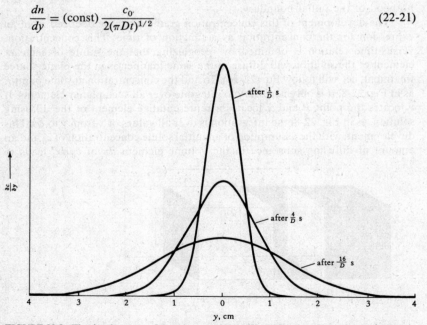

FIGURE 22-9 The development of the concentration gradient with time from an initial distribution as in Fig. 22-7.

where n is the refractive index. Furthermore, the area under the gradient curve is

$$\int_{-\infty}^{+\infty} \frac{c_0}{2(\pi Dt)^{1/2}} e^{-y^2/4Dt} \, dy = \frac{c_0}{2(\pi Dt)^{1/2}} (4\pi Dt)^{1/2} = c_0$$

Thus, the area under the refractive-index curve will be $(\text{const})(c_0)$. Finally, we can write, for the refractive-index-gradient curve

$$\frac{\text{Area}}{\text{Height}} = \frac{(\text{const})(c_0)}{(\text{const})(c_0)/2(\pi Dt)^{1/2}} = 2(\pi Dt)^{1/2} \tag{22-22}$$

Thus, measurements of the area and height of the refractive-index-gradient curve at various times yield values of D. Any concentration dependence can be attributed to the concentration dependence of D and can be removed by an extrapolation to zero concentration. Some results for diffusion coefficients obtained in this way are given in Table 22-5.

22-6 A Molecular Interpretation of Diffusion

To see how these experimental diffusion coefficients can be related to properties of the system, and particularly of the solute macromolecules, we take a molecular view of the diffusion process.

Consider diffusion across a distance interval dx over which the concentration changes from c to $c - dc$. The force that drives the molecules to the more dilute region can be related to the difference in the molar free energy of the solute at concentration c and at concentration $c - dc$. If ideal behavior is assumed, the free-energy difference *per molecule* is

$$G_{c-dc} - G_c = \frac{RT}{\mathfrak{N}} \ln \frac{c - dc}{c} \tag{22-23}$$

or

$$dG = \frac{RT}{\mathfrak{N}} \ln \left(1 - \frac{dc}{c} \right) \approx -\frac{RT}{\mathfrak{N}} \frac{dc}{c} \tag{22-24}$$

where the relation $\ln(1 - y) = -y$ for small y has been used.

This free-energy difference corresponds to the work done in the transfer of one macromolecule across the distance dx and can therefore be written as a force times the distance dx. Thus $dG = \text{driving force} \times dx$, or

$$\text{Driving force} = \frac{dG}{dx} = -\frac{RT}{\mathfrak{N}} \frac{1}{c} \frac{dc}{dx} \tag{22-25}$$

A frictional force sets and balances this diffusion force when some constant velocity is reached. The frictional force exerted by a viscous solvent fluid of viscosity η has been derived for a macroscopic sphere of radius r by G. G. Stokes as

$$\text{Frictional force} = 6\pi r\eta \frac{dx}{dt} \tag{22-26}$$

It appears suitable to apply this expression to the motion of reasonably spherical macromolecules. The diffusion velocity increases, therefore, until the force of Eq. (22-26) just balances that of Eq. (22-25). Then

$$6\pi r\eta \frac{dx}{dt} = -\frac{RT}{\mathfrak{N}} \frac{1}{c} \frac{dc}{dx}$$

or

$$c \frac{dx}{dt} = -\frac{RT}{6\pi r\mathfrak{N}\eta} \frac{dc}{dx} \tag{22-27}$$

If we agree that c implies a mass-per-unit-volume measure of concentration, it can be seen that the product $c \, dx/dt$ can be interpreted as the rate with which the diffusing substance moves through a unit cross section at x. This follows, as Fig. 22-10 suggests, from the fact that dx/dt, the average diffusion velocity in the x direction, is the distance the diffusing molecules will travel per unit time. Thus all molecules within a distance dx/dt of the cross section at x will cross in this unit time. These molecules are in a volume equal to dx/dt times the unit cross-section area. The mass of these molecules is the product of this

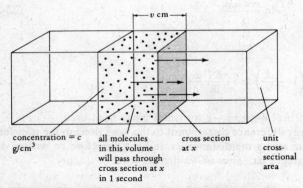

concentration = c
g/cm³

all molecules in this volume will pass through cross section at x in 1 second

cross section at x

unit cross-sectional area

FIGURE 22-10 Relation of velocity dx/dt and concentration to amount passing through a unit cross-section area.

volume and the concentration expressed as mass per unit volume. Thus $c\,dx/dt$ is the amount per unit time, i.e., the rate, with which the solute passes through the cross section. According to Eqs. (22-13) and (22-27), we can now write

$$-D\frac{\partial c}{\partial x} = -\frac{RT}{6\pi r\mathfrak{N}\eta}\frac{\partial c}{\partial x}$$

This leads to the identification

$$D = \frac{RT}{6\pi r\mathfrak{N}\eta} \tag{22-28}$$

Measurements of D and η could therefore lead to a value of the radius r for the macromolecule. Such a procedure is a little unsatisfactory. Molecules do not necessarily obey Stokes' law, even if they are spherical. Furthermore, macromolecules will generally be solvated and in moving through the solution will to some extent carry along this solvation layer. Equation (22-28) is important, however, in that it provides a way of determining the *effective* value of the group of terms $6\pi r\mathfrak{N}\eta$ for a solute characterized by molecules with radius r and a solvent characterized by viscosity η.

One can also investigate the extent to which the diffusing molecules act like Stokes'-law spheres. The frictional effect of such spheres can be expressed as the drag force per unit velocity. If this now is represented by f_0, we have, according to Eq. (22-26),

$$f_0 = 6\pi r\eta \tag{22-29}$$

A rearrangement of Eq. (22-28) shows that we have attempted to equate this frictional force to an effective frictional force by

$$6\pi r\eta = \frac{RT}{D\mathfrak{N}} \tag{22-30}$$

Now let f be the effective frictional force as given by

$$f = \frac{RT}{D\mathfrak{N}} \tag{22-31}$$

The extent to which the diffusing molecules perform like spheres that obey Stokes' law can be seen by the closeness of the so called *frictional ratio* f/f_0 to unity. We expect globular proteins to give values of this ratio near unity and rodlike molecules to give values considerably greater than unity.

An example is provided by hemoglobin, which has a molecular mass of $64{,}500$ g mol^{-1}, or 64.5 kg mol^{-1}, and a specific volume of 0.75 ml g^{-1}, or 0.75×10^{-3} m^3 kg^{-1}. If a spherical shape is assumed, a molecular radius of

26.8 × 10^{-10} m, or 26.8 Å, is calculated. The viscosity-of-water value of 1.005×10^{-3} kg m^{-2} s^{-1} at 20°C leads to

$$f_0 = 6\pi r\eta = 5.08 \times 10^{-11} \text{ kg s}^{-1}$$

With the value of D of 6.9×10^{-11} m^2 s^{-1} from Table 22-5 we have

$$f = \frac{RT}{D\mathfrak{N}} = 5.86 \times 10^{-11} \text{ kg s}^{-1}$$

The frictional ratio for hemoglobin is thus

$$\frac{f}{f_0} = 1.15$$

The closeness to unity again confirms the general spherical shape of such globular protein molecules. Some representative values of the frictional ratio are included in Table 22-5, page 777.

Finally, it is important to recognize that Eq. (22-28) is useful even if it is not satisfied when molecular radii are inserted for r. It is used as a means of expressing effective radii for diffusing molecules or effective values of the $6\pi r\eta$ term that Stokes' law has introduced.

22-7 The Ultracentrifuge and the Sedimentation-Velocity Method

In Sec. 22-5 the tendency of a solute to diffuse across a concentration gradient was treated. Macromolecules in solution can be made to alter their distribution in space by subjecting them to forces other than concentration gradients. If the macromolecule differs in density from the solvent, the simplest demonstration of this consists of allowing a solution to stand so that the force of gravity acts. A greater and more easily observed effect can be produced by using an ultracentrifuge, in which a sample of the macromolecule solution rotates at a very high speed, in the neighborhood of 10,000 to 80,000 min^{-1}. The ultracentrifuge, some features of which are shown in Fig. 22-11, is a very important tool for macromolecule research.

Two essentially different types of experiments can be performed to determine the behavior of solutions of macromolecules upon ultracentrifugation. In one, the rate of movement of the solute during the centrifugation is observed. In the other, the sample is centrifuged until an equilibrium distribution is obtained.

The first method starts with a well-defined boundary, or layer, of solution near the center of rotation and follows the movement of this layer toward the outside of the cell as a function of time. Such a method is termed a *sedimentation-velocity* experiment.

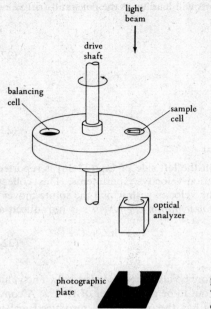

light
beam

drive
shaft

balancing
cell

sample
cell

optical
analyzer

photographic
plate

FIGURE 22-11
The basic features of an ultra-centrifuge.

A particle of mass m at a distance x from the center of rotation experiences a force given by

$$f_{centrif} = m'x\omega^2 \qquad (22\text{-}32)$$

where ω is the angular velocity in radians per second and m' is the effective mass of the solute particle, i.e., the actual mass corrected for the buoyancy effect of the solvent.

To express this buoyancy effect we first recognize that v, the specific volume of the solute, is the volume of 1 g of solute. The volume of m g of solute is mv, and the mass of this volume of solvent is $mv\rho$, where ρ is the solvent density. Thus the effective mass m' of the solute is $m - mv\rho = m(1 - v\rho)$. We now can rewrite Eq. (22-32) as

$$f_{centrif} = m(1 - v\rho)x\omega^2 \qquad (22\text{-}33)$$

This force is balanced for some constant-drift velocity dx/dt by a frictional force given by Stokes' law, Eq. (22-26), as

$$f_{fric} = 6\pi r\eta \frac{dx}{dt} \qquad (22\text{-}34)$$

Equating these two force expressions will lead us to the constant-drift velocity. A rearrangement of the equality

$$m(1 - \upsilon\rho)x\omega^2 = 6\pi\eta r \frac{dx}{dt} \tag{22-35}$$

that collects the dynamic variables gives

$$\frac{dx/dt}{x\omega^2} = \frac{m(1 - \upsilon\rho)}{6\pi r\eta} \tag{22-36}$$

The collection of dynamic terms on the left side of Eq. (22-36) is reported to describe the results of sedimentation-velocity experiments. This collection $(dx/dt)/x\omega^2$ can be looked on as the velocity with which the solute moves per unit centrifugal force field. The *sedimentation coefficient* s is introduced as

$$s = \frac{dx/dt}{x\omega^2} \tag{22-37}$$

The experimental results can therefore be tabulated as values of s. The value of s for many macromolecules comes out to be of the order of 10^{-13} s. A convenient unit having the value 10^{-13} s has therefore been introduced, called a *svedberg*, in honor of T. Svedberg, who did much of the early work with the ultracentrifuge.

According to Eq. (22-36),

$$s = \frac{dx/dt}{x\omega^2} = \frac{m(1 - \upsilon\rho)}{6\pi r\eta} \tag{22-38}$$

Rearrangement and multiplication by Avogadro's number gives

$$M = \mathfrak{N}m = \frac{6\pi r\eta\mathfrak{N}s}{1 - \upsilon\rho} \tag{22-39}$$

Now the troublesome terms involving η and r can be replaced by their effective values, such as appear in the measurable quantity D of Eq. (22-28) to give the desired result

$$M = \frac{RTs}{D(1 - \upsilon\rho)} \tag{22-40}$$

Thus, measurements of the sedimentation and diffusion coefficients and of the densities of the solvent and solute allow the deduction of the molecular

TABLE 22-5 Physical Data, for 20°C and Water Solutions of Some Proteins

Protein	Molecular mass, amu	Diffusion coefficient D, m^2 s^{-1} 10^{11}	Sedimentation coefficient s, 10^{13}s	Fractional ratio f/fo	Specific volume v, ml g^{-1}
Cytochrome c (bovine heart)	13,370	11.4	1.71	1.19	0.71
Myoglobin (horse heart)	16,900	11.3	2.04	1.11	0.74
Chymotrypsinogen (bovine pancreas)	23,240	9.5	2.54	1.19	0.73
β-Lactoglobulin (goat milk)	37,100	7.48	2.85	1.26	0.751
Serum albumin (human)	68,500	6.1	4.6	1.29	0.734
Hemoglobin (human)	64,500	6.9	4.46	1.16	0.75
Catalase (horse liver)	221,600	4.3	11.2	1.25	0.73
Urease (jack bean)	482,700	3.46	18.6	1.19	0.73
Fibrinogen (human)	339,700	1.98	7.63	2.34	0.71
Myosin (cod)	524,800	1.10	6.43	3.63	0.73
Tobacco mosaic virus	40,590,000	0.46	198	2.03	0.75

Source: All data except those for specific volume from A. L. Lehninger, "Biochemistry," 2d ed., p. 176, Worth Publishers, Inc., New York, 1975.

weight of the macromolecules. The entry of the diffusion coefficient might lead you to expect that the results are somewhat affected by the molecular shape. The necessary data for such calculations for a few macromolecular materials are included in Table 22-5.

A particular advantage of the sedimentation-velocity technique is that a macromolecule solution containing two or more types of macromolecules is separated according to the molecular masses of the components. Figure 22-12 shows the type of sedimentation diagram obtained for a system containing a number of macromolecular species.

Better resolution can be obtained by allowing the sedimentation to occur in a *density-gradient* solution, prepared, for example, by filling the centrifuge tube layer by layer with solutions of decreasing sucrose concentration. As the macromolecular substance or mixture of substances is centrifuged, it will then move through a solvent with gradually increasing density. The result is more stable macromolecular zones and a better "spectrum" of the components. The technique is thus a modification of the sedimentation-velocity method.

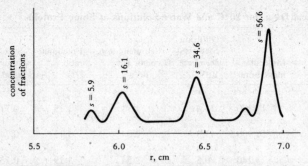

FIGURE 22-12 Separation of *Limulus* hemocyanin into fractions with different sedimentation constants, given in svedbergs (s). Centrifugal force is 120,000 times gravity, and time after reaching full speed is 35 min. [*From T. Svedberg, Proc. R. Soc. Lond.,* **B127:***1* (*1939*).]

22-8 The Sedimentation-Equilibrium Method

A second general centrifuge technique called *sedimentation equilibrium* allows the centrifugation process to proceed until an equilibrium distribution of the solute throughout the cell is obtained. Thermodynamics has introduced free energy as a convenient quantity for the study of equilibrium, and it can be used here to deal with the equilibrium-concentration gradient that develops. In particular, the centrifugal and diffusional contributions to the free energies G_{x_1} and G_{x_2} at the radial positions x_1 and x_2 are calculated. At equilibrium, the values of G_{x_1} and G_{x_2} must be equal.

The free-energy difference, as a result of the centrifugal effect, for particles at x_1 and at x_2 is obtained by finding the work required to move the particles from x_1 to x_2. The free energy is more negative at larger values of x and, on an individual molecule basis, is expressed by

$$\Delta G_{\text{centrif}} = -\int_{x_1}^{x_2} m'x\omega^2 \, dx = -\frac{m'\omega^2}{2}(x_2{}^2 - x_1{}^2) \tag{22-41}$$

With m' replaced by $m(1 - v\rho)$, this becomes

$$\Delta G_{\text{centrif}} = -\frac{m(1 - v\rho)\omega^2(x_2{}^2 - x_1{}^2)}{2} \tag{22-42}$$

This free-energy factor expresses the tendency of all the particles to congregate at large values of x, where the centrifugal free energy is low.

Balance is brought about by the diffusion tendency. Following Eq. (22-23), this is, per molecule,

$$\Delta G_{\text{diffus}} = \frac{RT}{\mathfrak{N}} \ln \frac{c_2}{c_1} \tag{22-43}$$

where c_2 and c_1 are concentrations at x_2 and x_1.

At equilibrium, the decrease in ΔG given by Eq. (22-42) just balances the increase given by Eq. (22-43), and for the process of moving solute from x_1 to x_2, one has the equilibrium condition

$$\Delta G_{\text{centrif}} + \Delta G_{\text{diffus}} = 0$$

On rearrangement after substitution of Eqs. (22-42) and (22-43), this yields

$$M = \mathfrak{N}m = \frac{2RT\ln(c_2/c_1)}{(1 - vp)\omega^2(x_2{}^2 - x_1{}^2)} \tag{22-44}$$

Thus, if measurements of the relative concentrations are made at two positions after equilibrium has been obtained, one can use Eq. (22-44) to calculate a value for the mass of the individual particles or the mass of an Avogadro's number of particles, i.e., the molar weight. This is the most accurate of the sedimentation methods for the determination of the molecular weight. Notice, for example, that Stokes' law was not used in the deduction of Eq. (22-44) and that the diffusion coefficient is absent from this equation. The principal drawback to the method is the time (as much as several days) it can take for equilibrium to be established.

A more recent variation on the sedimentation-equilibrium technique makes use of a density gradient. Most simply a solution is prepared that contains the macromolecular species and a heavy salt, e.g., cesium chloride. Centrifugation until equilibrium is reached produces a strong CsCl gradient and thus a density gradient throughout the tube. If the CsCl concentration has been appropriately chosen, the macromolecular substance will form a rather narrow band, as illustrated in Fig. 22-13. At this point the specific volume v of the macromolecular substance is equal to that of the solvent. Thus the term $1 - v\rho$ of Eq. (22-33) is unity, and there is no tendency for the macromolecular substance to move along the tube. Nearer the center of rotation, toward the top of the tube, the density ρ is less, and sedimentation will drive the macromolecules toward the band. Beyond the band, toward the bottom of the tube, the density ρ will be such that $v\rho$ will be greater than unity. The term $1 - v\rho$ is then negative, and macromolecules will be buoyed up toward the band.

22-9 Electrophoresis

In the studies of the preceding sections, macromolecule movements in solution have been due to diffusion and to the difference in density of the macromole-

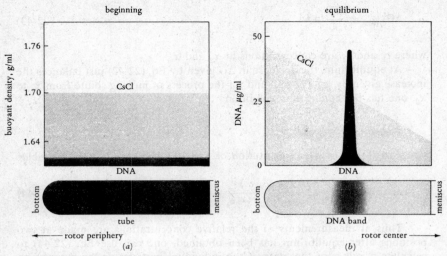

FIGURE 22-13 Concentration distribution of DNA and CsCl along the axis of the centrifuge tube at (a) the beginning of the CsCl equilibrium density-gradient centrifugation and (b) at the end of the run, i.e., after attainment of equilibrium. (*From W. Szybalski, Fractions, 1968, no. 1, Beckman Instruments, Inc.*)

cule and the solvent. Many of the macromolecules of interest, e.g., proteins, exist in solutions as charged species. It follows that movement of such particles can be produced by the application of an electric field. Such a process, known as *electrophoresis,* is the most important example of the more general electric-field motion effects described as *electrokinetic.*

Studies of the migration of charged solute particles under the influence of an applied electrical potential can be carried out in a *moving-boundary electrophoresis* apparatus shown schematically in Fig. 22-14. Depending on the charge carried by the particles, there will be a general movement of these species toward one electrode or the other. As a result, one of the original boundaries will move up, and the other will move down. Measurement of the movement of the boundary with time allows the *mobility* of the macromolecules to be deduced, at the pH of the buffer and at the temperature of the system. The mobility, defined as the rate of migration per unit voltage gradient, is usually given in units of centimeters per second per volt per centimeter, written cm^2 V^{-1} s^{-1}.

The mobility of a particle in an electrophoresis experiment is the velocity reached when the frictional drag just balances the electric force. The frictional drag is given approximately for spherical particles by Stokes' law, Eq. (22-26). The electric force is the charge eZ on the particle times the electrical potential gradient expressed in absolute units rather than in the practical units of volts, the absolute unit being $\frac{1}{300}$ V. The mobility u, which corresponds to a potential gradient of 1 V cm^{-1} can then be estimated from the relation

$$6\pi r\eta u = eZ(1 \text{ V m}^{-1})$$

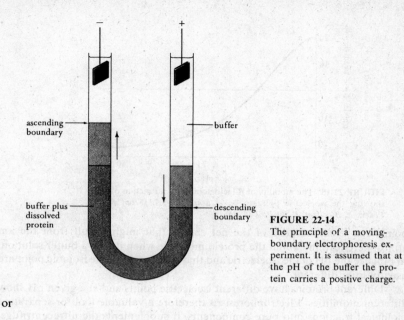

ascending boundary

buffer plus dissolved protein

buffer

ascending boundary

descending boundary

FIGURE 22-14
The principle of a moving-boundary electrophoresis experiment. It is assumed that at the pH of the buffer the protein carries a positive charge.

or

$$u = \frac{eZ}{6\pi r\eta} \tag{22-45}$$

The order of magnitude of protein mobilities can be estimated by introducing the representative and numerical values

$$e = 1.602 \times 10^{-19}\,\text{C} \qquad Z = 5$$
$$r = 20\,\text{Å} = 20 \times 10^{-10}\,\text{m} \qquad \eta = 1.005 \times 10^{-3}\,\text{kg m}^{-1}\,\text{s}^{-1}$$

Then

$$u = 40 \times 10^{-8}\,\text{m s}^{-1}$$

for a unit electric gradient.

The observed magnitude of protein mobilities and their dependence on pH is illustrated by the mobility-pH curve for β-lactoglobulin given in Fig. 22-15. The magnitude of the mobility at various pH values can be compared with typical mobilities of simple ions shown in Table 17-7. By comparison, protein molecules, particularly in the multicharged forms that exist at high or low pH, are not as resistant to movement as might be expected.

An important feature illustrated in Fig. 22-15 is the existence of a pH for which the mobility is zero. This pH is known as the *isoelectric point,* sometimes referred to as pH_I or even as pI. A closely related quantity is the isoionic point defined as the pH at which the macromolecule carries no net charge as a result of proton gains or losses in acid-base reactions. The isoelectric and the isoionic

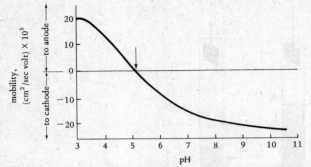

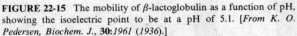

FIGURE 22-15 The mobility of β-lactoglobulin as a function of pH, showing the isoelectric point to be at a pH of 5.1. [*From K. O. Pedersen, Biochem. J.*, **30**:*1961* (*1936*).]

points can differ because of the net charge that might result from the ion atmosphere forming about the protein molecule when it is in a buffer solution. In practice the pH of the isoelectric and that calculated for the isoionic point are usually little different.

Different proteins have different isoelectric points and at a given pH show different mobilities. Electrophoresis is therefore a valuable tool for separating biological fractions into pure components. It supplements the ultracentrifuge, which separates according to molecular weight. Electrophoresis experiments can show that even if a sample is homogeneous with respect to molecular weight, it may contain different components having different electrical properties. Figure 22-16 shows the concentration gradients that develop in the rising and falling solution-solvent boundaries when a system of several species is subjected to moving-boundary electrophoresis.

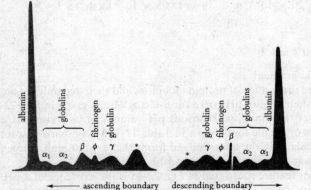

FIGURE 22-16 Electrophoretic patterns for normal human blood plasma at pH 8.6 showing the concentration gradients in the moving boundaries. The starred peaks are due to salt-concentration gradients. [*From R. A. Alberty, J. Chem. Educ.*, **25**:*426* (*1948*).]

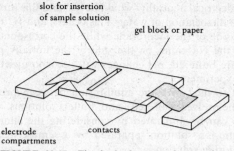

slot for insertion
of sample solution

gel block or paper

electrode
compartments

contacts

FIGURE 22-17 The basic features of zone electrophoresis.

Although the moving-boundary apparatus of Fig. 22-14 provides accurate mobility data, its use requires large amounts of material and considerable care to form and maintain sharp boundaries. Other techniques depending on solid or gelatinous supporting media are not preferred for the many analysis and separation uses to which electrophoresis is put. Such methods, known as *zone electrophoresis,* have generally supplanted the moving-boundary method. Simplest, and often used as a medium, is filter paper moistened with buffer solution and arranged as in Fig. 22-17. Also used are a variety of gels such as starch, agar, or polyacrylamide.

22-10 Donnan-Membrane Equilibria

Laboratory studies of macromolecule solutions, as in osmotic-pressure and dialysis studies, confine the macromolecules to one compartment while allowing passage of small ions or solvent in or out of that compartment. Much of the transport occurring in cells and cell compartments in living systems can be similarly described. In all such cases the equilibrium state that would be reached as a result of the net transport of the small ions can be markedly affected if the macromolecule carries a charge, as is generally the case.

Except at the isoionic pH, proteins and nucleic acids carry a charge as a result of a net gain or loss of protons. Additional charges are acquired by the binding of other species, e.g., the binding of Mg^{2+} ions by phosphate groups. Thus, macromolecules in laboratory or biological systems generally carry a charge. The overall electrical neutrality of the solution results from a corresponding opposite charge contributed by ions, called *counterions,* included in the remaining ionic makeup of the solution.

Suppose such a macromolecule or, more specifically, a protein solution is separated from pure water by a semipermeable membrane that allows passage of small ions but prohibits the passage of protein molecules. Such a situation could arise in an osmotic-pressure study or in the dialysis of the protein solution. Suppose the protein carries a net negative charge and that Na^+ ions are the counterions. The Na^+ ions will tend to diffuse to the low-concentration region of initially pure water. Electrical neutrality would be lost and this process prevented if it were not for the dissociation of water. This occurs, and H^+ tend to accumulate on the protein side of the membrane while the corresponding OH^- accumulate, along with the Na^+ ions, on the side of the initially pure water. Unless both solutions are buffered, pH changes will occur to upset the osmotic-pressure or dialysis experiment.

In such ways we are led to deal with the equilibrium between protein solutions, which are often themselves buffered, and buffer solutions. The complications that then arise can be illustrated by considering the simplest situation of the protein–sodium-ion solution separated by a semipermeable membrane from a sodium chloride solution.

Suppose the protein species P carries a negative charge of $-z$. The neutrality of the solution is achieved by the presence of z positive charges, Na^+ ions for example, for each protein molecule. At the start of a dialysis or osmotic-pressure study, if the protein concentration is c_P, as in Fig. 22-18, the initial Na^+ concentration in the protein compartment is zc_P.

Separated from this protein–sodium-ion solution, as in Fig. 22-18, is a salt solution with Na^+ and Cl^- ions at an initial salt concentration c_S.

Let us suppose that when equilibrium has been reached, an amount of chloride has diffused into the protein–sodium-ion compartment so that the chloride-ion concentration there has reached the value x. To maintain charge neutrality, an equal amount of sodium ions must accompany the chloride ions. (We shall assume that this effect overwhelms any H^+ or OH^- buildup that could result from water dissociation.) As a result, the concentrations of the species in the two compartments are those shown in Fig. 22-18.

The value of the unknown x in the expressions of Fig. 22-18 must now be deduced. When equilibrium is reached, the species that can penetrate the membrane will have equal activities in the two compartments. Here it is sodium chloride that establishes equilibrium, and thus the activity a_{NaCl} must be the same in the two compartments. Further, a_{NaCl} can be interpreted as $a_{Na^+}a_{Cl^-}$ or as $(\gamma_\pm)^2 c_{Na^+} c_{Cl^-}$. If such expressions are written for the two compartments, and if the mean-activity term is assumed to be equal in the two compartments, the condition for equilibrium can be described by

$$(zc_P + x)(x) = (c_S - x)(c_S - x) \tag{22-46}$$

species	salt compartment		protein compartment		
	Na^+	Cl^-	Na^+	Cl^-	P^{z-}
initial concentration	c_S	c_S	zc_P	0	c_P
change in concentration to reach equilibrium	$-x$	$-x$	$+x$	$+x$	
equilibrium concentration	$c_S - x$	$c_S - x$	$zc_P + x$	x	c_P

FIGURE 22-18 Species concentrations in a Donnan-membrane equilibrium study.

TABLE 22-6 Donnan-Membrane Equilibrium Results Calculated from Eq. (22-47) for $z = 1$

Initially		At equilibrium				
Salt compartment	Protein compartment	Salt compartment		Protein compartment		
$c_s = [Na^+] = [Cl^-]$	$c_P = [P^-] = [Na^+]$	$[Na^+]$ $= c_s - x$	$[Cl^-]$ $= c_s - x$	$[Na^+]$ $= c_P + x$	$[Cl^-]$ $= x$	$[P^-]$ $= c_P$
1.0	0	0.5	0.5	0.5	0.5	0
1.0	0.01	0.502	0.502	0.508	0.498	0.01
1.0	0.1	0.52	0.52	0.58	0.48	0.1
1.0	1.0	0.67	0.67	1.33	0.33	1.0

Rearrangement leads to x, the concentration of chloride that develops in the protein compartment

$$x = \frac{c_s^2}{zc_P + 2c_s} \qquad (22\text{-}47)$$

At large salt concentrations the effect of the protein is overwhelmed and $x \approx \frac{1}{2}c_s$. The two compartments achieve equal salt concentrations. On the other hand, at large protein concentrations, the passage of salt into the protein compartment is prevented, even though this entails the rejection of the chloride ion by a solution that contains none of that ion. Intermediate situations are illustrated by values calculated from Eq. (22-47) and shown in Table 22-6. Some chloride migrates into the protein compartment, along with the corresponding Na^+ that must accompany it. The idea that no NaCl would diffuse into the protein compartment and that the NaCl would diffuse until the inside and outside concentrations were equal is incorrect. The equilibrium, an example of the Donnan-membrane equilibrium, is deduced from Eq. (22-47).

The effects of various concentrations of protein and electrolyte are shown in Table 22-6. Only at high electrolyte concentrations relative to the protein concentration is the effect of the confined charged protein small. Therefore many studies of proteins or other polyelectrolytes in solution are made at high electrolyte concentration and at a pH near the isoionic point.

Many extensions and refinements of the development that led to Eq. (22-47) are possible and often necessary. Recognition of water dissociation and pH changes introduces additional complications. Even more difficult are the problems that arise from the nonideality of the two solutions and its effect on the activities or activity coefficients of the charged species.

22-11 Light Scattering

One of the most distinctive features of a colloidal, or macromolecule, solution is the scattered light, or *Tyndall effect*, observed when a light beam is passed

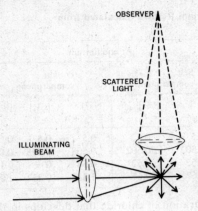

FIGURE 22-19
The detection of particles in
the ultramicroscope.

through such a solution. This scattered light can be used in two different ways to help elucidate the nature of colloidal solutions.

The first application is made in the *ultramicroscope*, shown schematically in Fig. 22-19. Here the sample is observed through a microscope at right angles to the direction of the entering light beam. Each colloid particle, larger than about 10 Å diameter in very favorable cases, will produce an observable point of scattered light. The individual particles can then be counted, and if the microscope focuses on a definite, known volume of solution, the number of particles per unit volume can be determined. Such data, along with the measurable mass of macromolecule material per unit volume, lead to a value of the average mass of the individual particles.

It should be emphasized that none of the details of the particles can be observed. They merely act as scattering centers, and one observes points of light. Furthermore, unless the refractive index of the colloid particle is very different from that of the solvent, the scattered light is too weak to be seen. The similarity of the refractive index of most macromolecules to the medium in which they are dispersed means that little scattered light will be given off. The method is therefore most applicable to inorganic colloids.

The second application of the scattering of light depends on the measurement and interpretation of the amount of light scattered in various directions as a beam of light passes through a solution of macromolecules. In some experiments the total amount of the scattered light is deduced from the decrease in intensity of the incident beam as it passes through the sample. Just as for Beer's law for the absorption of light (Sec. 20-3), one has the relation

$$I = I_0 e^{-\tau l} \tag{22-48}$$

where τ is the measure of the decrease in incident-beam intensity per unit length of a given solution and is known as the *turbidity*. In some experiments, on the other hand, the intensity of light scattered in various directions is measured

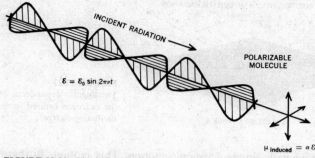

FIGURE 22-20 The induced dipole moments produced by the two components of incident radiation.

directly, rather than inferred, from the decrease in intensity of the incident beam.

That the scattered light is related to the particle size and shape can now be shown. We first consider the effect of particles that are small compared with the wavelength of the radiation. Incident plane-polarized radiation imposes, as Fig. 22-20 illustrates, an electric field

$$\mathcal{E} = \mathcal{E}_0 \sin 2\pi\nu t \tag{22-49}$$

as the particle. If the particle has a polarizability α, there will be an induced dipole moment given by

$$\mu_{\text{induced}} = \alpha \mathcal{E} = \alpha \mathcal{E}_0 \sin 2\pi\nu t \tag{22-50}$$

It is this oscillating dipole moment that emits secondary radiation and causes the particle to be a scattering center.

It has been mentioned in connection with the difficulties of early atomic theories that in classical electromagnetic theory an accelerated charge must emit electromagnetic radiation. This result can be applied to show what secondary radiation will be emitted by the oscillating induced dipole.

The oscillating dipole moment of Eq. (22-50) can be formally written as a charge of value $\alpha \mathcal{E}_0$ oscillating with a unit amplitude relative to an equal and opposite charge. Thus we can write

$$\mu_{\text{induced}} = (\alpha \mathcal{E}_0)x \tag{22-51}$$

with

$$x = \sin 2\pi\nu t \tag{22-52}$$

In this way a picture is obtained of an induced charge $\alpha \mathcal{E}_0$ in the irradiated

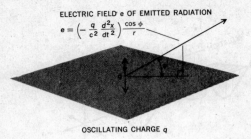

ELECTRIC FIELD e OF EMITTED RADIATION

$$e = \left(-\frac{q}{c^2}\frac{d^2x}{dt^2}\right)\frac{\cos\phi}{r}$$

OSCILLATING CHARGE q

FIGURE 22-21
The angular dependence of
the radiation emitted from an
oscillating charge.

particle vibrating with simple harmonic motion. This motion, furthermore, involves an acceleration d^2x/dt^2 which is calculated from Eq. (22-52) as

$$\frac{d^2x}{dt^2} = 4\pi^2\nu^2 \sin 2\pi\nu t \tag{22-53}$$

It is necessary now to quote, without derivation, the very important classical electromagnetic result that the acceleration of a charge q leads to the emission of electromagnetic radiation producing at a distance r and angle ϕ, as in Fig. 22-21, from the oscillating charge, an electric field e given by the expression

$$e = -\frac{q}{c^2}\frac{d^2x}{dt^2}\frac{\cos\phi}{r} \tag{22-54}$$

With this result one calculates that the radiation field of the dipole induced in the particle by one component of the incident radiation is

$$e = -\frac{\alpha\mathcal{E}_0 4\pi^2\nu^2 \sin 2\pi\nu t \cos\phi}{c^2 r} \tag{22-55}$$

The propagation of this radiation through space with a velocity c can be represented by including a sinusoidal space dependence to give

$$e = -\frac{4\pi^2\nu^2\mathcal{E}_0 \sin 2\pi\nu(t - x/c) \cos\phi}{c^2 r} \tag{22-56}$$

It is, however, not the electric field of the radiation but the energy content that is of interest. This energy is directly related to the square of the field amplitude, and with this relation the intensity, or energy, of the secondary beam is calculated as

$$i = \frac{16\pi^4\nu^4}{c^4 r^2}\alpha^2\mathcal{E}_0^2 \sin^2 2\pi\nu\left(t - \frac{x}{c}\right)\cos^2\phi \tag{22-57}$$

What is of importance for comparison with experimental results is the intensity of scattered radiation, at various angles, compared with the intensity of the incident radiation. This incident plane-polarized radiation can be depicted as entering the sample according to the relation

$$I_0 = \mathcal{E}_0{}^2 \sin^2 2\pi\nu \left(t - \frac{x}{c}\right) \tag{22-58}$$

and this expression can be inserted into Eq. (22-57) to give

$$\frac{i}{I_0} = \frac{16\pi^4\nu^4}{c^4 r^2} \alpha^2 \cos^2\phi \tag{22-59}$$

Intoduction of the radiation wavelength by the relation $\nu = c/\lambda$ then gives

$$\frac{i}{I_0} = \frac{16\pi^4}{r^2} \frac{\alpha^2 \cos^2\phi}{\lambda^4} \tag{22-60}$$

When ordinary, nonpolarized radiation is used for the incident beam, the induced dipole moment in the sample can be considered to have two mutually perpendicular components. The scattered beam consists, then, of two perpendicular components like that of Eq. (22-60). This net scattered beam is related to the angle θ of Fig. 22-21 by the equation

$$\frac{i}{I_0} = \frac{8\pi^4\alpha^2}{\lambda^4 r^2} (1 + \cos^2\theta) \tag{22-61}$$

This angular dependence is best verified by checking that it gives the correct summation of the two plane-polarized components in various special directions. The intensity predicted by Eq. (22-61) for the scattered beam from small particles is illustrated in Fig. 22-22.

It should be noticed that the forward and backward scattering are equal. Furthermore, the fourth-power dependence of the scattering on the wavelength shown by Eq. (22-61) should be noticed. It is, for example, to this enhanced scattering of short-wavelength radiation that the blue color of the sky is

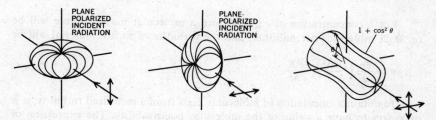

FIGURE 22-22 The angular dependence of secondary, or scattered, radiation from a particle that is small compared with the wavelength of the radiation.

attributed. The short-wavelength blue end of the visible spectrum is scattered more than the long-wavelength red end, and the "background" color of the sky is therefore blue.

The interpretation of the scattering of radiation that has culminated in Eq. (22-61) can be brought to a comparison with the experimental quantity, the turbidity. For many samples the amount of scattering is small, and the turbidity expression

$$\frac{I}{I_0} = e^{-\tau l}$$

or

$$\tau l = -\ln \frac{I}{I_0} \tag{22-62}$$

can be written, for unit-cell length, as

$$\tau = -\ln \left(\frac{I}{I_0} - \frac{I_0}{I_0} + 1 \right) = -\ln \left(\frac{I - I_0}{I_0} + 1 \right) \approx \frac{I_0 - I}{I_0} \tag{22-63}$$

The term $I_0 - I$ is the intensity removed from the incident beam and is therefore the integral over all angles of the scattered radiation of Eq. (22-61). The measure of turbidity can therefore be evaluated, according to the differential surface element of Fig. 22-23, as

$$\tau = \int_0^\pi \frac{i}{I_0} 2\pi r^2 \sin \theta \, d\theta \tag{22-64}$$

Substitution of the expression for scattered intensity i of Eq. (22-61) and integration gives

$$\tau = \frac{8\pi}{3} \left(\frac{2\pi}{\lambda} \right)^4 \alpha^2 \tag{22-65}$$

For a concentration of c g ml^{-1} and a molecular mass M there will be $(c/M)\mathfrak{N}$ molecules per milliliter, and the turbidity of such a material will be

$$\tau = \frac{8\pi}{3} \left(\frac{2\pi}{\lambda} \right)^4 \alpha^2 \frac{c\mathfrak{N}}{M} \tag{22-66}$$

To obtain a calculation of molecular mass from a measured turbidity, it is necessary to have a value of the molecular polarizability. The expression of Eq. (16-37) of Sec. 16-5 can be reduced for $n_R \approx 1$, as is the case for gases, to the relation between α and the refractive index n_R of

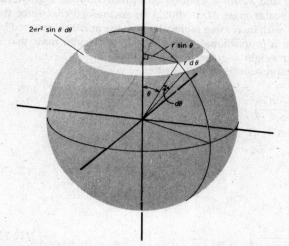

FIGURE 22-23 The surface element for the integration of the scattered radiation.

$$2\pi \left(\frac{c}{M} \mathfrak{N} \right) \alpha = n_R - 1 \tag{22-67}$$

With this result the turbidity of a gaseous system, in which the particles are small compared with the wavelength, can be written

$$\tau = \frac{32\pi^3 M (n_R - 1)^2}{3\lambda^4 c \mathfrak{N}} \tag{22-68}$$

With this expression the measurable turbidity can be related to the molecular mass of the gas-phase particles, the mass of material per unit volume, and the refractive index of the gaseous system. This expression can also be turned around so that a value for Avogadro's number can be obtained from the scattering produced by gas samples.

For the systems of interest here, i.e., macromolecules in a liquid medium, it is necessary to introduce the fact that the scattering depends on the *difference* between the refractive index of the particles and that of the medium. If n_R is the refractive index of the solution and n_R° that of the pure solvent, the appropriate relation comparable with Eq. (22-68) turns out to be

$$\tau = \frac{32\pi^3 M n_R^\circ}{3\lambda^4 c \mathfrak{N}} (n_R - n_R^\circ)^2 \tag{22-69}$$

Now measurements n_R° and n_R for a solution of a given value of c allow the calculation of the molecular mass M. It should be mentioned that since the polarizability increases with increasing molecular size, the amount scattered by an individual molecule is proportional to its size. The molecular mass that is obtained is therefore a weight-average molecular mass.

In practice, this expression is usually written

$$\tau = \frac{32\pi^3 n_R^\circ}{3\lambda^4 \mathfrak{N}} \left(\frac{n_R - n_R^\circ}{c}\right)^2 cM$$

or

$$\tau = HcM \tag{22-70}$$

where

$$H = \frac{32\pi^3 n_R^\circ}{3\lambda^4 \mathfrak{N}} \left(\frac{n_R - n^\circ}{c}\right)^2 \tag{22-71}$$

In dilute solutions, moreover, the term for the change of refractive index with concentration can be written as a differential, and H then is

$$H = \frac{32\pi^3 n_R^\circ}{3\lambda^4 \mathfrak{N}} \left(\frac{dn_R}{dc}\right)^2 \tag{22-72}$$

From measurements of refractive index for the wavelength of light used in the scattering experiments, H can be evaluated and the turbidity can be measured. Equation (22-70) can then be used to calculate a molecular mass. In practice, an extrapolation to infinite dilution is necessary, and for particles of appreciable size compared with the wavelength of light so also is recognition of the angular dependence of the scattered light.

A little must now be said about the scattering that results when the molecules are not small with respect to the wavelength of the light. Visible light has wavelengths between about 400 and 800 nm, and these lengths are just about the dimensions expected for many macromolecules. As for electron scattering from different atoms of a molecule in an electron-diffraction experiment, the scatterings from different parts of the molecule will now interfere with each other. The effect is, in fact, very similar to that studied in detail for electron diffraction. The macromolecule is best thought of as some geometric shape presenting a continuum of scattering centers rather than a few discrete centers. A detailed calculation for the amount of light scattered as a function of angle, for a given wavelength and assumed molecular size and shape, can be performed by integrating the Wierl equation of Sec. 15-14 over all parts of the

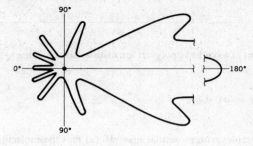

FIGURE 22-24
The scattering of visible light
from a spherical particle of
radius 5000 Å. [*From V. K.
LaMer and M. Kerker, Sci.
Am.* **188:***69 (1953).*]

molecule. The type of light-scattering angular dependence that can result for molecules with dimensions like that of the wavelength of the scattered light is indicated in Fig. 22-24. The details of the pattern are dependent on the shape of the molecule as well as on its overall size. Measurements of light scattering now give promise of being one of the most powerful methods for studying the geometry of macromolecules in solution.

In lieu of a detailed analysis of the molecular shape that would lead to the observed angular dependence of the scattered radiation, it is often sufficient to measure the intensity of the scattered beam at two angles, usually 45 and 135°, to the incident beam. The ratio of these intensities reflects the overall shape of the macromolecule in solution. Calculations have been made, using essentially the Wierl equation for some simple shapes, and these are shown in Fig. 22-25. From observations of the scattered intensity at the angles of 45 and 135°, such curves can be consulted, and lead to some information on the usually unapproachable quantity, the shape of a molecule in solution.

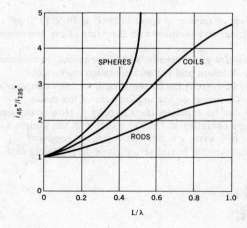

FIGURE 22-25
The ratio of the intensity of
the scattered light at 45° to
that at 135°. The wavelength
of the light is λ, and L is the
diameter for spheres, the rms
distance between ends for
coils, and the length for rods.

PROBLEMS

22-1. The molecular masses of a synthetic polymer are distributed according to the expression

$$\frac{1}{N}\frac{dN}{dM} = 0.61 \times 10^{-4}e^{-[(M-10,000)/10,000]^2}$$

where N is the number of molecules with molecular mass M. (a) Plot the molecular-mass-distribution curve. Determine graphically (b) the number and (c) mass-average molecular masses.

22-2. The molecular mass of egg albumin is about 40,000 g. Find (a) the freezing-point depression, (b) the vapor-pressure lowering, and (c) the osmotic pressure at 25°C of an aqueous solution containing 10 g liter^{-1}.

22-3. The viscosity of solutions of native DNA and of fractions of DNA produced by sonic breakup of the native material have been reported [J. Eigner and P. Doty, *J. Mol. Biol.*, **12**:549 (1965)]. For molecular masses in the range 2×10^6 to about 130×10^6, the intrinsic viscosities can be represented by the empirical relation $[\eta] = 0.069M^{0.70}$, where M is the molecular mass. (a) What value of $[\eta]$ does this equation yield for the high-molecular-mass fractions, with M of about 130×10^6, corresponding to unfragmented DNA? (b) What structure do this value and the dependence of $[\eta]$ on mass suggest for the DNA molecule in solution?

22-4. (a) For one of the substances for which the diffusion coefficient is given in Table 22-5, calculate and plot the concentration gradient as a function of y, as in Fig. 22-9, for two different times. (b) In view of the form of Eq. (22-20), compare the influences of different values of D and t on the development of the concentration-gradient curve.

22-5. The diffusion coefficient of oxygen dissolved in water is 200×10^{-11} m^2 s^{-1} at 25°C. How long, on the average, does it take an oxygen molecule to go a distance of 1 mm in a particular direction?

22-6. The diffusion coefficient of sucrose in water at 20°C is 40×10^{-11} m^2 s^{-1}. Estimate its sedimentation coefficient and compare with the value of the macromolecules of Table 22-5.

22-7. For spherical particles of a given density, what dependence on molecular mass would be expected for the diffusion and the sedimentation coefficients?

22-8. From the data of Table 22-5, verify the frictional ratio for one example other than myoglobin or hemoglobin. Comment on the implications of the result.

22-9. The force of gravity can be expressed as 9.80 N kg^{-1}. How many times greater is the force of a centrifuge operating at 75,000 r min^{-1} with the sample 6 cm from the center of rotation; i.e., how many g's does the centrifuge produce?

22-10. Calculate the frictional ratio for bovine serum given the following data, all applying to 25°C:

Molecular weight, 66,500 g mol^{-1}

Specific volume, 0.734 ml g^{-1}

Diffusion coefficient, 6.97×10^{-11} m^2 s^{-1}

22-11. Both myoglobin and hemoglobin are globular proteins that seem suitable for the spherical-particle Stokes'-law development that led to Eq. (22-28). The diffusion coefficients reported for myoglobin and hemoglobin in water at 20°C are 11.3×10^{-11} and 6.9×10^{-11} m^2 s^{-1}, respectively. (a) What radii do these data and Eq. (22-28) produce for these molecules? (b) It is known that hemoglobin is made up of four subunits, each subunit being similar to the myoglobin molecule. Are the radii estimates consistent with this fact?

22-12. About how long will it take the boundary of a myoglobin sample to move a distance of 1 mm in a centrifuge operating at 60,000 r min^{-1} if the initial distance of the sample boundary from the center of rotation is 6 cm? The sedimentation constant s reported for myoglobin is 2.04 svedbergs at 20°C.

22-13. Sedimentation-velocity studies of human hemoglobin in water at 20°C yield a sedimentation coefficient of 4.46 svedbergs. The specific volume v of hemoglobin is estimated to be 0.75 ml g^{-1}, and the density ρ of the solvent is 1 g ml^{-1}. The diffusion coefficient for hemoglobin under the same conditions is 6.9×10^{-11} m^2 s^{-1}. Use these data to estimate the molar mass of hemoglobin.

22-14. A sample of γ globulin gives the following experimental results at 20°C:

Specific volume v, 0.178 ml g^{-1}

Sedimentation coefficient s, 7.12×10^{-13} s

Diffusion coefficient D, 4.00×10^{-11} m^2 s^{-1}

Calculate the molecular mass of γ globulin.

22-15. The tabulated data were obtained[†] in a boundary sedimentation-velocity study with a 52,000r min^{-1} centrifuge.

Time, min	0	16.3	32.3	48.3	64.3	80.3
Radius to boundary	12.380	12.696	12.993	13.297	13.611	13.923

In view of Eq. (22-37), which can also be written

$$s = \frac{1}{\omega^2} \frac{d \ln x}{dt} \quad \text{or} \quad s = \frac{2.303}{\omega^2} \frac{d \log x}{dt}$$

use a graphical treatment to obtain a value for the sedimentation constant.

22-16. The following are additional data obtained in the sedimentation-equilibrium study on which the example of Sec. 22-8 was based:

x, cm	6.827	6.917	6.979	7.026	7.026	7.093
c, arbitrary units	3.52	5.52	7.52	9.52	11.52	13.52

Use a graphical procedure to show that these data correspond to the concentration-radius relation expected on the basis of Eq. (22-44).

22-17. Use data from Prob. 22-16 to deduce a value for the molecular mass (or use the slope of the best straight line in the graphical treatment developed to answer Prob. 22-16).

[†]From a more extensive listing given in C. H. Chervenka, "A Manual of Methods," Beckman Instruments, Inc.

22-18. Calculate the molecular mass of a macromolecular substance from the following sedimentation-equilibrium data.†

Rotor speed	15,000 r min^{-1}
Temperature	12.4°C
$1 - v\rho$	0.277
Concentration (arbitrary units):	
At $x = 6.827$	3.52
At $x = 7.093$	13.52

22-19. What would happen in a isoelectric-focusing study if the electrodes were connected improperly, i.e., the electrode at the basic end of the cell were made positive and that at the acidic end were made negative?

22-20. An aqueous colloidal solution of silver chloride was examined in an ultramicroscope. In a field of view of 0.05 mm diameter and 0.05 mm depth, an average of 8.4 particles were counted. If the solution had been prepared by the dilution of a solution containing 0.0032 g of AgCl per milliliter by a factor of 1:10,000, what was the average mass of the AgCl particles? Is this a number or mass average?

REFERENCES

KAUFMAN, M.: "Giant Molecules," Doubleday & Company, Inc., Garden City, New York, 1968.

FLORY, P. J.: "Principles of Polymer Chemistry," Cornell University Press, Ithaca, N.Y., 1953. The nature, synthesis, and characterization of polymeric materials. The emphasis is on synthetic polymers and on studies and properties of solutions of these polymeric materials.

MOROWETZ, H.: "Macromolecules in Solution," Wiley-Interscience, New York, 1965.

WILLIAMS, J. W.: "Ultracentrifugation of Macromolecules: Modern Topics," Academic Press, Inc., New York, 1973.

DICKERSON, R. E., and I. GEIS: "The Structure and Action of Proteins," Harper & Row, Publishers, Incorporated, New York, 1969. A magnificent introduction to the structures of proteins and the way these structures are related to some of the enzyme actions of these molecules.

SHAKMANN, M. A. (ed.): "Polyamino Acids, Polypeptides, and Proteins," University of Wisconsin Press, Madison, Wis., 1962. A summary of recent and current, as of 1961, research on various aspects of polymeric amino acid materials. The collection provides an illustration of the uses to which physical-chemical methods are put in this area of macromolecule studies.

STEINER, R. F., and R. F. BEERS, JR.: "Polynucleotides," Elsevier Publishing Company, Amsterdam, 1961. Included in this monograph are summaries of the physical methods that are of value for these compounds and a discussion of the results of application of these methods. An illustration of the extension of the material of this chapter for one type of macromolecule is thus provided.

GIMBLETT, F. G. R.: "Inorganic Polymer Chemistry," Butterworth & Co., Ltd., London, 1963. The chemical nature and synthesis of inorganic polymers, with some discussions of the properties and structures of these materials.

† From a more extensive listing given in C. H. Chervenka, "A Manual of Methods," Beckman Instruments, Inc.

APPENDIX A
MATHEMATICS

A-1 Evaluation of Integrals of the Type $\int_0^\infty x^n e^{-ax^2}\,dx$

a. Reduction of the integrals Integration by parts, using the general expression

$$\int u\,dv = uv] - \int v\,du$$

can be carried out with

$$dv = xe^{-ax^2}\,dx \qquad \text{and thus} \qquad v = -\frac{1}{2a}e^{-ax^2}$$

and

$$u = x^{n-1} \qquad \text{and thus} \qquad du = (n-1)x^{n-2}\,dx$$

With these identifications, integration by parts gives

$$\int_0^\infty x^n e^{-ax^2}\,dx = \frac{x^{n-1}}{2a}e^{-ax^2}\Big]_0^\infty - \int_0^\infty \left[-\frac{1}{2a}(n-1)x^{n-2}e^{-ax^2}\right]dx$$

$$= 0 + \frac{n-1}{2a}\int_0^\infty x^{n-2}e^{-ax^2}\,dx$$

In this way integrals of the general type can be reduced either to one involving the integral xe^{-ax^2} or to one involving the integral e^{-ax^2}.

b. For n odd In this case the method of part a leads to the integral

$$\int_0^\infty xe^{-ax^2}\,dx$$

which can be integrated directly to give

$$-\frac{1}{2a}e^{-ax^2}\Big]_0^\infty = \frac{1}{2a}$$

c. For n even Here, the method of part a leads to the integral

$$\int_0^\infty e^{-ax^2}\,dx$$

Evaluation is accomplished by writing the product of two such integrals based on two independent coordinates x and y which can be pictured as being cartesian coordinates. We thus investigate

$$\int_0^\infty e^{-ax^2}\,dx \int_0^\infty e^{-ay^2}\,dy = \int_0^\infty \int_0^\infty e^{-a(x^2+y^2)}\,dx\,dy$$

The coordinates x and y can now be related to new coordinates r and θ by the relations which associate cartesian coordinates with polar coordinates. Thus

$$x^2 + y^2 = r^2 \quad \text{and} \quad dx\,dy = r\,dr\,d\theta$$

Furthermore, since in the xy coordinate system the integration is over the first quadrant, the corresponding limits of the integration involving r and θ are 0 to ∞ and 0 to $\pi/2$. We thus have the problem, in r and θ, of

$$\int_0^{\pi/2} \int_0^\infty e^{-ar^2} r\,dr\,d\theta$$

Now the two integrations can be performed to give $(\pi/2)(1/2a)$, and therefore the original integral is evaluated as

$$\int_0^\infty e^{-ax^2}\,dx = \frac{1}{2}\sqrt{\frac{\pi}{a}}$$

d. Even and odd character and the limits of integration Functions of the type $x^n e^{-ax^2}$ are even if n is even and odd if n is odd. Integration from $-\infty$ to $+\infty$ will therefore give zero for n odd and will give twice the value of the integral from 0 to ∞ for n even.

e. Values of most often used integrals:

$$\int_{-\infty}^{+\infty} e^{-ax^2}\,dx = \sqrt{\frac{\pi}{a}} \qquad \int_0^\infty xe^{-ax^2}\,dx = \frac{1}{2a}$$

$$\int_{-\infty}^{+\infty} x^2 e^{-ax^2}\,dx = \frac{1}{2a}\sqrt{\frac{\pi}{a}} \qquad \int_0^\infty x^3 e^{-ax^2}\,dx = \frac{1}{2a^2}$$

$$\int_{-\infty}^{+\infty} x^4 e^{-ax^2}\,dx = \frac{3}{4a^2}\sqrt{\frac{\pi}{a}}$$

A-2 Stirling's Approximation

One form of Stirling's approximation for the value of the factorial of a large number can be derived as follows. One considers the natural logarithm of the factorial and expresses this as a summation:

$$\ln N! = \ln N + \ln(N-1) + \ln(N-2) + \cdots + \ln 2 + \ln 1$$

$$= \sum_{i=1}^N \ln i$$

For large N, the argument of Appendix A-4 can be used to replace the sum by an integral to obtain

$$\ln N! \approx \int_1^N \ln x \, dx$$

where x is a continuous function.

Integration by parts, with $u = \ln x$, $du = d \ln x = (1/x) \, dx$, and $dv = dx$, $v = x$, leads to the result

$$\ln N! \approx x \ln x \Big]_1^N - \int_1^N x \frac{1}{x} \, dx \approx N \ln N - N$$

Although this logarithmic form is often the one used, we can also write

$$N! \approx N^N e^{-N}$$

Finally, it should be mentioned that a better approximation, not derived here, is

$$N! \approx N^N e^{-N} (2N)^{1/2}$$

A-3 The Method of Lagrange Multipliers

An extremum of a function $f(x_1, x_2, \ldots, x_n)$ of a set of n variables $x_1, x_2, \ldots, x_n$ exists when df is zero for variation of any of the x_i's. Since

$$df = \frac{\partial f}{\partial x_1} dx_1 + \frac{\partial f}{\partial x_2} dx_2 + \cdots + \frac{\partial f}{\partial x_n} dx_n = \sum \frac{\partial f}{\partial x_i} dx_i \qquad \text{(A-3-1)}$$

and, for an extremum, df must be zero for all values of $dx_1, dx_2, \ldots, dx_n$, an extremum will occur when all the coefficients of the dx_i are zero. Thus an extremum can be found by writing the n equations

$$\frac{\partial f}{\partial x_i} = 0$$

$$\frac{\partial f}{\partial x_2} = 0$$

$$\cdots\cdots\cdots \qquad \text{(A-3-2)}$$

$$\frac{\partial f}{\partial x_n} = 0$$

and solving for the values of $x_1, x_2, \ldots, x_n$ that satisfy this set of n equations.

When, however, the x_i's cannot all be independently varied, the dx_i's cannot take on any value and we cannot require all $\partial f / \partial x_i$'s to be zero. We cannot proceed by the method outlined above to solve for the values of $x_1, x_2, \ldots, x_n$ that locate an extremum.

The procedure which locates an extremum in a function like $f(x_1, x_2, \ldots, x_n)$ when variations in the x_i's are subject to certain constraints depends on the introduction of *Lagrange multipliers*. If, to be specific, two constraining equations

$$g(x_1, x_2, \ldots, x_n) = 0 \qquad \text{and} \qquad h(x_1, x_2, \ldots, x_n) = 0 \qquad \text{(A-3-3)}$$

are assumed, the Lagrange method asserts that solution of the set of $n + 2$ equations

$$\frac{\partial f}{\partial x_i} + \alpha \frac{\partial g}{\partial x_i} + \beta \frac{\partial h}{\partial x_i} = 0 \qquad \text{for } i = 1, 2, \ldots, n \tag{A-3-4}$$

$$g(x_1, x_2, \ldots, x_n) = 0 \tag{A-3-5}$$

$$h(x_1, x_2, \ldots, x_n) = 0 \tag{A-3-6}$$

will yield values of $x_1, x_2, \ldots, x_n$ that locate an extremum subject to the constraints. The α and β are *undetermined multipliers* that are constants, not functions of the x_i.

That this procedure locates an extremum for a well-behaved function can now be shown.

Solutions that satisfy Eq. (A-3-4) allow the partial derivatives $\partial f/\partial x_i$ to be written

$$\frac{\partial f}{\partial x_i} = -\alpha \frac{\partial g}{\partial x_i} - \beta \frac{\partial h}{\partial x_i} \qquad \text{for all } i$$

These expressions can now be inserted into the total differential expression for df to give

$$df = -\alpha \sum \frac{\partial g}{\partial x_i} dx_i - \beta \sum \frac{\partial h}{\partial x_i} dx_i \tag{A-3-7}$$

Finally, if the constraining equations, Eqs. (A-3-5) and (A-3-6), are satisfied,

$$\sum \frac{\partial g}{\partial x_i} dx_i = 0 \qquad \text{and} \qquad \sum \frac{\partial h}{\partial x_i} dx_i = 0$$

and it follows from the substitution of these in Eq. (A-3-7) that $df = 0$.

Thus solution of Eqs. (A-3-4) to (A-3-6) for $x_1, x_2, \ldots, x_n$ locates an extremum when the x_i's are subject to constraints like those of the two expressions $g = 0$ and $h = 0$ used in this illustration. Whether the extremum is a maximum, minimum, or point of inflection is usually determined from physical considerations. The values of the undetermined multipliers, α and β in the example used here, may turn out to be of interest, but their determination is not central to the problem of locating an extremum.

A-4 Replacing a Sum by an Integral

Let us consider the condition under which a summation of terms, each term determined or indexed by the value of an integer, can be replaced by an integration.

Suppose a quantity A is given by a summation of terms according to

$$A = a(1) + a(2) + a(3) + \cdots + a(n) = \sum_{i=1}^{n} a(i) \tag{A-4-1}$$

where $a(i)$ implies a term whose value is determined by assigning an integral value to i.

Although only integral values of i are used to generate values for the terms of the summation, we can deal with i as a continuous variable. Then the summation over the range of i's can be written, in a way that turns out to be profitable, as

$$A = a(1) \int_0^1 di + a(2) \int_1^2 di + \cdots + a(n) \int_{n-1}^n di$$

$$= \int_0^1 a(1)\, di + \int_1^2 a(2)\, di + \cdots + \int_{n-1}^n a(n)\, di \tag{A-4-2}$$

Now, if each $a(i)$ does not vary very much in the unit range of i, that is, in the range of integration of each term, the constant values of $a(1)$, $a(2)$, and so on, obtained by using integers, can be replaced by the varying functions $a(i)$ obtained by using the continuous variable i in each term. When this condition holds, i.e., the variation in each term is small compared with the total variation in the values of the $a(i)$ terms, we can rewrite Eq. (A-4-2) as

$$A = \int_0^1 a(i)\, di + \int_1^2 a(i)\, di + \cdots + \int_{n-1}^n a(i)\, dn = \int_0^n a(i)\, di \tag{A-4-5}$$

By this development, the conditions under which a sum can be calculated by means of the corresponding integral have been displayed.

APPENDIX B
TABLES OF PROPERTIES

TABLE B-1 Thermodynamic Properties of Substances at 1 atm Pressure and 25°C in the Physical State Indicated

Note that $S°$ and $C_P°$ are the entropies and heat capacities of the listed substances; $\Delta H_f°$ are the values for the compounds compared with the elements of which they are composed; $\Delta G_f°$ values are related to $\Delta H_f°$ and $S°$ values by the relation $\Delta G_f° = \Delta H_f° - T\Delta S_f°$, where $\Delta S_f°$ can be calculated from the listed entropies of the compound and the elements of which it is composed; physical states are indicated by (c) for crystalline, (l) for liquid, and (g) for gas

	Element or compound	$\Delta H_f°$, kJ mol^{-1}	$S°$, J mol^{-1} K^{-1}	$\Delta G_f°$, kJ mol^{-1}	$C_P°$, J mol^{-1} K^{-1}
	$H_2(g)$	0.0	130.59	0.0	28.84
	$H(g)$	217.94	114.61	203.24	20.79
Group 0	$He(g)$	0.0	126.06	0.0	20.79
	$Ne(g)$	0.0	144.14	0.0	20.79
	$Ar(g)$	0.0	154.72	0.0	20.79
	$Kr(g)$	0.0	163.97	0.0	20.79
	$Xe(g)$	0.0	169.58	0.0	20.79
	$Rn(g)$	0.0	176.15	0.0	20.79
Group I	$Li(c)$	0.0	28.03	0.0	23.64
	$Li(g)$	155.10	138.67	122.13	20.79
	$Li_2(g)$	199.2	196.90	157.32	35.65
	$Li_2O(c)$	−595.8	37.91	−560.24	
	$LiH(g)$	128.4	170.58	105.4	29.54
	$LiCl(c)$	−408.78	(55.2)	−383.7	
	$Na(c)$	0.0	51.0	0.0	28.41
	$Na(g)$	108.70	153.62	78.11	20.79
	$Na_2(g)$	142.13	230.20	103.97	
	$NaO_2(c)$	−259.0		−194.6	
	$Na_2O(c)$	−415.9	72.8	−376.6	68.2
	$Na_2O_2(c)$	−504.6	(66.9)	−430.1	
	$NaCH(c)$	−426.73	(523)	−377.0	80.3
	$NaCl(c)$	−411.00	72.4	−384.0	49.71
	$NaBr(c)$	−359.95		−347.6	
	$Na_2SO_4(c)$	−1384.49	149.49	−1266.83	127.61
	$Na_2SO_4 \cdot 10H_2O(c)$	−4324.08	592.87	−3643.97	587.4
	$NaNO_3(c)$	−466.68	116.3	−365.89	93.05
	$Na_2CO_3(c)$	−1130.9	136.0	−1047.7	110.50
	$K(c)$	0.0	63.6	0.0	29.16
	$K(g)$	90.0	160.23	61.17	20.79
	$K_2(g)$	128.9	249.75	92.5	
	$K_2O(c)$	−361.5		−318.8	
	$KOH(c)$	−425.85		−374.5	

Element or compound	$\Delta H_f°$, kJ mol^{-1}	$S°$, J mol^{-1} K^{-1}	$\Delta G_f°$, kJ mol^{-1}	$C_p°$, J mol^{-1} K^{-1}
KCl(c)	−435.87	82.67	−408.32	51.50
KMnO$_4$(c)	−813.4	171.71	−713.79	119.2
Group II				
Be(c)	0.0	9.54	0.0	17.82
Mg(c)	0.0	32.51	0.0	23.89
MgO(c)	−601.83	26.8	−569.57	37.40
Mg(OH)$_2$(c)	−924.66	63.14	−833.74	77.03
MgCl$_2$(c)	−641.82	89.5	−592.32	71.30
Ca(c)	0.0	41.63	0.0	26.27
CaO(c)	−635.09	39.7	−604.2	42.80
CaF$_2$(c)	−1214.6	68.87	−1161.9	67.02
CaCO$_3$(c, calcite)	−1206.87	92.9	−1128.76	81.88
CaSiO$_3$(c)	−1584.1	82.0	−1498.7	85.27
CaSO$_4$(c, anhydrite)	−1432.68	106.7	−1320.30	99.6
CaSO$_4 \cdot \frac{1}{2}$H$_2$O(c)	−1575.15	130.5	−1435.20	119.7
CaSO$_4 \cdot 2$H$_2$O(c)	−2021.12	193.97	−1795.73	186.2
Ca$_3$(PO$_4$)$_2$(c)	−4137.5	236.0	−3899.5	227.82
Group III				
B(c)	0.0	6.53	0.0	11.97
B$_2$O$_3$(c)	−1263.6	54.02	−1184.1	62.26
B$_2$H$_6$(g)	31.4	232.88	82.8	56.40
B$_5$H$_9$(g)	62.8	275.64	165.7	80
Al(c)	0.0	28.32	0.0	24.34
Al$_2$O$_3$(c)	−1669.79	50.99	−1576.41	78.99
Group IV				
C(c, diamond)	1.90	2.44	2.87	6.06
C(c, graphite)	0.0	5.69	0.0	8.64
C(g)	718.38	157.99	672.97	20.84
CO(g)	−110.52	197.91	−137.27	29.14
CO$_2$(g)	−393.51	213.64	−394.38	37.13
CH$_4$(g)	−74.85	186.19	−50.79	35.71
C$_2$H$_2$(g)	226.75	200.82	209.2	43.93
C$_2$H$_4$(g)	52.28	219.45	68.12	43.55
C$_2$H$_6$(g)	−84.67	229.49	−32.89	52.65
C$_6$H$_6$(g)	82.93	269.20	129.66	81.67
C$_6$H$_6$(l)	49.03	124.50	172.80	
C$_6$H$_5$CH$_3$(l)	50.0	319.7	122.3	
CH$_3$OH(g)	−201.25	237.6	−161.92	
CH$_3$OH(l)	−238.64	126.8	−166.31	81.6
C$_2$H$_5$OH(l)	−277.63	160.7	−174.76	111.46
CH$_3$CHO(g)	−166.35	265.7	−133.72	62.8
HCOOH(l)	−409.2	128.95	−346.0	99.04
HCN(g)	130.5	201.79	120.1	35.90
CO(NH$_2$)$_2$(c)	−333.19	104.6	−197.15	93.14
CS$_2$(l)	87.9	151.04	63.6	75.7
CCl$_4$(g)	−106.69	309.41	−64.22	83.51
CCl$_4$(l)	−139.49	214.43	−68.74	131.75
CH$_3$Cl(g)	−81.92	234.18	−58.41	40.79
CH$_3$Br(g)	−34.3	245.77	−24.69	42.59
CHCl$_3$(g)	−100	296.48	−67.	65.81

	Element or compound	ΔH_f°, kJ mol^{-1}	S°, J mol^{-1} K^{-1}	ΔG_f°, kJ mol^{-1}	C_p°, J mol^{-1} K^{-1}
	CHCl$_3$(l)	−131.8	202.9	−71.5	116.3
	Si(c)	0.0	18.70	0.0	19.87
	SiO$_2$(c,quartz)	−859.4	41.84	−805.0	44.43
Group V	N$_2$(g)	0.0	191.49	0.0	29.12
	N(g)	472.64	153.19	455.51	20.79
	NO(g)	90.37	210.62	86.69	29.86
	NO$_2$(g)	33.85	240.45	51.84	37.91
	N$_2$O(g)	81.55	219.99	103.60	
	N$_2$O$_4$(g)	9.66	304.30	98.29	38.71
	N$_2$O$_5$(c)	−41.84	113.4	133	79.08
	NH$_3$(g)	−46.19	192.51	−16.63	35.66
	NH$_4$Cl(c)	−315.39	94.6	−203.89	84.1
	HNO$_3$(l)	−173.23	155.60	−79.91	109.87
	P(c,white)	0.0	44.0	0.0	23.22
	P(c,red)	−18.4	(29.3)	−13.8	
	P$_4$(g)	54.89	279.91	24.35	66.9
	P$_4$O$_{10}$(c)	−3012.5			
	PH$_3$(g)	9.25	210.0	18.24	
Group VI	O$_2$(g)	0.0	205.03	0.0	29.36
	O(g)	247.52	160.95	230.09	21.91
	O$_3$(g)	142.2	237.6	163.43	38.16
	H$_2$O(g)	−241.83	188.72	−228.59	33.58
	H$_2$O(l)	−285.84	69.94	−237.19	75.30
	H$_2$O$_2$(l)	−187.61	(92)	−113.97	
	S(c,rhombic)	0.0	31.88	0.0	22.59
	S(c,monoclinic)	0.30	32.55	0.10	23.64
	SO(g)	79.58	221.92	53.47	
	SO$_2$(g)	−296.06	248.52	−300.37	39.79
	SO$_3$(g)	−395.18	256.22	−370.37	50.63
	H$_2$S(g)	−20.15	205.64	−33.02	33.97
	SF$_6$(g)	−1096	290.8	−992	
Group VII	F$_2$(g)	0.0	203.3	0.0	31.46
	HF(g)	268.6	173.51	−270.7	29.08
	Cl$_2$(g)	0.0	222.95	0.0	33.93
	HCl(g)	−92.31	186.68	−95.26	29.12
	Br$_2$(l)	0.0	152.3	0.0	
	Br$_2$(g)	30.71	245.34	3.14	35.98
	HBr(g)	−36.23	198.48	−53.22	29.12
	I$_2$(c)	0.0	116.7	0.0	54.98
	I$_2$(g)	62.24	260.58	19.37	36.86
	HI(g)	25.9	206.33	1.30	29.16
Transition metals	Pb(c)	0.0	64.89	0.0	26.82
	Zn(c)	0.0	41.63	0.0	25.06
	ZnS(c,sphalerite)	−202.9	57.74	−198.3	45.2
	ZnS(c,wurtzite)	−189.5	(57.74)	−242.5	
	Hg(l)	0.0	77.4	0.0	27.82

Element or compound	ΔH_f°, kJ mol^{-1}	S°, J mol^{-1} K^{-1}	ΔG_f°, kJ mol^{-1}	C_p°, J mol^{-1} K^{-1}
HgO(c,red)	−90.71	72.0	−58.53	45.73
HgO(c,yellow)	−90.21	73.2	−58.40	
HgCl$_2$(c)	−230.1	(144.3)	−185.8	
Hg$_2$Cl$_2$(c)	−264.93	195.8	−210.66	101.7
Cu(c)	0.0	33.30	0.0	24.47
CuO(c)	−155.2	43.51	−127.2	44.4
Cu$_2$O(c)	−166.69	100.8	−146.36	69.9
CuSO$_4$(c)	−769.86	113.4	−661.9	100.8
CuSO$_4 \cdot$5H$_2$O(c)	−2277.98	305.4	−1879.9	281.2
Ag(c)	0.0	42.70	0.0	25.49
Ag$_2$O(c)	−30.57	121.71	−10.82	65.56
AgCl(c)	−127.03	96.11	−109.72	50.79
AgNO$_3$(c)	−123.14	140.92	−32.17	93.05
Fe(c)	0.0	27.15	0.0	25.23
Fe$_2$O$_3$(c,hematite)	−822.2	90.0	−741.0	104.6
Fe$_3$O$_4$(c,magnetite)	−1120.9	146.4	−1014.2	
Mn(c)	0.0	31.76	0.0	26.32
MnO$_2$(c)	−519.6	53.1	−466.1	54.02
PbCl$_2$	−85.9	32.5	−75.06	18.4

Source: Values mostly from Selected Values of Chemical Thermodynamic Properties, *Natl. Bur. Stand. Circ.* 500, 1952.

TABLE B-2 Thermodynamic Properties of Substances in Aqueous Solution at Unit Activity and 25°C

Note that the values are for an effective concentration of 1 M, that is, unit activities; particularly for the ionic species, this can be somewhat different from 1 M concentration; ionic properties are based on the assignment of zero value for ΔH_f°, ΔG_f°, and S° for $H^+(aq)$; (aq) = aqueous

	Species in solution	ΔH_f°, kJ mol^{-1}	S°, J mol^{-1} K^{-1}	ΔG_f°, kJ mol^{-1}
	$H^+(aq)$	0.0	0.0	0.0
	$H_3O^+(aq)$	−285.85	69.96	−237.19
	$OH^-(aq)$	−229.95	−10.54	−157.27
Group I	$Li^+(aq)$	−278.44	14.2	−293.80
	$Na^+(aq)$	−239.66	60.2	−261.88
	$K^+(aq)$	−251.21	102.5	−282.25
Group II	$Be^{2+}(aq)$	−389		−356.48
	$Mg^{2+}(aq)$	−461.95	−118.0	−456.01
	$Ca^{2+}(aq)$	−542.96	−55.2	−553.04
Group III	$H_3BO_3(aq)$	−1067.8	159.8	−963.32
	$H_2BO_3^-(aq)$	−1053.5	30.5	−910.44
Group IV	$CO_2(aq)$	−412.92	121.3	−386.22
	$H_2CO_3(aq)$	−698.7	191.2	−623.42
	$HCO_3^-(aq)$	−691.11	95.0	−587.06
	$CO_3^{2-}(aq)$	−676.26	−53.1	−528.10
	$CH_3COOH(aq)$	−488.44		−399.61
	$CH_3COO^-(aq)$	−488.86		−372.46
Group V	$NH_3(aq)$	−80.83	110.0	−26.61
	$NH_4^+(aq)$	−132.80	112.84	−79.50
	$HNO_3(aq)$	−206.56	146.4	−110.58
	$NO_3^-(aq)$	−206.56	146.4	−110.58
	$H_3PO_4(aq)$	−1289.5	176.1	−1147.2
	$H_2PO_4^-(aq)$	−1302.5	89.1	−1135.1
	$HPO_4^{2-}(aq)$	−1298.7	−36.0	−1094.1
	$PO_4^{3-}(aq)$	−1284.1	−218	−1025.5
Group VI	$H_2S(aq)$	−39.3	122.2	−27.36
	$HS^-(aq)$	−17.66	61.1	12.59
	$S^{2-}(aq)$	41.8		83.7
	$H_2SO_4(aq)$	−907.51	17.1	−741.99
	$HSO_4^-(aq)$	−885.75	126.85	−752.86
	$SO_4^{2-}(aq)$	−907.51	17.1	−741.99

	Species in solution	ΔH_f°, kJ mol^{-1}	S°, J mol^{-1} K^{-1}	ΔG_f°, kJ mol^{-1}
Group VII	$F^-(aq)$	-329.11	-9.6	-276.48
	$HCl(aq)$	-167.44	55.2	-131.17
	$Cl^-(aq)$	-167.44	55.2	-131.17
	$ClO^-(aq)$		43.1	-37.2
	$ClO_2^-(aq)$	-69.0	100.8	-10.71
	$ClO_3^-(aq)$	-98.3	163	-2.60
	$ClO_4^-(aq)$	-131.42	182.0	-8
	$Br^-(aq)$	-120.92	80.71	-102.80
	$I_2(aq)$	20.9		16.44
	$I_3^-(aq)$	-51.9	173.6	-51.50
	$I^-(aq)$	-55.94	109.36	-51.67
Transition metals	$Cu^+(aq)$	(51.9)	(-26.4)	50.2
	$Cu^{2+}(aq)$	64.39	-98.7	64.98
	$Cu(NH_3)_4^{2+}(aq)$	(-334.3)	806.7	-256.1
	$Zn^{2+}(aq)$	-152.42	-106.48	-147.19
	$Pb^{2+}(aq)$	1.63	21.3	-24.31
	$Ag^+(aq)$	105.90	73.93	77.11
	$Ag(NH_3)_2^+(aq)$	-111.80	241.8	-17.40
	$Ni^{2+}(aq)$	(-64.0)		-48.24
	$Ni(NH_3)_6^{2+}(aq)$			-251.4
	$Ni(CN)_4^{2-}(aq)$	363.6	(138.1)	489.9
	$Mn^{2+}(aq)$	-218.8	-84	-223.4
	$MnO_4^-(aq)$	-518.4	189.9	-425.1
	$MnO_4^{2-}(aq)$			-503.8
	$Cr^{2+}(aq)$			-176.1
	$Cr^{3+}(aq)$		-307.5	-215.5
	$Cr_2O_7^{2-}(aq)$	-1460.6	213.8	-1257.3
	$CrO_4^{2-}(aq)$	-894.33	38.5	-736.8

Source: Values from Selected Values of Chemical Thermodynamic Properties, *Natl. Bur. Stand. Circ.* 500, 1953.

TABLE B-3 Free Energies Based on H_{298}° for Some Elements and Inorganic Compounds

Melting points of the halides are in the intervals marked by m

	$-(G^\circ - H_{298}^\circ)/T$, JK^{-1}				ΔH_{298}°, kJ
	298.15 K	500 K	1000 K	1500 K	
Elements (gases)					
Cl_2	223.0	226.9	241.1	252.4	0
F_2	202.7	206.4	219.9	230.8	0
H_2	130.6	133.9	145.4	154.6	0
N_2	191.5	194.9	206.6	216.2	0
O_2	205.1	206.6	220.8	230.9	0
Halides (solids and liquids)					
$AgCl$	96.2	102.4 m	130.7	(154)	-127.0
BaF_2	96.3	105	137	(160)	-1200
CaF_2	68.9	70.0	107	133	-1214
$CaCl_2$	114	122	153 m	187	-795
Hg_2Cl_2	193	(200)			-265
$HgCl_2$	144	153 m			-223
KCl	82.5	88.3	110.2 m	(137)	-435.9
KBr	96.1	102.1	124.2 m	(151)	-392.2
KI	105.4	112.1 m	(135)	(161)	-327.6
$LiBr$	35.6	40.7	60.2 m	(83.0)	-609
$LiCl$	59.3	64.9 m	88.9	(113.5)	-400
$MgCl_2$	89.5	97.9 m	129.4	169.2	-641
$MnCl_2$	117	126 m	160	199	-481.9
$NaCl$	72.5	78.3	99.8 m	125.2	-411
NaI	98.5	104.6 m	(129)	(155)	-288
$PbCl_2$	136	145 m	185		-358
$TiCl$	111.2	117.3 m	146.1		-204.1
$ZnCl_2$	111.5	(120) m	(178)	(214)	-417
Oxides, etc. (solids)					
Ag_2O	122	129.7			-30
CaO	40	44.9	63.8	79.2	-635.1
$Ca(OH)_2$	83.4	94.1	134.6		-986.0
$CaSO_4$	106.7	118.7	166.3	211	$-1432.$
Cu_2O	93.7	101.8	131.7	(156)	-169
CuO	42.6	47.8	67.3	84.0	-157
FeS	60.3	68.3	96.8	117.5	-95.1
FeS_2	53.1	60.9	89.2		-177.9
MgO	27.4	31.9	48.9	63.3	-601.5
$Mg(OH)_2$	63.1	72.0			-924.5
Na_2CO_3	136	149.1	204.1	259	-1131
$NaNO_3$	116.5	128.5	194.3		-466.7
Na_2O	76.1	84.5	(115)	(148)	-416
NaO_2	115	(122)	(153)		-259
SiO_2	41.8	48.4	72.5	92.5	-877.0
TiO_2	50.4	57.6	84.1	105.6	-944.5

Source: K. S. Pitzer and L. Brewer, "Thermodynamics," McGraw-Hill Book Company, New York, 1961.

TABLE B-4 Free Energies Based on H_0° for Some Elements and Inorganic and Organic Substances

All substances are gaseous except where state is indicated

	$-(G^\circ - H_0^\circ)/T$, J K^{-1}					$H_{298}^\circ - H_0^\circ$, kJ	ΔH_0°, kJ
	298 K	500 K	1000 K	1500 K	2000 K		
Br	154.1	164.9	179.3	187.8	194.0	6.20	112.5
Br$_2$	212.7	230.1	254.4	269.1	279.6	9.73	35.0
Br$_2(l)$	107					13.55	0
C	136.1	147.3	162.0	170.6	176.6	6.53	710
C(gr)	2.22	4.85	11.6	17.5	22.5	1.050	0
Cl	144.0	155.0	170.2	179.2	185.5	6.27	119.4
Cl$_2$	192.2	208.6	231.9	246.2	256.6	9.180	0
F	136.8	148.1	163.4	172.2	178.4	6.520	77
F$_2$	173.1	188.7	211.0	224.8	235.0	8.828	0
H	93.8	104.5	119.0	127.4	133.4	6.196	216.0
H$_2$	102.2	116.9	137.0	149.0	157.6	8.468	0
I	159.9	170.6	185.0	193.5	199.5	6.196	107.1
I$_2$	226.7	244.6	269.4	284.3	295.0	8.987	65.5
I$_2(s)$	71.9					13.20	0
N	132.4	143.2	157.6	166.0	172.0	6.197	470.9
N$_2$	162.4	177.5	198.0	210.4	219.6	8.669	0
O	138.4	150.0	165.1	173.8	179.9	6.724	246.8
O$_2$	176.0	191.1	212.1	225.1	234.7	8.66	0
O$_3$	204.1	222.9	251.7	270.7	284.5	10.35	144.8
S	145.4	157.1	172.7	181.7	188.0	6.66	276
S(rh)	17.1	27.1				4.41	0
PCl$_3$	258.0	288.1	335.0			16.1	−276
PCl$_5$	279.3	319.2	383.1			21.8	−365
SF$_6$	235.2	270.6	337.0	385.0	422.1	16.74	−1195.0
B$_2$O$_3$	229.7	252.2	291.4	320.0	342.7	11.84	−876
HO	154.0	169.4	189.9	202.1	210.9	8.81	38.8
H$_2$O	155.5	172.8	196.7	211.7	223.1	9.908	−238.9
H$_2$O$_2$	196.4	216.4	247.5	268.9		10.84	−129.9
NH$_3$	158.9	176.9	203.5	221.9	236.6	9.92	−39.2
NO^3	179.8	195.6	217.0	229.9	239.5	9.18	89.9
N$_2$O	187.8	205.5	233.3	252.2		9.58	85.0
NO$_2$	205.8	224.3	252.0	270.2	284.0	10.31	36.3
SO	192.6	202.9	229.6	243.0	252.8	8.74	6.3
SO$_2$	212.6	231.7	260.6	279.6	293.7	10.54	−294.4
SO$_3$	217.1	239.1	276.5	302.9	322.6	11.6	−389.4
CO	168.4	183.5	204.0	216.6	225.9	8.673	−113.81
CO$_2$	182.2	199.4	226.4	244.7	258.8	9.364	−393.17
CS$_2$	202.0	221.9	253.2	273.8	289.1	10.7	115.
CH$_4$	152.5	170.5	199.4	221.1	238.9	10.03	−66.90
CH$_3$Cl	198.5	217.8	250.1	274.2		10.41	−74.0
CH$_2$Cl$_2$	230.4	252.5	291.1	318.7		11.86	−79.

	$-(G° - H_0°)/T$, J K^{-1}					$H_{298}° - H_0°$, kJ	$\Delta H_0°$, kJ
	298 K	500 K	1000 K	1500 K	2000 K		
$CHCl_3$	248.1	275.3	321.2	353.0		14.18	−96.
CCl_4	251.7	285.0	340.6	376.4		17.20	−104.
$COCl_2$	240.6	255.0	304.5	331.1	351.1	12.86	−217.8
CH_3OH	201.4	222.3	257.6			11.42	−190.2
CH_3SH	214.1	237.1	275.8			12.1	−5.0
CH_2O	185.1	203.1	230.6	250.2	266.0	10.01	−112.
$HCOOH$	212.2	232.6	267.7	293.6	314.4	10.88	−370.9
HCN	170.8	187.6	213.4	230.7	244.0	9.24	131
C_2H_2	167.3	186.2	217.6	239.4	256.6	10.01	227.3
C_2H_4	184.0	203.9	239.7	267.5	290.6	10.56	60.75
C_2H_6	189.4	212.4	255.7	290.6		11.95	−69.12
C_2H_5OH	235.1	262.8	315.0	356.3		14.2	−219.3
CH_3CHO	221.1	245.5	288.8			12.84	−155.4
CH_3COOH	236.4	264.6	317.6	357.1		13.8	−420.
CH_3CN	203.1	225.9	266.0			12.04	99.2
CH_3NC	204.0	227.6				12.53	161.1
C_3H_6	221.5	248.2	299.4	340.7		13.54	35.4
C_3H_8	220.6	250.2	310.0	359.2		14.69	−81.50
$(CH_3)_2CO$	240.4	272.1	331.4	378.8		16.27	−199.7
n-C_4H_{10}	244.9	284.1	362.3	426.5		19.43	−99.03
i-C_4H_{10}	234.6	271.7	348.9	412.7		17.89	−105.8
n-C_5H_{12}	269.9	317.7	413.7	492.5		13.16	−113.9
i-C_5H_{12}	269.3	315.0	409.9	488.6		12.08	−120.5
neo-C_5H_{12}	235.8	280.5	376.1	455.7		10.77	−130.9
C_6H_6	221.4	252.0	320.4	378.4		14.23	100.4
cy-C_6H_{10}	252.2	290.5	378.6	454.7		17.44	24.1
cy-C_6H_{12}	238.8	277.8	371.3	455.2		17.73	−83.72

Source: From K. S. Pitzer and L. Brewer, "Thermodynamics," McGraw-Hill Book Company, New York, 1961.

TABLE B-5 Properties of Diatomic Molecules (Homonuclear Molecules)

	Reduced mass, amu	$v = 0$ state				Equilibrium "state"			
		$r_{v=0}$, Å	$I_{v=0}$, 10^{-47} kg m^2	$\bar{v}_{0-1}$, cm^{-1}	D_0, kJ mol^{-1}	r_e, Å	I_e, 10^{-47} kg m^2	$\bar{v}_e$, cm^{-1}	D_e, kJ mol^{-1}
H$_2$	0.5039	0.7510	0.472	4162	432.1	0.7412	0.460	4404	458.1
HD	0.6717	0.7495	0.627	3634	435.5	0.7413	0.613	3815	458.0
D$_2$	1.0070	0.7481	0.936	2992	439.6	0.7414	0.919	3114	458.0
Li$_2$	3.47	2.69	41.8	346	99.0	2.68	41.6	351	348
Na$_2$	11.495	3.081	181.2	158	72	3.077	180.8	159	73
K$_2$	19.55	3.92	499	93	49	3.92	498	93	50
C$_2$	6.006	1.248	15.5	1828	602	1.242	15.4	1855	613
N$_2$	7.0034	1.100	14.07	2330	942	1.098	14.01	2358	956
P$_2$	15.487	1.896	92.4	775	620	1.893	92.2	781	780
O$_2$	7.9997	1.211	19.47	1556	494	1.208	19.36	1580	503
F$_2$	9.4992	1.42	31.7	894	155	1.41	31.5	918	160
Cl$_2$	17.726	1.991	115.0	554	239.3	1.988	114.7	560	242.6
Br$_2$	39.952	2.283	345.8	322	190.1	2.281	345.1	324	192.0
I$_2$	63.452	2.669	750.5	213	148.8	2.666	748.7	214	150.0
Ar$_2$	19.97	3.8	480	25	0.92	3.8	470	31	1.1
Xe$_2$	65.65	4.44	2150	20	1.38	4.44	2150	21	1.5
H$_2^+$	0.5036	1.07	0.96	2173	242	1.06	0.94	2297	255
N$_2^+$	7.003	1.119	14.56	2175	599	1.116	14.49	2207	612
O$_2^+$	7.999	1.126	16.84	1843	614	1.123	16.74	1876	625

TABLE B-5 Properties of Diatomic Molecules (Heteronuclear Molecules)

	Reduced mass, amu	$v = 0$ state				Equilibrium "state"			
		$r_{v=0}$, Å	$I_{v=0}$, 10^{-47} kg m^2	$\bar{v}_{0\to1}$, cm^{-1}	D_0, kJ mol^{-1}	r_e, Å	I_e, 10^{-47} kg m^2	$\bar{v}_e$, cm^{-1}	D_e, kJ mol^{-1}
CH	0.9299	1.13	1.972	2732	333	1.12	1.973	2859	350
NH	0.9402	1.05	1.713	3047	310	1.04	1.679	3203	329
OH	0.9482	0.980	1.512	3570	425	0.9705	1.483	3735	447
HF	0.9570	0.926	1.362	3959		0.917	1.336	4139	
HCl	0.9800	1.283	2.679	2885	427	1.274	2.641	2990	444
HBr	0.9953	1.423	3.348	2559	362	1.414	3.304	2650	378
HI	0.9988	1.617	4.330	2230	295	1.605	4.270	2310	309
CO	6.8606	1.131	14.56	2143	1069	1.128	14.50	2170	1082
NO	7.4684	1.154	16.51	1876	627	1.151	16.42	1904	638
SO	10.673	1.48	39.0	1138	517	1.48	38.8	1149	524
PN	9.645	1.49	35.7	1323	730	1.49	35.6	1337	738
NaCl	13.946	2.365	129.5	360	345	2.361	129.0	364	347
KCl	18.593	2.670	220.2	276	426	2.666	219.5	279	428

Source: "Spectroscopic Data," vol. 1, S. N. Suchard (ed.) and vol. 2, S. N. Suchard and J. E. Metzer (eds.), Plenum Press, London, 1975 and 1976, and from D. R. Shull and H. Prophet, Project Directors, JANAF Thermodynamic Tables, 2d ed, 1971 and Supplement 1977, *Natl. Bur. Stand. (U.S.)* nos. 37 and 48.

TABLE B-6 Properties of Small Polyatomic Molecules

All values for the $v = 0$ state

Molecule	Vib. spacing, cm^{-1}	Moment of inertia (each I in units of 10^{-47} kg m^2)	Structure (r in Å)	Symmetry number
CO_2	667(2) 1343 2349	$I_A = I_B = 71.70$	$r(C-O) = 1.162$ (linear)	2
HCN	713(2) 2097 2349	$I_A = I_B = 18.93$	$r(C-H) = 1.066$ $r(C-N) = 1.153$	1
N_2O	589 1276 2224	$I_A = I_B = 66.47$	$r(N-N) = 1.128$ $r(N-O) = 1.19$	1
NO_2	757 1358 1665	$I_A = 3.50$ $I_B = 64.5$ $I_C = 68.1$	$r(N-O) = 1.197$ $\angle(ONO) = 134.2°$	2
SO_2	518 1151 1362	$I_A = 13.8$ $I_B = 81.3$ $I_C = 95.3$	$r(S-O) = 1.432$ $\angle(OSO) = 119.5°$	2
O_3	705 1042 1110	$I_A = 7.87$ $I_B = 62.8$ $I_C = 70.8$	$r(O-O) = 1.278$ $\angle(OOO) = 116.8°$	2
H_2O	1595 3657 3756	$I_A = 1.02$ $I_B = 1.92$ $I_C = 2.94$	$r(O-H) = 0.958$ $\angle(HOH) = 104.5°$	2
D_2O	1178 2672 2788	$I_A I_B I_C = 39.95$	$r(O-D) = 0.958$ $\angle(DOD) = 104.4°$	2
H_2S	1183 2615 2626	$I_A I_B I_C = 46.9$	$r(S-H) = 1.328$ $\angle(HSH) = 92.2°$	2
NH_3	1022 1692(2) 3506 3577	$I_A I_B I_C = 34.82$	$r(N-H) = 1.012$ $\angle(HNH) = 106.7°$	3
H_2CO	1163 1247 1501 1746	$I_A = 2.97$ $I_B = 21.6$ $I_C = 24.7$	$r(C-H) = 1.12$ $r(C-O) = 1.210$ $\angle(HCH) = 120°$ (planar)	2
C_2H_2	612(2) 629(2) 1974 3282 3373	$I_A = I_B = 23.78$	$r(C-H) = 1.058$ $r(C-C) = 1.208$ (linear)	2

Molecule	Vib. spacing, cm^{-1}	Moment of inertia (each I in units of 10^{-47} kg m^2)	Structure (r in Å)	Symmetry number
CH_4	1306(3) 1534(2) 2916 3019	$I_A = I_B = I_C = 5.313$	$r(C{-}H) = 1.091$ (tetrahedral)	12
CH_3Cl	932 1017(2) 1355 1455(2) 2968 3054(2)	$I_A I_B I_C = 21{,}500$	$r(C{-}H) = 1.096$ $r(C{-}Cl) = 1.781$ $\angle(HCCl) = 110.9°$	3
$CHCl_3$	261(2) 363 680 774(2) 1220(2) 3034	$I_A I_B I_C = 32.8 \times 10^6$	$r(C{-}H) = 1.100$ $r(C{-}Cl) = 1.758$ $\angle(ClCCl) = 111.3°$ $\angle(HCCl) = 107.6°$	3
CCl_4	218(2) 314(3) 458 776(3)	$I_A = I_B = I_C = 486.3$	$r(C{-}Cl) = 1.760$ (tetrahedral)	12
C_2H_4	826 1443 943 1623 949 2989 1023 3026 1222 3102 1342 3105	$I_A I_B I_C = 5450$	$r(C{-}H) = 1.086$ $r(C{-}C) = 1.337$ $\angle(HCH) = 117.4°$ $\angle(HCC) = 121.3°$ (planar)	4
SF_6	347(3) 525(3) 615(3) 642(2) 773 947(3)	$I_A = I_B = I_C = 308.6$	$r(S{-}F) = 1.56$ (octahedral)	16

Source: D. R. Shull and H. Prophet. Project Directors, JANAF, 2d ed., 1971 and Suppl. 1977, *Natl. Bur. Stand.* (*U.S.*) nos. 37 and 48.

APPENDIX C
CHARACTER TABLES FOR A SELECTION OF POINT GROUPS

C_s	E	σ_h		
A'	1	1	x, y, R_z	x^2, y^2, z^2, xy
A''	1	-1	z, R_x, R_y	yz, xz

C_i	E	i		
A_g	1	1	R_x, R_y, R_z	x^2, y^2, z^2
A_u	1	-1	x, y, z	xy, xz, yz

C_2	E	C_2		
A	1	1	z, R_z	x^2, y^2, z^2, xy
B	1	-1	x, y, R_x, R_y	yz, xz

C_{2v}	E	C_2	σ_v	σ_v'		
A_1	1	1	1	1	z	x^2, y^2, z^2
A_2	1	1	-1	-1	R_z	xy
B_1	1	-1	1	-1	x, R_y	xz
B_2	1	-1	-1	1	y, R_z	yz

$\mathbf{C}_{2h}$	E	C_2	σ_h	i		
A_g	1	1	1	1	R_z	x^2, y^2, z^2, xy
A_u	1	1	-1	-1	z	
B_g	1	-1	-1	1	R_x, R_y	xz, yz
B_u	1	-1	1	-1	x, y	

$\mathbf{C}_{3v}$	E	$2C_3$	$3\sigma_v$		
A_1	1	1	1	z	$x^2 + y^2, z^2$
A_2	1	1	-1	R_z	
E	2	-1	0	$(x, y)(R_x, R_y)$	$(x^2 - y^2, xy)(xz, yz)$

$\mathbf{C}_{4v}$	E	C_2	$2C_4$	$2\sigma_v$	$2\sigma_d$		
A_1	1	1	1	1	1	z	$x^2 + y^2, z^2$
A_2	1	1	1	-1	-1	R_z	
B_1	1	1	-1	1	-1		$x^2 - y^2$
B_2	1	1	-1	-1	1		xy
E	2	-2	0	0	0	$(x, y)(R_x, R_y)$	(xz, yz)

$\mathbf{C}_{6v}$	E	C_2	$2C_3$	$2C_6$	$3\sigma_v$	$3\sigma_d$		
A_1	1	1	1	1	1	1		$x^2 + y^2, z^2$
A_2	1	1	1	1	-1	-1	R_z	
B_1	1	-1	1	-1	1	-1		
B_2	1	-1	1	-1	-1	1		
E_1	2	-2	-1	1	0	0	$(x, y)(R_x, R_y)$	(xz, yz)
E_2	2	2	-1	-1	0	0		$(x^2 - y^2, xy)$

$\mathbf{D}_{2d}$	E	C_2	$2S_4$	$2C_2'$	$2\sigma_d$		
A_1	1	1	1	1	1		$x^2 + y^2, z^2$
A_2	1	1	1	-1	-1	R_z	
B_1	1	1	-1	1	-1		$x^2 - y^2$
B_2	1	1	-1	-1	1	z	xy
E	2	-2	0	0	0	$(x, y)(R_x, R_y)$	(xz, yz)

$\mathbf{D}_{2h}$

	E	C_2^z	C_2^y	C_2^x	i	σ_{xy}	σ_{xz}	σ_{yz}		
A_{1g}	1	1	1	1	1	1	1	1		x^2, y^2, z^2
A_{1u}	1	1	1	1	-1	-1	-1	-1		
B_{1g}	1	1	-1	-1	1	1	-1	-1	R_z	xy
B_{1u}	1	1	-1	-1	-1	-1	1	1	z	
B_{2g}	1	-1	1	-1	1	-1	1	-1	R_y	xz
B_{2u}	1	-1	1	-1	-1	1	-1	1	y	
B_{3g}	1	-1	-1	1	1	-1	-1	1	R_x	yz
B_{3u}	1	-1	-1	1	-1	1	1	-1	x	

$\mathbf{D}_{3d}$

	E	$2C_3$	$3C_2$	i	$2S_6$	$3\sigma_d$		
A_{1g}	1	1	1	1	1	1		$x^2 + y^2, z^2$
A_{1u}	1	1	1	-1	-1	-1	R_z	
A_{2g}	1	1	-1	1	1	-1		
A_{2u}	1	1	-1	-1	-1	1	z	
E_g	2	-1	0	2	-1	0	(x, y)	$(x^2 - y^2, xy)$
E_u	2	-1	0	-2	1	0	(R_x, R_y)	(xz, yz)

$\mathbf{D}_{3h}$

	E	σ_h	$2C_3$	$2S_3$	$3C_2$	$3\sigma_v$		
A_1	1	1	1	1	1	1		$x^2 + y^2, z^2$
A_2	1	1	1	1	-1	-1	R_z	
A_1	1	-1	1	-1	1	-1		
A_2	1	-1	1	-1	-1	1	z	
E	2	2	-1	-1	0	0	(x, y)	$(x^2 - y^2, xy)$
E	2	-2	-1	1	0	0	(R_x, R_y)	(xz, yz)

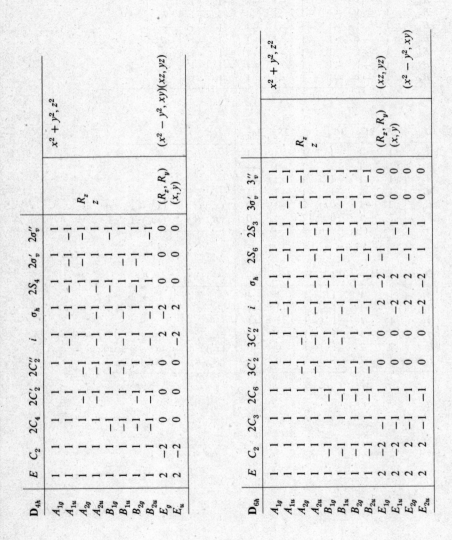

D_{4h}

D_{4h}	E	C_2	$2C_4$	$2C_2'$	$2C_2''$	i	σ_h	$2S_4$	$2\sigma_v$	$2\sigma_v''$		
A_{1g}	1	1	1	1	1	1	1	1	1	1		$x^2+y^2,\ z^2$
A_{1u}	1	1	1	1	1	-1	-1	-1	-1	-1		
A_{2g}	1	1	1	-1	-1	1	1	1	-1	-1	R_z	
A_{2u}	1	1	1	-1	-1	-1	-1	-1	1	1	z	
B_{1g}	1	1	-1	1	-1	1	1	-1	1	-1		
B_{1u}	1	1	-1	1	-1	-1	-1	1	-1	1		
B_{2g}	1	1	-1	-1	1	1	1	-1	-1	1		
B_{2u}	1	1	-1	-1	1	-1	-1	1	1	-1		
E_g	2	-2	0	0	0	2	-2	0	0	0	(R_z, R_y)	$(x^2-y^2, xy)(xz, yz)$
E_u	2	-2	0	0	0	-2	2	0	0	0	(x, y)	

D_{6h}

D_{6h}	E	C_2	$2C_3$	$2C_6$	$3C_2'$	$3C_2''$	i	σ_h	$2S_6$	$2S_3$	$3\sigma_v'$	$3\sigma_v''$		
A_{1g}	1	1	1	1	1	1	1	1	1	1	1	1		$x^2+y^2,\ z^2$
A_{1u}	1	1	1	1	1	1	-1	-1	-1	-1	-1	-1		
A_{2g}	1	1	1	1	-1	-1	1	1	1	1	-1	-1	R_z	
A_{2u}	1	1	1	1	-1	-1	-1	-1	-1	-1	1	1	z	
B_{1g}	1	-1	1	-1	1	-1	1	-1	1	-1	1	-1		
B_{1u}	1	-1	1	-1	1	-1	-1	1	-1	1	-1	1		
B_{2g}	1	-1	1	-1	-1	1	1	-1	1	-1	-1	1		
B_{2u}	1	-1	1	-1	-1	1	-1	1	-1	1	1	-1		
E_{1g}	2	-2	-1	1	0	0	2	-2	-1	1	0	0	(R_z, R_y)	(xz, yz)
E_{1u}	2	-2	-1	1	0	0	-2	2	1	-1	0	0	(x, y)	
E_{2g}	2	2	-1	-1	0	0	2	2	-1	-1	0	0		(x^2-y^2, xy)
E_{2u}	2	2	-1	-1	0	0	-2	-2	1	1	0	0		

T_d	E	$8C_3$	$3C_2$	$6\sigma_d$	$6S_4$		
A_1	1	1	1	1	1		$x^2 + y^2 + z^2$
A_2	1	1	1	-1	-1		
E	2	-1	2	0	0		$(x^2 - y^2, 2z^2 - x^2 - y^2)$
T_1	3	0	-1	-1	1	(R_x, R_y, R_z)	
T_2	3	0	-1	-1	-1	(x, y, z)	(xy, xz, yz)

O_h	E	$8C_3$	$6C_2$	$6C_4$	$3C_4^2$	i	$6S_4$	$8S_6$	$3\sigma_h$	$6\sigma_d$		
A_{1g}	1	1	1	1	1	1	1	1	1	1		$x^2 + y^2 + z^2$
A_{1u}	1	1	1	1	1	-1	-1	-1	-1	-1		
A_{2g}	1	1	-1	-1	1	1	-1	1	1	-1		
A_{2u}	1	1	-1	-1	1	-1	1	-1	-1	1		
E_g	2	-1	0	0	2	2	0	-1	2	0		$(2z^2 - x^2 - y^2, x^2 - y^2)$
E_u	2	-1	0	0	2	-2	0	1	-2	0		
T_{1g}	3	0	-1	1	-1	3	1	0	-1	-1	(R_x, R_y, R_z)	
T_{1u}	3	0	-1	1	-1	-3	-1	0	1	1	(x, y, z)	
T_{2g}	3	0	1	-1	-1	3	-1	0	-1	1		(xz, yz, xy)
T_{2u}	3	0	1	-1	-1	-3	1	0	1	-1		

APPENDIX D
SI UNITS

Some details of the system of units, known as SI units (for Système International d'Unités) that are likely to be encountered in physicochemical studies are given here. For more complete tables and for the rationale of the system, the following references can be consulted:

HALLIDAY, R. I.: Electrolyte Theory and SI Units, *J. Chem. Educ.*, **53**:21 (1976).
MCGLASHEN, M. L.: Internationally Recommended and Symbols for Physicochemical Quantities and Units, *Annu. Rev. Phys. Chem.*, **24**:51 (1973).
NORRIS, A. C.: SI Units in Physico-chemical Calculations, *J. Chem. Educ.*, **48**:797 (1971).
Policy for NBS Usage of SI Units, *J. Chem. Educ.*, **48**:569 (1971).
TAYLOR, B. N., D. N. LANGENBERG, and W. H. PARKER: The Fundamental Physical Constants, *Sci. Am.*, **223**(4):62 (1970).

TABLE D-1 Basic SI Units

Physical quantity	Name of unit	Symbol
Length	meter	m
Mass	kilogram	kg
Time	second	s
Electric current	ampere	A
Thermodynamic temperature	kelvin	K
Amount of substance	mole	mol

TABLE D-2 Derived SI Units

Physical quantity	SI name or special name and symbol	SI symbol
Area	square meter	m^2
Volume	cubic meter	m^3
Density	kilogram per cubic meter	$kg\,m^{-3}$
Velocity	meter per second	$m\,s^{-1}$
Angular velocity	radian per second	$rad\,s^{-1}$
Acceleration	meter per second squared	$m\,s^{-2}$
Force	newton (N)	$kg\,m\,s^{-2} = J\,m^{-1}$
Pressure	newton per square meter	$N\,m^{-2}$
Energy	joule (J)	$kg\,m^2\,s^{-2} = N\,m$
Power	watt (W)	$kg\,m^2\,s^{-3} = J\,s^{-1}$
Electric charge	coulomb (C)	$A\,s$
Electric potential difference	volt (V)	$kg\,m^2\,s^{-3}\,A^{-1} = J\,A^{-1}\,s^{-1}$
Electric field strength	volt per meter	$V\,m^{-1}$
Electric resistance	ohm (Ω)	$kg\,m^2\,s^{-3}\,A^{-2} = V\,A^{-1}$
Electric capacitance	farad (F)	$A^2\,s^4\,kg^{-1}\,m^{-2} = A\,s\,V^{-1}$

TABLE D-3 Examples of Non-SI Units

Physical quantity	Name	SI equivalent
Length	angstrom (Å)	10^{-10} m
	inch (in)	0.0254 m
	foot (ft)	0.3048 m
	mile (mi)	1609 m
Volume	liter	10^{-3} m^3
Mass	pound (lb)	0.4535924 kg
Force	dyne (dyn)	10^{-5} N
	poundal	0.138255 N
Pressure	atmosphere (atm)	101,325 N m^{-2}
	torr (mmHg)	133.322 Nm^{-2}
	bar	10^5 N m^{-2}
Energy	erg	10^{-7} J
	calorie (cal)	4.1840 J
	electronvolt (eV)	0.16021×10^{-18} J
Power	horsepower (hp)	745.700 W
Viscosity	poise (P)	10^{-1} kg m^{-1} s^{-1}
Dipole moment	debye	3.338×10^{-30} m C

TABLE D-4 Prefixes for Fractions and Multiples in the SI System

10^{12}	tera	T
10^{9}	giga	G
10^{6}	mega	M
10^{3}	kilo	k
10^{-1}	deci	d
10^{-2}	centi	c
10^{-3}	milli	m
10^{-6}	micro	μ
10^{-9}	nano	n
10^{-12}	pico	p

INDEX

Page numbers in *italic* indicate tables.

Brunauer, S., 744
Butler-Volmer equation, 649
tert-Butyl bromide, rate of hydrolysis, 660

Cage effect, 692
Calomel electrode, 620, 621
Calorie, unit, 8
Calorimeter, 166–167
Capacitance of condenser, 546
Capillary-rise method, 733
Carbon dioxide:
  PV isotherms for, 54
  Raman spectrum of, 449
Carbon monoxide:
  bond length, 463
  rotational spectrum, 446
Carnot, S., 205
Carnot cycle, 205–213
β-Carotene, 468
Catalysis:
  by enzymes, 674
  heterogeneous, 748–752
Cathode, 579
Cathodic current, 645, 648
Cavity radiation, 709
Cell constant, 573
Cell reactions, 621–624
  and free-energy changes, 624
Center of symmetry, 384
Character of representation, 395
Character tables, 383, 396–398, 815–819
  vector-like properties of, 397–398
Charge density in Debye-Hückel theory, 601, 605
Charles, J., 4
Chemical bonding, theory of, 411–443
Chemical equilibria and free energy, 237–273
Chemical potential, 287
Chemical reactions:
  energy changes in, 168–172
  rates of, 657–706
Chemical shifts, 480–483
  chart, 482
Chemisorption, 739
Chloroform-acetone solutions:
  activities, 289
  boiling-point diagram, 337
  thermodynamics of, 280
  vapor pressure diagram, 280, 335
Clapeyron equation, 314
Clausius, R. J. E., 28
Clausius-Clapeyron equation, 311–314
Clausius-Mosotti equation, 550
Closed systems, 282
Coherent radiation, 723
Coherent scattering, 531
Colligative properties, 293–301
  of solutions of electrolytes, 576
Collision cross-section, 683
Collision diameter, 44–46, *51*
Collision energy, 684
Collision frequency, 46, *51*
Collision properties, values for gases, 49–51
Collision rate, 46, *51*
Collision theory, 683–690
  compared to transition-state theory, 697
Collisions, types of, 45
Colloids, types of, 756

Combustion, enthalpies of, 168
Components, number of, 317
Compound formation and freezing-point diagrams, 327
Compressibility factor, 13–15, 19–20
  and fugacities, 260
  and van der Waals' equation, 58
Concentration cells, 634–641
  electrode, 634
  electrolyte, 636, 637
Condenser, electrical, 545
Conductance, 571
  ionic, 585
Conductance measurements, applications of, 590–593
Conductimetric titrations, 590
Conductivity cell, 571
Conjugated systems, 469
Conservation of energy, 122
Constant-boiling mixture, 339
Constantan, 329
Cooling curves, 325
Coordination compounds, bonding in, 435–439
Correlation diagram for atomic states, 404–407
Correlation energy, 378
Corresponding states, law of, 17–19, 57
Coulomb's law, 544, 546, 593
Counterions, 783
Covalent radii, 526, *527, 528*
Critical isotherm, 18, 19
Critical point, 17–19
  data for, *19*
  and van der Waals' equation, 55–58
Critical pressure, 18, 19
Critical solution temperature, 323
Critical volume, 18, 19
Cross sections:
  for elastic collisions, 685
  for reactive collisions, 686–688
Crystal field, 403
Crystal-field splitting factor, 406
Crystal planes, 500
Crystal shapes, 493–497
Crystal systems, 495, 496
Crystals, heat capacity of, 150–155
Cubic lattices, 510
Curie's law, 565

Dalton's law of partial pressures, 9
de Broglie, L., 79
Debye, P., 589
Debye (unit), 543
Debye characteristic temperature, 153, 154
Debye equation, 553, 554
Debye-Hückel limiting law, 608
Debye-Hückel theory, 599–608
  and activity coefficients, 606
Debye's theory of heat capacity of crystals, 153–155
Degeneracy of quantum states, 76
Degree of advancement of chemical reaction, 244
Degree of dissociation, 576
  and van't Hoff i factors, 578
Degree of ionization from conductance measurements, 590
Degrees of freedom:
  of molecules, 35, 73
  in phase equilibria, 318

LIST OF THE ATOMIC MASSES OF THE ELEMENTS

Element	Symbol	Atomic Number	Atomic Mass*	Element	Symbol	Atomic Number	Atomic Mass*
Actinium	Ac	89	(227)	Hafnium	Hf	72	178.49
Aluminum	Al	13	26.98	Hahnium	Ha	105	(260)
Americium	Am	95	(243)	Helium	He	2	4.003
Antimony	Sb	51	121.75	Holmium	Ho	67	164.93
Argon	Ar	18	39.95	Hydrogen	H	1	1.0080
Arsenic	As	33	74.92				
Astatine	At	85	(210)	Indium	In	49	114.82
				Iodine	I	53	126.90
Barium	Ba	56	137.34	Iridium	Ir	77	192.2
Berkelium	Bk	97	(249)	Iron	Fe	26	55.85
Beryllium	Be	4	9.012				
Bismuth	Bi	83	208.98	Krypton	Kr	36	83.80
Boron	B	5	10.81	Kurchatovium	Ku	104	(257)
Bromine	Br	35	79.91				
				Lanthanum	La	57	138.91
Cadmium	Cd	48	112.40	Lawrencium	Lw	103	(257)
Calcium	Ca	20	40.08	Lead	Pb	82	207.19
Californium	Cf	98	(251)	Lithium	Li	3	6.939
Carbon	C	6	12.011	Lutetium	Lu	71	174.97
Cerium	Ce	58	140.12				
Cesium	Cs	55	132.91	Magnesium	Mg	12	24.31
Chlorine	Cl	17	35.45	Manganese	Mn	25	54.94
Chromium	Cr	24	52.00	Mendelevium	Md	101	(256)
Cobalt	Co	27	58.93	Mercury	Hg	80	200.59
Copper	Cu	29	63.54	Molybdenum	Mo	42	95.94
Curium	Cm	96	(247)				
				Neodymium	Nd	60	144.24
Dysprosium	Dy	66	162.50	Neon	Ne	10	20.18
				Neptunium	Np	93	(237)
Einsteinium	Es	99	(254)	Nickel	Ni	28	58.71
Erbium	Er	68	167.26	Niobium	Nb	41	92.91
Europium	Eu	63	151.96	Nitrogen	N	7	14.007
				Nobelium	No	102	(253)
Fermium	Fm	100	(253)				
Fluorine	F	9	19.00	Osmium	Os	76	190.2
Francium	Fr	87	(223)	Oxygen	O	8	15.999
Gadolinium	Gd	64	157.25	Palladium	Pd	46	106.4
Gallium	Ga	31	69.72	Phosphorus	P	15	30.97
Germanium	Ge	32	72.59	Platinum	Pt	78	195.09
Gold	Au	79	196.97	Plutonium	Pu	94	(242)